...d by the monographs, by furnishing a well-digested survey of the progress
...and by pointing out directions in which investigation needs to be extended.
...the attainment of this purpose, extended references to the literature enable
...ested to follow up the subject in more detail. If the literature is so volumi-
...complete bibliography is impracticable, a critical selection is made of those
...ch are most important.

The
SULFONAMIDES
and
ALLIED COMPOUNDS

by
ELMORE H. NORTHEY, Ph.D.

Administrative Director
Stamford Research Laboratories
American Cyanamid Company
Stamford, Connecticut

American Chemical Society
Monograph Series

REINHOLD PUBLISHING CORPORATION
330 West Forty-second Street, New York, U. S. A.

1948

Copyright 1948 by

REINHOLD PUBLISHING CORPORATION

———

Printed in United States of America
WAVERLY PRESS, INC., BALTIMORE, MD.

American Chemical Socie

Scientific and Technologic M

By arrangement with the Interallied Conference of Pu
met in London and Brussels in July, 1919, the American C
take the production and publication of Scientific and Technol
subjects. At the same time it was agreed that the National Re
tion with the American Chemical Society and the American
undertake the production and publication of Critical Tables of
Constants. The American Chemical Society and the National Resea
agreed to care for these two fields of chemical development. The
Society named as Trustees, to make the necessary arrangements for the
monographs, Charles L. Parsons, secretary of the society, Washington,
John E. Teeple, then treasurer of the society, New York; and Professor Geh
Swarthmore College. The Trustees arranged for the publication of the A.
(a) Scientific and (b) Technologic Monographs by the Chemical Catalog Con
(Reinhold Publishing Corporation, successors) of New York.

The Council, acting through the Committee on National Policy of the A.
Chemical Society, appointed editors (the present list of whom appears at the close
introduction) to have charge of securing authors, and of considering critically the m
scripts submitted. The editors endeavor to select topics of current interest, and auth
recognized as authorities in their respective fields.

The development of knowledge in all branches of science, especially in chemistry, has
been so rapid during the last fifty years, and the fields covered by this development so
varied that it is difficult for any individual to keep in touch with progress in branches of
science outside his own speciality. In spite of the facilities for the examination of the
literature given by Chemical Abstracts and by such compendia as Beilstein's Handbuch
der Organischen Chemie, Richter's Lexikon, Ostwald's Lehrbuch der Allgemeinen Chemie,
Abegg's and Gmelin-Kraut's Handbuch der Anorganischen Chemie, Moissan's Traité
de Chimie Minérale Générale, Friend's and Mellor's Textbooks of Inorganic Chemistry
and Heilbron's Dictionary of Organic Compounds, it often takes a great deal of time to
coördinate the knowledge on a given topic. Consequently when men who have spent
years in the study of important subjects are willing to coördinate their knowledge and
present it in concise, readable form, they perform a service of the highest value. It was
with a clear recognition of the usefulness of such work that the American Chemical Society
undertook to sponsor the publication of the two series of monographs.

Two distinct purposes are served by these monographs: the first, whose fulfillment
probably renders to chemists in general the most important service, is to present the
knowledge available upon the chosen topic in a form intelligible to those whose activities
may be along a wholly different line. Many chemists fail to realize how closely their
investigations may be connected with other work which on the surface appears far afield
from their own. These monographs enable such men to form closer contact with work
in other lines of research. The second purpose is to promote research in the branch of

Preface

This monograph attempts to cover the chemical side of the new chemotherapy which has revolutionized medicine in recent years. Progress has been so rapid and the number of new compounds synthesized (now over 5000) so great, that it has been all but impossible for chemists active in the field to keep up with developments. Duplication of effort has been enormous. It is hoped that by listing most of the compounds that have been made as the result of the discovery of antibacterial properties of sulfonamides and related compounds, some of the waste of duplication can be avoided and the assembled information can be used as background for further conquest of disease. It is also an aim of this monograph to provide pharmacologists and clinicians with data on activities and sources of information on other important properties of the drugs. It is anticipated that further study will be stimulated because, unquestionably, there are valuable compounds passed over in the first cursory tests which may prove to be the answer to some specific need. A further aim is to provide all research workers in the field with a brief summary on medical uses and abuses of these drugs. Such information is not intended as a therapeutic guide but as a research tool, since final proof of usefulness is obtained only by widespread employment of the drugs in human and veterinary medicine. Success or failure in medical practice is the criterion by which experimental results are finally judged.

The importance of these drugs to modern medicine may be gauged from the fact that the United States produced 10,005,307 pounds of the sulfonamide drugs in 1943. If we assume that an average course of treatment requires 35 grams of drug, this would mean that an incredible number of patients (129,000,000) could have been treated with the drugs produced in 1943! Undoubtedly much of this huge production was used in stocking the needs of our armed forces and those of our allies all over the world, and may represent a peak production which will not be duplicated now that penicillin and other antibiotics are replacing the sulfonamides for certain uses and supplementing them in many other uses.

The author shares with many others active in the field the inner satisfaction of having contributed in some measure to the accomplishments which are reflected in otherwise cold life insurance statistics. Death rates are now the lowest in history for many infectious diseases. The lives of at least twenty-five thousand wage earners are being saved yearly in the United States through the use of sulfa drugs in the treatment of pneumonia. Spectacular accomplishment credited wholly to the new chemotherapy is shown by reduction in mortality from meningitis in United States Army camps from 39 per cent in the World War I to 3.5 per cent in World War II.

This monograph is an outgrowth of a review prepared and presented before Section C of the American Association for the Advancement of Science at the Research Conference in Chemistry held at Gibson Island, Maryland, July, 1939. The original review was revised and enlarged under sponsorship of the Division of Medicinal Chemistry of the American Chemical Society and was published in *Chemical Reviews*, *27*, 85–196 (1940). Since then the literature has expanded so enormously that a real need for revision and amplification was felt. Press of war work delayed completion of these efforts, but delay brought the benefits of broader scope and better evaluation of data.

The present monograph owes much to the cooperative spirit demonstrated by the drug industry and various medical research institutions of the country who supplied much unpublished data on new compounds and the chemotherapeutic evaluation of both old and new compounds. Exceptionally large contributions were made by Eli Lilly and Co. (activities on about 600 old and new compounds), The American Cyanamid Co. (data on 600 old and new compounds), The Upjohn Co., Sharpe and Dohme, Inc., and Abbott Laboratories.

Clinical applications have not been reviewed with thoroughness but it is hoped that the most important papers on recent developments have been surveyed. The literature on these applications is huge and much of it is now merely of historical interest, so rapid has been the obsolescence of compounds in the field. A number of reviews have been written which cover special fields of medical literature up to the date of their publication. The literature up to 1940 is adequately covered by several of these.

Some of the more important reviews are:

Buttle, G. A. H., *Trans. Roy. Soc. Trop. Med. Hyg.*, **33,** 141–168 (1939).
    [Particularly good on applications to tropical medicine.]
Marshall, E. K., Jr., *Ann. Rev. Physiol.*, **3,** 643–670 (1941).
    [Review of experimental chemotherapy from 1938 to Sept., 1940.]
Findlay, G. M., "Recent Advances in Chemotherapy", Philadelphia, Blakiston, 1939.
Long, P. H., and Bliss, E. A., "Clinical and Experimental Use of Sulfanilamide, Sulfa-
    pyridine and Allied Compounds, New York, The Macmillan Co., 1939.
    [Very complete literature on pharmacological and clinical findings to 1939.]
Mellon, R. R., Gross, P., and Cooper, F. B., "Sulfanilamide Therapy of Bacterial Infec-
    tions", Springfield, Ill., Charles C. Thomas, 1939.
Spink, W. W., "Sulfanilamide and Related Compounds in General Practice", Chicago, Ill.,
    The Yearbook Publishers Inc., 2nd. Ed., Revised reprint (July, 1943).
    [An authoritative handbook on clinical applications.]
Goodman, L., and Gilman, A., "The Pharmacological Basis of Therapeutics", Chap. 56 to
    60, New York, The Macmillan Co., 1941.
Henry, R. J., "The Mode of Action of Sulfonamides", *Bact. Revs.*, **7,** 175–262 (1943); En-
    larged reprint, Josiah Macy Jr. Foundation (1944).
    [An excellent critical review stressing the bacteriological side of the subject.]
Rune Frisk, A., "Sulfanilamide Derivatives", English translation by Helen Frey, Stock-
    holm, Sweden, P. A. Norstedt & Söner, 1943.
    [A very complete description of the pharmacology of 29 N^1-substituted sulfanilamides
    including literature and the author's own extensive studies.]
Special Chemotherapy Number, *Schweiz. med. Wochschr.*, **73,** 549–684 (1943).
    [An excellent presentation by Swiss medical authorities of the clinical use of sulfon-
    amides, including a bibliography of 958 references. Mode of action, nomenclature
    and structure are also discussed.]
Medical Research Council, War Memorandum No. 10, "The Medical Use of Sulphon-
    amides", London, His Majesty's Stationery Office, 1943.
    [An excellent short guide in use of the sulfa drugs, but colored by the supply situation
    in England at time of issuance.]
Kolmer, J. A., "Chemotherapy of Bacterial Diseases", *Arch. Internal Med.*, **65,** 671–743
    (1940).
    [A review of the medical literature on the Prontosils, sulfanilamide and sulfapyridine;
    about 400 references.]
Circular Lettter No. 17 (Feb. 23, 1942) Office of the Surgeon General United States Army,
    Washington, D. C., *War Med.*, **2,** 466–481 (1943).
    [An excellent guide to military uses of the sulfonamides.]

Bickel, G., "*La Sulfanilamide et ses Dérivés en Thérapeutique*", 687 references, Lausanne, Switzerland, Librairie Payot, 1940.

[Covers the therapeutic uses of sulfanilamide, Prontosil, Septazine, Uleron, sulfapyridine, sulfathiazole, Rodilone and sulfacetamide.]

Schnitker, M. A., "Sulfanilamide, Sulfapyridine and Allied Compounds in Infections", 202 references, New York, Oxford University Press, Inc., 1940.

"The Prevention of Respiratory Tract Bacterial Infections by Sulfadiazine Prophylaxis in the United States Navy, *NavMed* 284, Bureau of Medicine and Surgery, Navy Department, Wash., D. C., U. S. Govt. Printing Office (1944)-599351.

[This is a full report covering the mass prophylactic use of sulfadiazine on 600,000 naval trainees.]

Harold J. White, author of Chapter VIII dealing with measurement of chemotherapeutic activities of sulfonamide drugs, has charge of *in vitro* and *in vivo* antibacterial testing of new drugs at the Stamford Research Laboratories of the American Cyanamid Company. He has described methods of testing new chemotherapeutic agents which should be of value to those engaged in, or wishing to undertake, such studies. In addition to pointing out many of the pitfalls which abound in this work, he has prepared a key to the literature so that the published data on studies of the action of sulfa drugs against particular bacteria may be readily found.

Chapter X, which covers the pharmacology of the more important sulfonamide and sulfone drugs, was written by J. T. Litchfield, Jr., pharmacologist at the Stamford Research Laboratories of the American Cyanamid Company. In addition to his experience at these laboratories, he has conducted pharmacological researches on the sulfonamide drugs at Johns Hopkins University and the University of Minnesota.

Benjamin W. Carey has reviewed and edited the clinical material assembled by the author and is responsible for any unsupported medical opinion expressed in Chapter XII. Dr. Carey is in an excellent position to evaluate such work because he is Director of Lederle Laboratories Division of American Cyanamid Co., in charge of clinical investigations carried out by that company. A major portion of his efforts is directed to evaluation of new chemotherapeutic drugs and to widening the field of usefulness of the existing sulfonamide drugs through sponsoring further clinical research.

The author wishes to thank R. O. Roblin, Jr., Jackson P. English, and Paul H. Bell for constructive criticism of much of the manuscript and particularly the section dealing with mechanism of action.

In addition to the above, the author has been very considerably aided by Doris R. Seeger who arranged the compounds within tables in Beilstein order and who helped in proofreading. The author's wife, Alberta V. Northey, assisted materially in compilation of references and in the difficult task of typing the manuscript.

Stamford, Conn.　　　　　　　　　　　　　　　　　ELMORE H. NORTHEY
March, 1947

List of Abbreviations

ASC	acetylsulfanilyl chloride
cc.	cubic centimeters
CSF	cerebrospinal fluid
Gm.	gram(s)
M.	molar
mg.	milligram(s)
mg.%	milligram per cent (usually mg per 100 cc)
ml.	milliliters
mM	millimoles
PABA	p-aminobenzoic acid
pH	logarithm of the reciprocal of the hydrogen ion concentration
pKa	logarithm of the reciprocal of the acid dissociation constant

Abbreviations of names of scientific journals correspond to those used in *Chemical Abstracts*.

Abbreviations for organisms or diseases are given in Appendix A.

CONTENTS

Where boldface and lightface numbers occur together within parentheses, the boldface numbers are table numbers and the lightface numbers following the colon give the page location for these tables.

* Not discussed specifically in text.

⌈Where boldface and lightface numbers occur together within parentheses, the boldface⌉
 numbers are table numbers and the lightface numbers following the colon give the page
⌊location for these tables.   ⌋

* Not discussed specifically in text.

* Not discussed specifically in text.

[Where boldface and lightface numbers occur together within parentheses, the boldface numbers are table numbers and the lightface numbers following the colon give the page location for these tables.]

* Not discussed specifically in text.

⌈Where boldface and lightface numbers occur together within parentheses, the boldface⌉
|numbers are table numbers and the lightface numbers following the colon give the page|
⌊location for these tables.⌋

* Not discussed specifically in text.

⎡Where boldface and lightface numbers occur together within parentheses, the boldface⎤
│numbers are table numbers and the lightface numbers following the colon give the page│
⎣location for these tables.⎦

* Not discussed specifically in text.

┌Where boldface and lightface numbers occur together within parentheses, the boldface┐
│numbers are table numbers and the lightface numbers following the colon give the page│
└location for these tables.

* Not discussed specifically in text.

⌈Where boldface and lightface numbers occur together within parentheses, the boldface⌉
│numbers are table numbers and the lightface numbers following the colon give the page│
⌊location for these tables.⌋

* Not discussed specifically in text.

⌈Where boldface and lightface numbers occur together within parentheses, the boldface⌉
│numbers are table numbers and the lightface numbers following the colon give the page│
⌊location for these tables.⌋

* Not discussed specifically in text.

⎡Where boldface and lightface numbers occur together within parentheses, the boldface⎤
│numbers are table numbers and the lightface numbers following the colon give the page│
⎣location for these tables.⎦

  * Not discussed specifically in text.

⌈Where boldface and lightface numbers occur together within parentheses, the boldface⌉
│numbers are table numbers and the lightface numbers following the colon give the page│
⌊location for these tables.⌋

* Not discussed specifically in text.

[Where boldface and lightface numbers occur together within parentheses, the boldface
numbers are table numbers and the lightface numbers following the colon give the page
location for these tables.]

⌈Where boldface and lightface numbers occur together within parentheses, the boldface⌉
│numbers are table numbers and the lightface numbers following the colon give the page│
⌊location for these tables.   ⌋

* Not discussed specifically in text.

⌈Where boldface and lightface numbers occur together within parentheses, the boldface⌉
│numbers are table numbers and the ligtface numbers following the colon give the page│
⌊location for these tables.⌋

Chapter I

HISTORY OF BACTERIAL CHEMOTHERAPY

Specific chemical compounds have been used for the treatment of human diseases of protozoal origin with some success for a great many years. Mercury for treatment of syphilis was introduced by Jacobus Carpensis about 1500. The usefulness of quinine in malaria dates from the seventeenth century. Hexamethylenetetramine was first employed as a urinary antiseptic by Nicolaier in 1895. Modern chemotherapy of blood stream infections using synthetic drugs dates from 1910 when Ehrlich developed arsphenamine, and later neoarsphenamine, for the successful treatment of syphilis and trypanosome infections. This started a search for other chemotherapeutic agents which would effectively kill not only protozoal but bacterial invaders without seriously injuring the host in the process. Much of this work was carried out with products that were strongly bactericidal *in vitro*. Little or no success attended these efforts, because either the animal detoxified the drug before it could exert its effect on bacteria in the blood stream and tissues, or the drug killed the animal.

(I) DYES

Among the many compounds tested, certain of the dyes were highly effective against bacteria *in vitro* and some had slight effect *in vivo*. Examples were such dyes as gentian violet, acriflavine and methylene blue. The latter has been used for some time as an urinary antiseptic but has only a slight action in the leuco form to which it is reduced in passing through the animal body. Against certain of the trypanosomes, trypan red and trypan blue were moderately effective *in vivo*, and these in turn led to development of the more effective but colorless Germanin. Other dyes showing a measure of effectiveness against bacteria were: 4,6-diamino-3-(phenylazo)pyridine (Pyridium), synthesized by Tschitschibabin and introduced as a urinary antiseptic by Ostromislensky, who also introduced 2,4-diamino-4'-ethoxy-azobenzene for the same use; and the butoxypyridylazodiaminopyridine of Dohrn and Diedrichs, also a urinary antiseptic.

(II) SEARCH FOR AN AGENT ACTIVE *in Vivo*

The only partial success in combatting bacterial infection of the blood stream was the discovery by Morgenroth and Levy in 1911 that ethylhydrocupreine, or Optochin, (a quinine derivative) would protect mice against small inocula of pneumococci. This drug was tried clinically and was not sufficiently effective to be of real value; besides it had the unhappy effect of blinding a proportion of the patients by selective action on the optic nerve.

Heidelberger and Jacobs[188], while following this lead and that offered by the dyes, coupled diazotized *p*-aminobenzenesulfonamide with dihydrocupreine. This had only slight activity and was not investigated further. It is regrettable that this compound did not have appreciable activity, as later dyes made with *p*-aminobenzenesulfonamide were found to possess. The world might then have had the benefits of the miraculous curative power of *p*-aminobenzenesulfonamide, now known as sulfanilamide, a full fifteen years earlier.

It remained for a team composed of Fritz Mietzsch and Joseph Klarer, chemists, and

1

Gerhard Domagk, pharmacologist, working in the laboratories of the I. G. Farbenindustrie in Wuppertal-Elberfield, Germany, to continue the long search.   Mietzsch and others had developed Atabrine, an acridine derivative useful in treating malaria.   Encouraged by this success, they sought antibacterial compounds by the same kind of patient research, which involved finding a suitable therapeutic nucleus and by proper substitution on this, enhancing the effect to the maximum.

As Mietzsch[357] tells the story, they followed the lead offered by the azo compounds and over a period of years synthesized many different dyes.   One large series, in which an alkylated amino group was substituted onto the azo dye nucleus, showed interesting therapeutic activity in trypanosome infections in mice and important bactericidal powers *in vitro*; however, action against bacteria in living animals was not attained.   This tended to confirm their growing belief that there was no correlation between chemotherapeutic activity *in vivo* and *in vitro*.   They, therefore, resolved to test all further compounds *in vivo*.   Another important decision made about the same time was to introduce the sulfamyl (NH_2SO_2—) group into the dye molecule, para to the azo linkage. There was no previous knowledge to indicate that introduction of a sulfamyl group would create therapeutic activity, hence this important decision was the result of a chemist's "hunch".   This "hunch" was partly based on knowledge Horlein, Dressel, and Kothe had found, that introduction of a sulfamyl group into acid wool dyes favorably influenced a number of important dying properties, such as fastness to washing, fulling, and light. This indicated affinity for protein molecules.   However, none of these sulfonamide dyes had been investigated therapeutically up to this point.

As the study progressed, the sulfamyl group was introduced into one of the alkylated amine-azo compounds, giving:

$$NH_2SO_2-\langle\ \rangle-N{=}N-\langle\ \rangle(CH_3)-N\ (C_2H_5)(CH_2CHOHCH_2NH_2)$$

This compound, and others, for the first time showed a specific action against streptococcal infections in mice; it also showed *in vitro* activity.   This historically important compound was probably made in early 1931, since the German patent covering it was applied for on November 7, 1931.

(III) PRONTOSIL

Soon after this, the compound was made now known as Prontosil (rubrum),

$$NH_2SO_2-\langle\ \rangle-N{=}N-\langle\ \rangle(NH_2)-NH_2\cdot HCl$$

This showed still better *in vivo* activity against beta hemolytic streptococci in mice, but almost no activity *in vitro*.   Thus it was demonstrated that a compound could be highly active *in vivo* without showing *in vitro* activity, whereas the opposite had always been true in the past.

The epoch making discovery of the effectiveness of Prontosil was probably made sometime early in 1932, because the German patent application was applied for by Mietzsch and Klarer[213] on December 24, 1932. Clinical work was started in 1932, and on May 17, 1933, Dr. Foerster, at the monthly meeting of the Dusseldorf dermatological society, reported the cure of what would otherwise have been a fatal case of staphylococcal septicemia in a 10 month old boy, through use of "Streptozon" (as Prontosil was then called). This was followed in 1934 by several brief clinical reports on the effectiveness of Prontosil, but it was not until February 15, 1935 when Domagk[987] published the results of his animal studies, that the scientific world outside of Germany awoke to the importance of Prontosil. It is interesting to note that Domagk did not publish the work done two years earlier, until after issuance of the Prontosil patent in Germany on January 2, 1935.

The French seem to have recognized the importance of what was happening in Germany somewhat ahead of the rest of the world, with the result that intensive work was started at the Pasteur Institute in Paris, and in several industrial laboratories, early in 1935. 2,4-Diamino-4'-sulfamylazobenzene hydrochloride (the original Prontosil) was synthesized and sold under the name Rubiazol. Later the compound 2,4-diamino-6-carboxy-4'-sulfamylazobenzene was substituted without change of trade name. Many other azo compounds were made and tested.

(IV) SULFANILAMIDE

Late in 1935, Trefouel, Trefouel, Nitti and Bovet[511], working at the Pasteur Institute under M. Fourneau, made a very fundamental discovery which they described as follows (freely translated): "Having prepared and tested different products resulting from the coupling of diazotized p-aminobenzenesulfonamide with mono-, or polyphenols, either alkylated or not, we have reached the conclusion that some derivatives, although different from Prontosil in regard to their physical and chemical properties, show an analogous antistreptococcic action. Only relatively slight variations of protective action are caused by remarkable differences of oil solubility and surface tension. This has been verified with the azo compounds of non-aminated poly-phenols, especially with those of resorcinol and of ethyl-, propyl- and hexylresorcinols, to which we will have occasion to return. On the other hand, the same derivatives in which the p-aminobenzenesulfonamide is replaced by aminobenzamide, aminophenylacetonitrile, aminobenzonitrile, or phenetidine are without therapeutic action. Is not the reason that such different compounds act in an almost identical manner because, in the organism, they undergo a series of modifications, the first step of which would be the breaking of the double bond with the formation of p-aminobenzenesulfonamide? This hypothesis led us to study the activity of p-aminobenzenesulfonamide hydrochloride (1162F)".

They then described experiments on mice and rabbits which showed practically the same protective action obtained with sulfanilamide as with Prontosil, and concluded: "The protective action of p-aminobenzenesulfonamide is also present in numerous similar derivatives differing by the substitution on the amide, by the nature and position on the benzene ring of the substituent amines, phenols, alkylphenols, halogens, etc. The therapeutic activity of such a simple molecule, which is itself not a coloring matter, opens the way to a systematic study of chemotherapy comparable to that which has been followed in the case of pentavalent arsenic". This, in view of the developments during the years which followed, was a prophetic understatement!

Early in 1936, Goissedet, Despois, Gailliot and Mayer[170] confirmed the work of Trefouel, *et al.*, that dyes were not essential to activity and announced the synthesis of p-benzylaminobenzenesulfonamide which was sold under the name "Septazine" or "Setazine" and had a vogue among European clinicians for some time. Later work has shown its activity to be due, solely, to cleavage to sulfanilamide.

Work started in England sometime in 1935, but it was not until June 6, 1936 that two publications in *The Lancet* really opened the eyes of the rest of the English-speaking world. The first by Colebrook and Kenny[904] reported on the effectiveness of Prontosil in combatting puerperal sepsis; the second by Buttle, Gray, and Stephenson[61] stressed the effectiveness of sulfanilamide and its derivatives against streptococcal and meningococcal infections in mice. The results were so convincing that almost every large medical research institution and pharmaceutical manufacturing concern in the world initiated research on derivatives of sulfanilamide. Intensive pharmacological and clinical work, which paralleled the chemical studies, rapidly broadened the field of usefulness of the parent compound and its early derivatives.

(V) SULFAPYRIDINE

Although many hundreds of derivatives had been made and studied, it was not until 1938 that a really outstanding advance was made by Whitby's[549] publication in May of that year that sulfapyridine showed an outstanding curative effect in pneumonia. It now seems reasonably certain that Ewins and Phillips of May and Baker, Ltd. were the first to synthesize pure sulfapyridine, although others had independently synthesized and tested it before Whitby's publication. Crossley, Northey, and Hultquist[102] in this country and Goldirev and Postovski[171] in Russia published the fact that they had synthesized the compound independently. Still others have been involved in various patent interferences which have now been settled with issuance of patents in most countries to May and Baker[341].

Sulfapyridine, as the first heterocyclic derivative, was followed by many others, a few of which have proven much more effective and less toxic, so that sulfapyridine is now rarely prescribed in the United States. This is an illustration of the high obsolescence of products in the drug field and explains why patents have not been particularly important. With many parties involved, it takes so long to settle a patent interference that by the time the patent is published, the product has been superseded by a new and better drug.

(VI) MODERN SULFA DRUGS

Sulfathiazole, which is perhaps the most potent "sulfa" drug, was first published by Fosbinder and Walter[149], but was independently synthesized by many others in this country and abroad. Its medical use started in 1940.

Sulfadiazine, which is considerably less toxic while nearly as potent as sulfathiazole is rated "drug of choice" for most uses. It was first synthesized by Roblin, Williams, Winnek, and English[43] It s introduced into medical practice in 1941 and was employed in very large quantities by the armed forces during World War II. Sulfamethyldiazine, or sulfamerazine, was synthesized by this same group and published at the same time as sulfadiazine, but its introduction into medical use was delayed until 1943 by a strong but unfounded prejudice among clinicians against "sulfa" drugs containing methyl groups. Sulfadimethyldiazine or sulfamethazine was also passed up by American clinicians but found favor in England and was responsible for overcoming the prejudice on methyl groups (based largely on the toxicity of 4-methyl-2-sulfanilamidothiazole).

Sulfacetamide, introduced in Europe as "Albucid" in 1938, was synthesized by Dohrn and Diedrich[115] and independently by Crossley, Northey, and Hultquist[101]. Because of its low toxicity, it has found favor in treatment of urinary infections, and in the form of its highly soluble, neutral sodium salt for ophthalmic and other topical uses.

Sulfaguanidine, synthesized by Winnek[17] and introduced by Marshall and coworkers[335] in 1940 for treatment of intestinal infections, proved its value by preventing any major epidemic of bacillary dysentery among troops during World War II. Succinylsulfa-thiazole and phthalylsulfathiazole, synthesized by Moore[2183] in 1941 and proved clinically by Poth, *et al.*[1950], are used for the same purpose.

(VII) Theories

Modern theories of the mechanism of action of sulfonamide drugs stem from the fundamental postulations of Woods and Fildes[145] made in 1940. This theory ascribed the action of many chemotherapeutic agents to interference with essential bacterial metabolites. In the case of sulfanilamide, the action was postulated as a displacement of *p*-aminobenzoic acid (PABA) from a bacterial enzyme necessary to growth of the organism. The general concept has been verified by the synthesis of other types of chemotherapeutic agents closely allied in structure to vitamins essential to bacterial growth.

In 1942, Bell and Roblin[719] using the Woods-Fildes theory as a basis, introduced molecular structural considerations and were finally able to predict *in vitro* activities of new sulfanilamide derivatives with reasonable accuracy and to offer a reasonable explanation for many of the observed variations of *in vitro* activities among known sulfanilamide derivatives.

Based on current theories, it appears possible that the most effective sulfanilamide derivatives have now been made.

(VIII) Future Developments in Chemotherapy

If this were so, future advances might be made with greater profit in other fields. The extensions of Fildes' theory offer many such attractive fields based on present knowledge of bacterial metabolism, which is still scanty. In addition, further fundamental study by bacteriologists and biochemists is almost sure to open new opportunities for the synthetic approach to new types of chemotherapeutic agents. Empirical testing of many different organic compounds will also continue to open up new fields of exploration.

A vast amount of effort is now being spent in structure determination and synthesis of the highly potent antibiotic substances produced by molds and other microorganisms. Synthesis of structurally related compounds may result in improvement of these naturally occurring chemotherapeutic agents.

The next ten years will see many of the common infectious diseases of bacterial and protozoal origin conquered by present and future chemotherapeutic agents. Unfortunately, no such prediction is possible for virus diseases; it is probable that medicine will have to continue with vaccines, serums and other biological products in treatment of virus diseases for some time to come. The helminthic diseases offer another promising and important field for chemotherapy. The present agents which contain antimony or arsenic should be superseded by less toxic and more effective synthetic organic drugs.

When chemotherapy has conquered infectious diseases, there will still remain the vast field of non-infectious diseases. A little progress has been made on these; synthetic vitamins and hormones might properly be called chemotherapeutic agents for treatment of non-infectious diseases.   Thiouracil for treatment of thyrotoxicosis is another example and would seem to point the way to chemotherapeutic control of other glandular diseases. Also, much research on the chemotherapy of cancer is in progress, though whether this is an infectious or noninfectious disease is a moot point.

If mankind is now willing to support the war against disease with but a small fraction of the wealth and determination it has put into self-destruction, we have every reason to expect continued victories against our oldest and deadliest enemies.   Chemotherapy is a weapon of wide application in this fight.

Chapter II

NOMENCLATURE, CLASSIFICATION AND SYNTHESIS OF SULFANILAMIDE DERIVATIVES

(I) NOMENCLATURE

(A) Sulfanilamide Derivatives

The system of nomenclature for sulfanilamide derivatives now in general use throughout the world was developed by the author and associates in collaboration with Austin M. Patterson[98]. The parent compound, sulfanilamide, has a perfectly proper chemical name, since it is the amide of sulfanilic acid, name long recognized in dye chemistry for p-aminobenzenesulfonic acid.

Other groups may be substituted for any of the hydrogens in sulfanilamide:

(N^1) SO_2NH_2	SO_2NHCH_3	SO_2NH_2	SO_2NH_2
NH_2 (N^4)	NH_2	$NHCH_3$	NH_2 (with CH_3)
Sulfanilamide	*N^1-Methyl-sulfanilamide*	*N^4-Methyl-sulfanilamide*	*3-Methyl-sulfanilamide*

In naming simple derivatives as substituted sulfanilamides, it is necessary to distinguish between derivatives of amide and amino nitrogens. Since the sulfamyl group (—SO_2NH_2) is the most important functional group, it occupies the 1 position on the ring and derivatives of the amide nitrogen are designated as N^1-substituents. Thus in the simple methyl-substituted sulfanilamides, the N^1-, N^4-, and 2- or 3-methylsulfanilamides are derived as illustrated. For more complex compounds, radical names for the sulfanilamide part of the molecule are useful:

SO_2—	SO_2NH—	SO_2Cl
NH_2	NH_2	$NHCOCH_3$
Sulfanilyl—	*Sulfanilamido—*	*Acetylsulfanilyl chloride*

2,4-Bis-(sulfanilamido)toluene-5-sulfonic acid

$$NH_2\langle\;\rangle SO_2NH\langle\overset{*}{\;}\rangle SO_2N\begin{matrix} CH_2CH_2NHSO_2\langle\;\rangle NHSO_2\langle\;\rangle NH_2 \\ \\ CH_2CH_2NHSO_2\langle\;\rangle NHSO_2\langle\;\rangle NH_2 \end{matrix}$$

N^1,N^1-Bis-[2-($N^{4'}$-sulfanilylsulfanilamido)ethyl]-N^4-sulfanilylsulfanilamide*

The compound having six benzene rings illustrates the usefulness of all three types of names. By starting with the starred ring as parent, the full name is readily derived. Similar considerations apply to the naming of derivatives of orthanilamide and metanilamide.

$$SO_2NH_2 \qquad\qquad SO_2NH_2$$
$$\langle\;\rangle NH_2 \qquad\qquad \langle\;\rangle$$
$$\qquad\qquad\qquad\qquad NH_2$$

Orthanilamide   Metanilamide

Non-proprietary medical and trade names for therapeutically important sulfanilamide derivatives are usually derived from the chemical name through shortening the radicals sulfanilamido- or sulfanilyl- to "sulfa" and appending the name of the parent ring system or substituted amine. The following well known derivatives illustrate this:

$$SO_2NH{\overset{S}{\underset{N}{\langle\;\rangle}}}$$
$$\langle\;\rangle$$
$$NH_2$$

2-Sulfanilamidothiazole	Chemical name
2-(Sulfanilylamino)thiazole	Chemical name
Sulfathiazole	Trade name

$$SO_2N{=}C{\overset{NH_2}{\underset{NH}{\langle}}}$$
$$\langle\;\rangle$$
$$NH_2$$

| Sulfanilylguanidine | Chemical name |
| Sulfaguanidine | Trade name |

$$\overset{O}{\overset{\|}{SO_2NHCCH_3}}$$
$$\langle\;\rangle$$
$$NH_2$$

| N-Sulfanilylacetamide | Chemical name |
| Sulfacetamide | Trade name |

In the latter case the term "sulfacetimide" which is also used, should be discouraged, since the term "imide" is reserved for cyclic disubstituted amides where the nitrogen is part of a heterocyclic ring as in phthalimide,

$$\text{[structure of phthalimide]}$$

Collectively these drugs have come to be known as "sulfa" drugs. Since this term is useful, it will be employed in this monograph but will refer only to derivatives of sulfanilamide and will exclude compounds having similar activities but different structures such as the bis(4-aminophenyl) sulfones. Elsewhere the term is loosely used to include all compounds of similar activity; it is felt that this should be discouraged.

The structural formulae for ring compounds will omit ring carbons and double bonds. Modern theories of resonance in systems of conjugated double bonds, such as occur in carbocyclic and heterocyclic rings exhibiting aromatic character, make location of such double bonds meaningless, unless all resonance forms of such a system are shown. It is, therefore, better to omit these double bonds entirely to avoid the mental "booby traps" which entice the unwary when fixed positions are shown. Ring hydrogens are also omitted except in the case of partially or wholly saturated rings, where one or two hydrogens will be appended to the atoms of the ring as required to show the saturation of the adjacent bond.

(B) Sulfones, Sulfoxides, Sulfides and Disulfides

According to the International Union Rules for the Naming of Organic Compounds,[a] sulfones, sulfoxides, sulfides and disulfides are to be named by the same system as used for the others, oxy being replaced by sulfonyl, sulfinyl, thio and dithio respectively. Elsewhere in the rules, ethers are to be considered as hydrocarbons substituted by alkoxy groups. An exception is made in naming symmetrical ethers where the older system may be retained. Presumably this exception would apply to symmetrically substituted sulfur derivatives also.

While the International Union Rules stipulate that the "principal" function in a complex molecule is to be expressed in the ending of the name, no order of preference of functions is specified. For indexing purposes in *Chemical Abstracts*, however, an arbitrary order of preference of functions has been established so as to avoid a multiplicity of entries. Thus if a compound has an acid function, it will be named as an acid regardless of what other functional groups may be present. "Sulfone" has been placed after "amine", hence, *Chemical Abstracts* names compounds containing both functions as amines rather than sulfones. Thus the parent drug of the sulfone series

$$NH_2 \langle \quad \rangle SO_2 \langle \quad \rangle NH_2$$

is named "*p,p'*-sulfonyldianiline". Unfortunately, this name does not correspond with common usage, the name most frequently encountered being, "4,4'-diaminodiphenyl-sulfone". However, this type of name is considered poor because it leads to confusion

[a] *J. Am. Chem. Soc.* **55**, 3905–3925 (1933).

if extended to more complex molecules. A better name is bis(4-aminophenyl) sulfone and this will be employed throughout this monograph.

In order to relate the large number of compounds in Chapter VI to the common functional group, $-SO_2-$, symmetrically substituted sulfones will be named as bis( ) sulfones. Unsymmetrically substituted sulfones will be named by the International Union Rules, but because a large class of them contain the 4-aminophenylsulfonyl radical, for which the name "sulfanilyl" has been generally adopted, this will be applied where particularly useful and where no flagrant violation of the rule for naming a compound for its principal function is involved. The compound

for example, will be named 5-amino-2-sulfanilylthiazole, rather than *p*-aminophenyl 5-amino-2-thiazolyl sulfone, or 2-(*p*-aminophenylsulfonyl)-5-aminothiazole.

Symmetrical sulfides, sulfoxides, disulfides, and disulfoxides will be named as bis( ) sulfides, etc. For unsymmetrical compounds, the International Union Rules will be used. Examples are:

Bis(4-aminophenyl) sulfoxide   4-(4'-Nitrophenyldithio)acetanilide

(II) System of Classification

(A) General Considerations

In order to classify the 5400 compounds, which have been published (or disclosed to the author for publication) as a part of the intensive study of sulfonamides and related compounds in the current renaissance of chemotherapy, the author has devised a system which is partly his own but is fundamentally that of Beilstein, "Handbuch der Organischen Chemie". The strict order in Beilstein has been departed from most notably in establishing the main and subclassifications of sulfanilamide derivatives and sulfones. This was done to bring compounds together which were closely related according to both chemical and pharmacological properties but which may have had other functions which would have placed the compounds outside of the desired categories if the Beilstein system had been followed rigorously. Within individual tables, however, an attempt has been made to list substituents in the order employed in Beilstein.

(B) Classification of Sulfanilamide Derivatives

Compounds which are derivatives of sulfanilamide are classified as indicated under Chapters III and IV in the Table of Contents. A simple derivative (Chapter III) is first classified as to whether the substituent is on the nucleus, N^1 or N^4 positions. It is further classified under these main divisions as to whether the substituent is acyclic, isocyclic, heterocyclic, anil, sugar, acyl or inorganic. In the case of two substituents on the same position, the substituent highest in this order will govern the placement of the compound, *i.e.*, the compound

would be listed under N^4-acyl- rather than N^4-isocyclicsulfanilamides.

Complex derivatives where combinations of the nucleus, N^1, or N^4 positions are involved (Chapter IV) are classified similarly with first the position, then the nature of the substituent determining the placement. Thus, if a compound is substituted in all three positions, the nature of the N^4-substituent will determine its placement among nuclear, N^1, N^4-substituted sulfanilamides. The compound:

$$\text{CH}_3\text{CONH} \overset{\text{CH}_3}{\underset{\text{CH}_3}{\diamondsuit}} \text{SO}_2\text{NH} \overset{\text{S}}{\underset{\text{N—CH}_3}{\diamondsuit}}$$

for example, obviously belong to the main class of nuclear, N^1, N^4-substituted sulfanilamides. It will next be classified for its N^4-substituent and will appear in a table of nuclear, N^1-substituted-N^4-acylsulfanilamides. If there were a sufficient number of such compounds, it might then appear in a sub-classification of N^4-acyclicacyl derivatives. Again, if there were a sufficient number of this type of compounds, it would next be classified as to the specific grouping, N^4-acetyl. If there were a large number of compounds of this specific class, it would next be classified according to its N^1-substituent and finally, if there were many nuclear-substituted, N^1-(4-methyl-2-thiazolyl)-N^4-acetylsulfanilamides, it would be classified according to the nature of the nuclear-substituents.

Fortunately, there have been comparatively few nuclear, N^1, N^4-substituted sulfanilamides made so that the classification does not extend lower than nuclear, N^1-substituted-N^4-acylsulfanilamides. In the case of N^1, N^4-substituted sulfanilamides, however, there have been a large number of N^1-substituted-N^4-acetylsulfanilamides prepared, so that these compounds are classified to a rather low level according to the N^1-substituent.

(C) Classification of Compounds Related to Sulfanilamide

Here the main classifications have been arbitrary so as to group compounds of related pharmacological and chemical properties. A system similar to that used for sulfanilamide derivatives has been employed for sub-classifications, while the Beilstein order of substituents is adhered to in the individual tables.

(D) Classification of Sulfones, Sulfoxides, Sulfides, Disulfides, etc

An arbitrary main classification has again been used. Because of the apparent importance of the p-aminophenylsulfonyl, or sulfanilyl, radical in the pharmacological properties of these compounds, the classification has been such as to place compounds containing this group together. A further consideration, partly for ease of tabulation, was to make a separation between symmetrically and unsymmetrically substituted sulfones. In other particulars, the system follows that employed for sulfanilamide derivatives.

(III) Synthesis of Sulfanilamide Derivatives and Sulfones

(A) Intermediates

(1) *N*-Acetylsulfanilyl Chloride

The intermediate most generally employed for preparation of sulfanilamide derivatives is N-acetylsulfanilyl chloride (ASC), which may be purchased under that name, or as p-acetylaminobenzenesulfonyl chloride.   A satisfactory laboratory method of preparation is given by H. Gilman.[a]

This involves sulfonation of acetanilide with a 5 to 1 molar ratio of chlorosulfonic acid at 15 to 20°C, followed by gradual heating to 60°C and holding for one hour to complete the reaction.   The reaction mixture is drowned in ice.   The precipitate of ASC is filtered and washed to remove acid.   The wet paste may be used for many purposes, but when it is necessary to use purified ASC (as for reaction with expensive amino heterocycles) it may be air dried in thin layers on porous plates, or in a vacuum desiccator, and, when dry, recrystallized from a solvent.   Benzene and ether, as described in the literature, are poor solvents.   Much better results are obtained by using chloroform or ethylene dichloride.

The commercial product assays about 98% pure.   Repeated recrystallizations, with care to exclude moisture (which can destroy thirteen times its weight of ASC), are necessary to obtain an analytically pure material.   This is not necessary for most synthetic work.

N-Acetylsulfanilyl chloride was first prepared by Schroeter[464] in 1906 by reacting sodium acetylsulfanilate with phosphorous oxychloride.

(2) p-Nitrobenzenesulfonyl Chloride

This is a useful intermediate, particularly in making sulfanilamide derivatives which are sensitive to strong acids or alkalies, because the nitro group may be reduced to amino under nearly neutral conditions.   A satisfactory method of preparation is that of Barber[701].

The author has used essentially the same method.   A solution of sodium disulfide is first prepared.   This should be as free from oxidation products and other impurities as possible and may be prepared by absorption of H_2S into 20% sodium hydroxide followed by addition of the stoichiometric amount of sulfur and heating to solution, all with exclusion of air.   The solution of sodium disulfide containing 1 mole Na_2S_2 is then added to a boiling solution of 2 moles of p-nitrochlorobenzene in 3 times its weight of 95% alcohol at such a rate as to maintain constant boiling under reflux without further application of heat.   At the end the reaction mixture is heated for 30 minutes, cooled and the impure bis(p-nitrophenyl) disulfide is filtered, washed with alcohol, then with water.

The wet cake is suspended in about 5 parts of 95% acetic acid and a rapid stream of chlorine is passed in.   The temperature is held at 50°C.   After chlorination is complete and almost all the solid has dissolved (1 to 2 hours), the warm solution is treated with activated charcoal and clarified then drowned in eight times its volume of ice and water.

The crude p-nitrobenzenesulfonyl chloride which crystallizes is filtered, washed well with water, sucked as dry as possible then dried in thin layers in an air dryer at not over 40°C.   This product contains considerable amounts of bis(p-nitrophenyl) sulfoxide, bis(p-nitrophenyl) sulfone and other impurities which may not be objectionable if they can be removed after reaction of the sulfonyl chloride.   Partial purification with considerable loss can be effected by crystallization from such solvents as ethylene dichloride, trichloroethylene, glacial acetic acid or mixtures of these.   The pure product, melting point 80°C., can be obtained by vacuum distillation at 1–2 mm. pressure but this is dangerous since violent decomposition may occur even at early stages in the distillation.

(B) Manufacture of Sulfanilamide

Sulfanilamide is made by reacting crude wet acetylsulfanilyl chloride (ASC) with a large excess of strong ammonium hydroxide at 40–50°C. to give N^4-acetylsulfanilamide,

[a] "Organic Synthesis," Col. Vol. 1, p. 8, John Wiley and Sons, Inc., New York, 1932.

which may be isolated by filtration and washing of the reaction slurry. Since in the sulfonation of acetanilide with chlorosulfonic acid, there is a small amount of bis(4-acetamidophenyl) sulfone formed, this occurs as an impurity in the crude N^4-acetylsulfanilamide. In a series of patents to the I.G. and affiliates, Mietzsch, Behnish and Klarer[223, 231, 234, 554] disclosed a method of purification in which the crude N^4-acetylsulfanilamide (which they said contained about 1% of the sulfone) was dissolved as its sodium salt, in one normal concentration in water at a temperature of 25°C., treated with activated charcoal to remove the alkali insoluble sulfone, and precipitated from the filtrate by acidification. The purified N^4-acetylsulfanilamide was then hydrolyzed to sulfanilamide by boiling with acid or alkali. Instead of isolating the purified N^4-acetylsulfanilamide, the clarified solution containing one mole dissolved as the sodium salt, could be boiled for one hour after addition of 85 Gm. solid sodium hydroxide. Crude sulfanilamide was obtained by neutralization and cooling of the hydrolysate. It may be recrystallized from water or alcohol, using activated charcoal to give pure sulfanilamide meeting U.S.P. requirements. Alkaline hydrolysis of N^4-acetylsulfanilamide has been patented in Switzerland[195].

Instead of acetanilide, oxanilide[539], formanilide or carbanilide[1142] may be converted to sulfanilamide by the same general process. In the case of 4,4'-disulfamylcarbanilide, it is necessary to autoclave with 22% sulfuric acid at 150–160° to hydrolyze[1142].

Another process for producing sulfanilamide[411] starts with chlorobenzene which is sulfonated with 3 to 4 times its weight of chlorosulfonic acid at 25 to 35°C. to give p-chlorobenzenesulfonyl chloride. This is reacted with strong ammonium hydroxide to give the amide, which is then heated with concentrated ammonium hydroxide in an autoclave at 160°C. for 12 hours, with a copper catalyst, to produce crude sulfanilamide. This must be treated with hydrogen sulfide to remove copper, then undergo extensive purification to remove tarry impurities before a U.S.P. product is obtained.

It is not known whether this process is in commercial use. In the author's experience, high amounts of bis(4-chlorophenyl) sulfone are encountered. This loss, plus the poor yields on the amination of 4-chlorobenzenesulfonamide and difficulties in purification, mean that advantages over production from the relatively expensive acetanilide are counterbalanced in large measure.

A third process[256] starts with p-toluenesulfonamide which is oxidized to the acid, converted to the amide, and then subjected to Hofmann degradation to give sulfanilamide. The number of steps, coupled with expensive reagents and starting materials, make it certain that this process has not been applied commercially.

The possibility of dehydrating ammonium sulfanilate to sulfanilamide, analogous to dehydration of ammonium acetate to acetamide, has undoubtedly received attention, but with what success is not known. If satisfactory yields could be obtained, this would give the cheapest sulfanilamide. The difficulty seems to be that the temperature for the reaction is well above the decomposition point of sulfanilamide. A novel proposal[366] for accomplishing the dehydration of other ammonium aromatic sulfonates to the corresponding aromatic sulfonamides consists of suspending the dry ammonium salt in an inert gas and passing through a heated tube at 225 to 400°C. This apparently works well if the resulting sulfonamide is volatile at the reaction temperature.

(C) Manufacture of Sulfapyridine

Sulfapyridine is manufactured by reacting dry ASC with 2-aminopyridine in the presence of pyridine as a solvent and HCl acceptor at 60 to 100°C. Use of acetone[602], methanol or dioxane[11] as solvents together with pyridine or excess 2-aminopyridine as HCl acceptors are also mentioned. The reaction mixture may be diluted with water and acidified to precipitate 2-(N^4-acetylsulfanilamido)pyridine which can then be filtered.

Hydrolysis of the 2-(N^4-acetylsulfanilamido)pyridine is best accomplished by boiling with excess sodium hydroxide until test by diazotization indicates hydrolyis to be complete. Boiling with strong acids not only hydrolyzes the acetyl group, but cleaves at the amide linkage giving sulfanilic acid and the salt of 2-aminopyridine[102]. The solution of sodium sulfapyridine resulting from the hydrolysis is acidified preferably with SO_2[638] and the crude sulfapyridine filtered. It may be purified by dissolving as its sodium salt in water, treating with an activated charcoal and reprecipitating with acid. The final purification involves recrystallization from acetone or alcohol with use of an activated charcoal.

Many other methods of manufacture have been devised largely for patent purposes. A fairly obvious method consists of reacting *p*-nitrobenzenesulfonyl chloride or 4-azobenzenesulfonyl chloride with 2-aminopyridine in pyridine, followed by reduction of the nitro or azo group with iron[341]. Less obvious is heating a mixture of 2-bromo (or iodo) pyridine with sulfanilamide, potassium carbonate and copper powder at 180° for two hours[1749].

A novel method of manufacture[540] consists in converting sulfanilic acid to sulfanilyl fluoride by treatment with fluorosulfonic acid. This is reacted with a large excess of 2-aminopyridine (40 Gm. to 10 Gm. sulfanilyl fluoride) at 180°. After addition of a little water to the melt, sulfapyridine crystallizes, while a considerable amount of 2-(N^4-sulfanilylsulfanilamido)pyridine is retained in the 2-aminopyridine mother liquor, from which it is recovered as the sodium salt by extraction with sodium hydroxide.

Another procedure[1563] involves formation of the sodium derivative of 2-aminopyridine by reaction with sodamide in benzene, then reaction with dry ASC. This same procedure is said to work with other amino heterocycles such as various aminoquinolines and 2-aminothiazole.

A method which is interesting chemically, if not practically[76], discloses that compounds of the type:

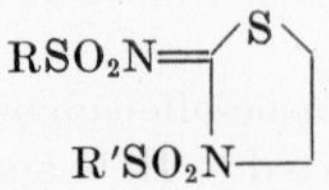

$$RSO_2N = \underset{R'SO_2N}{\overset{S}{\diagup\!\!\!\diagdown}}$$

are acylating agents. Thus the following reaction is described:

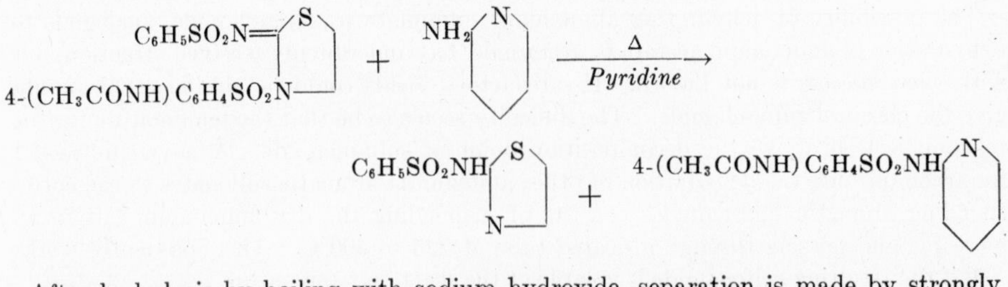

$$C_6H_5SO_2N = \overset{S}{\diagup\!\!\!\diagdown} \quad + \quad NH_2 \overset{N}{\diagup\!\!\!\diagdown} \quad \xrightarrow[\textit{Pyridine}]{\Delta}$$
$$4\text{-}(CH_3CONH)C_6H_4SO_2N$$

$$C_6H_5SO_2NH \overset{S}{\underset{N}{\diagup\!\!\!\diagdown}} \quad + \quad 4\text{-}(CH_3CONH)C_6H_4SO_2NH \overset{N}{\diagup\!\!\!\diagdown}$$

After hydrolysis by boiling with sodium hydroxide, separation is made by strongly acidifying. The sulfapyridine remains in solution while the 2-phenylsulfonamidothiazole crystallizes and is filtered off. On neutralizing, sulfapyridine is obtained. A number of similar reactions are described, including the synthesis of sulfathiazole.

Still another method involves preparation[1747] of *p*-nitrobenzenesulfenyl chloride,

$4\text{-NO}_2\text{C}_6\text{H}_4\text{SCl}$, reaction of this with excess 2-aminopyridine in dry ether to form 2-(p-nitrophenylsulfenamido)-pyridine, oxidation to the corresponding sulfonamide by use of permanganate and, finally, reduction of the nitro group by suitable means to give sulfapyridine.

Instead of p-nitrobenzenesulfenyl chloride, p-acetamidobenzenesulfenyl bromide may be carried through a similar series of reactions and the acetyl group finally hydrolyzed. Similar syntheses of sulfathiazole are described.

Use of the sulfinyl halides (*e.g.*, $4\text{-NO}_2\text{C}_6\text{H}_4\text{SOCl}$) as intermediates is also described[457, 1804]. The steps follow those for the corresponding sulfenyl halides.

The process for making p-acetamidobenzenesulfonyl bromide by bromination of bis(4-acetamidophenyl) disulfide in slightly diluted acetic acid has been patented[1705].

The patenting of such a large number of impractical processes may be bewildering to the reader. Most of these have been worked out in Europe where, in general, the product cannot be patented. To protect himself, it is necessary for an inventor to work out not only the most practical synthesis, but all possible syntheses, since anyone with a new process can sell the product.

(D) Manufacture of Sulfathiazole and Derivatives

(1) 2-Aminothiazole

The process for 2-aminothiazole described in the older literature, which consisted in the reaction of 1,2-dichloroethyl ethyl ether with thiourea, is not used commercially. Most 2-aminothiazole is manufactured from vinyl acetate. In the simplest process[2264], this is chlorinated at -10 to $0°$C. with an equimolar amount of chlorine to give as the main product 1,2-dichloroethyl acetate, $\text{ClCH}_2\text{CH(Cl)OCOCH}_3$. The entire reaction mixture is fed into an aqueous suspension of thiourea at $100°$C. with cooling, and ring closure takes place:

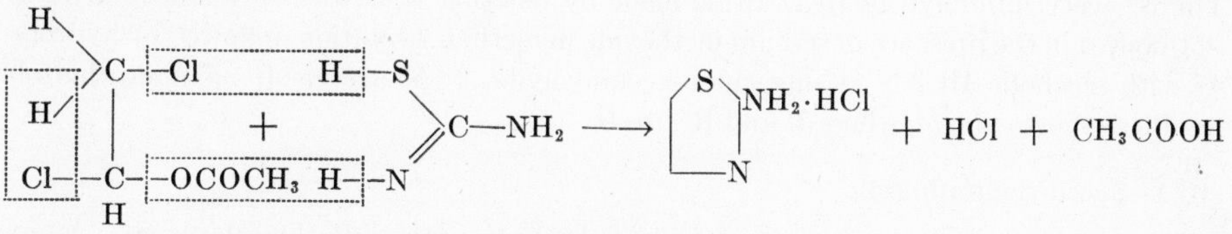

The 2-aminothiazole can be recovered as the base by neutralizing the reaction mixture, cooling and filtering off the 2-aminothiazole with some salt. It may be purified by drying, then vacuum distilling at 3 mm. The yield is 84% of theory.

In a second process[1798], the chlorination of vinyl acetate is carried out at -5 to $-10°$C. in the presence of 3.85 moles of anhydrous ethyl alcohol with production of diethylchloroacetal, $\text{ClCH}_2\text{CH(OC}_2\text{H}_5)_2$. This may be isolated by distillation, or the crude reaction mixture (which contains ethyl acetate and other by-products) may be condensed directly with thiourea in aqueous alcohol at 70–$75°$C. giving a solution of 2-aminothiazole hydrochloride from which the base is liberated by neutralization with sodium carbonate. Salts are filtered off, the solution evaporated, then the 2-aminothiazole is flash distilled under vacuum. In another variation[787], the diethylchloroacetal is reacted with thiourea in the presence of dilute hydrochloric acid giving about a 68% yield.

Still another process[1703] utilizes paraldehyde which is brominated with an equal volume of bromine to give tribromoparaldehyde. This is condensed with thiourea in water at 80 to $90°$C. and the 2-aminothiazole isolated by extraction with ether after making alkaline with sodium carbonate.   The crude yield is 65 to 70%.   Instead of isolating the base, the solution of 2-aminothiazole hydrobromide may be treated with the sodium salt of a suitable aromatic sulfonic acid and the resulting salt of 2-aminothiazole filtered off and condensed with ASC in pyridine[1704].

(2) Sulfathiazole

2-Aminothiazole is reacted with dry ASC in dry pyridine and the resulting N^4-acetyl-sulfathiazole is hydrolyzed with sodium hydroxide.   The process is analogous to that used for sulfapyridine and the alternative methods described there have been used on 2-aminothiazole as well.   Other 2-aminothiazoles substituted in the 4 or 5 position are condensed similarly.

A second general method of synthesis involves condensation of halogenoketones, aldehydes or esters with N^4-acetylsulfanilylthioureas giving rise to the corresponding 2-(N^4-acetylsulfanilamido)thiazoles[622] when boiled in alcohol or alcohol-pyridine mixture:

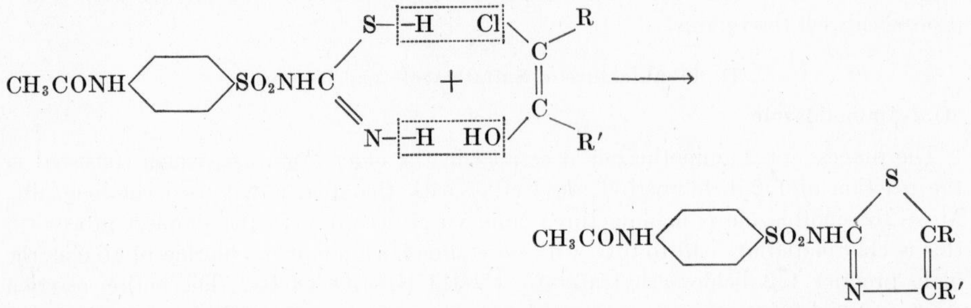

The isomeric isothiourea structure, and enol form of the halogenoketone are shown. The N^4-acetylsulfanilylthiourea can be made by reacting ASC with S-(methoxymethyl)-isothiourea in the presence of sodium methoxide in methanol solution, followed by hydrolysis with alcoholic HCl[622].   Using chloroacetaldehyde, 2-(N^4-acetylsulfanilamido)thiazole results as shown above, where R and R′ are H.

(3) N^4-Succinylsulfathiazole

This may be made by fusing succinic anhydride with sulfathiazole[372, 2183].   As an alternative synthesis, succinylaniline may be converted to succinylsulfanilyl chloride and this reacted with 2-aminothiazole in dry pyridine to give the desired product[372].

The corresponding N^4-phthalylsulfathiazole is made similarly[372].

(E) Manufacture of Sulfaguanidine

Various processes have been described in the patent literature and elsewhere for the manufacture of sulfaguanidine.   Condensation of acetylsulfanilyl chloride with guanidine nitrate in the presence of considerable excess of sodium hydroxide in an aqueous acetone medium[17, 335] gives N^4-acetylsulfanilylguanidine which is isolated by dilution with water. This is also made[1354] by fusing N^4-acetylsulfanilamide and dicyanodiamide at 205°C.   The acetyl group is removed by hydrolysis with 4% HCl at 90°C.

Another method uses p-nitrobenzenesulfonyl chloride under essentially the same conditions as above to give p-nitrophenylsulfonylguanidine[17].   This is also made by condensing p-nitrobenzenesulfenyl chloride (or ethyl p-nitrobenzenesulfenate) with guanidine nitrate in dry ether in the presence of sodium ethoxide followed by permanganate oxidation to the corresponding sulfonyl derivative[1706].   The nitro group can be reduced by iron, ferrous sulfate, or sodium sulfhydrate.

Direct fusion of sulfanilamide and dicyanodiamide has been shown by White, *et al.*[2441] to give sulfaguanidine rather than 4-guanylbenzenesulfonamide as claimed by Buttle, *et al.*,[60].

An interesting synthesis of sulfaguanidine resulted from attempts to hydrolyze N^4-acetylsulfanilamidotetrazole or to reduce *p*-nitrophenylsulfonamidotetrazole. Ring cleavage to sulfaguanidine occurred[434].

Another synthesis[1357] started with S-benzylisothiourea which was converted to the sulfanilyl derivative with *p*-nitrobenzenesulfonyl chloride followed by reduction with iron. The sulfanilyl derivative was heated with ammonia under pressure to give sulfaguanidine and benzyl mercaptan. In a similar synthesis[1356], sulfanilamide was dissolved as its sodium salt in phenol at 160°C. and S-ethylisothiourea sulfate was added gradually. When evolution of ethyl mercaptan had ceased, benzene was added to the melt and crude sulfaguanidine was precipitated.

(F) Manufacture of Sulfadiazine

(1) 2-Aminopyrimidine

Synthesis of this compound starts with isocytosine as the first main intermediate[434, 1861]. This may be made by the series of reactions[642]:

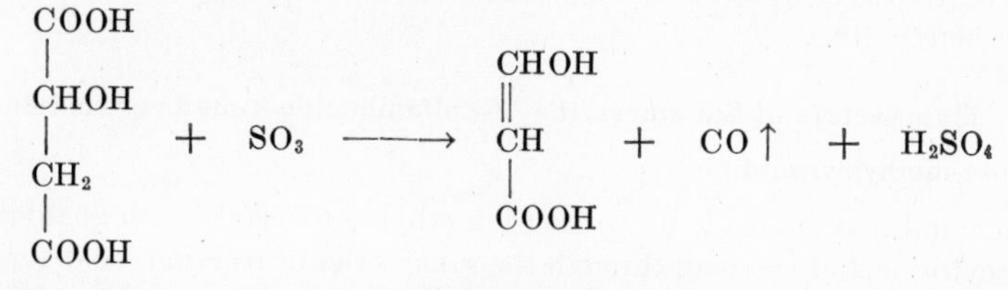

Malic acid   *Formylacetic acid*

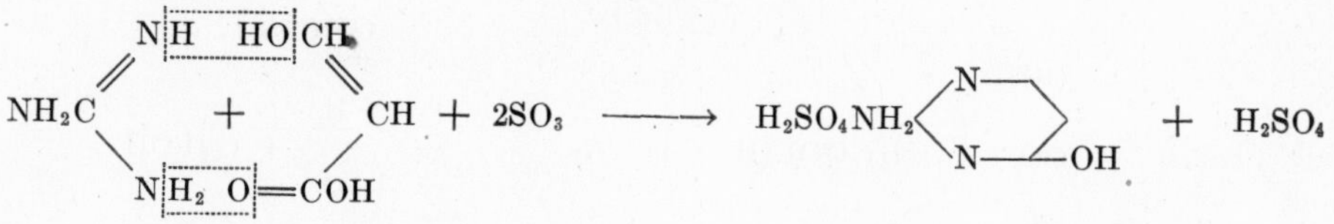

Guanidine   *Isocytosine acid sulfate*

The malic acid is dissolved in 20% oleum with cooling below 10°C. Guanidine carbonate is added and the reaction mixture warmed to about 40°C. until gas evolution ceases. Isocytosine is best isolated by drowning the sulfuric acid solution in refrigerated methanol when isocytosine acid sulfate precipitates. This is filtered and free isocytosine precipitated by treatment with aqueous ammonia with cooling. This is the most convenient laboratory process.

Commercially[1861] the following reactions are used:

$$HCOOC_2H_5 + CH_3COOC_2H_5 + NaOC_2H_5 \longrightarrow NaOCH = CHCOOC_2H_5$$

Sodium formylacetic ester

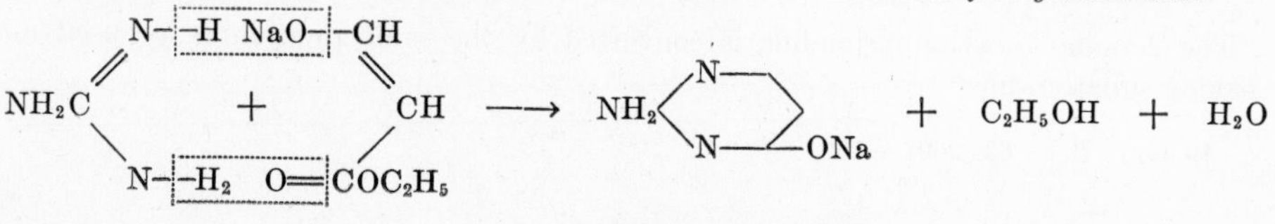

Sodium isocytosine

The slurry of sodium formylacetic ester is condensed with guanidine nitrate and additional sodium hydroxide to give sodium isocytosine. This is precipitated with acid giving isocytosine. Isocytosine is converted to 2-amino-4-chloropyrimidine by treatment with 1.5 moles phosphorous oxychloride and 0.25 mole sulfuric or chlorosulfonic acid[635]. The 2-amino-4-chloropyrimidine is isolated by drowning the reaction mixture in ice and neutralizing.

2-Amino-4-chloropyrimidine may be dechlorinated by treatment with hydrogen under pressure using palladium catalyst in the presence of barium hydroxide[434]. Commercially the dechlorination is carried out with zinc dust in the presence of ammonia and sodium bicarbonate. 2-Aminopyrimidine is isolated from the filtrate of the zinc sludge by extraction with an organic solvent such as isopropyl acetate[637] or by precipitation as the insoluble sulfite followed by conversion to free 2-aminopyrimidine with aqueous ammonia[636].

In another process[1830], the dechlorination is carried out with zinc dust and acid and the 2-aminopyrimidine is isolated as an equimolecular complex with zinc chloride.

(2) Sulfadiazine

2-Aminopyrimidine is condensed with dry ASC in dry pyridine to give 2-(N^4-acetylsulfanilamido)pyrimidine which is hydrolyzed to sulfadiazine with sodium hydroxide. All the alternative syntheses for sulfapyridine starting with 2-aminopyridine will work analogously here[434, 1748].

(G) Manufacture of Sulfamerazine (2-Sulfanilamido-4-methylpyrimidine)

(1) 2-Amino-4-methylpyrimidine

This compound may be made by condensing ethylacetoacetate with guanidine to give 6-methylisocytosine and carrying through the same series of reactions as described under sulfadiazine[637]. A more direct synthesis is as follows:[a]

Sodium formylacetone

Guanidine nitrate   *2-Amino-4-methylpyrimidine*

(2) Sulfamerazine

The 2-amino-4-methylpyrimidine is converted by the same procedures as used for making sulfapyridine[434, 493].

[a] Benary, *Ber.*, **63**, 2601 (1930).

(H) Manufacture of "Sulfamethazine" (2-Sulfanilamido-4,6-dimethylpyrimidine)

(1) 2-Amino-4,6-dimethylpyrimidine

Acetylacetone (prepared by the condensation of ethyl acetate and acetone in the presence of sodium or sodium methylate; or by pyrolysis of dehydroacetic acid) is condensed with guanidine carbonate in a suitable solvent such as toluene, giving excellent yields of the free base.

(2) Sulfamethazine

2-Amino-4,6-dimethylpyrimidine is converted by the same procedures as for sulfapyridine[436, 1747, 2399].

In a second process, acetylacetone and sulfaguanidine condense directly by 18 hour heating at 130°C.[1355].

Sulfanilylguanidine
(Sulfaguanidine)

Acetylacetone

2-Sulfanilamido-4,6-dimethyl-
pyrimidine (Sulfamethazine)

(3) Other Condensations with Sulfaguanidine

Similar condensation of N^4-acetylsulfanilylguanidine with sodium formylacetic ester gives 2-(N^4-acetylsulfanilamido)-4-hydroxypyrimidine[1146]. The reaction can also be carried out with substituted acetoacetic esters, using sodium ethoxide as condensing agent, giving 2-(N^4-acetylsulfanilamido)-4-hydroxy-5-alkyl-6-methylpyrimidines.

(I) Manufacture of Bis(4-aminophenyl) Sulfone and Derivatives

A satisfactory laboratory procedure[433, 1077] involves reduction of ASC with sodium sulfite to give sodium p-acetamidobenzenesulfinate. This is condensed with p-nitrochlorobenzene to give 4-(4′-nitrophenylsulfonyl)acetanilide which can be simultaneously reduced and hydrolyzed with tin and hydrochloric acid to give bis(4-aminophenyl) sulfone[77, 458]. The reaction of sodium or silver sulfinate with active halogen compounds is quite general and may be used to prepare mixed alkyl or heterocyclic aryl sulfones as well[433].

The intermediate, 4-(4′-nitrophenylsulfonyl)acetanilide, is a convenient starting material for unsymmetrically substituted phenyl sulfones. By hydrolysis with acid 4-(4′-nitrophenylsulfonyl)aniline results. The free amino group can then be alkylated, acylated, converted to an anil, diazotized and coupled, etc. The nitro group can later be reduced and a different substituent introduced on the resulting 4′-amino group[433].

Another method of synthesizing sulfones is by oxidation of the corresponding sulfides or sulfoxides, with peroxides, permanganate or wet chlorine. Any amino groups should be protected by acetylation before oxidation, but normally these are not present because the starting compounds will be acylamino or nitro derivatives[155, 237, 419, 525, 1137], which can later be hydrolyzed or reduced.

The bis(4-halophenyl) sulfones may be aminated under pressure at 230°C. with a copper catalyst and ammonia or amines to give the corresponding bis(4-aminophenyl) sulfones[220, 281, 1095]. The bis(4-halophenyl) sulfones may be made by the reaction of a 4-halobenzene-sulfonyl chloride with a halobenzene in the presence of aluminum chloride.[a]

[a] For further references on the synthesis and chemistry of sulfones see C. M. Suter, "The Organic Chemistry of Sulfur, Tetracovalent Sulfur Compounds," John Wiley and Sons, Inc., New York, 1944.

Chapter III

STRUCTURE AND ACTIVITIES OF SIMPLE SULFANILAMIDE DERIVATIVES

In this chapter, all of the derivatives of sulfanilamide are considered in which either the nucleus (benzene ring), N^1-(amide nitrogen) or N^4-(amine nitrogen) positions are mono- or polysubstituted but where substitution in more than one of these positions is excluded. Also included are the various salts of sulfanilamide. Salts of sulfanilamide derivatives are listed in the tables following the parent compound, but no attempt has been made to search the literature exhaustively for such salts.

A key to the activities is given in Appendix A.

(I) Salts of Sulfanilamide (Tables 1, 2 and 3, p. 51)

Sulfanilamide and its N^1-monosubstituted derivatives are amphoteric compounds capable of forming salts with both acids and bases. Sulfanilamide is a very weak acid having an acid dissociation constant, Ka, of 3.7×10^{-11}. Its base constant, Kb, is 2.3×10^{-12}. It would, therefore, be expected that both types of salts would be highly hydrolyzed and that well characterized salts would be formed only with the stronger acids and bases. This seems true of salts with acids but it is surprising to find such salts as those of aluminum and bismuth listed; however, proof of their existence as true salts is lacking.

Many mixed salts with the chinchona alkaloids have been made. There would seem to be many such compounds possible but little urge to make them because stoichiometric proportions of drugs are not always proper combinations for best therapeutic response and compounds of this type are probably too loosely bound to have any therapeutic value *per se*.

None of the salts of sulfanilamide are thought to be used clinically at present because free sulfanilamide is well absorbed when given orally and for intravenous injection the sodium salts of the more potent derivatives are now used. These are more effective and less dangerous because they are not as highly alkaline.

Todd[2332] reported a cuprous complex with sulfanilamide which interfered when making the usual test for sugars in urine. This was formed as a white crystalline product which on analysis gave the formula $(C_6H_8N_2SO_2)_2Cu_3(OH)_2$.

(II) Nuclear-substituted Sulfanilamides (Tables 4 and 5, p. 52)

The nuclear-substituted derivatives of sulfanilamide have not been extensively investigated either chemically or pharmacologically. The reason for this appears to be the uniform low activities so far encountered in this series.

(III) N^1-Substituted Sulfanilamides

This class of sulfanilamide derivatives has been very extensively explored and now numbers 963 compounds. Most of the therapeutically important new sulfonamide drugs are members of this series.

(A) N^1-Acyclicsulfanilamides

(1) $R = C_nH_{2n+1}$ to C_nH_{2n-1} (Table 6, p. 54)

Synthesis. These compounds are readily synthesized from the corresponding aliphatic amines by reaction with acetylsulfanilyl chloride, usually in aqueous solution at 40–50°C. and with gradual addition of sufficient sodium hydroxide or sodium carbonate to maintain

21

a pH of 8 to 11. The N^4-acetyl-N^1-alkylsulfanilamides may be isolated by acidification to pH 3 to 6, filtration, and washing with dilute acid to remove unreacted amine. The acetyl group may then be hydrolyzed by boiling with 10 to 20% hydrochloric acid or by boiling with about 2.5 moles of sodium hydroxide in about 1 molar concentration of drug. N^1,N^1-dialkyl derivatives are best hydrolyzed with acid because they are incapable of forming soluble sodium salts.

Long chain aliphatic amines having poor water solubility may be reacted with ASC in acetone, dioxane or pyridine solution.

Pharmacology. The N^1-alkylsulfanilamides show somewhat lower activities than sulfanilamide for the methyl and ethyl derivatives, then a rapidly decreasing activity *in vivo* with increased length of carbon chain.   Probably low absorption accounts for the lack of *in vivo* activity of long chain derivatives, while low water solubility prevents determination of *in vitro* activity. N^1,N^1-dimethylsulfanilamide is slightly less active than the monomethyl.   Inability of N^1-disubstituted sulfanilamide derivatives to ionize probably accounts for the low activities of such compounds (see Ionization Theories, Chapter XI).

(2) Oxy and Oxo Derivatives (Table 7, p. 55)

Synthesis. These compounds can be made by the same methods as (1) above.

Pharmacology. These compounds appear slightly more active as a class *in vivo* than are the corresponding unsubstituted alkyl derivatives.   This is probably because of better absorption characteristics rather than higher inherent activity because comparative *in vitro* studies on *E. coli*[719, 1057] show lower rather than higher activities for these compounds. There is some indication, however, both *in vitro*[2441] and *in vivo* of a moderate degree of specificity of action against different organisms but much more work would be necessary to draw definite conclusions.   There is no great urge to do this work because of the lack of sufficient activity in the series to justify it on practical grounds.

Studies of the distribution of N^1-hydroxyethylsulfanilamide in the body tissues showed it to be similar to sulfanilamide at the start.   At the end of 24 hours, however, the distribution had changed until it closely resembled sulfanilylglycine, *i.e.* the hydroxymethyl group had probably been oxidized to carboxy[1097].

(3) Carboxy and Sulfo Derivatives (Table 8, p. 56)

Synthesis. The amino acids can be reacted with ASC under much the same conditions as above, under (1).

Pharmacology. Sulfanilylglycine (2-sulfanilamidoacetic acid) has been studied fairly extensively but all *in vivo* tests indicate a lack of appreciable activity.   Some activity was shown against pneumococcus *in vitro*[2441] and slight activity against streptococcus and *E. coli*[1057, 2441].   The lack of *in vivo* activity may be explained by the fact that the drug is poorly absorbed, rapidly excreted, and does not penetrate the tissues of the body well[1097].   It, therefore, does not reach the site of an infection in sufficient concentration to be effective.   The esters of sulfanilylamino acids are no better, probably because they are readily hydrolyzed in the body.

The sulfanilamidoaliphaticsulfonic acids would be expected to have even poorer absorption-excretion characteristics because of a further increase in anionic strength and this seems borne out in their lack of activity.

(4) Amino Derivatives (Table 9, p. 57)

Pharmacology. The activities of these derivatives are of a very low order.   Theoretical considerations, would predict that a strong cationic group such as a tertiary aliphatic amine would lead to absorption difficulties and low activity (see Cowles-Brueckner Theory, Chapter XI).

A number of these compounds were made from the dialkylaminoalkylamine intermediates found useful as antimalarials when linked to quinoline or acridine nuclei. No antimalarial activity appears to be present in sulfanilyl derivatives of these amines.

(B) N^1-Isocyclicsulfanilamides

The availability from the dyestuff industry of a wide variety of aromatic amines stimulated the synthesis of the corresponding sulfanilyl derivatives. Some of the derivatives showed slightly greater therapeutic effect than sulfanilamide and this further encouraged synthesis so that some 223 members of this class have now been made. Several of these compounds were studied clinically but none has survived competition from the more potent drugs now available.

(1) $R = C_nH_{2n-1}$ to C_nH_{2n-25} (Table 10, p. 58)

Synthesis. The general method works well for almost all these derivatives.

Pharmacology. The N^1-cycloalkylsulfanilamides are similar to the long chain N^1-alkylsulfanilamides in showing little or no activity.

N^1-Phenylsulfanilamide (sulfanilanilide) was one of the first derivatives of sulfanilamide to be made[168] and studied[61]. It was said to be slightly more potent than sulfanilamide *in vivo*. This was verified for its *in vitro* activity against *E. coli*[719] and pneumococci[1057] but not against streptococci[1057]. Further *in vivo* studies have also failed to verify a higher activity than sulfanilamide. Probably a large share of the reason for low *in vivo* activity is because the compound is actively secreted by the renal tubules of the kidney so that blood levels of the drug are poorly maintained[1097].

N^1-(4-Fluorophenyl)sulfanilamide was said to have a delayed toxic effect, following a single intraperitoneal dose, in which deaths occurred 30 to 50 hours after administration.

N^1-(4-Nitrophenyl)sulfanilamide has had varying reports of relative activity but the more recent work would indicate that it is less potent and more toxic than sulfanilamide against streptococci and has little or no activity against other test organisms *in vivo*. *In vitro* results indicate some activity against streptococci, pneumococci, *staphylococci* and *E. coli*[332].

1-Sulfanilamido-2-methylnaphthalene was so insoluble that *in vitro* studies could not be made at concentrations in excess of 1 mg.% at which level it was inactive against *E. coli* and pneumococci, (types I and III). It was also almost completely inactive against mouse pneumonia, but this could be explained by the low blood levels of drug, which did not exceed 0.4 mg. per 100 cc.[1135]

(2) **Oxy Derivatives** (Table 11, p. 60)

Synthesis. Synthesis of derivatives with free phenolic hydroxyls is complicated by the formation of appreciable quantities of the phenol esters of acetylsulfanilic acid during condensation of the aminophenol with ASC. This necessitates using excess ASC and using sufficient excess sodium hydroxide during hydrolysis to take care of the increased amount of acidic products formed.

Pharmacology. The isomeric and substituted sulfanilamidophenols appear to have slight but definite activity against the usual test organisms both *in vitro*[2441] and *in vivo* but in no case has the activity been sufficiently high to warrant clinical use. 2-Methyl-4-sulfanilamido-1-naphthol was somewhat more active than sulfanilamide *in vitro* against *E. coli* and pneumococci, types I and III, but showed practically no activity *in vivo* in mouse pneumonia[1135]. Low blood levels probably accounted for the low survival rate in part.

Not shown in Table 11 is the compound,

$$H_2N\langle \rangle SO_2N\langle \rangle OC_2H_5$$
$$|$$
$$CH(CH_3)_2$$

which was reported as saving 100% of mice infected with streptococci[2583]. This result is so unusual in sulfonamide compounds devoid of acid dissociation characteristics that it is hoped others will study this compound.

(3) Thio Derivatives (Table 12, p. 61)

A number of these derivatives have been made and patented but do not appear to have been sufficiently active to have been extensively studied pharmacologically.

(4) Oxo Derivatives (Table 13, p. 61)

Synthesis. 2-Sulfanilamido-1,4-naphthoquinone was prepared by the fusion of the sodium salt of sulfanilamide and 2-chloro-1,4-naphthoquinone.

Pharmacology. 4-Sulfanilamidoacetophenone was said to be about as active as sulfanilamide against streptococci but to be less toxic. Its rate of excretion in the dog was about the same as sulfanilamide[363]. Others have failed to verify appreciable activity for the compound either *in vitro* or *in vivo*[332] against the common test organisms.

2-Sulfanilamido-1,4-naphthoquinone was said to have an *in vitro* bacteriostatic activity comparable to sulfapyridine against pneumococci (types I and III) and *E. coli*[1135] but was synthesized in the hope of finding antitubercular activity[2207]. Of fifteen naphthoquinone derivatives tested *in vitro*, it was the only one worthy of further study in experimental tuberculosis[1593].

(5) Carboxy Derivatives (Table 14, p. 62)

Synthesis. These are readily prepared from the aminobenzoic acids by reaction with ASC in aqueous solution with addition of base to keep the pH 6–10. The acetyl derivative is readily hydrolyzed by boiling with about 3.5 moles of sodium hydroxide.

Pharmacology. Wide variations in activities *in vivo* have been reported for the isomeric sulfanilamidobenzoic acids. Studies of distribution and excretion[1097] show that the compounds appear in the tissues in very low concentrations as compared with the blood level, are bound in high percentage to the plasma proteins, and are excreted very rapidly by the kidney. Hence, locus of an experimental infection and dosage schedule would have a profound influence on the *in vivo* results. *In vitro* results[1057, 2441] indicate appreciable activity for the three isomers, particularly against pneumococcus. The poor absorption-distribution-excretion characteristics make the compounds as a class impractical as chemotherapeutic agents, however.

(6) Sulfino and Sulfo Derivatives (Table 15, p. 63)

Synthesis. See (5) above.

Pharmacology. Activities of the sulfinic acid derivatives have not been reported. The sulfonic acid derivatives have been studied rather extensively but have still less favorable absorption-distribution-excretion characteristics than the corresponding carboxylic acids[1097], hence are of no importance in systemic infections.

Sodium sulfanilylsulfanilate has been studied by a number of workers in virus diseases. Dochez and Slanetz[114] tried it against dog distemper in ferrets and dogs and claimed it to be effective. MacIntyre and Montgomerie[326] and Plummer, *et al.*[1937] were unable to duplicate these results. Hebb, Sullivan and Felton[187, 1069] claimed it to be effective in treatment of lymphogranuloma venereum. It was ineffective against rabies virus[1214] and influenza[112, 1147, 1864].

Ratish and Bullowa[2003] studied the pharmacology of the compound in both animal and human subjects. They found that when it was given orally only trace amounts appeared in the blood. About 5% was recovered from the urine and 40% from the feces over a 72-hour period. A considerable concentration was found in the bile. High blood levels appeared on intravenous injection but excretion in the urine was rapid; 3/4 of the total recovered was excreted within two hours. The high concentrations of drug obtainable in feces were probably responsible for favorable effects on lesions of the bowel, as reported by Levy, Holder and Bullowa[1562].

This compound is unusual in that it forms a comparatively stable crystalline salt containing benzene of crystallization[98].

(7) Amino and Azo Derivatives (Table 16, p. 64)

Synthesis. N^1-Aminophenylsulfanilamides are best synthesized from the corresponding monoacetylphenylenediamines (or nitroanilines) by the general reaction with ASC, followed by hydrolysis of both acetyl groups (or by hydrolysis and reduction).

Pharmacology. The isomeric N^1-aminophenylsulfanilamides have been extensively studied, particularly in Europe. Conflicting reports of *in vivo* activities have been made, reflecting different techniques of testing. Absorption-distribution-excretion characteristics of the 4-isomer appear favorable[1097], and as a matter of historical interest this compound in the form of its tartrate salt was used clinically in Europe but was withdrawn because it caused a high incidence of peripheral neuritis. *In vitro* activities[332, 1057, 2441] of the three isomers were definite but of a lower order than sulfanilamide.

(8) Miscellaneous Derivatives (Table 17, p. 66)

(C) N^1-Heterocyclicsulfanilamides

The N^1-heterocyclic derivatives of sulfanilamide comprise most of the important new derivatives of the parent compound showing increased bacteriostatic potencies and better therapeutic response in clinical practice. They have received very intensive study, such that the published members of this general class increased from 76 compounds in 1940 to 393 in 1945. This represents a considerable expenditure of effort because the amino-heterocycles are not easy intermediates to synthesize. Many were synthesized for the first time as part of this program.

Structure. The structure of heterocyclic derivatives of sulfanilamide has been studied by a number of investigators. The N^1-pyridyl and N^1-thiazolyl derivatives have received the most attention. Enough work has been done to state definitely that many assigned structures in the literature are incorrect. It is obviously of considerable importance to workers in the field to know the structure of compounds they are making and testing, since erroneous conclusions and deductions can be made on the basis of faulty structures particularly when attempts are made to correlate structures with chemotherapeutic activities. An attempt has been made on the basis of what is now known of structures to classify the older compounds in the literature correctly, based on the method of synthesis rather than on the name originally assigned.

Three structures are conceivable for the reaction product of acetylsulfanilyl chloride with 2-aminopyridine. These are:

$$CH_3CONH \langle\rangle SO_2N-\underset{H}{N} \qquad\qquad CH_3CONH \langle\rangle SO_2N=\overset{H}{N}$$

(I)   (II)

and $CH_3CONH \langle\rangle SO_2$

$$NH=\overset{N}{\langle\rangle}$$

(III)

Of these, (III) is ruled out by the preparation of *two* isomeric methyl derivatives by alkylation with diazomethane[2189] and by the fact that no ammonia is lost with production of a pyridone derivative by alkaline hydrolysis[102]. The isomeric methyl derivatives of structures (IV) and (V) differ markedly in melting point and in chemotherapeutic activity.

$$NH_2 \langle\rangle SO_2N-\underset{CH_3}{N} \qquad\qquad NH_2 \langle\rangle SO_2N=\overset{CH_3}{\overset{N}{\;}}$$

(IV)   *Mpt. 86.5-87.0°*   (V)   *Mpt. 232-233°*

Compounds of type (IV) are low melting, toxic and practically devoid of activity, while compounds of type (V) are high melting and have slight to moderate chemotherapeutic activity.

Structure of N^1-methyl-2-sulfanilamidopyridine (IV) has been established by synthesis from 2-bromopyridine and N^1-methylsulfanilamide (or the corresponding nitro or acetyl derivative[341] and through degradation by acid hydrolysis to sulfanilic acid and 2-methyl-aminopyridine[2189].

Structure of 1-methyl-2-sulfanilimido-1,2-dihydropyridine (V) was established by synthesis from 1-methyl-2-pyridoneimine[413], and by acid hydrolysis to the 1-methyl-2-pyridoneimine and sulfanilic acid[2189].

Alkylation of the sodium salt of sulfapyridine with usual alkylating agents, such as the dialkylsulfates and alkyl halides, leads to compounds of structure (V). Reaction of sulfapyridine with diazomethane gives compounds of structures both (IV) and (V), in the yield ratio of 70:30 (or 60:40 starting with N^4-acetylsulfapyridine)[2189].

The ultraviolet absorption spectra of a number of the N^4-acetyl compounds were investigated[2189]. It was found that compounds of type (IV) show an absorption maxima at about 2650 Å, while compounds of type (V) show maxima at both this point and at 3215 Å. 1-Alkylpyridoneimines show a single absorption band with a maximum absorption at 3050 Å. It was, therefore, reasoned that this second band was characteristic for the pyridoneimine structure. N^4-Acetylsulfapyridine was found to show both maxima;

however, the absorption at 3215 Å was weaker than that shown by the alkylated compound of structure (V). On the basis of this evidence it was estimated that N^4-acetylsulfapyridine contains about 60% structure (II).

The absorption spectrum evidence was weakened by findings on the corresponding derivatives of sulfathiazole where the bond at 2600 Å was assigned to the 2-imino-4-thiazoline structure. This was singular since absorption in this region was supposedly a function of the rest of the molecule in the sulfapyridine series and it was to be expected that the sulfanilyl group in sulfathiazole would also absorb in the region. It was probably fortuitous that 2-imino-3-methyl-4-thiazoline happened to absorb at about 2600 Å also.

In a more thorough study of the absorption spectra of sulfathiazole and related compounds, Vandenbelt and Doub[2650] ascribed the 2670–2590 Å band to the sulfanilamide portion of the molecule and the 2800–2830 Å band to the thiazole structure. These authors investigated the effects of pH on the absorption spectra of various heterocyclic sulfonamides including the sulfanilamido-, acetylsulfanilamido-, and benzenesulfonamido-derivatives of thiazole, pyridine and pyrimidine, from which the above conclusions were reached.

It appears that the question of the structure, or specifically the distribution of tautomeric and resonance structures, of the heterocyclic derivatives has not been settled as yet. The possible correlations between structures and chemotherapeutic activities in this series of compounds make further study of this subject desirable (see Resonance Theories, Chapter XI).

Druey[184, 1007], Jensen[246, 249] and others have studied the structure of sulfathiazole and related compounds. The isomeric compounds:

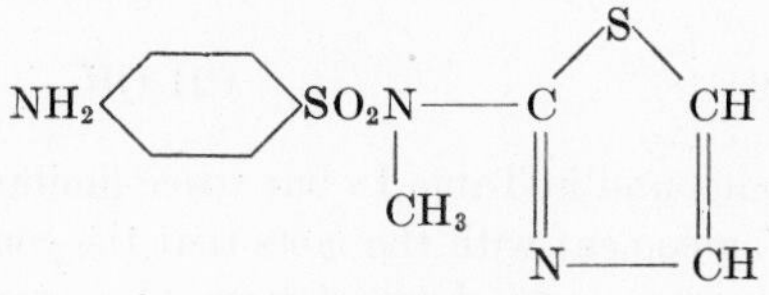

(I)   *Mpt. 109°*

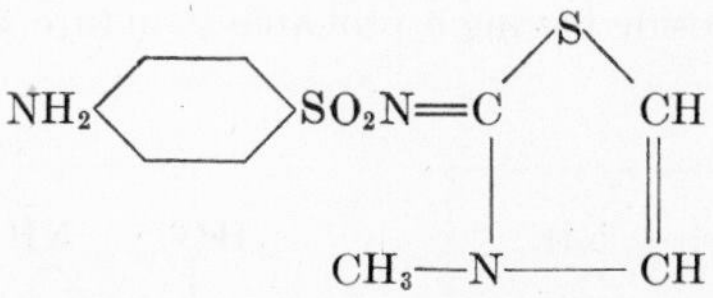

(II)   *Mpt. 245°*

are both known. Structure (II) results from methylation of acetylsulfathiazole with dimethylsulfate (or methyl iodide) followed by alkaline hydrolysis of the acetyl group with acid; or by reaction of ASC with the corresponding 2-imino-3-methyl-4-thiazoline, followed by hydrolysis. Structure (I) results from reaction of 2-methylaminothiazole with acetylsulfanilyl chloride, followed by hydrolysis; or by reaction of 2-bromothiazole with N^1-methyl-N^4-acetylsulfanilamide in the presence of copper powder, followed by hydrolysis of the acetyl group.

Druey[1007] suggested because compound (II) was active therapeutically, while compound (I) was inactive, that it was possibly the imino form of sulfathiazole which was active.   He pointed out that amino-imino tautomerism was possible in all the highly active commercial sulfanilamide derivatives; *viz.* sulfapyridine, sulfadiazine, sulfaguanidine and N^1-acetylsulfanilamide (Albucid, sulfacetamide).

Synthesis.   The aminoheterocycles are such weak bases that appreciable yields of the desired sulfonamides are rarely obtained in aqueous reaction media.   Instead, dry ASC is usually reacted with the aminoheterocycle in dry pyridine.   For further details of this and other methods of synthesis see Chapter II under Manufacture of Sulfapyridine or Sulfathiazole.   See also above, under discussion of Structure.

(1) One or More O- or S-Atoms in the Heterocyclic System (Table 18, p. 66)

Structure.   The compounds listed in Table 18 offer no problems in determination of structure.   Jackson[1366] has prepared the sulfanilyl derivative of D-glucosamine for which he gives the structure:

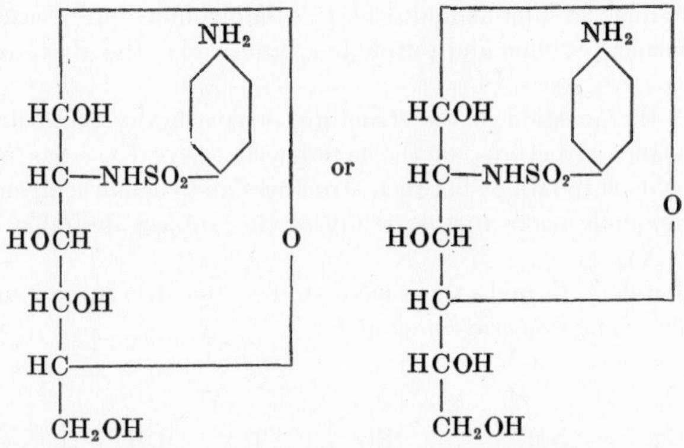

$$
\begin{array}{ccc}
& \text{NH}_2 & \\
\text{HCOH} & & \\
\text{HC—NHSO}_2\text{—} & & \\
\text{HOCH} \qquad \text{O} & & \\
\text{HCOH} & & \\
\text{HC—} & & \\
\text{CH}_2\text{OH} & &
\end{array}
\qquad \text{or} \qquad
\begin{array}{c}
\text{NH}_2 \\
\text{HCOH} \\
\text{HC—NHSO}_2\text{—} \\
\text{HOCH} \qquad \text{O} \\
\text{HC—} \\
\text{HCOH} \\
\text{CH}_2\text{OH}
\end{array}
$$

This would place the compound in Table 18 but space limitations prevented inclusion.

These structures are in agreement with the facts that the compound reduces Fehling's solution, undergoes diazotization, and shows downward mutarotation in aqueous solution.   Melting point was 202° with decomposition.   On treatment with 50% acetic acid the compound forms a glucoside having a probable structure represented by either of the two formulae:

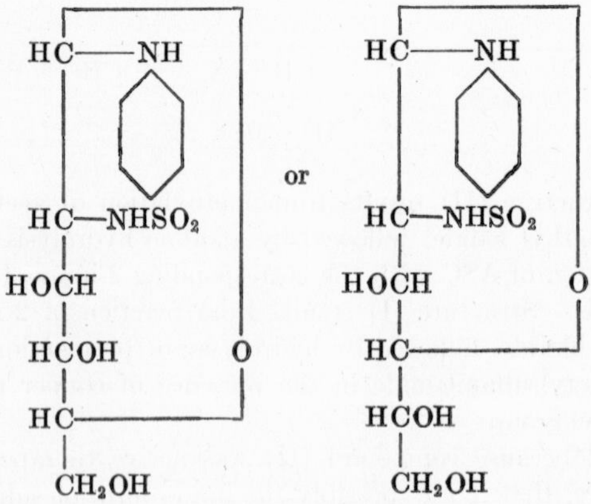

$$
\begin{array}{c}
\text{HC——NH} \\
\text{HC—NHSO}_2 \\
\text{HOCH} \\
\text{HCOH} \qquad \text{O} \\
\text{HC—} \\
\text{CH}_2\text{OH}
\end{array}
\qquad \text{or} \qquad
\begin{array}{c}
\text{HC——NH} \\
\text{HC—NHSO}_2 \\
\text{HOCH} \qquad \text{O} \\
\text{HC—} \\
\text{HCOH} \\
\text{CH}_2\text{OH}
\end{array}
$$

This compound does not undergo mutarotation and cannot be diazotized. It decomposes above 235°C. On heating with $N/10$ hydrochloric acid it is apparently hydrolyzed back to N-sulfanilyl-D-glucosamine. This compound is covered in the German patent literature[1858].

Pharmacology. Pharmacological tests indicate that N-sulfanilyl-D-glucosamine is poorly absorbed but that given subcutaneously adequate blood levels are reached. The compound is completely inactive *in vivo* and has little or no activity *in vitro* on pneumococcus (type I) or hemolytic streptococci[1366].

The other compounds of Table 18 have not received extensive study but do not appear to have much promise as therapeutic agents. 2-Sulfanilamidothiophene showed activity equal to sulfapyridine *in vitro* against *E. coli*, and pneumococci (type I and type III) but showed no protection against pneumococci *in vivo*. It did not give blood concentrations of more than 1 mg./100 cc.; further, it was fairly toxic ($LD_{50} = 0.45$ Gm./kilo[1135].)

(2) One N-Atom in the Heterocyclic System

(a), (b), (c) *Sulfanilamidopyridines* (Tables 19, 20, 21, p. 68-70)

The success of 2-sulfanilamidopyridine in treatment of pneumonia (Chapter XII) led to synthesis of many substituted and isomeric sulfanilamidopyridines. The only one of these to have survived screening tests and other considerations is 2-sulfanilamido-6-methylpyridine which apparently is used to some extent in Russia under the name, methylsulfidine. The intermediate, 2-amino-6-methylpyridine, can be produced by the sodamide process starting with the readily available 2-picoline. The 3-sulfanilamidopyridine, which is said to be as active as sulfapyridine, has not been extensively investigated because there is no economical method of producing the intermediate, 3-aminopyridine.

Synthesis. For synthesis of sulfapyridine see Chapter II. Derivatives can be made by the same general methods.

Pharmacology. For the pharmacology of sulfapyridine see Chapter X. 2-Sulfanilamido-6-methylpyridine was said to be slightly inferior to sulfapyridine in potency while causing an even higher incidence of nausea[1740].

Substitution of long chain alkyl groups on the amide nitrogen of sulfapyridine gave a series of compounds which proved ineffective in experimental tuberculosis[2260]. Substitution of the pyridine ring with carboxyl, carbonyl, sulfo, sulfanilamido or sulfamyl groups appeared to destroy *in vivo* activity but this may have been through introduction of poor absorption-excretion characteristics to the compounds. 2-Sulfanilamido-5-sulfamyl-pyridine was said to have slight *in vitro* activity against staphylococci[1364].

An interesting series of isomeric compounds is provided by the 5-amino(and halo)-2-sulfanilamidopyridines and the corresponding 2-amino(and halo)-5-sulfanilamidopyridines. In *in vivo* studies[435], 5-amino-2-sulfanilamidopyridine was comparable with sulfapyridine in potency while the isomer was considerably less active. Exactly opposite results were obtained with the halogen derivatives, where the 2-halo-5-sulfanilamidopyridines were much more active than the isomers. Differences in absorption-excretion characteristics did not explain variations in activity.

(d) *2-Sulfanilimido-1,2-dihydropyridines* (Table 22, p. 70)

Synthesis. Most of these compounds were made by alkylation of the sodium salt of 2-(N^4-acetylsulfanilamido)pyridine with the corresponding halide of the R^1 substituent, followed by acid hydrolysis.

Pharmacology. Although more active than the isomeric N^1-alkyl-2-sulfanilamido-pyridines, the 1-alkyl-2-sulfanilimido-1,2-dihydropyridines are less active than sulfa-pyridine. Thus, the 1-methyl derivative had 1/4 activity of sulfapyridine against *E. coli*, *in vitro*, while the 1-(β-hydroxyethyl) derivative had 1/128 and the 1-(carboxymethyl) derivative had 1/256 the activity[2189].

(e) *Miscellaneous Pyridine Derivatives* (Table 23, p. 70)

Pharmacology. While results of the pharmacological study of these compounds have not been published, it may be predicted that such compounds would behave more as N^1-alkylsulfanilamides than as N^1-pyridylsulfanilamides and hence have activities of the order of sulfanilamide or less.

(f) *x-Sulfanilamidoquinolines* (Table 24, p. 71)

Structure. The structure of the (N^1-substituted sulfanilamido)-quinolines[338] listed is open to serious doubt since they were made by reaction of diethylaminoethyl chloride with the respective sulfanilamidoquinolines. In the case of other sulfanilamido hetero-cycles this type of reaction leads to substitution on the ring nitrogen giving rise to 1-alkyl-2-sulfanilimido-1,2-dihydroheterocycles. It would be surprising to find these compounds exceptions, yet the low melting points are characteristic of N^1 rather than ring-N-sub-stitution.

Pharmacology. The seven isomeric sulfanilamidoquinolines have each been tested *in vitro* and claimed to be as active as sulfapyridine against type I pneumococci[463]. *In vivo*, however, the compounds are less active and more toxic. Certain of the substituted sulfanilamidoquinolines have been tested against duck malaria with disappointing results.

(g) *x-Sulfanilamidoisoquinolines* (Table 25, p. 72)

Pharmacology. The results of activity tests on 1-sulfanilamidoisoquinoline are quite discordant. The antistreptococcal activity is said in one case[97] to be comparable with sulfadiazine and in other cases to be almost nil[137, 1057].

(h) *Miscellaneous N^1-Heterocyclicsulfanilamides with one N-Atom in the Heterocyclic System* (Table 26, p. 73)

Pharmacology. The pharmacology of these compounds has not been disclosed but based on analogy, few of them would be expected to show appreciable activity *in vivo*, either because the substitution is through an aliphatic chain or because the molecular size is so great for the number of solubilizing groups present that absorption of the drug becomes questionable. 2-Sulfanilamidopyrrole showed a low order of activity *in vitro* against *E. coli*, type I and III pneumococci, hence was not further investigated[1135]. It is soluble—4.8 gm./liter.

(3) Two or More N-Atoms in the Heterocyclic System

Because of the wide variety of compounds in this classification it has been further subdivided.

(a) *5-Membered Heterocyclic Rings* (Table 27, p. 75)

Pharmacology. These compounds have not proved to have as interesting chemothera-peutic properties as the six membered heterocyclic rings containing two nitrogens. 3-Sulfanilamidopyrazole was slightly inferior to sulfapyridine against *E. coli* and pneumo-cocci, type I and III, *in vitro*[1135].

(b) *2-Sulfanilamidopyrimidines* (Table 28, p. 77)

The success of 2-sulfanilamidopyrimidine, or sulfadiazine, which is considered the most valuable of all the sulfa drugs, stimulated the synthesis of a very large number of derivatives. Of these, 2-sulfanilamido-4-methylpyrimidine (sulfamerazine) and 2-sulfanilamido-4,6-dimethylpyrimidine (sulfamethazine) have developed into important drugs. The synthesis of all of these is described in Chapter II. The other derivatives have been made by analogous methods.

Large differences in reported melting points of 2-sulfanilamido-4,6-dimethylpyrimidine are recorded. According to Sprague[2180] the lower melting form, melting at 175 to 178° crystallizes as an unstable hydrate which melts with effervescence, if heated rapidly, in the range 110 to 130°. The melt solidifies and remelts at 175–178°. If the heating is carried out slowly, the water is lost gradually and first melting occurs at 175–178°. On standing this low melting form changes to the form melting at 198–200°. Once this stable form has been produced in a laboratory it is difficult to prepare the low melting form. The still higher melting point of 236–240°[162] was a typographical error (personal communication).

The hydration of sulfamethazine also accounts for wide differences in reported solubilities. If the anhydrous, high-melting-point material is dissolved to form a saturated solution at a high temperature and the solution is cooled while in contact with the solid, the solution remains indefinitely supersaturated, apparently because it is not in equilibrium with another phase of the same material. Evidently the compound is hydrated in solution, or possibly is converted to the isomeric low melting form, so that it cannot crystallize on the particles of anhydrous, high-melting sulfamethazine. Thus Roblin, *et al.*[436] reported the solubility at 37° as 75 mg. per 100 cc. which was obtained by long standing of the anhydrous-high-melting sulfamethazine in contact with water at this temperature; while Caldwell, *et al.*[66] reported a solubility at 29° of 150 mg. per 100 cc. and Macartney, *et al.*[1645] gave 191 mg. per 100 cc. at 37° and pH 5.5.

The 2-sulfanilamido-4-methyl-5-*n*-amylpyrimidine melting at 188–190°[66] was shown not to be this, but 2-sulfanilamido-4-*n*-hexylpyrimidine instead, for which a higher melting point of 206–207° was found[493].

Pharmacology. The pharmacology of the clinically important drugs is discussed in Chapter X while their activities against experimental infections are given in Chapter VIII in the tables indicated.

It appears that substitution of long chain alkyl groups on the pyrimidine ring is detrimental to activity *in vivo*. Introduction of hydroxyl, a second sulfanilamido, or dialkylamino groups also lowers the activity markedly, probably by changing the absorption-excretion characteristics to the point where inadequate blood levels are achieved[653].

(c) (d) *4-and 5-Sulfanilamidopyrimidines* (Tables 29 and 30, p. 78)

Pharmacology. While both the 4 and 5-sulfanilamidopyrimidines appear active *in vitro* they do not appear to be as active *in vivo* as the 2-isomer. This cannot be blamed on inadequate blood levels and should be accepted with reservation since difficulties in synthesis have prevented adequate testing on experimental animals.

(e) *Miscellaneous N¹-Heterocyclicsulfanilamides Having 6-Membered Rings with Two N-Atoms* (Table 31, p. 79)

Synthesis. The isomers of sulfadiazine, 3-sulfanilamidopyridazine and 2-sulfanilamidopyrazine (sulfapyrazine), offer considerable difficulties in synthesis so that, while sulfapyrazine appears equal or superior to sulfadiazine in activity, its commercialization has not been accomplished, possibly for lack of a good commercial synthesis.

The structure of the compound having an N^1-methyl group[1146] is open to question because it was made by reaction with dimethylsulfate and this reagent is known to alkylate other sulfanilamidoheterocycles on the ring nitrogen.

Pharmacology. The pharmacology of sulfapyrazine is discussed in Chapter X. 3-Sulfanilamidopyridazine while it appeared as active as sulfadiazine against, *E. coli, streptococci or pneumococci, in vitro,* showed little or no activity against streptococci and pneumococci *in vivo* despite adequate blood levels of drug. No explanation for this anomaly has been found but further work would seem indicated since the preliminary results were obtained on too few animals to be reliable.

(f) *Miscellaneous N^1-Heterocyclicsulfanilamides with two N-Atoms in the Heterocyclic System* (Table 32, p. 81)

Pharmacology. Addition of a fused, saturated carbocyclic ring to the pyrimidine ring of sulfadiazine appeared to destroy activity.

The sulfanilamidoindazoles appeared to have good activity *in vitro* against *E. coli*[432] and streptococci[1502], but in the case of 3-sulfanilamidoindazole, the compound was not active against streptococci *in vivo* even though moderately good blood levels of drug were achieved[1057]. The *in vitro* activities against a large number of organisms were determined by Lawrence and Goetchius[2584] for the 3-, 5-, 6-, and 7-sulfanilamidoindazoles. The compounds were found to be comparable to sulfathiazole or sulfadiazine against the common test pathogens and against the gas gangrene organisms. They seemed more active than sulfathiazole against three species of *Brucella* in bacteriostatic tests where dilutions between 1:16,000 and 1:32,000 stopped growth. The organisms were not killed by concentrations of 0.1%, however. The bacteriostatic effect on *Brucella* was not as sensitive to antagonism by PABA, by several thousand fold, as the similar relationship with sulfathiazole. This would seem another exception to the contention that sulfa drugs are non-specific *in vitro* (see Chapter XI).

2-Sulfanilamidoquinoxaline, or sulfaquinoxaline, appeared to have only 1/32 the activity of sulfadiazine *in vitro* against *E. coli*[2639]; however, *in vivo* tests where the drugs were given only once per day gave considerably higher survival rates on pneumococcal and streptococcal infections with sulfaquinoxaline than with sulfathiazole or sulfadiazine. When the drugs were given on a six hourly schedule, sulfathiazole and sulfadiazine were superior. These results also held for *S. schottmülleri* and *S. aertrycke* infections in mice and probably indicated that sulfaquinoxaline maintained blood levels of drug over a much longer time than the other drugs but was not as effective a chemotherapeutic agent at a given blood level of drug.

(g) *N^1-Heterocyclicsulfanilamides with Three or More N-Atoms in the Heterocyclic System* (Table 33, p. 83)

Structure. The compound listed as 6-sulfanilamidopurine is open to some doubt as to its constitution because it is not readily soluble in dilute sodium hydroxide. It may be 7-sulfanilyl-6-aminopurine instead[1135]. This compound was so insoluble in water (1.3 mg. per 100 cc. at 20°) that its bacteriostatic activity could not be determined.

(4) One N-Atom and One O-, S- or Se-Atom in the Heterocyclic System

This general class of N^1-heterocyclicsulfanilamides contains some very active members and has been well investigated. Some 142 compounds have been described of this type.

Many of these compounds involve complications in synthesis through tendency of ASC to react with the ring nitrogen in the tautomeric form, as well as with the amino group.

(a) *One N- and One O-Atom in the Heterocyclic System* (Table 34, p. 85)

Pharmacology. 2-Sulfanilamidooxazole showed the anomalous behavior of being highly active *in vitro* against *E. coli* and pneumococci yet showing no activity *in vivo* against streptococci despite adequate blood levels of drug[653].

2-(O-Sulfanilamidophenyl)oxazole was found to be about as active as sulfadiazine against streptococci in mice and to have a low order of toxicity[846]. 2-Sulfanilamido-5-phenyloxazole was of comparable activity to sulfathiazole against *E. coli* and pneumococci type I and III *in vitro*[1135].

(b) *2-Sulfanilimidothiazolidines* (Table 53, p. 86)

(c) *2-Sulfanilamido-2-thiazolines* (Table 36, p. 87)

Synthesis. If 2-amino-2-thiazoline is reacted with ASC in aqueous sodium carbonate the product is largely 3-(N^4-acetylsulfanilyl)-2-iminothiazolidine which on acid hydrolysis gives 3-sulfanilyl-2-thiazolidone (Table 44)[1344]. When the reaction is run in anhydrous pyridine[240, 416] the product is largely 2-(N^4-acetylsulfanilimido)-3-(N^4-acetylsulfanilyl)-thiazolidine which on acid hydrolysis gives mainly 2-sulfanilamido-2-thiazoline but also some 2-sulfanilimido-3-sulfanilylthiazolidine and 3-sulfanilyl-2-thiazolidone.

Pharmacology. The parent compound of the series, 2-sulfanilamido-2-thiazoline, or sulfathiazoline, has been fairly well studied for activities against various pathogens and the results are given in Table 281. It has also received a certain amount of clinical study, the results of which apparently do not justify marketing the drug in competition with such drugs as sulfathiazole.

In vitro against *E. coli* and type I and III pneumococcus, sulfathiazoline had 1/5 the activity of sulfathiazole[1135].

Kolmer, Rule and Groskin[1473] studied the chronic toxicity of sulfathiazoline, as compared to sulfathiazole in rabbits and found the drugs very similar. Doses of 0.2 Gm. per kilo twice daily were borne for 10 days without fatality although there was kidney damage because of obstruction of the tubules, sometimes associated with tubular necrosis. There was also slight evidence of damage to liver and spleen. At 0.05 Gm. dosage there was no observable toxicity. Raiziss, Severac, and Moetsch[1977] also studied the chronic toxicity of the drug in dogs and the acute toxicity in mice and rabbits and found it slightly less toxic than sulfathiazole. Chemotherapeutic tests in mice on *Staphylococcus aureus* and pneumococcus showed the drug to be approximately equivalent to sulfathiazole.

Jacoby, Baron and Ollswang[1369] studied sulfathiazoline versus sulfathiazole in gonorrhea. With sulfathiazoline 83% of 88 cases were cured in 20 days with 5 cases showing toxic reactions, while with sulfathiazole 89% of 100 cases were cured in 12 days with 5 cases showing toxic reactions. Leberman and Alexander[1533] obtained 87.5% cures of 88 cases in an average of 3.2 days. Dosage was 4 Gms. per day for ten days.

Substitution of the N^1-nitrogen of sulfathiazoline by any of various groups appears to destroy the activity. A methyl group in either the 4 or 5 position on the thiazoline ring has little effect on activity, apparently.

(d) *2-Sulfanilamido-4-thiazolines* (Table 37, p. 87)

Synthesis. These compounds, which are isomeric with the 2-(N^1-substituted-sulfanilamido)thiazoles, were the subject of considerable confusion as to their structure in the early literature. They result from the alkylation of 2-(N^4-acetylsulfanilamido)thiazole in alkaline solution with alkyl halides or alkyl sulfates followed by hydrolysis with hydrochloric acid. Alternatively, 2-aminothiazole may be alkylated to 2-imino-3-alkyl-4-thiazoline before condensation with ASC or p-nitrobenzenesulfonyl chloride[1007]. These compounds are incapable of forming sodium salts. They are higher melting than the isomeric 2-(N^1-alkylsulfanilamido)thiazoles.

Pharmacology. While substitution of a methyl or an allyl group in the 3 position in these compounds gives lower activities (probably through prevention of ionization) than shown by sulfathiazole, the compounds still are comparable in activity to sulfanilamide. *In vitro* studies on *E. coli* showed 1/16 the activity of sulfathiazole for 3-methyl-2-sulfanilimido-4-thiazoline but only 1/1024 the activity for the isomeric 2-(N^1-methylsulfanilamido)thiazole[2189]. Substitution of longer chain alkyl groups or introduction of highly ionic substituents destroyed activity.

The 3-alkyl-2-sulfanilimido-4-thiazolines appear to be less toxic than the isomeric 2-(N^1-alkylsulfanilimido)thiazoles[2189] based on comparison of the methyl derivatives.

3-(2-Bromoallyl)-2-sulfanilamido-4-thiazoline was said to be toxic[1007].

(e) *2-Sulfanilamidothiazoles* (Table 38, p. 88)

Synthesis. See Chapter II for synthesis of sulfathiazole. Its homologues are made similarly.

The 2-(N^1-alkylsulfanilamido)thiazoles can be made by reaction of ASC or p-nitrobenzenesulfonyl chloride with 2-(alkylamino)thiazoles followed by hydrolysis or reduction. They may also be made by reaction of 2-bromothiazole with N^4-acetyl-N^1-alkylsulfanilamides in the presence of potassium carbonate and copper powder, followed by hydrolysis of the acetyl group[1007].

The 2-sulfanilamidocarboxythiazoles appear to decarboxylate readily. This may account for melting point discrepancies on these compounds because rate of heating will determine the composition of the material at the observed melting range.

Pharmacology. Sulfathiazole is the most potent of the sulfa drugs in general use. Its activities against a large number of organisms are given in Table 282, while its pharmacology is discussed in Chapter X and its clinical applications appear in Chapter XII.

2-Sulfanilamido-4-methylthiazole or sulfamethylthiazole ("Ultraseptyl", "Toriseptin, M", "M & B 838", "Ciba 3753") was studied clinically in this country for a brief period and said to be the best sulfa drug against staphylococcal infections. However, it was hastily withdrawn because it appeared to cause a high (2%) incidence of peripheral neuritis among patients. Its use seems to have continued in Europe despite this and other severe toxic reactions. Its activity appears to be equal to sulfathiazole against the common pathogens (see Table 283) and also in clinical studies[2546]. Like sulfathiazole it fails to reach really effective concentrations in the cerebrospinal fluid and is highly bound to blood proteins[1097]. A considerable portion of the drug also appeared to be metabolized to other products[2546].

2-Sulfanilamido-4-ethylthiazole was said to be considerably more toxic than the methyl derivative[39]. 2-Sulfanilamido-4-phenylthiazole had an LD_{50} of about 2.5 Gm./kilo, in comparison to 6.0 Gm./kilo for sulfamethylthiazole and 7.0 Gm./kilo for sulfathiazole[29].

(f) *2-Sulfanilamidobenzothiazoles* (Table 39, p. 90)

Pharmacology. Based on *in vivo* results these do not appear to hold much promise as chemotherapeutic agents. 2-Sulfanilamidobenzothiazole did not reach effective blood levels in mice[1057]. This is the probable cause of poor *in vivo* activities since the compound is comparable with sulfathiazole *in vitro*.

(g) *2-Sulfanilamido-4-thiazolones* (Table 40, p. 90)

Synthesis. These may be synthesized from the 2-amino-4-thiazolones by reaction with ASC (or better, *p*-nitrobenzenesulfonyl chloride) in pyridine followed by hydrolysis (or reduction). Another synthesis is from N^4-acyl-N^1-(α-haloacyl)sulfanilamides by treatment with potassium thiocyanate[371].

Pharmacology. These compounds possess definite therapeutic activity in mice. They do not appear to have received much clinical study, probably because of adverse toxic reactions.

Cooper, *et al.*[95] reported 2-sulfanilamido-5-ethyl-4-thiazolone (sulfaethylthiazolone) to have less antistreptococcal activity but approximately the same antipneumococcal activity as sulfapyridine; activity against staphylococci was about the same as sulfathiazole or sulfadiazine. The compound did not produce urolithiasis, as has been caused by large doses of the other drugs, but instead entailed risk of fatal anemia. Mice and rats were used as test animals.

The compounds appeared to be readily absorbed so that 2-sulfanilamido-5-ethyl-4-thiazolone, for example, reached a higher peak blood level for a given dose than sulfathiazole or sulfapyridine. However, excretion was also rapid so that little drug remained at the end of eight hours[371].

(h) *Miscellaneous N^1-Heterocyclicsulfanilamides with One N- and One S- or Se-Atom in the Heterocyclic System* (Table 41, p. 91)

Pharmacology. The 2-sulfanilamidoselenazoles were claimed to be as active *in vitro* as sulfathiazole against pneumococci, type I and III, and *E. coli*[1135]; however, *in vivo* they were not active[25].

5-Sulfanilamidothiazole was claimed by Jensen and Schmith[1384] to be as active as the 2-isomer, in support of their thesis that position isomerism among sulfanilamidoheterocycles does not materially change activities.

(5) Two N-Atoms and One O- or S-Atom in the Heterocyclic System

(a) *2-Sulfanilamido-1,3,4-thiadiazoles* (Table 42, p. 92)

Synthesis. The general method for synthesis of sulfanilamidoheterocycles has been used for most of these compounds.

A novel method of synthesizing 2-sulfanilamido-1,3,4-thiadiazoles has been patented[2487]. ASC is condensed with an aldehyde thiosemicarbazone in pyridine, to give the *N*-acetyl-sulfanilyl derivative which is then oxidized with potassium ferricyanide in alkaline solution to close the thiadiazole ring and hydrolyze the acetyl group.

Pharmacology. 2-Sulfanilamido-1,3,4-thiadiazole was found by Bell and Roblin[719] to be a fairly strong acid (pKa 4.77) and to be too highly ionized for best activity. 2-Sulfanilamido-5-methyl-1,3,4-thiadiazole was less acidic (pKa 5.45) and showed somewhat greater activity *in vitro* against *E. coli*.

Because of the comparatively high acidity of the sulfathiadiazole it is possible to obtain salts with ammonia and various amines in solid form[2486].

Frisk[1135] found sulfathiadiazole to have about the same activity as sulfanilamide *in vitro* against *E. coli*, and type I and III pneumococci.

Anderson, Schmith and Søbye[657] have studied 2-sulfanilamido-5-methyl-1,3,4-thiadiazole (Lucosil, Tetracid) both pharmacologically and clinically. *In vitro* it appeared to be almost as potent as sulfathiazole. In mice it was less toxic and as potent as sulfapyridine in protecting against pneumonia. In the clinic 50 cases of pneumonia responded favorably with few side effects. The compound appeared to be absorbed and excreted rapidly. An oral dose of 2 Gm. was completely (85–100%) excreted in the urine in seven hours. Only 5 to 10% was acetylated in the body.

Others have failed to show appreciable activity *in vivo*, possibly because the drug was not administered frequently enough to maintain an appreciable blood concentration. Frisk[1135] found that the drug when given in 1 Gm. doses on a 4 hourly schedule 5 times per day gave an average blood level of less than 2 mg.% in man. This was caused by very rapid excretion rather than poor absorption. Better blood levels (4–6 mg.%) were obtained in mice but survivals at a given drug intake were inferior to sulfapyridine in pneumonia. *In vitro* the drug was almost as active as sulfathiazole against *E. coli* and pneumococci, type I and III.

Osterberg[1879] found it non-irritating in the eye and an excellent healing agent in several eye infections.

2-Sulfanilamido-5-ethyl-1,3,4-thiadiazole (Globucid) has received greatest study of the members of this series and the experimental activities are shown in Table 284. Sapinsky[2087] studied the clinical toxicity of 2-sulfanilamido-5-ethyl-1,3,4-thiadiazole and found no indication of toxicity to the blood or damage to the bone marrow. No toxicity to liver, kidney or intestines was noted. Shreus[2142] recommended the drug for both oral and local application, in prophylaxis against wound infections for gas gangrene, but Klöse and Schröer[1453] considered it much inferior to serum. Frisk[1135] obtained average blood levels of 10–11 mg. per 100 cc. in man on a dosage of 1 Gm. at 4 hourly intervals, 5 times per day; or slightly higher blood levels than obtained with sulfadiazine. The drug showed very low conjugation in either blood or urine. Against pneumococci type I in mice the drug was slightly inferior to sulfapyridine, sulfathiazole or sulfadiazine at a given dosage. It produced blood levels in mice slightly greater than sulfapyridine. These results paralleled the *in vitro* bacteriostatic and bactericidal results, which showed the drug to be less potent than sulfathiazole and about equal to sulfapyridine or sulfadiazine against *E. coli* and pneumococci, type I and III[1135].

The sulfathiadiazoles appear to be unusual in their distribution in the body. 2-Sulfanilamido-5-ethyl-1,3,4-thiadiazole had a plasma concentration many times that in the red cells; in a third of the cases no drug could be detected in the red cells. Sulfamethylthiadiazole showed slightly more affinity for the red cells. Neither drug penetrated to the cerebrospinal fluid in concentrations higher than 10% of the blood level[1135].

Janbon, *et al.*,[1370] noted that 2-sulfanilamido-5-isopropyl-1,3,4-thiadiazole showed low conjugation in the blood and urine. They also noted a marked hypoglycemic effect three hours after administration of a 3 Gm. dose. Döring[997] found no cyanosis or inclusion body anemias from use of this or 2-sulfanilamido-5-isobutyl-1,3,4-thiadiazole.

Frisk[1135] found 2-sulfanilamido-5-isopropylthiadiazole slightly less active than the methyl or ethyl derivative *in vitro* and definitely less active in mouse pneumonia despite adequate blood levels of drug. The isobutyl derivative was still less active *in vitro*.

(b) *Miscellaneous N^1-Heterocyclicsulfanilamides with Two N-Atoms and One O- or S-Atom in the Heterocyclic System* (Table 43, p. 93)

Pharmacology. The sulfanilamidooxadiazoles appear to be strongly acidic. Thus 4-methyl-3-sulfanilamido-1,2,5-oxadiazole, or 4-methyl-3-sulfanilamidofurazan, has a pKa of 4.1 and 5-methyl-3-sulfanilamido-1,2,4-oxadiazole has a pKa of 4.4[719]. In spite of this acidity the compounds are about as active as sulfapyridine against *E. coli, in vitro.* A third isomer, 5-methyl-2-sulfanilamido-1,3,4-oxadiazole was said to have the activity of sulfanilamide against pneumococci *in vitro*[1384]. The activities *in vivo* do not appear high but very little work has been done on these compounds in exploration of their possibilities.

(6) N^1-Nitrogen a Member of the Heterocyclic System (Table 44, p. 94)

Chemistry. A considerable number of sulfanilyl derivatives of hydrogenated, nitrogen-containing heterocycles have been made. These compounds resemble the N^1,N^1-dialkyl-sulfanilamides in their properties more than they do the sulfanilamido heterocycles. Because no hydrogen is associated with the amide nitrogen these compounds are incapable of salt formation with bases.

Pharmacology. These compounds further resemble the N^1,N^1-dialkylsulfanilamides in possessing little or no chemotherapeutic activity.

The sodium salt of 1-sulfanilyl-4-carbethoxy-5-hydroxy-1,2,3-triazole was found to have slightly greater activity than sulfanilamide against *E. coli* and pneumococci, types I and III[1135]. This compound is very unstable, however, and undergoes decomposition with loss of nitrogen to form an N^1-acylsulfanilamide[106]. This may possibly account for the activity.

(D) N^1-Acylsulfanilamides

These comprise a potentially very large class of derivatives and have been explored to a total of 188 compounds. Several clinically useful drugs have been derived from the study. As proof that further work in a field that appears to be fairly well investigated will often develop unexpected results, the recent work of Pulver and Martin[1966] has uncovered unique properties in N^1-(3,4-dimethylbenzoyl)sulfanilamide, or "Irgafen". This will be discussed more in detail below.

All N^1-acylsulfanilamides derived from carboxylic acids are strong acids and form neutral sodium salts which are usually highly soluble. This makes these salts useful for local treatment where the high alkalinity of the sodium salts of other sulfa drugs would prove objectionable. This property also means that the drugs will be excreted without danger of crystallization in the kidney.

Synthesis. N^1-Acylsulfanilamides of monobasic carboxylic acids are prepared most conveniently by treating 1.2 moles of N^4-acetylsulfanilamide dissolved in 250 cc. of dry pyridine with 1 mole of the acyl chloride at 90–110°C. Crude N^4-acetyl-N^1-acylsulfanilamide is isolated by drowning the reaction mixture in water and acidifying. The N^4-acetyl group is hydrolyzed by boiling 1 mole of the diacylsulfanilamide dissolved in 800 cc. of water and 2.4 moles of sodium hydroxide for about 90 minutes. The pH is then adjusted between 8 and 9, the solution is cooled and filtered to remove any sulfanilamide or N^4-acetylsulfanilamide. The crude N^1-acylsulfanilamide is precipitated with acid and is recrystallized from 80% alcohol or other solvent[101].

Instead of N^4-acetylsulfanilamide, N^4-carbethoxysulfanilamide or 4-nitrobenzene-sulfonamide may be acylated and instead of the acid chloride, the acid anhydride may be used as acylating agent[2100].

Another method of synthesis[2396] is to fuse the sodium salt of sulfanilamide with a carboxamide at 170–200°, where the N^1-nitrogen is mainly acylated. At higher temperatures both nitrogens are acylated.

(1) N^1-Acyclicacylsulfanilamides (Table 45, p. 99)

Pharmacology. N^1-Acetylsulfanilamide (Albucid, Sulamyd, Sulfacetamide) has been used mainly for urinary tract infections[584, 2426] where it is claimed superior to sulfanilamide in effectiveness while not involving risk of kidney stoppage, as in the case of the more potent drugs such as sulfathiazole and sulfadiazine. It has also been employed in the form of its very soluble, neutral sodium salt for treatment of eye infections where higher concentrations of the drug may be used than is possible with other sulfa drugs.

Robinson and Crossley[2037] have investigated the metabolism of N^1-acyclicacylsulfanilamides in various animals. By extracting with ether at pH 9, sulfanilamide was extracted but the highly ionized N^1-acylsulfanilamides were not extracted from body fluids; however, by reducing the pH to 3.5 they could also be extracted with ether. Using this technique, as well as ultraviolet absorption spectra, it was shown that N^1-acetylsulfanilamide was for the most part unchanged in passing through the body, while the higher homologues such as N^1-butyrylsulfanilamide were largely broken down to sulfanilamide and only about 15% remained unchanged in the urine. It was shown that this breakdown did not occur in the digestive tract but that the liver, kidney and spleen contained an enzyme capable of bringing it about. They showed that this enzyme gave an increased rate of hydrolysis with increasing length of carbon chain of the acyl group, but showed less activity against branched chain acyl groups. Thus N^1-isobutyrylsulfanilamide was excreted 35% unchanged.

Since the longer chain N^1-acylsulfanilamides form neutral, highly soluble sodium salts and are cleaved largely to sulfanilamide, they offer a means of injecting the equivalent of sulfanilamide in highly concentrated form.

The long chain N^1-acylsulfanilamides, and particularly N^1-dodecanoylsulfanilamide, were studied in experimental tuberculosis with encouraging results in preliminary work[90] which was not duplicated in further animal or clinical studies[386, 498, 673]. This is fairly typical of work on chemotherapy of tuberculosis where the slow progress of the disease makes evaluation of drugs especially difficult.

Pulver and Martin[1966] studied nine unsaturated or branched chain N^1-acylsulfanilamides. Of these, N^1-senecioylsulfanilamide (N^1-dimethylacroylsulfanilamide, or "Irgamid") appeared most active. They were unable to see any correlation between the structures of these and the therapeutic effectiveness in mice; further, their results indicated high specificity of effect against various organisms by various of the drugs. One of the striking results was that N^1-isobutyrylsulfanilamide saved 80% of mice infected with streptococci, 20% with pneumococci and 80% with *E. coli* where N^1-isovalerylsulfanilamide showed 0%, 0%, and 100% respectively. Each drug was equally well absorbed; however, the rough toxicity data indicated that N^1-isovalerylsulfanilamide was 20 times as toxic as N^1-isobutyrylsulfanilamide. It is felt that these results are in need of confirmation by others because the number of experimental animals used were insufficient to permit definite conclusions.

Irgamid has been studied clinically in Switzerland on a variety of diseases with results that are difficult to evaluate. According to Löffler and Hegglin[1607] it was inferior to sulfathiazole in pneumonia and showed more undesirable secondary effects, particularly on the circulatory system. In contrast to these results, Markoff[1722], who used it in 43, and Scherer[2099], who used it in 60 miscellaneous cases of pneumococcal, staphylococcal, E. coli and streptococcal infections, claimed results equivalent to those obtained with sulfapyridine and sulfathiazole and with a low incidence of toxic reactions. Muller[1815] also used it successfully in veterinary medicine.

Frisk[1135] found the drug to be slowly but completely absorbed so that 93–100% of the dose given could be accounted for in the urine. It was slowly eliminated (35 to 67% in 24 hours) and about half of the excreted product was acetylated.

It now appears that this drug has been superseded by Irgafen.

(2) N^1-Isocyclicacylsulfanilamides (Table 46, p. 101)

Pharmacology. N^1-Benzoylsulfanilamide, sulfabenzamide, appears to be fairly well absorbed[186, 801, 1057] in men and mice. There have been a few studies where its use in treatment of dysentery has been investigated with promising results[801, 2437]. No large scale clinical studies have been reported, however.

Pulver and Martin[1966] studied 18 derivatives of N^1-benzoylsulfanilamide in which alkyl groups were introduced at various points on the benzoyl ring. Much valuable data were collected on the acute and chronic toxicities in mice; absorption and extent of acetylation in rabbits; therapeutic effect against streptococci, pneumococci and E. coli infections in mice; *in vitro* effect on growth of E. coli (measured manometrically on O_2 consumption) and action against the enzymes; catalase, cholinesterase and diaminoxidase.

Of these compounds, N^1-(3,4-dimethylbenzoyl)sulfanilamide ("Irgafen") was outstanding. This was exceptionally well absorbed and very slowly excreted so that very high blood levels were reached with low dosage. The activity against mouse infections was comparable with sulfathiazole or sulfapyridine. In contrast, the isomeric N^1-(2,3-; 2,4-; and 2,5-dimethylbenzoyl)sulfanilamides, while they were equally well absorbed, had practically no activity *in vivo* and only slight activity *in vitro!* Hydrogenation of the ring, giving N^1-(3,4-dimethylhexahydrobenzoyl)sulfanilamide, markedly decreased the activity. Increase in number of methyl groups also brought about much lower activities.

The authors were unable to explain these results in terms of any existing theories. They found no parallel between the observed activities and the inhibition of enzyme actions nor was there any correlation of activity with structure. Since too few experimental animals were used in the *in vivo* studies to give significant results and since there is no assurance that conditions were sufficiently controlled to permit quantitative comparisons of one drug with another, these results are in need of confirmation.

In further studies, Irgafen, N^1-(3,4-dimethylbenzoyl)sulfanilamide, was claimed by Pulver and Suter[1967] to be as active as other commonly used sulfa drugs against pneumococci, staphylococci, haemolytic streptococci or E. coli, but less active against Friedländer's bacillus than sulfadiazine. Mice tolerated 1.25 Gm./kilo given twice daily for 5 days or single oral doses of 7.5 Gm./kilo. The tolerated dose of the sodium salt injected by any of the usual routes was 0.5 Gm./kilo for mice and rabbits. The free compound is almost insoluble in water, but the sodium salt is quite soluble and has a pH of 8.2 for a 5% solution.

According to Michaud[1775] a blood level of 5 to 10 mg. per 100 cc. can be maintained in man with a daily dose of 2 Gm. of Irgafen, following an initial dose of 3 Gm. Rieben[2622] found it effective when given rectally as a solution of the sodium salt; 1 Gm. in 100 cc.

water given rectally every 12 hours produced and maintained blood levels of 6–8 mg. per 100 cc.

Löffler[1606] recommended Irgafen as one of the drugs useful in treating pneumonia but placed it as less active than sulfapyridine, sulfathiazole and sulfadiazine. Gsell[2547] treated 255 patients with the drug, of which 45 cases had pneumonia and 62 had urinary infections. The drug was very well absorbed but so slowly excreted that daily doses of 2 Gm. gave 15 mg.% concentration of free drug and 17 mg.% total drug in the blood. The drug did not penetrate to the cerebrospinal fluid in amounts greater than 20% of the blood level. The toxic reactions noted were 5 cases of vomiting, 5 of diarrhea, 1 of drug fever, 2 of exanthemata, 1 of neuritis and 1 case of toxic liver damage. It was recommended that total dosage of 18 Gm. should not be exceeded because of the slowness with which the drug is excreted.

(3) N^1-Heterocyclicacylsulfanilamides (Table 47, p. 103)

The low or uncertain activity of the few derivatives made plus the difficulty of synthesis has not encouraged an extensive study of this series.

(4) (5) Sulfanilylimido Esters and Sulfanilylamidines (Tables 48, 49, p. 103, 104)

Synthesis. The sulfanilylamidines may be prepared by reaction of p-nitrobenzenesulfonyl chloride with the amidine in acetone solution in the presence of a considerable excess of sodium hydroxide at 10–20°C. The nitro group may be reduced with iron or catalytically with hydrogen[165, 1862]. As by-products in this reaction N,N^1-bis(p-nitrobenzenesulfonyl)amidines result which form neutral monosodium salts and are readily separated from the p-nitrobenzenesulfonylamidines, which do not form sodium salts[1862].

Another general method of synthesis is by conversion of an N-acyl-p-nitrobenzenesulfonamide to the corresponding imido chloride by reaction with phosphorous pentachloride, then by reaction with ammonia or amines form the amidine. This is the best procedure for arriving at compounds whose probable structure is[165, 1862]:

$$-SO_2N=C-R$$
$$|$$
$$R'-N-R''$$

The sulfanilylamidines were of interest because all of the potent N^1-heterocyclicsulfanilamides have an amidine structure where the amidine carbon and one of the amidine nitrogens are members of the heterocyclic ring.

Structure. The structure of the sulfonylamidines has not been established with certainty. The author and coworkers[1862] favored the structure,

$$RSO_2N=CR'$$
$$|$$
$$NH_2$$

(I)

on the basis of the inability of the compounds to form alkali salts, which would seem possible were the structure of the type

$$RSO_2N-CR'$$
$$|\quad\ ||$$
$$H\quad NH$$

(II)

This argument is, however, weak since the presence of the HN= group which is a powerful electron donor may repress the ionization of the amide hydrogen in formula (II) below its ability to form salts.

H. J. Barber[701] has prepared several sulfonyl derivatives of imido esters of the type

$$RSO_2N{=}CR'$$
$$|$$
$$OR''$$

and finds that on converting these to the sulfonylamidines by treatment with cold alcoholic ammonia, low melting sulfonylamidines result which are converted to the higher melting forms (the forms which result on direct synthesis from amidines and a sulfonyl chloride) by long boiling in alcohol. The low melting form of p-nitrobenzenesulfonylbenzamidine (159–165°) decomposed at 195 to 200° while the high melting form (179°) decomposed at or slightly above its melting point. This decomposition was accompanied by evolution of SO_2 and the formation of N-(4-nitrophenyl)benzamidine, m.p. 167–168°. The imido-ester did not undergo this reaction.

Barber believed the low melting form to be represented by formula (I) and the high melting form by formula (II). In further support of this he stated (but did not give the evidence) that hydrolysis of the high melting form gave a mixed amide, RSO_2NHCOR', plus ammonia, while the low melting form gave some sulfonamide. Definite evidence could not be obtained because of ready transformation of the isomers.

Pharmacology. Despite the structural analogy to the highly active N^1-heterocyclic-sulfanilamides, the sulfanilylamidines have shown disappointingly low activities in the few reported studies on experimental infections. This was not through lack of absorption in the case of sulfanilylacetamidine[1057] because adequate blood levels of drug were reached and fairly well maintained. Bis-sulfanilylacetamidine was not well absorbed, nor was it active against *E. coli, in vitro.*

(6) Derivatives of Carbonic Acid (Table 50, p. 105)

The wide variety possible in derivatives of carbonic acid plus the success of one member of the series, sulfanilylguanidine, (sulfaguanidine) has led to the synthesis of at least 56 such compounds representing urethanes, ureas, isoureas, the corresponding sulfur analogues, guanidines, guanylureas, biguanides, aminoguanidines, etc.

Synthesis. Sulfanilylureas may be made by treating an N^4-acylsulfanilamide with potassium cyanate in 85% alcohol (or with nitrourea and sodium carbonate in 80% alcohol). The soluble alkali salts result. The acyl group can by hydrolyzed either with concentrated hydrochloric acid or with sodium hydroxide but the compound itself is converted to sulfanilamide by prolonged boiling with strong acids or bases[1224]. Sulfanilamide is slowly converted by boiling with urea and sodium carbonate in 75% alcohol to sulfanilylurea[1224]. N^1-Substituted sulfanilylureas are readily prepared from the corresponding isocyanates.

Migliardi and Tappi[1781] claimed to have made N^4-acetylsulfanilylurea and the corresponding thiourea by reacting acetylsulfanilyl chloride with urea or thiourea in pyridine; however, the melting points of the products did not agree with those of the corresponding compounds synthesized as above.

Reaction of acetylsulfanilylcyanamide with alcoholic HCl gives the sulfanilylalkyl-isourea directly[2461]. Acetylsulfanilylmethylisourea on treatment with an alkyl amine gives the corresponding substituted acetylsulfanilylalkylguanidine. Such substituted guanidines can also be made from acetylsulfanilylcyanamide by treatment with an amine[2461].

The synthesis of sulfaguanidine is given in Chapter II. Various acid salts of sulfanilylguanidine have been made to produce a more water-soluble product[19]. The lactate, phosphate, sulfate, salicylate, and mandelate are described, but these have not proved to be therapeutically important.

Pharmacology. Sulfanilylurea has been given the trade name Euvernil in Germany. It is said to be rapidly absorbed and evenly distributed throughout all the body fluids and organs; however, in the first two hours 32% of the drug is excreted. It is claimed to be particularly valuable in urinary infections. Dosage is 6 to 15 Gm. per day in divided doses[1135, 2618]. Acetylation of the drug was low, amounting to about 10% of the total blood concentration and 10–20% of the urinary concentration.

Low blood concentrations of drug probably accounted for low survivals in mice infected with type I pneumococcus because *in vitro* the drug had an activity comparable with sulfapyridine against *E. coli*, and pneumococci, type I and III. The acute toxicity in mice was very low (LD$_{50}$ 6.99 Gm./kilo)[1135].

Sulfanilylthiourea "Badional", had an equivalent activity *in vitro* but gave slightly higher survivals in mouse pneumonia than sulfanilylurea in spite of still lower blood levels of drug[1135].

Sulfaguanidine which has reached great importance in treatment of intestinal infections in both man and domestic animals is discussed in Chapters X and XII. Activities against a variety of experimental infections are listed in Table 287.

The other derivatives of carbonic acid have not been studied in great detail but do not appear to have much promise as chemotherapeutic agents against the common pathogens treated by other sulfa drugs. The only compound of the series showing activity *in vitro* equal to or possibly greater than sulfaguanidine was sulfanilylaminoguanidine[2459]. Its lack of activity against streptococcal infections in mice may be explained by inability to obtain adequate blood concentrations of the drug[1057]. It appears to be more toxic than sulfaguanidine[1057].

(E) N^1-Inorganic Derivatives of Sulfanilamide

(1) N^1-Sulfonylsulfanilamides (Table 51, p. 106)

Chemistry. Introduction of a sulfonyl group on the sulfonamide group of sulfanilamide gives a disulfonamide structure, —SO$_2$ NH SO$_2$—. This grouping ionizes as a strong acid having a pKa of about 3.[719] The compounds can be synthesized by reacting a sulfonyl chloride with N^4-acetylsulfanilamide in the presence of excess sodium hydroxide at about 40°C. followed by alkaline hydrolysis of the acetyl group.

The compound disulfanilamide,

$$NH_2 \langle \rangle SO_2NHSO_2 \langle \rangle NH_2 ,$$

is subject to confusion in the literature with N^4-sulfanilylsulfanilamide,

$$NH_2 \langle \rangle SO_2NH \langle \rangle SO_2NH_2$$

Pharmacology. The N^1-alkanesulfonylsulfanilamides have little or no activity either *in vitro* or *in vivo* against common test organisms.

Disulfanilamide, or its soluble sodium salt, has given various results in the hands of different investigators in experimental streptococcal infections. It is not well absorbed and is excreted rapidly so that adequate blood levels are not reached when the drug is given per os nor adequately maintained when given parenterally. This may explain part of the variation in results. Measurements of activity *in vitro* have also given variable results in the hands of different investigators against streptococci, pneumococci *Strep. viridans*, and *E. coli*[719, 1057, 2441] but most of these tests indicate a low order of activity. Preliminary tests against influenza virus were not confirmed by later work[89].

(2) **Miscellaneous N^1-Inorganic Derivatives** (Table 52, p. 107)

Synthesis. These compounds can be synthesized by reaction of ASC with hydroxylamine, sulfamic acid, hydrazines, etc., followed by hydrolysis of the acetyl group using any of the general methods.

Pharmacology. One of the few of these derivatives which appears to have appreciable activity is N^1-hydroxysulfanilamide. The activity seems inferior to that of sulfanilamide *in vivo*. It was active against streptococci and pneumococci but not against *Strep. viridans, in vitro*.[2441] It appeared to distribute in the cat much the same as sulfanilamide and to have similar excretion characteristics[1097]. N^1-Aminosulfanilamide (sulfanilylhydrazine) was active *in vitro* against streptococci and pneumococci but not against *Strep. viridans*[2441]. The lack of *in vivo* activity may be linked to the toxicity of the drug[1733] but is not a function of excretion-distribution characteristics[1097] which were favorable.

Sulfanilylazide showed slightly inferior activity to sulfanilamide *in vitro* against *E. coli* and pneumococci, type I and III,[1135] but greater activity against gonococcus and meningococcus[1021].

N-Sulfanilylcholhydrazide, "sulfacholazine" which has the formula:

$$CH_3CH(CH_3)CH_2CH_2CONHNHSO_2\langle\quad\rangle NH_2$$

is a derivative of cholic acid and was tested[702] to see whether it would be excreted into the bile after intravenous injection. This was found to be the case, whereas sulfanilamide and sulfapyridine were found not to be excreted in bile. The compound is bacteriostatic *in vitro* against *Strep. haemolyticus* and pneumococcus but has little activity against coliform bacteria. Its activity could not be measured in bile because bile was itself bactericidal.

The statement that sulfapyridine is not excreted into the bile is challenged by Gough[1196] who found in a series of eight patients recovering from operation for biliary fistula that the concentration of sulfapyridine in the bile was almost twice as great as the blood concentration.

(IV) N^4-Substituted Sulfanilamides

(A) N^4-Acyclicsulfanilamides (Table 53, p. 108)

Synthesis. N^4-Monoalkylsulfanilamides may be prepared by chlorosulfonation, amidation and hydrolysis of *N*-alkylacetanilides or by amidation of *p*-bromobenzenesulfonamide with an alkyl amine in the presence of a copper salt in an autoclave at about 180°. Alkylation of sulfanilamide with an alkyl halide will probably go either in the N^1 or N^4-position depending on the alkalinity of the reaction mixture, high alkalinity favoring N^1-substitution[409].

N^4,N^4-dialkylsulfanilamides can be prepared only with great difficulty. Jensen and Schmith[1384] were unable to prepare N^4,N^4-dimethylsulfanilamide by treatment of p-bromobenzenesulfonamide with dimethylamine solution at 180° for 12 hours in the presence of $CuSO_4$, nor were they able to make it by amidation of N,N-dimethylsulfanilyl chloride. Lewis and Tager[291] prepared the compound in 5% yields by the latter method.

The aldehyde-bisulfite and aldehyde-dithionite (sulfoxylate) derivatives of sulfanilamide are readily prepared as concentrated solutions in water by reaction of sulfanilamide with an equimolecular amount of an aldehyde bisulfite, or aldehyde dithionite. Preparation of such compounds in pure, dry form is much more difficult because of their high solubility, ease of oxidation, and tendency to decompose. Usually the reaction is run in an organic solvent such as alcohol and the product precipitated by addition of ether.

Pharmacology. The question of whether N^4-substituted sulfanilamides are active as such or must be converted to a free amino group by removal of the N^4-substituent, either by the catabolism of the host or of the bacteria, remains unanswered with certainty. In the majority of compounds where a N^4-substituent is present it has been demonstrated that a diazotizable amine will appear in the blood of the host if the compound shows *in vivo* activity. A number of such compounds are inactive *in vitro*. There is thus good basis for the inference that a free amino group is essential to activity.

In the case of N^4-methyl- and N^4,N^4-dimethylsulfanilamide, Lewis and Tager[291] showed that these compounds had some activity *in vivo* against streptococci. In both man and mice it was also shown that a diazotizable amine (presumably sulfanilamide) appeared in the blood stream in levels as high as 10.6 mg. per 100 cc. in mice. Both drugs showed some inhibition of growth of β-hemolytic streptococci *in vitro* but not of type I pneumococci nor of *Strep. viridans*. In no case could a diazotizable amine be demonstrated in a culture media which had been sterilized by the drugs. All cultures were sterilized by equivalent amounts of sulfanilamide.

This evidence does not permit the conclusion that these drugs are inactive *per se*. It would be necessary to show that β-hemolytic streptococci are able to remove N^4-methyl groups to give free sulfanilamide and that the degree of inhibition is parallel to the free sulfanilamide produced. There are obvious experimental difficulties in such a demonstration.

It is quite certain, and not too surprising that aldehyde bisulfite and dithionite derivatives break down *in vivo* to give sulfanilamide, since these compounds are known to hydrolyze readily. These compounds are also active *in vitro*[1384, 2441]. Again there is no convincing proof that they must be converted to sulfanilamide as the active form but it seems reasonable to assume that the activity of these compounds is that of sulfanilamide, *in vivo*. It may be significant that none of these compounds is more active than sulfanilamide, while most are less active.

According to Mutch[387] N^4-(sodium 1-sulfoethyl)sulfanilamide (sulfonamide E.O.S.) forms 50% aqueous solutions suitable for administration by nasal tube, rectal tube or by intravenous drip. When given intravenously 16% was recovered unchanged in the urine within 30 minutes. Half of the amount administered ultimately appeared in the urine as sulfanilamide, or N^4-acetylsulfanilamide. At the end of 2 hours no more of the original material could be detected in the urine.

(B) N^4-Isocyclicsulfanilamides (Table 54, p. 109)

Synthesis. Many of the compounds in this series are N^4-(substituted benzyl)sulfanilamides. These are made by reduction of the anils resulting from the reaction of substituted benzaldehydes with sulfanilamide. By addition of sodium bisulfite to such anils, soluble sodium sulfonates are obtained.

Pharmacology. N^4-benzylsulfanilamide was used in Europe during the early days of sulfonamide therapy under the name "Septazine" but has now been superseded by more potent drugs. It was shown to break down in the body to give free sulfanilamide[245, 364] and its total activity was explainable on the basis of the liberated sulfanilamide. N^4-(Disodium 1,3-disulfo-3-phenylpropyl)sulfanilamide, "Soluseptazine", also owes its effect to breakdown to sulfanilamide. Through its high solubility it offers a means of parenteral therapy. Because sulfanilamide is the effective agent this compound has also been supplanted by more potent chemotherapeutic agents.

The reported slight activity against streptococci *in vivo* of N^4-phenylsulfanilamide should be checked and presence of diazotizable amine in the blood stream should be investigated, to see if the activity can be ascribed to breakdown of this diphenylamine derivative by body catabolism.

(C) N^4-Heterocyclicsulfanilamides (Tables 55–58, p. 110)

Pharmacology. Very little has been published on the pharmacology of these compounds. Probably the compounds are inactive or nearly so.

(D) N^4-Anils of Sulfanilamide

(1) Acyclicanils of Sulfanilamide (Tables 59, 60, p. 119)

Pharmacology. Two of the N^4-alkylidine-bis-sulfanilamides have been investigated[841] and found to be active *in vivo* when tested in mice. N^4-Camphorylidine-bis-sulfanilamide seemed somewhat more active than sulfanilamide when tested against β-hemolytic streptococci, and N^4-dodecylidine-bis-sulfanilamide less active. Against type I pneumococcus both compounds appeared equal or superior to sulfapyridine. The drugs were inactive against *Staphylococcus aureus* and gonococcus *in vitro*. Both appeared to be partially (or wholly) converted to sulfanilamide in the body. After administration of 100 mg. of N^4-camphorylidine-bis-sulfanilamide to a rat the total drug in the blood expressed as sulfanilamide was 8 mg. per 100 cc., while the free sulfanilamide was 7 mg. per 100 cc. and the difference was in a conjugated form which may have been unchanged drug or N^4-acetylsulfanilamide. N^4-Dodecylidine-bis-sulfanilamide was absorbed less regularly and more of the drug appeared in a conjugated form. Average 2-hour blood levels after 100 mg. were administered to rats were 14.7 mg. per 100 cc. total drug expressed as sulfanilamide, with 9.5 mg. per 100 cc. free sulfanilamide.

Belief was expressed that the superior results obtained with these drugs were a result of the combined action of sulfanilamide and the unchanged drug. The presence of unchanged drug in the blood still remains to be demonstrated, however.

(2) Isocyclicanils of Sulfanilamide (N^4-Aralkylidenesulfanilamides) (Table 61, p. 120)

Synthesis. These compounds are readily synthesized by reaction of an aromatic aldehyde with sulfanilamide, usually in alcohol. The compounds are stable to bases but are readily cleaved by mineral acids.

Pharmacology. These compounds are usually active *in vivo* but are probably cleaved to sulfanilamide as the active agent.

(3) Heterocyclicanils of Sulfanilamide (Table 62, p. 121)

Pharmacology. These compounds are also broken down to sulfanilamide as the active form, in all probability.

(E) N^4-Sugar Derivatives of Sulfanilamide

(1) Glycosides of Sulfanilamide (Table 63, p. 122)

Structure. There has been some doubt as to the constitution of sugar derivatives of sulfanilamide. The anil structure,

$$RCH{=}N\langle\quad\rangle SO_2NH_2$$

has been suggested by a few authors[132, 173] while the majority have favored the glycoside structure

$$\underset{O}{\boxed{\qquad}}{-}CHNH\langle\quad\rangle SO_2NH_2$$

Braun, *et al.*[52] confirmed the work of Kuhn and Birkofer[275], (by synthesis through N^4-tetraacetyl-*d*-glucosidosulfanilamide) that the condensation of glucose with sulfanilamide in 95% alcohol using ammonium chloride as catalyst, gives N^4-*d*-glucosidosulfanilamide. They also stated this to be a β-glucoside and gave a melting point of 204°C., $[\alpha]_D^{23}$ − 123° (water, C = 0.418, + = 105 min.); $[\alpha]_D^{24}$ + 29.7° (0.1 N HCl, C = 0.4212, + = 390 min.). The structure would thus be:

$$
NH_2SO_2\langle\quad\rangle NH{-}\overset{H}{\underset{\begin{array}{l}HCOH\\HOCH\\HCOH\\HC\\CH_2OH\end{array}}{C}}
$$

That both types of structures may exist was indicated by Klingel and MacLennen[558] who described two maltosides of sulfanilamide, one a water-soluble form, α_D + 50° to + 80°, for which they gave the anil structure:

$$\begin{array}{l} \text{HC}\!\!=\!\!\text{N}\!\!\left\langle\right\rangle\!\!\text{SO}_2\text{NH}_2 \\ \text{CHOH} \\ \text{CHOH} \\ \text{CH}\!-\!\!-\!\!-\!\!-\!\!\text{O}\!-\!\!-\!\!-\!\!-\!\!\text{CH}\!-\!\rceil \\ \text{CHOH} \qquad\qquad\quad \text{CHOH}\ | \\ \text{CH}_2\text{OH} \qquad\qquad\ \ \text{CHOH}\ \ \text{O} \\ \qquad\qquad\qquad\qquad\ \ \text{CHOH}\ | \\ \qquad\qquad\qquad\qquad\ \ \text{CH}\!-\!\rfloor \\ \qquad\qquad\qquad\qquad\ \ \text{CH}_2\text{OH} \end{array}$$

and an insoluble form, $\alpha_D - 12°$ to $-14°$, for which they gave the glycoside structure:

$$\begin{array}{l} \lceil\!-\!\!\text{CH}\!-\!\!-\!\!\text{NH}\!\!\left\langle\right\rangle\!\!\text{SO}_2\text{NH}_2 \\ |\quad \text{CHOH} \\ \text{O}\quad \text{CHOH} \\ |\quad \text{CH}\!-\!\!-\!\!-\!\!-\!\!-\!\!-\!\!\text{O}\!-\!\!\text{CH}\!-\!\rceil \\ \lfloor\!-\!\!\text{CH} \qquad\qquad\quad \text{CHOH}\ | \\ \quad\ \text{CH}_2\text{OH} \qquad\qquad \text{CHOH}\ \ \text{O} \\ \qquad\qquad\qquad\qquad\ \text{CHOH}\ | \\ \qquad\qquad\qquad\qquad\ \text{CH}\!-\!\rfloor \\ \qquad\qquad\qquad\qquad\ \text{CH}_2\text{OH} \end{array}$$

They stated that the insoluble form could be converted to the soluble by hydrolysis with $0.005N$ hydrochloric acid.

Pharmacology. The reported *in vivo* activity of N^4-glucosidosulfanilamide against streptococci[52, 1574] is lower than the activity of sulfanilamide, not only on an equal weight basis, as might be expected, but also on an equimolecular basis. This suggests that the compound is active because broken down to sulfanilamide, but that absorption is not as complete as with free sulfanilamide.

(2) N^4-Sugar Sodium Bisulfite Derivatives of Sulfanilamide (Table 64, p. 123)

Pharmacology. The pharmacology of these very soluble derivatives has not been reported in the literature.

(F) N^4-Acylsulfanilamides (Tables 65–68, p. 123)

Synthesis. These derivatives are readily synthesized either by starting with an acylated aniline and treating with chlorosulfonic acid to make the corresponding N-acylsulfanilyl chloride, followed by amidation with ammonia; or by acylation of sulfanilamide with the acid chloride or anhydride in a suitable solvent such as the corresponding acid, or pyridine. Care must be taken not to use excess of the acid chloride or anhydride, because a N^1,N^4-diacylsulfanilamide may result.

The N^4-guanylsulfanilamide listed[60] has been shown to be sulfanilylguanidine instead[2441].

Pharmacology. It is believed by most investigators that N^4-acylsulfanilamides are devoid of chemotherapeutic activity except as the N^4-acyl group is cleaved by enzyme action in the bacteria or host to give free sulfanilamide. In the case of N^4-acetylsulfanilamide the amount of deacetylation is slight in man because the reverse process of acetylation is an important mechanism. Acetylation and deacylation vary considerably from animal to animal and this leads to confusion in interpretation of therapeutic assays of these drugs unless understood. Further, the rate at which various N^4-acylsulfanilamides are deacylated has been shown by Kohl and Flynn[264] to increase with increased length of chain of the acyl group. This was studied by exposing the drug to the action of liver suspension which contains an acylase. Their data[a] are:

	% Hydrolysis		
	2 hr.	5 hr.	8 hr.
N^4-Acetylsulfanilamide	9.1	9.1	8.1
N^4-Butyrylsulfanilamide	14.1	27.8	30.4
N^4-Valerylsulfanilamide	21.7	24.0	25.0
N^4-Caproylsulfanilamide	38.3	41.0	41.9
N^4-Heptanoylsulfanilamide	63.9	80.1	89.6

Similar results were obtained with the corresponding N^4-acyl-N^1-hydroxysulfanilamides.

Other results[264, 2191] show that a deacylating enzyme is present in blood and kidney as well as liver.

N^4-Acetyl-N^4-hydroxysulfanilamide (Table 65) was active against streptococcus, pneumococcus and *Strep. viridans*, *in vitro*[2441]. This hydroxylamine derivative probably has a different mechanism of action than most sulfanilamide derivatives.

It should not be concluded that because the N^4-acyl group must be removed before the drug can be active, that such derivatives have no place in therapeutics. It may be that one of these drugs may prove useful for a specific therapeutic need because the active drug can be liberated as needed at the site of infection without maintaining toxic, high blood levels of the active drug.

Poth, *et al.*[1950] in investigating various compounds for use in intestinal infections found that while the N^4-succinyl derivatives of sulfanilamide had low toxicity, the corresponding N^4-maleyl derivative produced vomiting, diarrhea, paralysis and after a few days or weeks death ensued. These were probably toxic effects of maleic acid.

(G) N^4-Inorganic Derivatives of Sulfanilamide

(1) N^4-Sulfonylsulfanilamides (Tables 69–71, p. 130–132)

Synthesis. These compounds are readily synthesized by reacting a sulfonyl chloride with sulfanilamide in aqueous solution, using sodium carbonate to neutralize the liberated acid. Use of excess of the sulfonyl chloride, particularly in the presence of excess sodium hydroxide, will give N^1,N^4-bis-(sulfonyl)sulfanilamides. In very concentrated sodium hydroxide solution, N^1-sulfonylsulfanilamides may be the main product of the reaction.

Pharmacology. The only compounds showing appreciable activity are those in which the sulfonyl group is sulfanilyl or convertible thereto. In this case the active compound is behaving as an N^1-substituted sulfanilamide and might better be named and classified, N^1-(p-sulfamylphenyl)sulfanilamide instead of N^4-sulfanilylsulfanilamide; however, the confusion in the literature on the name of this compound (improperly called disulfanilamide) is too great to warrant further change.

[a] Data quoted with the permission of the authors and copyright owner.

N^4-Sulfanilylsulfanilamide has been used abroad under such trade names as "Disulon", "Diseptal C", Albasil C" and "Disulfane". It has been largely displaced by more potent and less toxic sulfa drugs. One of the serious toxic reactions ascribed to the drug was peripheral neuritis (see Chapter XII).

It would appear that the sulfonyl group cannot be removed by catabolic reactions of the host or parasite and that such derivatives are inactive because of the unavailability of a free N^4-amino group.

(2) Azo Derivatives of Sulfanilamide (Tables 72–78, p. 133–142)

Because the discovery of chemotherapeutic activity in the sulfonamide drug field occurred in the dyes derived by diazotization and coupling of sulfanilamide, this particular class of sulfanilamide derivatives has been extensively investigated. Some 215 such dyes have been made and described, largely in the patent literature.

Synthesis. Sulfanilamide is readily diazotized in the presence of excess mineral acid by addition of sodium nitrite solution at a temperature of 10–15°. The diazo compound is relatively stable and couples well to reactive methylene groups in the aliphatic series and to hydroxy and amino substituted aromatic compounds of both the carbocyclic and heterocyclic series. Usually red dyes result.

Pharmacology. "Prontosil", 4'-sulfamyl-2,4-diaminoazobenzene hydrochloride, was of therapeutic importance in the early days of sulfonamide therapy, but caused so many toxic reactions that it was replaced by "Neoprontosil" [Azosulfamide, disodium 2-(4'-sulfamylphenylazo)-7-acetamido-1-hydroxynaphthalene-3,6-disulfonate] which is still marketed. While indicated by the work of Trefouel, Trefouel, Nitti and Bovet[511] and Fuller[153] who showed that sulfanilamide was excreted when the dye was given, conclusive evidence was obtained by Litchfield, White and Marshall[310] "that the entire therapeutic activity of Neoprontosil depends on the sulfanilamide formed from it." In mice it was shown that administration of four times the dosage of Neoprontosil in the diet produced the same blood levels of sulfanilamide and the same curative effect against streptococcal infections as the standard dosage of sulfanilamide. In its effects Neoprontosil behaves as a diluted sulfanilamide and modern judgement is that it has little place in therapy[2248]. It produces the same toxic reactions as sulfanilamide. Bernheim[732] showed that the liver was the probable site of the reduction of the dye to sulfanilamide.

"Rubiazole", when first introduced was apparently identical chemically with Prontosil but later the coupling component was changed to 3,5-diaminobenzoic acid and a more soluble product resulted.

The fact that there is considerable variation in the *in vivo* activities of various azo derivatives of sulfanilamide is probably to be explained on the basis of different absorption-distribution-excretion characteristics and perhaps also on different rates of cleavage at the azo linkage. *In vitro* the dyes are not active as far as is known.

(3) Diazoamino Compounds Derived from Sulfanilamide (Table 79, p. 146)

The reported activities of these compounds do not appear to encourage further synthesis in the series.

(4) Salts of 4-Sulfamylphenylaminophosphamic Acid (Table 80, p. 147)

These compounds are described in a patent but nothing has been published on their activities.

(5) **Miscellaneous Inorganic Derivatives** (Table 81, p. 147)

N^4-Hydroxysulfanilamide, or p-hydroxylaminobenzenesulfonamide, has received a considerable amount of attention because of various theories of the mechanism of action of sulfanilamide derivatives which postulated an oxidation of sulfanilamide to the hydroxylamine derivative as the active form. These theories have now been largely discarded. There has been confusion in the literature on the properties of this compound. The pure product is rather difficult to prepare because of its great reactivity and ease of decomposition. Bratton, White and Marshall[50] first prepared it in pure form, as was finally established by Sevag[2169], who showed that the product melting at 161.5° which had been reported by several investigators[58, 813, 1753, 2172] was actually a complex of two moles of N^4-hydroxysulfanilamide and one mole of sulfanilamide. Burton and Walker[815] verified these results.

Pharmacology. Bratton, White and Marshall[50] found that N^4-hydroxysulfanilamide was apparently converted to sulfanilamide within 5 minutes when injected into dogs. *In vitro*, they found it no more than ten times as active as sulfanilamide. Mayer[1753] claimed it to be 100 times as potent *in vitro* and to act immediately without the characteristic lag of sulfanilamide.

N^4-Aminosulfanilamide (p-hydrazinobenzenesulfonamide) is inactive and toxic *in vivo*. The corresponding sulfonic acid[1384] was said to have slight activity *in vitro* against pneumococci but its activity was not reversed by p-aminobenzoic acid (see Chapter XI).

TABLE 1

I. Salts of Sulfanilamide
   A. Salts with Bases

Salt	Melting Range	Activities	References
Sodium·2.5H$_2$O		++(S)	105, 311, 383
Potassium			383
Copper			383
Silver			51, 383, 467, 574
Magnesium			383
Zinc			383
Mercuric			383, 467
Aluminum		+(S)	178, 383
Bismuth			383
Manganese			383
Phenylmercuric	208.5–11.5°		290
Diphenylmercuric			290

TABLE 2

I. Salts of Sulfanilamide
   B. Salts with Acids

Salt	Melting Range	Activities	References
Hydrochloride		++, +(S)	170, 213, 311
Phosphate	158–62°		565
Adipate			151
Picrate			467
Camphorate	156–8°		134
Salicylate	133–5°		565
Acetylsalicylate	210–2°		565
Phenylglycolate			565
Quinate		++(S)	353
Benzenesulfonate	213–7°	++(S)	133, 478
Phenolsulfonate	216–20°	++(S)	133, 478
10-Camphorsulfonate	180–2°	++(S)	133, 377, 478
Sulfosalicylate	214–20°	++(S)	133, 478
Quinolinate			126
3-Pyridinesulfonate			126
8-Hydroxyquinolinesulfonate	280–90°		565

TABLE 3

I. Salts of Sulfanilamide
   C. Mixed Salts

Salt	Melting Range	Activities	References
Cinchonine-sulfanilamide·2HCl	135°		306, 500
Cinchonine-sulfanilamide·2HBr	130°		306, 500
Cinchonine-sulfanilamide·H$_2$SO$_4$	130°	+(S)	306, 500
Cinchonidine-sulfanilamide·2HCl	136°		306, 500

TABLE 3—(*Continued*)

Salt	Melting Range	Activities	References
Cinchonidine-sulfanilamide·2HBr	136°		306, 500
Cinchonidine-sulfanilamide·H₂SO₄	180°	+(S)	306, 500
Quinidine-sulfanilamide·2HCl	135°		306, 500
Quinidine-sulfanilamide·2HBr	130°		306, 500
Quinidine-sulfanilamide·H₂SO₄	172°	+(S)	306, 500
Quinine-sulfanilamide·2HCl	130°	++(S)	305, 397, 500, 891
Quinine-sulfanilamide·3HCl	130–50°		306
Quinine-sulfanilamide·2HBr	210°		306, 500
Quinine-sulfanilamide·2HI	70°		306, 500
Quinine-sulfanilamide·H₂SO₄	208°	++(Pk), +(S)	306, 500
Quinine-sulfanilamide·1.5H₂SO₄	186°		500
Quinine-sulfanilamide·NH₂SO₃H	133°		500
Quinine-sulfanilamide salicylate		++(S)	305, 500
Quinine-sulfanilamide camphorsulfonate		±(S), 0(I)	500
Quinine-sulfanilamide·4-[4′-(NH₂)C₆H₄SO₂NH]C₆H₄SO₃H	153°		500
Euquinine-sulfanilamide·2HCl	135°		306, 500
Euquinine-sulfanilamide·2HBr	135°		306, 500
Euquinine-sulfanilamide·H₂SO₄	91°	+(S)	306, 500

TABLE 4

II. Nuclear-substituted Sulfanilamides
  A. Inorganic Substituents

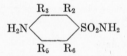

R₂	R₃	R₅	Melting Range	Activities	References
			164.5–6.5°ᵃ	See Table 275	168, 223, 231, 234, 554, 1489, 2424
Cl—					207
	Cl—		161°		228, 485, 1182
	Cl—	Cl—	205–5.5°		472
	Br—	Br—	239–40°	0	61, 154, 1973, 2427
	I—		179–80°, 183–4°		359, 466, 720
	I—	I—	265°D		466, 467
	NO₂—		207°	0	147, 261, 512, 531, 623
	NO₂—	NO₂—		0(P, S, Sa)	432, 1057
HO—				0	508
CH₃O—					207

ᵃ Sulfanilamide.

TABLE 4—*(Continued)*

R_2	R_3	R_5	Melting Range	Activities	References
	HO—		166°	±(S), 0(P, Sa)	508, 640, 1057
	CH_3O—				485, 1182
	NCS—		161.5–2°		1411
	NH_2		278–9°		1411
	![S–S– ring with SO₂NH₂]				
CH_3O—	NH_2SO_2—	CH_3O—			211
	NH_2SO_2—			0	140, 213
	do	NH_2SO_2—	291°	0	61, 322
	NH_2—		174–5°	0(S)	151, 213, 512, 623, 1427, 1574, 2441
NH_2—		NH_2SO_2—	187°		322
	—N=N— ![quinoline ring]		176–8°		369
	—N=N— ![pyrazolone ring with CH₃, CH₃, N, NC₆H₅, =O]		159–60°D		407
	4-$(HO_3S)C_6H_4N=N$—		145–50°D		407
	N=N ![ring with SO₂NH₂] N=N—			0(I, R)	1447, 1574
	ClHg—	ClHg—		0(S)	1427, 1574

TABLE 5

II. Nuclear-substituted Sulfanilamides
   B. Acyclic Substituents

$$H_2N \overset{R_3 \quad R_2}{\underset{R_5 \quad R_6}{\bigcirc}} SO_2NH_2$$

R_2	R_3	R_5	Melting Range	Activities	References
CH_3-				0	171, 213
CH_3-		$Cl-$			211
CH_3-		$Br-$ (?)	185°		684
CH_3-	$Br-$	$Br-$ (?)	198°		684
	CH_3-		172°	0	151, 418, 512, 684
CH_3-		CH_3-	189–90°		207, 211, 453
	CH_3-	CH_3-			228
CH_3-		CH_3O-	183°		208, 211, 226, 560
CH_3-		CH_3CH_2O-	139°		208, 226, 560
CH_3-		$4-(NO_2)C_6H_4CH_2O-$			226, 560
$HOOC-$				0	254
	$HOOC-$			0	146, 254, 2441

TABLE 6

III. N^1-Substituted Sulfanilamides
   A. N^1-Acyclicsulfanilamides
      1. $R = C_nH_{2n+1}$ to C_nH_{2n-1}

$$H_2N \bigcirc SO_2N \overset{R^1}{\underset{R^{1'}}{}}$$

R^1	$R^{1'}$	Melting Range	Activities	References
CH_3-		111–2°	+, ++(S), 0(I, Po), ++(Pl), +(Ec)	151, 213, 311, 512, 719, 892, 1322, 1713, 1733, 1734
CH_3-	CH_3-	168°, 171–2°	±, +, ++(S), +(Ec), +(Pl)	74, 151, 207, 213, 216, 228, 450, 512, 536, 719, 1384, 1491, 1574, 1713, 1733, 1734, 2373
CH_3CH_2-		106–7°	+, ++(S)	151, 213, 512, 536, 1057, 1322, 1713
$BrCH_2CH_2-$		69–70°, 78–80°	0(P, S, Sa)	249, 477, 968, 1574, 2373

TABLE 6—(*Continued*)

R^1	$R^{1'}$	Melting Range	Activities	References
CH_3CH_2-	CH_3CH_2-	105–6°	++(S)	151, 173, 213, 512, 536, 1322, 1713
$CH_3(CH_2)_2-$		85°		1713
$CH_3CHClCH_2-$			+(S)	1427, 1574
$CH_3CHBrCH_2-$			+(S)	1427, 1574
$CH_3(CH_2)_2-$	$CH_3(CH_2)_2-$		±(S)	151, 512
$(CH_3)_2CH-$			±(S)	151, 512
$CH_3(CH_2)_3-$			±(S)	151
do	$CH_3(CH_2)_3-$		±(S)	151, 1057
$CH_3CH_2(CH_3)_2C-$		109–110°, 154–5°	++(S)	1322, 1574, 2373
$CH_3(CH_2)_7-$		114–9.5°	0(P, S)	103, 137
$CH_3(CH_2)_{11}-$		122–4°	0(I, P, R, S, Tt)	103, 137, 204, 1057, 1574, 2373
$CH_3(CH_2)_{16}-$		118°	0(S, T)	2260
$CH_3(CH_2)_{17}-$		127–30°	±(S, Sa), 0(P)	103, 137, 204, 1057, 1557, 2373
$CH_3(CH_2)_{17}(CH_3)_2C-$		81–3°		1770
$CH_2=CHCH_2-$		85–6°, 104–4.5°	+(S)	151, 512, 1322, 1713
$CH_3(CH_2)_7CH=CH(CH_2)_8-$		120.0–2.5°	+(Sa), 0 Le, P, S, Tt	103, 137, 673, 1057

TABLE 7

A. N^1-Acyclicsulfanilamides
  2. Oxy and Oxo Derivatives

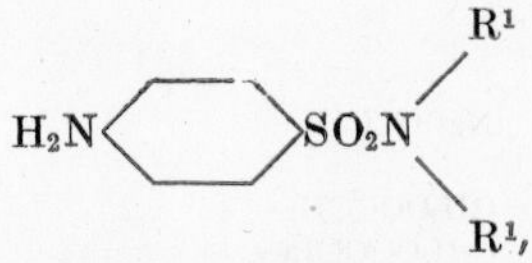

$$H_2N\langle\ \ \rangle SO_2N \begin{array}{c} R^1 \\ R^{1'} \end{array}$$

R^1	$R^{1'}$	Melting Range	Activities	References
$HOCH_2-$				568
$HOCH_2CH_2-$		100–1°	0, +(S), ±(Ec), 0, +(P), +(M), 0(I, Po, T)	5, 33, 35, 105, 213, 296, 332, 477, 719, 892, 1574, 1734, 2441
$CH_3(CH_2)_{10}COOCH_2CH_2-$		63.4–4.8°	±(S, Sa), 0(P)	103, 1057
$HOCH_2CH_2-$	CH_3-	124.5–6.3°	0(S, P)	103, 311, 1057
do	$HOCH_2CH_2-$	110–1°	++, +, 0(S), +(Ec), 0(I, M, P, Pl, R)	5, 105, 214, 267, 311, 1057, 1427, 1574, 1733, 1734, 2441
$HSCH_2CH_2-$			+(S)	1427, 1574
$CH_3CHOHCH_2-$		115–6°	++(M), ±(Sa), +, ±, 0(S), 0(I, Pl, R, Tt), −(P)	5, 105, 296, 1574, 1733, 2373, 2441

TABLE 7—(*Continued*)

R^1	$R^{1'}$	Melting Range	Activities	References
$CH_3CHOHCH_2-$	$CH_3CHOHCH_2-$	162.0–3.5°	±(S), 0(P)	105, 1057
$HOCH_2(CH_3)CH-$			+(S), 0(I, R)	1574, 2373
$CH_3CH(SH)CH_2-$			±(S)	1574
$HOCH_2(CH_2)_2-$		124.5°	0(I, R, Tt), ±, +(S), ++(M)	5, 212, 297, 1574, 2373, 2441
$C_2H_5OCH_2CH_2CH_2-$		59.8–60.8°		105
$C_2H_5CHOHCH_2-$				296
$HOCH_2(C_2H_5)CH-$		105–7°	+(S), 0(I)	1574, 2373
$(CH_3)_2COHCH_2-$		102–3°, 157–9°	0, ±, +(S), 0(I)	5, 103, 311, 1574, 2373, 2441
$HOCH_2(CH_3)_2C-$		139–41°, 154–6°	+(S), 0(I, P)	103, 1057, 1574, 2373
$CH_3(HO)CH(C_2H_5)CH-$		102–4°	+(S), 0(I)	1574, 2373
$HOCH_2(C_2H_5)(CH_3)C-$		118–20°	+(S), 0(I)	1574, 2373
$CH_3(CH_2)_2CHOH(C_3H_7)CH-$		84–6°	+(S), 0(I)	1574
$HOCH_2CHOHCH_2-$		102–4°	++(M), 0(S)	5, 296, 2441
$(HOCH_2)_2CH-$				296
$(HOCH_2)_2(CH_3)C-$		131.8–4.0°	+(S), 0(P)	103, 1057
$(HOCH_2)_2(C_3H_7)C-$			0(P, S)	1574, 2373
NaO_2SCH_2-		227–9°	++(S)	1
HO_3SCH_2-			0(G)	2654
$H_2O_3PCH_2-$			0(I, P, R, S)	1427, 1574

TABLE 8

A. N^1-Acyclicsulfanilamides
3. Carboxy and Sulfo Derivatives

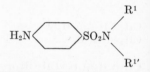

R^1	$R^{1'}$	Melting Range	Activities	References
$HOOCCH_2-$		154°	±, 0(Ec, S), 0(P, Pl), 0(En, Po)	33, 35, 62, 92, 207, 255, 267, 269, 348, 398, 719, 968, 1485, 1574, 1733, 1734, 2373, 2441
$NaOOCCH_2-$			+(P), ±, 0(S)	62, 254, 311, 1057, 1459
CH_3OOCCH_2-		88.5–9.0°		91
$C_2H_5OOCCH_2-$		90.4–2.0°	0, ±(P, S), 0(Tt)	91, 103, 1427, 1574, 2422
NH_2OCCH_2-		155°	0(S, Tt)	1574, 2422
$NCCH_2-$		163–5°	±(S)	432, 1057
$HCl·NH_2C(=NH)CH_2-$		189–90°		45
CH_3OOCCH_2-	CH_3-	105–6°		91
$C_2H_5OOCCH_2-$	CH_3-	115°		91
CH_3OOCCH_2-	C_2H_5-	85°		91
$C_2H_5OOCCH_2-$	do	88–9°		91
$HOOCCH_2-$	$HOOCCH_2-$			1702
$HOOC(CH_3)CH-$		107–8°	0(S, Tt)	348, 1427, 1459, 1574
$HOOCCH_2CH_2-$			0	1459
$CH_3CH_2(HOOC)CH-$			0	1459
$CH_3(CH_2)_2(HOOC)CH-$			0	1459
$(CH_3)_2CH(HOOC)CH-$			0	1459
$CH_3(CH_2)_3(HOOC)CH-$			0	1459
$(CH_3)_2CHCH_2(HOOC)CH-$			0	1459

TABLE 8—(*Continued*)

R^1	$R^{1'}$	Melting Range	Activities	References
$SCH_2(HOOC)CH-$				
$SCH_2(HOOC)CHNHSO_2C_6H_4NH_2-4$		193-4°	0(P, S, Sa, I)	1137, 1574, 2373
$CH_3SCH_2CH_2(HOOC)CH-$			0	1459
$NH_2OCCH_2(HOOC)CH-$				1459
$HOOCCH_2CH_2(HOOC)CH-$		192-4°	0(P, S)	968
$NaOOCCH_2CH_2(HOOC)CH-$			±(S)	62, 968, 1057
$NaOOCCH_2CH_2(NaOOC)CH-$				968
$C_2H_5OOCCH_2CH_2(C_2H_5OOC)CH-$		127°		2179
$C_4H_9OOCCH_2CH_2(C_4H_9OOC)CH-$		138.4-41.6° (HCl)	0(S)	103
$HO_3SCH_2CH_2-$			0(S)	159, 160, 209
$H_2O\cdot NaO_3SCH_2CH_2-$			0(S)	311

TABLE 9

A. N^1-Acyclicsulfanilamides
4. Amino Derivatives

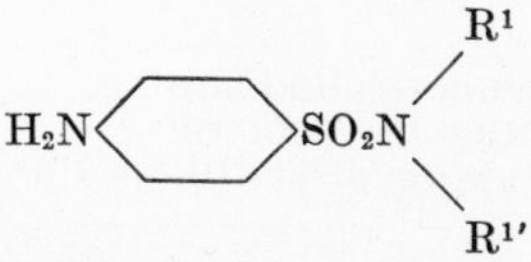

R^1	$R^{1'}$	Melting Range	Activities	References
$2HCl\cdot NH_2CH_2CH_2-$		217-20°		22
$2HCl\cdot (C_2H_5)_2NCH_2CH_2-$		190-5°		22
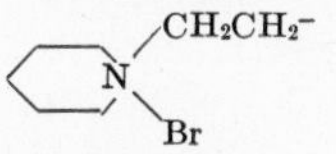 (structure) CH_2CH_2-		218°	0	968
(structure) NCH_2CH_2-		157°		320
(structure) NCH_2CH_2-				321
(structure) NCH_2CH_2-				318
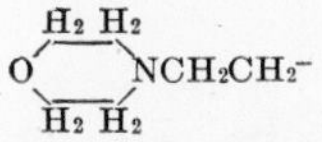 (structure) NCH_2CH_2-		98-100.4°	0(P, S)	103, 1057
$[4-(NH_2)C_6H_4SO_2NHCH_2CH_2]_2NCH_2CH_2-$		178.5-80°D	0(C, Pg, Pr, S, Sa)	1713
$4-(NH_2)C_6H_4SO_2NHCH_2CH_2-$		229.4-31.2°D	0(P, S)	103, 639, 1057, 1702
do	$HOCH_2CH_2-$	163.0-4.5°	0(P, S)	103, 639, 1057
do	$SO_2NHCH_2CH_2-$			
	$C_6H_4(NH_2)-4$	241-4°a	0(P), ±(S)	103, 639, 1057
$4-(NH_2)C_6H_4SO_2NHCH_2CH_2$				
$4-(NH_2)C_6H_4SO_2N$				
$(CH_2)_2$				
$4-(NH_2)C_6H_4SO_2NCH_2CH_2-$		208-9°	0(C, Pg, Pr, S, Sa)	1713

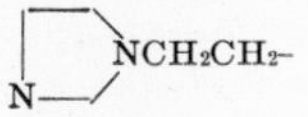

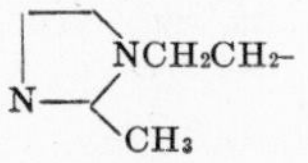

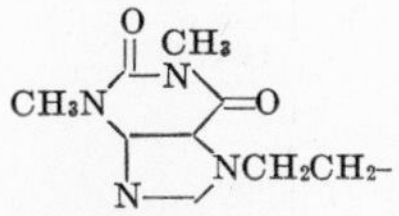

a Trihydrochloride.

TABLE 9—(Continued)

R^1	$R^{1\prime}$	Melting Range	Activities	References
4-$(NH_2)C_6H_4SO_2NHCH_2$				
|				
4-$(NH_2)C_6H_4SO_2NHCHCH_2-$		234.5–6°	0(C, Pg, Pr, S, Sa)	1713
$(C_2H_5)_2NCH(CH_3)(CH_2)_2-$				83
$HCl\cdot(C_2H_5)_2N(CH_2)_4-$		172°	±(S)	83, 84, 112, 710
4-$(NH_2)C_6H_4SO_2NH(CH_2)_4-$		205°	0(T)	2260
$(C_2H_5)_2N(CH_2)_2(CH_3)CH-$		198–200°	0(Pr)	122, 123
$(C_2H_5)_2NCH_2CHOHCH_2-$		oil	0(Pr)	122, 123
$\begin{array}{c}H_2\ \ H_2\\ H\langle\bigcirc\rangle NCH_2CHOHCH_2-\\ H_2\ \ H_2\end{array}$		151–2°	O(Pr)	122, 123
4-$(NH_2)C_6H_4SO_2NHCH_2CHOHCH_2-$		177–9°, 184.2–6.5°	0(Pr, Po), –, 0, ±, +(S), 0(P, Sa, Tt)	103, 505, 639, 1057, 1427, 1574, 1713
$NH_2(CH_2)_2(HOOC)CH-$		259–60°		612
$NH_2(CH_2)_4(HOOC)CH-$		286°D		612
$[4-(NH_2)C_6H_4SO_2NHCH_2]_2CCH_2-$		243.5–4°	0(C, Pg, Pr, S, Sa)	1713

TABLE 10

B. N^1-Isocyclicsulfanilamides
1. $R = C_nH_{2n-1}$ to C_nH_{2n-25}

$$NH_2\langle\bigcirc\rangle SO_2N\!\!\begin{array}{c}R^1\\R^{1\prime}\end{array}$$

R^1	$R^{1\prime}$	Melting Range	Activities	References
$\begin{array}{c}H_2\ \ H_2\\ H_2\langle\bigcirc\rangle\\ H_2\ \ H_2\ \ H\end{array}$		109–10° 227° (HCl)	0	173, 243, 1427, 1574, 1713
$\begin{array}{c}\quad\ \ H\\ CH_3\ \ H_2\ /\ \ H\\ \langle\bigcirc\rangle\\ H\ \ H_2\ \ H_2\ CH(CH_3)_2\cdot HCl\end{array}$			0(P)	1427, 1574
$\begin{array}{c}\square-(CH_2)_{11}-\\ H_2\ H_2\ H\end{array}$		116°	0(Le)	673
C_6H_5-		192°, 198°	+++, +(Ec), ±, +(S), ±(M, P)	61, 168, 269, 331, 442, 512, 719, 1574, 1734, 2441
do	$(CH_2)_2CH-$		+(S)	2583
4-FC_6H_4-		166.5°	±(S), 0(P)	179, 502, 1574
2-ClC_6H_4-		169.0–70.3°	0(P, S)	105, 1057
4-ClC_6H_4-		195.4–6.4°	±(S), 0(P)	105, 1057
3,5-$Cl_2C_6H_3-$		150°		555
3,4,5-$Cl_3C_6H_2-$		211°		555
4-BrC_6H_4-		178°	0(P)	332
3,5-$Br_2C_6H_3-$		150°		555
4-IC_6H_4-			0(I, R, S, Tt)	1427, 1574
2,4-$I_2C_6H_3-$		176–8°		812, 1609, 2094
3,5-$I_2C_6H_3-$		199°		555

TABLE 10—*(Continued)*

R¹	R¹′	Melting Range	Activities	References
4-(ON)C₆H₄—		133-4°		2262
2-(NO₂)C₆H₄—		179°, 167°	+, ±(Sa), 0(P)	160, 201, 332, 1147
3-(NO₂)C₆H₄—		171-2°	++(S), 0(P, T)	201, 331, **332, 544,** 1147
4-(NO₂)C₆H₄—		165-6°	+++, ±(S), ±(P), 0(En,P, Po, Sa, T), ±(Ec)	33, 35, 201, 268, 332, 544, 1147 1411, 1485
2,4-(NO₂)₂C₆H₃—			+(Cw)	989
C₆H₅—	C₆H₅—	225-30°	0(I, S)	1574, 2373
do	HOCH₂CH₂—	135.5-7.0°	++, ±(S), 0(P, Pl)	105, 1057, 1733, 2441
do	HO—		0(P)	1574
2-(CH₃)C₆H₄—		155.5°	+(Ec), ±(P), 0(Sa, T)	168, 218, 332, 719
2-CH₃-5(NO₂)C₆H₃—		199°	+(S), ±(P)	332
3-(CH₃)C₆H₄—		133.5°	+(Ec), 0(P, Sa, T)	168, 332, 719
4-(CH₃)C₆H₄—		183-4°, 190°	+(Ec), ±(P, T)	168, 331, 332, 719, 1411
4-(CH₃)-3(NO₂)C₆H₃—		189°	+(S), 0(P, Sa)	332
C₆H₅CH₂—		119.0-9.5°	±, +(S)	171, 213, 448, 512, 1322, 1602
C₆H₅CH₂CH₂—		143°	+(S), 0(P)	1574, 2001, 2373
4-(NO₂)C₆H₄CH₂CH₂—		207°		2001
2,6-(CH₃)₂C₆H₃—		231°	0(P, S)	332
2,4-(CH₃)₂C₆H₃—		149°	±(P)	332
3,5(F₃C)₂C₆H₃—		166°		555
2-CH₃-5-[(CH₃)₂CH]C₆H₃—		150.5°	0(P, S)	332
5-CH₃-2-[(CH₃)₂CH]C₆H₃—		>260°	0(S)	1574, 2373
C₆H₅CH = CHCH₂—		155-6°, 173-4°	0(I, S)	1503, 1574, 2373
		163°		2001
1-C₁₀H₇—				168
2-C₁₀H₇—				168
2-(CH₃)C₁₀H₆—(1)		247-8°	0(Ec, P)	1135, 2206, 2207, 2457
4-(C₆H₅)C₆H₄—		247°		2238
4-[C₆H₅C(C₂H₅)=C(C₂H₅)]C₆H₄—		180-2°	+(S, Sa)	800
		239°		2238
		213-5°		1985
		265°		1985

TABLE 11

B. N^1-Isocyclicsulfanilamides
   2. Oxy Derivatives

$$H_2N\langle\quad\rangle SO_2NHR^1$$

R^1	Melting Range	Activites	References
H₂ H₂ H H₂⟨ ⟩ H₂ H OH	141–2°	0(M, S)	5
2-(HO)C₆H₄–	182–3°	+++(Ec), –, 0, +(S)	105, 311, 544, 2437, 2441
2-(CH₃O)C₆H₄–	198–9.5°	0(P, S)	105, 137, 332
2-(C₆H₅O)C₆H₄–	149°		1985
2-CH₃O-5-(NO₂)C₆H₃–	188°	0(P)	332
3-(HO)C₆H₄–	195–6°	±, +(S)	311, 544, 1734, 2437, 2441
3-(CH₃O)C₆H₄–	163.5°	0(P, Sa, T)	332
4-(HO)C₆H₄–	199.5–201.5°, 234–5°	++(Ec), ++, ±(S), +(P), 0(Pl)	105, 311, 329, 449, 544, 1733, 1734, 2437, 2441
4-(CH₃O)C₆H₄–	195°	0(P, T, Tt)	83, 84, 331, 332, 1446, 1574
4-(C₂H₅O)C₆H₄–		±(S)	331, 512
4-(C₆H₅O)C₆H₄–	177–8°		1985
4-[4'-(4″-(NH₂)C₆H₄SO₂NH)C₆H₄O]C₆H₄–	105–15°		210
4-HO-3-(NO₂)C₆H₃–	189°	0(S)	311, 543
4-CH₃O-2-(NO₂)C₆H₃–	117°	0(P)	332
2-CH₃O-5-(CH₃)C₆H₃–	161°	0(P)	332
4-(CH₃O)C₆H₄CH₂CH₂–	149°		2001
C₆H₅CHOHCH₂–	164.1–5.1°		2370
2-CH₃-4-HO-5-[(CH₃)₂CH]C₆H₂–	220–3°D	+(Tv), ±(P, S, Sa)	105, 137, 407, 1057, 2489
Cholesteryl– (7)	234–6°		1503
3-CH₃-4-(HO)C₁₀H₅– (1)	209°D	++(Ec), 0(P)	1135, 2206, 2207
3-CH₂=CHCH₂-4-(HO)C₁₀H₅– (1)	195°D		817
2,6-(HO)₂C₆H₃–	180°D	+(S), 0(I, Tt)	1574, 2373
3-CH₃O-4-(HO)C₆H₃–	169.5–71.5°D	0(S)	105, 137, 2441, 2489
3,4-(CH₃O)₂C₆H₃CH₂CH₂–	126–7°		2001

TABLE 12

B. N^1-Isocyclicsulfanilamides
  3. Thio Derivatives

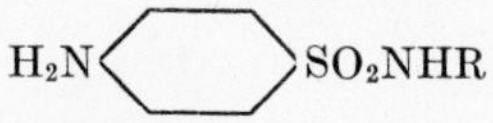

$H_2N\langle\quad\rangle SO_2NHR$

R^1	Melting Range	Activities	References
$3\text{-}(CH_3SO_2)C_6H_4-$			1349
$4\text{-}(CH_3S)C_6H_4-$	195–6°	+(S)	1057, 2323
$4\text{-}(C_2H_5S)C_6H_4-$	169–70°	±(S)	1057, 2323
$4\text{-}(C_2H_5SO_2)C_6H_4-$	190°	±(S)	1057, 2323
$4\text{-}[CH_3(CH_2)_3S]C_6H_4-$	162–5°		2323
$4\text{-}[CH_3(CH_2)_5S]C_6H_4-$	137°	+(S)	1057, 2323
$4\text{-}[CH_3(CH_2)_9S]C_6H_4-$	141–2°	±(S)	1057, 2323
$4\text{-}[CH_3(CH_2)_{13}S]C_6H_4-$	141.0–1.5°	±(S)	1057, 2323
$4\text{-}[CH_3(CH_2)_{15}S]C_6H_4-$	135–8°	±(S)	1057, 2323
$4\text{-}[4'\text{-}(NO_2)C_6H_4SO]C_6H_4-$	238–9°D		1176
$4\text{-}[4'\text{-}(NO_2)C_6H_4SO_2]C_6H_4-$	191–2°		1176
$4\text{-}[C_6H_5CH_2S]C_6H_4-$	204.5°	±(S)	1057, 2323
$4\text{-}(C_6H_5CH_2SO_2)C_6H_4-$	191–3°	±(S)	1057, 2323
$4\text{-}(HOOCCH_2S)C_6H_4-$	200–3°D		1808
$4\text{-}[CH_3(CH_2)_5(C_2H_5OOC)CHS]C_6H_4-$	oil		1808
$4\text{-}[CH_3(CH_2)_{15}(C_2H_5OOC)CHS]C_6H_4-$	wax		1808
$4\text{-}[4'\text{-}(4''\text{-}(NH_2)C_6H_4SO_2NH)C_6H_4S]C_6H_4-$	100°D		210, 225
$4\text{-}[4'\text{-}(4''\text{-}(NH_2)C_6H_4SO_2NH)C_6H_4S-S]C_6H_4-$	231–3°		2323
$4\text{-}[4'\text{-}(NH_2)C_6H_4SO_2]C_6H_4-$		±(S)	137, 432
$4\text{-}[4'\text{-}(4''(NH_2)C_6H_4SO_2NH)C_6H_4SO_2]C_6H_4-$		±(S)	60, 77, 152, 210, 225

TABLE 13

B. N^1-Isocyclicsulfanilamides:
  4. Oxo Derivatives

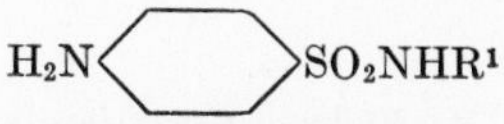

$H_2N\langle\quad\rangle SO_2NHR^1$

R^1	Melting Range	Activities	References
$4\text{-}(CH_3CO)C_6H_4-$	190°, 211°	±(Sa), +, 0(S), 0(P)	332, 352, 363, 431, 1983, 1984
$C_6H_5COCH_2-$	176–7°D		1983, 1984
$HCl\cdot C_6H_5COCH_2-$	200–2°D		1984
$4\text{-}(CH_3CH_2CO)C_6H_4-$	203°		352
$1\text{-}C_{10}H_7COCH_2-$	169°		1983
$4\text{-}(C_6H_5CO)C_6H_4-$	182–3°	0(P, S)	332, 352, 1574, 2373

TABLE 13—(*Continued*)

R¹	Melting Range	Activities	References
	226–7°	+++(Ec), +(T)	1135, 1593, 2206, 2207
	180–2°	0(I, P)	1574, 2373
	280°	0(P)	1574, 1823, 2373

TABLE 14

B. *N*¹-Isocyclicsulfanilamides
5. Carboxy Derivatives

H_2N⟨⟩SO_2NHR^1

R¹	Melting Range	Activities	References
2-(HOOC)C₆H₄—	215°D 225°D	+++, ±, 0(S), +(Ec), ±(P, Sa), 0(I, Pl, R, Tt)	98, 137, 159, 218, 267, 332, 556, 1574, 1733, 1734, 1984, 2373, 2441
2-(NaOOC)C₆H₄—		++, 0(S), +(P)	105, 269, 311
2-(C₂H₅OOC)C₆H₄—	165.5°	0(P)	105, 332
2-(NH₂OC)C₆H₄—	175°		2422
2-HOOC-4-ClC₆H₃—			83, 84
3-(HOOC)C₆H₄—	196°, 210°	+, ±, 0(S), +(Ec), ±(P, Pl), 0(I, R, Tt)	98, 218, 267, 269, 311, 332, 556, 1574, 1733, 1734, 2373, 2441
3-(C₂H₅OOC)C₆H₄—	105°	0(P)	332
3-(NH₂OC)C₆H₄—	217°		2422

TABLE 14—(*Continued*)

R^1	Melting Range	Activities	References
4-(HOOC)C$_6$H$_4$—	181–2°, 202°	++, +, ±, 0(S), ±(Ec, P), 0(I, R, Tt)	33, 35, 98, 137, 267, 269, 311, 332, 461, 556, 1574, 1734, 1984 2373, 2441
4-(NaOOC)C$_6$H$_4$—			556
4-(C$_2$H$_5$OOC)C$_6$H$_4$—	230°	±(Sa), 0(P)	332
4-(NH$_2$OC)C$_6$H$_4$—	202°		287, 2422
4-(HOOCCH$_2$)C$_6$H$_4$—		+(S), 0(I, R, Tt)	1574, 2373
C$_6$H$_5$CH$_2$(HOOC)CH—	196–7°D		159, 160, 1459
3-(HOOCCH=CH)C$_6$H$_4$—		0	158, 159
3-(NH$_2$OCCH=CH)C$_6$H$_4$—	246°		2422
4-(HOOCCH=CH)C$_6$H$_4$—			158
3-NH$_2$OC-2-(HO)C$_6$H$_3$—	193°		2422
4-HOOC-3-(HO)C$_6$H$_3$—	224°	0	105, 218, 556, 2441
3-HOOC-4-(HO)C$_6$H$_3$—	>285°D	0(En)	98, 556, 1485
3-C$_2$H$_5$OOC-4-(HO)C$_6$H$_3$—			2422
3-NH$_2$OC-4-(HO)C$_6$H$_3$—	215°		2422
4-(HO)C$_6$H$_4$CH$_2$(HOOC)CH—	230°D	0(Tt)	348, 1427, 1574
3-HOOC-4-(HO)C$_{10}$H$_5$— (1)	225°D		817

TABLE 15

B. *N^1*-Isocyclicsulfanilamides
6. Sulfino and Sulfo Derivatives

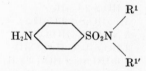

R^1	R$^{1'}$	Melting Range	Activities	References
2(HO$_2$S)-4-(NO$_2$)C$_6$H$_3$—		163°		228
4(HO$_2$S)C$_6$H$_4$—		228°D		228
2-(HO$_3$S)C$_6$H$_4$—		>100°D	++, ±, 0(S), 0(Ec, P)	64, 98, 137, 1734, 2441
2-HO$_3$S-4-FC$_6$H$_3$—		285°D	0(S)	502
2-HO$_3$S-4-ClC$_6$H$_3$—		300°D	0(S)	502
3-(HO$_3$S)C$_6$H$_4$—		>300°D	+, ±, 0(S), ±(Pl), 0(Ec)	98, 137, 218, 556, 1733, 1734, 2441
3-(NH$_2$O$_2$S)C$_6$H$_4$—		134–56°	++(Ec), ++, +(S)	100, 137, 719
3-HO$_3$S-4-FC$_6$H$_3$—		260°D	0(S)	502
3-HO$_3$S-4-ClC$_6$H$_3$—		310°D	0(S)	502
4-(HO$_3$S)C$_6$H$_4$—			0, ±(S), ±(Ec), 0(I, Pl, Pk, Po)	98, 158, 218, 267, 556, 890, 892, 1733, 1734, 2441
do	C$_2$H$_5$—	243–7°D	±(S), 0(P)	105, 1057

TABLE 15—*(Continued)*

R^1	$R^{1'}$	Melting Range	Activities	References
4-$(NaO_3S)C_6H_4-$		>300°D	+(Ca, L), ±(G, P, Pk, R), ±, 0(S), 0(En, I, Pc, Pl, Po, R)	48, 89, 98, 114, 187, 267, 269, 311, 326, 329, 421, 890, 1069, 1214, 1485, 1562, 1649, 1699, 1864, 2003
4-HO_3S-2-ClC_6H_3-			0(S, P)	105, 1057
4-NaO_3S-2,5-$Cl_2C_6H_2-$			±(S), 0(P)	105, 1057
2,5-$(HO_3S)_2C_6H_3-$		375–80°D	±(Sa), 0(I, S, Tt)	1574, 2373
3,5-$(HO_3S)_2C_6H_3-$			0(S)	100
4-HO_3S-2-$(CH_3)C_6H_3-$		>280°D	+, 0(S), 0(P)	98, 218, 311, 1057
5-HO_3S-2-$(CH_3)C_6H_3-$				218
4-HO_3S-3-$(CH_3)C_6H_3-$		>300°D	0(P, S)	98, 218, 1057
2-NaO_3S-4-$(CH_3)C_6H_3-$		>300°D	0(P, S)	64, 98, 1057
4-NaO_3S-2,5-$(CH_3)_2C_6H_2-$		>300°D	0(P, S)	98, 1057
4-NaO_3S-1-$C_{10}H_6-$		>245°D	++, ±, 0(S), 0(I, P, R, Tt)	98, 137, 218, 556, 1057, 1574, 2373
5-(NaO_3S)-1-$C_{10}H_6-$		>300°D	+, 0(S), 0(P)	98, 1057
3,6-$(HO_3S)_2$-1-$C_{10}H_5-$			0(S)	159, 160, 218, 556
3,8-$(HO_3S)_2$-1-$C_{10}H_5-$				218, 556
4,8-$(NaO_3S)_2$-1-$C_{10}H_5-$			0(S)	311
1-HO_3S-2-$C_{10}H_6-$		185–6°	±(S), 0(I, R, Tt)	1574, 2373
6-HO_3S-2-$C_{10}H_6-$		>300°D	±(P), 0, −(S)	98
5,7-$(HO_3S)_2$-2-$C_{10}H_5-$			0(S)	159, 160
5-NaO_3S-2-$(HO)C_6H_3-$			0(S)	311
3-HO_3S-4-$(C_2H_5O)C_6H_3-$		>245°D	0(P, S)	98, 1057
3,6$(HO_3S)_2$-8-HO-1-$C_{10}H_4-$			0(S)	159, 160
7-HO_3S-5-HO-2-$C_{10}H_5-$				218, 556
6-HO_3S-8-HO-2-$C_{10}H_5-$				218, 556
3,6-$(HO_3S)_2$-8-HO-2-$C_{10}H_4-$			0(S)	159, 160

TABLE 16

B. N^1-Isocyclicsulfanilamides
7. Amino and Azo Derivatives

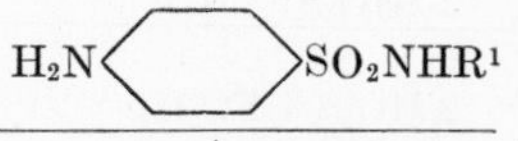

$H_2N\langle\ \rangle SO_2NHR^1$

R^1	Melting Range	Activities	References
2-$(NH_2)C_6H_4-$	201°, 208°	+++, ±, 0(S), ++(Ec), 0(I, P, R)	201, 311, 332, 544, 1446, 1574, 1734, 2441
2-[4'-$(NH_2)C_6H_4SO_2NH]C_6H_4-$	187.3–8.7°	+(S), ±(P)	639, 1057
3-$(NH_2)C_6H_4-$	160°, 177°	++, +, 0(S), +, ±(P), ±(M), 0(Sa)	67, 201, 311, 332, 544, 548, 1446, 1574, 2441
3-[4'-$(NH_2)C_6H_4SO_2NH]C_6H_4-$	220.5–21.7	±, 0(S), 0(P)	98, 210, 225, 233, 639, 1057

TABLE 16—(*Continued*)

R¹	Melting Range	Activities	References
4-$(NH_2)C_6H_4-$	138°, 156°	+++, +(Ec), +++, ++, +, ±(S), +, ±, 0, −(P), +(Sa), ±(M), 0(F, I, Pl, R)	33, 160, 201, 271, 311, 329, 332, 340, 448, 477, 544, 548, 719, 912, 913, 1214, 1574, 1734, 2441
4-$(CH_3NH)C_6H_4-$			201
4-$[(CH_3)_2N]C_6H_4-$	231–2°	+(S), ±, 0(P)	158, 201, 211, 331, 340, 639, 1147
4-$[(C_2H_5)_2N]C_6H_4-$		++, ±(S), 0(I, P)	201, 639, 1574, 2373
4-$(C_6H_5NH)C_6H_4-$	172°		211, 304
4-$(C_6H_5CH_2NH)C_6H_4-$	175.0–5.5°		270, 271
4-$[4'-(CH_3O)C_6H_4CH_2NH]C_6H_4-$	157.0–7.5°		270
4-$[4'-(4''-(NH_2)C_6H_4SO_2NH)C_6H_4NH]C_6H_4-$			210, 225
4-$(C_6H_5CH=N)C_6H_4-$	225°	+++(S), ±(P)	269, 271
4-$[4'-(NO_2)C_6H_4CH=N]C_6H_4-$	223–4°	+(S), 0(P)	269, 271
4-$[4'-(CH_3O)C_6H_4CH=N]C_6H_4-$	204–5°	++(S), ±(P)	269, 271
4-$[4'-[(CH_3)_2N]C_6H_4CH=N]C_6H_4-$	214–5°	++(S), 0(P)	269, 271
4-$[4'-(NH_2)C_6H_4SO_2NH]C_6H_4-$	263.5°, 273–4°D	++, +, 0(S), ±(Sa), 0(P)	98, 201, 210, 225, 332, 448, 639, 1057, 1411
3-NO_2-4-$(NH_2)C_6H_3-$	223–4°		543
2,4-$(NH_2)_2C_6H_3-$			211
3,4-$(NH_2)_2C_6H_3-$	208–9°		340, 543
3,5-$[4'-(NH_2)C_6H_4SO_2NH]_2C_6H_3-$	335–40°D	0(S)	639, 1057
2-CH_3-5-$(NH_2)C_6H_3-$	208.5°	0(P)	201, 332
3-CH_3-4-$(NH_2)C_6H_3-$	198°		211, 340
4-CH_3-3-$(NH_2)C_6H_3-$	185°	±(S), 0(P, Sa)	332
3-$[4'-(NH_2)C_6H_4SO_2NH]$-4-$(CH_3)C_6H_3-$	229°	±(S), 0(P)	332
5-CH_3-2-$(NH_2)C_6H_3-$	187°		201
4-$(NH_2CH_2CH_2)C_6H_4-$	223°		2001
4-$(NH_2)C_6H_4CH_2CH_2-$	154–5°		2001
2,3-$(CH_3)_2$-4-$(NH_2)C_6H_2-$	169°		201
4-$[4'-(NH_2)C_6H_4SO_2NH]$-1-$C_{10}H_6-$	257°		210, 225
5-$[4'-(NH_2)C_6H_4SO_2NH]$-1-$C_{10}H_6-$	285°		210, 225
8-$[4'-(NH_2)C_6H_4SO_2NH]$-1-$C_{10}H_6-$			210, 225
6-$[4'-(NH_2)C_6H_4SO_2NH]$-2-$C_{10}H_6-$	276°		210, 225
$NH_2\langle \rangle SO_2NH\langle \rangle - \langle \rangle -$	283°, 293°	±(S), 0(P)	210, 225, 332
$NH_2\langle \rangle SO_2NH\langle \rangle CH_2\langle \rangle -$	100–50°, 219.5–220°	±(S)	210, 225, 1057, 1176
$NH_2\langle \rangle SO_2NH\langle \rangle - \langle \rangle -$ with CH_3, CH_3	231–3°		210, 225
2-HO-5-$(NH_2)C_6H_3-$	167–8°		543
2-CH_3O-5-$(NH_2)C_6H_3-$	232°	0(P)	332
3-HO-4-$(NH_2)C_6H_3-$			211, 340
4-HO-3-$(NH_2)C_6H_3-$	204°	0(S)	311, 543
4-CH_3O-2-$(NH_2)C_6H_3-$		±(S), 0(P, Sa)	332
5-HO-2-$(NH_2)C_6H_3-$	205°		543
4-$[4'-(NH_2)C_6H_4SO_2NH]$-2-CH_3-5-$(CH_3O)C_6H_2-$	300°		210, 225
4-$\{[4'-(4''-(NH_2)C_6H_4SO_2NH)C_6H_4]_2C(OH)\}C_6H_4-$	150–5°D	+(S), 0(P)	105, 137, 1057
4-$[4'-(NH_2)C_6H_4SO_2NH]$-2,5-$(CH_3O)_2C_6H_2-$	288°		210, 225
$NH_2\langle \rangle SO_2NH\langle \rangle \overset{\parallel}{\underset{O}{C}}\langle \rangle -$	278°		210, 225

TABLE 16—(Concluded)

R^1	Melting Range	Activities	References
4-[4'-(NH$_2$)C$_6$H$_4$SO$_2$NH]-2-(HO$_3$S)C$_6$H$_3$—	>240°D	+++, ±, 0(S), 0(P)	89, 98, 137, 448, 639, 1057
4-NH$_2$-3-(HO$_3$S)C$_6$H$_3$—		+(S)	448
2-NH$_2$-5-(NaO$_3$S)C$_6$H$_3$—	>270°D	0(S)	98
3-[4'-(NH$_2$)C$_6$H$_4$SO$_2$NH]-4-(NaO$_3$S)C$_6$H$_3$—	>320°D	+++, ±, 0(S), 0(P)	98, 137, 639, 1057
2-[4'-(NH$_2$)C$_6$H$_4$SO$_2$NH]-4-(NaO$_3$S)C$_6$H$_3$—		+, ±(S), 0(P, Tv)	98, 639, 1057, 1393
3-[4'-(NH$_2$)C$_6$H$_4$SO$_2$NH]-4,6-(NaO$_3$S)$_2$C$_6$H$_2$—			639
2,6-(HO$_3$S)$_2$-4-(NH$_2$)C$_6$H$_2$—			218
5-[4'-(NH$_2$)C$_6$H$_4$SO$_2$NH]-2-NaO$_3$S-4-(CH$_3$)C$_6$H$_2$—	>300°D	0(S)	98, 639
NH$_2$⟨⟩SO$_2$NH⟨⟩ HO$_3$S SO$_3$H	>300°D	±(S), 0(P)	98, 639, 1057
NH$_2$⟨⟩SO$_2$NH⟨⟩CH=CH⟨⟩— SO$_3$H SO$_3$H	>330°D	+(S), 0(P)	98, 639, 1057
4-(C$_6$H$_5$N=N)C$_6$H$_4$—	249–50°	0(I, S)	1574, 2373
1-(C$_6$H$_5$N=N)-2-C$_{10}$H$_6$—	221–2°		728
3-[4'-[(HO)$_2$OAs]C$_6$H$_4$N=N]-4-(HO)C$_6$H$_3$CH$_2$(HOOC)CH—	>300°		348
4-[4'-(HO$_3$S)C$_6$H$_4$N=N]-3-(NH$_2$)C$_6$H$_3$—			127
4-[4'-(HO$_3$S)C$_6$H$_4$N=N]-3-[4''-(NH$_2$)C$_6$H$_4$SO$_2$NH]C$_6$H$_3$—			127

TABLE 17

B. N^1-Isocyclicsulfanilamides

8. Miscellaneous Derivatives

Compound	Melting Range	Activities	References
{4-[4'-(NH$_2$)C$_6$H$_4$SO$_2$NH]C$_6$H$_4$}$_2$PC$_6$H$_5$	202–4°		169
{4-[4'-(NH$_2$)C$_6$H$_4$SO$_2$NH]C$_6$H$_4$}$_2$AsC$_6$H$_5$	198°		169
4-[4'-(NH$_2$)C$_6$H$_4$SO$_2$NH]C$_6$H$_4$AsO$_3$H$_2$	244–5°, >241°D	+, 0(S), 0(Tt)	25, 331, 332, 504, 1574, 2192, 2437
4-[4'-(NH$_2$)C$_6$H$_4$SO$_2$NH]C$_6$H$_4$AsO$_3$HNa		±(S), 0(I, P, Po, Sa)	311, 892

TABLE 18

C. N^1-Heterocyclicsulfanilamides

1. One or More O- or S-Atoms in the Heterocyclic System

H$_2$N⟨⟩SO$_2$N⟨R^1 / $R^{1'}$

R^1	$R^{1'}$	Melting Range	Activities	References
S⟨⟩—		156.5 –7.5°	+++, +(Ec), +, 0(P), 0(S)	41, 47, 528, 1134–5
O⟨⟩CH$_2$—		153.3 –4.2°	+, 0(Ec), 0(I, P, Po, S)	105, 137, 719, 892

TABLE 18—(*Continued*)

R^1	R$^{1'}$	Melting Range	Activities	References
do	CH$_2$–	134–6.5°	+(P), O(S)	103
		195°		2456
		242–4°, 245°		394, 2456
		189–90°		1985
SO$_2$NH NH$_2$		267–8°		210
		168°		1174
		>120°D		1174
		>125°D		1174

TABLE 19

C. N^1-Heterocyclicsulfanilamides
  2. One N-Atom in the Heterocyclic System
    a. 2-Sulfanilamidopyridines

$$H_2N\text{—}\langle\ \rangle\text{—}SO_2N\ \begin{matrix}R^1\\|\\\end{matrix}\ \begin{matrix}N\diagdown R_6\\R_3\diagup\ \diagdown R_5\\R_4\end{matrix}$$

R¹	R₃	R₄	R₅	R₆	Melting Range	Activities	References
					190.4–1.5°ᵃ	See Table 276	11, 44, 102, 171, 272, 341, 409, 434, 435, 480, 481, 482, 486, 516, 540, 544, 553, 602, 868,1489,1707, 1749, 2188, 2210, 2424
Na−						+++(S), ++(P), ±(B)	95, 334, 434, 486, 1856
½ Cu−							870
Ag−							51, 574
½ Ca−					b	+(F, Ko, Kr)	575
CH₃−					86.5-7.0°		2189
CH₃(CH₂)₂−					108°	0(T)	2260
CH₃(CH₂)₄−					74-5°	0(T)	2260
CH₃(CH₂)₁₅−					77°	0(T)	2260
CH₃(CH₂)₁₇−					70-1°	0(T)	2260
C(CH₃)=CHCH₂− | (CH₂)₂CH=C(CH₃)₂					75-6°	0(T)	2260
HOOCCH₂−							408
NH₂OCCH₂−							408
			Br−		196-7°	++(Ec), +(S, Sa, P)	435, 719, 1057
			I−		220-1°		341, 435, 486, 1057
	I−		I−		217°D		827
			NO₂−		218-20°	0(En, Po)	409, 435, 1057, 1749, 1485
				CH₃−	219-20°, 222°ᶜ	++, ±(P), 0(Tt)	341, 486, 516, 517, 869, 1574, 1740, 2237, 2373
CH₃(CH₂)₁₇−				CH₃−	77-8°	0(T)	2260
	C₂H₅O−				198-200°	+(S, Sa)	435, 1057
				HO	239-40°		410
	HOOC−				176-9°		341, 486, 2210
	NH₂OC−					0(S)	358
			HO₃S−		305°		341, 486
			NH₂O₂S−		222°, 227°		80, 1364, 1819
			(CH₃)₂NO₂S−		151-3°		1819

ᵃ Sulfapyridine.
ᵇ Orsulon.
ᶜ Sulfamethylpyridine, Methylsulfidine.

TABLE 19—(*Continued*)

R^1	R_3	R_4	R_5	R_6	Melting Range	Activities	References
			NH_2-		157–9°	+++, ++(Ec, S), +(P)	390, 409, 435, 719, 1057
			SO_2NH- 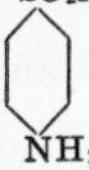 ⬡ NH_2		215–6°	+, 0(S), ± (Sa), 0(P)	435, 1057
				NH_2-	108°, 204–6°, 209–10°	++(P, S)	93, 149, 480, 516, 1829
				$(CH_2)_5=N-$	185°	±(P)	417
				SO_2NH-  ⬡ NH_2	255°		341, 486
		$HOOC-$		NH_2-		0(P, S)	95
	$C_6H_5N=N-$			NH_2-	230–2°		1829
	SO_2NH_2  ⬡ $N=N-$			NH_2-	264–5°		1829

TABLE 20

b. 3-Sulfanilamidopyridines

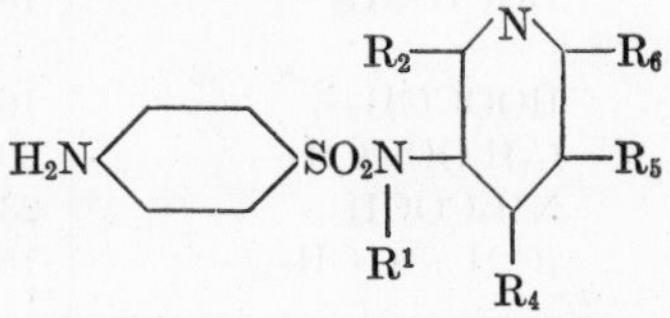

R^1	R_2	R_4	R_5	R_6	Melting Range	Activities	References
					258–9°D	+++(Ec, P), +(S, Sa)	137, 272, 435, 553, 719, 1057
				$Cl-$	186–7°	+++(Ec), ++(S), 0(P, Sa)	435, 643, 1057
				$Br-$	196–7°	+++, +(P), +++(Ec, S), ± (Sa)	435, 643, 719, 1057
				$I-$	205°D		827
				$HO-$	243–4°D	0(S)	435, 643
				CH_3O-	178°	±(P)	417
				C_2H_5O-	207–8°	+(Ec, S, Sa), 0(P)	435, 643, 1057
	NH_2CO-				182°		2422
				NH_2-	210–12°	++(Ec), +(Sa), ±(P), ±, 0(S)	435, 553, 719, 1829

TABLE 21

c. 4-Sulfanilamidopyridines

R^1	R$_2$	R$_3$	R$_5$	R$_6$	Melting Range	Activities	References
					240°, 245–7°	+(P)	272, 341, 480, 486, 1057

TABLE 22

d. 2-Sulfanilimido-1,2-dihydropyridines
  (2-Sulfanilylpyridonimines)

R$_1$	Melting Range	Activities	References
CH$_3$–	225°, 232–3°	+++(S), +(Ec), +(P)	341, 413, 486, 2189
C$_2$H$_5$–	189–92°		413
CH$_3$(CH$_2$)$_2$–	182–4°		413
CH$_3$(CH$_2$)$_3$–	194–7°		413
C$_6$H$_5$CH$_2$–	179°, 235°		341, 486, 2189
4-(NO$_2$)C$_6$H$_4$CH$_2$–	234°D		1984
HOCH$_2$CH$_2$–	184–5°	±(Sa), +, ±(S), +(Ec), 0(P)	1057, 1734, 2189
HOOCCH$_2$–	165°	+(Ec, P)	2189
C$_2$H$_5$OOCCH$_2$–	200.5–1.0°		2189
NH$_2$COCH$_2$–	230°D		2189
(C$_2$H$_5$)$_2$N(CH$_2$)$_2$–	155–7°		338

TABLE 23

3. Miscellaneous Pyridine Derivatives

R^1	Melting Range	Activities	References
	130.8–31°		272, 2378
	133–3.5°		272

TABLE 23—(*Continued*)

R¹	Melting Range	Activities	References
 (structure: N-heterocycle with CH₂–)	183–3.5°		272
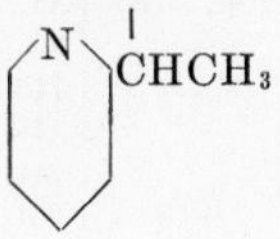 (structure: N-heterocycle with CHCH₃)	135–6°		272
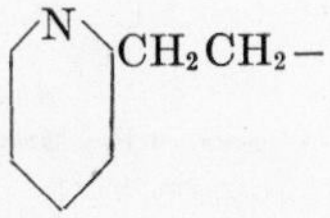 (structure: N-heterocycle with CH₂CH₂–)	248–50°D		368
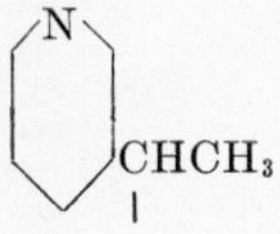 (structure: N-heterocycle with CHCH₃)	163.5–4.5°		272
 (structure: N-heterocycle with CHCH₃)	194–5°		272

TABLE 24

f. x-Sulfanilamidoquinolines

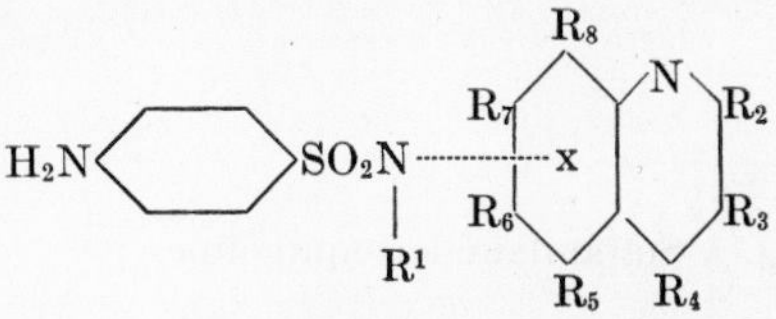

$$H_2N\langle\rangle SO_2N\text{---}x\text{ (quinoline with }R_2, R_3, R_4, R_5, R_6, R_7, R_8\text{)},\; R^1$$

R¹	R₂	R₃	R₄	R₅	R₆	R₇	R₈	Melting Range	Activities	References
	x							197.8–8.7°	++, ±(S), +(P)	105, 137, 248, 341, 409, 463, 486, 516, 517, 1057, 1384, 1563, 1749
N(CH₂)₂– | (C₂H₅)₂	x			NO₂–				132°		338
		x						185–6°D		248, 463, 553, 1384
			x					248°		248, 463, 1384
				x				228–30°		43, 248, 253, 463, 553, 1384, 1563

TABLE 24—(Continued)

R¹	R₂	R₃	R₄	R₅	R₆	R₇	R₈	Melting Range	Activities	References
					x			202-4°, 208°	0(P, Tt), 0, −(S)	43, 159, 160, 248, 253, 341, 426, 463, 486, 553, 1384, 1574, 2192
						x		206°		43, 248, 463, 1384
							x	188°, 194-5°	+, −(S)	43, 84, 248, 253, 463, 553, 710, 1384, 1563
	CH₃−				x			252°		341, 486
	x		CH₃−					230-1°	+(P)	604
					CH₃−	x				463
	CH₃−	CH₃−			x		CH₂−	219°, 226°	±(S), 0(P, Pl)	57, 812, 2098
	CH₃−	CH₃−			x		C₂H₅−	241-2°		2098
	CH₃−	CH₃−			x		CH₃(CH₂)₂−	208-9°	±(S), 0(P, Sa, Su)	2098
	C₆H₅−		x					293°		30
				x			CH₃O−	228-30°		341, 486
					HO−	x		222°		344
					CH₃O−	x		191°, 195-6°	+ (S)	84, 112, 248, 344, 710, 1384, 1563
N(CH₂)₂−					CH₃O−	x		91-2°		338
(C₂H₅)₂										
					C₂H₅O	x		193-4°		344
	HO−		CH₃−			x		289°		341, 486
	CH₃−	CH₃−		CH₃O−	x		CH₃−	230°	0(Pl)	57, 812
	C₆H₅−		x		CH₃O−			268°		30
	do		HOOC−		x					105, 1485
				NH₂SO₂−		x		201°		507
				do	CH₃O−	x		234°D		507

TABLE 25

g. x-Sulfanilamidoisoquinolines

H_2N⟨⟩SO_2N------x ... R_7 R_8 R_1 N R_6 R^1 R_5 R_4 R_3 R_2

R¹	R₁	R₃	R₄	R₅	R₆	R₇	R₈	Melting Range	Activities	References
	x							263°, 268-70°D	+++, 0(S), 0(P)	97, 105, 137, 341, 409, 486, 1057
			x					211.5-12.5°	++(S)	97
				x				223-4.5°D	0(S)	97, 1057, 1239

TABLE 26

h. Miscellaneous N^1-Heterocyclicsulfanilamides with One
N-Atom in the Heterocyclic System

H_2N⟨⟩SO_2NHR^1

R^1	Melting Range	Activities	References
	173–5°		1135
	202°D		2414
	194°	0(Pr)	572
	200°	0(Pr)	572
	240–50°		368
	224°D		1985
	256–7°		393
			163

TABLE 26—(*Continued*)

R[1]	Melting Range	Activities	References
CH₂CH₂— 	234–5°		368
CH₃CHCH₂— 	240–2°D		368
	178–80°	±(P)	417
	251–3°		1985
	194°	0(Pr)	572
	180°		110
			110

TABLE 26—(*Concluded*)

R¹	Melting Range	Activities	References
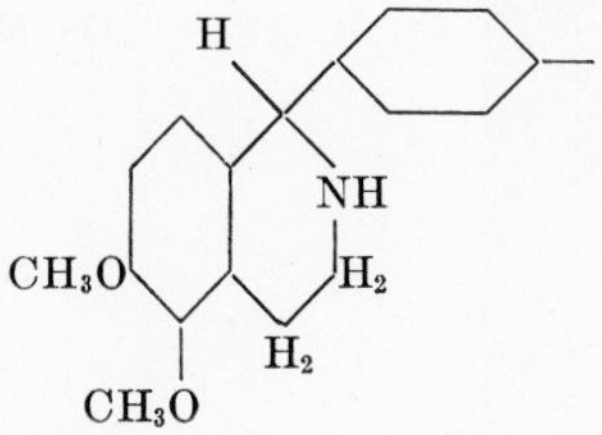	159–62°D		1985
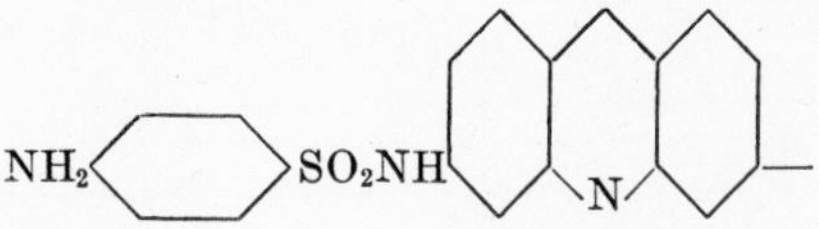			160, 163
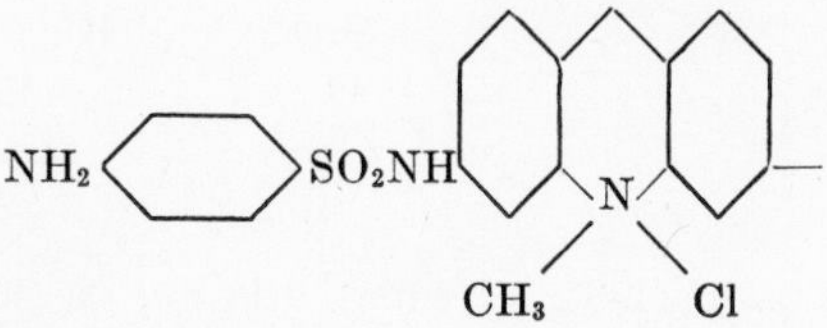		0(I, Po), ±(P, S), +(Sa)	105, 892, 1057

TABLE 27

C. *N*¹-Heterocyclicsulfanilamides
  3. Two or more N-Atoms in the Heterocyclic System
  a. 5-Membered Heterocyclic Rings

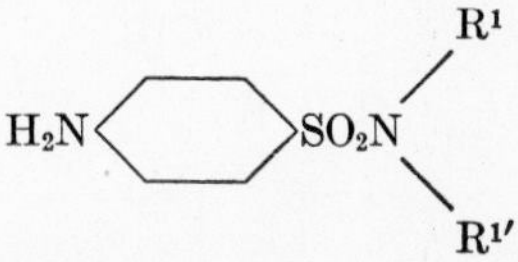

R¹	R¹′	Melting Range	Activities	References
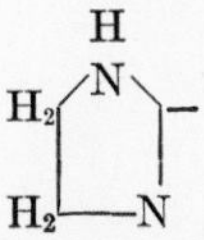		223–5°	0(P, S)	1574, 2192
		235°	+++(P), +(Ec)	1135, 1376, 1384
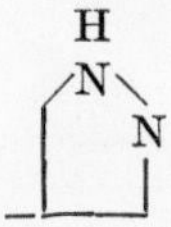		185°	+(S), ±(P)	417, 1057

TABLE 27—(*Continued*)

R^1	$R^{1\prime}$	Melting Range	Activities	References
(structure: H–N, N ring)		262°	+(Ec), 0(P, S)	339, 653, 719
(structure: N, NCH₃ ring)	CH₃–			339
(structure: –CH₂CH₂–N, H–N ring)			±(S), 0(P)	105, 137, 1057
(structure: CH₃, H–N, N, CH₃ ring)		233°	±(P)	417
(structure: C₆H₅, O=, NCH₃, CH₃ ring)		213°, 248°, 253–4°, 260–1°	+(Sa), 0(P, S)	32, 407, 434, 518, 1057, 2084
(structure: H H, N=O, O=NH ring)		122°D	++(P)	417
(structure: COOH, –CHCH₂–N, H–N ring)		263–4°		649
(structure: –CHCH₂–N, H–N ring, COOCH₃)		218–25°		649

TABLE 28

b. 2-Sulfanilamidopyrimidines

NH_2⟨ ⟩SO_2N — pyrimidine ring with substituents R^1 (on N), R_4, R_5, R_6

R^1	R_4	R_5	R_6	Melting Range	Activities	References
				$254\text{-}6°D^a$	See Table 277	162, 434, 493, 647, 1378, 1708, 1828, 1861, 2399
Na–						434, 647
½Cu–						647
Ag–						574
½Ca–						1826
CH_3–						647
		Cl–		246-7°	+++(Ec), +(P, S)	436, 1057
	CH_3–			235-6°, 236-8°^{b}	See Table 278	162, 434, 493, 687, 1378, 1384, 1828, 1975, 2378
Na–	CH_3–				+++	434, 493, 1816, 2419
	CH_3–	Br–		231-2°		493
		CH_3–		262-3°		493
	C_2H_5–			242°	+ (P)	1975
	CH_3–	CH_3–		222°	+++, +(Ec, P, S)	66, 143, 1645, 1975
	CH_3–		CH_3–	175.5-6.5°, 178-80°, 198-9°, 205-7°^{cc}	See Table 279	66, 162, 436, 493, 1355, 1378, 1384, 1708, 1828, 2399
Na–	CH_3–		CH_3–			1645
	$CH_3CH_2CH_2$–			217-8°	+, 0(P, S)	493, 1975, 2378
	C_2H_5–	CH_3–		215°	0(P)	1975
	CH_3–	CH_3–	CH_3–	241-2°		1355
		$CH_3(CH_2)_3$–		205-6°		493
	$(CH_3)_2CHCH_2$–			232°	0(P)	1975
	$CH_3(CH_2)_4$–			226°	0(P)	1975
	$CH_3(CH_2)_5$–			206-7°	0(P)	143, 493, 1975
	CH_3–	$CH_3(CH_2)_4$–		215-6°, 188-90°		66, 493
	C_6H_5–			268-9°	0(P)	493, 1975
	C_6H_5–		CH_3–	233°		1378
	morpholino (O⟨CH_2CH_2⟩$_2$N–)			>300°	0 (P)	432
	HO–			268-9°, 279°	±, 0(S)	432, 1057, 1146
	CH_3O–			241-2°, 251-2°	++, ±(P), +(S)	436, 604, 647, 1057
	C_2H_5O–			255-6°	±(P, S)	436, 647
	CH_3–		C_2H_5O–	151-2°		493

^{a} Sulfadiazine.
^{b} Sulfamerazine.
^{c} Sulfamezathine, Sulfamethazine

TABLE 28—(*Continued*)

R¹	R₄	R₅	R₆	Melting Range	Activities	References
CH_3-			$HO-$	253.5–4.0°	±(C)	493, 1146, 1951
do			CH_3S-	197.5–8.5°	++(P)	687
CH_3O-			CH_3-	203.5–4.5°	++(P)	687
CH_3-	CH_3-		$HO-$	238–9°		1146
do	C_2H_5-		do	208–9°		1146
do	$CH_3(CH_2)_3-$		do	121–2°		1146
do	$(CH_3)_2CH(CH_2)_2-$		do	190–3°		1146
do	$CH_3(CH_2)_5-$		do	108–10°		1146
CH_3O-			CH_3O-			647
C_2H_5OOC-			$HO-$	219°		1355
NH_2-				271–2°	+++, 0(S), ++ (Ec), 0(P)	653, 1057
$(C_2H_5)_2N-$				>300°	±(Ec), 0(P, S)	653, 1057

TABLE 29

c. 4-Sulfanilamidopyrimidines

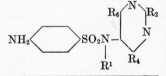

R₂	R₅	R₆	Melting Range	Activities	References
			231–2°D	+++(Ec), 0(P, S)	434, 436, 647, 719, 1007, 1057
CH_3-			207–8°	±(S)	436, 1057
		CH_3-	209–11°		687
CH_3-		do	233°, 243°	++, 0(P, I, R, Tt)	1007, 1161, 1427, 1574, 2233
C_2H_5-	CH_3-	C_2H_5-		0(P, Tt)	1427, 1574
CH_3O-					647
C_2H_5O-			256–7°		493
CH_3O-		CH_3-	188.5–9.5°	+(P)	687
C_2H_5O-		do	186–7°		493
C_2H_5S-		do	188–9°		493

TABLE 30

d. 5-Sulfanilamidopyrimidines

R¹	R₂	R₄	R₆	Melting Range	Activities	References
				260–1°	+++(Ec), +(S)	436, 647, 719, 1057

TABLE 30—(*Continued*)

R¹	R₂	R₄	R₆	Melting Range	Activities	References
	Cl			206–7°	+++(Ec), +(P, S)	436, 1057
		CH₃—		233.0–5.5°D	+(P)	687
	CH₃O—			232–4°	++(S), +(P)	436, 647, 1057
	CH₃O—	CH₃—		191–2°	—	687
	NH₂—			293–8°	±(P, S)	436, 647, 1057
Na—	NH₂—				+(P)	1057
	4-(NH₂)C₆H₄SO₂NH—			231–2°, 241–2°	0(S)	436, 647, 1057, 1975

TABLE 31

e. Miscellaneous N^1-Heterocyclicsulfanilamides Having 6-Membered Rings with Two N-Atoms

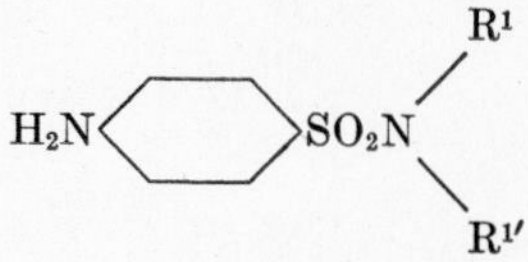

$$H_2N \langle\!\!\!\;\bigcirc\!\!\!\;\rangle SO_2N \begin{smallmatrix} R^1 \\ R^{1\prime} \end{smallmatrix}$$

R¹	R¹′	Melting Range	Activities	References
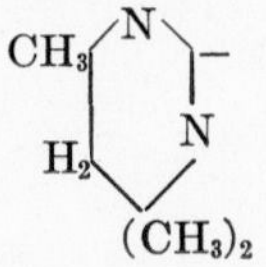 CH₃ / N / H₂ N (CH₃)₂		230–2°	+(S)	162, 1057, 1146
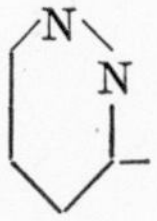		189–90°	+++(Ec), +(S), 0(P)	653, 719, 1057
		251°, 255–7°Dᵃ	See Table 280	130, 417, 452, 2373
do	Na·H₂O		+++(P)	130, 706
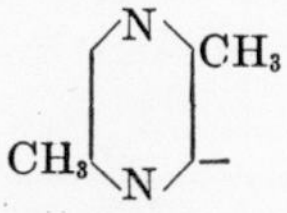 CH₃ N CH₃ / CH₃ N		227–8°		251

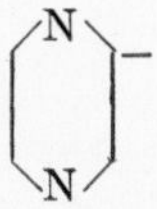

ᵃ Sulfapyrazine.

TABLE 31—(*Continued*)

R^1	$R^{1'}$	Melting Range	Activities	References
		190–3°	0(S)	1146
	CH₃–	160–5°		1146
			0	162, 1147
		277–9°D	±(S), 0(En, P, Sa)	26, 434, 436, 1057, 1485
		283°D		26
			0(P, S)	162, 1147

TABLE 32

f. Miscellaneous N^1-Heterocyclicsulfanilamides with Two
   N-Atoms in the Heterocyclic System

$$H_2N\langle\quad\rangle SO_2N\begin{smallmatrix}R^1\\ \\R^{1'}\end{smallmatrix}$$

R^1	Melting Range	Activities	References
H_2 N-N (see structure)	252–3°, 255–6°	0(P)	66, 143, 493, 1975
$CH(CH_3)_2$ structure	185–7°	0	66, 143
structure with CH_3	273–4°D	+(S), 0(P)	812
structure with CH_3	234–6°D	+++(Ec)	812
structure NH	225–6°	+++(Ec), 0(S)	432, 1502, 2584
structure NH	247–8°	0(I, PO)	892, 1502, 1983, 1984, 2584

TABLE 32—(*Continued*)

R¹	Melting Range	Activities	References
	195–6°		1502, 2584
	254–6°		1502, 1983, 2584
	213–4°	$\pm$(P, S), 0(I)	417, 1574, 2373
	267–7°	0	66, 143
	a	++(Ec, P, S, Ssc), +(Ae)	2635, 2639, 2656
	>350°		2635
	188°	$\pm$(P)	417
	230–40°		368

a Sulfaquinoxaline.

TABLE 32—(*Concluded*)

R¹	Melting Range	Activities	References
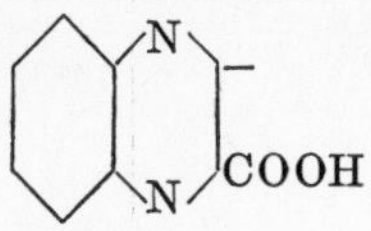 (structure: bicyclic N,N ring with COOH)	238–9°		2656

TABLE 33

g. *N¹*-Heterocyclicsulfanilamides with Three or More N-Atoms in the Heterocyclic System

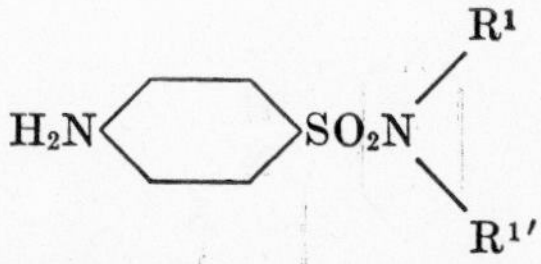

$$H_2N\!-\!\bigcirc\!-\!SO_2N\big\langle\begin{smallmatrix}R^1\\R^{1\prime}\end{smallmatrix}$$

R¹	R¹′	Melting Range	Activities	References
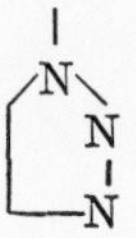 (triazole ring structure)		187°	+(Ec), 0(S)	432, 1057
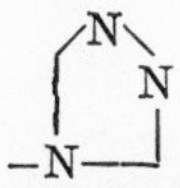 (triazole ring structure)		237°D	+, 0(S), ±(Ec), 0(P)	653, 719, 1057
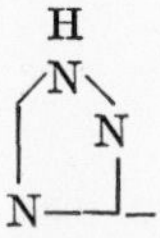 (triazole ring with H)		195–6°D, 210°D	±(Ec), 0(P, S)	653, 719, 1984
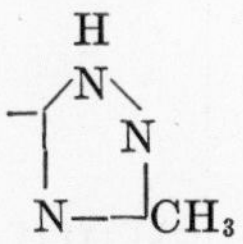 (triazole ring with H, CH₃)		244–5°	0(P)	686, 1381
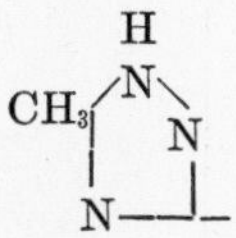 (triazole ring with H, CH₃)			0(G)	2384
do	Na–	>300°	±(P)	417
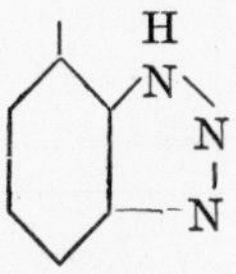 (benzotriazole ring with H)			0(I, Po)	892

TABLE 33—(*Continued*)

R^1	$R^{1\prime}$	Melting Range	Activities	References
		135–7°		1983, 1984
		·H_2O 210°		2378
		189°	±(P)	417
		290–5°D	+(Ec), 0(P, S)	653
		202°D		2378
			±(S)	162, 1057
		258–9°D	+(Ec), ±(P)	731, 1135
		200–1°D		1983, 1984

TABLE 33—(*Concluded*)

R^1	R$^{1'}$	Melting Range	Activities	References
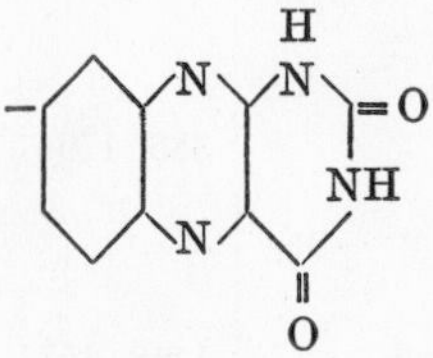			0	162, 1147

TABLE 34

C. N^1-Heterocyclicsulfanilamides
  4. One N-Atom and One O-, S- or Se-Atom in the Heterocyclic System
    a. One N- and One O-Atom in the Heterocyclic System.

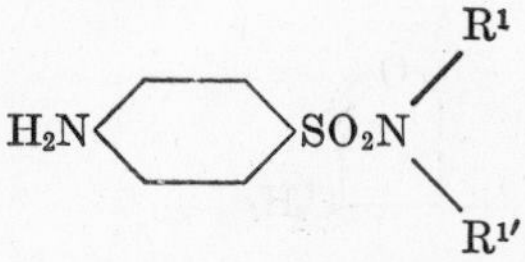

R^1	Melting Range	Activities	References
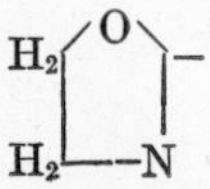	192–5°		2370
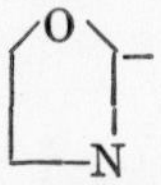	175–6°	+++(Ec), 0(P, S)	653, 719, 1057, 2492
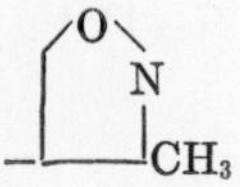	146–8°		385
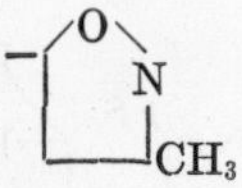	164–5°, 169–70°	++(Ec), +(P, S)	653, 685, 719

TABLE 34—(*Continued*)

R¹	Melting Range	Activities	References
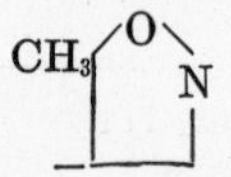	136–7°		385
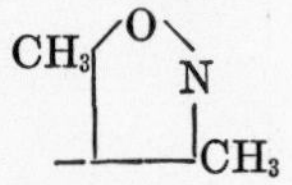	193–4°		385, 1794
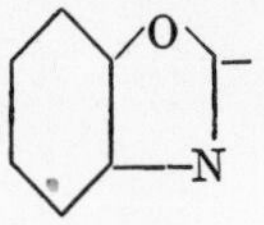	155–60°	0(P)	1448, 1574
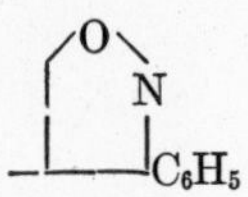	170–1°		385
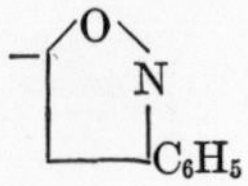	173–4°		685
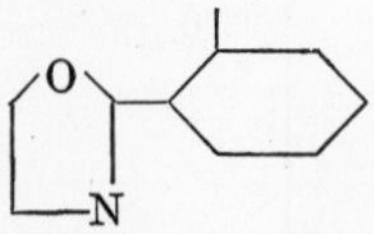	172.5–3.5°	+++(S)	846
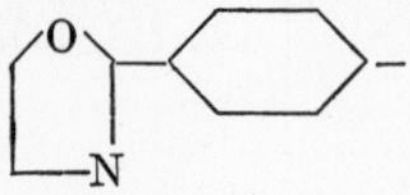	191.5–2.5°	+(S, Sa)	2052
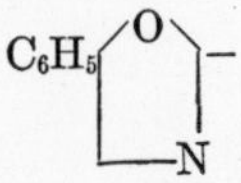	282–4°, 267–9°	+++(Ec)	685, 686, 1135, 1377, 1384

TABLE 35

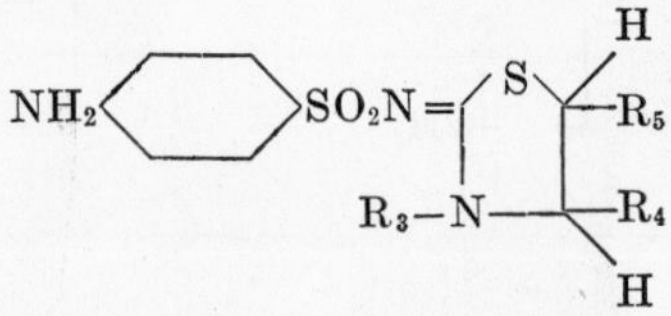

b. 2-Sulfanilimidothiazolidines

R₃	Melting Range	Activities	References
CH_3-	196–8°		1984
C_2H_5-	181–2°		1984

TABLE 36

c. 2-Sulfanilamido-2-thiazolines

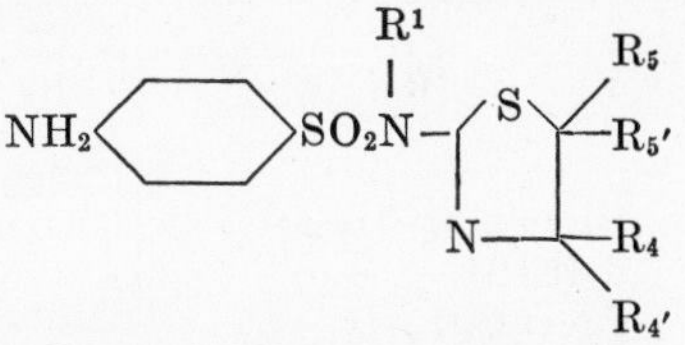

$$NH_2 \langle \rangle SO_2N - R^1 \begin{array}{c} S - R_5, R_5' \\ N - R_4, R_4' \end{array}$$

R^1	R_4	R_5	Melting Range	Activities	References
a			204–5°, 209–10°, 225°	See Table 281	25, 79, 249, 416, 417, 481, 492, 1384, 1448, 1574
$CH_2=CHCH_2-$			186–9°		1984
C_6H_5-			156–85°, 215–6°	0(P, Tt)	1448, 1574, 1984
$4-(Br)C_6H_4-$			149–55°	0(P, Tt)	1448, 1574
$4-(C_2H_5O)C_6H_4-$			211–3°	0(P, Tt)	1448, 1574
$4-(C_4H_9S)C_6H_4-$			214–5°	0(P, Tt)	1448, 1574
	CH_3-		176°	++(P, S)	1824
		CH_3-	177.5–8.5°	++(P, S)	1824

a Sulfathiazoline.

TABLE 37

d. 2-Sulfanilimido-4-thiazolines

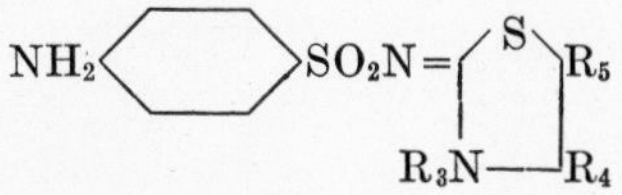

$$NH_2 \langle \rangle SO_2N = \begin{array}{c} S - R_5 \\ R_3N - R_4 \end{array}$$

R_3	R_4	R_5	Melting Range	Activities	References
CH_3-			246°, 250–1°	++(Ec, P, Pk, S) +(Pl, Pp)	184, 246, 249, 1007, 1145, 1384, 1733, 1896, 2189, 2232
C_2H_5-			183–5°, 192–4°	0, ++(S), 0(P, Pp)	1007, 1145, 2232
$CH_3(CH_2)_2-$			174°	+	1007, 2232
$(CH_3)_2CH-$			175–7°	±	1007, 2232
$CH_3(CH_2)_3-$			186–8°, 192–5°	0	1007, 1145, 2232
$(CH_3)_2CH(CH_2)_2-$			201–3°	0(S, P, Pp)	1145
$CH_3(CH_2)_5-$			156°	0(S, P, Pp)	1145
$CH_3(CH_2)_{11}-$			106°	0(P, S, Sa)	1007, 1574, 2232
$CH_3(CH_2)_{15}-$			106°	0	1007, 2232
$CH_2=CHCH_2-$			165–6°	+++	1007, 2232

TABLE 37—(*Continued*)

R_3	R_4	R_5	Melting Range	Activities	References
$CH_2=CBrCH_2-$			122–3°	+	1007
$C_6H_5CH_2-$			185–7°	±	249, 1007
$4-NO_2C_6H_4CH_2-$			199–200°D		1984
$HOCH_2CH_2-$			155°, 159-60°	++, +(S)	1007, 1145, 1734, 2189, 2232
CH_3COCH_2-			202°	0(S, P, Pp)	1145
$3-(NO_2)C_6H_4COCH_2-$			238–9°		1984
$HOOCCH_2-$			184–5°, 148°, 152–3°	0(S, P, Pp)	1007, 1145, 2232
$(C_2H_5)_2NCOCH_2-$			232–3°	0	1007, 2232
$(C_2H_5)_2NCH_2CH_2-$			147–8°	0	338, 1007, 2232
CH_3-	CH_3-		206°, 208°	±(P, S)	249, 343, 492
$C_6H_5CH_2-$	CH_3-		215–6°		343
$(C_2H_5)_2NCH_2CH_2-$	CH_3-		142–3°		338
C_2H_5-		CH_3-	193–4°		343
$(C_2H_5)_2NCH_2CH_2-$		CH_3-	140–1°		338
CH_3-	CH_3-	$HOOC-$	152–3°		249
CH_3-	CH_3-	$H_2O \cdot HOOC-$	207°		249

TABLE 38

e. 2-Sulfanilamidothiazoles

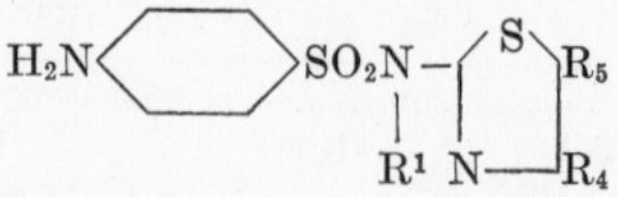

$$H_2N\langle\ \rangle SO_2N-\langle\overset{S}{\underset{N}{\ }}\rangle R_5$$
$$R^1 \quad R_4$$

R^1	R_4	R_5	Melting Range	Activities	References
			200–2°[a]	See Table 282	76, 79, 149, 163, 283, 316, 343, 434, 480, 481, 483, 492, 517, 540, 606, 615, 1384, 1489, 1563 2229
$Na-$			264.5–5.0°	+++, ++(S)	316, 526, 2229
$Na \cdot H_2O$					929
$Na \cdot 1\frac{1}{2}H_2O$				0(B)	865, 1856
$Na \cdot 5H_2O$			55°		1681
$\frac{1}{2}Cu-$					316
Ag					574
$\frac{1}{2}Ca-$					1826
$HOCH_2CH_2NH_3-$			110–2°	0(Tv)	2229
CH_3-			111–2°	++(Pk), 0(P, Pl, S)	184, 246, 249, 1007, 1384, 1733, 1896, 2189

[a] Sulfathiazole.

TABLE 38—(*Continued*)

R^1	R_4	R_5	Melting Range	Activities	References
C_2H_5-					343
	CH_3-		236-7[ob], 242-4°	See Table 283	69, 76, 79, 149, 249, 316, 343, 434, 480, 481, 483, 492, 516, 517, 540, 622, 1146, 1384, 1740, 1823
Na—	CH_3-				1543
	$ClCH_2-$		120°		622
	CH_3-	$Cl-$	ca. 260°		622
		CH_3-	243°, 247°		249, 343, 1384
	C_2H_5-		134°, 152-3°	+++(C), ++(P)	25, 39, 315, 316, 622, 2281
Na—	do				39
		C_2H_5-	170°	++(Pk)	343, 1148, 1896
	CH_3-	CH_3-	246°, 255°		25, 249, 343, 622, 1146, 1381, 1384
		$(CH_3)_2CH-$	217-8°	++(Pk)	1148, 1897
	CH_3-	C_2H_5-	193-4°		1148
	C_2H_5-	CH_3-	199-200°	++(S), ±(P)	492
		$CH_3(CH_2)_3-$	246°		1148
	$(CH_3)_3C-$		205-7°		25
	CH_3-	$CH_3(CH_2)_2-$	197-8°		1148
	$CH_3(CH_2)_4-$		163-4°		1381, 1384
		$CH_3(CH_2)_4-$	237°		1148
	CH_3-	$CH_3(CH_2)_3-$	192-3°		1148
	do	$CH_3(CH_2)_4-$	187-8°		1148
	do	$(CH_3)_2CH(CH_2)_2-$	202-4°		1148
	$CH_3(CH_2)_6-$		136-7°		1381, 1384
	CH_3-	$CH_3(CH_2)_5-$	191-2°		1148
	$CH_3(CH_2)_8-$		135-6°		1381
	$CH_3(CH_2)_{10}-$		144-5°		1381
	$CH_3(CH_2)_{12}-$		143-4°		1381
	$CH_3(CH_2)_{14}-$		144-5°		1381
	C_6H_5-		191°, 196-7°, 206°°	+(S), ±(P), ±(Aa, Et, pr, Sd, Se, Sp, Sse), +(Sa), 0(En, I, Po)	25, 29, 249, 259, 343, 492, 892, 1527, 1823, 2441
		C_6H_5-		+(S), 0(I, P, R, Sa)	1427, 1574
	CH_3-	C_6H_5-	140°		343
	C_6H_5-	CH_3-			79
	$4-(C_6H_5)C_6H_4-$		216-7°	+(P), ±(S)	434, 1057
	$HOCH_2-$		201°		622
	CH_3-	$HOCH_2CH_2-$	174-6°, 180.5-1.5°		343, 685, 1378, 1384
	$H_2O \cdot CH_3-$	do	145°		249
	$3,4-(HO)_2C_6H_3-$				622
	CH_3CO-				622
	CH_3-	CH_3CO-	213-4°		622
	$HOOC-$		224-5°, 241-2°D	0(S)	25, 2180
		$HOOC-$	213-4°D, 216°D	0(S)	685, 2180

[b] Sulfamethylthiazole.

[*] Sulfaphenylthiazole

TABLE 38—(*Concluded*)

R¹	R₄	R₅	Melting Range	Activities	References
		C_2H_5OOC-	227–8°		1146
	$HOOCCH_2-$		185°D		249, 1146, 1384
	$HCl \cdot HOOCCH_2-$		162°D		2180
	CH_3-	$HOOC-$	176–183° and 237°; 190°; 200–4°D	±(S)	25, 249, 343, 622, 1146, 1384, 2180
	CH_3-	C_2H_5OOC-	130–4°, 194–6°, 240°D	+(S), −(P)	343, 492, 622 1146
	$HOOC(CH_2)_2-$		143–5°	0(P, S)	595
	CH_3-	$C_2H_5OOCCH_2-$	183–4°		1146
	$HCl \cdot HOOC(CH_2)_3-$		204–6°		595
	$HOOC(CH_2)_2C-$		174°		1146
	$CH_3(CH_2)_3(HOOC)CH-$		157–8°		1146
	$4-(NH_2)C_6H_4-$		102–3°		622
	$4-(CH_3CONH)C_6H_4-$		275–7°		622

TABLE 39

f. 2-Sulfanilamidobenzothiazoles

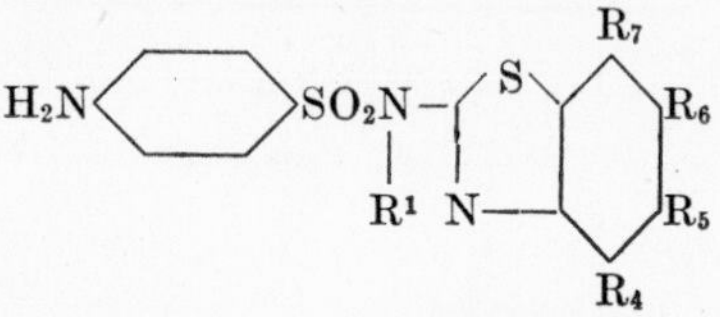

R¹	R₅	R₆	Melting Range	Activities	References
			304–5°D, 319°, 280–2°	±Sa, 0(En, I, P, Po, S, Tt)	343, 434, 892, 1057, 1485, 1574, 1714, 2373
		$Cl-$	267–8°	0(Tt)	1448, 1574
		NO_2-	292°		343
		CH_3-	282.5–284°	+(S), 0(P)	343, 492
		C_2H_5O-	257°		343
		C_4H_9O-	244–5°	0(P, Tt)	1448, 1574
CH_3-		do	218–9°	0(P, Tt)	1448, 1574
		NH_2SO_2-	285°		721
	NH_2-		270°		343
	CH_3CONH-		265°		343

TABLE 40

g. 2-Sulfanilamido-4-thiazolones

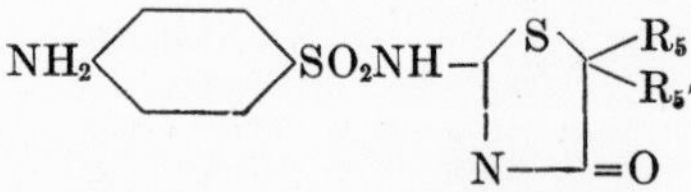

R₅	R₅′	Melting Range	Activities	References
CH_3-		235–8° 167–8°		371, 622 371

TABLE 40—(*Continued*)

R_5	$R_{5'}$	Melting Range	Activities	References
C_2H_5-		184–4.5°	++(P, S, Sa)	95, 371
CH_3-	CH_3-	210–1°	++(P, S, Sa)	371
$CH_3(CH_2)_2-$		160–1°	+++(S)	371
$CH_3(CH_2)_3-$		206.5–7.5°	+++(S), ++(P)	371
C_2H_5-	C_2H_5-	198–9°	++(P, S, Sa)	371
$CH_3(CH_2)_4-$		167–8°	+++(S)	371
$CH_3(CH_2)_{15}-$		129–31°		371
C_2H_5OOC-		138–9°		622

TABLE 41

h. Miscellaneous N^1-Heterocyclicsulfanilamides with One N- and One S- or Se-Atom in the Heterocyclic System.

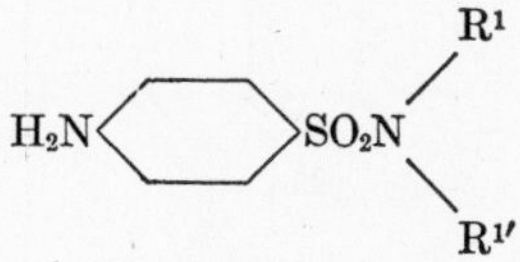

R^1	$R^{1'}$	Melting Range	Activities	References
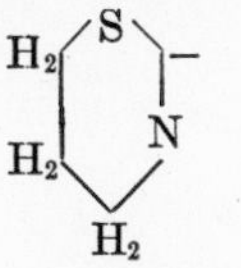		88°	±(P)	417
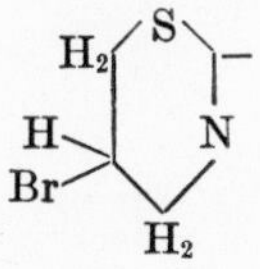		100°	±(P)	417
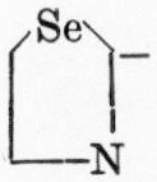		206°		1383, 1384
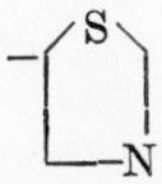		185°	++(S)	674
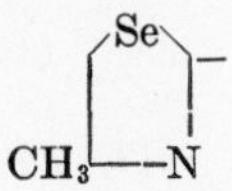		236–7°, 222–3°	+++(Ec), 0(P)	25, 1135, 1220, 1383, 1384
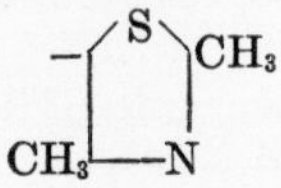				1381

TABLE 41—(Continued)

R¹	R¹ᵛ	Melting Range	Activities	References
		249–50°, ·H_2O 150°	++, +(S), ±(Sa), 0(P)	32, 95, 150, 492, 622, 1574
		209.5–10.5°, 231–2°	0(P)	25, 1220
		>315°	±(P)	417
		209–10°		343
		231–2°		1220

TABLE 42

C. *N*¹-Heterocyclicsulfanilamides
   5. Two N-Atoms and One O- or S-Atom in the Hetero-
      cyclic System.
      a. 2-Sulfanilamido-1,3,4-thiadiazoles

R₅	Melting Range	Activities	References
	213–4°[a], 216–8°, 221–2°	++(Ec, P), +(Sa), ±(S)	162, 434, 506, 719, 1134–5, 1218, 2312, 2491
CH_3-	186–7°[b], 190–2°, 204°, 208–9°	+++(Ec), ++, +, 0(P), +(Ko, Kr), ±(F), 0(Pv, S, Tt)	162, 432, 575, 657, 719, 1134–5, 1147, 1218, 1382, 1384, 1431, 1448, 1574, 1879, 2312, 2313, 2486, 2487, 2491, 2648
C_2H_5-	185.5–6.0°[c]	See Table 284	1135, 1431, 2087, 2384, 2486

TABLE 42—(*Continued*)

R_5	Melting Range	Activities	References
$CH_3(CH_2)_2-$	165–6°	++(Ec, G)	1134–5, 2384
$(CH_3)_2CH-$	195–7°d	+++, ++(Ec), ++(G), +(Cw, P)	1134–5, 1370, 1431, 2143, 2384
$(CH_3)_2CHCH_2-$	223.5–5°	++(G), +(Ec), 0(Pv)	1134–5, 1431, 2384, 2648
$(CH_3)_2CH(CH_2)_2-$			2384
$(C_2H_5)_2CH-$			1431
$CH_3(CH_2)_5-$		++(G)	2384
$CH_3(CH_2)_7CH=CH(CH_2)_7-$	109–11°		672
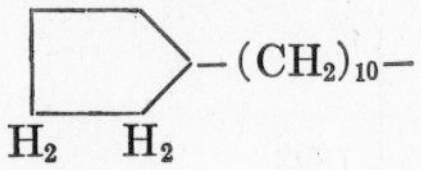 $-(CH_2)_{10}-$ H_2 H_2	117–8°	0(Le)	672, 673
C_6H_5-			2491
$C_6H_5CH=CH-$	285–6°D		672
CH_3S-	198°		1218
NH_2-	259°	++(Ec), +(S)	653, 1057
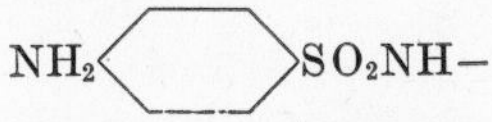 NH_2 SO_2NH-	223°		1218

a Sulfathiadiazole.
b Sulfamethylthiadiazole, Lucosil, or Tetracid.
c Sulfaethylthiadiazole, Globucid.
d Sulfaisopropylthiadiazole, VK57, 2254RP.

TABLE 43

b. Miscellaneous N^1-Heterocyclicsulfanilamides with Two N-Atoms and One O- or S-Atom in the Heterocyclic System H_2N SO_2NHR^1

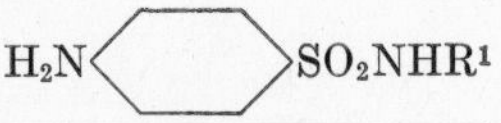

R^1	Melting Range	Activities	References
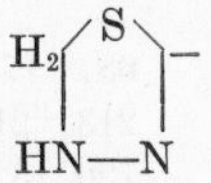	204–5°	++(Ec)	1135
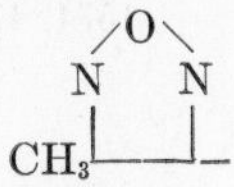	148–50°	++(Ec), 0(P, S)	653, 719, 2312, 2313
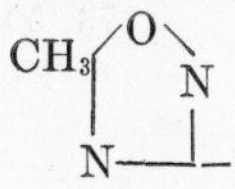	211–13°	+++(Ec), +(P, S)	653, 719, 1057, 2312, 2313

TABLE 43—(*Continued*)

R^1	Melting Range	Activities	References
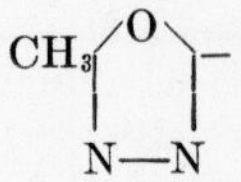 CH₃ ... N—N (structure)	172°		1381, 1384, 2312
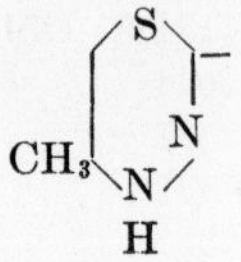 CH₃ ... N H (structure)		++(P), ++, +(S)	95, 150
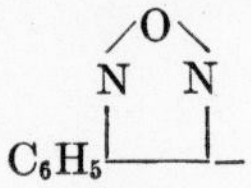 C₆H₅ ... N N (structure)	290°D		2313
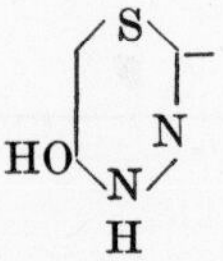 HO ... N H (structure)			1823

TABLE 44

C. N^1-Heterocyclicsulfanilamides
6. N^1-Nitrogen a Member of the Heterocyclic System N_2H⟨ ⟩SO_2N⊃

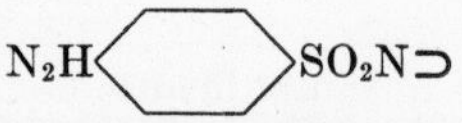

$-N$⊃	Melting Range	Activities	References
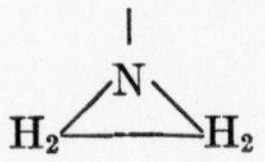 H₂ — N — H₂ (aziridine)	157.5–8.5°	−	2370
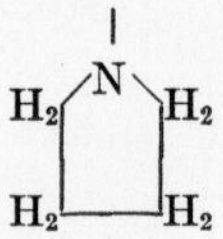 H₂ N H₂ / H₂ — H₂ (pyrrolidine)	167.5–8°	±(S)	68, 215
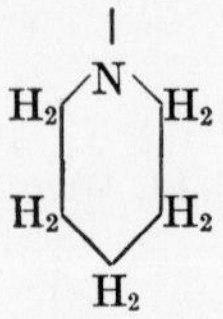 H₂ N H₂ / H₂ H₂ / H₂ (piperidine)	164°, 167–8°	±, 0(S), 0(Tt)	68, 171, 173, 213, 214, 215, 720, 1322, 1427, 1574, 1713
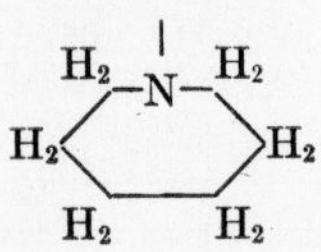 H₂ N H₂ / H₂ H₂ / H₂ H₂ (structure)		0(S)	173, 505

TABLE 44—(*Continued*)

$-N \supset$	Melting Range	Activities	References
	176–7°	±(S)	68
	125°	±, 0(S), 0(Tt)	417, 1427, 1574
	172–4°, 177–8°	0(P, S)	1057, 1239, 1329
	134.0–4.5°		1239
	58.0–8.5°		1239
	67.0–7.5°		1239

TABLE 44—(*Continued*)

$-N\subset$	Melting Range	Activities	References
 H (CH$_2$)$_{12}$CH$_3$ (structure) N– H$_2$ H$_2$	70.0–1.5°		1239
(structure) N	146–7°		1984
COOH N H$_2$ H H$_2$ H$_2$		0(S)	1459
N H$_2$ H$_2$ H$_2$ H$_2$ N H	204°	–, 0(S)	93, 262, 329
N H$_2$ H$_2$ H$_2$ H$_2$ N C$_6$H$_5$	169–70°		265
N H$_2$ H$_2$ H$_2$ H$_2$ N COOC$_2$H$_5$	170°		262
N H$_2$ H$_2$ H$_2$ H$_2$ N CH$_2$COOH		0(I, P, R, S)	1574

TABLE 44—(*Continued*)

$-N \supset$	Melting Range	Activities	References
 4-$(NH_2)C_6H_4SO_2$	331–2°		262, 2084
	228–30°		318
	285–8°		318
Hydroxyethylapocupreicine		0	426
 H_2——$NSO_2C_6H_4(NH_2)-4$	178–80°	+(P, S, Sa)	968
	167–8°	+(P, S), ±(Sa)	14, 434, 1057
Quinicine		0	426
	186–7°	0(P)	686
	209–10°	0(P)	686
		+(Ec, G, M, P)	106, 1021, 1135

TABLE 44—(*Continued*)

$-N\supset$	Melting Range	Activities	References
		$\pm$(Ec)	1134
	216–7°	+, $\pm$, 0(S), $\pm$(M, P), 0(I, Po, Tt)	5, 105, 311, 375, 892, 1057, 1427, 1574, 1733, 2441
	182–4°		2499
	187–8°, 192°		1377, 1384, 2370
4-(NH₂)C₆H₄SO₂N	220°		1377
	209–10°	0(P)	416, 1344, 2370
	144–5°		1344
			184
	259–61°, 265°		249, 416
	134.5–5.5°	0(P)	1344, 2370

TABLE 44—(*Concluded*)

−N⊃	Melting Range	Activities	References
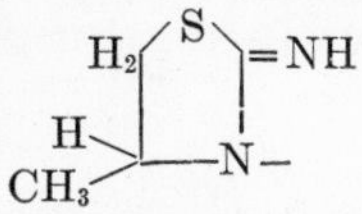	137–8°		1344
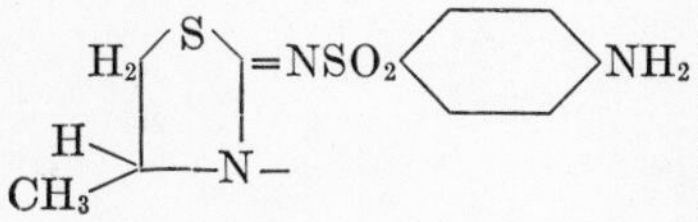	225–6°		1824
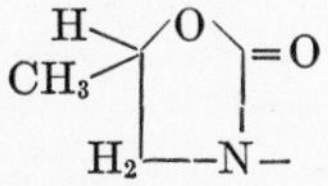	142–4°		2370
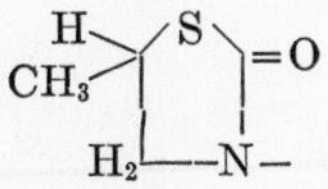	190.5–1.5°	+++(S), −(P)	1344, 2370
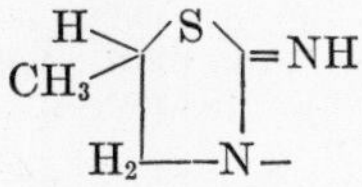	153–3.5°		1344
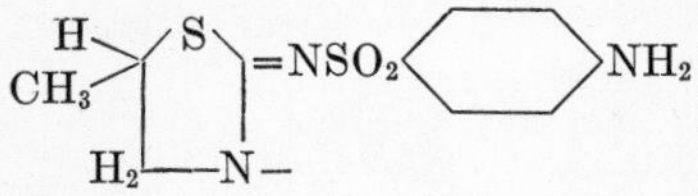	176.5–7.0°		1824
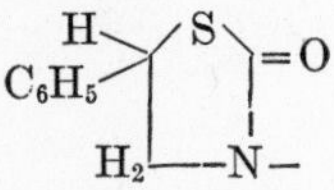	168–70°		1344
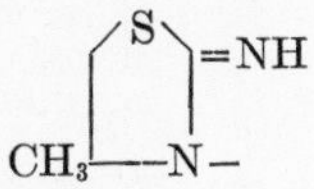	180°		1711

TABLE 45

D. N^1-Acylsulfanilamides
  1. N^1-Acyclicacylsulfanilamides

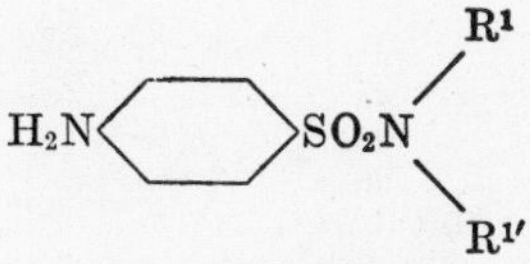

R^1	$R^{1\prime}$	Melting Range	Activities	References
HCO−		120–2°		2396
do	Na−	250–2°D		2396

TABLE 45—(*Continued*)

R^1	$R^{1'}$	Melting Range	Activities	References
CH_3CO-		182–4°a	See Table 285	101, 115, 137, 247, 1384, 1790, 2100, 2396
do	NH_4-	167–70°		101
do	$Na-$	257°	++(S), +, 0(Pa), ±(P)	101, 1450, 2044, 2100
do	½ Ca–			2100
do	½ Ba–	185°D		2100
do	½ Hg–	251°D		2100
do	$-NH_2(C_2H_5)_2$	180–2°D		101
do	*(structure)*	109°		2103
$ClCH_2CO-$		157–8°	+(Ec, S)	719, 1033, 1057
CH_3CH_2CO-		134–5°	++, +(S), ++(Sa) +(P), 0(G)	101, 137, 2037, 2100, 2654
do	½ Ca–	283°D		2100
$CH_3(CH_2)_2CO-$		125–6.6°	+++, ++(S), ++ +(Ec), +(P, Sa), ±(Cw), 0(En, I, Po)	101, 137, 892, 1057, 1221, 1485, 1966, 2037, 2100, 2175
$(CH_3)_2CHCO-$		198.5–200°	++, +(Ec, S), +(P), ±(Sa)	101, 137, 1057, 1966, 2037
$CH_3(CH_2)_3CO-$		117.5–8.5°	++, +(S), +(P, Sa)	105, 137, 1057, 2037
$(CH_3)_2CHCH_2CO-$		115–7°	+++(Ec), +, 0(P), ±(Sa), 0(S)	105, 137, 1057, 1966, 2583
$(CH_3)_3CCO-$		129.2–9.9°	+(Ec, S), 0(P)	1966
$CH_3(CH_2)_4CO-$		129.2–9.9°	++, +(S, Sa), +(P)	101, 137, 1057
$(C_2H_5)_2CHCO-$		189–93.5°	++(Sa), +(S)	101, 1057
$CH_3(CH_2)_5CO-$		121.8–3.8°	++(S), + (P, Sa)	101, 137, 1057
$CH_3(CH_2)_6CO-$		101–3°	++(P, S), +(Sa)	101, 137, 1057
$CH_3(CH_2)_3CH(C_2H_5)CO-$		165.5–8.0°	++(S), +(P)	101, 1057
$CH_3(CH_2)_8CO-$		119–21°	++(S), +(P, Sa), 0(Le)	101, 137, 673, 1057
$CH_3(CH_2)_9CO-$		112.5–5.0°	++(S), +(P, Sa) 0(Le)	101, 137, 673, 1057
$CH_3(CH_2)_{10}CO-$		115°, 127– 128.5°	+++, +(S), ++, 0(T), +, 0(P), +(Sa), 0(En, Po)	90, 101, 137, 386, 498, 673, 1057, 1485, 1734
do	$Ag-$	200–10°D		101
do	½ Ca–			101
do	½ Hg–	235–40°D		101
do	CH_3-	59.3–60.5°	++(S), +(P)	101, 1057
$CH_3(CH_2)_{12}CO-$		113.5–7.7°, 126°	++(S), ±(Ec), 0(En, P, Po)	101, 137, 968, 2441
$CH_3(CH_2)_{14}CO-$		102.5–8.5°	+(S), ±(P, Sa)	105, 137, 1057
$CH_3(CH_2)_{16}CO-$		98–102°	+(S), 0(P)	101, 137, 1057
$CH_3CH=CHCO-$			+++(Ec), ++(S), +(P)	1966, 2583
$ClC(CH_3)=CHCO-$			+++(S), ±(Ec), 0(P)	1966, 2583

a Sulfacetamide ("Albucid," "Sulamyd").

TABLE 45—(*Concluded*)

R¹	R¹′	Melting Range	Activities	References
$(CH_3)_2C=CHCO-$		b	$+++, ++(S),$ $+++, +(P),$ $+++, ++, +(Ec),$ $\pm(F)$	589, 1135, 1158, 1324, 1523, 1607, 1722, 1815, 1966, 2099, 2583
do	CH_3-		$0(Ec, P, S)$	1966, 2583
$(CH_3)_2CHCH=CHCO-$			$+(Ec, P, S)$	1966
$(CH_3)_2C=C(CH_3)CO-$			$++, +(Ec), 0(P, S)$	1966, 2583
$CH_3(CH_2)_7CH=CH(CH_2)_7CO-$				101
$HOOCCH_2CH_2CO-$				2179
$HOOC(CH_2)_4CO-$		178°	$\pm (S)$	968
$4-(NH_2)C_6H_4SO_2NHCO(CH_2)_8CO-$		173-4°		101
$C_2H_5OOCC(=N_2)CO-$				106

b Irgamid.

TABLE 46

2. N^1-Isocyclicacylsulfanilamides

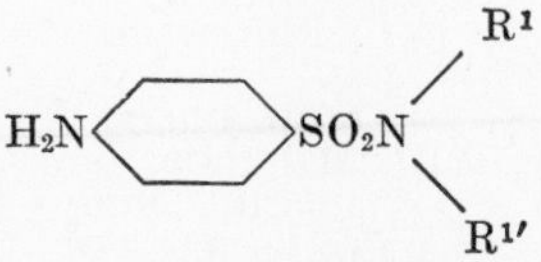

$$H_2N-\langle\ \rangle-SO_2N\begin{array}{c}R^1\\R^{1\prime}\end{array}$$

R¹	R¹′	Melting Range	Activities	References
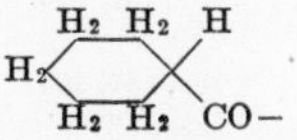 (cyclohexyl structure) H₂ H₂ H / H₂ / H₂ H₂ CO—		198.5-200°	$+++(S), +(P)$	101, 1057
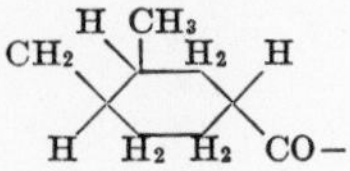 (methylcyclohexyl structure) H CH₃ / CH₂ H₂ H / H H₂ H₂ CO—			$+(S), \pm(Ec), 0(P)$	1966
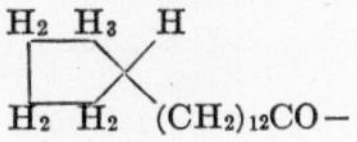 (cyclobutyl structure) H₂ H₃ H / H₂ H₂ (CH₂)₁₂CO—		78-80°		968
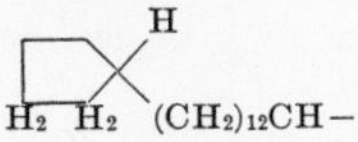 (cyclobutyl structure) H / H₂ H₂ (CH₂)₁₂CH—		97.9-99°	$++(S), \pm(P)$	101, 968, 1057
C_6H_5CO-		181.2- 2.3°ᵃ	$+++, +(Ec),$ $+++(S), +, \pm, 0(P)$ $+(M, Sa), +(Tv),$ $0(I, R)$	101, 137, 186, 365, 719, 801, 1057, 1393, 1574, 1966, 2100, 2196, 2437, 2583
$4-(NO_2)C_6H_4CO-$		218-9°, 235-40°	$++$ '), $+(P, S)$	101, 137, 1057, 2196
C_6H_5CO-	CH_3-	235-6.5°		105, 1381
$C_6H_5CH_2CO-$		182°		2100
$2-(CH_3)C_6H_4CO-$		176°	$++, +(Ec, S), +(P)$	1159, 1966, 2583
$3-(CH_3)C_6H_4CO-$		160°	$++, +(Ec), ++(P),$ $+(S)$	1159, 1966, 2583
$3-CH_3-4-ClC_6H_3CO-$			$++(P, S)$	2583

ᵃ Sulfabenzamide.

TABLE 46—(Continued)

R¹	R¹′	Melting Range	Activities	References
4-(CH₃)C₆H₄CO—		114°	+++(P, S), +++, +(Ec)	1159, 1966, 2583
do	CH₂=CHCH₂—		++(S)	2583
C₆H₅CH₂CH₂CO—		160.3–1.5°	+++(S), +(P)	101, 137, 1057
4-(C₂H₅)C₆H₄CO—			++(S), +(Ec), 0(P)	1966, 2583
2,3-(CH₃)₂C₆H₃CO—			0(Ec, P, S)	1966, 2583
2,4-(CH₃)₂C₆H₃CO—		222°	+(Ec), 0(P, S)	1159, 1966, 2583
2,5-(CH₃)₂C₆H₃CO—			+(Ec), 0(P, S)	1381, 1966, 2583
3,4-(CH₃)₂C₆H₃CO—		214–5°, 220°ᵇ	See Table 286	1159, 1314, 1381
do	CH₃—		++(S)	2583
do	CH₃CH₂(CH₃)CH—		++(S)	2583
4-(C₃H₇)C₆H₄CO—			+++(S), ++, +(Ec), 0(P)	1966, 2583
4-[(CH₂)₂CH]C₆H₄CO—			+++, ++(P), ++(S), +(Ec)	1966, 2583
3-CH₃-4-(C₂H₅)C₆H₃CO—			++(S), +(Ec, P)	1966
2,4,6-(CH₃)₃C₆H₂CO—			+(S), +, ±(Ec), 0(P)	1966, 2583
3,4,5-(CH₃)₃C₆H₂CO—			+++, ++(P),++, +(Ec, S)	1966, 2583
2,4,5-(CH₃)₃C₆H₂CO—			+(Ec), ±(S), 0(P)	1966, 2583
4-(C₄H₉)C₆H₄CO—			+++(S), 0(P)	2583
2,3,5,6-(CH₃)₄C₆HCO—			±(Ec), 0(P, S)	1966, 2583
2,3,4,5,6-(CH₃)₅C₆CO—			0(Ec, P, S)	1966, 2583
C₆H₅CH=CHCO—		130–3°, 174–5°	++(S), +(P)	101, 137, 1057
do	Na—		++(P, S), 0(Tu)	101, 137, 1057, 1393
(C₆H₅)₂CHCO—		210.5–2.5°	++(S), ±(P)	101, 137, 1057
2-(HOOC)C₆H₄CO—				2179
4-(HOOC)C₆H₄CO—		>225°D	+(P)	101, 137, 1057
2-(HO)C₆H₄CO—			++, +(S), ±(Sa), 0(I, P, R)	329, 1574
2-(CH₃S)C₆H₄CO—		177°		1159
2-[(CH₃)₂CHS]C₆H₄CO—		144°		1159
3-(CH₃S)C₆H₄CO—		185°		1159
3-[(CH₃)₂CHS]C₆H₄CO—		140°		1159
4-(CH₃O)C₆H₄CO—		160°		1159
4-(CH₃S)C₆H₄CO—		182°	++(P, S)	1159, 2583
4-[(CH₃)₂CHS]C₆H₄CO—		215°		1159
C₆H₅CH(OH)CO—		192.5–4.5°D	+(Sa), ±(S), 0(P)	101, 137, 1057
3-CH₃-4-(CH₃O)C₆H₃CO—		187°	+++, ++(Ec, P), +++(S)	1159, 1966, 2583
3-CH₃-4-(CH₃S)C₆H₃CO—		192°	+++(P, S), +, ±(Ec)	1159, 1966, 2583
3-CH₃-4-(C₂H₅S)C₆H₃CO—			+++(S), 0(P)	2583
3-CH₃S-4-(CH₃)C₆H₃CO—		217–8°		1159
3-HO-2-C₁₀H₆CO—		245–50°D		101
4-(NH₂)C₆H₄CO—		197.8–9.0°	++(Ec), +(P, S)	101, 719, 1057
3-CH₃-4-(NH₂)C₆H₃CO—			+++(S), 0(P)	2583

ᵇ "Irgafen."

TABLE 47

3. N^1-Heterocyclicacylsulfanilamides

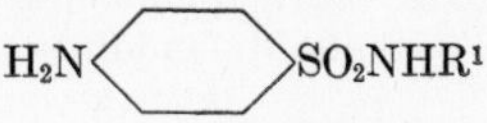

$$H_2N\langle\bigcirc\rangle SO_2NHR^1$$

R^1	Melting Range	Activities	References
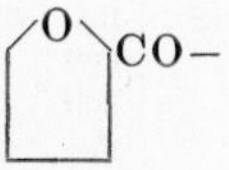	191.5–2.0°	+, 0(S), +(P), ±(Tv)	101, 1057, 1393
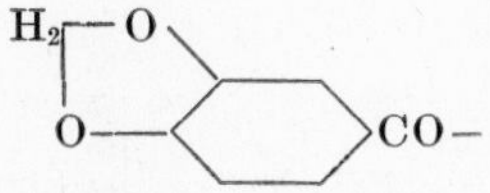		+++(S),0(P)	2583
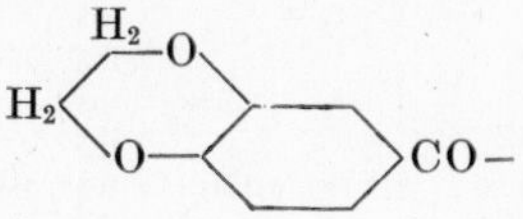		+++(S), 0(P)	2583
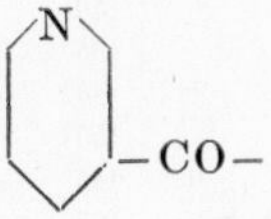	257–8°	+, 0(S), +(P)	101, 137, 1057, 1895
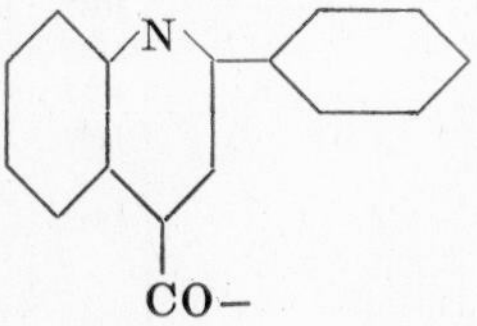	305–10°	0(P, S)	101, 137, 1057
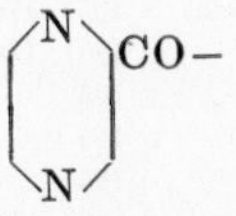	246–8°		108

TABLE 48

D. N^1.-Acylsulfanilamides

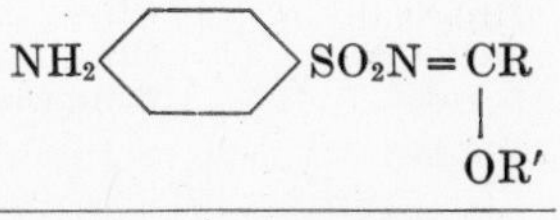

4. Sulfanilylimido Esters

$$NH_2\langle\bigcirc\rangle SO_2N=CR$$
$$OR'$$

R	R^1	Melting Range	Activities	References
C_6H_5-	C_2H_5-	98°		701

TABLE 49

D. N^1-Acylsulfanilamides
  5. Sulfanilylamidines

$$NH_2\langle\ \rangle SO_2N=C-R$$
$$\underset{R'-NR''}{|}$$

R	R'	R″	Melting Range	Activities	References
CH₃−			147-9°, 151-2°	+(Tv), ±(S), +(Ec)	165, 1057, 1393, 1501, 1862
do	CH₃−		201°		165
do	CH₃−	CH₃−	174°		165
do	C₂H₅−		160°		165
do	C₂H₅−	C₂H₅−	106°		165
do	CH₃(CH₂)₂−		167-8°		165
do	CH₃(CH₂)₃−		168-9°		165
do	CH₂=CHCH₂−		150°		165
do	do	CH₂=CHCH₂−	132-3°		165
do	HOCH₂CH₂−		178°		165
do	-(CH₂)₂O(CH₂)₂−		212°		165
do	-(CH₂)₅−		155°		165
do	4-(NH₂)C₆H₄SO₂−		191.6-1.8°	±(S), 0(Ec)	1057, 1862
CH₃CH₂−			151-2°		165, 1501
CH₃(CH₂)₂−			79-82°		1501
(CH₃)₂CHCH₂−			118-20°		165
(CH₃)₂CHCH₂CH₂−			126.0-7.2°		1862
CH₃(CH₂)₁₁−			94-5°		1501
C₆H₁₁−			150-1°		165
C₆H₅−			155-60°, 210.2-10.7°	+(Ec, S)	165, 701, 1057, 1501, 1862
do	CH₃−		228.1-9.1°	±(S)	1057, 1862
do	C₂H₅−	C₂H₅−	193.7-4.0°		1862
do	(pyridyl)		206.8-7.5°		1862
do	4-(NH₂)C₆H₄SO₂−		206.4-7.6°D	±(S), 0(Ec)	1057, 1862
C₆H₅CH₂−			177-9°		1501, 1862
4-ClC₆H₄CH₂−					165
do	CH₃−				165
do	C₂H₅−				165
4-(CH₃)C₆H₄−			234.9-5.4°	+(Ec), ±(S)	1057, 1862
do	4-(NH₂)C₆H₄SO₂−		166.9-7.5°	±(Ec, S)	1057, 1862
C₆H₅CH=CH−					165
(C₂H₅)₂NC(=O)−			Resin		165
(CH₃)₂NCH₂−	CH₃−	CH₃−	193-4°		165
4-(NH₂)C₆H₄−	CH₃−				165
do	(CH₃)₂CH−				165
(furyl)					165
do	(CH₃)₂CH−				165
do	CH₃(CH₂)₃−				165
(pyridyl)			208.1-8.2°	+(S)	1057, 1862

TABLE 50

D. N^1-Acylsulfanilamides
6. Derivatives of Carbonic Acid

$$H_2N\langle\ \rangle SO_2N-R^1$$
$$|$$
$$R^{1\prime}$$

R^1	$R^{1\prime}$	Melting Range	Activities	References
$C_2H_5OC(=O)-$		133°D, 270°D		166, 1781
$NH_2C(=O)-$		140-6°D, 149-54°, 155-8°, 303°D, 320° subl.	++, +(Ec), +(P), 0(S)	166, 719, 931, 1135, 1223, 1224, 1781, 2618
$H_2O\cdot NH_2C(=O)-$		125-7°D		1224
$NH_2C(=O)-$	NH_4-			931
do	$Na-$			931
do	$K-$			931, 1223
$CH_3NHC(=O)-$		173°		166
$(CH_3)_2NC(=O)-$		158-61°, 268-70°D	0(S)	1223, 1781
do	$Na-$			1223
$C_2H_5NHC(=O)-$		160°		166
$(C_2H_5)_2NC(=O)-$		170°D		166
$(CH_3)_2CH(CH_2)_2NC(=O)-$		150-2°		166
$(C_6H_5)_2NC(=O)-$		216°	0(S)	1781
$3-(NH_2)C_6H_4NHC(=O)-$		174°D		166
$4-(NH_2)C_6H_4NHC(=O)-$		250°D		166
$4-(NH_2)C_6H_4SO_2NHC(=O)-$		238°		1377
$CH_3OC(=NH)-$		172-3°	+(Ec)	1057, 2459
$C_2H_5OC(=NH)-$		126-7°	+(Ec), ±(S)	1057, 2459
$N\equiv C-$		292-5°	+, 0(Ec), ±(S)	719, 1057, 2459
$NH_2C(=NH)-$		190-2°a	See Table 287	17, 113, 162, 335, 434, 981, 1198, 1356, 2459, 2590
$CH_3NHC(=NH)-$		170.0-0.5°	++, +(S), ++(Ec), ±(Pl)	1733, 1734, 2180
$C_2H_5NHC(=NH)-$		160-1°	+(Ec)	645, 1057, 2459
$C_3H_7NHC(=NH)-$		147-8°	+(Ec), +, ±(S), 0(P, Sa)	645, 1057, 1574, 2373, 2459
$C_4H_9NHC(=NH)-$		184-6°	±(Ec)	645, 1057, 2459
$C_5H_{11}NHC(=NH)-$		221.0-1.5°	+(S), ±(Ec)	645, 1057, 2180
$C_7H_{15}NHC(=NH)-$		162.0-2.5°	0(S)	2180
$C_6H_5NHC(=NH)-$		231-3°	+(Ec)	631, 1057, 2459
$2-(CH_3)C_6H_4NHC(=NH)-$				631
$4-(CH_3)C_6H_4NHC(=NH)-$				631
⟨N⟩-NHC(=NH)-		239-41°	+(Ec)	1057, 2459
H₂ H₂ ⟨O NC(=NH)-⟩ H₂ H₂		145-6°		2180
$4-(HOOC)C_6H_4NHC(=NH)-$		234-5°	0(Ec)	1057, 2459
$4-(NH_2)C_6H_4NHC(=NH)-$		200-1°	+(Ec)	1057, 2459

a Sulfaguanidine.

TABLE 50—(*Continued*)

R^1	$R^{1\prime}$	Melting Range	Activities	References
H₂ H₂ H H₂〈 〉 H₂ H₂ C(=NH)NHC(=NH)−		155–8°		1353
NH₂C(=O)NHC(=NH)−		225–6°	+(Ec)	646, 1057, 2459
N≡CNHC(=NH)−		236–7°	+	2459
NH₂C(=NH)NHC(=NH)−		231°, 244–5°	+(S), ±(Ec)	20, 1057, 1353, 2459
(CH₃)₂NC(=NH)NHC(=NH)−		191–2°	+(Ec)	20, 1057, 2459
C₄H₉NHC(=NH)NHC(=NH)−		214–5°	±(Ec)	20, 1057, 2459
C₆H₅NHC(=NH)NHC(=NH)−		188°		641, 1353
2-(CH₃)C₆H₄NHC(=NH)NHC(=NH)−		214–6°	+(Ec)	20, 641, 1057, 2459
HOCH₂CH₂NHC(=NH)NHC(=NH)−		140°		1353
H₂ H₂ O〈 〉NC(=NH)NHC(=NH)− H₂ H₂			+(Ec)	20, 1057
4-(CH₃O)C₆H₄NHC(=NH)NHC(=NH)−		198–200°		641, 1353
NH₂C(=S)NHC(=NH)−			±(Ec)	646, 1057
NH₂NHC(=NH)−		209–10°	++, +(Ec), 0(S)	633, 719, 1057, 1427, 1574, 2459
NO₂NHC(=NH)−		194–5°	±(Ec)	1057, 2459
NH₂C(=S)−		174–5° 203°	++(Ec, P, T)	1135, 1756, 1781
C₆H₅NHC(=S)−		276°	0(S)	1781
CH₃SC(=NH)−		184–5°	++, +(S), +(Ec)	932, 1057, 2459
C₂H₅SC(=NH)−		154–5°, 160–1.5°, 168°	++, 0(S), +(Ec)	1057, 1357, 1756, 2180, 2459, 2549
C₃H₇SC(=NH)−		133–4°		2549
C₄H₉SC(=NH)−		116°		2549
C₆H₁₃SC(=NH)−		129–30.5°	+(S)	2180
CH₂=CHCH₂SC(=NH)−		170°		2549
C₆H₅CH₂SC(=NH)−		143°, 145–6°	0(S)	432, 1357

TABLE 51

E. *N¹*-Inorganic Derivatives of Sulfanilamide
1. *N¹*-Sulfonylsulfanilamides

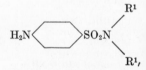

R^1	$R^{1\prime}$	Melting Range	Activities	References
CH₃CH₂SO₂−		206.5–7.5°	±(S, Sa), 0(Ec, P)	104, 717, 1057
CH₃(CH₂)₃SO₂−		209–10.5°	0, ±(S)	104, 494
do	Na−		+(Sa), ±(S), 0(P)	105, 1057
CH₃(CH₂)₄SO₂−		183–4.5°	0, ±	104, 494
do	Na−		0(P, S, Sa)	105, 1057
CH₃(CH₂)₃CH(C₂H₅)CH₂SO₂−		189–91°	0(En, P, Po, S, Sa)	104, 1057, 1485
CH₃(CH₂)₁₁SO₂−		188.8–9.9°	0(P, S)	104, 1057
H₂ H₂ H H₂〈 〉 H₂ H₂ SO₂−		230°D	0(P)	104, 137, 1057, 1485

TABLE 51—(*Continued*)

R^1	$R^{1\prime}$	Melting Range	Activities	References
4-$(NO_2)C_6H_4SO_2-$		280-5°D		105
do	Na-		$\pm$(Sa), 0(P, S)	105, 1057
$C_6H_5CH_2SO_2-$		226-7°, 242.0-3.5°	0(P, S, Sa)	104, 494
4-$(NO_2)C_6H_4CH_2SO_2-$				105
4-$(HO)C_6H_4SO_2-$		248.5-50.0°	$\pm$(S), 0(P)	105, 1057

		213-4.5°	+(Sa), 0(P, S)	104, 137, 1057
4-$(NH_2)C_6H_4SO_2-$		260.5-1.5°	+++, +, 0(S), $\pm$(Ec), 0(En, I, Po)	63, 99, 137 395, 399, 448, 658, 719, 1057, 1485, 2441
do	NH_4-			63, 99
do	Li-			63, 99
do	Na-	>340°D	+++, +, 0(S), $\pm$(P)	63, 89, 99, 137, 399, 1057
do	$\frac{1}{2}$Cu-			63, 99
do	Ag-			63, 99
do	$\frac{1}{2}$Mg-		++, 0(S), 0(P)	63, 99, 1057
do	$\frac{1}{2}$Ca-			63, 99
do	$\frac{1}{2}$Ba-			63, 99
do	$\frac{1}{2}$Zn-			63, 99
do	$\frac{1}{2}$Hg-			63, 99
do	$\frac{1}{3}$Al-		0(En)	105, 1485
do	$\frac{1}{2}$Pb-			63, 99
do	$\frac{1}{2}$Ni-			63, 99
do	$(C_2H_5)_2NH_2-$			63, 99
do	$C_5H_{11}NH_3-$			63, 99
do	$(HOCH_2CH_2)_3NH-$			63, 99
do	CH_3-	180-1°	+++, $\pm$(S), 0(P)	63, 99, 137, 1057
do	C_2H_5-	153.3-4.7°	+++, $\pm$(S), $\pm$(P)	63, 99, 137, 1057
do	$C_{12}H_{23}-$	123.8-5.4°	0(P, S)	105, 137
4-$(NH_2)C_6H_4CH_2SO_2-$				105

TABLE 52

E. N^1-Inorganic Derivatives of Sulfanilamide
  2. Miscellaneous Inorganic Derivatives

R^1	$R^{1\prime}$	Melting Range	Activities	References
HO-		156-65°D	++, +(S), ++(C), +(M), $\pm$(Ec, Pl), 0(I, P, R, Tt)	58, 182, 297, 1574, 1733, 1734, 2441

TABLE 52—*(Continued)*

R^1	$R^{1\prime}$	Melting Range	Activities	References
$(C_6H_5)_2S=$		183–4°	0	2331
NaO_3S-			0	311
NH_2-		131°, 136–7°	0(S), − (Pl)	106, 432, 1329, 1427, 1574, 1733, 2441, 2630
$(CH_3)_2C=N-$				106
$C_6H_5CH=N-$				106
C_6H_5CONH-		190–2°		185
![N-CONH- structure]				1041
$NH_2C(=O)NH-$			0(I, S)	18, 1219, 1574
$C_6H_5NHC(=O)NH-$				1219
$4\text{-}(CH_3)C_6H_4NHC(=O)NH-$				1219
$NH_2C(=S)NH-$				1219
$C_6H_5NHC(=S)NH-$				1219
$4\text{-}(CH_3)C_6H_4NHC(=S)NH-$				1219
$Cholyl\text{-}NH-$		Indefinite		185, 702
$4\text{-}(H_2N)C_6H_4SO_2NH-$		190–203°D	0(Sa)	1329
$N_2=$		38–9°	+(Ec, G, M, P)	106, 1021, 1135

TABLE 53

IV. N^4-Substituted Sulfanilamides
    A. N^4-Acyclicsulfanilamides

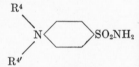

R^4	$R^{4\prime}$	Melting Range	Activities	References
CH_3-		164°, 173°	+(S)	291, 309, 1384, 2441
CH_3-	CH_3-	213°	+(S)	291
C_2H_5-		134–5.5°	0(Pr)	536
$C_5H_{11}-$			±(S, P)	92, 1702
$CH_3(CH_2)_5-$				1702
$HOCH_2CH_2-$			±, −(S)	418, 505
$HOCH_2(CHOH)_4CH_2-$				132
$HOOCCH_2SCH_2-$				1573
$NH_4OOCCH_2SCH_2-$				1573
$NaOOCCH_2SCH_2-$				1573
$NH_2CH_2CH_2NH_3OOCCH_2SCH_2-$				1573
$4\text{-}(HO_3S)C_6H_4SCH_2-$				1573
$4\text{-}(NaO_3S)C_6H_4SCH_2-$				1573
$CH_3CONHCH(COONa)CH_2SCH_2-$			+(S), 0(I, R)	1570, 1574
HO_2SCH_2-		158–60°		257
NaO_2SCH_2-		a	++, +(S), ++(Ba) +(Sa, M), ±(Bm, Bs, G, P)	1, 34, 73, 146, 216, 255, 257, 274, 311, 442, 1369, 1467, 2441

a Aldanil.

TABLE 53—(*Continued*)

R⁴	R⁴′	Melting Range	Activities	References
HO_3SCH_2-				132
$NH_4O_3SCH_2-$		$175°D$		1322
NaO_3SCH_2-			$++(S)$	132, 146, 170, 190, 225, 448, 524, 1182, 1322
KO_3SCH_2-				1322
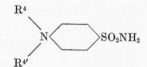 $NH\cdot HO_3SNHCH_2-$				1023
$CH_3(NaO_3S)CH-$		b	$++(S), +(Sa)$	174, 175, 387, 1467
$HOOCCH_2-$		$175°, 265-6°$	$++, \pm(S)$	78, 132, 146, 190, 216, 254, 255, 418, 448, 512, 524
$C_2H_5OOCCH_2-$		$144°$		216
NH_2OCCH_2-		$207°$	$++, \pm(S)$	216, 448, 512, 524
$HOOCCH_2-$	$ON-$		$\pm(S)$	146
$HOOC(CH_3)CH-$				132
$HOOCCH_2CH_2-$			$+(S)$	418
$NCCH_2CH_2-$	$NCCH_2CH_2-$	$151-2°$	$0(S)$	604
$HOOCCH_2(HOOC)CH-$				132
$NaOOCCH_2(NaOOC)CH-$				105
$NaO_3SCH_2CH_2(NaO_3S)CH-$				487
$CH_3(NaO_3S)CHCH_2(NaO_3S)CH-$				487
$(C_2H_5)_2NCH_2CH_2-$		$141-2°$		54
$(C_2H_5)_2N(CH_2)_3-$		$119-20°, 140-2°$	$+, -(S)$	54, 122, 123, 448
$HCl\cdot(C_2H_5)_2N(CH_2)_3-$		$135-57°$		54
$(C_2H_5)_2N(CH_2)_4-$		$155°$		54
$(C_2H_5)_2NCH_2CHOHCH_2-$		$112°$	$\pm(S)$	448

b Sulfonamide E.O.S.

TABLE 54

B. *N⁴*-Isocyclicsulfanilamides

$$R^4-N(R^{4\prime})-\langle\ \rangle-SO_2NH_2$$

R⁴	R⁴′	Melting Range	Activities	References
$\langle\ \rangle(CH_2)_{11}-$		$116°$		673
C_6H_5-		$143-5°$	$+(S), 0(I, P, R)$	217, 1574, 2373
$2,4,6-(NO_2)_3C_6H_2-$			$0(S, Tt)$	1427, 1574
$C_6H_5CH_2-$		$174.5-5.8°ᵃ$	$+, \pm(S), +(Pf), \pm(M, P, Pm, Pv), 0(En, L, T)$	170, 173, 180, 245, 270, 347, 360, 442, 448, 488, 548, 973, 1011, 1057, 1207, 1485, 1602, 1646, 1734, 1981, 2441
$4-(NO_2)C_6H_4CH_2-$		$178-9°$	$+++(S)$	203, 347, 440, 504

a Septazine.

TABLE 54—(Continued)

R⁴	R⁴'	Melting Range	Activities	References
C₆H₅CH₂—	Cl₂PO—			191
do	NH₂(HO)PO—			191
do	NH₂(NH₄O)PO—			191
do	NH₂(NaO)PO—			191
C₆H₅(CH₂)₃—				217
2-(HO)C₆H₄CH₂—		183°	±(S)	170, 217, 488
4-(HO)C₆H₄CH₂—		206°	±(S)	170, 217, 488
4-(CH₃O)C₆H₄CH₂—		177-8°	+(S)	270
2,4-(HO)₂C₆H₃CH₂—			±(S)	170
3-CH₃O-4-(HO)C₆H₃CH₂—		167°	+(S)	159, 160
2,4,6-(HO)₃C₆H₂CH₂—			±(S)	170
C₆H₅(NaO₂S)CH—				487
C₆H₅CH₂(NaO₂S)CH—				487

R⁴	R⁴'	Melting Range	Activities	References
(structure: CH₃, H₂, CH₃CCH₃, H₂, H, =O, =CH—) d,l			±(S)	1427, 1574
(structure: naphthalenedione with O, O)		286-8°		2207
3-Cl-4-(HOOC)C₆H₃—		207°		31
3-(NaO₂S)C₆H₄CH₂—				488
C₆H₅CH(SO₃Na)CH₂(NaO₂S)CH—		b	+(L, Pf, Pk, Pv, S), ±(M, P, Pm, Pp), 0(Cd)	487, 548, 697, 861, 1011, 1050, 1818, 2150
4-(NH₂)C₆H₄CH₂—		152-3°		203, 224
4-[(CH₃)₂N]C₆H₄CH₂—				203
4-(NaO₂SNH)C₆H₄CH₂—				224, 2462

ᵃ Septazine.
ᵇ Soluseptazine.

TABLE 55

C. N⁴-Heterocyclicsulfanilamides
1. One O- or One N-Atom in the Heterocyclic System

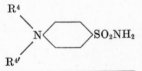

$$R^4 \diagdown N \diagup \langle \rangle SO_2NH_2 \diagup R^{4'}$$

R⁴	R⁴'	Melting Range	Activities	References
(piperidine ring, N—)		223-4°, 235°	0(S)	172, 409

TABLE 55—(*Continued*)

R⁴	R⁴′	Melting Range	Activities	References
(NO₂-substituted bicyclic N-ring structure)		209–10°		409
(bicyclic N-ring structure)		257°, 263°	0(S)	43, 172, 409
(bicyclic N-ring structure)		262–3°		43
(bicyclic N-ring structure)		275°		409
(N-CH₃ bicyclic ring structure)		280°D		683
(CH₃-substituted bicyclic N-ring structure)		258°		683
(tricyclic N-ring structure)		245–6°	+(S), 0(P)	161, 1147
(N–C_6H_5 bicyclic ring structure)		250°		30

TABLE 55—(*Continued*)

R^4	$R^{4'}$	Melting Range	Activities	References
		301°D		683
		308°D		683
		293°D		683
		277°D		683
		249°		683
		278°		683
		286°, >300°	0(I, Po)	72, 110, 514, 892
		304°D		124

TABLE 55—(*Concluded*)

R⁴	R⁴′	Melting Range	Activities	References
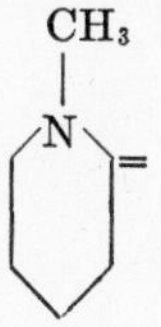 CH₃ (structure)		245–6°		2187
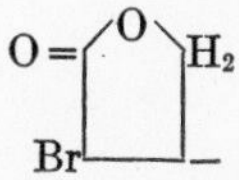 O= ... Br (structure)			++(S)	77, 276, 277
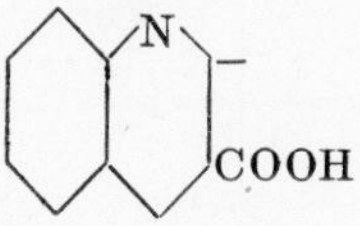 COOH (structure)		>280°	+(S), ±(P)	160, 1147
NH₂ (structure)		221°		409
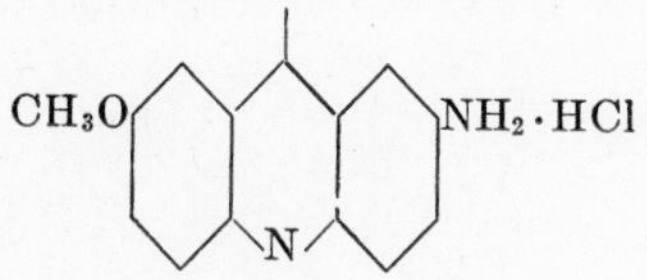 CH₃O ... NH₂·HCl (structure)		315°D		124
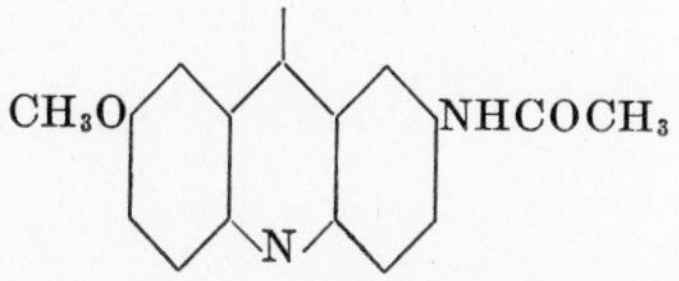 CH₃O ... NHCOCH₃ (structure)		185°		124

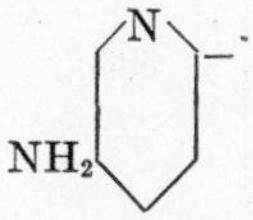

TABLE 56

C. *N⁴*-Heterocyclicsulfanilamides
  2. Two or More N-Atoms in the Heterocyclic System.

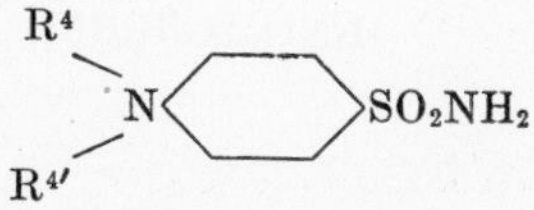

$$\begin{matrix} R^4 \\ \diagdown \\ N \\ \diagup \\ R^{4\prime} \end{matrix}\!-\!\!\diagup\diagdown\!\!-\!SO_2NH_2$$

R⁴	Melting Range	Activities	References
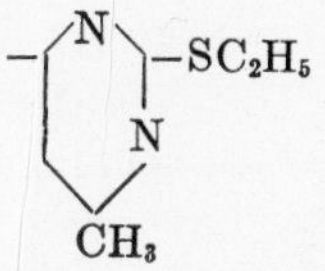 –N ... –SC₂H₅ ... N ... CH₃ (structure)	188–9°		2180

TABLE 56—(Continued)

R⁴	Melting Range	Activities	References
	237–9°		503
	280–2°		503
	239–40°		503
	218–20°		503
	240–255°		1164
			1164
			1164

TABLE 57

C. N^4-Heterocyclicsulfanilamides
   3. One N- and One S-Atom in the Heterocyclic System.

R^4	$R^{4\prime}$	Melting Range	Activities	References
H ICH₂ (ring) H₂ N			0	1147
S N (ring)			0(I, P, R, Tt)	1147, 1427, 1574
CH₃ S N (ring)		234–5°		537
S N (ring)				1345
HOCH₂CH₂ S CH₃ N (ring)		211–2°		537
S NH (ring)		240°D	0	161
S NCH₂CH=CH₂ (ring)		139.5–41°	0	161, 1147
S NC₆H₅ (ring)		193°	0	161
ICH₂ S NH (ring)		115–9°	0	161

TABLE 57—*(Continued)*

R^4	$R^{4'}$	Melting Range	Activities	References
C_6H_5—NH (thiazoline ring, S, =)		228–30°	0	161, 1147
C_6H_5—$NCH_2CH=CH_2$ (thiazoline ring, S, =)		209–10°	0	161, 1147
H_2, $O=$—N (thiazolidine ring, S)		240–55°	±, 0(S) 0(I, R)	161, 311, 1147, 1427, 1574
$C_2H_5OOCCH_2$—N (thiazoline ring, S)			0	1147
C_2H_5OOC, CH_3—N (thiazoline ring, S)			0	1147
$C_2H_5OOCCH_2$, CH_3—N (thiazoline ring, S)			0	1147
$C_2H_5OOCCH_2$—NH (thiazoline ring, S, =)		219–20°	0	161
C_2H_5OOC, CH_3—NH (thiazoline ring, S, =)		243–5°	0	161
$C_2H_5OOCCH_2$, CH_3—NH (thiazoline ring, S, =)		163°	0	161
—N (thiazoline ring, S, NH_2)			0(I, P, R, Tt)	1427, 1574

TABLE 58

C. N^4-Heterocyclicsulfanilamides
 4. N^4-Nitrogen a Member of the Heterocyclic System ⊂N⟨ ⟩SO₂NH₂

⊂N—	Melting Range	Activities	References
CH₃ N— CH₃		0(En, I, Po)	892, 1485
H₂ N— H₂ H₂	161–3°, 182–4°		1329
H₂ H₂ H—N N— H₂ H₂	210–1°		265
H₂ H₂ 4-(NH₂SO₂)C₆H₄N N— H₂ H₂			2084
N—NC₆H₅ N— CH₃—N Cl	198°		1388
N—NC₆H₅ N— CH₃CH₂CH₂—N Cl	179°		1388
N—NC₆H₅ N— n-C₆H₁₃—N Cl	147°		1388

TABLE 58—(Continued)

$\subset N-$	Melting Range	Activities	References
N—NC₆H₅ / N— / n-C₇H₁₅—N Cl	142°		1388
N—NC₆H₅ / N— / n-C₁₁H₂₃—N Cl	135°		1388
O ‖ N— / CH₃—N / CH₃	237°		448, 935
O ‖ H₂— / N— / H₂— ‖ O	282.3°		360
O ‖ CH₃— / N— ‖ O	210–3°, 217-8°		40, 729
O ‖ N— ‖ O	320–2°		150, 2371
O= N =O			40

TABLE 58—*(Concluded)*

⊏N–	Melting Range	Activities	References
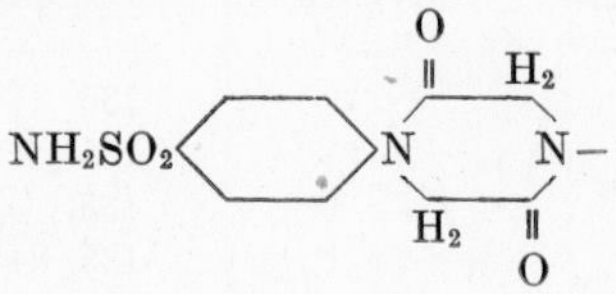 (structure)	325°D	0	4
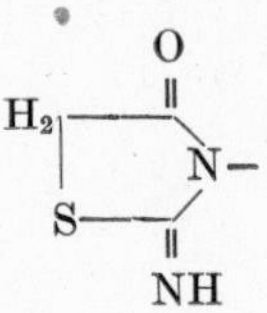 (structure)	258°D	0	4
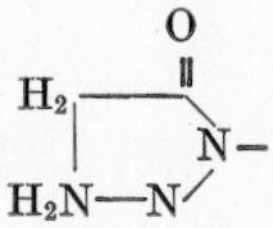 (structure)	257–60°D		2658, 2659
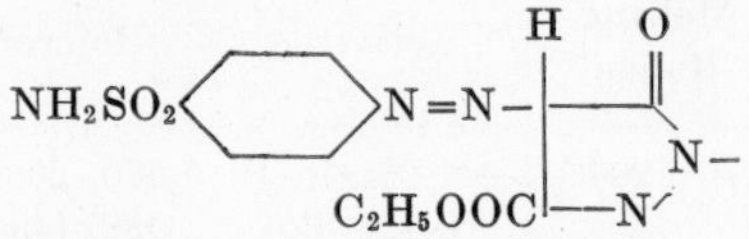 (structure)	258–60°		1071

NH_2SO_2—◯—N(=O)(H_2)N(H_2)(=O)N–

H_2—(=O)—N–, S—(=NH)— NH

H_2—(=O)—N–, H_2N—N

NH_2SO_2—◯—N=N—C(H)(=O)N–, C_2H_5OOC—N

TABLE 59

D. N^4-Anils of Sulfanilamide
  1. Acyclicanils of Sulfanilamide $R^4 = N$◯SO_2NH_2
    a. N^4-Alkylidenesulfanilamides

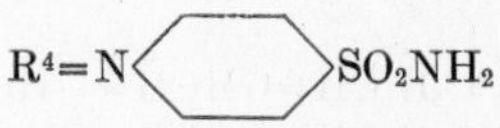

R^4	Melting Range	Activities	References
$CH_2=$		+	385, 489, 568
$CH_3(CH_2)_4CH=$		0(I)	1901, 1962
$CH_3(CH_2)_5CH=$	171–2°	0(Ca)	48
$HOOCCH=$			74, 132
$NaOOCCH=$			132
$CH_3(HOOC)CH=$			74, 132
$CH_3(NaOOC)CH=$			132

TABLE 60

b. N^4-Alkylidenebis(sulfanilamides) $R^4 = \left(-NH\bigcirc SO_2NH_2 \right)_2$

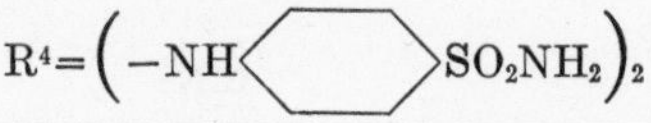

R^4	Melting Range	Activities	References
$CH_3(CH_2)_6CH=$	140–2°		135
$CH_3(CH_2)_7CH=$	138–40°		135
$CH_3(CH_2)_9CH=$	133–6°	*	135
$CH_3(CH_2)_{10}CH=$	140–4°	++(S, P)	135, 841
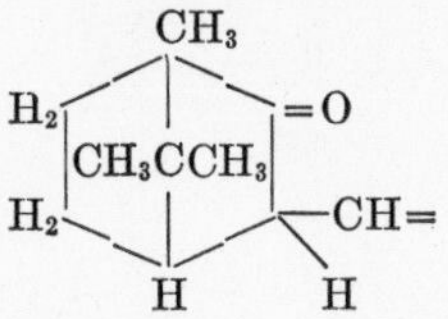 (structure)	145–8°	+++(S, P)	136, 841

TABLE 61

2. Isocyclicanils of Sulfanilamide $R^4 = N\bigcirc SO_2NH_2$
  (N^4-Aralkylidenesulfanilamides)

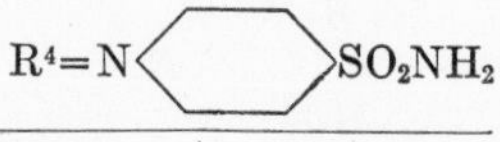

R^4	Melting Range	Activities	References
$C_6H_5CH=$	176°, 204°	++(S), +(P), 0(En, Po)	170, 268, 487, 488, 1485
$2\text{-}(NO_2)C_6H_4CH=$			1984
$3\text{-}(NO_2)C_6H_4CH=$	173°	+(S)	173
$4\text{-}(NO_2)C_6H_4CH=$		++(S)	74, 270
$C_6H_5CH=CHCH=$	215°, 240°	+, +++(S), 0(En, Po)	173, 270, 471, 487, 1485
$C_6H_5CH=CHCH=(\cdot HCl)$	203–5°D		471
$C_6H_5CH=C(C_5H_{11})CH=$		0(P)	315
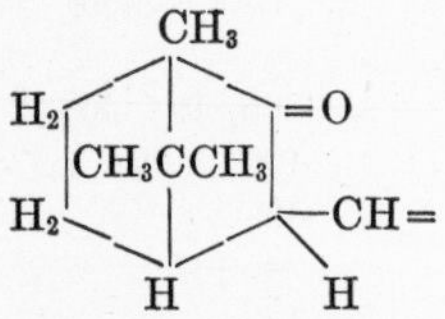 (structure)	194–7°		136
$2\text{-}(HO)C_6H_4CH=$		++(S)	170, 418, 488, 1962
$3\text{-}(HO)C_6H_4CH=$	138°		1984
$6\text{-}NO_2\text{-}3\text{-}(HO)C_6H_3CH=$	197°	+(S)	173
$4\text{-}(HO)C_6H_4CH=$		+++(S)	170, 488, 504
$4\text{-}(CH_3O)C_6H_4CH=$	193°, 200°	++, +(S), +(P)	173, 268, 269

TABLE 61—(*Continued*)

R^4	Melting Range	Activities	References
2-HO-3-(CH₃O)C₆H₃CH=	208°		566
2,4-(HO)₂C₆H₃CH=		++, +(S)	170, 418
4-HO-3-(CH₃O)C₆H₃CH=	198–9°	+, ++(S)	159, 160, 407, 418
3,4-(CH₃O)₂C₆H₃CH=	196°	+(S)	173
3-CH₃O-4-(C₂H₅O)C₆H₅CH=	164–5°		407
3,4-(C₂H₅O)₂C₆H₃CH=	216°		173
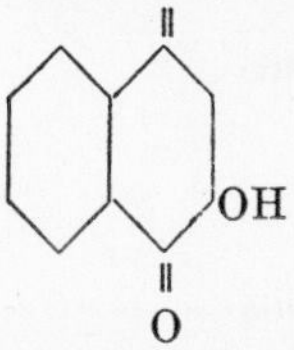 [naphthoquinone structure with OH, =O groups]	271–3°		1361
2,4,6-(HO)₃C₆H₂CH=		++(S)	170
2-(HOOC)C₆H₄CH=	276°	++(S)	60
3-(HOOC)C₆H₄CH=	202°		461
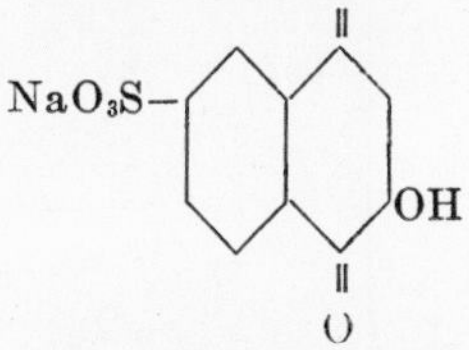 [NaO₃S— naphthoquinone structure with OH, =O]			1361
4-(CH₃)₂NC₆H₄CH₂=	216°, 229°	++(S), ±(P)	173, 203, 268, 269, 376
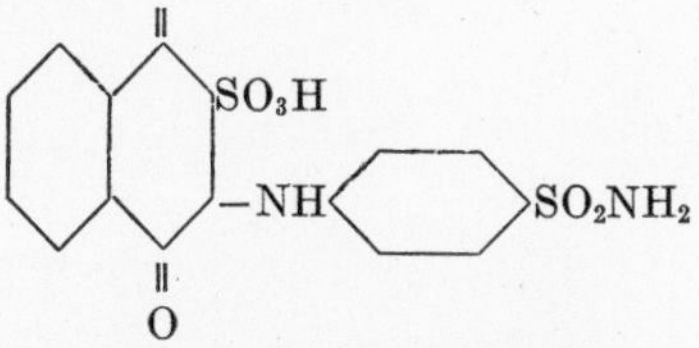 [naphthoquinone structure with SO₃H, —NH⟨ ⟩SO₂NH₂, =O]	276–8°		1361
2-CH₃COOHg-3-(HO)C₆H₃CH=	282°	+(S), 0(P, Sa)	968

TABLE 62

3. Heterocyclicanils of Sulfanilamide $R^4 = N\langle\ \rangle SO_2NH_2$

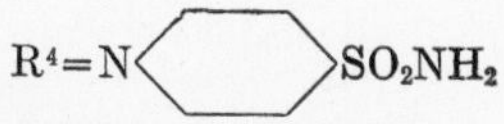

R^4	Melting Range	Activities	References
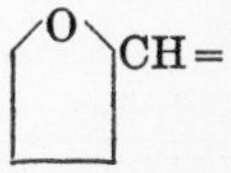 [furan-type ring]CH=	196°	+(S)	173

TABLE 62—(*Continued*)

R^4	Melting Range	Activities	References
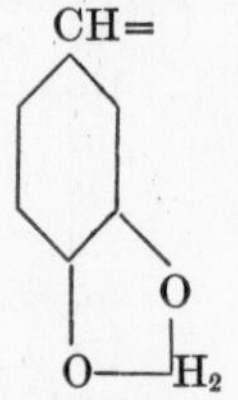 CH= (structure)	219°	+(S)	173
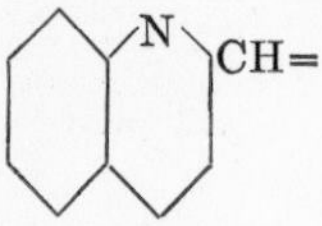 (structure) CH=	188–9°		1405
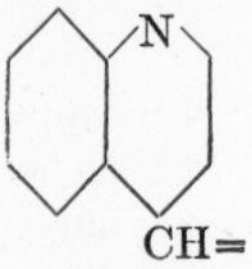 (structure) CH=	151–3°		1405
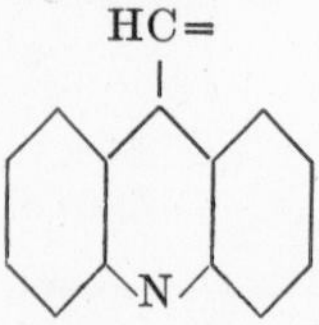 HC= (structure)	248–50°		367
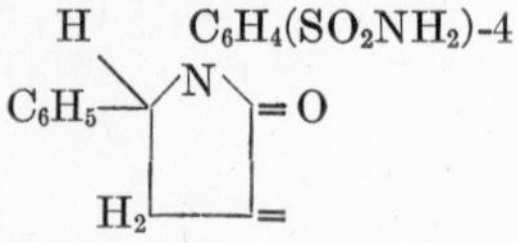 H C$_6$H$_4$(SO$_2$NH$_2$)-4 (structure) C$_6$H$_5$—N =O, H$_2$ =	260–3°	+, 0(P, S)	105, 1057, 2512
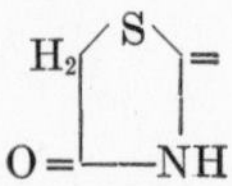 H$_2$ S = (structure) O= —NH		0(S)	311

TABLE 63

E. *N*^{4}-Sugar Derivatives of Sulfanilamide
  1. Glycosides of Sulfanilamide

Sugar	Melting Range	Activities	References
Arabinose	195°D		275, 456
Xylose	150°	+(G)	354, 355, 356, 456, 1699
Rhamnose	208–10°D		456

TABLE 63—(*Continued*)

Sugar	Melting Range	Activities	References
Glucose	207–8°, 210°D	+(S)	52, 60, 132, 173, 275, 456, 524, 2434
Tetraacetylglucose	191°		52, 275
Mannose	202°, 196°D		275, 456
Galactose	142–4°		354, 356, 456
Tetraacetylgalactose			355, 356
Maltose (soluble)		++(S), +(G) ·	456, 558, 1699
Maltose (insoluble)	236°		558
Lactose	190°		354, 356, 456, 849

TABLE 64

2. N^4-Sugar Sodium Bisulfite Derivatives of Sulfanilamide

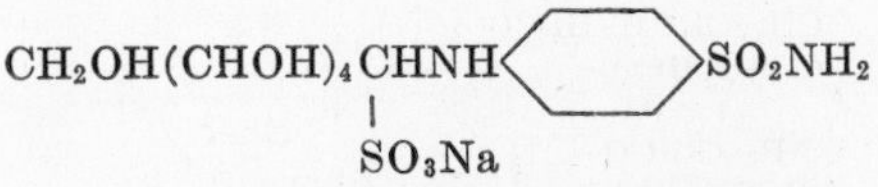

$$CH_2OH(CHOH)_4 CHNH\langle\hspace{1cm}\rangle SO_2NH_2$$
$$|$$
$$SO_3Na$$

Probable Type Formula

Sugar	Melting Range	Activities	References
Glycerose			1894
Glucose		+++(S)	504, 1894
d-Galactose			1894
Maltose			1894
Lactose			1894

TABLE 65

F. N^4-Acylsulfanilamides
1. N^4-Acyclicacylsulfanilamides

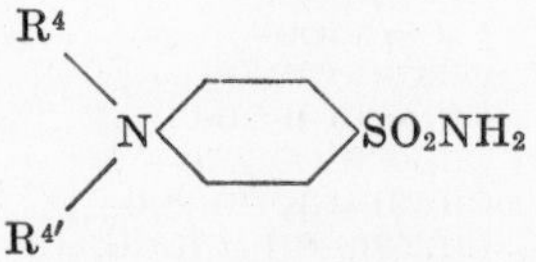

$$\begin{matrix} R^4 \\ \diagdown \\ N\langle\hspace{1cm}\rangle SO_2NH_2 \\ \diagup \\ R^{4'} \end{matrix}$$

R^4	$R^{4'}$	Melting Range	Activities	References
HCO—			+(S)	151, 512
do	C_2H_5—	187–8°	0(Pr)	536
CH_3CO—		215–6°	+(Pl), ±, 0(S)	61, 151, 360, 512, 973, 1733, 2441
do	CH_3—	153°	±(S)	61, 201, 512
do	C_2H_5—	126–7°		536
do	HO—	227–9.5°	+, 0(S)	50, 244, 440, 713, 815, 2441
$ClCH_2CO$—		214°, 215–7°	+(S), ±(P)	40, 157, 217, 242, 412, 1086, 1427, 1574, 2464
Cl_2CHCO—		215–6°, 218°	+++(S), 0(I)	40, 725, 1574, 1578
Cl_3CCO—		197–8°, 205°	++(S), 0(I)	40, 1574, 1578
$BrCH_2CO$—		218°D		40

TABLE 65—(*Continued*)

R^4	$R^{4\prime}$	Melting Range	Activities	References
CH_3CH_2CO-		221°, 226.5–7.5°	$+(M, S)$	5, 360
$CH_3CHClCO-$		210–2°	$++(S), \pm(P, Sa), 0(I)$	1574, 2373
CH_2ClCH_2CO-		225–6°		217
$CH_3CHBrCO-$		209–10°	$+(S)$	1574, 2373
$CH_3CH_2CH_2CO-$		231°, 236–7°	$++(M), +, \pm(S)$	5, 360
$CH_3CH_2CHClCO-$		175–7°	$++(S), \pm(P), 0(I, Sa)$	1574, 2373
$CH_3CHClCH_2CO-$		202–3°	$+(S), 0(I)$	1574, 2373
$CH_3CHClCHClCO-$		183–5°	$0(P, S)$	1574, 2373
$(CH_3)_2CHCO-$		241°, 248–9°	$++(M), \pm(S)$	5, 211, 341, 360
$CH_3(CH_2)_3CO-$		197–8°, 214°	$++, +(S)$	5, 211, 311, 360
$(CH_3)_2CHCH_2CO-$		213°, 216–7°	$\pm(S)$	211, 360
$CH_3(CH_2)_4CO-$		205°	$++(S), \pm(P)$	211, 270, 360, 2191
$CH_3(CH_2)_3CHBrCO-$		186–7°	$+(S), 0(I, P, Sa)$	1574
$(CH_3)_2CHCH_2CH_2CO-$		193–4°	$0(S)$	211, 360
$(C_2H_5)_2CHCO-$			$+(S), 0(I, P, R)$	217, 904, 1574, 2464
$(C_2H_5)_2CBrCO-$				1574, 2373
$CH_3(CH_2)_5CO-$		192–202°	$\pm(S)$	211, 360
$CH_3(CH_2)_2(C_2H_5)CBrCO-$		118–20°	$0(I, P, S)$	1574, 2373
$CH_3(CH_2)_6CO-$		189°, 200°	$+, \pm(S)$	211, 360
$(CH_2)_2CHCH_2(C_2H_5)CHCO-$			$+(S), 0(I, P, R)$	904, 1574
$(CH_3)_2CHCH_2[(CH_3)_2CH]CHCO-$		229–30°	$+(S), 0(I, P)$	1574, 2373
$CH_3(CH_2)_8CO-$		198°	$\pm(S), 0(Le)$	211, 673
$CH_3(CH_2)_9CO-$		203–5°D	$0(Le, P)$	49, 673
$CH_3CHBrCHBr(CH_2)_7CO-$		173–5°		40
$CH_3(CH_2)_{10}CO-$		205°, 207–8°	$+, 0(S, P), +(Sa)$	211, 360, 673, 1057
$CH_3(CH_2)_9CHBrCO-$				384
$CH_3(CH_2)_9CHICO-$				384
$CH_3(CH_2)_{12}CO-$		203°		211
$CH_3(CH_2)_{14}CO-$		202°		211
$CH_3(CH_2)_{16}CO-$		201°, 245°		40, 211
$CH_3(CH_2)_{15}CHBrCO-$				384
$CH_3(CH_2)_{20}CO-$		171°		211
$Cl_2C=CClCO-$		258°		40
$CH_3CH=CHCO-$		237–9°D	$+(S), 0(I)$	1574, 2373
$CH_2=CHCH_2CH_2CO-$		169–71°	$++(S), 0(I)$	1574, 2373
$CH_2=CH(CH_2)_8CO-$		196–8°	$\pm(P)$	673
$CH_3CH=CH(CH_2)_7CO-$		199°		40, 211
$CH_3(CH_2)_7CH=CH(CH_2)_7CO-$		197°, 204°	$0(S)$	40, 211
$cis\text{-}CH_3(CH_2)_7CH=CH(CH_2)_{11}CO-$		171°		211
$CH_3(CH_2)_7C\equiv C(CH_2)_7CO-$		189°		40
$HOOCCO-$		208–10°		530
$HOOCCH_2CO-$		172°		530
$4\text{-}(NH_2SO_2)C_6H_4NHOCCH_2CO-$			$0(P)$	315
$HOOC(CH_2)_2CO-$		202°, 213.5°, 217°	$++, +, \pm(S), ++(C), \pm(Dy)$	40, 292, 360, 406, 444, 461, 530, 788, 1574, 1950, 1951, 2373
$NaOOC(CH_2)_2CO-$			$+(Sa), 0(S)$	67, 311, 444
$NH_2OC(CH_2)_2CO-$		234–8°	$0(S)$	4
$HOOC(CH_2)_4CO-$		184°		530
$4\text{-}(NH_2SO_2)C_6H_4NHOC(CH_2)_4CO-$		>300°		40
$4\text{-}(NH_2SO_2)C_6H_4NHOCC(C_2H_5)_2CO-$			$0(P)$	315
$4\text{-}(NH_2SO_2)C_6H_4NHOC(CH_2)_8CO-$		>300°		40
$trans\text{-}HOOCCH=CHCO-$		295°		729
$trans\text{-}C_2H_5OOCCH=CHCO-$		219°		729
$cis\text{-}HOOCCH=CHCO-$		208–9°, 209–10°	$0, -(S)$	360, 729, 1950

TABLE 65—(*Continued*)

R⁴	R⁴′	Melting Range	Activities	References
cis-NaOOCCH=CHCO—			0(S)	311
cis-C₂H₅OOCCH=CHCO—		204–5°		729
cis-HOOCC(CH₃)=CHCO—				729
HOCH₂CO—		190°	±(P), 0(S)	217, 311, 315, 2464
CH₃OCH₂CO—		194°		217, 2464
do	C₆H₅—	>284°D		217, 2464
C₂H₅OCH₂CO—		165–6°, 172°	++(S), 0(I)	217, 1574, 2373, 2464
C₄H₉OCH₂CO—		157°		217, 2464
C₆H₅OCH₂CO—		205°		217, 2464
2-ClC₆H₄OCH₂CO—		232°		217, 2464
CH₃COOCH₂CO—				311
CH₃CH₂SCH₂CO—		164.5–5.0°	+(S), ±(Sa), 0(I, P, R)	1574, 2193
C₆H₅CH₂CH₂SCH₂CO—		169–70.5°	+(S), 0(I, P, R, Sa)	1574, 2193 1164
H₂N⟨N⟩SCH₂CO— (N, NH₂)				
H₂N⟨N⟩SCH₂CO— (N N, NH₂)				1164
CH₃CHOHCO—		187°, 196°	+, 0(S)	4, 217, 311, 2464
CH₃(CH₃COO)CHCO—		195.2°	0(S)	4
2-(CH₃)₂CH-5-(CH₃)C₆H₃OCH₂CH₂CO—				217, 2464
2-CH₃O-5-(CH₃)C₆H₃OCH₂CH₂CO—		191°		2464
CH₃COCH₂CO—		176–8°, 258–8°	+(S), 0(1, Tt)	217, 1574, 1799, 2373, 2464
NaO₃SCH₂CO—			0	432, 504
NH₂CH₂CO—		217°	+(S)	217, 346, 1068, 1427, 1574, 2464
HCl·NH₂CH₂CO—		287°		217, 2464
HCl·C₂H₅NHCH₂CO—		247°		217, 2464
(C₂H₅)₂NCH₂CO—		153°		157, 217, 2464
C₃H₇NHCH₂CO—		181°		217, 2464
C₄H₉NHCH₂CO—		167°		217, 2464
CH₂=CHCH₂NHCH₂CO—		193°		217, 2464
C₆H₅NHCH₂CO—		196°		157
2-(CH₃)C₆H₄NHCH₂CO—		212°		157
3-(CH₃)C₆H₄NHCH₂CO—		166°		157
4-(CH₃)C₆H₄NHCH₂CO—		189°		157
3,4-(CH₃)₂C₆H₄NHCH₂CO—		163°		157
2-(CH₃O)C₆H₄NHCH₂CO—		189°		157
2-(C₂H₅O)C₆H₄NHCH₂CO—		221°		157
3-(CH₃O)C₆H₄NHCH₂CO—		155°		157
3-(C₂H₅O)C₆H₄NHCH₂CO—		173°		157
4-(CH₃O)C₆H₄NHCH₂CO—		189°		157
4-(C₂H₅O)C₆H₄NHCH₂CO—		209°D		157
H₂⟨⟩NCH₂CO— (H₂ H₂ / H₂ H₂)		204°		217, 2464
Cl⟨⟩N–CH₂CO—		256°		217, 2464

TABLE 65—(*Concluded*)

R^4	$R^{4'}$	Melting Range	Activities	References
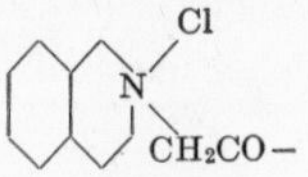 [structure: decahydroquinoline with Cl and CH_2CO-]		250°		217, 2464
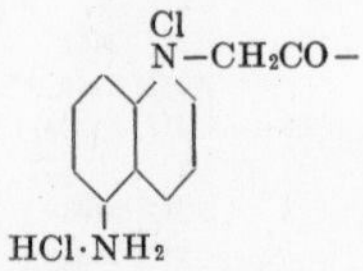 [structure: Cl $N-CH_2CO-$, $HCl\cdot NH_2$]		236°		157
$4(NH_2SO_2)C_6H_4NHCH_2CO-$			$+(S)$, $0(Tt)$	1574
$4\text{-}(C_6H_5N=N)C_6H_4NHCH_2CO-$		261°D		157
$C_4H_9NHCH_2CH_2CO-$		163°		217, 2464
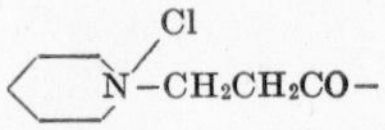 [structure: Cl $N-CH_2CH_2CO-$]		223°		217, 2464
$4\text{-}(NH_2SO_2)C_6H_4NHCOCH_2NHCH_2CO-$		256–8°, 260°		412, 1086
$C_4H_9NHC(C_2H_5)_2CO-$		177°		217, 2464
$CH_3C(NH_2)=CHCO-$		175°	$\pm(S)$	1427, 1574

TABLE 66

2. N^4-Isocyclicacylsulfanilamides $R^4NH\langle\quad\rangle SO_2NH_2$

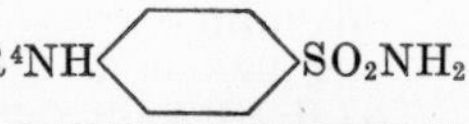

R^4	Melting Range	Activities	References
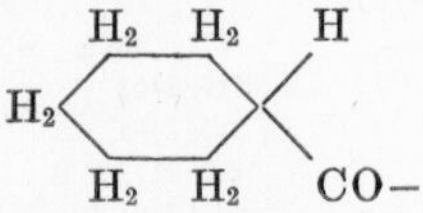 [structure: dimethyl-cyclohexane, H_2 H_2 H / H_2 / H_2 H_2 $CO-$]	238°		1983
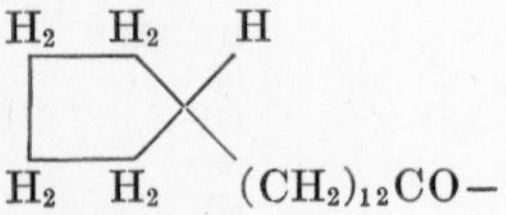 [structure: dimethyl-cyclopentane, H_2 H_2 H / H_2 H_2 $(CH_2)_{12}CO-$]	208°	$\pm(L, S)$, $0(I, Le, P, Sa, Y)$	968, 1082
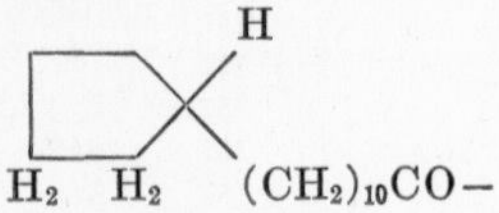 [structure: methyl-cyclopentane, H / H_2 H_2 $(CH_2)_{10}CO-$]	185–7°	$0(Le)$	673
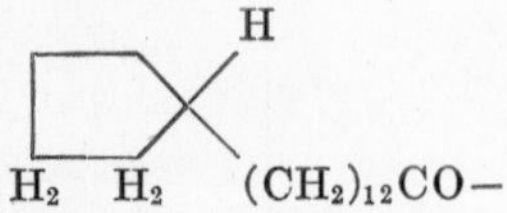 [structure: methyl-cyclopentane, H / H_2 H_2 $(CH_2)_{12}CO-$]		$0(Le, T)$	672

TABLE 66—(*Continued*)

R^4	Melting Range	Activities	References
C_6H_5CO-	284°	0(S)	331, 360, 968
2-FC_6H_4CO-	264°		764
3-$(NO_2)C_6H_4CO-$	245°		217, 2464
4-$(NO_2)C_6H_4CO-$	252°, 260°	±, 0(S), 0(I, L, Le, P, Y)	440, 1082, 1574, 2196, 2298
3,5-$(NO_2)_2C_6H_3CO-$			217, 2464
$C_6H_5CH_2CO-$	201°		211
$C_6H_5(CH_2)_3CO-$			384
$C_6H_5(CH_2)_2CHBrCO-$			384
$C_6H_5CH=CHCO-$	265°		40, 211
trans-$C_6H_5CBr=CBrCO-$	266°		40
$C_6H_5C{\equiv}CCO-$	254°		40
2-$(HO)C_6H_4CO-$	245°	0(S, Tt)	1574, 2298
2-$(CH_3COO)C_6H_4CO-$	150°	±(S), 0(Tt)	1574, 2298
$C_6H_5CHOHCO-$	232°	++(S), 0(C, Tt)	305, 1574, 2395
$C_6H_5CH(OOCCH_3)CO-$	187.5-9.5°		305
d-$C_6H_5CH(OOCCH_3)CO-$	127°	++(S), 0(Tt)	305, 1574
l-$C_6H_5CH(OOCCH_3)CO-$	198°	++(S), 0(Tt)	305, 1574
d,l-$C_6H_5CH(OOCC_6H_5)CO-$	242°	+(S), 0(Tt)	305, 1574
$C_6H_5CH(CH_2OOCCH_3)CO-$	190°	0(S)	1574, 2298
Cholyl-	244-6°D		185
2-$(HOOC)C_6H_4CO-$	338°	0(C)	40, 444, 461, 505, 530, 1951
2-$(NaOOC)C_6H_4CO-$		0	311, 461
2-HOOC-3,4,5,6-$(Cl)_4C_6CO-$	332°D		40
6-NO_2-2-$(HOOC)C_6H_3CO-$	259-60°		461
4,6-$(NO_2)_2$-2-$(HOOC)C_6H_2CO-$	274-5°		461
3-[4′$(NH_2SO_2)C_6H_4NHOC$]C_6H_4CO-	>360°		40
COOH CO- (two hexagons)	278-9°		40
3-$(HO_3S)C_6H_4CO-$	256°		461
4-$(NH_2SO_2)C_6H_4CH_2CO-$		-(S)	1427, 1574
3-$(NH_2)C_6H_4CO-$	275°		217, 2464
3,5-$(NH_2)_2C_6H_3CO-$	285°		217, 2464
$HCl\cdot$3,5-$(NH_2)_2C_6H_3CO-$	289-90°		2464

TABLE 67

3. N^4-Heterocyclicacylsulfanilamides   R^{4}NH⟨ ⟩SO$_2$NH$_2$

R^4	Melting Range	Activities	References
O⟩CO–	273.5°	±(S), 0(En, P, Po)	270, 1485
S⟩CO–	278.5°	±(S)	270
N⟩CO–	257–8°	+++, ++(S), ++, 0(P), ++(M), 0(I, R, Tt)	55, 107, 270, 427, 1408, 1574, 2298
N⟩C$_6$H$_5$ CO–		0(P)	1574, 2298
N⟩CO–	247–8°		108
N⟩COOH CO–	268°		444, 461
N⟩COONa CO–		++(S)	205, 444, 461
CH$_3$O⟩N CO–		0(S)	968
CH$_3$O⟩N CO–	255°	0(I, L, Le, P, S, Sa, Y)	968, 1082

TABLE 67—(*Continued*)

R^4	Melting Range	Activities	References
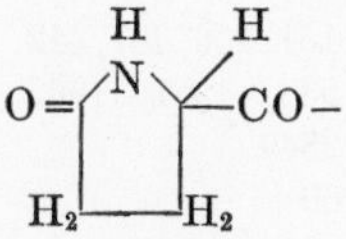 [structure: O=, N, H, H, —CO—, H$_2$, H$_2$]	262°	+++(S)	173, 2441
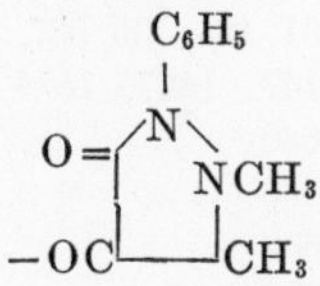 [structure: O=, N, C$_6$H$_5$, NCH$_3$, —OC, CH$_3$]	261°		1412

TABLE 68

F. *N*^{4}-Acylsulfanilamides
4. Derivatives of Carbonic Acid

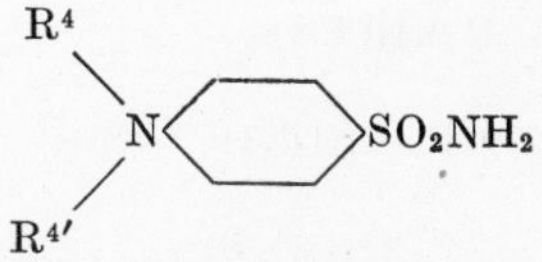

[structure: R^4, R$^{4\prime}$, N, —SO$_2$NH$_2$]

R$_4$	R$^{4\prime}$	Melting Range	Activities	References
C$_2$H$_5$OCO—		241.5–2.6°	±(M, S)	5, 151, 217, 512, 2100, 2464
C$_{12}$H$_{25}$OCO—			0(P)	315
(CH$_3$)$_3$N(Cl)CH$_2$CH$_2$OCO—		250–1°		6
NH$_2$CO—		172–3° 181°, 208–9°	++, +, 0(S), ++(M),±(P, Sa), 0(I, R, Tt)	96, 217, 267, 295, 1574, 2349, 2469
C$_6$H$_5$NHCO—		231–3°		2630
4-ClC$_6$H$_4$NHCO—		239–40°		2630
4-(NO$_2$)C$_6$H$_4$NHCO—		258–9°		2630
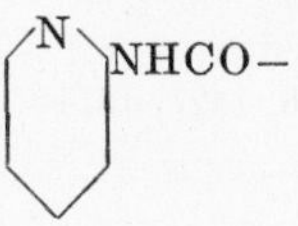 [pyridyl]NHCO—				1160
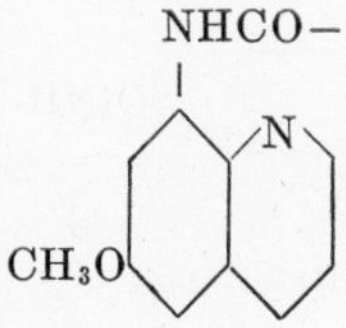 [structure: CH$_3$O, N, NHCO—]				1160
CH$_3$CONHCO—		246–7°	0	96

TABLE 68—*(Continued)*

R^4	$R^{4\prime}$	Melting Range	Activities	References
4-$(NH_2SO_2)C_6H_4NHCO-$		272–4°D	$\pm$(S), 0(I)	151, 206, 467, 512, 538, 1901, 1962, 2349
$NH_2C(=NH)-$		185°	++(S)	60
4-$(NH_2SO_2)C_6H_4NHC(=NH)-$		225–6°D		2540
$NH_2C(=S)-$		197°D, 205–6°	+(P, Sa), 0(Tt), 0, −(S)	161, 125, 505, 537, 1147, 1427, 1574
$CH_3NHC(=S)-$		205–6°		2630
$C_2H_5NHC(=S)-$		201–2°		2630
$C_3H_7NHC(=S)-$		182–3°		2630
$C_4H_9NHC(=S)-$		170–1°		2630
$C_5H_{11}NHC(=S)-$		157–8°		2630
$CH_2=CHCH_2NHC(=S)-$		189–90°	0	158, 159, 161, 2630
$C_6H_5NHC(=S)-$		190–1°	+(S), 0(I, P, R, Sa, Tt)	1147, 1427, 1574, 2630
2-$(CH_3)C_6H_4NHC(=S)-$		215–6°		2630
$NHC(=S)-$ 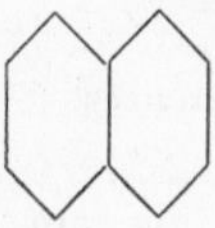 (naphthyl)		193–4°		2630
 N (quinolyl) $NHC(=S)-$				125
4$(C_2H_5O)C_6H_4NHC(=S)-$				125
3$(HOOC)C_6H_4NHC(=S)-$				125
4-$(NH_2SO_2)C_6H_4NHC(=S)-$				125, 538
4-$(H_2O_3As)C_6H_4NHC(=S)-$				125
4-$(H_2O_3Sb)C_6H_4NHC(=S)-$				125
$O=C=$				1160
$S=C=$			0(I, P, R, Tt)	125, 1427, 1574

TABLE 69

G. N^4-Inorganic Derivatives of Sulfanilamide
   1. N^4-Sulfonylsulfanilamides R^4NH⟨⟩SO_2NH_2
     a. N^4-Acyclicsulfonylsulfanilamides

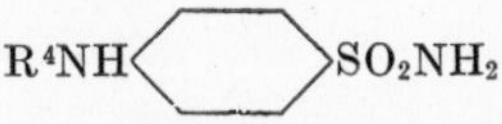

R^4	Melting Range	Activities	References
CH_3SO_2-	180–1°	$\pm$, 0, −(S), 0(P, Sa)	494, 505, 772, 1574
$C_2H_5SO_2-$	175–6°	$\pm$, 0(S), 0(P, Sa)	494, 772, 1574

TABLE 69—(*Continued*)

R^4	Melting Range	Activities	References
$CH_3(CH_2)_2SO_2-$		$+(S), 0(P, Sa)$	772, 1574
$CH_3(CH_2)_3SO_2-$	160–1°	$0, -(S), 0(P, Sa)$	494, 505, 772, 1574
$CH_5(CH_2)_4SO_2-$	156.0–6.5°	$\pm, 0(S), 0(P, Sa)$	494, 772, 1574
$CH_3(CH_2)_5SO_2-$	153.0–3.5°	$\pm, 0(S), 0(I, P, R, Sa)$	494, 1574, 2192
$CH_3(CH_2)_{11}SO_2-$	157–8°	$0(S)$	494

TABLE 70

b. N^4-Isocyclicsulfonylsulfanilamides $\qquad R^4NH\langle\hexagon\rangle SO_2NH_2$

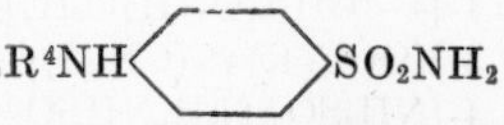

R^4	Melting Range	Activities	References
$C_6H_5SO_2-$	147–8°	$0(S)$	494
$3-(NO_2)C_6H_4SO_2-$	195°		217, 2464
$4-(NO_2)C_6H_4SO_2-$			209, 217
$C_6H_5CH_2SO_2-$	226–7°	$0(S)$	494
$4-[2'-(NO_2)C_6H_4]C_6H_4SO_2-$	239.5–40°	$0(S)$	1940
$C_6H_5OCH_2CH_2SO_2-$	145°		217, 2464
$2-CH_3O-5-(CH_3)C_6H_3O(CH_2)_3SO_2-$	159°		217, 2464
$3,4-(CH_3O)C_6H_3SO_2-$	155°		217, 2464
$3-(HOOC)C_6H_4SO_2-$			461
$3-HOOC-4-ClC_6H_3SO_2-$	240°		109
$3-HOOC-4-(HO)C_6H_3SO_2-$	247°	$0(R, S, Tt)$	430, 1574, 2373
$3-(NH_2)C_6H_4SO_2-$	168°	$\pm(S), 0(P, Pl)$	100, 217, 1075, 1733, 2441, 2464
$4-(NH_2)C_6H_4SO_2-$	137°[a]	See Table 288	33, 217, 269, 448, 450, 2368, 2464
$4-(HCl\cdot NH_2)C_6H_4SO_2-$	224°	$+++(S)$	173
$4-[(CH_3)_2N]C_6H_4SO_2-$	213°		217, 2461
$4-(C_6H_5CH_2NH)C_6H_4SO_2-$			2368
$4-(NaO_2SCH_2NH)C_6H_4SO_2-$			2368
$4-(CH_3CONH)C_6H_4SO_2-$	280°	$++(A, B), +, \pm(S)$	173, 217, 340, 448, 512, 999, 1411, 2368, 2464
$4-[CH_3(CH_2)_2CONH]C_6H_4SO_2-$	235–6°		1984
$4-[CH_3(CH_2)_4CONH]C_6H_4SO_2-$	184–6°		1984
$4-[C_6H_5(CH_3COO)CHCONH]C_6H_4SO_2-$	214–5°D	$+(S), 0(Tt)$	1446, 1574
$4-[4'(HOOC)C_6H_4CH_2NH]C_6H_4SO_2-$			2368
$4-[4'-(NH_2)C_6H_4SO_2NH]C_6H_4SO_2-$	203°, 210–1.5°	$++(S)$	33, 35, 100, 217, 2368, 2441, 2464

[a] Diseptyl C, Disulon.

TABLE 70—(*Continued*)

R^4	Melting Range	Activities	References
4-[4'-(CH$_3$CONH)C$_6$H$_4$SO$_2$NH]C$_6$H$_4$SO$_2$—	118°, 268°	+(S), 0(Tt)	33, 100, 217, 1574, 2368, 2464
4-[2'-(NH$_2$)C$_6$H$_4$]C$_6$H$_4$SO$_2$—	197.2–8.2°	0(S)	1940
4-[2'-(CH$_3$CONH)C$_6$H$_4$]C$_6$H$_4$SO$_2$—	231.5–2.5°	0(S)	1940
4-[4'(NH$_2$)C$_6$H$_4$]C$_6$H$_4$SO$_2$—	252°D		527
4-[4'-(CH$_3$CONH)C$_6$H$_4$]C$_6$H$_4$SO$_2$—	274°		527
3-HOOC-4-[4'-(CH$_3$O)C$_6$H$_4$NH]C$_6$H$_3$SO$_2$—	246°		109
4-(NH$_2$SO$_2$)C$_6$H$_4$NHSO$_2$—		+(S, Sa), 0(P)	538, 1427, 1574

TABLE 71

c. N^4-Heterocyclicsulfonylsulfanilamides   R^{4}NH⟨ ⟩SO$_2$NH$_2$

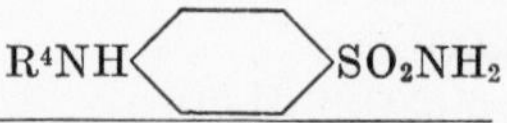

R^4	Melting Range	Activities	References
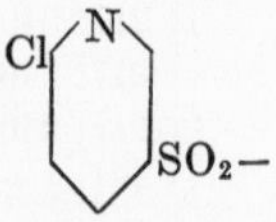			388
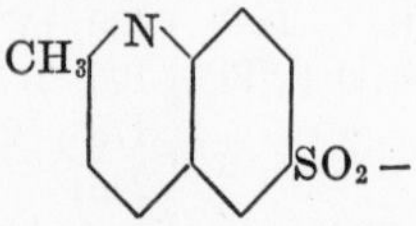	202°		217, 2464
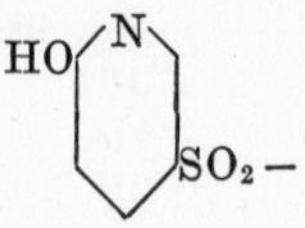			389
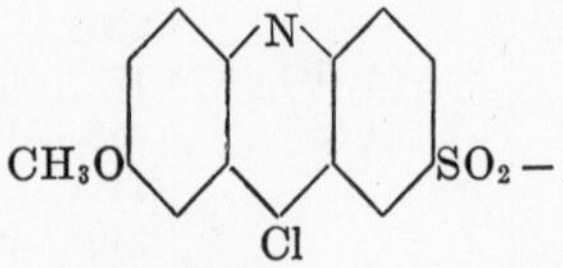	212–5°		109
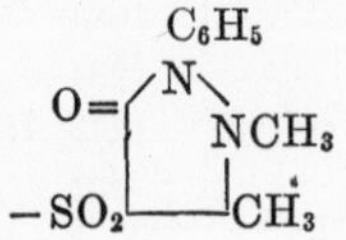	213°		2084

TABLE 71—(*Continued*)

R^4	Melting Range	Activities	References
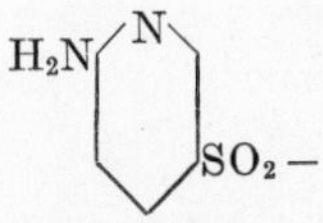			388
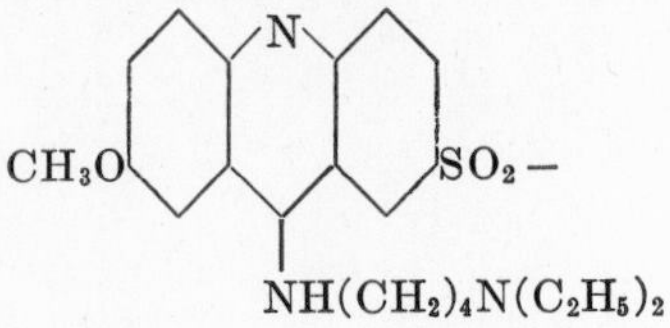	220–2°		109
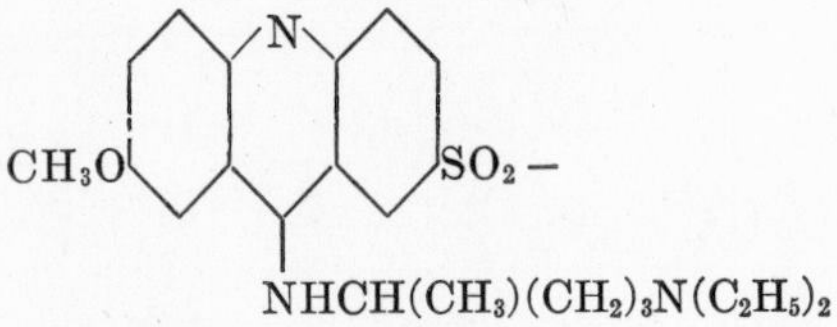	254–6°		109

TABLE 72

G. N^4-Inorganic Derivatives of Sulfanilamide
  2. Azo Derivatives of Sulfanilamide $R^4N=N$$SO_2NH_2$
    a. Acylicazo Derivatives

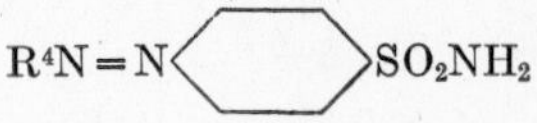

R^4	Melting Range	Activities	References
$HOOCCOCH_2-$	182°		382
$AgOOCCOCH_2-$			382
$CH_3CO(HOOC)CH-$	182°		378
$C_6H_5NHN=C(CH_3)-$	235°		1388
$C_6H_5NHN=C(CH_2CH_2CH_3)-$	200°		1388
$C_6H_5NHN=C(n\text{-}C_6H_{13})-$	181°		1388
$C_6H_5NHN=C(n\text{-}C_7H_{15})-$	176°		1388
$C_6H_5NHN=C(n\text{-}C_{11}H_{23})-$	167°		1388
$4\text{-}(NH_2SO_2)C_6H_4NHN=C(COCOOH)-$	232°		382

TABLE 73

$$R_3\quad R_2$$
$$R_4\!\!-\!\!\bigcirc\!\!-\!\!N\!=\!N\!\!-\!\!\bigcirc\!\!-\!\!SO_2NH_2$$
$$R_5\quad R_6$$

b. Isocyclicazo Derivatives

1. Azo Derivatives of Sulfanilamide and Benzene

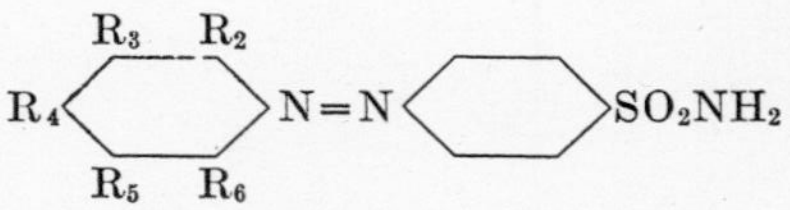

R_2	R_3	R_4	R_5	R_6	Melting Range	Activities	References
Cl–					225°	+(S)	85, 173, 218, 499, 2349
HO–	NO₂–	HO–	Cl–				521
HO–		CH₃–	Br–				605
HO–		HO–	Cl–			+(S)	605
CH₃–		HO–				+(S)	170, 512
C₂H₅–		HO–				+(S)	605
CH₃– (?)	CH₃– (?)	HO–	Cl– (?)				512
HO–	CH₃–	HO–	CH₃–			±(S)	512
CH₃–	CH₃–	HO–	CH₃–			±(S)	1962
HO–		HO–	CH₃–			±(S)	7, 61, 213
CH₃–		HO–	(CH₃)₂(C₂H₅)C–				512, 605
CH₂–		HO–	CH₃(CH₂)₂–				512
HO–		HO–	(CH₃)₂CH–			±(S)	512
HO–		HO–					605
HO–		HO–					512
HO–	C₆H₅–	HO–	C₆H₅–		207–8°	±(S)	7, 61, 213, 380, 407, 605
HO–		HO–					605
HO–		HO–					605
HO–		HO–				++, +(S)	170, 269, 328, 512
HO–		HO–				+(S)	512
CH₃O–	CH₃O–	HO–		Cl–		0(T)	605, 1469
HO–	C₆H₁₁S–	HO–				+, 0(S), +(Sa)	380, 512, 1057
HO–		HO–				+(S)	269
HO–		HO–				+(S)	512
HO–		HO–					512
HO–		HO–	CH₃–			+, 0(S), 0(Sa)	512, 1057
HO–		HO–	C₂H₅–			+(S)	170, 512
HO–		HO–	CH₃(CH₂)₂–				512
HO–	KOOC–	HO–	CH₃(CH₂)₅–	HO– C₂H₅O–	220°ᵃ	++, +(S), +, ± (L), 0(I, Lc, Y)	170, 269, 288, 289, 328, 605, 1082

ᵃ "Tutazol."

R₂	R₃	R₄	R₅	R₆	Melting Range	Activities	References
HO−	HOOC−	HS−			312°D	0(S)	170
HO−		NH₂SO₂−	NaO₃S−				264, 466, 472, 499, 1427, 1574, 1790, 1791, 2349
NH₂−			NH₂SO₂−		152-2.5°	±(P, S), 0(Ae, Sa)	605
	CH₃CONH−		Cl−				327
		(CH₃)₂N−					240
		(C₂H₅)₂N(CH₂)₂NH−			185-6°	+, −(S)	521
		CH₂CHOHCH₂NH−			166-7°	++, −(S)	171
Cl−	Cl−	N(C₂H₅)₂					328
Cl−		NH₂−					328
CH₃−	Cl−	NaO₃SCH₂NH−			153-4°D		240
		NH₂−			224-5°		240
		NH₂CH₂CHOHCH₂−			141-2°D		240
		HCl C₂H₅N−			212°	+(S)	116, 557
NH₂−		HCl·NH₂−			247-51°ᵇ	See Table 290	213, 240, 328
HCl·NH₃−		(C₂H₅)₂N−			198°		213
HCl·(C₂H₅)₂N−		NaO₃SCH₂NH−			235°		213
NaO₃SCH₂NH−		NH₂−					215
HOOCCH₂NH−		[bicyclic imide structure]					215
NH₂−		NH₂−		CH₃CONH−	337-8°		2372
HO−		NH₂−			172-5°D		407
HCl·NH₂−		NH₂−		HO−	228°		214
NH₂−		HO−		HO−	113°		213
NaO₃SNH−		HO−			>300°		213
		HO−			106°, 228°	+	214, 215, 328
		NH₂−				±	215
							512
NH₂−	(C₂H₅)₂N(CH₂)₃NH−			HOOC−	>300°ᶜ	±, ++(S), ±(G, L, Pf, Pm, Pv)	286, 328, 973, 1011, 1549, 1555

ᵇ "Prontosil."
ᶜ "Rubiazol."

TABLE 73—(*Concluded*)

R_2	R_3	R_4	R_5	R_6	Melting Range	Activities	References
NH_2-	$HOOC-$	NH_2-	$NaOOC-$		161-3°D, 225-6°	+	240, 328
NH_2-		NH_2-	$HOOC-$				1962
CH_2CONH-		NH_2-	do				215
$HO-$			NH_2CH- / $HOOC$			++(G), +(S)	215
							405
NH_2-	$Cl-$	NH_2-	HO_3S-	NaO_3S-			240
NH_2-		NH_2-	do				215
CH_2CONH-		$HO-$	do				215
NH_2-		$HO-$	H_2O_2As-				1962
$NHCSNH-CH_2CH=CH_2$		NH_2-					158

TABLE 74

2. Azo Derivatives of Sulfanilamide and Naphthalene

Structure: naphthalene ring bearing $R_1, R_2, R_3, R_4, R_5, R_6, R_7, R_8$ and position x, linked by $-N=N-$ to a benzene ring carrying SO_2NH_2.

R_1	R_2	R_3	R_4	R_5	R_6	R_7	R_8	Melting Range	Activities	References
HO—	HO—	CH_3—	HO—							168, 171, 605
x	CH_3—	C_2H_5—	HO—							605
x		$CH_3(CH_2)_2$—	x	CH_3—				249°	0(Ec)	2457
HO—		$CH_3(CH_2)_3$—	HO—					249°D	0(Ec)	866
x		$(CH_3)_2CHCH_2$—	HO—					251°	0(Ec)	2457
x		$CH_3(CH_2)_4$—	HO—					280°	0(Ec)	866
x		$C_6H_5CH_2CH_2$—	HO—					260°	0(Ec)	866
x		CH_3—	HO—					261°		866
x	HO—		NaO₃S—	NaO₃S—	HO₃S—	NaO₃S—	NaO₃S—		0(T)	605, 1469, 2101
HO—	x						HO₃S—		0(T)	605, 1469, 2101
HO—	x						NaO₃S—		0(T)	605, 1469, 2101
x	HO—				NO_2—		do			2101
x	HO—				NaO₃S—		do			2101
x	HO—	NaO₃S—	NaO₃S—		NaO₃S—					215
HO—	x	do			HO₃S—					2101
HO—	x				do					2101
HO—	x	HO₃S—								605, 2101
x	x	do								605
HO—			x	NH_2—			HO—	220°D	+(S)	328
x	HO—		HCl·NH_2—					>250°		2457
NH₂—	NH₂—		x					>300°		2457
x	x	CH_3—						226°D	+(T)	213
NH₂—	CH_3—		HO—					239°		2457
NH₂—	CH_3—			NH_2—				232°D		2457
x	x									214

TABLE 74—(Continued)

R_1	R_2	R_3	R_4	R_5	R_6	R_7	R_8	Melting Range	Activities	References
x	HO—									215
x	NH₂—									605
NH₂—	x		NaO₃S—	NaO₃S—	NH₂—		HO₃S—		0(T)	605, 1469
NH₂—	x	HOOC—	HO₃S—		HO₃S—		HO—			605
NH₂—	x		HO₃S—		do	x	do		+(S)	328
	NH₂—				do	x	HO₃S—			215
C₂H₅CONH—	CH₃CONH—				NH₂—	x	HO—			215
	HO—	HO₃S—	HO₃S—		HO₃S—	x	do			215
NH₂—	CH₃CONH—	NH₃O₃S—			NH₃O₃S—	x	do	a	See Table 291	215, 240
CH₃CONH—	do	—CONH₂			—CONH₂	x	do		++(S)	38
		HO₃S—			HO₃S—	x	do			
NH₂—	NH₂—	do			do	HO₃S—			++(S), 0(Pf, Pv)	328
CH₃CONH—	CH₃NH—			HO—		do			++(S)	328
x	(C₂H₄)₂N—			HO—		do				215
x	CH₃CONH—			HO—		do				215
x	NH₂CONH—			HO—		do				215
x	NHC(=NH)NH—			HO—		do				215
x	C(=NH)NH₂									215
x	NH₂OCCH₂NH—			HO—		do				215
x	CONH—			HO—		do				215
	⬡NH₂									

ᵃ Azosulfamide, "Neoprontosil."

TABLE 75

3. Azo Derivatives of Sulfanilamide and Miscellaneous
   Isocyclic Compounds

$$RN=N\langle\ \rangle SO_2NH_2$$

R–	Melting Range	Activities	References
HN$\langle$H₂ H₂ / H₂ H₂$\rangle$N$-\langle\ \rangle-$			265
HCl·C₂H₅N$\langle$H₂ H₂ / H₂ H₂$\rangle$N$-\langle\ \rangle-$			265
HCl·HOCH₂CH₂N$\langle$H₂ H₂ / H₂ H₂$\rangle$N$-\langle\ \rangle-$	200°D		265
CH₃CON$\langle$H₂ H₂ / H₂ H₂$\rangle$N$-\langle\ \rangle-$			265
HOOCCH₂N$\langle$H₂ H₂ / H₂ H₂$\rangle$N$-\langle\ \rangle-$			265
NH₂OCCH₂N$\langle$H₂ H₂ / H₂ H₂$\rangle$N$-\langle\ \rangle-$			265
(structure: $-\langle\ \rangle-C\langle\ \rangle-$ with NH·HCl on C, and N(CH₃)₂ on both rings)			1962
HO₃S$\langle\ \rangle$NHCNH$\langle\ \rangle$SO₃H (with O above C, HO and OH below)			215
HO₃S$\langle\ \rangle$NHCNH$\langle\ \rangle$SO₃H (with NH above C, HO and OH below)			215

TABLE 75—(*Continued*)

R—	Melting Range	Activities	References
			215
			215
			215
			215
			215
			215
			215

TABLE 75—(*Concluded*)

R—	Melting Range	Activities	References
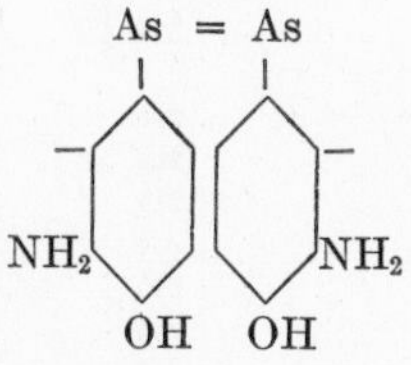			1962
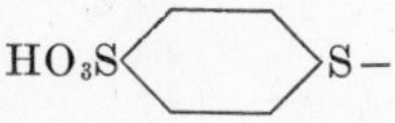		+(P, Sa), ±(S), 0(Tt)	1427, 1574

TABLE 76

c. Heterocyclicazo Derivatives
1. Azo Derivatives of Sulfanilamide and Pyridine

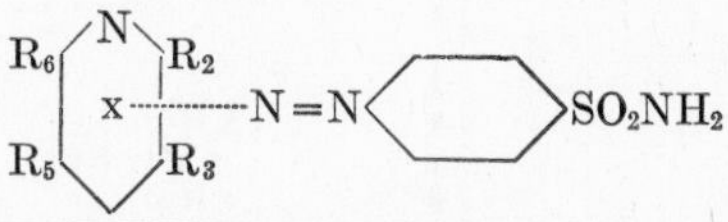

R_2	R_3	R_4	R_5	R_6	Melting Range	Activities	References
HO—			x	CH_3—			214
HO—		HO—	x	CH_3—	>300°		214
NH_2—			x			0(I)	214, 1901, 1962
NH_2—			x	—NH_2·HCl	266°	+, 0(S), 0(P)	93, 149, 150, 214, 1715
HO—			x	do	268°		214
NH_2—	HO_3S—		x	NH_2—			215

TABLE 77

2. Azo Derivatives of Sulfanilamide and Quinoline

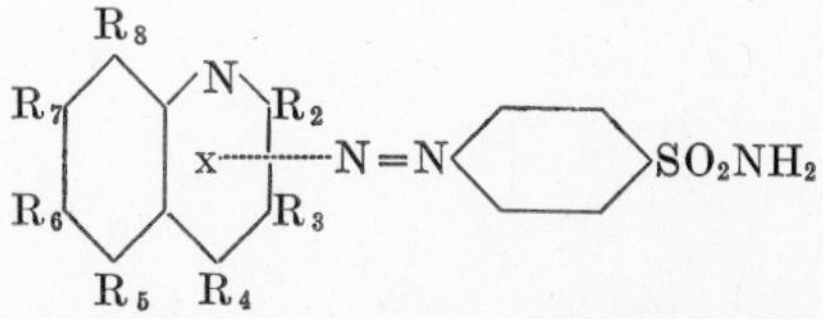

R_2	R_4	R_5	R_6	R_7	R_8	Melting Range	Activities	References
		x	HO—			268°, >290°D	++(S)	214, 328, 369
		HO—			x	171°		214, 380
				x	HO—	234°, 252-4°D	0(Ae, P, S, Sa)	214, 327, 369
		Cl		x	do	154°		214
				HO—		228°		214
		CH_3—		x	HO—	232°		214
		HO—			CH_3—	253°		214
		x	HO—		HO—	232°D		214
		x		HOOC—	do			215

TABLE 77—(*Continued*)

R₂	R₄	R₅	R₆	R₇	R₈	Melting Range	Activities	References
		HO₃S−		x	do		0(I, P, R)	215, 1427, 1574
		x	NH₂−			240°, 281°	++, 0(S)	328, 426
		x	HCl·NH₂−			271°		214
		x	C₂H₅NH−			124°		214
		x	(CH₃)₂CH(CH₂)₅NH−			183°		214
		x	CH₃(CH₂)₁₁NH−			126°		214
		x	NaO₂SCH₂NH−					215
		x	NaO₃SCH₂NH−					215
		x	HOOCCH₂NH−					215
		x			NH₂−	245°D	0(S)	426, 507
		x			−NH₂·HCl	212°		214
		−NH₂·HCl				192°		214
				−NH·HCl $\mid$ C₂H₅		180°		214
				−NH·HCl $\mid$ C₄H₉		178°		214
		x	CH₃−		−NH₂·HCl	>300°		214
		x	−NH₂·HCl		CH₃−	>300°		214
		x	CH₃O−		−NH₂	300°D	0(I, Po, S)	504, 507, 892
		x	HO−		−NH₂·HCl	370°D		214
		x	CH₃O−		do	>300°		214
		x	HO−	NH₂CH₂−		245-7°		369
		x		do	HO−	248-50°		369
HOOC−	HO−		NH₂−					215
		NH₂O₂S−		x	NH₂−	234°D		507
		do	CH₃O−	x	do	285°D		507

TABLE 78

3. Azo Derivatives of Sulfanilamide and Miscellaneous Heterocyclic Compounds

$$RN=N\langle\;\rangle SO_2NH_2$$

R	Melting Range	Activities	References
		++(S), ±(Sa), 0(P)	432, 1057
		++(S), +(Sa), 0(P)	432, 1057
		+(P, Sa), ±(S)	432, 1057

TABLE 78—(*Continued*)

R	Melting Range	Activities	References
CH₃ OSO₂CH₃ HO (structure)		$\pm$(Sa), 0(S, P, Ae)	327
(structure) HO	232°D		214
Dihydrocupreidine		$\pm$(S)	61
Dihydrocupreine	155–190°	$\pm$(S)	61, 188
Apoquinine		$\pm$(S)	61
Isoapoquinine		$\pm$(S)	61
(structure) —CH₂— OH HO	262–4°		369
(structure) O= N N CH₃ H	263°		1633
SO₃H (structure) O= N N CH₃ H	>350°		1633

TABLE 78—(Continued)

R	Melting Range	Activities	References
	204°D		378
		++(S)	159, 160
		++(S)	158, 159
	121°	++(S)	349
	93°	++(S)	349
			520

TABLE 78—(*Continued*)

R	Melting Range	Activities	References
			215
	218°		214
			2018
			1962, 2018
	240–50°D,[a] >250°D	+(Aa, Ec, Et, Sd, Se, Sp, Tc, Vc), ±(S), 0(I)	1528, 1677, 1901, 1962, 1963, 2018
5-(amino)ethylhydrocupreine		+(S)	362
		++,±(S)	405
			215

[a] Sulfazoacridine.

TABLE 78—(*Concluded*)

R	Melting Range	Activities	References
Casein		+(S)	504
Eggalbumin			545
Human serum			545
Antipneumococcus horse serum		±(S)	405

TABLE 79

G. N^4-Inorganic Derivatives of Sulfanilamide
3. Diazoamino Compounds Derived from Sulfanilamide

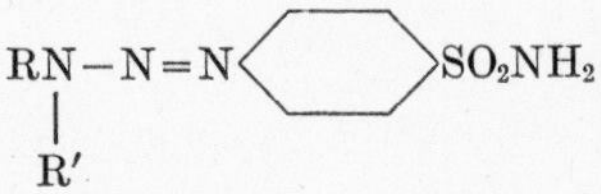

$$RN-N=N\langle\bigcirc\rangle SO_2NH_2$$
$$\underset{R'}{|}$$

R	R'	Melting Range	Activities	References
C_6H_5-			0(S, Tt)	1427, 1574
 [triazole, H]		175°		506
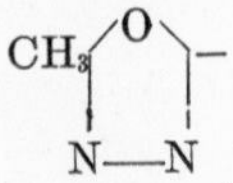 [CH₃ oxadiazole]		216°		506
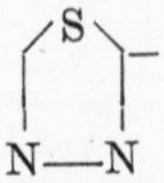 [thiadiazole]		193°D		506
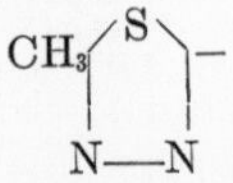 [CH₃ thiadiazole]		126°D		506
$HOCH_2(CHOH)_4CH_2-$	CH_3-		±(S), 0(Tt)	1427, 1574
$HOOCCH_2-$	CH_3-		0(I, R, S, Tt)	1427, 1574
do	$HOCH_2CH_2-$			2460
$4-(NaOOC)C_6H_4-$				2460
$NaO_3SCH_2CH_2-$	CH_3-			2460
$4-(NH_2SO_2)C_6H_4-$		172°	±(S)	173
$2-HOOC-4-(HO_3S)C_6H_3-$				2460
$2-HOOC-5-(HO_3S)C_6H_3-$				2460
$4-(Na_2O_3As)C_6H_4-$		>240°D	+(Tb)	1963, 2019

TABLE 80

G. N^4-Inorganic Derivatives of Sulfanilamide
4. Salts of 4-Sulfamylphenylaminophosphamic Acid

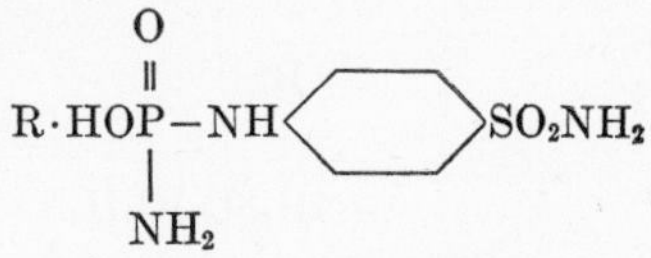

$$R \cdot HOP-NH\langle\hphantom{xx}\rangle SO_2NH_2$$

(with O double-bonded to P above, and NH$_2$ below P)

R	Melting Range	Activities	References
Hexamethylene tetramine			202
Tyramine			202
Hordenine			202
N-Diethylaminoisopentyl-6-methoxy-8-aminoquinoline, "Plasmochin"			202
2-Methoxy-6-chloro-9(α-diethylamino-δ-pentylamino)-acridine, "Atebrin"			202
2-Ethoxy-6,9-diaminoacridine			202
Hydroquinine			202
Quinine			202
Emetine			202

TABLE 81

G. N^4-Inorganic Derivatives of Sulfanilamide
5. Miscellaneous Inorganic Derivatives

$$\begin{matrix} R^4 \\ {\Large\diagdown} \\ N\langle\hphantom{xx}\rangle SO_2NH_2 \\ {\Large\diagup} \\ R^{4\prime} \end{matrix}$$

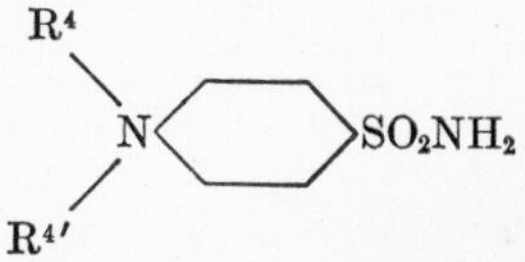

R^4	$R^{4\prime}$	Melting Range	Activities	References
HO−		141.5°, 143–4°	++, +(S)	50, 58, 346, 450, 451, 477, 713, 813, 815, 2169
CH$_3$C(=O)O−		138°		713
HO$_3$S−				230, 2462
NaO$_3$S−			±(S)	224, 448
NH$_2$−		155°	−, 0(S), 0(I, P)	346, 520, 935, 1057, 1384, 1574, 1753, 2373
C$_6$H$_5$NH−				218
CH$_3$CONH−		224°		935
C$_2$H$_5$OOCCH$_2$C(=NH)NH−		168–9°, 200°D		2659
C$_2$H$_5$OOCCH$_2$(CH$_3$)C=N−		142°		935
4-(NH$_2$SO$_2$)C$_6$H$_4$NH−		224–4.5°	0(S)	346, 472
	−N$_2$−	119°D	++(S), +(Sa), 0(En, P)	12, 1057, 1485
ON−	HO−	120°		713

TABLE 81—(*Continued*)

R^4	R$^{4'}$	Melting Range	Activities	References
4-(NH$_2$SO$_2$)C$_6$H$_4$N= ‖ O		301–2°D	±(S)	50, 346, 472, 843
H$_2$O$_2$P—			±(S)	505
(HO)$_2$P(=O)—				202
(C$_6$H$_5$CH$_2$O)(HO)P(=O)—		171–2°		1321
Cl$_2$P(=O)—				192
(NH$_2$)(HO)P(=O)—		167–9°		191, 198, 202
(NH$_2$)(NaO)P(=O)—				191, 202
(CH$_3$NH)(HO)P(=O)—				191
C$_6$H$_5$NH(HO)P(=O)—				191
4-(NH$_2$SO$_2$)C$_6$H$_4$NH(HO)P(=O)—				194

Chapter IV

STRUCTURE AND ACTIVITIES OF COMPLEX SULFANILAMIDE DERIVATIVES

The compounds tabulated and discussed in this chapter are derivatives of sulfanilamide in which combinations of the nucleus, N^1- and N^4-positions are substituted.

While the number of possible compounds of this type are practically unlimited, and some 1545 are listed in the tables, there have been comparatively few such compounds that have reached commercial importance. The reason for this is that nuclear substitution appears to have an adverse effect on chemotherapeutic activity, as does substitution on the N^4-nitrogen by groups which are not capable of being removed by known catabolic reactions of living organisms. This leaves as the most promising line of attack the N^1,N^4-disubstituted derivatives of sulfanilamide in which the N^4-substituent is capable of being removed in the animal body. Since the N^4-substituent probably does not alter the fundamental activities of the parent N^1-substituted sulfanilamide, to which the disubstituted compound is thought to revert before exerting its chemotherapeutic effect, the effect of the N^4-substituent is beneficial only as it modifies the general pharmacological properties of the drug so as to provide the effective agent at the site of the infection in ample concentration when needed. Certain of the N^4-acyl-N^1-heterocyclicsulfanilamides appear to accomplish this effect and are important drugs for special uses as will appear later in this chapter.

(I) NUCLEAR-N^1-SUBSTITUTED SULFANILAMIDES (Tables 82–86, p. 156–159)

Practically nothing has been published on the activities of these compounds. Some of the highly iodinated derivatives were prepared for test as x-ray contrast agents for use in diagnosis but with what success is not known.

(II) NUCLEAR-N^4-SUBSTITUTED SULFANILAMIDES (Tables 87–91, p. 159–162)

What little has been published on the pharmacology of these compounds indicates that they are inactive or nearly so.

(III) N^1,N^4-SUBSTITUTED SULFANILAMIDES

(A) N^4-Acyclic-N^1-substituted Sulfanilamides (Table 92, p. 162)

Structure. The structure of the 2-(N^4-dimethyl-N^1-methylsulfanilamido)pyridine listed[341] is questionable. Probably it should be 1-methyl-2-(N^4-dimethylsulfanilamido)-1,2-dihydropyridine since it was obtained by methylation with dimethyl sulfate.

Pharmacology. The activities of these derivatives in no case appear to exceed that of the corresponding N^1-substituted sulfanilamide. Further, the only compounds of this series which are active contain N^4-substituents known to be removed by catabolic reactions, such as CH_3—, NaO_2SCH_2—, NaO_3SCH_2—, etc.

(B) N^4-Isocyclic-N^1-substituted Sulfanilamides (Table 93, p. 165)

Pharmacology. The remarks under (A) above also apply here. Groups known to be removable are benzyl and substituted benzyl groups.

149

(C) N^4-Heterocyclic-N^1-substituted Sulfanilamides (Tables 94, 95, p. 166, 167)

Pharmacology. Very little has been published on the activities of these compounds but few, if any, appear to be active. The possible exception is the derivative having a N^4-(9-acridyl) radical but the authors[160] were of the opinion that this was removed in the body.

(D) N^4-Anils of N^1-substituted Sulfanilamides (Table 96, p. 168)

Pharmacology. Many of these compounds show a considerable amount of activity but this appears to be because of breakdown to the corresponding N^1-substituted sulfanilamide. Such anils are known to be easily hydrolyzed.

(E) N^4-Sugar Derivatives of N^1-substituted Sulfanilamides (Tables 97, 98, p. 170, 171)

Structure. The same considerations on structure of sugar derivatives of sulfanilamide, Chapter III, (IV) (E), apply here. Most of the derivatives are probably glycosides.

Pharmacology. The glucose derivative of sulfapyridine (10% sulfapyridine boiled in 30% glucose) received study as a form of parenteral therapy in treatment of pneumonia but had the disadvantage for this use that free sulfapyridine was not obtained in as satisfactory concentration as by giving an equivalent amount of sodium sulfapyridine. When taken *per os*, absorption in man was delayed as compared with the equivalent amount of sulfapyridine[131].

It seems very likely that all such N^4-derivatives are broken down to the free drug in the body.

(F) N^4-Acyl-N^1-substituted Sulfanilamides

(1) N^4-Acetyl-N^1-substituted Sulfanilamides (Tables 99–131, p. 191–209)

Classification. Because of the occurrence of a very large number of N^4-acetyl-N^1-substituted sulfanilamides, through the fact that most N^1-substituted sulfanilamides are synthesized through the corresponding N^4-acetyl derivatives as intermediates, these compounds have been separately classified.

Synthesis. These compounds result from the reaction of acetylsulfanilyl chloride with a wide variety of amines. Because the amino group is protected from oxidation, these compounds can frequently be purified with greater ease than the corresponding N^1-substituted sulfanilamides.

Reaction of ASC with 2-Aminothiazole. According to Deliwala, Ganapathi and Shirsat[962] when 2-aminothiazole reacts with 2 moles of ASC in dry pyridine at water bath temperatures, or in aqueous sodium bicarbonate medium, the product is 2-[bis-(N^4-acetylsulfanilyl)amino]thiazole, (Table 120).

melting at 127–129°C. Upon boiling for one to two hours in alcohol this was transformed to 2-N^4-acetylsulfanilimino-3-(N^4-acetylsulfanilyl)-4-thiazoline (Table 125)

decomposing at 190–225°.

Structure. The structure of 1-methyl-2-(N^1-methyl-N^4-acetylsulfanilamido)imidazole (Table 116) is open to question because it was made by alkylating 2-(N^4-acetylsulfanilamido)imidazole[339]. By analogy with other known reactions this may have resulted in 1,3-dimethyl-2-(N^4-acetylsulfanilimido)-2-imidazoline, *i.e.* in alkylation of the ring nitrogen rather than the N^1-nitrogen. The high melting point strengthens this belief.

5-(N^4-Acetylsulfanilamido)tetrazole (Table 117) has led to some controversy as to its constitution. Jensen and Hansen[1376, 1580] obtained a product melting at 170°, which they thought was 5-(N^4-acetylsulfanilamido)tetrazole, by reaction of acetylsulfanilyl chloride and 5-aminotetrazole in pyridine. This material decomposed to sulfanilic acid, acetic acid, urea and ammonia on hydrolysis. By reaction in aqueous solution they obtained a product melting at 202°, which gave sulfanilic acid and 5-aminotetrazole on hydrolysis. This they thought was a ring substituted acetylsulfanilyl derivative. Veldstra and Wiardi[2378] disagreed with these findings. Repeated purification by dissolving in dilute NaOH and reprecipitating with HCl resulted in separating the products of reaction in pyridine into products melting at 170° (*A*) and 207° (*B*). Similar purification of the product prepared in aqueous solution gave a compound melting at 207° (*C*) which was different than (*B*). (*A*) behaved as a weak monobasic acid while (*B*) and (*C*) were dibasic, with (*B*) somewhat weaker than (*C*). (*A*) could not be deacetylated without opening the ring, while (*B*) and (*C*) each gave the same compound, melting at 202–203°. On the basis of analogies in the absorption spectrum when compared with sulfanilamidotriazoles, they concluded that (*A*) was 5-(N^4-acetylsulfanilamido)-4,5-dihydrotetrazole, while (*B*) and (*C*) were isomeric 5-(N^4-acetylsulfanilamido)tetrazoles. The postulated structures are:

Pharmacology. N^4-Acetyl-N^1-substituted sulfanilamides are important pharmacologically because they represent the main conjugation products of the corresponding N^1-substituted sulfanilamides formed in the body. Such conjugated drugs are thought to be inactive, but it has been shown that both acetylation and deacetylation processes occur in the blood, liver and kidney[264, 2191]. Administration of one of the N^4-acetyl-N^1-substituted sulfanilamides therefore can lead to low blood concentrations of the free N^1-substituted sulfanilamide and show slight to moderate chemotherapeutic activity. None of the N^4-acetyl-N^1-substituted sulfanilamides is an important drug because its activity is invariably of a lower order than the deacetylated compound.

In vitro studies have shown little or no activity for N^4-acetylsulfanilamides and where very slight activity has been found this has been ascribed to the free drug resulting from slight hydrolysis of the acetyl group.[1135, 1384, 2441] The free drug has actually been demonstrated in some of these cases[2441].

For pharmacology of acetyl derivatives of important sulfonamide drugs consult Chapter X.

(2) N^4-Acyl (Other than Acetyl)N^1-substituted Sulfanilamides

Synthesis. There are two lines of synthesis which may be followed in arriving at these compounds. In the first, the N^1-substituted sulfanilamide may be acylated in the N^4-position using the acid anhydride or acid chloride with pyridine or other solvent. The other procedure starts with aniline which is acylated, then chlorosulfonated to give the N^4-acylsulfanilyl chloride which is reacted with the desired amine, to give the N^4-acyl-N^1-substituted sulfanilamide. If the acyl group is derived from expensive intermediates the first procedure will be most economical since it involves lower losses of this part of the molecule.

(a) *N^4-Acyclicacyl-N^1-substituted Sulfanilamides*

[1] $R^4 = C_nH_{2n+1}CO-$ to $C_nH_{2n-3}CO-$ (Table 132, p. 209)

Pharmacology. As indicated by the studies of Kohl and Flynn[264] N^4-acyl groups derived from the straight chain aliphatic acids vary considerably in the ease with which they are removed by body enzymes. The rate increases with increasing length of carbon chain reaching a maximum at 5- and 6-carbon acyl groups then declining. The N^4-caproyl-N^1-substituted sulfanilamides have been most extensively studied because of this. Since the activity of such derivatives does not exceed that of the corresponding N^1-substituted sulfanilamides (except that more prolonged blood levels of active drug may possibly be maintained in certain cases) these compounds have not been of sufficient interest to be marketed.

"Sulfabenamide" or N^4-caproyl-N^1-hydroxysulfanilamide has been studied both pharmacologically and clinically. It has been stated to exert its therapeutic effect promptly without the "lag" characteristic of sulfanilamide[2191]. This appeared to be a transient effect (also produced by *p*-toluenesulfonhydroxamide) which was then succeeded by a second period of bacteriostasis probably resulting from hydrolysis of the caproyl group and very similar to the effect of sulfanilamide itself.

Shank, *et al.*[474] used "Sulfabenamide" for treating 34 cases of erysipelas and found that it produced results equal to sulfanilamide without the accompanying toxic symptoms.

Gubner[2548] treated 5 cases of pulmonary tuberculosis for an average of ten months with a daily dose of 4 Gm. of "Sulfabenamide" and obtained favorable but inconclusive results. *In vitro* it had an inhibiting action on growth of the tubercle bacillus at a level of 5 mg. per 100 cc. and above.

[2] *Monosubstituted Derivatives of Dicarboxylic Acids* (Table 133, p. 217)

Pharmacology. Because these compounds have a free carboxyl group they are capable of forming highly soluble, neutral sodium salts. They first attracted chemists as a means of making a sulfonamide drug soluble for parenteral administration. This use did not develop because adequate blood levels of the active N^1-substituted sulfanilamide were not obtained; the N^4-carboxyacyl-N^1-substituted sulfanilamides were actively excreted by the kidneys[1950].

A use for such compounds was found in treatment of intestinal infections[372, 1949, 1950, 1951]. The compounds found most effective for such use were 2-(N^4-succinylsulfanilamido)thiazole, or succinylsulfathiazole, ("Sulfasuxidine") and 2-(N^4-phthalylsulfanilamido)thiazole, or phthalylsulfathiazole, ("Sulfathalidine") (Table 137). It has been supposed that these compounds were effective because they were not readily absorbed from the intestinal tract and were excreted rapidly by the kidney so that high doses of the drug could be given *per os* without production of toxic blood levels. Because of their high solubility under alkaline conditions they would mix well with the intestinal contents and undergo slow hydrolysis, giving a relatively high local concentration of sulfathiazole as the effective agent in dealing with the susceptible bacteria in the intestine. Because much of the liberated sulfathiazole would be low down in the intestine where absorption is poor the drug would not appear in the blood in dangerous amounts.

The above may be the main reason for effectiveness, without being the only mechanism of action. If sulfathiazole were the only agent involved one would not predict any characteristic differences in the bacterial population, consistency and odor of the feces. Such differences are observed in practice, however[1951].

Poth and Ross[1951] studied the hydrolysis rates of N^4-succinyl-(and N^4-phthalyl-) sulfaguanidines, sulfapyridines, sulfathiazoles, sulfamerazines, and sulfadiazines in normal hydrochloric acid and normal sodium hydroxide and compared with the relative bacteriostatic activity of the drugs as measured *in vivo* by effect on the coliform organisms in the bowel of the dog. The succinyl derivatives were readily hydrolyzed by either hydrochloric acid or sodium hydroxide. The phthalyl derivatives were not appreciably hydrolyzed by sodium hydroxide and varied in the hydrolysis produced by hydrochloric acid, with the sulfaguanidine, sulfapyridine, and sulfamerazine derivatives being readily hydrolyzed while the sulfathiazole derivative was slightly more resistant and phthalylsulfadiazine was not appreciably hydrolyzed. Further studies were made of hydrolysis rates in feces at pH 7. The phthalyl derivatives were not appreciably hydrolyzed while the succinyl derivatives showed some hydrolysis.

The authors were unable to see any parallel between the relative activities and rates of hydrolysis of the various compounds. They thought that these and other results indicated that the antibacterial activity was not solely the result of the free drug produced by hydrolysis. They believed that the activity resided partly in the N^4-acylsulfonamide, but also suggested that the acid cleavage products might contribute to the total bacteriostatic action.

No studies on *in vitro* inhibition of bacterial growth were reported in this paper but an earlier report[1950] showed that against *E. coli*, *in vitro*, succinylsulfathiazole had only one tenth the bacteriostatic activity of sulfanilamide and trace amounts of sulfathiazole in the sample were suggested as the probable source of the slight activity found.

The reasons why there are such striking differences between phthalylsulfathiazole and phthalylsulfadiazine in their effects on coliform organisms of the dog is not apparent. The fact that sulfadiazine appears in the blood shows that the phthalylsulfadiazine is being hydrolyzed but does not indicate whether such cleavage occurs in the intestine with absorption of the liberated sulfadiazine or after the phthalylsulfadiazine is absorbed and cleaved by the enzymes of the blood, liver or kidney. If phthalylsulfadiazine were not appreciably hydrolyzed in the gut, this might explain its lack of activity in intestinal infections.

Callomon and Raiziss[832] studied the action of 2-(N^4-succinylsulfanilamido)pyrazine, or "succinylsulfapyrazine", in reducing the count of coliform bacteria in mice and found it equal to sulfaguanidine. Succinylsulfapyrazine showed a blood level of sulfapyrazine from 2 to 5 mg. per 100 cc. in mice, or comparable to the blood levels in humans on oral dosage with sulfapyrazine.

There would seem to be little reason for using the succinyl-derivative if it breaks down to give the free drug rapidly enough so that the same blood levels are reached. Probably the free drug is the active agent in the intestine and for prompt and full therapeutic effect it would appear more rational in the author's opinion to use sulfapyrazine itself.

[3] *Disubstituted Derivatives of Dicarboxylic Acids* (Table 134, p. 219)

Pharmacology. These compounds appear to be uniformly inactive according to the published information.

[4] *Derivatives of Hydroxy Acids* (Table 135, p. 221)

Pharmacology. 2-(N^4-Malylsulfanilamido)thiazole was comparable to succinylsulfathiazole in reducing the coliform bacterial population in mice[832].

The high activity of 2-(N^4-acetoacetylsulfanilamido)pyridine against streptococci and its low activity against pneumocci *in vivo* is difficult to explain. If the activity is the result of cleavage to sulfapyridine, activity should be high against both organisms. This result should be checked.

[5] *Derivatives of Amino Acids* (Table 136, p. 222)

Pharmacology. Some of these compounds are said to be active against streptococci, staphylococci, pneumococci, and *Salmonella schottmülleri* in mice by the drug-diet method but detailed information was not given. They were also active, but no more so than the parent N^1-substituted sulfanilamides, against *Plasmodium lophurae* in ducks[1086]. The solubility of the compounds was less than 0.4 mg./100 cc. at 37° except 2-[N^4-(aminoacetyl)sulfanilamido]thiazole which had a solubility of 0.7 mg./100 cc.

(b) *N^4-Isocyclicacyl-N^1-substituted Sulfanilamides* (Table 137, p. 224)

Pharmacology. The only compound in this group of therapeutic importance is phthalylsulfathiazole which was discussed with compounds of Table 133.

(c) *N^4-Heterocyclicacyl-N^1-substituted Sulfanilamides* (Table 138, p. 226)

Pharmacology. Most of these compounds have little or no activity against blood stream infections. It is surprising to find two of the compounds claimed active against streptococci and inactive against pneumococci when each would be expected to break down to sulfapyridine as the active agent. The results should be rechecked.

2-(N^4-Quinolinyl)sulfathiazole was claimed by Poth and Ross[1951] to be effective in reducing the coliform population in the intestines of dogs when given in total daily dose of 1 Gm./kilo. No effect was produced at an eighth of this dosage, however. Cost was a deciding factor against its further study.

(d) *N^4-Derivatives of Carbonic Acid* (Table 139, p. 227)

Pharmacology. While some N^4-acylsulfanilamides show slight *in vitro* activity, presumably through hydrolysis of the acyl group, 2-(N^4-ureidosulfanilamido)thiazole was completely inactive *in vitro*. The ureido group is known to be especially resistant to hydrolysis with acids or bases. Such compounds also appear to be inactive *in vivo*.

(G) N^4-Inorganic Derivatives of N^1-Substituted Sulfanilamides

(1) N^4-Sulfonyl-N^1-substituted Sulfanilamides (Table 140, p. 229)

Synthesis. These compounds are readily synthesized by reacting an N^1-substituted sulfanilamide with the desired sulfonyl chloride, in aqueous solution, in the presence of a base or under anhydrous conditions using pyridine as solvent.

Pharmacology. These compounds were extensively studied in the early days of sulfonamide chemotherapy. The only compounds of interest are those in which the N^4-sulfonyl substituent is sulfanilyl. In these cases the drugs are behaving as N^1-substituted sulfanilamides.

Two of these drugs were marketed in Europe but it is believed have now been superseded by more potent and less toxic drugs. N^4-Sulfanilyl-N^1-methylsulfanilamide was sold under the name "Diseptal B", while N^4-sulfanilyl-N^1-dimethylsulfanilamide was used extensively for treating gonorrhea under the name "Uleron"[735, 2375]. The latter drug had a bad record in causing peripheral neuritis. Some of the reports of its activities against experimental infections are listed in Table 289, p. 410.

Because many of the reported results on activities of these compounds date from very early work before test methods were well established, they should not be given too much credence if claimed to be highly active. As compared to the more potent drugs now available their activities would be inferior.

(2) (3) (4) Azo Derivatives of N^1-Substituted Sulfanilamides (Tables 141–143, p. 235–243)

The possibilities for synthesizing these derivatives are enormous and in view of the fact that the initial lead on sulfa drugs came from an azo dye derived from sulfanilamide it is surprising that more of these dyes were not made by diazotizing N^1-substituted sulfanilamides and coupling to a variety of coupling components. The fact that the list is not longer can be ascribed to the early realization that such dyes owe their activity to reduction in the body to the active N^1-substituted sulfanilamides. *In vitro* those studied have been inactive.[1384]

(5) Miscellaneous N^4-Inorganic Derivatives of N^1-Substituted Sulfanilamides (Table 144, p. 244)

Pharmacology. There is very little literature on activities of these compounds. The azide derived from sulfapyridine appeared to be broken down to sulfapyridine on absorption since it gave a diazotizable amine in the blood of mice[1057]. Its activity is not surprising, therefore. Similar conversion of the hydroxylamine derivatives might be expected in view of what is known about 4-hydroxylaminobenzenesulfonamide.

(IV) NUCLEAR-N^1,N^4-SUBSTITUTED SULFANILAMIDES (Table 145, p. 246)

Pharmacology. In view of the generally adverse effect of nuclear and N^4-substitution on activities it would not be surprising to find these derivatives inactive against bacteria. This prediction seems verified in the few instances where activities are available.

The compounds described in the patent under reference number 560 are said to possess activity against ascarides. Such a result merely emphasizes that it is impossible to predict activities of compounds in unrelated species of parasites and shows that there is no adequate substitute for experiment in finding fundamentally new uses for drugs.

(V) UNCLASSIFIED DERIVATIVES OF SULFANILAMIDE (Table 146, p. 248)

Compounds of uncertain constitution or with structures such that they do not readily fit into classified tables are listed here. These do not appear to have importance as chemotherapeutic agents.

TABLE 82

I. Nuclear-N^1-substituted Sulfanilamides
  A. Nuclear-substituted N^1-Acyclicsulfanilamides

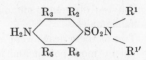

R^1	$R^{1\prime}$	R_2	R_3	R_5	Melting Range	Activities	References
CH_3-		C_2H_5-					207
CH_3-		CH_3-		CH_3O-	139°		226, 560
CH_3-		CH_3-		C_2H_5O-	167°		226, 560
CH_3-	CH_3-	CH_3-		CH_3O-	128°		226, 560
C_2H_5-	C_2H_5-	CH_3-		do	124°		226, 560
do	do	CH_3-		C_2H_5O-	92°		226, 560
$CH_3(CH_2)_3-$		CH_3-		CH_3O-	97°		226, 560
$HOCH_2CH_2-$			CH_3O-				212
do		CH_3-		CH_3O-	136°		226, 560
do		CH_3-		C_2H_5O-	122°		226, 560
$HOOCCH_2-$			$I-$	$I-$	249.5°		1451

TABLE 83

B. Nuclear-substituted N^1-Isocyclicsulfanilamides

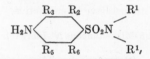

R^1	R_2	R_3	R_5	Melting Range	Activities	References
$(CH_3)_2C_6H_3-$		$Cl-$				37
$4-(HOOC)C_6H_4-$	$I-$		$I-$	261°D		1451
$4-(KO_3S)C_6H_4-$	$I-$		$I-$			1451

TABLE 83—(*Continued*)

R^1	R_2	R_3	R_5	Melting Range	Activities	References
$2\text{-}(HO)C_6H_4-$		NO_2-		205–6°		623
$4\text{-}(CH_3CONH)C_6H_4-$		NO_2-		265–6°		623
C_6H_5-	NH_2-		NH_2SO_2-	236°		322
do	do		$C_6H_5NHSO_2-$			322
do		NH_2SO_2-	NH_2SO_2-	240–1°		322
do		$C_6H_5NHSO_2-$	$C_6H_5NHSO_2-$			140
$4\text{-}(NH_2SO_2)C_6H_4-$		SO_2NH_2 	 SO_2NH_2			551
C_6H_5-	$HO-$	$NHSO_2-$	$NHSO_2-$	184°		2455

TABLE 84

C. Nuclear-substituted N^1-Heterocyclicsulfanilamides

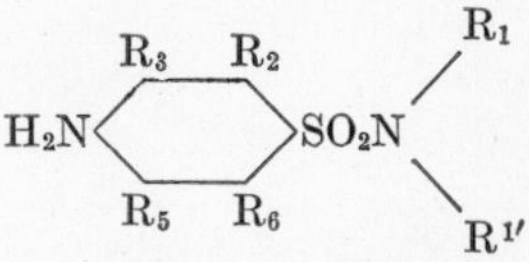

R^1	$R^{1\prime}$	R_2	R_3	R_5	Melting Range	Activities	References
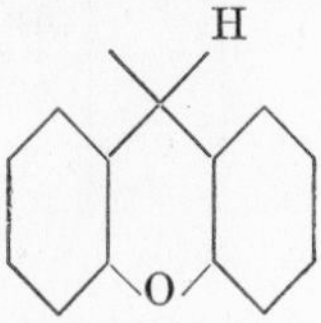			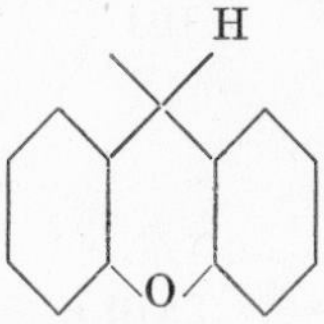		207–8°, 209°		1921
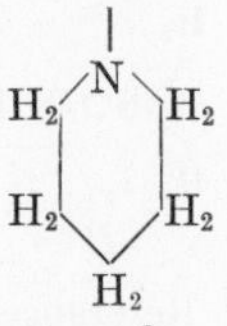			NCS–		140–1°		720
do			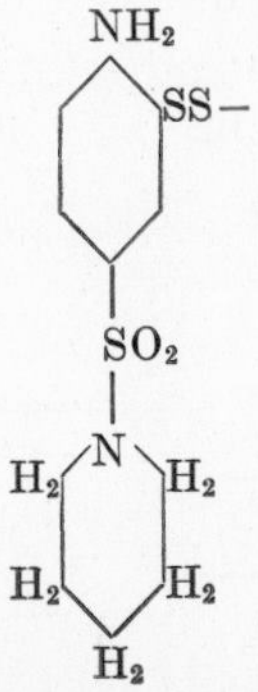		223–6°		720

TABLE 84—(*Continued*)

R¹	R¹′	R₂	R₃	R₅	Melting Range	Activities	References
[N-ring]			NO_2-		232°		262
do		CH_3-		CH_3-	217–8°		453
do			$HO-$		257°		640
do			$NCS-$		180–1°		721
do			NH_2 (—SS— / O₂S—HN[N-ring])		240–3°		721
[N,N-ring]			$HO-$				640
[S,N-ring]			$HO-$				640

TABLE 85

D. Nuclear-substituted N^1-Acylsulfanilamides

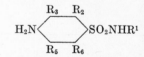

R¹	R₃	R₅	Melting Range	Activities	References
CH_3CO-	$Br-$	$Br-$	193.8–4.6°		2427

TABLE 86

E. Nuclear-substituted N^1-Sulfonylsulfanilamides

$$H_2N\underset{R_5\quad R_6}{\overset{R_3\quad R_2}{\bigcirc}}SO_2N\overset{R^1}{\underset{R^{1\prime}}{<}}$$

R^1	$R^{1\prime}$	R_3	R_5	Melting Range	Activities	References
4-NH_2-3-$IC_6H_3SO_2$—		I—	I—	249.2°D		1451
do	Na—	I—	I—			1451
4-NH_2-3,5-$(I)_2C_6H_2SO_2$—		I—	I—	259–60°		1451
do	NH_4—	I—	I—			1451

TABLE 87

II. Nuclear-N^4-substituted Sulfanilamides
   A. Nuclear-substituted N^4-Acyclic-, Isocyclic- or Hetero-cyclicsulfanilamides

$$\overset{R^4}{\underset{R^{4\prime}}{>}}N\underset{R_5\quad R_6}{\overset{R_3\quad R_2}{\bigcirc}}SO_2NH_2$$

R^4	$R^{4\prime}$	R_2	R_3	R_5	Melting Range	Activities	References
CH_3—	CH_3—	CH_3—		CH_3O—			560
C_2H_5—	C_2H_5—	CH_3—		do			560
NaO_3SCH_2—			Cl—				485, 1182
do			CH_3O—				485, 1182
C_6H_5—			NO_2—				140
do			NH_2SO_2—				140
4-$(CH_3O)C_6H_4$—			HOOC—		239–40°		31
—$(CH_2)_5$—		NO_2—					317

TABLE 88

B. Nuclear-substituted N^4-Acylsulfanilamides
   1. Nuclear-substituted N^4-Acetylsulfanilamides

$$CH_3CONH\underset{R_5\quad R_6}{\overset{R_3\quad R_2}{\bigcirc}}SO_2NH_2$$

R_2	R_3	R_5	Melting Range	Activities	References
Cl—					512
	Cl—		199°		485, 1182
	I—		216°		466
	NO_2—		186°		140, 261, 512
CH_3—			204°	0 (S)	211, 684
CH_3—		Cl—			211
CH_3—		Br— (?)	262°		684
	CH_3—			0 (S)	151, 211, 512
CH_3—		CH_3—	242–3°		211, 453

TABLE 88—(*Continued*)

R_2	R_3	R_5	Melting Range	Activities	References
HO—				0 (S)	508
	CH_3O—		213°		485, 489
	NHCOCH₃		307–8°		1412
	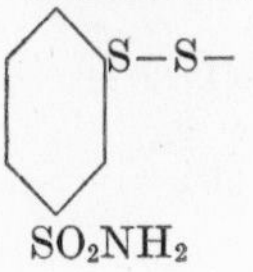 (ring)S—S— ... SO₂NH₂				
CH_3—	CH_3O—		234°		211, 226, 560
CH_3—	C_2H_5O—				226, 560
CH_3—	CH_2O—		>250°		560
		 (ring)NO₂			
HOOC—				0 (S)	255
	HOOC—			0 (S)	255
	NH_2SO_2—				140
	do	NH_2SO_2—			322
NH_2—		do			322
	N=N— ... SO₂NH₂				407
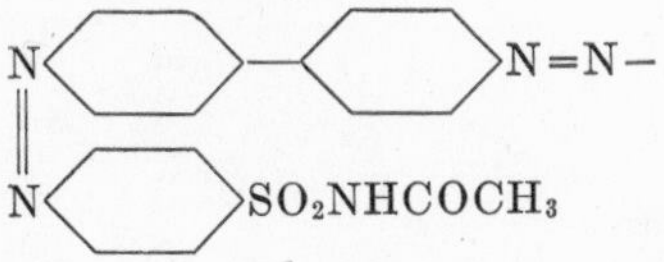	(biphenyl azo structure)	N=N—		0(I, R, Tt)	1447, 1574
	SO₂NHCOCH₃				

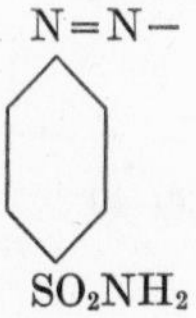

TABLE 89

2. Other Nuclear-substituted N^4-Acylsulfanilamides

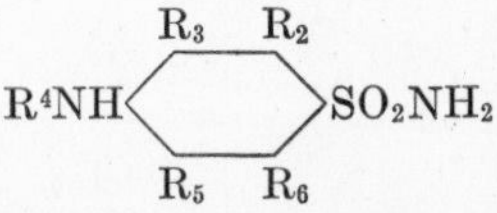

$$R^4NH\langle \overset{R_3 \quad R_2}{\underset{R_5 \quad R_6}{}}\rangle SO_2NH_2$$

R^4	R_2	R_3	R_5	Melting Range	Activities	References
$ClCH_2CO$—	CH_3—		C_2H_5O—	207°		217, 2464
$(CH_3)_2CHCH_2CO$—	CH_3—		Cl—			211
do	CH_3—		CH_3O—	187°		73, 211

TABLE 89—(*Continued*)

R^4	R_2	R_3	R_5	Melting Range	Activities	References
$CH_3(CH_2)_{16}CO-$		NO_2-				1163
$CH(CH_2)_7CO-$ ‖ $CH(CH_2)_7CH_3$	CH_3-			150°		73, 211
do		CH_3-		138–40°		73, 211
do	CH_3-		CH_3-	207°		73, 211
do	CH_3-		CH_3O-	148°		73, 211
do	CH_3O-		do	145°		73, 211
C_6H_5CO-		CH_3-		265°		684
do		$HO-$				508
do		$NHCOC_6H_5$ 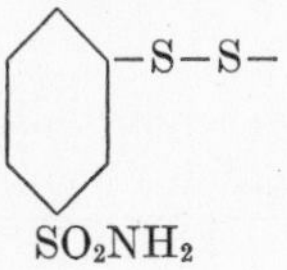		319–20°		1411
NH_2CO-	CH_3-	 —S—S— SO_2NH_2		209–10°	0	96
do		CH_3-		223–5°	0	96
$CH_3CONHCO-$	CH_3-			226–7°	0	96
do		CH_3-		231–3°	0	96
$NHC(=NH)-$ 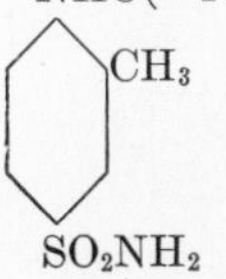 CH_3 SO_2NH_2	CH_3-			220°D		2540
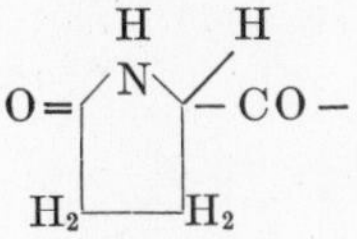 $O=$ N—$CO-$ (H, H ; H_2, H_2)	CH_3-			222°	±(P, S), 0(I, L, Lc, Sa, Y)	968, 1082
$C_4H_9NHCH_2CO-$	CH_3-		C_2H_5O-	154°		217, 2464

TABLE 90

C. Nuclear-substituted N^4-Sulfonylsulfanilamides

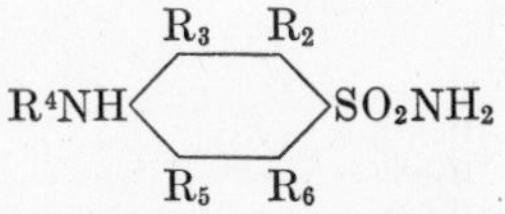

$R^4NH\langle\ \rangle SO_2NH_2$ (R_3 R_2 / R_5 R_6)

R^4	R_2	R_5	Melting Range	Activities	References
NaO_3S-	CH_3-	CH_3O-			224, 2462
$C_6H_5O(CH_2)_3SO_2-$	do	do			217
$4-(NH_2)C_6H_4SO_2-$	do	do	212°		217, 2464
$4-(CH_3CONH)C_6H_4SO_2-$	do	do			217

TABLE 91

D. Nuclear-substituted Azo Derivatives of Sulfanilamide $R^4N=N$⟨benzene ring with R_3, R_2 top and R_5, R_6 bottom⟩SO_2NH_2

R^4	R_2	R_3	R_5	Melting Range	Activities	References
$4\text{-}NH_2SO_2\text{-}2\text{-}IC_6H_3-$		$I-$		$>270°D$		466
$HCl\cdot 2,4\text{-}(NH_2)_2C_6H_3-$	CH_3-			$238°$		213, 215
do		NH_2SO_2-		$>250°$		213
$2\text{-}CH_3\text{-}4\text{-}(CH_3CONH)C_6H_3-$	CH_3-		C_2H_5O-	$208°$		226, 560
HO		CH_3-				215

TABLE 92

III. N^1,N^4-Substituted Sulfanilamides
A. N^4-Acyclic-N^1-substituted Sulfanilamides

⟨R^4 / $R^{4'}$ $N-$ benzene ring $-SO_2N$ R^1 / $R^{1'}$⟩

R^4	$R^{4'}$	R^1	$R^{1'}$	Melting Range	Activities	References
CH_3-		CH_3-	CH_3-	$152°$	$+(S),$ $0(P)$	216, 1057
CH_3-				$154°$		341
CH_3-		$CH_3CHOHCH_2-$		$90\text{-}1°$		5
CH_3-		CH_3CO-			$0(G)$	2654
CH_3-		$4\text{-}(NH_2)C_6H_4-$		$191\text{-}3°$		201
CH_3-	CH_3-	C_6H_5-		$176°$		144
CH_3-	CH_3-	$3,5\text{-}Cl_2C_6H_3-$		$195°$		555
CH_3-	CH_3-			$218\text{-}20°$		341, 486
CH_3-	CH_3-	do	CH_3-	$155°$		341
CH_3-	CH_3-	$4\text{-}(HOOC)C_6H_4-$				218
CH_3CH_2-		$(CH_3)_2COHCH_2-$		$131.5°$	$0(S)$	5
$HOOCCH_2SCH_2-$						1573
do						1573

TABLE 92—(*Continued*)

R⁴	R⁴′	R¹	R¹′	Melting Range	Activities	References
do		CH₃—N, S ring				1573
do		C₆H₅—N, S ring				1573
do		HOCH₂CH₂—				1573
do		HO—				1573
NaOOCCH₂SCH₂—		N-ring (piperidine)				1573
do		S, N thiazoline ring				1573
do		CH₃—N, S ring				1573
do		C₆H₅—N, S ring				1573
do		HOCH₂CH₂—				1573
do		HO—				1573
HOOCCH₂CH₂SCH₂—		N-ring (piperidine)				1573
NaOOCCH₂CH₂SCH₂—		do				1573
2-(HOOC)C₆H₄SCH₂—		CH₃—N, S ring				1573
2-(NaOOC)C₆H₄SCH₂—		do				1573
CH₃CONHCH(COONa)CH₂SCH₂—		N-ring (piperidine)				1570
do		CH₃—N, S ring				1570
do		HOCH₂CH₂—				1570
do		HO—				1570
BrCH₂CH₂CONHCH(COONa)CH₂SCH₂—		S, N thiazoline ring				1570
C₆H₅CONHCH(COONa)CH₂SCH₂—		HOCH₂CH₂—				1570

TABLE 92—(Continued)

R⁴	R⁴'	R¹	R¹'	Melting Range	Activities	References
HO₂SCH₂−		[piperidine ring, N]		206–10°D		1771
do		HO₂SCH₂−		170–2°D		257
NaO₂SCH₂−		[piperidine ring, N]		198–200°D	++(P, S)	255, 1771
do		do	Na−	225–30°D		1771
do		[thiazoline ring, S/N]			++(P)	315, 432
do		NaO₂SCH₂−			−	73, 254, 257
do		CH₃CO−		glass		788
do		CH₃(CH₂)₁₀CO−			+(S), 0(P)	101, 1057
HO₃SCH₂−		[piperidine ring, N]		216–20°D		1772
NaO₃SCH₂−		CH₃−				1322
do		C₂H₅−				1322
do		do	C₂H₅−			1322
do		CH₃CH₂(CH₃)₂C−				1322
do		CH₂=CHCH₂−				1322
do		HC=CH(CH₂)₈− ∣ (CH₂)₇CH₃		>260°D		673
do		C₆H₅CH₂−		234°D		1322
do		[piperidine ring, N]			++(P, S)	255, 1772, 2399
do		do	Na−			1772
do		[thiadiazole ring, S/N–N]				2491
do		−(CH₂)₅−				1322
do		CH₃CO−		212–13°D		788
do		4-(NH₂SO₂)C₆H₄−			±(S)	524
NaO₃S(CH₃)CH−		[thiazoline ring, S/N]		a	++(S)	604, 2537
do		CH₃CO−		165–197°D		788
HOOCCH₂−		CH₃−	CH₃−	187°		216
NaO₃SCH₂CHOHCH₂−	CH₃−	CH₃−	CH₃−			216

a STAB,

TABLE 92—(*Concluded*)

R^4	$R^{4'}$	R^1	$R^{1'}$	Melting Range	Activities	References
$HCl \cdot (C_2H_5)_2N(CH_2)_2-$		CH_3-	CH_3-	159–60°	0(Pr)	536
do		C_2H_5-	C_2H_5-	138–9°	0(Pr)	536
do		$-(CH_2)_5-$		201–3°	0(Pr)	536
$(C_2H_5)_2N(CH_2)_3-$		$N(CH_2)_3CH-$ | | $(C_2H_5)_2 \ CH_3$			0(Pr)	122, 123
$HCl \cdot (C_2H_5)_2N(CH_2)_3-$		C_2H_5-	C_2H_5-	180–1°	0(Pr)	536

TABLE 93

B. *N^4-Isocyclic-N^1-substituted Sulfanilamides* $R^4NH\!\!\bigcirc\!\!SO_2N{<}^{R^1}_{R^{1'}}$

R^4	R^1	$R^{1'}$	Melting Range	Activities	References
$2,4\text{-}(NO_2)_2C_6H_3-$	[N-heterocyclic ring]		230–3°		341, 486
do	CH_3O- [fused N-heterocyclic ring]		180°		344
$C_6H_5CH_2-$	$HOCH_2CH_2-$		115–6°	±(S)	5
do	C_6H_5-		177.5–8.1°		270
do	[N-heterocyclic ring]		200°	·	341, 486
do	CH_3O- [fused N-heterocyclic ring]		181–2°		344
do	CH_3CO-		143–4°		2100
$4\text{-}(NO_2)C_6H_4CH_2-$	$4\text{-}(NO_2)C_6H_4CH_2$ [N-heterocyclic ring]		208–10°		1984
$4\text{-}(CH_3O)C_6H_4CH_2-$	C_6H_5-		162.0–2.4°	±(S)	270
do	[N-heterocyclic ring]		216.5–7.5°		270
do	$4\text{-}[4'\text{-}(CH_3O)C_6H_4NH]C_6H_4-$		184–5°		270
$C_6H_5CH(SO_3Na)-$	CH_3CO-		185–90°		788
$C_6H_5CH(SO_3Na)CH_2(SO_3Na)CH-$	do				771
[fused bicyclic ketone structure] $=O$	[N–N heterocyclic ring]			0(T)	1593

TABLE 94

C. N^4-Heterocyclic-N^1-substituted Sulfanilamides
  1. N^4-Nitrogen not a Member of the Heterocyclic System

$$R^4NH\text{—}\langle\ \rangle\text{—}SO_2N\begin{smallmatrix}R^1\\R^{1\prime}\end{smallmatrix}$$

R^4	R^1	$R^{1\prime}$	Melting Range	Activities	References
(structure)	(structure)		204°		409
(structure)	4-(NO$_2$)C$_6$H$_4$—		>285°	0(P)	161
do	(structure)		268–9°D	+(S), 0(P)	161, 1147
do	4-(NH$_2$SO$_2$)C$_6$H$_4$—		>280°	0(P)	161
do	4-(NH$_2$)C$_6$H$_4$—		278–82°	0(P)	161
(structure)	C$_6$H$_5$—	C$_2$H$_5$—	144°		30
(structure)	C$_2$H$_5$—	do	263–4°		110
do	CH$_3$CO—		143–5°		110
(structure)	C$_2$H$_5$—	C$_2$H$_5$—	175°		110
do	CH$_3$CO—		248–50°		110

TABLE 95

C. N^4-Heterocyclic-N^1-substituted Sulfanilamides
   2. N^4-Nitrogen a Member of the Heterocyclic System

$$CN \langle\ \rangle SO_2N \begin{smallmatrix} R^1 \\ R^{1\prime} \end{smallmatrix}$$

CN	R¹	Melting Range	Activities	References
H₂⟨ ⟩N— (piperidine, H₂ H₂ / H₂ H₂)	$3,5\text{-}Cl_2C_6H_3-$			555
CH₃ / N— / CH₃	N⟨ ⟩ (piperidine)		0(En, I, Po)	892, 1485
do	(thiazoline, S/N)		0(En, I, Po)	892, 1485
(decahydroquinoline, H₂ N— H₂)	(decahydroquinoline, H₂ N— H₂)	153–7°		1329
HN⟨ ⟩NSO₂C₆H₄N⟨ ⟩N—	HN⟨ ⟩N— (piperazine, H₂ H₂)			2084
C₆H₅ / N—N / N—N (triazole)	C_6H_5-	213°		53
CH₃—N / H₂⟨ ⟩N— / O (pyrazolone)	N⟨ ⟩ (piperidine)	248°		21
do	$4\text{-}(HOOC)C_6H_4-$			206
H₂ / H₂⟨ ⟩N— (succinimide, O...O)	N⟨ ⟩ (piperidine)			475
do	(thiomorpholine, S/N)	266–7°		372
⟨ ⟩CO\N— / CO (phthalimide type)	N⟨ ⟩ (piperidine)			475
do	$HOOCCH_2-$	231°		2179
do	$HOOCCH_2CH_2CH(COOH)-$	227°D		2179
$4\text{-}(HOCH_2CH_2NHSO_2)C_6H_4N$ / H₂ N— / H₂ O	$HOCH_2CH_2-$	260–70°D	0(S)	4

TABLE 95—(*Continued*)

$\subset N$	R^1	Melting Range	Activities	References
4-(CH₃CHOHCH₂NHSO₂)C₆H₄N⟨⟩N– (with O, H₂ structure)	CH₃CHOHCH₂–	280–4°D	0(S)	4
HON= structure with CH₃, N	N⟨⟩–	237–9°		21
Cl Cl / Cl COOH structure –N=N– with CH₃–N	4-(HOOC)C₆H₄–			206

TABLE 96

D. N^4-Anils of N^1-substituted Sulfanilamides $R^4{=}N\langle\rangle SO_2N{<}^{R^1}_{R^{1\prime}}$

R^4	R^1	$R^{1\prime}$	Melting Range	Activities	References
CH₂=	N⟨⟩–			±(S)	420
CH₂=	HOCH₂–			0(S, Tt)	1427, 1574
C₆H₅CH=	C₆H₅–		175–5.5°	+, ±(S), ±(P)	268, 270
do	3,5-Br₂C₆H₃–				555
do	4-(NO₂)C₆H₄–		192°	++(S), +(P)	268, 270
do	N⟨⟩–		245–6°	++(S), +(P)	268, 270, 362
do	HOOCCH₂–		185–6°	0(S)	968
do	2(HOOC)C₆H₄–		226–6.5°		270
2-(NO₂)C₆H₄CH=	N⟨⟩–		193–4°	++(S), 0(En)	270, 1485
do	S⟨⟩–N structure				1984
3-NO₂C₆H₄CH=	do		220–2°D		1984
4-(NO₂)C₆H₄CH=	CH₃–	CH₃–			217
do	C₆H₅–		196–7°		270
do	3,5-Br₂C₆H₃–		239°		555
do	4-(NO₂)C₆H₄–		201.5–2.0°	+(S)	270

TABLE 96--(*Continued*)

R⁴	R¹	R¹′	Melting Range	Activities	References
do	(N-piperidyl ring)–		245–6.2°	++(S)	270
do	N=CH ring–NO₂		230°	±(S), 0(P)	269, 271
$C_6H_5CH=CHCH=$ do	C_6H_5- $3,5-Br_2C_6H_3-$		214°		270 355
do	(N-piperidyl ring)–		215–7.5°	++, +(S), 0(En, Po)	270, 471
do	CH_3CO-				751
O=N(H) ring, H₂...H₂	$HOCH_2CH_2-$		85–93°	0(S)	4
H₂ S ring, O=NH	$CH_3CHOHCH_2-$		209–12°	0(S)	4
CH₃ H S ring, O=NH	do		190–2°	0(S)	4
$2-(HO)C_6H_4CH=$	$3,5-Cl_2C_6H_3-$		164°		555
$3-(HO)C_6H_4CH=$	(N-pyridyl ring)–		242–3.5°	+++(S), +(P)	270
$4-(CH_3O)C_6H_4CH=$ do do	C_6H_5- $3,5-Cl_2C_6H_3-$ $4-(NO_2)C_6H_4-$		166° 176° 213.5°	+(S), 0(P) +(S), ±(P), 0(En, Po)	268, 269 555 268, 269, 1485
do	(N-pyridyl ring)–		212–2.5°	+(S, P), 0(En, Po)	268, 269, 1485
do	$2-(HOOC)C_6H_4-$		233–3.5°		270
do	N=CH ring–OCH₃		183–4°	++(S), ±(P)	269, 271
O=C= $4-[(CH_3)_2N]C_6H_4CH=$ do	CH_3- C_6H_5- $4-(NO_2)C_6H_4-$	CH_3-	231° 231°	+(S), 0(P) +(S, P)	1160 268, 269 268, 269
do	(N-pyridyl ring)–		238–40°	+(S, P)	268, 269
do	$2(HOOC)C_6H_4-$		247–8°		270
do	N=CH ring–N(CH₃)₂		238.2°	++(S), 0(P)	269, 271

TABLE 97

E. N^4-Sugar Derivatives of N^1-Substituted Sulfanilamides

1. Glycosides of N^1-Substituted Sulfanilamides

Sugar	R^1	$[\alpha]_D$	Melting Range	Activities	References
d-Arabinose	(N-ring structure)	+6°			304
l-Arabinose	do	− 6°			304
Xylose	do	−16°			304
Rhamnose	do	+76°			304
Glucose	do	−43°		++(P)	131, 304, 432, 604, 849, 1086, 1534
do	(S, N—N ring structure)				2491
do	CH$_3$CO−		188°, 192°		771, 788
do	4-(NH$_2$SO$_2$)C$_6$H$_4$−				8
do	4-(CH$_3$NHSO$_2$)C$_6$H$_4$−				8
do	4-[(CH$_3$)$_2$NSO$_2$]C$_6$H$_4$−				8
Mannose	4-(NH$_2$SO$_2$)C$_6$H$_4$−				8
Galactose	(N-ring structure)	−67°		+	304, 432, 849
do	(S, N—N ring structure)				2491
do	4-(NH$_2$SO$_2$)C$_6$H$_4$−				8
Maltose	(N-ring structure)	+48°			304
do	4-(NH$_2$SO$_2$)C$_6$H$_4$−				8
do	4-(CH$_3$NHSO$_2$)C$_6$H$_4$−				8
do	4-[(CH$_3$)$_2$NSO$_2$]C$_6$H$_4$−				8
do	4-(HOCH$_2$CH$_2$NHSO$_2$)C$_6$H$_4$−				8
do	4-[(HOCH$_2$CH$_2$)$_2$NSO$_2$]C$_6$H$_4$−				8
do	4-NH$_2$SO$_2$-2-CH$_3$-5-(CH$_3$O)C$_6$H$_2$−				8

TABLE 98

2. N^4-Sugar Sodium Bisulfite Derivatives of N^1-Substituted Sulfanilamides

$$CH_2OH(CHOH)_4CHNH\!\!\left\langle\right\rangle\!\!SO_2N\begin{smallmatrix}R^1\\ \\ R^{1\prime}\end{smallmatrix}$$

$$\underset{SO_3Na}{|}$$

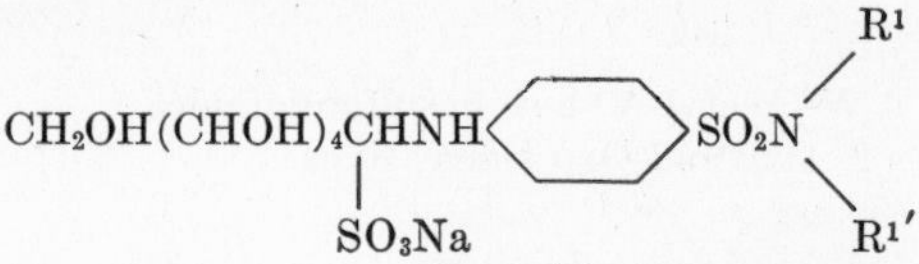

Probable Type Formula

Sugar	R^1	Melting Range	Activities	References
Glucose	4-$(NH_2SO_2)C_6H_4-$			1894

TABLE 99

F. N^4-Acyl-N^1-substituted Sulfanilamides
  1. N^4-Acetyl-N^1-substituted Sulfanilamides
    a. N^4-Acetyl-N^1-acyclicsulfanilamides
      1. R = C_nH_{2n+1} to C_nH_{2n-1}

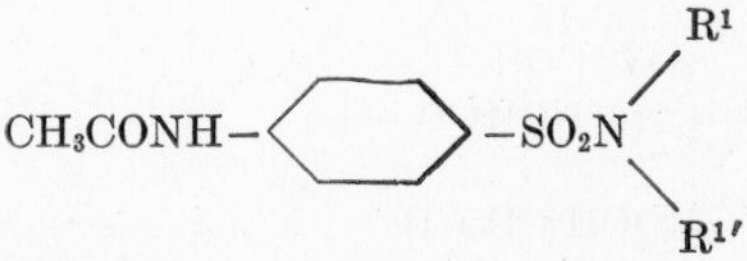

$$CH_3CONH-\!\!\left\langle\right\rangle\!\!-SO_2N\begin{smallmatrix}R^1\\ \\ R^{1\prime}\end{smallmatrix}$$

R^1	$R^{1\prime}$	Melting Range	Activities	References
Ag$-$				51
CH$_3-$		190–0.5°		151, 512, 1733, 1734
CH$_3-$	CH$_3-$	145–6°	$+$(S)	53, 151, 158, 412, 450, 512, 1733, 1734
C$_2$H$_5-$		153–5°	$+$(S)	61, 151, 512, 536, 1733
ClCH$_2$CH$_2-$		173.5–4.0°	$+$(S), 0(I)	1574, 2370
BrCH$_2$CH$_2-$		163–5°	$+$(S), 0(P, Sa)	968, 1574, 2373
C$_2$H$_5-$	C$_2$H$_5-$	77–8°; 82°	$+$(S)	151, 173, 512, 536, 1733
ClCH$_2$CH$_2-$	ClCH$_2$CH$_2-$	122–3°	$+$(S), 0(I)	1574, 2373
CH$_3$(CH$_2$)$_2-$		130–1°		1733
do	CH$_3$(CH$_2$)$_2-$		$\pm$(S)	151, 512
CH$_3$(CH$_2$)$_3-$			$\pm$(S)	151, 512
(CH$_3$)$_2$CH$_2$CH$_2-$			$\pm$(S)	151, 512
CH$_3$(CH$_2$)$_9$(CH$_3$)$_2$C$-$		107°		1770
CH$_3$(CH$_2$)$_{11}$(CH$_3$)$_2$C$-$		102°		1770
CH$_3$(CH$_2$)$_{16}-$		128°	0(T)	2260
C$_{18}$H$_{37}-$			0(S)	1427, 1574
CH$_3$(CH$_2$)$_{17}$(CH$_3$)$_2$C$-$		105°		1770
CH$_2$=CHCH$_2-$		154–5°	$\pm$(S)	512, 1733
CH$_3$(CH$_2$)$_7$CH=CH(CH$_2$)$_8-$		126–7°		673

TABLE 100

a. N^4-Acetyl-N^1-acyclicsulfanilamides
2. Oxy and Oxo Derivatives

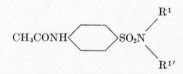

R^1	$R^{1'}$	Melting Range	Activities	References
HOCH$_2$CH$_2-$		150–1°	++(M), ±, 0(S)	5, 105, 297, 311, 332, 2441
do	CH$_3-$		0(S)	311
do	HOCH$_2$CH$_2-$	161–2°	±(M), 0(P, S)	5, 105, 214, 267, 269
HSCH$_2$CH$_2-$			0(P)	1427, 1574
CH$_3$CHOHCH$_2-$		166–7°	±, 0(S), 0(M)	5, 105, 297, 1427, 1574
HOCH$_2$CH$_2$CH$_2-$		133.5–5.0°	±(M), 0(S)	5, 212, 297
CH$_3$CH$_2$CHOHCH$_2-$				297
(CH$_3$)$_2$COHCH$_2-$		185–7°	+(M), ±, 0(S)	5, 1574
HOCH$_2$(CH$_3$)$_2$C$-$		223.3–4.5°		105
HOCH$_2$CHOHCH$_2-$		132–3°	0(M, S)	5, 297
(HOCH$_2$)$_2$CH$-$				297
(HOCH$_2$)$_2$(CH$_3$)C$-$		212.5–3.8°		105
HOCH$_2$(CHOH)$_4$CH$_2-$	CH$_3-$	87–91°	0(M, S)	5
NaO$_3$SCH$_2-$			0(I, P, R)	1427, 1574
H$_2$O$_3$PCH$_2-$			+(S), 0(I, P, R)	1427, 1574

TABLE 101

a. N^4-Acetyl-N^1-acyclicsulfanilamides
3. Carboxy and Sulfo Derivatives

R^1	$R^{1'}$	Melting Range	Activities	References
HOOCCH$_2-$		237°	+(S)	33, 62, 209, 267, 269, 348
NaOOCCH$_2-$			0(S)	311
C$_2$H$_5$OOCCH$_2-$		128°		91, 158
H$_2$NOCCH$_2-$		224–5°	0(S)	91
C$_2$H$_5$O(HN)CCH$_2-$				45
NCCH$_2-$		194–5°	+++(S)	45, 91
H$_2$N(HN)CCH$_2-$				45
H$_2$NOCCH$_2-$	CH$_3-$	185–6°	0(S)	91
do	C$_2$H$_5-$	167–8°		91

TABLE 101—(*Concluded*)

R¹	R¹′	Melting Range	Activities	References
$NCCH_2-$	CH_3-	158–9°	+++, −(S)	91
do	C_2H_5-	128–8.5°	+++, −(S)	91
$HOOC(CH_3)CH-$		208°		348
$NaOOC(CH_3)CH-$			0(S)	311
$lSCH_2(HOOC)CH-$				

$$SCH_2CHCOOH$$

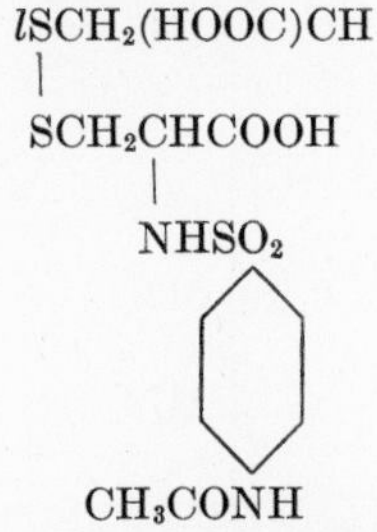		204–6°D		1360
CH_3CONH				
$HOOCCH_2CH_2(HOOC)CH-$		142°D		62, 968
$HO_3SCH_2CH_2-$				209

TABLE 102

a. *N*⁴-Acetyl-*N*¹-acyclicsulfanilamides
   4. Amino Derivatives

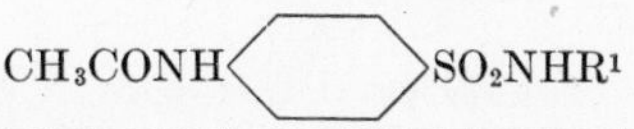

$$CH_3CONH \langle \rangle SO_2NHR^1$$

R¹	Melting Range	Activities	References
$H_2NCH_2CH_2-$			22
$(C_2H_5)_2N(CH_2)_2-$		0 (S)	22, 311, 338
CH_2CH_2-	228°		320
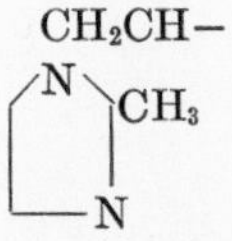 CH_2CH-	212–4°		321
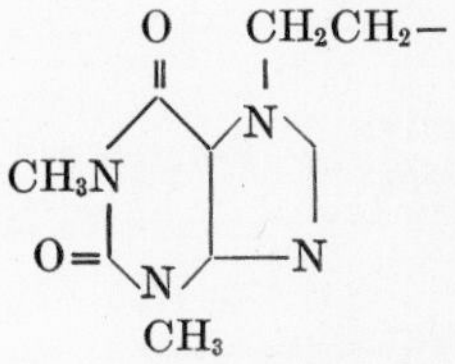	250–1°		318
$[4\text{-}(CH_3CONH)C_6H_4SO_2NHCH_2CH_2]_2NCH_2CH_2-$	198.5–200.5°		1716

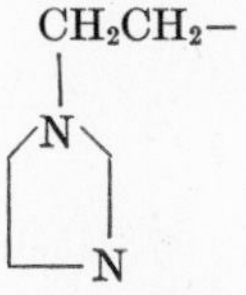

TABLE 102—(*Concluded*)

R^1	Melting Range	Activities	References
4-(CH₃CONH)C₆H₄SO₂NH | (CH₂)₂ | 4-(CH₃CONH)C₆H₄SO₂N | (CH₂)₂ |	290.5–291.5°		1716
4-(CH₃CONH)C₆H₄SO₂NCH₂CH₂— (C₂H₅)₂N(CH₂)₃—		0 (S)	512
NH(CH₂)₃— (ring structure with N, OCH₃)	189°		1179
4-(CH₃CONH)C₆H₄SO₂NHCH₂ | 4-(CH₃CONH)C₆H₄SO₂NHCHCH₂— (C₂H₅)₂N(CH₂)₄—	218.5–220.5°		1716 83, 84
4-(CH₃CONH)C₆H₄SO₂NH(CH₂)₄—	233°	0(T)	2260
[4-(CH₃CONH)C₆H₄SO₂NHCH₂]₃CCH₂—	304–6°		1716
(C₂H₅)₂N(CH₂)₃(CH₃)CH—		0(Pr)	122, 123
(C₂H₅)₂NCH₂CHOHCH₂—		0(Pr)	122, 123
(cyclohexyl ring) NCH₂CHOHCH₂—		0(Pr)	122, 123
4-(CH₃CONH)C₆H₄SO₂NHCH₂CHOHCH₂—	232.5–233.5°	0(S)	1427, 1574, 1716

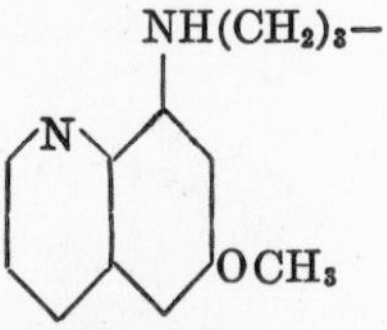

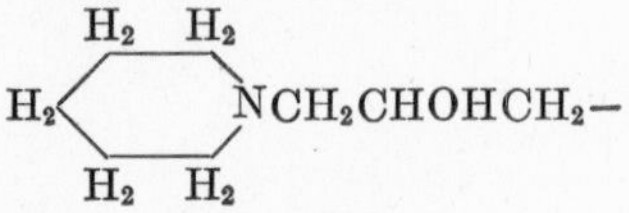

TABLE 103

b. N^4-Acetyl-N^1-isocyclicsulfanilamides   CH₃CONH⟨ ⟩SO₂NHR¹

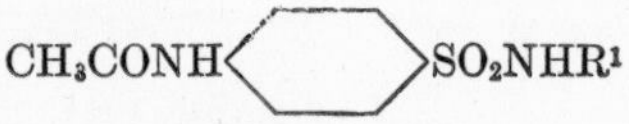

1. R=CₙH₂ₙ₋₁ to CₙH₂ₙ₋₂₅

R^1	Melting Range	Activities	References
(cyclohexyl ring structure with H₂ groups and H)	217.5–8.5°, 224°		173, 1713

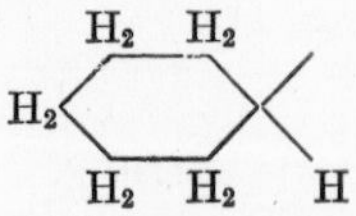

TABLE 103—(*Continued*)

R^1	Melting Range	Activities	References
C_6H_5-	210, 214°	±(S)	61, 168, 218, 331, 512
$4\text{-}FC_6H_4-$			179
$3,5\text{-}(Cl)_2C_6H_3-$	238°		555
$3,4,5(Cl)_3C_6H_2-$	271°		555
$4\text{-}BrC_6H_4-$	208°		332
$3,5(Br)_2C_6H_3-$	244°		555
$2,4\text{-}I_2C_6H_3-$	230–1°		812, 1609, 2094
$3,5\text{-}I_2C_6H_3-$	277°		555
$4\text{-}(ON)C_6H_4-$	198–212°		2262
$2\text{-}(NO_2)C_6H_4-$	200–1°		267, 332, 544
$3\text{-}(NO_2)C_6H_4-$	237°, 244°		331, 332, 544
$4\text{-}(NO_2)C_6H_4-$	240°, 258°, 264°		33, 201, 331, 332, 544, 1411
$3,5(NO_2)_2C_6H_3-$	273°		555
$2\text{-}(CH_3)C_6H_4-$	244.5°		168, 332
$2\text{-}(CH_3)\text{-}5\text{-}(NO_2)C_6H_3-$	266.5°		332
$3\text{-}(CH_3)C_6H_4-$	205°		168, 332
$4\text{-}(CH_3)C_6H_4-$	208°, 212°		168, 218, 331 332
$4\text{-}(CH_3)\text{-}3\text{-}(NO_2)C_6H_3-$	239°		332
$C_6H_5CH_2-$		±(S)	205, 512
$C_6H_5CH_2CH_2-$	126°		2001
$4\text{-}(NO_2)C_6H_5CH_2CH_2-$	183–4°		2001
$2,4\text{-}(CH_3)_2C_6H_3-$	214.5°		332
$2,6\text{-}(CH_3)_2C_6H_3-$	236.5°		332
$3,5\text{-}(F_3C)_2C_6H_3-$	211°		555
$2\text{-}CH_3\text{-}5\text{-}[(CH_3)_2CH-]C_6H_3-$	160.5°		332
	190–1°		2001
$1\text{-}C_{10}H_7-$			168
$2\text{-}C_{10}H_7-$			168
$2\text{-}(CH_3)C_{10}H_6\text{-}(1)$	230–1°		2207
$4\text{-}(C_6H_5)C_6H_4-$	169°		2238
$4\text{-}[C_6H_5C(C_2H_5)=C(C_2H_5)]C_6H_4-$	207–8°		800
	245°		2238

TABLE 103—(*Concluded*)

R^1	Melting Range	Activities	References
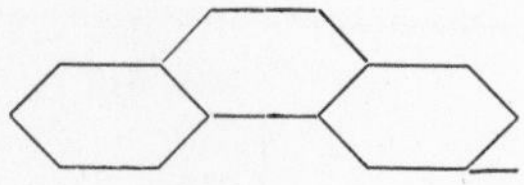	244–5°		1985
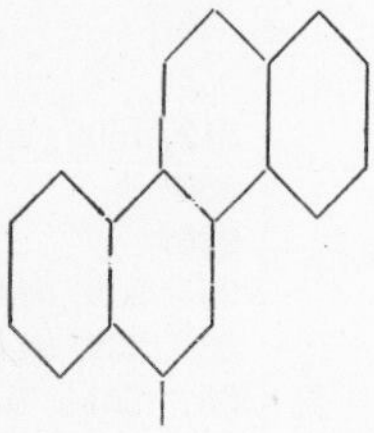	265°		1985

TABLE 104

b. N^4-Acetyl-N^1-isocyclicsulfanilamides

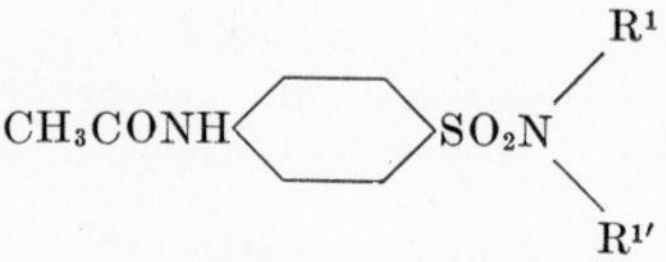

2. Oxy Derivatives

R^1	$R^{1'}$	Melting Range	Activities	References
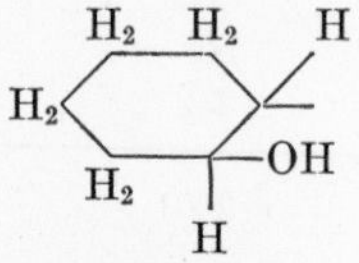		218°	0(M, S)	5, 311
2-(HO)C_6H_4—		216–7°	0 (S)	105, 311, 544
2-(CH_3O)C_6H_4—		212°	0 (S)	105, 332
2-(C_6H_5O)C_6H_4—		162°		1985
2-HO-4-(NO_2)C_6H_3—		222–3°		543
2-CH_3O-5-(NO_2)C_6H_3—		261.5°D		332
3-(HO)C_6H_4—		217–8°	0 (S)	311, 544
3-(CH_3O)C_6H_4—		193°		332
4-(HO)C_6H_4—		>260°	0 (S)	105, 311, 544
4-(CH_3O)C_6H_4—		200°		83, 84, 331, 332
4-(C_2H_5O)C_6H_4—		204°	± (S)	331, 464, 512
4-(C_6H_5O)C_6H_4—		183°		1985
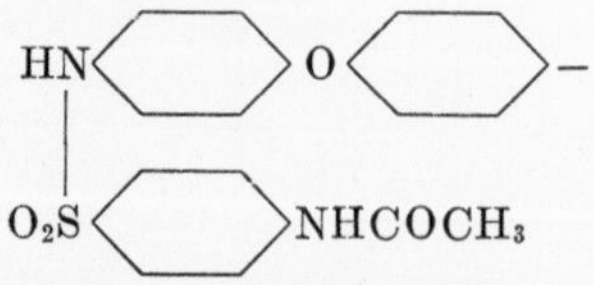		150°		225

TABLE 104—(*Concluded*)

R^1	$R^{1'}$	Melting Range	Activities	References
$4\text{-HO-2-}(NO_2)C_6H_3-$		$217°$	0 (S)	311, 543
$4\text{-}CH_3O\text{-2-}(NO_2)C_6H_3-$				332
$4\text{-HO-3-}(NO_2)C_6H_3-$		$236°$	0 (S)	311, 543
$3\text{-}NO_2\text{-4}(CH_3COO)C_6H_3-$	CH_3CO-			543
$2\text{-}CH_3O\text{-5-}(CH_3)C_6H_3-$		$206°$		332
$4\text{-}(HOCH_2)C_6H_4-$		$175°$		218
$4\text{-}(CH_3O)C_6H_4CH_2CH_2-$		$157°$		2001
$2\text{-}[(CH_3)_2CH]\text{-3-HO-5-}(CH_3)C_6H_2-$		$235\text{-}6°$		407
$1\text{-HO-2-}(CH_3)C_{10}H_5\text{-}(4)$		$250°$		2207

	$CH_2CH=CH_2$	$240°D$		749
$3,4\text{-}(CH_3O)_2C_6H_3CH_2CH_2-$				2001

TABLE 105

b. N^4-Acetyl-N^1-isocyclicsulfanilamides $CH_3CONH\langle\ \rangle SO_2NHR^1$

3. Thio Derivatives

R^1	Melting Range	Activities	References
$4\text{-}(HS)C_6H_4-$			218
$4\text{-}(CH_3S)C_6H_4-$	$171.5°$		2323
$4\text{-}(C_2H_5S)C_6H_4-$	$159.5°$		2323
$4\text{-}(C_2H_5SO_2)C_6H_4-$	$234°$		2323
$4\text{-}[CH_3(CH_2)_3S]C_6H_4-$	$120°$		2323
$4\text{-}[CH_3(CH_2)_5S]C_6H_4-$	$141.5\text{-}2.5°$		2323
$4\text{-}[CH_3(CH_2)_9S]C_6H_4-$	$106°$		2323
$4\text{-}[CH_3(CH_2)_{13}S]C_6H_4-$	$116.5\text{-}7.5°$		2323
$4\text{-}[CH_3(CH_2)_{15}S]C_6H_4-$	$96\text{-}108°$		2323
$4\text{-}(C_6H_5SO)C_6H_4-$	$112\text{-}3°$		1808
$4\text{-}[4'\text{-}(NO_2)C_6H_4SO]C_6H_4-$	$263\text{-}4°D$		1176
$4\text{-}[4'\text{-}(NO_2)C_6H_4SO_2]C_6H_4-$	$279\text{-}80°$		1176
$4\text{-}[4'\text{-}CH_3C_6H_4SO]C_6H_4-$	$125\text{-}6°$		1808
$4\text{-}(C_6H_5CH_2S)C_6H_4-$	$210.5\text{-}1.5°$		2323
$4\text{-}(C_6H_5CH_2SO_2)C_6H_4-$	$229°$		2323
$4\text{-}(HOOCCH_2S)C_6H_4-$	$185°$	$++$(S)	1057, 1808
$4\text{-}(C_2H_5OOCCH_2S)C_6H_4-$	$149\text{-}50°$	$+$(S)	1057, 1808
$4\text{-}(HOOCCH_2SO)C_6H_4-$	$134\text{-}6°$		1808
$4\text{-}[HOOC(CH_3)CHS]C_6H_4-$	$163\text{-}5°$		1808
$4\text{-}[CH_3(CH_2)_9(C_2H_5OOC)CHS]C_6H_4-$			1808
$4\text{-}[CH_3(CH_2)_{11}(C_2H_5OOC)CHS]C_6H_4-$	$261\text{-}4°D$		1808
$4[4'\text{-}(4''\text{-}NH_2C_6H_4SO_2NH)C_6H_4S\text{-}S]C_6H_4-$	$237\text{-}9°$		2323
$4[4'\text{-}(4''\text{-}CH_3CONHC_6H_4SO_2NH)C_6H_4SO_2]C_6H_4-$	$175°D$		225, 1176
$5\text{-}HS\text{-2-}(CH_3)C_6H_3-$			218

TABLE 106

b. N^4-Acetyl-N^1-isocyclicsulfanilamides

4. Oxo and Carboxy Derivatives

$$CH_3CONH\langle\ \rangle SO_2NHR^1$$

R¹	Melting Range	Activities	References
2-(OHC)C₆H₄—			218
4-(CH₃CO)C₆H₄—	241°, 254.5°		332, 352, 400
C₆H₅COCH₂—	151–2°D		1984
4-(CH₃CH₂CO)C₆H₄—			352, 400
1-C₁₀H₇COCH₂—	202–4°D		1984
4-(C₆H₅CO)C₆H₄—	216–8.5°		332, 352, 400
			1823
2-(HOOC)C₆H₄—	233°, 245°	±, 0(P)	98, 100, 267, 269, 311, 332, 556
2-CN-4-ClC₆H₃—			218
4-NO₂-2-(HOOC)C₆H₃—			218
3-(HOOC)C₆H₄—	261°, 274°	0(P)	98, 218, 267, 269, 332, 556
3-(CN)C₆H₄—	236°		218, 556
3-HOOC-4-ClC₆H₃—	263°		110
4-(HOOC)C₆H₄—	252°D	0(P)	33, 98, 218, 267, 269, 311, 332, 556
4-(C₂H₅OOC)C₆H₄—	220°		84, 218, 556
4-(NH₂OC)C₆H₄—			218
4-HOOC-3-ClC₆H₃—	142°		110
3-(HOOCCH=CH)C₆H₄—			158
4-(HOOCCH=CH)C₆H₄—			158
C₆H₅CH₂(HOOC)CH—	205–6°		160
4-HOOC-3-(HO)C₆H₃—	242–5°		105, 218, 556
4-(HO)C₆H₄CH₂(HOOC)CH—	221–2°		348
	240°D		817

TABLE 107

b. *N*-4-Acetyl-*N*1-isocyclicsulfanilamides   CH₃CONH⟨ ⟩SO₂NHR¹

5. Sulfino and Sulfo Derivatives

R^1	Melting Range	Activities	References
2-HO₂S-4-(NO₂)C₆H₃—	212°		228
4-(HO₂S)C₆H₄—	143–4°D		228
2-(HO₃S)C₆H₄—			64, 98
3-(HO₃S)C₆H₄—			98, 556
4-(HO₃S)C₆H₄—			98, 158, 218, 267, 556
4-(NaO₃S)C₆H₄—		0(En, P)	269, 1485
4-(C₆H₅O₃S)C₆H₄—			218
4-(ClO₂S)C₆H₄—			218, 228
2,6-(NO₂)₂-4-(HO₃S)C₆H₂—			218
4-ClO₂S-2-(CH₃)C₆H₃—			218
4-HO₃S-1-C₁₀H₆—			98, 218, 556
4-NaO₃S-1-C₁₀H₆—		0(S)	311
3,6-(HO₃S)₂-1-C₁₀H₅—			218, 556
3,8-(HO₃S)₂-1-C₁₀H₅—			218, 556
4,8-(NaO₃S)₂-1-C₁₀H₅—		0(S)	311
3,6,8-(NaO₃S)₃-1-C₁₀H₄—		0(S)	311
7-HO₃S-5-HO-2-C₁₀H₅—			218, 556
6-HO₃S-8-HO-2-C₁₀H₅—			218, 556

TABLE 108

b. *N*⁴-Acetyl-*N*1-isocyclicsulfanilamides   CH₂CONH⟨ ⟩SO₂NHR¹

6. Amino and Azo Derivatives

R^1	Melting Range	Activities	References
2-(NH₂)C₆H₄—	222–3°	0(S)	311, 544
3-(NH₂)C₆H₄—	217–8°	0(S)	311, 544
3-[4′-(CH₃CONH)C₆H₄SO₂NH]C₆H₄—	289–90°		557
3-(NaO₃SNH)C₆H₄—			224, 2462
4-(NH₂)C₆H₄—	220°, 235°	+(S), ±(P)	201, 228, 271, 311, 332, 544
4-[(CH₃)₂N]C₆H₄—	195–6°		211, 311, 340
4-[(C₂H₅)₂N]C₆H₄—			201
4-(C₆H₅NH)C₆H₄—	221°		211, 340
4-(C₆H₅CH₂NH)C₆H₄—	182–2.5°		270
4-[4′-(CH₃O)C₆H₄CH₂NH]C₆H₄—	208–8.5°		270
4-(C₆H₅CH=N)C₆H₄—	206.5–7.0°	+(S), ±(P)	269, 271
4-[4′-(NO₂)C₆H₄CH=N]C₆H₄—	255.5–7.5°	+(S), 0(P)	271

TABLE 108—(*Continued*)

R^1	Melting Range	Activities	Reference
4-[4'-(CH$_3$O)C$_6$H$_4$CH=N]C$_6$H$_4$—	246.5–7.5°	+++(S), ±(P)	269, 271
4-(CH$_3$CONH)C$_6$H$_4$—	>260°		201, 211, 340, 544
4-[CH$_3$CO(CH$_3$)N]C$_6$H$_4$—			201
4-[4'-(NH$_2$)C$_6$H$_4$NH]C$_6$H$_4$—			340
4"-[4'-(4-(CH$_3$CONH)C$_6$H$_4$SO$_2$NH)C$_6$H$_4$NH]C$_6$H$_4$—	157–8°D		225
4-[4'-(CH$_3$)$_2$NC$_6$H$_4$CH=N]C$_6$H$_4$—	242°	++(S), 0(P)	269, 271
4-[4'-(CH$_3$CONH)C$_6$H$_4$SO$_2$NH]C$_6$H$_4$—	316.5°D		225, 332
3-NO$_2$-4-(NH$_2$)C$_6$H$_3$—	258–9°		543
2,4-(CH$_3$CONH)$_2$C$_6$H$_3$—			211, 340
2,5-(CH$_3$CONH)$_2$C$_6$H$_3$—	227–8°		543
3,4-(NH$_2$)$_2$C$_6$H$_3$—	230–1°		543
3,4-(CH$_3$CONH)$_2$C$_6$H$_3$—			340
3,5-(NH$_2$)$_2$C$_6$H$_3$—	264°		555
2-CH$_3$-5-(CH$_3$CONH)C$_6$H$_3$—			201
3-CH$_3$-4-(CH$_3$CONH)C$_6$H$_3$—	280°		211, 340
5-CH$_3$-2-(CH$_3$CONH)C$_6$H$_3$—			201
3-[4'-(CH$_3$CONH)C$_6$H$_4$SO$_2$NH]-4-(CH$_3$)C$_6$H$_4$—	278°		332
2,3-(CH$_3$)$_2$-4-(CH$_3$CONH)C$_6$H$_2$—			201
4-(C$_6$H$_5$CONHCH$_2$CH$_2$)C$_6$H$_4$—	223°		2001
4-(CH$_3$CONH)C$_6$H$_4$CH$_2$CH$_2$—	230°		2001
6-[4'-(CH$_3$CONH)C$_6$H$_4$SO$_2$NH]C$_{10}$H$_6$-(2)			225
4-(CH$_3$CONH)C$_6$H$_4$SO$_2$NH⟨ ⟩–⟨ ⟩–	288°		225, 332
4-(CH$_3$CONH)C$_6$H$_4$SO$_2$NH⟨ ⟩CH$_2$⟨ ⟩–	180°, 244–5°		225, 1176
4-(CH$_3$CONH)C$_6$H$_4$SO$_2$NH⟨ ⟩–⟨ ⟩– (CH$_3$, CH$_3$ substituents)			225
2-HO-5-(CH$_3$CONH)C$_6$H$_3$—	239–40°		543
3-HO-4-(CH$_3$CONH)C$_6$H$_3$—			211, 340
2-CH$_3$CONH-5-(HO)C$_6$H$_3$—	239–40°		543
2-CH$_3$CONH-5-(CH$_3$COO)C$_6$H$_3$—	200–1°		543
4-(CH$_3$CONH)C$_6$H$_4$SO$_2$NH⟨ ⟩–C(=O)–⟨ ⟩–	140–5°		225
4-[4'-(CH$_3$O)C$_6$H$_4$NH]-3-(HOOC)C$_6$H$_3$—	158–60°		110
3-[4'-(CH$_3$O)C$_6$H$_4$NH]-4-(HOOC)C$_6$H$_3$—	218–20°		110

TABLE 108—(*Concluded*)

R^1	Melting Range	Activities	References
2,6-(HO$_3$S)$_2$-4-(NH$_2$)C$_6$H$_2$—			218
4-(C$_6$H$_5$N=N)C$_{10}$H$_6$-1—	270°		728
1-(C$_6$H$_5$N=N)C$_{10}$H$_6$-2—	206–7°		728
3-NH$_2$-4-[4'-(NaO$_3$S)C$_6$H$_4$N=N]C$_6$H$_3$—			127
3-[4'-(CH$_3$CONH)C$_6$H$_4$SO$_2$NH]-4-[4''-(NaO$_3$S)C$_6$H$_4$N=N—]C$_6$H$_3$—			127

TABLE 109

b. N^4-Acetyl-N^1-isocyclicsulfanilamides
   7. Phosphorus and Arsenic Derivatives

Compound	Melting Range	Activities	References
{4-[4'-(CH$_3$CONH)C$_6$H$_4$SO$_2$NH]C$_6$H$_4$}$_2$PC$_6$H$_5$			169
{4-[4'-(CH$_3$CONH)C$_6$H$_4$SO$_2$NH]C$_6$H$_4$}$_2$AsC$_6$H$_5$			169
4-[4'-(CH$_3$CONH)C$_6$H$_4$SO$_2$NH]C$_6$H$_4$AsO$_3$H$_2$	275°D		322

TABLE 110

c. N^4-Acetyl-N^1-heterocyclicsulfanilamides
   1. One or more O- or S-Atoms in the Heterocyclic System

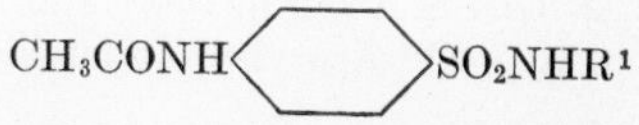

CH$_3$CONH⟨ ⟩SO$_2$NHR^1

R^1	Melting Range	Activities	References
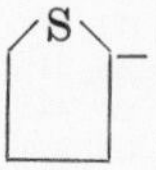	196°		41, 47, 528
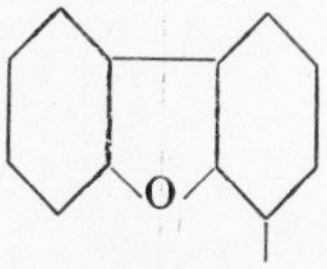	218°		2456
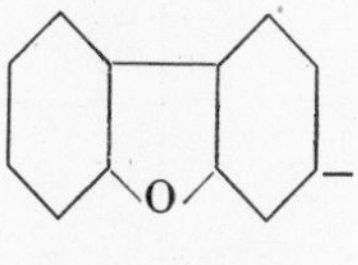	223°, 240–2°		394, 2456
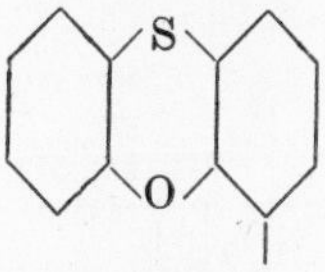	192°		1174

TABLE 110—(Concluded)

R^1	Melting Range	Activities	References
(structure)	154°		1174
(structure)	163°		1174
4-$(CH_3CONH)C_6H_4SO_2NH$ *(structure)*	180°D		1217

TABLE 111

c. N^4-Acetyl-N^1-heterocyclicsulfanilamides
 2. One N-Atom in the Heterocyclic System
 a. x-(N^4-Acetylsulfanilamido)pyridines

$$CH_3CONH\!\!-\!\!\langle\ \rangle\!\!-\!\!SO_2N\ (R^1)\ \cdots\ \text{pyridine } R_2,R_3,R_4,R_5,R_6$$

R^1	R_2	R_3	R_4	R_5	R_6	Melting Range	Activities	References
	x					195–6°, 225–8°ᵃ	0(Br)	11, 44, 102, 171, 272, 331, 334, 341, 409, 434, 482, 486, 516, 549, 553, 868, 1278, 1384, 1707, 2598
								334
Na–	x							
CH₃–	x					119.5–120.0°		2189
CH₃(CH₂)₄–	x					83°	0(T)	2260
CH₃(CH₂)₁₅–	x					88°	0(T)	2260
CH₃CO–	x					194°		1984
N(CH₂)₂– | (C₂H₅)₂	x							338
	x			I–		234°		341, 486
	x	I–		I–		242°D		827
	x			NO₂–		264°, 277–9°		341, 409, 486
		x				280°D		272, 341, 553
		x			I–	217°		827
		x	x			256–7°		272, 341, 486
	CH₃–		x				0, (I, P, R, Tt)	1427, 1574

ᵃ Acetylsulfapyridine.

TABLE 111—(*Concluded*)

R[1]	R₂	R₃	R₄	R₅	R₆	Melting Range	Activities	References
$CH_3(CH_2)_{17}-$	x				CH_3-	215-7°		341, 516, 869
	x				CH_3-	84°	0(T)	2260
	x				$NHCOOCH_3$	222°		410
					(ring) SO_3-			
	C_2H_5OOC-	x				182°		2422
	x	$HOOC-$				175°		341, 486, 2210
	x			HO_3S-		326-8°		1819
	x			$C_6H_5OSO_2-$		175-85°		341
	x			NH_2SO_2-		247°		80, 1819
	x			NSO_2- $\vert$ $(CH_3)_2$		151-3°		1819
	x			NH_2-				390, 409, 435
	x				NH_2-	195°, 238°	±, +, ++ (S), 0(P, Sa, Tt)	93, 149, 150, 516, 1574, 2373
	x				CH_3CONH-	230°		1829
	x				 $NHCOCH_3$	275°		341
		x			(ring) SO_2NH- CH_3CONH-	288-90°D		553, 1829

TABLE 112

b. 2-(N^4-Acetylsulfanilyl)pyridonimines

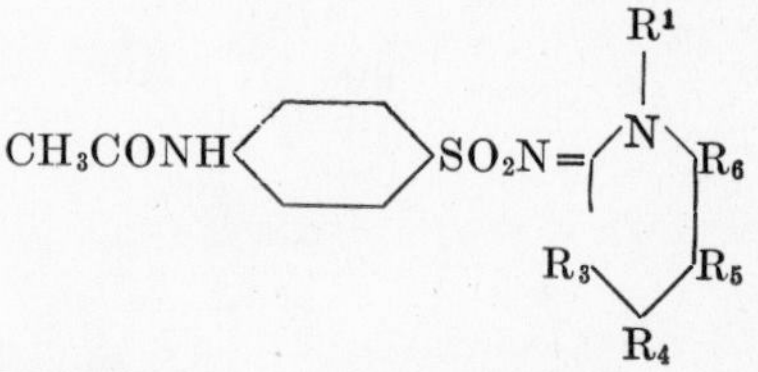

$$CH_3CONH\langle\ \rangle SO_2N=\left(\begin{matrix}R^1 \\ N \\ R_3 \end{matrix}\right)\begin{matrix}R_6\\R_5\\R_4\end{matrix}$$

R[1]	Melting Range	Activities	References
CH_3-	232-3°, 239-40°		381, 413, 486, 2189
C_2H_5-	222-4°		413
$CH_3(CH_2)_2-$	165-8°		413
$CH_3(CH_2)_3-$	178-80°		413
$C_6H_5CH_2-$	188-90°, 213-4°		341, 413, 486, 2189
$4-(NO_2)C_6H_4CH_2-$	215-8°		1984
$HOCH_2CH_2-$	217-8°		2189
$C_2H_5OOCCH_2-$	212-3°		2189

TABLE 113

$$CH_3CONH\!\!-\!\!\langle\ \rangle\!\!-\!\!SO_2N\!\!-\!\!x\ \ \begin{array}{c}R_8\ \ N\ \ R_2\\R_7\ \ \ \ \ \ R_3\\R_6\ \ \ \ \ \ R_4\\R_5\ \ R_4\end{array}$$

(with R^1 on the nitrogen)

c. x-(N^4-Acetylsulfanilamido)quinolines

R^1	R_2	R_3	R_4	R_5	R_6	R_7	R_8	Melting Range	Activity	References
	x							216°		341, 409, 516
(C₂H₅)₂N(CH₂)₂—	x			NO₂—						338
		x						250–3°		553
				x				256–8°D		43, 253, 553
					x			275°, 283°	0(S)	43, 253, 341, 426, 553
						x		238°		43
							x	193–4°		43, 84, 253, 553
	CH₃—				x			272°		341, 486
	CH₃—	CH₃—	x				CH₃—	253–5°, 260.5–1.5°		57, 2098
	CH₃—	CH₃—	x				CH₃CH₂—	244–5°		2098
	CH₃—	CH₃—	x				CH₃(CH₂)₂—	237–8°	0(Pl)	2098
	C₆H₅—		x					269–70°, 293°		30, 321
			x				CH₃O—	185°		341, 486
				HO—			x			344
				CH₃O—			x	222–3°		84, 344
				CH₃O—			x			338
				C₂H₅O—			x	225°		344
(C₂H₅)₂N(CH₂)₂—	HO—		CH₃—			x		304°		341, 486
	CH₃—	CH₃—		CH₃O—x			CH₃—	274°		57
	C₆H₅—		x	CH₃O—				268°		30

TABLE 114

d. Miscellaneous N^4-Acetyl-N^1-heterocyclicsulfanil-amides with One N-Atom in the Heterocyclic System.

$$CH_3CONH\!\!-\!\!\langle\ \rangle\!\!-\!\!SO_2NHR^1$$

R^1	Melting Range	Activities	References
(piperidin-N-yl)—CH₂—	121°, 124–5°		272, 2378
(piperidin-N-yl)—CH₂—	181–1.5°		272

TABLE 114—(*Continued*)

R^1	Melting Range	Activities	References
	196–200°		272
	240°D		2390
	142–2.5°		272
	249°		272
	205°		272
	203°D	0(Sa)	1329
	225°, 246–7°		97, 341, 409, 486
	304–6°D		97

TABLE 114—(Continued)

R¹	Melting Range	Activities	References
	284–8°D		97, 1239
	134–6°, 185–90°		572
	194°		572
	202–3°D		1985
			393
	273–5°D		1985
			368
	215°		572

TABLE 114—(*Concluded*)

R^1	Melting Range	Activities	References
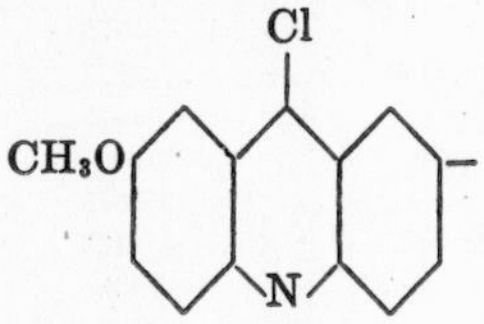	243–4°D		110
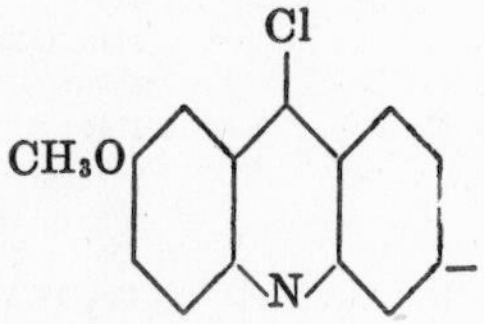	245–7°D		110
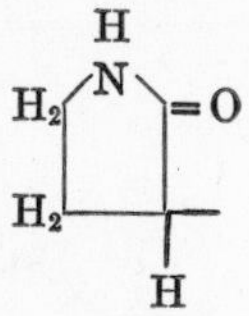	222–4°D		612
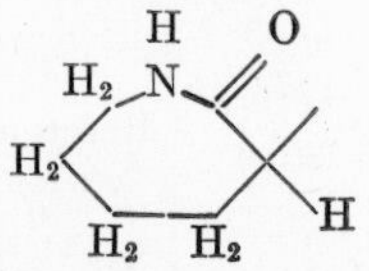	286–8°D		612

TABLE 115

c. N^4-Acetyl-N^1-heterocyclicsulfanilamides
  3. Two or More N-Atoms in the Heterocyclic System
  a. x-(N^4-Acetylsulfanilamido)pyrimidines

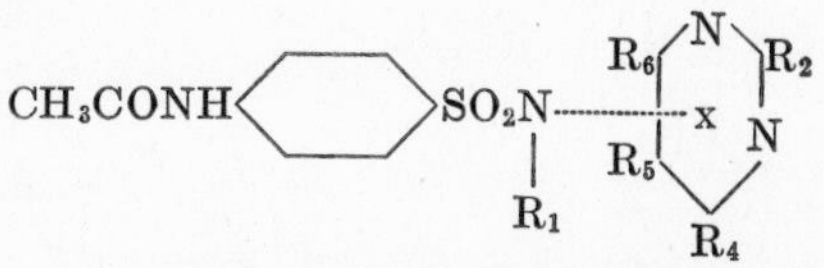

$$CH_3CONH\langle\rangle SO_2N$$

R_2	R_4	R_5	R_6	Melting Range	Activities	References
x				**258–9**°a		**434, 647, 1378,** 1708
	x					647
		x				436, 647
x	CH₃–			**248–9**°b		**434, 436, 687,** 1378, 1828, 1975, 2378
x	CH₃–		Cl–	>280°		1146
	CH₃–	x		246–7.5°D		687
x	C₂H₅–			274°		1975
x	CH₃–	CH₃–		272–3°, 276–7°		1975
x	CH₃–		CH₃–	**246.8–7.4**°c		**66, 436, 1378,** 1708, 1828
x	CH₃CH₂CH₂–			258°		1975
x	C₂H₅–		CH₃–	286°		1975

a Acetylsulfadiazine.
b Acetylsulfamerazine.
c Acetylsulfamethazine.

TABLE 115—(*Concluded*)

R_2	R_4	R_5	R_6	Melting Range	Activities	References
x	$(CH_3)_2CHCH_2-$			233°		1975
x	$CH_3(CH_2)_4-$			222-3°		1975
x	$CH_3(CH_2)_5-$			216°		1975
x	CH_3-	$CH_3(CH_2)_4-$		208.3-9°		66
x	C_6H_5-			287°		1975
x	do	CH_3-		235°		1378
x	CH_3O-					436
x	C_2H_5O-					436, 647
CH_3O-		x				436
x	CH_3-		$HO-$	279°		1146, 1355
x	CH_3-		CH_3O-	263-5°		687
x	CH_3-	$(CH_3)_2CH(CH_2)_2-$	$HO-$	228-9°		1146
$HO-$	$HO-$	x				436, 647
x	NH_2-					653
x	$(C_2H_5)_2N-$					653
x		x		295°D		436, 1975
CH_3CONH-		x				436, 647

TABLE 116

b. Miscellaneous N^4-Acetyl-N^1-heterocyclicsulfanila-
mides with Two N-Atoms in the Heterocyclic
System

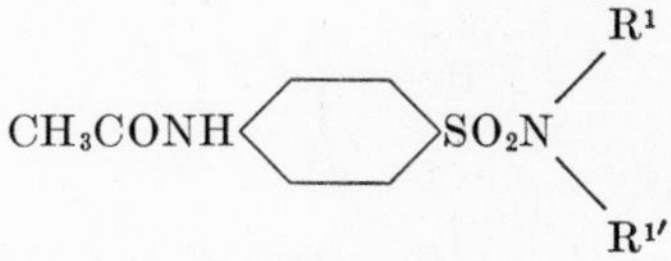

$$CH_3CONH\langle\rangle SO_2N\diagdown^{R^1}_{R^{1'}}$$

R^1	$R^{1'}$	Melting Range	Activities	References
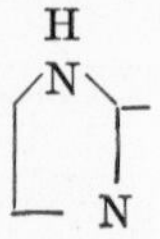 H (heterocycle)		259°		339
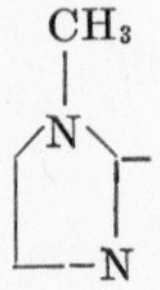 CH_3 (heterocycle)	CH_3-	227-8°		339
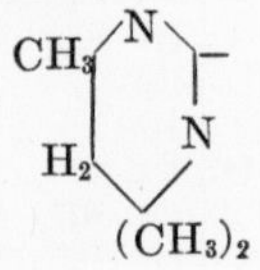 CH_3 ... H_2 ... $(CH_3)_2$ (heterocycle)		217-8°		1146
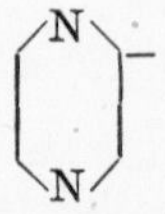 (heterocycle)		240-2°, 250-2°D		130, 452, 1248
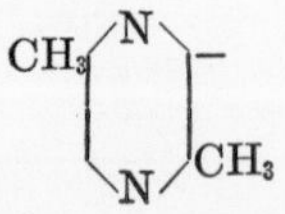 CH_3 ... CH_3 (heterocycle)		238-9°		251

TABLE 116—(*Continued*)

R¹	R¹'	Melting Range	Activities	References
		259°		66, 1975
		227.5–8.5°		66
		253–5°		1502
		250–2°, 262°D		1502, 1984
		245–6°		1502
		258–60°		1502
		261.5–2°		66
		238–40°		2635

TABLE 116—(*Concluded*)

R[1]	R[1]′	Melting Range	Activities	References
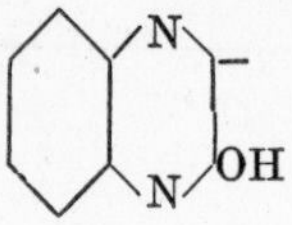				2635
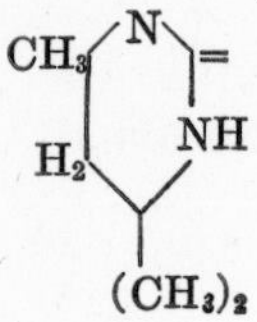		241–2°		1146
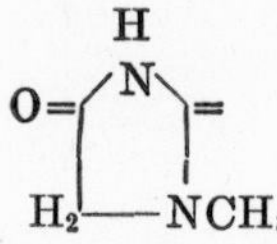		266°D		1734
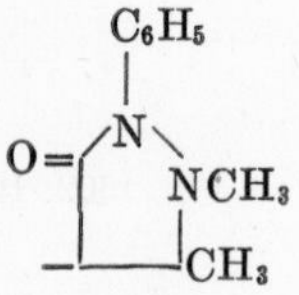		244–5°, 264–5°, 267°	0(S)	32, 407, 518, 2084
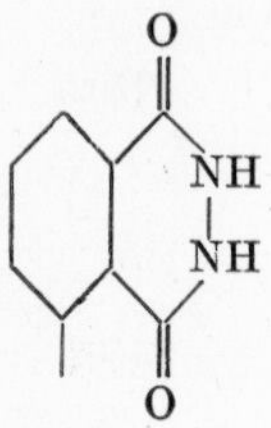		170–2°	0(I, S)	1574, 2373
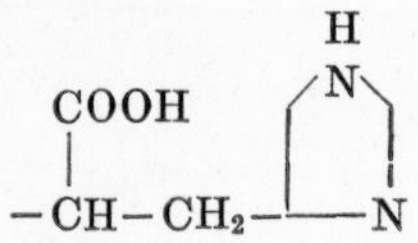		242–3°		649
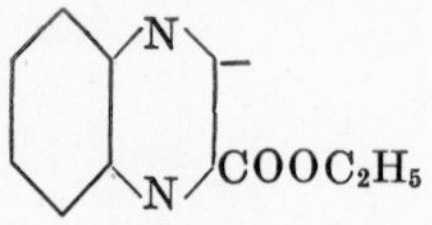		236–7°		2656

TABLE 117

c. N^4-Acetyl-N^1-heterocyclicsulfanilamides with Three or More N-Atoms in the Heterocyclic System

$$CH_3CONH\langle\ \rangle SO_2NHR^1$$

R^1	Melting Range	Activities	References
N–N, N (heterocyclic ring)	237°		653
H, N–N, N (heterocyclic ring)	193.5°, 204°, 210°D	0(S)	1983, 1984, 2370
H, N–N, N (heterocyclic ring)	272–3°	0(P)	686
H, N–N, N–CH₃ (heterocyclic ring)	298–9°	0(P)	686
H, CH₃–N–N (heterocyclic ring)	230–2°	0(S)	2370
H, C_2H_5–N–N (heterocyclic ring)	216–7°		2370
H, $CH_3(CH_2)_2$–N–N (heterocyclic ring)	216.5–7.5°		2370
H, $(CH_3)_2CH$–N–N (heterocyclic ring)	216–7°		2370

TABLE 117—(*Concluded*)

R¹	Melting Range	Activities	References
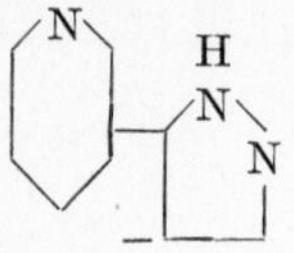	234–6°		2378
	163°D, 207°, 171–2°, 202°D		1376, 1380, 2312, 2313, 2378
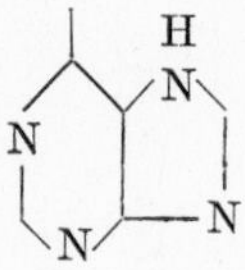	234°D		731
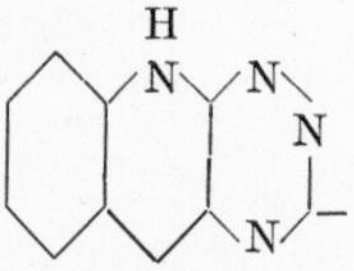	261–2°D		1984

TABLE 118

c. N^4-Acetyl-N^1-heterocyclicsulfanilamides
   4. One N-Atom and One O-, S- or Se-Atom
      in the Heterocyclic System
      a. 2- (N^4 - Acetylsulfanilamido) - 2 - thia-
        zolines

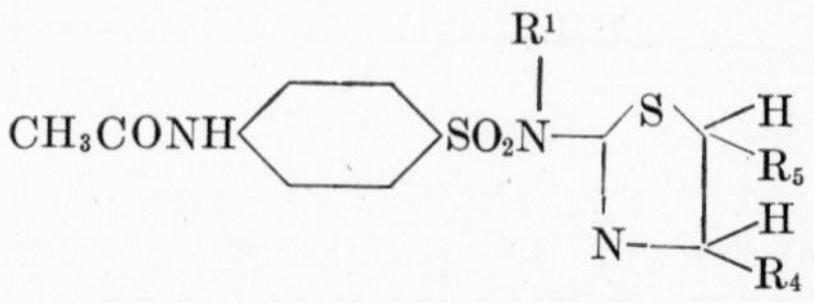

R¹	Melting Range	Activities	References
$CH_2=CHCH_2-$	256–8°[a]		79, 249, 416
	179–81°		1984
C_6H_5-	230°		1984

[a] Acetylsulfathiazoline.

TABLE 119

b. 2-(N^4-Acetylsulfanilimido)-4-thiazolines

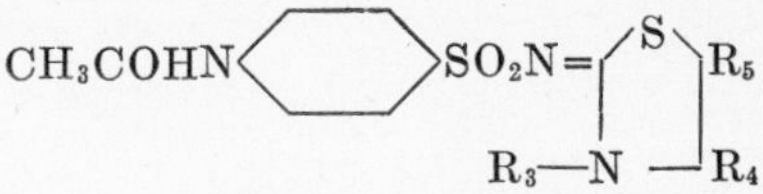

$$CH_3COHN\langle\hspace{1em}\rangle SO_2N=\underset{R_3-N\underset{}{\quad}R_4}{\overset{S}{\diagup}}R_5$$

R_3	R_4	Melting Range	Activities	References
CH_3-		272–3°		184, 246, 249, 1943, 2189, 2232
C_2H_5-		192–4°		1007, 2232
$CH_3(CH_2)_2-$		178–80°		1007, 2232
$CH_3(CH_2)_3-$		213°		1007, 2232
$CH_2=CHCH_2-$		110–2°		1007, 2232
$CH_2=CBrCH_2-$		205–7°		1007
$C_6H_5CH_2-$		203–4°		249, 1007, 2232
$HOCH_2CH_2-$		231–2°D		1007, 2189, 2232
$3\text{-}NO_2C_6H_4COCH_2-$		216–8°		1984
$C_2H_5OOCCH_2-$		222–3°		1007, 2232
$(C_2H_5)_2NCOCH_2-$		245–6°		1007, 2232
$(C_2H_5)_2NCH_2CH_2-$		86–8°		1007, 2232
$C_6H_5SO_2-$		180°		76
CH_3-	CH_3-	237–9°		492
$C_6H_5CH_2-$	CH_3-			343
$(C_2H_5)_2NCH_2CH_2-$	CH_3-	156°		338

TABLE 120

c. 2-(N^4-Acetylsulfanilamido)thiazoles

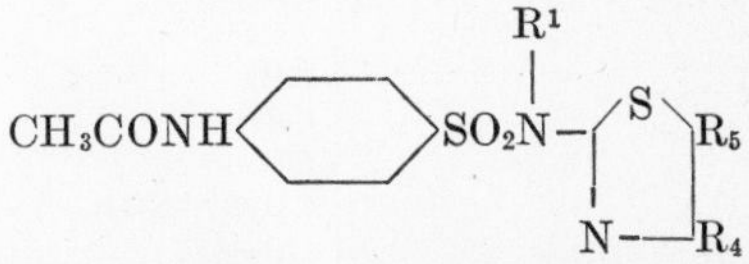

$$CH_3CONH\langle\hspace{1em}\rangle SO_2N-\underset{N-R_4}{\overset{R^1}{\diagup}}\overset{S}{R_5}$$

R^1	R_4	R_5	Melting Range	Activities	References
			256–7°[a]	0(Ec, P)	76, 79, 149, 249, 316, 343, 434, 480, 483, 1057, 1823
CH_3-			103–5°		1007
$H_2O\cdot CH_3-$			115°		249
$(C_2H_5)_2N(CH_2)_2-$					338
$CH_3CONHC_6H_4SO_2-$			127–9°		483, 962
do	CH_3-		194°		483

[a] Acetylsulfathiazole.

TABLE 120—*(Concluded)*

R^1	R_4	R_5	Melting Range	Activities	References
	CH_3-		259–60°	O(I, P, R, Tt)	76, 79, 149, 249, 316, 343, 434, 480, 483, 516, 1427, 1574, 2598
CH_3-	CH_3-		172–3°		492
$C_6H_5CH_2-$	CH_3-				343
$(C_2H_5)_2N(CH_2)_2-$	CH_3-				338
	CH_3-	$Cl-$	217°		622
	$ClCH_2-$		203°D		622
		CH_3-	240°		249, 343
$(C_2H_5)_2N(CH_2)_2-$	CH_3-				338
	C_2H_5-		218°, 230.5–1.0°		39, 622
		C_2H_5-	241–2°		1148
	CH_3-	CH_3-	290°, 264°		249, 622
	$CH_3(CH_2)_2-$		182–3°		592
		$(CH_3)_2CH-$	200–1°		1148
	C_2H_5-	CH_3-	230–1°		492
		$CH_3(CH_2)_3-$	211–2°		1148
	CH_3-	$CH_3(CH_2)_2-$	237–8°		1148
	$CH_3(CH_2)_4-$		163–4°, 184°		591, 1381
		$CH_3(CH_2)_4-$	229°		1148
	CH_3-	$CH_3(CH_2)_3-$			1148
	CH_3-	$(CH_3)_2CH(CH_2)_2-$	234–6°		1148
	$CH_3(CH_2)_6-$		166–7°, 168°		591, 1381
	CH_3-	$CH_3(CH_2)_5-$	216–8°		1148
	$CH_3(CH_2)_8-$		169°		1381
	$CH_3(CH_2)_{10}-$		175°		1381
	$CH_3(CH_2)_{12}-$		175°		1381
	$CH_3(CH_2)_{14}-$		176°		1381
	C_6H_5-		227–9°, 235°		249, 343, 492, 1146
	CH_3-	C_6H_5-			343
	C_6H_5-	CH_3-	285°		79
	CH_3-	$HOCH_2CH_2-$	264°		249, 343, 685
	$CH_3C(=NOH)-$		204°		622
	CH_3-	CH_3CO-	280°		622
		C_2H_5OOC-	228–9°		685, 1146
	$C_2H_5OOCCH_2-$		172–3°		249, 1146
	CH_3-	C_2H_5OOC-	152–3°, 249°		249, 343, 492, 622, 1146
	CH_3-	$C_2H_5OOCCH_2-$	203–4°		1146
	$C_2H_5OOC(CH_3)_2C-$				1146
	$HOOC(CH_2)_{11}-$		98–100°		595
	$4-(NH_2)C_6H_4-$		173–5°		622
	$4-(CH_3CONH)C_6H_4-$		280–1°		622

TABLE 121

d. 2-(N^4-Acetylsulfanilamido)benzothiazoles

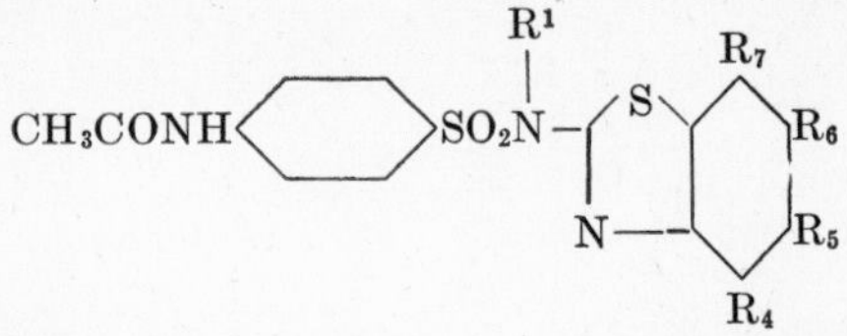

$$CH_3CONH\langle\quad\rangle SO_2N\text{—}\begin{smallmatrix}R^1\\ \\ \end{smallmatrix}\begin{smallmatrix}S\quad R_7\\ \\N\text{——}R_5\\R_4\end{smallmatrix}R_6$$

R_5	R_6	Melting Range	Activities	References
		265°, 286°		249, 343
	NO_2-	303°		343
CH_3-		297–9°		492
	C_2H_5O-	280–1°		343
NH_2SO_2-		240°D		720, 721
CH_3CONH-				343

TABLE 122

e. 2-(N^4-Acetylsulfanilamido)-4-thiazolones

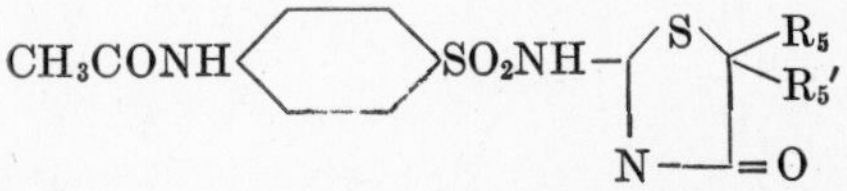

$$CH_3CONH\langle\quad\rangle SO_2NH\text{—}\begin{smallmatrix}S\diagdown R_5\\ \diagup R_5'\\N\text{——}=O\end{smallmatrix}$$

R_5	R_5'	Melting Range	Activities	References
		258–9°, 266.5°		371, 622
CH_3-		244–5°		371
C_2H_5-		200–1°		371
CH_3-	CH_3-	247–8°		371
$CH_3(CH_2)_2-$		187–8°		371
$CH_3(CH_2)_3-$		184–5°		371
C_2H_5-	C_2H_5-	210–1.5°		371
$CH_3(CH_2)_4-$		190–1°		371
$CH_3(CH_2)_{15}-$		143°		371
C_2H_5OOC-		165–6°		622

TABLE 123

f. Miscellaneous N^4-Acetyl-N^1-heterocyclicsulfa-
nilamides with One N- and One O-, S- or Se-
Atom in the Heterocyclic System

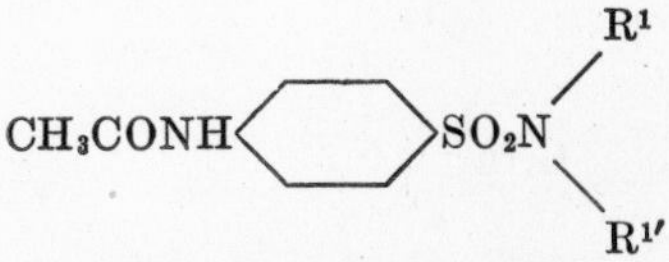

$$CH_3CONH\langle\quad\rangle SO_2N\begin{smallmatrix}R^1\\ \\R^{1'}\end{smallmatrix}$$

R^1	$R^{1'}$	Melting Range	Activities	References
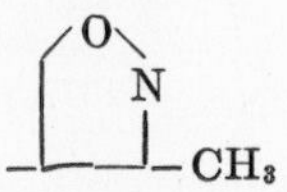 $\begin{smallmatrix}O\\ \diagdown N\\ \text{—}\rfloor\text{—}CH_3\end{smallmatrix}$		192°		385

TABLE 123—(*Continued*)

R¹	R¹′	Melting Range	Activities	References
(structure)		222–4°		385
(structure)		228–9°, 255°		1220, 1383
(structure)		245–6°		385
(structure)		277–8° (·H₂O)180°		32, 150, 492, 622
(structure)		239–40°D		685
(structure)		207–8°		846
(structure)		226.5–8°		2052
(structure)		48–9°		687
(structure)		238–9°		1220
(structure)		220°		1377

TABLE 123—(*Concluded*)

R^1	$R^{1\prime}$	Melting Range	Activities	References
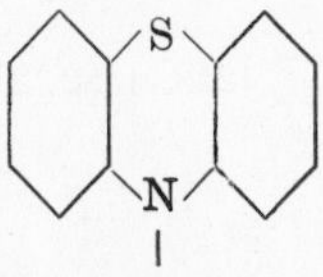		209°		1382
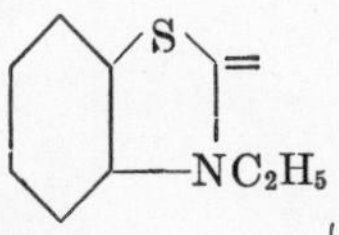	=			343
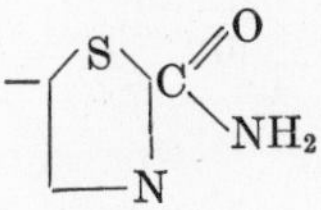		253–5°D		674
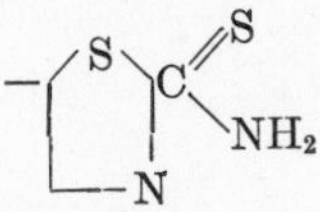		237°D	0(S)	674
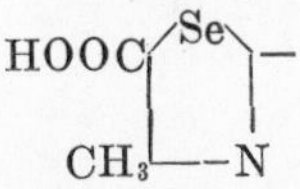		238–9°		1220

TABLE 124

c. N^4-Acetyl-N^1-heterocyclicsulfanilamides

5. Two N-Atoms and one O- or S-Atom in the Heterocyclic System   CH₃CONH⟨ ⟩SO₂NHR¹

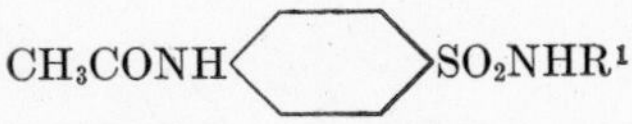

R^1	Melting Range	Activities	References
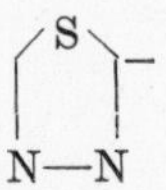	183°, 214–5°, >300°		506, 1218, 2312
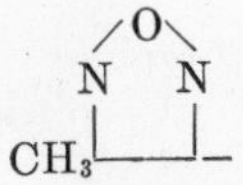	214°, 157°D		2312, 2313
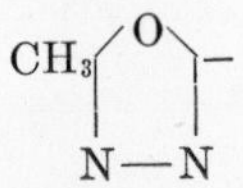	193°, 213°		2312, 2313

TABLE 124—(Concluded)

R¹	Melting Range	Activities	References
CH₃ —[S,N—N ring]—	200°D, 234–5°, 238°		1218, 1382, 2312
CH₃ —[S,N,N–H ring]—			150
$CH=CH(CH_2)_7$—[S,N—N ring]—; $(CH_2)_7CH_3$	104–6°		672
[cyclopentyl] $-(CH_2)_{10}-$[S,N N ring]— ; H_2 H_2 H	117–9°		672
C_6H_5 [O,N N ring]	165°		2313
$C_6H_5CH=CH$—[S,N—N ring]—	202–4°		672
CH_3S—[S,N—N ring]—	216–8°		1218
HO—[S,N,N–H ring]—			1823
NH_2—⟨ ⟩—SO_2NH—[S,N—N ring]—	250–4°		1218

TABLE 125

c. N^4-Acetyl-N^1-heterocyclicsulfanilamides

6. N^1-Nitrogen a Member of the Heterocyclic System

$$CH_3CONH\langle\quad\rangle SO_2N{\supset}$$

$-N{\supset}$	Melting Range	Activities	References
(pyrrolidine ring: H_2 H_2 / $N-$ / H_2 H_2)	179°	±(S)	68, 215
(piperidine ring: H_2 H_2, H_2, $N-$, H_2 H_2)	157–8°	0(S)	5, 36, 171, 173, 213, 214, 215, 720, 1713
(azetidine ring: H_2 H_2 / $N-$)	201–2°	±(S)	68
(decahydroquinoline, N bridged: N, H_2, H_2, H_2)		0(S)	504
(bicyclic amine: H_2, $N-$, H_2, H_2)	174–6°		1329
H C_2H_5 (bicyclic amine: $N-$, H_2, H_2)	156–7.5°		1239
H $(CH_2)_5CH_3$ (bicyclic amine: $N-$, H_2, H_2)	102–3°		1239

TABLE 125—(Continued)

$-N\supset$	Melting Range	Activities	References
H (CH₂)₆CH₃ structure	indefinite		1239
H (CH₂)₁₂CH₃ structure	56–8°		1239
C₆H₅N ... N— structure	260–2°D		265
C₂H₅OOCN ... N— structure	132°		262
CH₃CONH⟨ ⟩—SO₂N ... N— structure	324°	0(S, Sa)	105, 262, 1057, 2084
N / N structure	167°		320
N—CH₃ / N structure	93–4.5°	0(S)	95, 318, 321
N / N cyclohexyl structure	197–200°		318

TABLE 125—(*Continued*)

−N⊃	Melting Range	Activities	References
H₂ H₂ O N− H₂ H₂	165–6°, 105–6°	0(S)	5, 375
Hydroxyethylapocupreicine	105°	0(S)	426
H₂—N = NH H₂—N SO₂⟨⟩NHCOCH₃	245°		968
N–N N NHSO₂⟨⟩NHCOCH₃	220–2°D		1376
H HN=⟨N N −N−	203–4°	0(P)	686
H HN=⟨N N −N—CH₃	245°, 240–1°	0(P)	686, 1376, 2378
NH ‖ N HN N −N			1378
N S	204–6°		2499
H₂⟨O⟩=O H₂− N−	175°, 189–90°		1377, 2370

TABLE 125—(*Continued*)

$-N\supset$	Melting Range	Activities	References
H_2C—O—$C=NH$, H_2C—$N-$	177–8, 198°		1377, 2370
H_2C—O—$C=NSO_2$⟨⟩$NHCOCH_3$, H_2C—$N-$	250–3°D, 310°D		1377, 2370
H_2C—S—$C=NH$, H_2C—$N-$	183°	0, $-$(S)	246, 249, 686, 1344, 1377, 2370
S—$C=NSO_2C_6H_5$, $-N-$	169°		76
H_2C—S—$C=NSO_2$⟨⟩$NHCOCH_3$, H_2C—$N-$	207°, 250°		246, 249, 416, 492
H_2C—S—$C=NH$, CH_3—CH—$N-$	178–9°	$-$(S)	1344, 2370
H_2C—S—$C=NSO_2$⟨⟩$NHCOCH_3$, CH_3—CH—$N-$	145–7°, 150–3°		492, 1824
CH_3, H, C—O—$C=NH$, H_2C—$N-$	191–2°		2370
CH_3, H, C—S—$C=NH$, H_2C—$N-$	162–3°	$-$(S)	1344, 2370
CH_3, H, C—S—$C=NSO_2$⟨⟩$NHCOCH_3$, H_2C—$N-$	185.5–6.5°, 192°		249, 1824

TABLE 125—(*Concluded*)

—N⊃	Melting Range	Activities	References
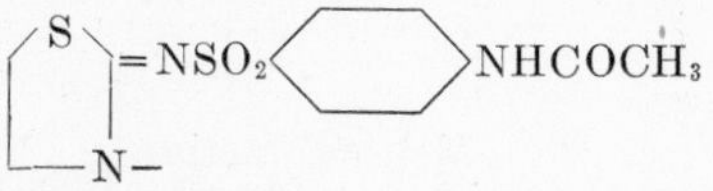	200–20°		76, 249, 962
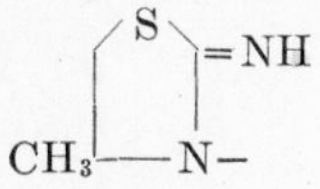	273°		1711
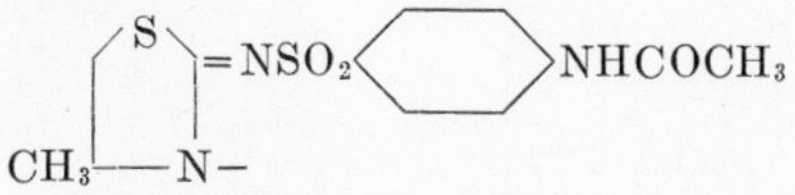	150°, 250°		76, 249
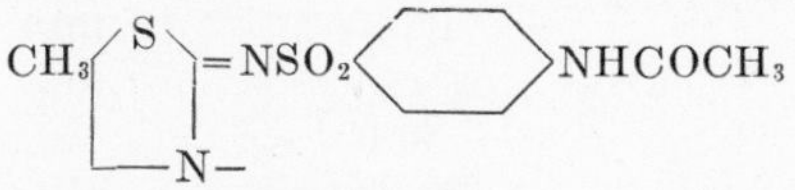	200°D		249
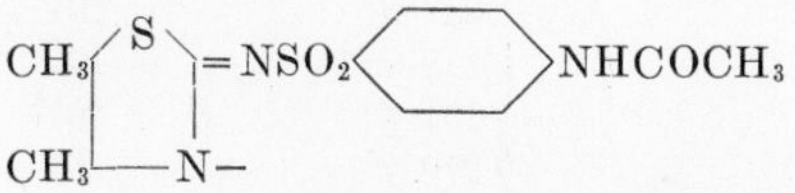	200–20°D		249
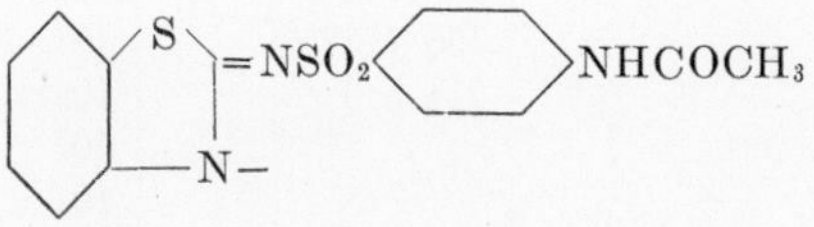	180°		249
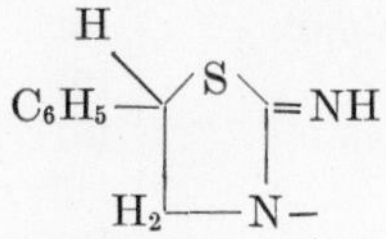	181–3°		1344
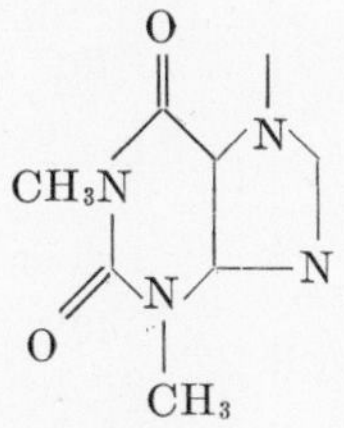	200–3°		318
Quinicine		0(S)	426
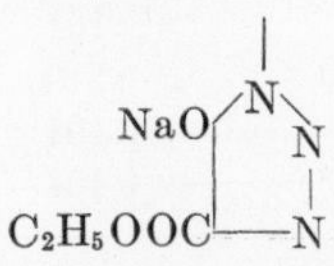			106

TABLE 126

d. N^4-Acetyl-N^1-acylsulfanilamides
 1. N^4-Acetyl-N^1-acyclic-, isocyclic- or heterocyclicacylsulfanilamides

$$CH_3CONH \overset{R^1}{\underset{R^{1\prime}}{\diagdown N}} SO_2N$$

R^1	$R^{1\prime}$	Melting Range	Activities	References
CH₃CO—		258–9°, 253.5–5.5°	0(P, S)	101, 467, 1137, 1702, 1790, 2100
CH₃CO—	CH₃COO⟨ ⟩— (NO₂)	191°		534
CH₂ClCO—		241–2°		371
CH₃CH₂CO—		242.5–4.3°		101
CH₃(CH₂)₂CO—		238.2–40.0°		101
CH₃CH₂CHBrCO—		230–2°		371
(CH₃)₂CHCO—		247–8°		101
(CH₃)₂CHCH₂CO—		215–7.5°		101
CH₃(CH₂)₄CO—		191–3°		101
(C₂H₅)₂CHCO—		270–2°		101
CH₃(CH₂)₅CO—		205–7.5°		101
CH₃(CH₂)₆CO—		195–7.6°		101
CH₃(CH₂)₃CH(C₂H₅)CO—		214–5.6°		101
do	Na—			101
do	½ Mg—			101
CH₃(CH₂)₈CO—		143.2–4.8°		101
CH₃(CH₂)₉CO—		153.2–5.0°		101
CH₃(CH₂)₁₀CO—		130–6°		101
CH₃(CH₂)₁₂CO—		144.2–5.0°		101
(CH₃)₂C=CHCO—		231°		1158
CH₃(CH₂)₇CH=CH(CH₂)₇CO—		131–5°		101
(cyclohexyl CO—)		210–22°		101
(spirocyclic (CH₂)₁₂CO—)				101
C₆H₅CO—		280–5°		101, 365, 2100
4-(NO₂)C₆H₄CO—		270–2°		101
C₆H₅CH₂CH₂CO—		160–205°		101

TABLE 126—(*Concluded*)

R^1	$R^{1\prime}$	Melting Range	Activities	References
$C_6H_5CH=CHCO-$		228–9.5°		101
$(C_6H_5)_2CHCO-$		248.5–51°		101
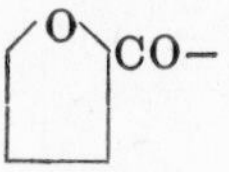 [structure: tetrahydrofuran ring with O and CO−]		240.5–1.5°		101
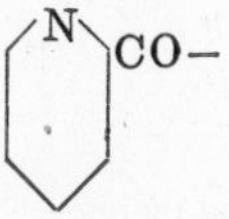 [structure: piperidine ring with N and CO−]		295–300°		101, 107
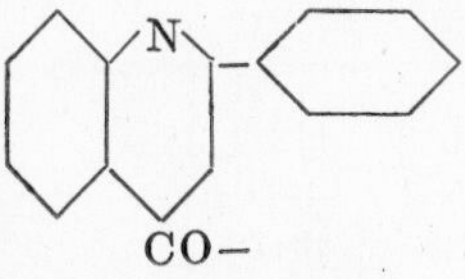 [structure: bicyclic ring with N bridging phenyl, CO−]		166–70°		101
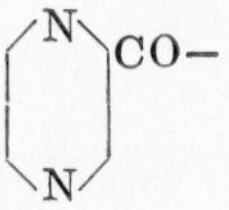 [structure: piperazine ring with two N and CO−]		262–4°		108
$4-(HOOC)C_6H_4CO-$		330°D		105
$4-(NH_2)C_6H_4CO-$		260–3°		101
$C_2H_5OOCCN_2CO-$				106

TABLE 127

2. N^4-Acetylsulfanilylimido Esters

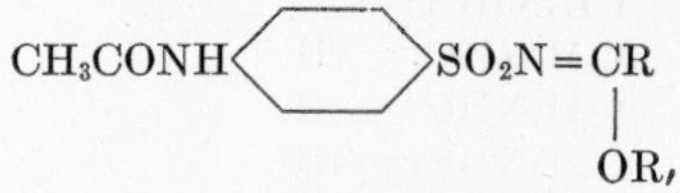

$$CH_3CONH\langle\ \rangle SO_2N=CR$$
$$|$$
$$OR\prime$$

R	R′	Melting Range	Activities	References
C_6H_5-	C_2H_5-	100–102°, 136–7°		701

TABLE 128

3. N^4-Acetylsulfanilylamidines

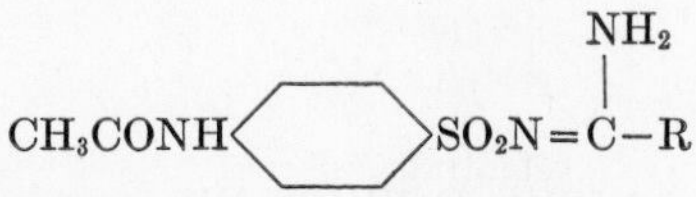

$$CH_3CONH\langle\ \rangle SO_2N=\overset{\overset{NH_2}{|}}{C}-R$$

R	Melting Range	Activities	References
CH_3-		244.2–4.7°	1501, 1862
CH_3CH_2-		192–5°	1501

TABLE 128—(*Concluded*)

R	Melting Range	Activities	References
$CH_3(CH_2)_2-$ ·		149–51°	1501
$CH_3(CH_2)_{11}-$		114–6°	1501
C_6H_5-		180–5°, 211–2°	701, 1501
$C_6H_5CH_2-$		193–4°	1501

TABLE 129

d. N^4-Acetyl-N^1-acylsulfanilamides
4. Derivatives of Carbonic Acid

$$CH_3CONH\langle\ \rangle SO_2NHR^1$$

R^1	Melting Range	Activities	References
$C_2H_5OC(=O)-$	172°		1781
$NH_2C(=O)-$	185–8°, 241–2°		1224, 1781
$CH_3NHC(=O)-$		0(S)	311
$(CH_3)_2NC(=O)-$	>330°		1781
$C_6H_5NHC(=O)-$			1224
$(C_6H_5)_2NC(=O)-$	201°		1781
$4-(CH_3CONH)C_6H_4SO_2NHC(=O)-$	320°		1377
$CH_3OC(=NH)-$	208–9°		1223, 2469
$C_2H_5OC(=NH)-$	223–4°		931
$N\equiv C-$			2469
$NH_2C(=NH)-$	266°, 117–8°D[a]	++(Dy), 0(S)	17, 162, 311, 335, 981, 1354, 1983, 1984, 2214
$CH_3NHC(=NH)-$	246–7°		1734
$C_2H_5NHC(=NH)-$			645
$C_3H_7NHC(=NH)-$			645, 2469
$C_4H_9NHC(=NH)-$			645
$C_5H_{11}NHC(=NH)-$			645
$C_6H_5NHC(=NH)-$			631
$2-(CH_3)C_6H_4NHC(=NH)-$			631
$4-(CH_3)C_6H_4NHC(=NH)-$			631
 $\langle N\rangle-NHC(=NH)-$			2469
$NH_2C(=O)NHC(=NH)-$			646
$N\equiv CNHC(=NH)-$			2469
$NH_2C(=NH)NHC(=NH)-$			20
$(CH_3)_2NC(=NH)NHC(=NH)-$			20
$C_4H_9NHC(=NH)NHC(=NH)-$			20

[a] Acetylsulfaguanidine

TABLE 129—(*Concluded*)

R^1	Melting Range	Activities	References
$C_6H_5NHC(=NH)NHC(=NH)-$			641
$2\text{-}(CH_3)C_6H_4NHC(=NH)NHC(=NH)-$			20, 641, 2469
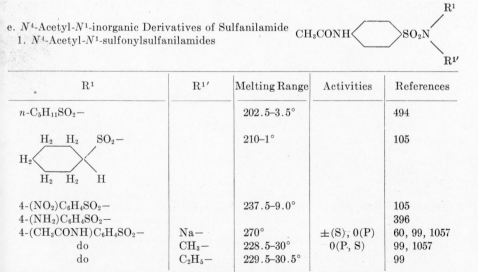 $O\langle\ \rangle NC(=NH)NHC(=NH)-$			20
$4\text{-}(CH_3O)C_6H_4NHC(=NH)NHC(=NH)-$			641
$4\text{-}(CH_3CONH)C_6H_4NHC(=NH)-$			2469
$NH_2NHC(=NH)-$	256–7°		633, 2469
$NO_2NHC(=NH)-$			631, 2469
$NH_2C(=S)-$	200.5°, 285°		622, 1378, 1781
$C_6H_5NHC(=S)-$	>330°		1781
$CH_3SC(=NH)-$	230–2°, 236°		932, 1357
$C_2H_5SC(=NH)-$	180–1°, 188°		1357, 2549
$C_3H_7SC(=NH)-$	174°		2549
$C_4H_9SC(=NH)-$	157°		2549
$CH_2=CHCH_2SC(=NH)-$	173–4°		2549
$C_6H_5CH_2SC(=NH)-$	168°, 171–3°		1357, 2549
$CH_3OCH_2SC(=NH)-$	167°		622
$CH_3OC[N(CH_3)_2]=$	136–44°		1223

TABLE 130

e. N^4-Acetyl-N^1-inorganic Derivatives of Sulfanilamide
  1. N^4-Acetyl-N^1-sulfonylsulfanilamides

$CH_3CONH\langle\ \rangle SO_2N\begin{smallmatrix}R^1\\R^{1\prime}\end{smallmatrix}$

R^1	$R^{1\prime}$	Melting Range	Activities	References
$n\text{-}C_5H_{11}SO_2-$		202.5–3.5°		494
(cyclohexyl)SO_2-		210–1°		105
$4\text{-}(NO_2)C_6H_4SO_2-$		237.5–9.0°		105
$4\text{-}(NH_2)C_6H_4SO_2-$				396
$4\text{-}(CH_3CONH)C_6H_4SO_2-$	Na–	270°	±(S), 0(P)	60, 99, 1057
do	CH_3-	228.5–30°	0(P, S)	99, 1057
do	C_2H_5-	229.5–30.5°		99

TABLE 131

e. N^4-Acetyl-N^1-inorganic Derivatives of Sulfanilamide
2. Miscellaneous Inorganic Derivatives

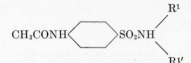

R^1	$R^{1\prime}$	Melting Range	Activities	References
HO—		194–6°	+, ±, 0(S)	182, 297, 373
Cl—	Na—	195–205°D		2331
Cl—	K—	190–200°D		2331
Br—	Na—	250–60°D		2331
Br—	K—	210–20°D		2331
$(CH_3)_2S=$		141–2°D		2331
$(CH_3CH_2)_2S=$		181–2°D		2331
$[CH_3(CH_2)_2]_2S=$		166–7°D		2331
$[CH_3(CH_2)_3]_2S=$		160.0–0.5°D	0(S)	2331
$[CH_3(CH_2)_4]_2S=$		158.5–160°D		2331
$(C_6H_5)_2S=$		204–204.5°	0(S)	2331
$[4-(CH_3)C_6H_4]_2S=$		180.0–0.5°	+(S)	2331
$(C_6H_5CH_2)_2S=$		192.5–193.0°		2331
$[4-(CH_3CONH)C_6H_4]_2S=$		163.5–164.5°D	0(S)	2331
$H_2N—$		183°D, 194–6°	0, —(S)	106, 505, 1427, 1574, 2630
$C_6H_5NH—$		157–9°D		2630
$3-(NO_2)C_6H_4NH—$		180–1°D		2630
$4-(NO_2)C_6H_4NH—$			0(I, P, R)	1427, 1574
$(CH_3)_2C=N—$				106
$C_6H_5CH=N—$				106
$C_6H_5CONH—$		219–20°		185
⟨N⟩CONH—				1041
⟨N⟩(CO)₂N—				1041
$NH_2C(=O)NH—$		227°D		18, 1219, 2630
$C_6H_5NHC(=O)NH—$				1219
$4-BrC_6H_4NHC(=O)NH—$		215–6°D		2630
$4-(NO_2)C_6H_4NHC(=O)NH—$		214.5–5.5°D		2630

TABLE 131—(*Concluded*)

R^1	R$^{1\prime}$	Melting Range	Activities	References
2-(CH$_3$)C$_6$H$_4$NHC(=O)NH—		206.5–7.5°D		2630
4-(CH$_3$)C$_6$H$_4$NHC(=O)NH—				1219
NH$_2$C(=NH)NH—				1219, 1983
NH$_2$C(=S)NH—		193–4°D		18, 1219, 2630
CH$_3$NHC(=S)NH—		228°D		2630
C$_2$H$_5$NHC(=S)NH—		214°D		2630
C$_3$H$_7$NHC(=S)NH—		210°D		2630
C$_4$H$_9$NHC(=S)NH—		212–3°D		2630
C$_5$H$_{11}$NHC(=S)NH—		204°D		2630
CH$_2$=CHCH$_2$NHC(=S)NH—		212.5–14°D		2630
C$_6$H$_5$NHC(=S)NH—		216–7°D		1219, 2630
4-(CH$_3$)C$_6$H$_4$NHC(=S)NH—				1219
NHC(=S)NH— 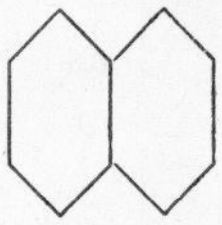		232–3°D		2630
4-(CH$_3$O)C$_6$H$_4$NHC(=S)NH—		209–10°D		2630
4-(HO$_3$S)C$_6$H$_4$NH—		218–20°D	0(I, P, Tt)	1574, 2373
4-(CH$_3$CONH)C$_6$H$_4$SO$_2$NH—		>300°		1329
-N$_2$—				106

TABLE 132

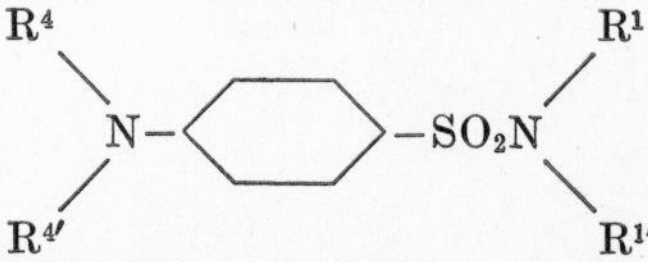

2. N^4-Acyl (other than Acetyl)-N^1-substituted Sulfanilamides
   a. N^4-Acyclicacyl-N^1-substituted Sulfanilamides
      1. R^4 = C$_n$H$_{2n+1}$CO— to C$_n$H$_{2n-3}$CO—

$$R^4\diagdown N{-}\langle\ \rangle{-}SO_2N\diagup R^1_{R^{1\prime}}$$

R^4	R$^{4\prime}$	R^1	R$^{1\prime}$	Melting Range	Activities	References
HCO—		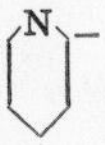 ⟨N⟩—			+(P)	315
ClCH$_2$CO—		CH$_3$—		137°		217, 2464
do		C$_2$H$_5$—	C$_2$H$_5$—	114°		217, 2464
do		BrCH$_2$CH$_2$—		149–50°	+(S), ±(P)	1574, 2373
do		C$_4$H$_9$—		153°		217, 2373 2464,
do		C$_6$H$_5$—				412
do		C$_6$H$_5$CH$_2$—		165°		217, 2464

TABLE 132—(Continued)

R⁴	R⁴′	R¹	R¹′	Melting Range	Activities	References
ClCH₂CO—		(piperidin-1-yl)		188–9°, 192–3°	++(Sa), ±(P)	1086, 1574, 2373
do		HCl (decahydroquinolinyl)		226°		253
do		HCl (decahydroquinolinyl)		166–8°D		253
do		HCl (decahydroquinolinyl)		220°D		253
do		(piperazin-1-yl)		208–210°		1086
do		(thiazolidin-3-yl)		160–5°, 205–6°	0(P, Sa)	1086, 1574, 2373
do		CH₃—(thiazolidinyl)		231–2°		1086
do		CH₃CHOHCH₂—		125–9°		4
do		HOCH₂CH₂—		147°		2464
Cl₃CCO—		CH₂=CH—		138–40°	+(S), 0(P)	1574, 2373
do		CH₂=CHCH₂—		146–7°	+(S), 0(P)	1574, 2373
do		(piperidin-1-yl)		230–1°	±(P), 0(Sa)	1574, 2373
do		(thiazolidin-3-yl)		250–1°	0(I, P)	1574, 2373
do		C₆H₅—(thiazolidinyl)		214–5°	+(S), 0(P)	1574, 2373
do		NH₂C(=NH)—		178–80°	0(P)	1574, 2373
do		HO—		190°D	++(S)	1574, 2373
CH₃CO—	CH₃—	4-(NO₂)C₆H₄—				201
do	CH₃—	4-CH₃COO-3-NO₂C₆H₃—			0(S)	311
do	CH₃—	4-(CH₃CONH)C₆H₄—				201
do	C₂H₅—	(CH₃)₂C(OH)CH₂—		134°		5
do	HC(CH₂)₈— ‖ HC(CH₂)₇CH₃	HC(CH₂)₅— ‖ HC(CH₂)₇CH₃		92°		673
do	C₆H₅CH₂—	(piperidin-1-yl)		177°		341, 486

TABLE 132—(*Continued*)

R⁴	R⁴′	R¹	R¹′	Melting Range	Activities	References
CH₃CO	C₆H₅CH₂–			143–4°		344
do	NCH₂CH₂– / (C₂H₅)₂	CH₃–	CH₃–			536
do	do	C₂H₅–	C₂H₅–			536
do	do	–(CH₂)₅–		oil		536
do	Cl–	Cl–	Na–	200–10°D		634
CH₃CH₂CO–		3,5-Cl₂C₆H₃–		236°		555
do		–(CH₂)₂O(CH₂)₂–		189–90°	±(M, S)	5
do		CH₃CHOHCH₂–		148°	+(M), 0(S)	5
do		(CH₃)₂COHCH₂–		172–2.5°	+(M), ±(S)	5
do		CH₃CH₂CO–		232°		2150
do		4-(HO₂S)C₆H₄–		145–7°		228
do		4-(CH₃CONH)C₆H₄–				201
do		HO–		174–8°	±(S)	182, 373
CH₃CHClCO–		BrCH₂CH₂–		141–3°	++(S)	1574, 2373
do				195–6°	++(Sa), 0(P)	1574, 2373
do						253
do				228°D		253
CH₃CHBrCO–		CH₃CHOHCH₂–		140–3°		4
CH₃(CH₂)₂CO–		4-(NO₂)C₆H₄–		248–50°D		1984
do				206°, 114–5°	++(Sa), +(S), ±(P)	105, 868, 1057, 1983, 1984
do				224–5°		1983
do				244–6°		1983
do		HOCH₂CH₂–		139°	±(M), 0(S)	5
do		HOCH₂CH₂–	HOCH₂CH₂–	114–5°	±(M), 0(S)	5
do		–(CH₂)₂O(CH₂)₂–		191–3°	±(M, S)	5
do		CH₃CHOHCH₂–		127–8°	+(M), 0(S)	5
do		(CH₃)₂COHCH₂–		166°	++(M), ±(S)	5

TABLE 132—(*Continued*)

R⁴	R⁴′	R¹	R¹′	Melting Range	Activities	References
CH₃(CH₂)₂CO—		(structure: N—CH₃ ring)		213°		1984
do		CH₃(CH₂)₂CO—		217–20°		1983
do		2-(HOOC)C₆H₄—		226–8°D		1984
do		4-(HOOC)C₆H₄—		224–6°		1984
do		HO—		172–8°D	+, ±(S)	182, 373, 374
do	Cl—	Na—	Cl—	140–150°D	+(S), ± (P), 0 (Sa)	105, 634, 1057
CH₃CH₂CHClCO—		BrCH₂CH₂—		131–3°	++(S), 0(P)	1574, 2373
do		(N ring structure)		179–82°	+(P, Sa)	1574, 2373
CH₃CH₂CHBrCO—		(N ring structure)		180–2°	0(P, Sa)	1574, 2373
do		(S–N ring structure)		250–1°	0(P)	1574, 2373
(CH₃)₂CHCO—		HOCH₂CH₂—		116.5°	+(S), ±(M)	5
do		—(CH₂)₂O(CH₂)₂—		147°	±, 0(M, S)	5, 311
do		CH₃CHOHCH₂—		144°	+(M), ±(S)	5
do		(CH₃)₂COHCH₂—		173°	++(M), ±(S)	5
do		HO—		172–6°D	±(S)	182, 373, 2181
CH₃(CH₂)₃CO—		CH₃CHOHCH₂—		121.5°	++(M), ±(S)	5
do		(CH₃)₂COHCH₂—		136–6.5°	+(M), ±, 0(S)	5, 311
do		HO—		178–9.5°D	++(S), +(P)	94, 182, 330, 373, 374, 2181
(CH₃)₂CHCH₂CO—		(cyclohexyl structure)		197°		211
do		(CH₃)₂COHCH₂—		146–7°	0(M, S)	5
do		HO—		168.5–73°D	+, ±(S)	182, 373, 374, 2181
CH₃(CH₂)₄CO—		C₆H₅—		190–0.5°	++(S), ±(P)	270
do		4-(NO₂)C₆H₄—		152°, 225°	++(S), ±(P)	270, 1984
do		(N ring structure)		200–1°	++, + (S), ±, 0(P)	270, 272, 904, 1574, 1983, 2179

TABLE 132—(*Continued*)

R^4	R$^{4'}$	R^1	R$^{1'}$	Melting Range	Activities	References
CH$_3$(CH$_2$)$_4$CO—		(structure)		174–5°		272
do		(structure)		222–3°	0(P)	269, 272
do		(structure) –CH$_2$–		129.5–30.5°		272
do		(structure) –CH$_2$–		97.5–9.5°		272
do		(structure) CH$_2$–		131°		272
do		(structure) –CHCH$_3$		143.5–4.0°		272
do		(structure) –CHCH$_3$		168.5°		272
do		(structure) CHCH$_3$		159–60°		272
do		(structure)		214–5°		1086
do		(structure)		199–200°		2656
do		(structure)		182–2.5°	0(P)	2370
do		CH$_3$–(structure)		193–4°	0(P)	2370
do		C$_2$H$_5$–(structure)		206–7°	+(S), 0(P)	2370
do		CH$_3$(CH$_2$)$_2$–(structure)		174–4.5°		2370

TABLE 132—(Continued)

R^4	$R^{4\prime}$	R^1	$R^{1\prime}$	Melting Range	Activities	References
$CH_3(CH_2)_4CO-$		(CH$_3$)$_2$CH— [triazole ring]		182–3°		2370
do		[thiazolidine ring H$_2$S, H$_2$—N]		181–2°		1983
do		[thiazoline ring S—N]		198–9°	++(S), ±(P)	491, 904, 1574, 1983
do		[thiazoline ring S, CH$_3$—N]		171–2°	++(S), 0(P)	492
do		$HOCH_2CH_2-$		116°	++, + (S), 0 (I)	904, 1574, 2179
do	do		$HOCH_2CH_2-$	105°	0(S)	2179
do		$-(CH_2)_2O(CH_2)_2-$		161–1.5°	0(S)	2179
do		$CH_3(CH_2)_4COOCH_2CH_2-$			±(S)	904, 1574
do		[pyridine ring CH$_3$N=]		213–15°		1984
do		[thiazoline ring H$_2$S=, H$_2$—NCH$_3$]		201–3°		1984
do		[thiazoline ring S=, NCH$_3$]		215°		1984
do		[thiazolidinone ring C$_2$H$_5$, H, O=, S, N]		174–5°		371
do		[thiazolidinone ring CH$_3$(CH$_2$)$_3$, H, O=, S, N]		134–5°	++(P, S)	371
do		CH_3CO-		166–9°D		1983
do		$CH_3(CH_2)_2CO-$		164–8°		1983
do		$CH_3(CH_2)_4CO-$		164–72°		1983
do		do	[piperidine ring N—]	155–7°		1984
do		$CH_3(CH_2)_5CO-$		148–52°		1983
do		$CH_3(CH_2)_{14}CO-$		123–6°		1983
do		$CH_3(CH_2)_{16}CO-$		127–30°		1983
do		[cyclohexane ring H$_2$ H$_2$ H, H$_2$, H$_2$ H$_2$ CO—]		185–7°		1983

TABLE 132—(*Continued*)

R^4	$R^{4\prime}$	R^1	$R^{1\prime}$	Melting Range	Activities	References
$CH_3(CH_2)_4CO-$		$-CH_2CH_2OC(=NH)-$		156–7°	+(S), 0(P)	2370
do		$-CH_2CHOC(=NH)-$ | CH_3		155–7°	++(S)	2370
do		$-CH_2CH_2SC(=NH)-$		160–0.5°	+(S), 0(P)	1344, 2370
do		$-CHCH_2SC(=NH)-$ | CH_3		145–6°	0(P)	1344, 2370
do		$-CH_2CHSC(=NH)-$ | CH_3		164–5°	0(P, S)	1344, 2370
do		$-CH_2CHSC(=NH)-$ | C_6H_5		203–4°		1344
do		$HOOCCH_2CH(COOH)-$		216–7°	0(S)	2179
do		$4\text{-}(NH_2)C_6H_4-$		197.5–8.0°	++(S), ±(P)	270
do		[piperazine ring structure]		154°	±(S)	2179
do		$HO-$		175–9°D[a]	++(S), +(Et, P, T)	94, 182, 330, 373, 374, 470, 474, 904, 1257, 1574, 1734, 2181, 2191, 2548
do		$HO-$	CH_3-		+(P), 0(S)	904, 1574
do		$CH_3(CH_2)_3SO_2-$		182–3°	±(S)	494
do		$CH_3(CH_2)_4SO_2-$		152.5–3.0°	±(S)	494
do		$4\text{-}NO_2C_6H_4SO_2-$		201–4°		105
do		$4\text{-}NH_2C_6H_4SO_2-$		245.5–7.0°	0(P, Sa)	105, 1057
do		C_6H_5NH-			0(I, P, R, S)	904, 1574
$CH_3(CH_2)_3CHBrCO-$		[pyridine ring structure]		133–5°	±(P)	1574
do		[thiazole ring structure with CH_3-]		152–4°	±(Sa), 0(P)	1574, 2373
do		$HOCH_2CH_2-$		119–20°	+(S)	1574, 2373
do		$HO-$		110–1°	+(S), 0(P)	1574, 2373
$(CH_3)_2CH(CH_2)_2CO-$		$HO-$		153–7°D	++, ±(S)	182, 373, 374, 2181
$(C_2H_5)_2CHCO-$		$3,5\text{-}Cl_2C_6H_3-$		192°		555
do		[thiazoline ring structure]			0(P)	315
$CH_3(CH_2)_5CO-$		[pyridine ring structure]		193°		1983, 1984

[a] Sulfabenamide.

TABLE 132—(Continued)

R⁴	R⁴'	R¹	R¹'	Melting Range	Activities	References
CH₃(CH₂)₅CO−		(H₂C–S / H₂C–N) thiazolidinyl−		175–6°		1983
do		(S / N) thiazolinyl−		202–3°		1983
do		(H₂C–S= / H₂C–NCH₃)		170°		1984
do		(S= / NCH₃)		173–4°		1984
do		C₂H₅ (H / O= S N)		140–1°		371
do		CH₃(CH₂)₃ (H / O= S N)		139–40°	++(S)	371
do		CH₃(CH₂)₅CO−		131–4°		1983
do		HO−		166–9°D	++(S), 0(P)	94, 182, 330, 373, 374, 904, 1574
CH₃(CH₂)₆CO−		CH₃−	CH₃−	79–82°		1984
do		(N) piperidinyl−		213–4°, 218–9°	++(S), +(Sa), ±(P)	105, 1057, 1984
do		(S= / N–CH₃)		153–4°		1984
do		CH₃(CH₂)₆CO−	(N) piperidinyl−	135°		1984
do		HO−		160–3°D	++(S)	182, 373
CH₃(CH₂)₇CO−		HO−		168–72°D	±, 0(S)	182, 373
CH₃(CH₂)₈CO−		(N) piperidinyl−		168°	0(T)	848
CH₃(CH₂)₉CO−		(N) piperidinyl−		154°	0(T)	848
CH₃(CH₂)₁₀CO−		C₄H₉−		113°		211
do		C₆H₅CH₂−		134°		211
do		(N) piperidinyl−		151.6–3.0°	±(P, S), 0(Le, T)	105, 137, 673, 848, 1057

TABLE 132—*(Concluded)*

R^4	$R^{4'}$	R^1	$R^{1'}$	Melting Range	Activities	References
$CH_3(CH_2)_{10}CO-$			$-(CH_2)_5-$	103°		211
do		$CH_3(CH_2)_{10}CO-$		144–5°	0(P, S)	101, 1057
do		$4-NO_2C_6H_4SO_2-$		185–6.5°		105
do		$4-NH_2C_6H_4SO_2-$		260°D	±(Sa), 0 (P, S)	105, 1057
$CH_3(CH_2)_{14}CO-$		 (thiazolyl ring)		140–7°		1983, 1984
$CH_3(CH_2)_{16}CO-$		 (thiazolyl ring)		148–50°		1983, 1984
$CH_2=CH(CH_2)_8CO-$		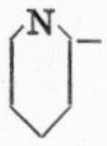 (pyridyl ring)		160°	0(T)	848
$CH_3(CH_2)_7CH=CHCH_2$ $-OC(CH_2)_4CH=CH$		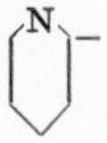 (pyridyl ring)		98–100°	0(T)	848

TABLE 133

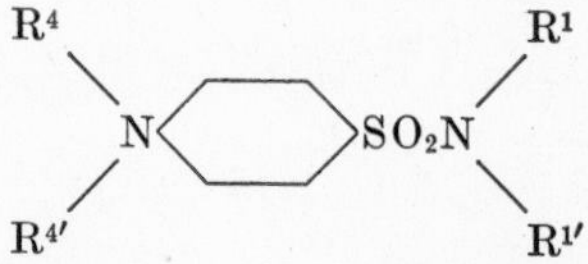

a. N^4-Acyclicacyl-N^1-substituted Sulfanilamides
2. Monosubstituted Derivatives of Dicarboxylic Acids

$$R^4 \diagdown N \diagup \bigcirc \diagdown SO_2N \diagup R^1$$
$$R^{4'} \qquad\qquad\qquad R^{1'}$$

R^4	R^1	$R^{1'}$	Melting Range	Activities	References
$HOOCCO-$	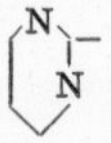 (pyrimidyl ring)		250°D		372
do	 (thiazolyl ring)		203–5°, 207–8°	+(C)	372, 1951, 2182, 2183
$C_2H_5OOCCO-$	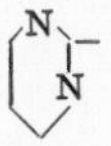 (pyrimidyl ring)		230–5°		372
do	 (thiazolyl ring)		231–2°, 233–4°D		372, 2182, 2183
$HOOCCH_2CO-$	CH_3-	CH_3-			216
do	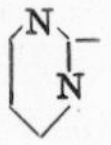 (pyrimidyl ring)		215–6°		372
do	 (thiazolyl ring)		240–50°D	0(C)	372, 1951, 2182, 2183

TABLE 133—(*Continued*)

R⁴	R¹	R¹′	Melting Range	Activities	References
HOOCCH₂CO−	NH₂C(=NH)−		172-5°		372
C₂H₅OOCCH₂CO−	[pyrimidinyl N⌉/N]		198-9°		372
do	[thiazolyl S⌉/N]		193-4.5°	/	372, 2182, 2183
do / HOOC(CH₂)₂CO−	NH₂C(=NH)− / CH₃−	CH₃−	225-6° / ·		372 / 444
do	[pyridyl N⌉]		135-40°	++(C)	372, 475, 1950, 2057
do	[pyrimidinyl N⌉/N]		212-3°	++(C)	372, 1950
do	[pyrazinyl N⌉/N]			+++(C)	832
do	[pyrimidinyl N⌉/N, CH₃]		201-2°	+(C)	372, 1950
do	[quinoxalinyl N⌉/N]		234-5°		2656
do	[thiazolyl S⌉/N]		184-6°, 192-5°ᵃ	See Table 292	372, 2182, 2183
do	[CH₃—thiazolyl S⌉/N]		257.5-8°		2182
do	CH₃CHOHCH₂−		179-92°D	0(S)	4
do	[C₂H₅ C₂H₅ S⌉ O=N]		161-2°	++(C)	372, 1950
do	[C₂H₅ H S⌉ O=N]		208-9°		372
do	NH₂C(=NH)−		214-5°	+(C)	372, 1950
do	HOOCCH₂−		189-90°		2179
do	HOOCCH₂CH₂ | HOOCCH−		165-7°	·	2179
do	4-NH₂SO₂C₆H₄−		234°	++(C)	372, 1951

ᵃ Succinylsulfathiazole ("Sulfasuxidine").

TABLE 133—(*Concluded*)

R⁴	R¹	R¹′	Melting Range	Activities	References
HOOC(CH₂)₂CO—	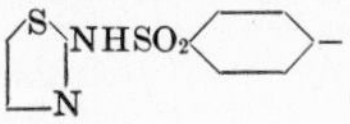 (thiazoline ring)—NHSO₂—⟨ ⟩—		237°	0(C)	372, 1951
do	HO—		170–4°D	0(S), —(C)	182, 373, 1950
C₂H₅OOC(CH₂)₂CO—	CH₃CHOHCH₂—		125–8°	±(S)	4
HOCH₂CH₂NHCO(CH₂)₂CO—	HOCH₂CH₂—		137–42°	0(S)	4
HOOC(CH₂)₃CO—	 (thiazoline ring)—		196–7°		372, 2182
HOOC(CH₂)₄CO—	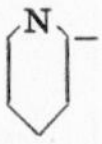 (pyridine ring)—		184–5°		372
do	 (pyrimidine ring)—		188°	±(Ec)	372, 1057
do	 (thiazoline ring)—		196–7°		372, 2182, 2183
do	NH₂C(=NH)—		132–3°		372
HOOC(CH₂)₈CO—	 (thiazoline ring)—		171–2°		372, 2182
HOOCCH=CHCO—	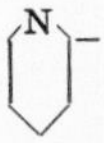 (pyridine ring)—		193–4°		372, 475
do	 (thiazoline ring)—		215–6°	+++(C)	372, 1951, 2182, 2183
do	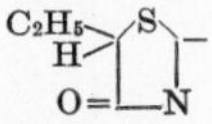 C₂H₅—NH—(thiazolidinone ring)—O=—		179–81°		372
do	NH₂C(=NH)—		201–2°		372
do	HOOCCH₂—		202°D		2179
do	HO—		184–5°D	0, —	182, 373, 1950

TABLE 134

a. *N*⁴-Acyclicacyl-*N*¹-substituted Sulfanilamides

3. Disubstituted Derivatives of Dicarboxylic Acids

$$R^4 = \left[-HN\langle\ \rangle SO_2NHR^1 \right]_2$$

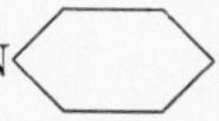

R⁴	R¹	Melting Range	Activities	References
—COCH₂CO—	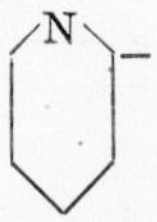 (pyridine ring)—		0(P)	315

TABLE 134—(*Concluded*)

R^4	R^1	Melting Range	Activities	References
$-COCH_2CO-$	(thiazole ring: S, N)	233–6°	0(P)	315, 372
do	$HOCH_2CH_2-$	203–8°D	0(S)	4
do	$CH_3CHOHCH_2-$	173–6°D	0(S)	4
$-COCH_2CH_2CO-$	(thiazoline ring: S, N)	277–9°D		372
do	$HOCH_2CH_2-$	243–50°D	0(S)	4
do	$CH_3CHOHCH_2-$	265–70°D	0(S)	4
$-CO(CH_2)_3CO-$	(thiazoline ring: S, N)	251–4°		372
do	$HOCH_2CH_2-$	196–8°	0(S)	4
do	$CH_3CHOHCH_2-$	187–90°	0(S)	4
$-CO(CH_2)_4CO-$	$NH_2C(=NH)-$	268–9°D		372
$(C_2H_5)_2C\big\langle\!\!\begin{smallmatrix}CO-\\CO-\end{smallmatrix}$	(piperidine ring: N)		0(P)	315
do	(thiazoline ring: S, N)		0(P)	315
$-CO(CH_2)_8CO-$	(thiazole ring: S, N)	245–6°		372

TABLE 135

a. N^4-Acyclicacyl-N^1-substituted Sulfanilamides
   4. Derivatives of Hydroxy Acids

$$R^4NH\!\!-\!\!\langle \rangle\!\!-\!\!SO_2N\!\!<^{R^1}_{R^{1\prime}}$$

R^4	R^1	$R^{1\prime}$	Melting Range	Activities	References
$HOCH_2CO-$	(N-heterocycle)			$\pm(P)$	315
do	(S,N-heterocycle)			$\pm(P)$	315
CH_3OCH_2CO-	$HOCH_2CH_2-$		125–7°	$+, 0(S)$	4, 311
do	$CH_3CHOHCH_2-$			$0(S)$	311
do	CH_3OCH_2-			$\pm(S)$	311
$C_2H_5OCH_2CO-$	C_2H_5-	C_2H_5-	90–1°		217, 2464
do	(bicyclic H_2 structure)		133°		217, 2464
do	$C_6H_5CH_2-$		108°		217, 2464
do	$-(CH_2)_5-$		150°		217, 2464
CH_3COOCH_2CO-	$HOCH_2CH_2-$			$0(S)$	311
do	$CH_3CHOHCH_2-$			$0(S)$	311
do	$(CH_3)_2CCH_2-$ $\|$ OH			$0(S)$	311
$CH_3COOCHCO-$ $\|$ CH_3	$CH_3CHOHCH_2-$		97–103°	$0(S)$	4
$HOOCCHOHCH_2CO-$	(S,N-heterocycle)			$++(C)$	832
do	(S,N-heterocycle with CH_3)				2182
CH_3COCH_2CO-	(N-heterocycle)		176–7°	$+++(S),$ $\pm(P),$ $0(I)$	1574, 2373
do	$HO-$		221–2°		374

TABLE 136

a. N^4-Acyclicacyl-N^1-substituted Sulfanilamides
  5. Derivatives of Amino Acids

$$R^4NH\underset{}{\bigcirc}SO_2N\diagup^{R^1}_{\diagdown R^{1\prime}}$$

R^4	R^1	$R^{1\prime}$	Melting Range	Activities	References
NH_2CH_2CO-			220–1°		1086
do			238–40°		1086
do			215–6°		1086
do			205–6°		1086
$(C_2H_5)_2NCH_2CO-$	C_2H_5-	C_2H_5-	77°		157
do			137°		253
do			115–6°		253
$C_4H_9NHCH_2CO-$	C_4H_9-		85°		217, 2464
do	$C_6H_5CH_2-$		117°		217, 2464
do	$HOCH_2CH_2-$		133°		217, 2464
$C_6H_5NHCH_2CO-$	C_6H_5-		202°		157
$2\text{-}CH_3C_6H_4NHCH_2CO-$	$2\text{-}CH_3C_6H_4-$		170°		157
$3\text{-}CH_3C_6H_4NHCH_2CO-$	$3\text{-}CH_3C_6H_4-$		188°D		157
$4\text{-}CH_3C_6H_4NHCH_2CO-$	$4\text{-}CH_3C_6H_4-$		296°		157

TABLE 136—(*Concluded*)

R^4	R^1	$R^{1\prime}$	Melting Range	Activities	References
H_2 H_2 / H_2 — N—CH_2CO— / H_2 H_2			217–8°		253
do			131°		253
do			172–3°		253
Cl / N—CH_2CO—	CH_3—		272°		217, 2464
do	C_2H_5—	C_2H_5—	158°		217, 2464
4-$CH_3OC_6H_4NHCH_2CO$—	4-$CH_3OC_6H_4$—		185°		157
$(C_2H_5)_2NCH(CH_3)CO$—			137°		253
do			115–6°		253
H_2 H_2 / H_2 — N—$CH(CH_3)CO$— / H_2 H_2					253
do			178°		253

TABLE 137

b. N^4-Isocyclicacyl-N^1-substituted Sulfanilamides

R⁴	R⁴′	R¹	R¹′	Melting Range	Activities	References
[cyclohexyl] H₂ H₂ CO—, H₂, H₂ H₂ H		[thiazolidinyl]		220°		1983
do		[thiazolinyl]		222–3°		1983
do		[pyridyl]	[cyclohexyl] H₂ H₂ H, H₂, H₂ H₂ —CO—	193–5°		1984
(CH₂)₁₂CO—, H₂ H₂ H [cyclobutyl]		[piperidyl]		134–6°	0(T)	848
C_6H_5CO-		CH_3-		156–7°		331
do		CH_3-	CH_3-	177–8°		331
do		C_2H_5-		192–3°		331
do		$CH_3CH_2CH_2-$		192–3°		331
do		$CH_2{=}CHCH_2-$		186–7°		331
do		$C_6H_{11}-$		199–200°		331
do		C_6H_5-		220–1°, 222.5°	0(S)	331, 360
do		$3\text{-}NO_2C_6H_4-$		194–5°		201, 331
do		$4\text{-}NO_2C_6H_4-$		242–3°		331
do		$4\text{-}CH_3C_6H_4-$		209–10°		331
do		$4\text{-}C_2H_5C_6H_4-$		202–3°		331
do		[pyridyl]		251–1.5°		331
do		[quinoxalinyl]		259–60°		2656
do		$-(CH_2)_2O(CH_2)_2-$		241–1.5°		2179
do		$-(CH_2)_5-$		194–5°		331
do		$4\text{-}CH_3OC_6H_4-$		212–3°		331
do		CH_3CO-		262–3°		1597
do		C_6H_5CO-		252°D, 268–70°	+(S), 0(P)	968, 1597, 2196
do		do	[piperidyl]	217°		1984
do		$4\text{-}(CH_3)_2NC_6H_4-$		217–8°		331
do		$4\text{-}H_2O_3AsC_6H_4-$		205.5–6.5°		331
do		$HO-$			0(S)	182
$4\text{-}(NO_2)C_6H_4CO-$		[pyridyl]		248°, 272°	0(I, P), −(S)	341, 486, 1574, 2298

TABLE 137—(*Concluded*)

R⁴	R⁴'	R¹	R¹'	Melting Range	Activities	References
4-(NO₂)C₆H₄CO—		4-NO₂C₆H₄CO—		268°D	0(P, S, M)	2196
C₆H₅CO—	Cl—	Cl—	Na—	160–170°		634
C₆H₅CH₂CO—		3,5-Cl₂C₆H₃—		204°		555
C₆H₅CH=CHCO—		C₂H₅—	C₂H₅—	157°		211
do		C₆H₅CH=CHCO—	[pyridyl ring]	196–8°		1984
2-HOOCC₆H₄CO—		[pyridyl ring]				475
do		[pyridazinyl ring, N–N]		320–2°D	0(C)	1951, 2152, 2179
do		[pyrimidinyl ring, N–N–CH₃]		282–7°D	0(C)	1951, 2152, 2179
do		[thiazolyl ring, S, N]		>260°Dᵃ	+++(C)	372, 1442, 1745, 1947, 1951, 2152, 2182, 2183
do		NH₂C(=NH)—		266–7°		372
do		HOOCCH₂—		184°		2179
do		HOOCCH₂CH₂ | HOOCCH—		176–8°		2179
COOH CO— [dicyclohexyl]		[pyridyl ring]		266–7°		2179
do		[pyrimidinyl ring, N–N]		250–3°		2179
do		[thiazolyl ring, S, N]		270°D		2179
C₆H₅CHOHCO—		[pyridyl ring]		258°	0(P, Tt)	1446, 1574
do		CH₃CO—		246–7°		2395

ᵃ Phthalylsulfathiazole, "Sulfathalidine."

TABLE 138

c. N^4-Heterocyclicacyl-N^1-substituted Sulfanilamides
$$R^4NH\!-\!\!\langle\ \rangle\!-\!SO_2N\!\!\begin{smallmatrix}R^1\\[2pt]R^{1\prime}\end{smallmatrix}$$

R^4	R^1	$R^{1\prime}$	Melting Range	Activities	References
(furan-2) CO—	C_6H_5—		243.5–4.0°	±(S, P)	270
do	4-$(NO_2)C_6H_4$—		259°	±(S, P)	270
do	(pyridyl)—		242°	++(S), 0(P)	270
do	(thiazolyl)—		>240°D		1951
do	4-$(NH_2)C_6H_4$—		238–8.5°	±(S), 0(En, Po)	270, 1485
(thiophen-2) CO—	C_6H_5—		228–30°	±(S, P)	270
do	4-$(NO_2)C_6H_4$—		261–2.5°	±(S, P)	270
do	(pyridyl)—		257–8°	±(S, P)	270
do	4-$(NH_2)C_6H_4$—		267.2°	±(S, P)	270
(pyridin-2) CO—	C_6H_5—		222.8°	0(P)	270
do	4-$NO_2C_6H_4$—		267–9°	0(P, S)	270
do	(pyridyl)—		265–6°	0(P)	270, 307, 308, 2378
do	do	Na—	275°D		307
do	(thiazolyl)—			±(S), 0(P)	95, 150
do	CH_3—(thiazolyl)—				150
do	CH_3CO—		255–6°		107
do	(pyridyl)CO—		222°, 248°		107, 1887
do	4-$NH_2C_6H_4$—		227°		270

TABLE 138—(*Concluded*)

R⁴	R¹	R¹′	Melting Range	Activities	References
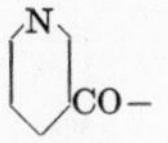 (piperidine-N-CO−)	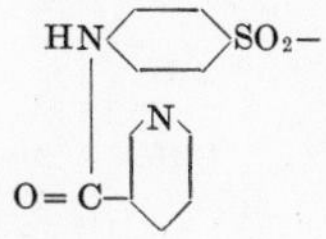 HN⟨ ⟩SO₂− with O=C−N⟨ ⟩	HO−	>250°	0(P, Tt)	1446, 1574
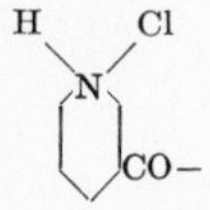 (N(H)(Cl)CO−)	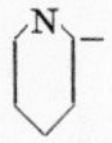 (N-piperidinyl)		148°	++(S), ± (P), 0(I, R, Tt)	307, 1574
do	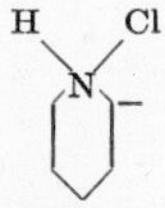 H Cl N⟨ ⟩		115–45°D		307
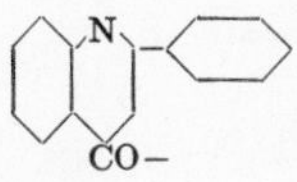 (N-phenyl-piperidine-CO−)	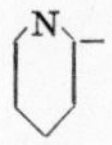 (N-piperidinyl)			0(I, P, R, Tt)	1446, 1574
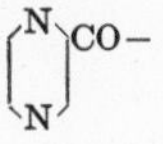 (N,N-piperazine-CO−)	CH₃CO−		249–50°		108
do	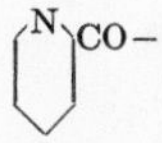 (N-piperidinyl-CO−)		286–90°		108
(N-COOH piperidine-CO−)	(thiazoline S,N)			+++(C)	1951
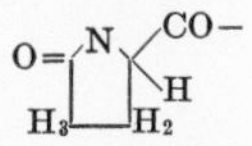 (O=N−C(CO−)(H) H₃ H₂)	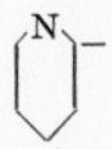 (N-piperidinyl)		273°	0(P, Sa)	968
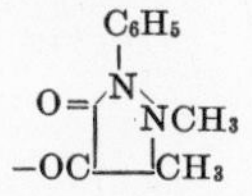 (C₆H₅ O=N−NCH₃ −OC−CH₃)	C₂H₅−	C₂H₅−	174°		1412

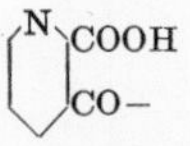

TABLE 139

2. *N*⁴-Acyl (Other Than Acetyl)*N*¹-substituted Sulfanilamides
   d. *N*⁴-Derivatives of Carbonic Acid

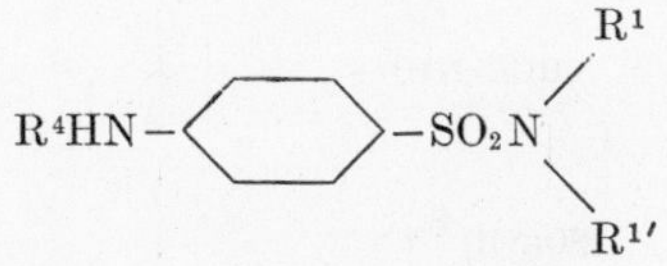

$$R^4HN-\langle\ \rangle-SO_2N\begin{matrix}R^1\\R^{1\prime}\end{matrix}$$

R⁴	R¹	R¹′	Melting Range	Activities	References
C₂H₅OCO−	4-(NO₂)C₆H₄−				224
do	HOCH₂CH₂−		176°	++(M), +(S)	5
do	−CH₂CH₂OCH₂CH₂−		157–8°	+(M), 0(S)	5
do	CH₃CHOHCH₂−		132°	+(M), ±(S)	5
do	CH₃CO−		244°		2100
do	CH₃CH₂CO−		208°		2100
do	CH₃(CH₂)₂CO−		217–8°		2100
do	C₆H₅CH₂CO−		209°		2100
do	4-(NH₂)C₆H₄−		170°		224

TABLE 139—(*Concluded*)

R⁴	R¹	R¹′	Melting Range	Activities	References
C_2H_5OCO-	$4-(NaO_2SNH)C_6H_4-$				224
NH_2CO-	CH_3-	CH_3-		0(S)	1160, 1427, 1574
do	C_2H_5-	C_2H_5-	206–7°	0(S)	96
do	C_6H_5-		207°		2349
do	(thiazoline ring)			0(S)	1384
do	C_6H_5-(thiazoline ring)			0(I, P, R, S, Sa)	1427, 1574
do	$HOCH_2CH_2-$			0(S)	1427, 1574
do	$4-(CH_3O)C_6H_4-$			0(S)	1427, 1574
do	$NH_2C(=NH)-$			0(I, P, R)	1427, 1574
do	$HOOCCH_2-$		202–3°D		2349
do	$CH_3CH(CN)CH_2-$			0(S, Tt)	1427, 1574
do	$4-(NH_2CONH)C_6H_4-$			–(S)	1427, 1574
C_6H_5NHCO-	$COOC_2H_5$ HCS ⬡ $(CH_2)_5CH_3$		129°		1808
do	$COOC_2H_5$ HCS ⬡ $(CH_2)_{15}CH_3$		80°		1808
$NHC(=NH)-$ ⬡ $SO_2NHC_6H_5$	C_6H_5-		245–8°		2540
$NHC(=NH)-$ ⬡ SO_2NH(pyridyl)	(pyridyl)		210–20°D		2540
$NHC(=NH)-$ ⬡ SO_2NH(thiazoline)	(thiazoline)		205–10°D		2540
$NHC(=NH)-$ ⬡ $SO_2NHC(=NH)NH_2$	$NH_2C(=NH)-$		209–10°		2540
$CH_3NHC(=S)-$	(thiazoline)		190–3°		2630
$CH_2=CHCH_2NHC(=S)-$	CH_3-	CH_3-			158
do	$4-(HO_3S)C_6H_4-$				158
do	$4-(NH_2SO_2)C_6H_4-$				158

TABLE 140

$$R^4 \diagdown N \diagup R^{4'} \quad \text{—} \quad SO_2N \diagup R^{1} \diagdown R^{1'}$$

G. N^4-Inorganic Derivatives of N^1-Substituted Sulfanilamides

1. N^4-Sulfonyl-N^1-substituted Sulfanilamides

R^4	$R^{4'}$	R^1	$R^{1'}$	Melting Range	Activities	References
CH_3SO_2—		CH_3—	CH_3—			505
do		$HOCH_2CH_2$—	$HOCH_2CH_2$—		—	505
do		$4\text{-}(NH_2SO_2)C_6H_4$—				505
$C_6H_5SO_2$—		CH_3—	CH_3—	173°		74
do		C_2H_5—	C_2H_5—			74
do		CH_3—				217
$4\text{-}BrC_6H_4SO_2$—		$3\text{-}(NO_2)C_6H_4SO_2$—				63, 100
$3\text{-}(NO_2)C_6H_4SO_2$—		CH_3—				209
$4\text{-}(NO_2)C_6H_4SO_2$—		CH_3—	CH_3—			209
do		C_4H_9—				209
do		C_6H_5—				209
do		$HOOCCH_2$—				209
do		HO_3SCH_2—				100
$4\text{-}(CH_3)C_6H_4SO_2$—		$HOCH_2CH_2$—	$HOCH_2CH_2$—	187–90°	+(S)	639, 1057
do		$HN\text{—}C_6H_4\text{—}O_2S\text{—}C_6H_4\text{—}CH_3$ (structure)		100–50°	0(P, S)	100
(Cl–N / O_2S ring structure)		(N-piperidine structure)				389
(HO–N / O_2S ring structure)		do				389
($CH_3O\text{···}N\text{···}SO_2\text{···}Cl$ fused structure)		C_2H_5—	C_2H_5—	187–9°		109

TABLE 140—(Continued)

R⁴	R⁴'	R¹	R¹'	Melting Range	Activities	References
3,4-(CH₃O)₂C₆H₃SO₂—		CH₃—	CH₃—	168°		217, 2464
do		CH₃—	C₂H₅—	201°		217, 2464
3-HOOC-4-ClC₆H₃SO₂—		C₂H₅—		194–5°		109
4-(HOOC)C₆H₄SO₂—		CH₃—				217
4-(ClOC)C₆H₄SO₂—		CH₃—				217
4-(NH₂OC)C₆H₄SO₂—		CH₃—				217
4-(NH₂NHOC)C₆H₄SO₂—		CH₃—				217
4-(N₃OC)C₆H₄SO₂—		CH₃—				217
3-(HOOC)-4-(HO)C₆H₃SO₂—		CH₃—	CH₃—	205°		430
3-(HOOC)-4-(HO)C₆H₃SO₂—		CH₃—	Na—	203°		430
3-(NH₂)C₆H₄SO₂—		3-(NH₂)C₆H₄SO₂—		>280°D	+(S)	100
4-(NH₂)C₆H₄SO₂—		CH₃—	CH₃—	141ᵃ	+, ++(S), ++(G), +(L)	217, 697, 989, 1302, 1312, 2464
do		CH₃—		194ᵇ	See Table 289	73, 74, 217, 450, 2464
do		CH₃—		190°		217, 2464
do		do	C₂H₅—	164°, 176°		73, 74, 75, 109, 217, 2464
do		C₄H₉—		183°		217, 2464
do		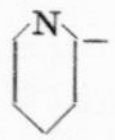 (pyridyl ring structure)		235–8°	±(P, S)	160, 163, 480, 540, 1147
do		 (thiazolyl ring structure)		163–4°	+(S), 0(P)	161, 1147
do		HOCH₂CH₂—	CH₃—	145°	++, ±, 0(S), 0(En, P, Po)	33, 35, 100, 137, 217, 1057, 1485, 2368, 2441, 2464
do		do	C₆H₅—	183–5°	++(S), 0(P)	103, 1057
do		do			++, 0(S), 0(P)	100, 1057
do		do	HOCH₂CH₂—	122.5–2.8°	±(S), 0(En, P, Po)	100, 217, 1057, 1485, 2441, 2464
do		-(CH₂)₂O(CH₂)₂-			±(S)	311

ᵃ "Diseptal B."
ᵇ "Uleron."

			M.P.	Activity	References
4-(NH₂)C₆H₄SO₂—	CH₃CHOHCH₂—		127.3-9.6°	++(M), +, 0(S), ±(P)	5, 100, 1057
do	(CH₃)₂C(OH)CH₂—		184-5°	++(M), 0, ±	5, 311
do	CH₃CO—		187°, 209°		2100, 2102
do	CH₃(CH₂)₁₀CO—		102-4°		101
do	HN⟨C₆H₄⟩SO₂NHCO— / O₂S⟨C₆H₄⟩NH₂				519
do	NH₂(NH=)C— HOOCCH₂—		155-60°	0(S)	162, 1147
do			188°	±(S)	33, 35, 217, 2368, 2464
do	2-(HOOC)C₆H₄—		200-3°	++(S)	100
do	4-(HOOC)C₆H₄—			0(P)	315
do	2-(NaO₃S)C₆H₄—				64
do	4-(NaO₃S)C₆H₄—		>220°D	+, ±(S), 0(P)	100, 1057
do	3,6,8-(HO₃S)₃C₁₀H₄—			0(P)	315
do	HN⟨C₆H₄⟩SO₂NHCH₂CH₂— / O₂S⟨C₆H₄⟩NH₂		120-60°D	±(S), 0(P)	103, 639, 1057
do	HN⟨C₆H₄⟩SO₃Na / O₂S⟨C₆H₄⟩NH₂			0(P, S)	639
do	4-(HO)C₆H₄SO₂—	Na—		±(S), 0(P)	105
do	3-(NH₂)C₆H₄SO₂—		198.5-206°	+(S), ±(P), 0(En, Po)	105, 1057
do	4-(NH₂)C₆H₄SO₂—	CH₃—	218°	++(S)	100, 396, 486, 1057, 1485, 2441
do	CH₃—				217, 2464
4-[(CH₃)₂N]C₆H₄SO₂—	C₂H₅—	C₂H₅—	133-4°		109

TABLE 140—(Continued)

R^4	$R^{4'}$	R^1	$R^{1'}$	Melting Range	Activities	References
CH_3O / Cl, N (quinoline) — NH—C_6H_4—SO_2—		C_6H_5-	C_2H_5-	160-1°		109
$4-(CH_3CONH)C_6H_4SO_2-$		CH_3-	CH_3-	218°		217, 2464
do		CH_3-		183°		217, 450, 2464
do		C_2H_5-	C_2H_5-	225-8°		217, 2464
do		do				109, 217, 2464
do		C_4H_9-				217, 2464
do		$HOCH_2CH_2-$		153°		33, 102, 217, 2368, 2464
do		do	$HOCH_2CH_2-$			2464
do		$-(CH_2)_2O(CH_2)_2-$		121°	0(S)	311
do		$CH_3CHOHCH_2-$		127-8°	0(M, S)	5
do		$(CH_3)_2COHCH_2-$		213°	0(M, S)	5
do		CH_3CO-		178°		2100
do		$CH_3(CH_2)_{10}CO-$		120-152°		101
do		$HOOCCH_2-$		247°		33, 2368
do		$NH_2(NH=)C-$		143-5°D		162
do		$(C_2H_5)_2N(CH_2)_3(CH_3)CH-$			0(Pr)	122, 123
do		$4-(CH_3CONH)C_6H_4SO_2-$				396
$4-[CH_3(CH_2)_2CONH]C_6H_4SO_2-$		$-(CH_2)_2O(CH_2)_2-$		194°		262
C_2H_5OOCN(piperazine, H₂ H₂ / N— / H₂ H₂)$C_6H_4SO_2-$		CH_3-	CH_3-	282°	0(S)	311
(phthalimide: CO—N—CO, fused cyclohexane)SO_2-						2371
$4-(C_2H_5OCONH)C_6H_4SO_2-$		$CH_3CHOHCH_2-$		175-7°	++(M), 0(S)	5
do		CH_3CO-		212°		2102

Structure		4-(HOOC)C₆H₄–	M.p.	0(P)	Ref.
O₂S⟨⟩NHCONH⟨⟩SO₂–					315
HN⟨⟩SO₂NH⟨⟩COOH					
4-[(CH₃)₂NCH₂CONH]C₆H₄SO₂–		CH₃–	113°		217, 2464
4-(C₄H₉NHCH₂CONH)C₆H₄SO₂–		CH₃–	200°		217, 2464
4-(CH₃SO₂NH)C₆H₄SO₂–		CH₃–	192°		217, 2464
CH₃N⟨⟩SO₂NH⟨⟩SO₂–		CH₃–	147–9°		88, 1819
HO₂N⟨⟩SO₂NH⟨⟩SO₂–		CH₃–	188°D		88, 1819
4-[4'-(NH₂)C₆H₄SO₂NH]C₆H₄SO₂–		CH₃–	124°	±(S)	217, 2464
do		HOCH₂CH₂–	137–43°	±(S)	100, 2441
do		do	115.5–20.5°	++(S), 0(Pl)	100, 2441
do		4-(NaO₃S)C₆H₄–	>250°D		100, 1733
SO₂⟨⟩NHSO₂⟨⟩NHCOCH₃		CH₃–	125°		217, 2464
H₂N⟨⟩SO₂NH⟨⟩SO₂–		CH₃–	171–2°		1819
4-(Cl₂PONH)C₆H₄SO₂–		CH₃–			193
HN⟨⟩SO₂– / HOP=O / HN⟨⟩SO₂NH₂		CH₃–			194
4-(NH₂)C₆H₄SO₂–	Na–	CH₃–		++(S)	989, 2464
do	Na– or K–	C₂H₅–			217, 2464

TABLE 140—(Concluded)

R⁴	R⁴'	R¹	R¹'	Melting Range	Activities	References
4-(NH₂)C₆H₄S₂O–	Na–	NaN〈 〉SO_2– O_2S〈 〉NH_2	Na–	340°D	0(P, S)	100, 1057, 2441
do	K–	CH₃– C₂H₅–	CH₃– C₂H₅–		++(S)	989, 2464
						109
SO_2–〈 〉COOH NHC₆H₄(OCH₃)-4						
〈 〉N–〈 〉SO₂– CH₃O NH(CH₂)₃N(C₂H₅)₂		do	do	200°		109
〈 〉N–〈 〉SO₂– CH₃O NH(CH₂)₄N(C₂H₅)₂		do	do	130°		109
〈 〉N–〈 〉SO₂– CH₃O NHCH(CH₂)₃N(C₂H₅)₂ CH₃		do	do	160°		109
O_2S〈 〉N=N〈 〉SO₂– HN〈 〉SO₂N(CH₃)₂		CH₃–	CH₃–	244-51°		843

$$R^4N=N\!\!-\!\!\langle\!\!\bigcirc\!\!\rangle\!\!-\!\!SO_2N\!\!<^{R}_{R^{1\prime}}$$

2. N^4-Acyclic- and Isocyclicazo Derivatives of N^1-Substituted Sulfanilamides

R^4	R^1	$R^{1\prime}$	Melting Range	Activities	References
C_6H_5–	CH_3–	CH_3–			218
do	C_2H_5–				218
do	$3,5$-$Br_2C_6H_3$–		$134°$		555
do	(thiazolyl, CH_3)		$208°$		343
do	4-$(HOOC)C_6H_4$–				218
do	3-CH_3-4-$(HO_3S)C_6H_3$–				218
do	Cl–	Na–			85, 499
do	Cl–	Cl–			85
do	Br-·$3H_2O$	Na–			86
do	do	K–			86
(naphthol structure)	4-$[(CH_3)_2NSO_2]C_6H_4$–				380
2-(HO)-1-$C_{10}H_6$–	$CH_3(CH_2)_{11}$–		163-$4°$		204
do	$CH_3(CH_2)_{17}$–		158-$9.5°$		204
do	$-CHCH_2-N$ (imidazolyl) $\mid$ COOH		255-$7°$		649
do	$-CHCH_2-N$ (imidazolyl) $\mid$ COOCH$_3$		165-$80°$		649

TABLE 141—(Continued)

R⁴	R¹	R¹'	Melting Range	Activities	References
2-HOC₁₀H₆—(1)	NCH₂CH₂CH₂CH— $\overset{\mid}{(C_2H_5)_2}$ $\overset{\mid}{CH_3}$		158°	0(S)	122, 123
do	—N₂—				106
1-HOC₁₀H₆—(2)	N		240–2°		21
2,4-(HO)₂C₆H₃—	C₆H₅—	C₂H₅—		+(S)	512
4-(HO)-3-(CH₃O)C₆H₃—	4-[(CH₃)₂NSO₂]C₆H₄—				380
4,6-(HO)₂-2-(C₅H₁₁)C₆H₂—	C₆H₅—	C₂H₅—		±(S)	512
3-(HOOC)-4-(HO)C₆H₃—	S—N		a	+	2302
do					1384
do	4-[(CH₃)₂NSO₂]C₆H₄—			0	
CH₃CO(HOOC)CH—	CH₃CO(HOOC)CH—	C₂H₅—	200°		127
4-[(C₂H₅)₂NSO₂]C₆H₄—	do	CH₃(CH₂)₂—	171–2°		378
4-[[CH₃(CH₂)₂]₂NSO₂]C₆H₄—	C₂H₅—		140–5°		1791
4-(C₆H₅NHSO₂)C₆H₄—	CH₃(CH₂)₂—		255–6°		1791
4-(C₆H₅CH₂NHSO₂)C₆H₄—	C₆H₅—		252–3°		1791
	C₆H₅CH₂—				1791
N—NHSO₂	N		274–6°		1791
4-(CH₃CONHSO₂)C₆H₄—	CH₃CO—		273°		1791
O₂S—HN—SO₂NH₂	4-NH₂SO₂C₆H₄—		310°		1791

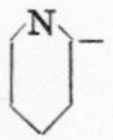

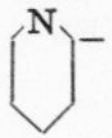

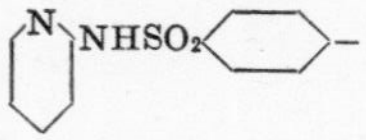

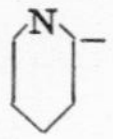

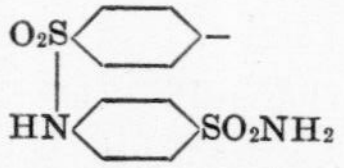

a Salazopyrin

			M.p.		Ref.
4-[Na(Cl)NSO₂]C₆H₄– 1-(HO)-4-(HO₃S)C₁₀H₅–(2)	Na– HO(CH₂)₃–	Cl–			499 212
4-(CH₃)₂NC₆H₄–	[H₂ H₂ N–S ring]				481
do	[N ring]				481
do	[CH₃ N–S ring]				481
4-[(C₂H₅)₂N]C₆H₄–	[N piperidine]				341
2,4-(NH₂)₂C₆H₃–	[N piperidine]		213-4°		21, 160, 171, 1147
do	CH₃CO–		180°D		2100
do	HOOC(CH₂)₂CH–		118-9°D		348
do	HOOC(CH₃)CH–		114°D		348
do	4-(HO)C₆H₄CH₂(HOOC)CH–		158-60°D		348
do	4-(NH₂SO₂)C₆H₄–		223-5°		328
2,4-(NH₂)₂C₆H₃–	NCH₂CH₂CH₂CH– CH₃			+O(Pr)	122
HCl·2,4-(NH₂)₂C₆H₃–	(C₂H₅)₂ CH₃–	CH₃–	181°		213
do	CH₃–		234°		213
do	C₂H₅–	C₂H₅–	160°		213
do	do		221°		213
do	[H₂ H₂ H / H₂ H₂ cyclohexane]		234°		213
do	C₆H₅CH₂–		288°		171, 213
do	CH₃OHCH₂–		194°		213

TABLE 141—(Continued)

R⁴	R¹	R¹'	Melting Range	Activities	References
HCl·2,4-(NH₂)₂C₆H₃—	—(CH₂)₅—		241°		171, 213
1-NH₂C₁₀H₆—(2)	(piperidine ring, N—)		236-8°		21
1-NH₂-2-CH₃-4-C₁₀H₅—	2-CH₃-1-C₁₀H₆—				2457
do	(piperidine ring, N—)		239°D	0(T)	2457
do	(thiazolidine ring, S, N—)	CH₃—	218°	0(T)	2457
4-HOOCCH₂O-2-(NH₂)C₆H₃—	CH₃—				215
6-(HOOC)-2,4-(NH₂)₂C₆H₂—	4-(NH₂SO₂)C₆H₄—				127
6-NH₂-1-HO-3-HO₃S-2-C₁₀H₄—	(piperazine ring, N, N—)			++(L, Mp)	2572
do	(ring, N, N—CH₃)			++(L, Mp)	2572
do	(CH₃—ring, N, N—CH₃)			++(L, Mp)	2572
6-NH₂-1-HO-3-NaO₃S-2-C₁₀H₄—	—(CH₂)₅—		>300°		171
7-NH₂-1-HO-3-HO₃S-2-C₁₀H₄—	HOOCCH₂—		>300°		348
do	HOOC(CH₃)CH—		>300°		348
do	4-(HO)C₆H₄CH₂CH₂(HOOC)CH—				348
2-(C₂H₅)₂N-5-HO-7-(HO₃S)C₁₀H₄—	CH₃—	CH₃—			215

			Ref.
CH₃CONH— / HO₃S— ring —OH / —SO₃H	(pyridine ring)	++(L, Mp, Tr)	2572
do	(N–N pyrimidine ring)	++(L, Mp)	2572
do	(N–N ring, CH₃)	++(L, Mp)	2572
do	(CH₃, N–N, CH₃ ring)	++(L, Mp)	2572
CH₃CONH— / NaO₃S— ring —OH / —SO₂Na	(pyridine ring)		1529
do	(quinoline ring)		1529
do	(N–N ring)		1529
do	(S, N thiazole ring)		1529

TABLE 141—(Concluded)

R⁴	R¹	R¹'	Melting Range	Activities	References
(structure)	(thiazoline-N ring)				1529
(structure)	$NCH_2CH_2CH_2CH-$ $(C_2H_5)_2$　CH_3			0(Pr)	122, 123
(structure)	C_2H_5-	C_2H_5-			215
do	$-(CH_2)_4-$				215
do	$-(CH_2)_5-$				215
(structure)	(piperidine-N ring)			++(T)	830
(structure)	(thiazoline-N ring)				807

TABLE 142

3. N^4-Heterocyclicazo Derivatives of N^1-Substituted Sulfanilamides

$$R^4N=N\left\langle\right\rangle SO_2N\begin{smallmatrix}R^1\\ \\R^{1'}\end{smallmatrix}$$

R⁴	R¹	R¹′	Melting Range	Activities	References
	4-[(CH₃)₂NSO₂]C₆H₄–				380
	do		146°	++(S)	349
	do		258°D		378
				+(S)	1147
					160
do				0(P)	161, 1147
	C₂H₅–				215
	CH₃–	CH₃–	168°		215
do	C₄H₉–		>300°		215
do				0(I, P, R)	1427, 1574
do	–(CH₂)₅–		164°		215

TABLE 142—(*Continued*)

R^4	R^1	$R^{1'}$	Melting Range	Activities	References
NH₂–N–NH₂ (ring)	CH_3-		207°	0(S)	1713, 1714
do	CH_3-	CH_3-	177–8°		1713
do	C_2H_5-		170–1°	0(S)	1713, 1714
do	do	C_2H_5-	219–20°		1713
do	$CH_3CH_2CH_2-$		182–3°	0(S)	1713, 1714
do	$CH_3CH=CH-$		149–50°	0(S)	1713, 1714
do	$C_5H_{11}-$	$C_5H_{11}-$		0(S)	1714
do	$C_6H_{11}-$		160–1°		1713
do	C_6H_5-		208°	+(S)	331, 1714
do	$3\text{-}(NO_2)C_6H_4-$		232–3°		331
do	$4\text{-}(NO_2)C_6H_4-$		265–6°	+(S)	331, 1714
do	$4\text{-}(CH_3)C_6H_4-$		193–4°		331
do	N (ring)–		200–1°	++(S)	331, 1714
do	$HOCH_2CH_2-$	$HOCH_2CH_2-$	165°		214
do	–(CH₂)₅–		195–6°		1713
do	$4\text{-}(CH_3O)C_6H_4-$		187°		331
do	$4\text{-}(C_2H_5O)C_6H_4-$		197–8°	+(S)	331, 1714
do	$4\text{-}[(CH_3)_2N]C_6H_4-$		201–2°	++(S)	331, 1714
do	$4\text{-}(H_2O_2As)C_6H_4-$		275–7°	++(S)	331, 1714
do	C_6H_5NH-			0(S)	1714
NH₂–N–NH₂·HCl (ring)	CH_3-		214°		214
do	CH_3-	CH_3-	233°		214
NH₂ (ring), N	H₂ H₂ / H₂ (ring) / H₂ H₂ H		270°		214
do		–(CH₂)₅–	280°		214
HCl·NH₂ (ring), N	CH_3-	CH_3-	258°		214
NH₂CH₂ (ring), N / HO	C_2H_5-	C_2H_5-	212–4° *		369
HO / NH₂CH₂ (ring), N	CH_3-	CH_3-	183–5°		369

TABLE 142—(*Concluded*)

R⁴	R¹	R¹′	Melting Range	Activities	References
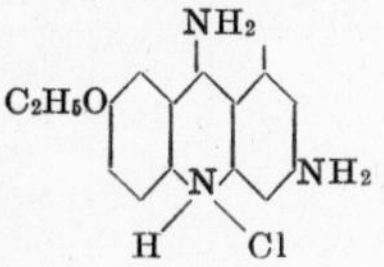 C_2H_5O ... NH_2 ... NH_2 ... N, H, Cl (acridine structure)	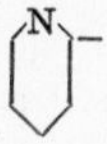 pyridyl		>250°D		1962, 2018
do	 thiazolyl		>250°D	0(I)	1528, 1901, 1962
Egg albumin	 pyridyl				545
Egg albumin	 thiazolyl				545
Human serum	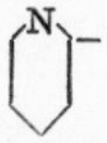 pyridyl				545
Human serum	 thiazolyl				545
Horse serum albumin	 thiazolyl				807
Horse serum globulin	 thiazolyl				807
Human serum globulin	 thiazolyl				807

TABLE 143

4. Diazoamino Compounds Derived from N^1-Substituted Sulfanilamides

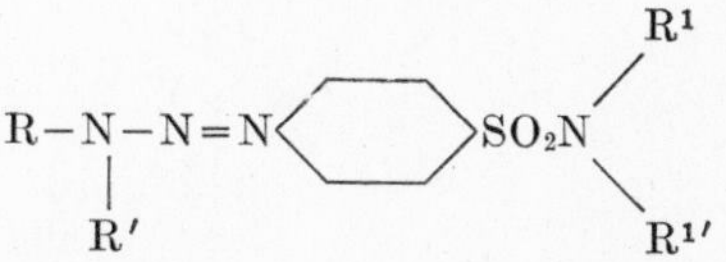

$$R-N-N=N\langle\ \rangle SO_2N\begin{smallmatrix} R^1 \\ \\ R^{1\prime} \end{smallmatrix}$$
$$\overset{|}{R'}$$

R	R′	R¹	R¹′	Melting Range	Activities	References
NaO_3SCH_2-	$HOCH_2CH_2-$	$4-[(CH_3)_2NO_2S]C_6H_4-$				2460
$HO_3SNHCONHC(=NH)-$		CH_3-	CH_3-			2460
$HOOCCH_2-$	CH_3-	CH_3-	CH_3-			2460
$4-(HOOC)C_6H_4-$		CH_3-	CH_3-			2460
do		CH_3CO-				2460
do		$4-(NH_2O_2S)C_6H_4-$				2460
do		$4-[(CH_3)_2NO_2S]C_6H_4-$				2460

TABLE 143—(*Concluded*)

R	R′	R¹	R¹′	Melting Range	Activities	References
4-$(C_2H_5OOC)C_6H_4-$		CH_3-	CH_3-			2460
$-(CH_2)_4CH(COOH)-$		CH_3-	CH_3-			2460
$NaO_3SCH_2CH_2-$	CH_3-	CH_3-	CH_3-			2460
4-$(NaO_3S)C_6H_4-$		CH_3-	CH_3-			2460
4-$(N_3SO_2)C_6H_4-$		$N_2=$				106
2-(HOOC)-4-$(HO_3S)C_6H_3-$		CH_3-	CH_3-			2460
do	C_2H_5-	CH_3-	CH_3-			2460
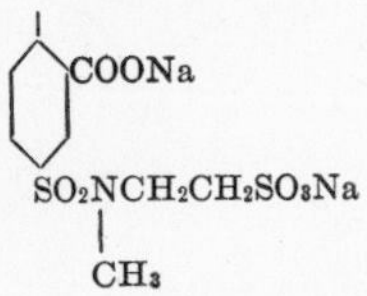 (structure: ring with COONa; SO₂NCH₂CH₂SO₃Na; CH₃)	CH_3-	CH_3-	CH_3-			2460
2-(HOOC)-5-$(HO_3S)C_6H_3-$		CH_3-	CH_3-			2460
do		4-$(NH_2O_2S)C_6H_4-$				2460
do		4-$[(CH_3)_2NO_2S]C_6H_4-$				2460
4-$(Na_2O_3As)C_6H_4-$	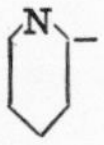 (pyridyl structure)					2019

TABLE 144

G. N^4-Inorganic Derivatives of N^1-Substituted Sulfanilamides
5. Miscellaneous Inorganic Derivatives

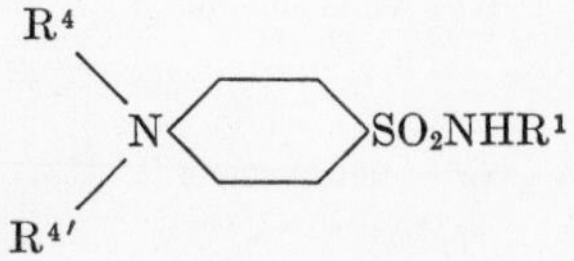

R⁴	R⁴′	R¹	Melting Range	Activities	References
$HO-$		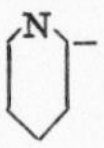 (pyridyl structure)	147°D		58
$HO-$		 (thiazolyl structure)	240–50°D		1384, 2230
$HO-$		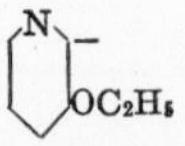 (pyridyl with OC_2H_5)	189–90°D		435
NaO_3S-		$HC(CH_2)_8-$ ‖ $HC(CH_2)_7CH_3$	235–60°D		673
do		4-$[(CH_3)_2NO_2S]C_6H_4-$			224, 2462
do		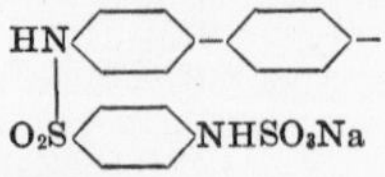 HN (biphenyl structure) O_2S (ring) $NHSO_2Na$			224, 2462
NH_2-		 (pyridyl structure)	190°		21

TABLE 144—(*Concluded*)

R⁴	R⁴'	R¹	Melting Range	Activities	References
C₆H₅NH—		3,5-Br₂C₆H₃—			555
(CH₃)₂C=N—		(structure)	229–30°		21
C₆H₅CH=N—		do	243–4°		21
HOOCCH₂CH₂(CH₃)C=N—		do	209–10°		21
C₂H₅OOCCH₂(CH₃)C=N—		do	187°		21
—N₂—		do	186–7°D	++(S, Sa), + (P), 0(En)	12, 1057, 1485
—N₂—		(structure)			12
—N₂—		(structure)			12
—N₂—		(structure)			12
(structure) NHSO₂—⟨⟩—N= (with ‖O)		(structure)	280–5°		843
(structure) NHSO₂—⟨⟩—N= (with ‖O)		(structure)			843
CH₃—N (structure) NHSO₂—⟨⟩—N= (with ‖O)		CH₃—N (structure)	298°		843
HO₂P(=O)—		(structure)		+(P)	604
do		(structure)		++(P)	604
Cl₂P(=O)—		CH₃—			192
do		4-(NO₂)C₆H₄—			193
do		4-(NH₂SO₂)C₆H₄—			193
do		4-[(CH₃)₂NSO₂]C₆H₄—			194
do		4-[Cl₂PONH]C₆H₄—			193
4-(NH₂SO₂)C₆H₄NHP— (with ‖O above, OH below)		4-(NO₂)C₆H₄—			194
do		4-[(CH₃)₂NSO₂]C₆H₄—			194
do		HN—⟨⟩— / HOP=O / HN—⟨⟩—SO₂NH₂			194
4-[(structure)—NHSO₂]C₆H₄NHP— (with ‖O, OH)		(structure)		±	505

245

TABLE 145

IV. Nuclear-N^1,N^4-substituted Sulfanilamides

Structure: $\dfrac{R^1}{R'}$N–SO$_2$– (benzene ring: R$_2$, R$_3$, R$_5$, R$_6$) –N$\dfrac{R^4}{R^{4'}}$

R⁴	R⁴'	R¹	R¹'	R₂	R₃	R₅	Melting Range	Activities	References
A. N⁴-Acyclic									
CH₃–		CH₃CH₂–	CH₃–		HOOC–				2460
	CH₃–	SO₃H					182°		111
CH₃–		C₆H₅–					158°		623
B. N⁴-Isocyclic									
C₆H₅–		HOCH₂CH₂–			NO₂–				140
do		CH₃–			NO₂–				140
do		do			NO₂–				140
3-CH₃C₆H₄–		CH₃–	CH₃–		C₆H₄NHSO₂–		158-9°		219
4-CH₃C₆H₄–		CH₃–	CH₃–		NH₂–		187°		219
4-CH₃OC₆H₄–		CH₃–	CH₃–		HOOC–		173-4°		219
do		CH₃–	CH₃–		do		115°		219
do		CH₃–			do		oil		219
do		C₆H₅–			ClOC–				219
do		C₆H₅–	C₂H₅–		–CH₂CH₂NHCO–N(C₂H₅)₂		170-1°		31, 219
do					HOOC–		233°		31
C. N⁴-Heterocyclic									
–(CH₂)₅–		–(CH₂)₅–	C₂H₅–	NO₂–	do		121°		317
D. N⁴-Acyl									
CH₃CO–		CH₃–		CH₃–		CH₃O–			560
do		CH₃–		CH₃–		C₂H₅O–			560
do		CH₃–	CH₃–	CH₃–		do			560
do		C₂H₅–	C₂H₅–	CH₃–		C₂H₅O–			560
do		do	do	CH₃–		CH₃O–			560
do		C₄H₉–							560
do		C₆H₅–		CH₃COO–			213-4°		2455

do			N⟨pyridine⟩		NO₂–	CH₃–	270°		262
do			do		NCS–		243.5–4.5°		453
do			⟨CH₃–thiazole⟩				237–8°D		721
do			⟨CH₃–thiazole⟩		⟨H₂N–S–S–SO₂ structure / S–N–CH₃ / NH⟩		232–5°D		721
do / do			HO(CH₂)₄– / HOCH₂CH₂–	CH₃–	CH₃O–	CH₃O–			311 / 560
CH₃(CH₂)₁₆CO–			ClCH₂–		NO₂–		oil / 165–7°	0	1163 / 96
NH₂CO– / do			C₂H₅– / do		CH₃–		147–8°	0 / 0	96
E. N⁴-Sulfonyl									
4-NO₂C₆H₄SO₂–	C₂H₅–	CH₃– / C₂H₅– / CH₃– / CH₃–	CH₃– / C₂H₅– / CH₃– / CH₃–	CH₃–	HOOC– / do / NaOOC–		246–7°		209 / 209, 214 / 209, 217, 2464 / 217, 2464
do		CH₃–	CH₃–		NH·HOOC– / (C₂H₅)₂				217, 2464
4-(NH₂)C₆H₄SO₂–	C₂H₅– / do / do	C₂H₅– / do / do	C₂H₅– / do / do		HOOC– / NaOOC– / NH·HOOC– / (CH₂CH₂OH)₂		205–6°		217, 2464 / 217, 2464 / 217, 2464

TABLE 146

V. Unclassified Derivatives of Sulfanilamide

Formula	Melting Range	Activities	References
$SO_2NH-N=N$ (ring) $N=N--NHSO_2$ (ring)	>240°D	+	301
$\overset{Na}{\underset{\vert}{SO_2N}}-N=N$ (ring) $N=N-N-SO_2$ (ring) $\underset{\vert}{Na}$		+	301
$SO_2NH-N=N$ (ring) NH SO₂ SO₂ NH (ring) $N=N--NHSO_2$		+	301
$4-[C_6H_4CH=N]C_6H_4SO_2NH_2$ $\overset{\Vert}{O}$		++(S)	347
$4-[4'-(NO_2)C_6H_4CH=N]C_6H_4SO_2NH_2$ $\overset{\Vert}{O}$		++(S)	347
SO_2NH Hg NH or $SO_2NH-Hg-NHSO_2$ $NH-Hg----NH$	240°D		1973

TABLE 146—(*Concluded*)

Formula	Melting Range	Activities	References
SO₂NH ... Hg ... NH (Br Br) or SO₂NH—Hg—NHSO₂ (Br Br Br Br) NH—Hg———NH			1973
Condensation product of Cl, NO₂, NO₂ with HON= CH₃—N, N—⟨ ⟩SO₂NH⟨ ⟩ O			21
Reaction product of NH₂SO₂⟨ ⟩N=NCH₂COCOOH with diaminoacridine		+	381
"Tropinone bis-sulfonamidophenylhydrazone acetate"		±	61
"N,N'bis(tetrahydroanacardyl)sulfanilamide"	154.5°		1149

Chapter V

STRUCTURE AND ACTIVITIES OF COMPOUNDS RELATED TO SULFANILAMIDE

In this chapter are listed many of the compounds, outside the classification of derivatives of sulfanilamide, which were made or studied as part of the extensive research originating from the discovery of the chemotherapeutic activity of sulfanilamide.

(I) 4-Nitrobenzenesulfonamides (Tables 147–161, p. 261–274)

Synthesis. Many of these compounds were made as intermediates by reaction of an amine with 4-nitrobenzenesulfonyl chloride. By reduction with neutral iron, hydrogen and a catalyst, or with ammonium sulfide, the corresponding sulfanilamide derivatives were formed.

Pharmacology. Reduction of the nitro group also occurs in the body as has been repeatedly demonstrated by the appearance of a diazotizable amine in the blood.[148, 542, 1007, 1702] Whether the nitro compounds owe their entire *in vivo* activity to the fraction reduced to amino has not been established with absolute certainty but appears highly probable. *In vitro*, 4-nitrobenzenesulfonamide had no inhibiting effect on type I pneumococci at a concentration of 200 mg. per 100 cc.[1384] This confirmed an earlier report[346] which had also demonstrated no *in vitro* activity.

Mayer and Oechslin[346] who favored a theory that an oxidation product of sulfanilamide was the active agent, claimed that *in vivo*, 4-nitrobenzenesulfonamide was five times as potent as sulfanilamide, presumably because by partial reduction it gave a higher concentration of the postulated active drug. This theory has now been discarded by most investigators and the apparent greater activity is probably to be explained by better maintenance of blood levels of sulfanilamide in mice.

Flynn and Kohl[148] demonstrated that liver suspension will reduce 4-nitrobenzenesulfonamide to a diazotizable amine and that 80% of ingested nitro compound was so reduced in rats.

Weber, Lalich and Major[542] studied the pharmacology of 2-(4-nitrophenylsulfonamido)-pyridine ("Nisulfadine"), (Table 150). Its solubility in water was less than 1 mg. per 100 cc. at 20°C. which made *in vitro* studies difficult. They studied its blood levels in dogs, rabbits and man by a modification of the Bratton-Marshall method in which one aliquot of the sample was determined, as is, to give the sulfapyridine content and a second aliquot was reduced with zinc in the presence of acid before determination. The difference in the results then represented the content of "Nisulfadine" (valid in dogs where no conjugation of sulfapyridine takes place).

They found the drug to be very poorly absorbed in dogs when given by the oral route. Following 0.5 Gm./kilo, maximum blood levels of 0.5 mg./100 cc. of nitro compound were produced in 4 to 8 hours while the blood level of sulfapyridine rose to a maximum of 3.2 mg./100 cc. in 12 hours. In the urine 27 mg./100 cc. of nitro compound and 114 to 514 mg./100 cc. of sulfapyridine were noted after 8 and 24 hours. When given intravenously at 0.1 Gm./kilo every 4 hours, urinary levels up to 815 mg./100 cc. of nitro compound after 36 hours were noted but blood levels did not exceed 0.8 mg./100 cc., while blood levels of sulfapyridine did not exceed 0.5 mg./100 cc. This suggested that the nitro compound was very rapidly excreted and that not much reduction occurred in the circulatory system although both liver and kidney suspension were capable of bringing it about. The authors thought that the higher levels of sulfapyridine following oral ingestion were brought about by reduction in the large intestine before absorption. They showed that the contents of the dog's ileus or colon would bring about such a reduction and so would incubation with *E. coli*.

"Nisulfadine" was studied clinically[1702] for treatment of ulcerative colitis but was inferior to 2-(4-nitrophenylsulfonamido)thiazole, ("Nisulfazole"), (Table 154), for this use because it caused a much higher incidence of nausea.

A patient receiving 3 Gm. of "Nisulfadine" daily developed blood levels of 2.3 to 7.9 mg./100 cc. of sulfapyridine and 1.5 to 3.6 mg./100 cc. of "Nisulfadine". When receiving 4 Gm. of "Nisulfazole" daily he showed 0.7 to 1.6 mg./100 cc. of sulfathiazole and 5.8 to 9.2 mg./100 cc. of "Nisulfazole".

The authors considered their results in treatment of 5 cases of ulcerative colitis as suggestive of further trial of the compounds. Further reports have not been noted in the last three years, however.

Only one derivative in the class of nuclear-N^1-substituted-4-nitrobenzenesulfonamides was noted. This was 2,4-dinitrophenylsulfonylpiperidine, melting at 130°[317].

(II) Derivatives of Orthanilamide and Metanilamide (Tables 162–169, p. 274–278)

Synthesis. Derivatives of orthanilamide are less readily synthesized than sulfanilamide and metanilamide derivatives, not only because the starting intermediate is more difficult to prepare but the reaction with amines frequently leads to low yields, because of steric hindrance. The best method of preparing such derivatives is to start with *o*-nitrochlorobenzene and proceed to *o*-nitrobenzenesulfonyl chloride by the series of reactions used in preparing *p*-nitrobenzenesulfonyl chloride (Chapter II). The reactions of this with amines and subsequent reduction of the nitro group are similar to those with the para isomer.

Metanitrobenzenesulfonyl chloride is readily prepared by heating 1 mole of nitrobenzene with 3 moles of chlorosulfonic acid at 125–130° until a sample of the reaction mixture, when boiled with sodium hydroxide, gives complete solution and absence of nitrobenzene odor. The reaction mixture is then cooled, drowned in ice and water and the product recovered by filtration. It may be recrystallized from such solvents as toluene, chloroform, or ethylene dichloride, if desired.

Another procedure is the nitration of benzenesulfonyl chloride with oleum and fuming nitric acid.[a]

Purification of *m*-nitrobenzenesulfonyl chloride is most conveniently carried out by dissolving in glacial acetic acid, treating with an activated charcoal and precipitating by dilution with water.[b]

Pharmacology. The derivatives of orthanilamide and metanilamide have not been extensively studied because of the lack of activity found in early work. It was demonstrated that orthanilamide and metanilamide were inactive both *in vivo* and *in vitro*[513, 1384, 2441]. Further, each was adequately absorbed into the blood stream and into bacterial cells[140] so that the compounds appeared to be inherently inactive.

The N^1-derivatives of 6-methylmetanilamide (Table 166) are claimed to be active against pneumococcal and brucella infections in the patent literature[2463] but no scientific

---

[a] Gurdzhi, I. H., *Chem. Abstracts*, **34**, 2343 (1940).
[b] Hodgson, H. H., and Whitehurst, J. S., *J. Chem. Soc.*, **1944**, 482.

publication has given the details of this work so it is difficult to judge its significance. Such activity, if verified, would be important to current theories of mechanism of action and the future development of the field.

Other derivatives of orthanilamide and metanilamide which show activity are N^2- or N^3-sulfanilyl derivatives (Tables 162, 165) but these are in reality N^1-substituted sulfanilamides, hence would be expected to show some activity. Note that N^3-metanilylmetanilamide is inactive.

One or two other derivatives have been said to be slightly active. It is well, therefore, not to jump to the conclusion that all orthanilamide and metanilamide derivatives will be inactive against all organisms. Thus far there has been little incentive to further synthesis of such derivatives, however.

(III) Acyclic Compounds (Tables 170–173, p. 280–281)

Pharmacology. Many of the acyclic compounds were synthesized because of their analogy to sulfanilamide; *i.e.*, an aliphatic chain of carbons was substituted for the benzene ring. These were inactive.

The compound called pantoyltaurine was synthesized by Snell[479] and later by others[709, 1493, 1664] as a result of the essential metabolite theory of chemotherapy as developed by Fildes and Woods (see Chapter XI). Since pantothenic acid had been shown to be an essential metabolite for many bacteria, Snell reasoned that by replacing the carboxyl group of pantothenic acid by an —SO_2OH group (analogous to the substitution of —COOH by —SO_2NH_2 in *p*-aminobenzoic acid) he might obtain a compound which, if present in sufficient concentration, might substitute for pantothenic acid in a bacterial enzyme system essential to growth and thus inhibit growth of the organism. Such inhibition should be reversed by pantothenic acid. This he found to be the case.

McIllwain[1669] defined an antibacterial index as the ratio of the molar concentration of metabolite substitute to the molar concentration of the essential metabolite required to prevent growth. Pantoyltauramide had an antistreptococcal index of 100 and an antipneumococcal index of 10,000. Pantoyltaurine (Table 172) had an antistreptococcal index of 500 and an antipneumococcal index of 1,000. Homopantoyltaurine was less active. He pointed out that only organisms needing an exogenous supply of pantothenic acid were inhibited. Some organisms are capable of synthesizing their own pantothenic acid and these were not inhibited. The *in vitro* studies of the analogues of pantothenic acid on various bacteria and the reversal by pantothenic acid is somewhat afield from the subject of this book and the original references should be consulted for further information.

(IV) Isocyclic Compounds

(A) Isocyclicsulfonamides

(1) 4-Aminoalkylbenzenesulfonamides (Table 174, p. 282)

Pharmacology. 4-(Aminomethyl)benzenesulfonamide hydrochloride (homosulfanilamide, "Sulfamylon") was introduced in Europe under the name "Marfanil" (Mesudin is an obsolete name). This compound well illustrates the danger of overlooking potentially important drugs by inadequate testing, since the compound was synthesized in this country, tested *in vitro* against streptococci, found inactive and abandoned[361]. In Germany it was tested against anaerobic organisms *in vitro* and found more effective than any other sulfonamide drug[990]. It was extensively used in the German army for prophylaxis against gas gangrene.

Jensen and Schmith[1384, 1385] found that the effect of "Marfanil" on anaerobic organisms, or on pneumococci, was not reversed by PABA or by *p*-(aminomethyl)benzoic acid, nicotinamide, or vitamin B₁. This indicated that it acts through a different mechanism of action than sulfa drugs, which are strongly antagonized by PABA. Others[1581, 2505] confirmed this finding. Methionine and peptone were found to antagonize its action, however[2502]. It was also shown[1385, 1581] that organisms made resistant to sulfathiazole are still susceptible to "Marfanil" and *vice versa*.

Attempts[1581] to repeat the experiments *in vivo* using guinea pigs infected with *Clostridium septicum* showed that the drug was apparently antagonized by PABA. This result is probably an artifact caused by toxicity of PABA or through some other mechanism which would come to light on further study.

(2) **4-Aminophenylalkanesulfonamides** (Table 175, p. 284)

Pharmacology. The reported activities on these compounds were obtained *in vivo* and while they showed the compounds to be inactive it would be rash, in view of the lesson provided by "Marfanil", to assume that the compounds would be inactive under other conditions and against other organisms.

(3) **4-Aminoalkylphenylalkanesulfonamides** (Table 176, p. 285)

Pharmacology. The above remarks also apply to these compounds.

(4) **Miscellaneous 4-Alkyl (or Substituted Alkyl)benzenesulfonamides** (Table 177, p. 285)

p-Toluenesulfonamide was said by a few authors to have slight activity *in vivo* but this has been called questionable by more recent work. *In vitro* it was inactive against streptococci, pneumococci and *Strep. viridans*[2441]. It was surprising to find *p*-toluenesulfonanilide claimed active *in vitro* against streptococci and pneumococci (but not against viridans)[2441].

The patent[476] claims activity comparable with sulfapyridine for *N*-nicotinyl-*p*-toluenesulfonamide and its isomers. The author has seen nothing published in the scientific literature to justify such a comparison.

Andrewes, *et al.*[659] reported very promising results in treatment of typhus (Rp) infections in mice with *p*-sulfamylbenzamidine hydrochloride (V-147) and *p*-sulfamylbenzamidoxime hydrochloride (V-186). It was necessary to give repeated doses and administer the drugs before, or soon after, infection to secure the best therapeutic effect. Clinical trials were unsuccessful, and typhus infections in guinea pigs were not satisfactorily treated. All closely related derivatives were less active.

One of these same drugs (V-147) was found by Evans, Fuller and Walker[2533] to be highly active *in vitro* against *Clostridium welchii* and against streptococci but to have practically no activity against *E. coli*, staphylococci and Gram-negative organisms. Activity was demonstrated against *Clostridium welchii* in guinea pigs as well. Like "Marfanil", "V-147" was not antagonized by PABA, hence probably was active through a different mechanism.

(5) **Miscellaneous Benzenesulfonamides** (Table 178, p. 287)

Benzenesulfonamide was completely inactive *in vitro* against streptococci, pneumococci and *Strep. viridans*[2441] and *in vivo* against streptococci.[512, 2441] The same was true of 4-chlorobenzenesulfonamide. 4-Nitrosobenzenesulfonamide was active against streptococci *in vivo* and this might be anticipated because it is an oxidation product of sulfanil-amide and might be reduced by the body. 4-Hydroxybenzenesulfonamide was inactive against streptococci, pnenumococci and *Strep. viridans, in vitro*[2441]. A large number of the ethers of *N*-substituted-4-hydroxybenzenesulfonamides have been unsuccessfully tested for activity against *Trypanosoma equiperdum*[2574].

3-Nitro-4-hydroxybenzenesulfonamide was said to have a marked curative effect on streptococcal septicemias and to be less toxic than sulfanilamide[327]. Since this work was done before the effect of PABA antagonism was known it would be interesting to see whether the activity of this compound would be antagonized.

(6) Naphthalenesulfonamides (Table 179, p. 295)

Pharmacology. These do not appear to have been extensively investigated but the reported activities are not encouraging. Introduction of a nitro group in the 8-position on naphthionic acid was said to have an "activating" influence on the activity[1222].

(7) 2'-Substituted Biphenyl-4-sulfonamides (Table 180, p. 296)

Pharmacology. All of these compounds proved inactive *in vitro* against *E. coli* and also *in vivo* against streptococci.

(8) 4'-Substituted Biphenyl-4-sulfonamides (Table 181, p. 297)

Pharmacology. These compounds, which are vinylogues of sulfanilamide and its N^1 derivatives, are of theoretical interest but their activities have not been revealed.

(9) Miscellaneous Isocyclicsulfonamides (Table 182, p. 298)

Pharmacology. These have not shown appreciable activity.

(B) Derivatives of 4-Aminobenzoic Acid

The Woods-Fildes theory (Chapter XI) postulates that *p*-aminobenzoic acid (PABA) is an essential metabolite for many bacteria and that compounds which are closely related structurally may substitute for PABA without performing the functions of PABA essential for growth of the organisms. It was, therefore, logical to look for bacterial inhibitors among the derivatives of PABA and many such active compounds have now been found. None have proved to be the equal of the more active sulfanilamide derivatives, however.

As an aid in understanding the complex relationships found among these compounds it should be noted that the nature of the effect will depend very largely on the concentration. Thus at very high concentrations most drugs can be bactericidal, *i.e.*, the bacteria are killed so that they cannot grow if transferred to fresh culture medium free of drug or be restored by addition of an antagonist. At lower concentrations the drugs may be bacteriostatic, *i.e.*, growth is stopped but the bacteria are still viable and may be restored to growth, as above. At still lower concentrations the drug may be inert or may even show growth stimulation or perhaps antagonism for other drugs. The range of concentrations at which these effects are observed will vary with the drug, with different species of bacteria, with temperature, with pH and with the composition of the substrate.

In the case of derivatives of PABA which show bacteriostatic activity over a wide range of concentrations, the inhibition of growth is completely antagonized by low concentrations of PABA and such relationships obey the law of mass action over a certain range of concentrations, in accordance with the Woods-Fildes theory.   McIlwain's antibacterial, or chemotherapeutic, index:

$$\frac{\text{Molar Concentration of inhibitor}}{\text{Molar Concentration of PABA}}$$

at bacteriostasis therefore applies and offers a convenient method for expressing the potency of the drug.   The smaller the index the greater the potency.   Where data are available on this index they have been substituted for the less significant expressions used elsewhere in this monograph.

Some of the derivatives of PABA behave as antagonists of sulfonamide drugs and of other PABA derivatives.   Similar relationships have previously been noted in vitamin analogues and derivatives but as yet there is no way of predicting whether a newly synthesized derivative will show vitamin or antivitamin activity, or merely be inert. Sufficient members of the PABA family have been made so that Johnson, Green and Pauli[1395] have arrived at the following generalizations[a] correlating structure and activity:

"1. Monosubstitution by neutral or weakly electropositive groups in the 2 or 3 position of PAB yields compounds with bacteriostatic properties.   There is little to choose between the two positions as far as activity is concerned.

2. Disubstitution whether in the 2,3 position or in the 3,5 position results in compounds which exhibit no bacteriostatic action.

3. Replacement of the amino group by any of the groups thus far studied, other than nitro, results in inactive compounds.

4. Variation of the carboxyl group by replacement or by derivative formation may give compounds which exhibit PAB activity, bacteriostatic activity or neither.   No rational conclusions can be drawn.

5. Simultaneous variation of the amino group, including replacement by the nitro group, and substitution in the benzene nucleus result in inactive compounds.

6. Simultaneous variation of the amino and carboxy groups gives inactive compounds."

They were unable to correlate the structures and activities of heterocyclic isosteres of PABA, however.

(1) Nuclear-substituted (Table 183, p. 298)

Pharmacology.   Wyss, *et al.*[580] found that 2-fluoro-4-aminobenzoic acid had 1/3 the activity of PABA as a sulfonamide antagonist and as a growth factor for *Cl. acetobutylicum* or a mutant of *Neurospora crassa*.   The 2-bromo derivative had 1/200, the 2-iodo 1/1500 and the 3-carboxy 1/2000 the activity of PABA as a sulfonamide antagonist.   The most active compound as a bacteriostatic agent in their series was 2-chloro-4-aminobenzoic acid which was almost as active as sulfapyridine against *E. coli* in a synthetic medium; however, this compound was very susceptible to antagonism by methionine.   Also it was not active *in vivo* partly because blood levels could not be maintained.   When 3% drug was fed in the rations of mice the blood level did not exceed 1 mg. per 100 cc.   Johnson, Green and Pauli[1395] found this drug to have bacteriostatic properties against *E. coli* reversable by PABA at concentrations greater than 10 mg./100 cc., while exhibiting antagonism to sulfanilamide at concentrations less than 2 mg./100 cc.   They found it to have

[a] Data quoted with the permission of the authors and copyright owner.

strongly antagonistic effects to the action of sulfonamide drugs on streptococcus and pneumococcus.

(2) Carboxy-substituted (Table 184, p. 299)

Pharmacology. It would be reasonable to suppose that derivatives of PABA formed by making acid derivatives of the carboxyl group, could revert to PABA in some cases by bacterial enzyme action and in most cases by the catabolic processes of the host. This seems verified in many cases where such derivatives show a brief period of bacteriostasis followed by normal growth. It has also been verified where the compounds show delayed antagonism of sulfa drugs. *p*-Aminobenzamide has been shown to have weak bacteriostatic properties which are lost after a few hours[1313, 1315].

(3) Amino-substituted (Table 185, p. 300)

Pharmacology. These derivatives appear uniformly inactive. In view of the fact that most of the substituents listed can be removed by catabolic processes of the host, these would be expected to show a PABA effect *in vivo*.

(4) Nuclear-carboxy-substituted (Table 186, p. 301)

Pharmacology. Substitution of the carboxyl by making the amide of 3-methyl-4-aminobenzoic acid (see Table 183) weakened the bacteriostatic powers by a factor of 6 to 9 depending on the organism tested[1395].

(5) Carboxy-amino-substituted (Table 187, p. 301)

The only two derivatives for which activities are shown were inactive *in vitro*. One might expect most such compounds to show PABA action *in vivo* through removal of the substituent groups.

(C) Derivatives of 4-Nitrobenzoic Acid

(1) (2) (3) Esters (Table 188, p. 301)

Pharmacology. The bacteriostatic activity of 4-nitrobenzoic acid offers special interest to theories of action of sulfonamide drugs because if the drug is reduced by bacterial enzymes, or by catabolic processes of the host, it gives rise to PABA, the antagonist of its action and that of sulfa drugs in general. That it does have typical sulfanilamide type bacteriostatic activity over a narrow concentration range and for a brief time has been amply demonstrated[1384, 1395, 1785, 2441] against several organisms in which reversal by PABA has also been observed, as well as its self-reversal through reduction to PABA. The compound is unique in that it is one of the few compounds where the amino group has been substituted by a different group (active *per se* and not by reconversion to amino) with retention of typical sulfanilamide type of bacteriostatic effect. Against Streptococcus *in vitro* it showed little effect and was able to antagonize the effect of sulfapyridine[1395]. This was explained as rapid transformation to PABA by the organism (see Chapter IX (II) for further discussion of 4-nitrobenzoic acid).

n-Hexyl 4-nitrobenzoate has been given the trade name "Amonal A" in Europe where it is said to be particularly effective against types I, II, III and X pneumonia in animal studies.[a]

---

[a] *Schweiz. med. Wochschr.*, **73**, 664 (1943).

The large number of other esters of *p*-nitrobenzoic acid have shown varying degrees of activity in mice probably reflecting different rates of absorption, hydrolysis and excretion and, perhaps rates of reduction. Many of these drugs are too insoluble to test *in vitro*.

(4) Miscellaneous Derivatives (Table 189, p. 303)

Pharmacology. Neither the *N*-substituted 4-nitrobenzamides nor the nuclear-substituted 4-nitrobenzoic acids have shown appreciable activity. Many of these were prepared as intermediates on the way to the amino compounds.

(D) Derivatives of Sulfanilic Acid (Table 190, p. 304)

Pharmacology. Sulfanilic acid (or its sodium salt) has been found to have slight bacteriostatic powers by some workers both *in vivo*[61] and *in vitro*[1364, 1384]. The *in vitro* activity was reversible by PABA[1364, 1384, 1491]. Others [151, 512, 2241, 2654] have found it inactive against bacteria both *in vitro* and *in vivo*. It was ineffective against gonorrhea in clinical studies [1699, 2654]. Studies of its action against *lymphogranuloma venereum* virus in animals and in man indicated slight activity[1069].

Studies of other pharmacological properties of sodium sulfanilate showed an excretion ratio of 0.91, low binding to plasma proteins and lack of penetration to the cerebrospinal fluid in concentrations greater than 3% of the plasma concentration[2178].

In contrast to the amides of sulfanilic acid (sulfanilamides) the esters appear to be nearly devoid of activity.

(E) Ketones

(1) Substituted Benzephenones (Table 191, p. 305)

Pharmacology. A large number of substituted benzophenones were studied for *in vitro* effectiveness against the tubercle bacillus. Where available, the concentrations in mg. per 100 cc. at which the compounds produced tuberculostasis have been listed. While several of these compounds appeared fairly active *in vitro*, in at least one case, that of 2,4'-dichlorobenzophenone, the compound did not show *in vivo* activity[1064] when tested by the drug-diet method on infected guinea pigs. Because no method was available for determination of blood levels of the drug, it was not possible to tell whether 2,4'-dichlorobenzophenone owed its lack of *in vivo* activity to lack of absorption or to some other explanation.

4,4'-Diaminobenzophenone has been shown by several authors[680, 1491] to possess weak bacteriostatic properties against *Streptobacterium plantarum* which are antagonized by 1/2000th the concentration of PABA. Slight activity *in vivo* against gonococcus and *Hemophilus pertussis* have also been noted[1574]. Others have not found the compound active *in vitro* against pneumococcus[1384] or *in vivo* against streptococcus[441].

4-Aminobenzophenone was a still weaker bacteriostatic agent against *Streptobacterium plantarum* and was antagonized by 1/50,000th its concentration of PABA[680]. 4,4'-Bis(dimethylamino)benzophenone was claimed somewhat active *in vivo* against streptococcus and staphylococcus[1574] but earlier reports[60, 441] had found it inactive.

(2) Miscellaneous Phenylketones (Table 192, p. 306)

Pharmacology. 4-Aminoacetophenone was somewhat more active than 4-aminobenzophenone against *Streptobacterium plantarum in vitro* and was antagonized by 1/10,000th its concentration of PABA[680, 1491]. Higher antibacterial indices were found against streptococcus and *E. coli, in vitro*[1395]. The corresponding nitro compound was slightly more active[1491].

The most active compound of the phenyl ketones appears to be 4,4'-diaminobenzil[1490], which was twice as active as sulfanilamide on *Staph. aureus* and 4 to 6 times as active on *Streptobacterium plantarum, in vitro*. The action was antagonized by PABA.

4,4'-Diaminobenzoin was found to lose its activity with time. This indicated breakdown of the molecule to give PABA by bacterial catabolism[1490]. 4,4'-Diaminodesoxybenzoin did not show this effect but had very weak antibacterial powers[1490].

(F) Quinones (Table 193, p. 307)

Pharmacology. While the quinones have bactericidal power *in vitro*, those listed do not appear to be active *in vivo*.

(G) Isocyclicsulfenamides

(1) 4-Nitrobenzenesulfenamides (Table 194, p. 309)

Synthesis. These compounds are of interest as possible intermediates for synthesis of sulfanilamide derivatives, because by oxidation the sulfenamide group can be changed to sulfonamide, then the nitro group may be reduced to amino, finally giving an N^1-substituted sulfanilamide.

4-nitrobenzenesulfenyl chloride may be made by treating bis(4-nitrophenyl)disulfide with dry chlorine in a suitable solvent, such as dry ether. By reaction in ether solution with excess of an amine, the sulfenamide is formed[1747].

Pharmacology. Slight *in vivo* activity against streptococci and staphylococci has been reported for the parent 4-nitrobenzenesulfenamide[968].

(2) 4-Acetamidobenzenesulfenamides (Table 195, p. 310)

These compounds also seem to be of interest largely as trick methods of synthesizing some of the valuable sulfonamide drugs in countries where product patents are not issued.

(H) Derivatives of Isocyclicsulfinic Acids

(1) 4-Nitrobenzenesulfinamides (Table 196, p. 310)

Synthesis. These compounds are again chiefly of interest as novel methods of synthesizing the valuable sulfa drugs which are obtainable from these intermediates by oxidation of the sulfinamide and reduction of the nitro group.

Pharmacology. The parent compound and 2-(4-nitrobenzenesulfinamido)pyridine were so toxic that treated animals died before the controls[2370].

(2) Miscellaneous Derivatives (Table 197, p. 311)

Pharmacology. It seems strange that the 4-(acylamino)benzenesulfinic acids have appreciable *in vivo* activity while the corresponding sulfonic acids are inactive. It would be of interest to know whether these compounds are antagonized by PABA.

(I) Isocyclic Selenium Compounds (Table 198, p. 311)

A number of compounds have been made in the effort to produce selenium analogues of the sulfa drugs. No exact analogue appears to have been synthesized because selenium does not undergo all the reactions of sulfur.

(J) Miscellaneous Isocyclicamines (Table 199, p. 311)

Pharmacology. A large number of substituted anilines have been studied in the hope of finding other para substituents besides the sulfamyl, sulfonyl or carbonyl types which would confer chemotherapeutic activity. Most of these attempts have been complete failures, but there are a few compounds, such as the 4-fluoro- or 4-chloroanilines, said to have slight activity against streptococcus *in vivo*[1574]. It would be interesting to know whether such activity is antagonized by PABA.

Several compounds have shown *in vitro* activity, such as 4-aminophenol, 4-aminodimethylaniline, 4-aminodiphenylamine, phenylthiourea and *N*-(2-aminoethyl)naphthylamine, without exhibiting *in vivo* activity[2441]. Such action may be a nonselective toxic effect against cells of both bacteria and the host.

(K) Miscellaneous Azo Compounds (Table 200, p. 317)

Pharmacology. In the early days of sulfonamide chemotherapy, following the announcement of the activity of "Prontosil", a large number of simple azo dyes were tested for activity against streptococcus *in vivo* but no activity was found unless the dye was derived from sulfanilamide or an *N*[1]-substituted derivative[512].

It is interesting to note that 4,4'-dicarboxyazobenzene was found inactive while 4-nitrobenzoic acid exhibited some activity[441].

(L) Miscellaneous Isocyclic Compounds (Table 201, p. 318)

Pharmacology. A number of the compounds listed here were tested because of their resemblance to known active compounds or because they might be converted by known catabolic reactions of the host to active compounds. It is possible that the activity of compounds containing CH_3—, —CH_2OH, —CH_2Cl, —$CHCl_2$, —$CHBr_2$, or —CHO in the para position on nitrobenzene is through biological oxidation to 4-nitrobenzoic acid, which is known to be active.

4,4'-Dihydroxybiphenyl was active *in vitro* against streptococci and pneumococci and showed a trace of antistreptococcal activity *in vivo*[2441]. Hydroquinone was also active *in vitro* but showed no *in vivo* activity.

(V) HETEROCYCLIC COMPOUNDS

(A) Heterocyclicsulfonamides

(1) 5-Aminopyridine-2-sulfonamides (Table 202, p. 323)

Synthesis. 2-Aminopyridine was nitrated, diazotized and converted to 5-nitro-2-pyridone, which was converted with PCl_5 to 2-chloro-5-nitropyridine. This was reacted with thiourea to give 5-nitro-2-pyridylpseudothiourea hydrochloride and this hydrolyzed with NaOH to 2-mercapto-5-nitropyridine. This was reduced to the amino with sodium dithionite and acetylated to give 2-mercapto-5-acetamidopyridine which was oxidized with chlorine in ice water to 5-acetamido-2-pyridinesulfonyl chloride. This then underwent reactions similar to acetylsulfanilyl chloride in preparing the desired sulfonamides[65].

Pharmacology. In a personal communication[826] it is stated that none of the 5-aminopyridine-2-sulfonamide analogues of the potent sulfonamide drugs "shows any promise as an agent against streptococcic infections. However, the compound derived from 2-amino-5-iodopyridine is quite active and is being studied further".

(2) **2-Aminopyridine-5-sulfonamides** (Table 203, p. 326)

Synthesis. 2-Aminopyridine can be directly sulfonated to 2-aminopyridine-5-sulfonic acid. On diazotization and heating in water, 2-pyridone-5-sulfonic acid was formed which was converted to 2-chloropyridine-5-sulfonyl chloride by reaction with PCl_5. By reaction with amines, 2-chloropyridine-5-sulfonamides were formed and by heating with ammonia or amines under pressure the 2-chlorine was replaced with amino or substituted amino groups[388].

Pharmacology. These compounds have been claimed active in the patent literature but pharmacological reports are not available. Because these compounds are isosteric with active sulfonamide drugs, they are of scientific interest. Studies on their antagonism by PABA would be especially welcome.

(3) **Miscellaneous Pyridinesulfonamides** (Table 204, p. 327)

Pharmacology. 3-Pyridinesulfonamide and some of its amide derivatives have been studied as inhibitors of bacteria requiring nicotinic acid. As yet, such studies have not resulted in compounds active against pathogenic bacteria *in vivo*. For further discussion, see Chapter XI under Vitamin Antagonists.

(4) **Quinolinesulfonamides** (Table 205, p. 329)

Pharmacology. The disodium salt of 2-methyl-6-sulfamylcinchoninic acid was found active against streptococci and less active against pneumococci[1574]. The disodium salt of 2-methyl-6-sulfamylcinchoninamide was inactive against streptococci. While these compounds can be viewed as nuclear-N^4-substituted sulfanilamides it appeared that the activity was associated with the free carboxyl group in some way since conversion to the amide removed the activity. Studies on antagonism by PABA would be of interest.

(5) (6) **2- and 3-Acridinesulfonamides** (Tables 206 and 207, p. 329–330)

Pharmacology. Many of these compounds are described in the patent literature and have presumably been tested as antimalarials but reports of the studies are not available.

(7) **1-Phenyl-2,3-dimethyl-5-pyrazolone-4-sulfonamides** (Table 208, p. 331)

Pharmacology. The parent compound of the series was practically inactive.

(8) **Benzimidazole-5-sulfonamides** (Table 209, p. 332)

Pharmacology. These compounds are structurally related to sulfanilamide or its N^1-derivatives. The only one on which activities are available appears inactive.

(9) **Benzotriazole-5-sulfonamides** (Table 210, p. 332)

Pharmacology. No activities have been reported for these compounds but would be of interest because of the structural relationships to sulfanilamides.

(10) **Isoxazolesulfonamides** (Table 211, p. 333)

Pharmacology. No information is available on the pharmacology of these compounds.

(11) **2-Aminothiazole-5-sulfonamides** (Table 212, p. 333)

Pharmacology. These isosteres of sulfanilamide derivatives were not active against pneumococcal infections in mice. High toxicity was found for 2-amino-4-methyl-5-thiazolesulfonanilide[686].

(12) **Benzoxazolone-6-sulfonamides** (Table 213, p. 334)

Pharmacology. These compounds may be viewed as sulfanilamide derivatives where the nucleus and N^4-positions are linked in a ring. The parent compound does not appear to be active.

(13) **2-Mercaptobenzothiazole-5-sulfonamides** (Table 214, p. 334)

Pharmacology. Not available.

(14) **2-Aminobenzothiazole-6-sulfonamides** (Table 215, p. 334)

Pharmacology. These compounds may be viewed as nuclear-N^4-substituted sulfanilamides where the nuclear and N^4-substituents are part of the thiazole ring. In view of the inactivity of this class of compounds in the sulfanilamide series, the low activities of the 2-aminobenzothiazole-6-sulfonamides cause no surprise.

(15) **Miscellaneous Heterocyclicsulfonamides** (Table 216, p. 335)

(B) **Miscellaneous Heterocyclic Compounds** (Table 217, p. 335–339)

These compounds are of considerable theoretical interest because many are isosteric with *p*-aminobenzoic acid or *p*-nitrobenzoic acid. Several show antibacterial activity *in vitro* which is antagonized by PABA.[a]

Pharmacology. While several of these compounds have shown definite *in vitro* activity against such organisms as *E. coli*, pneumococci and streptococci, none has been shown to possess *in vivo* activity against these or other organisms.

[a] For further discussion of the theoretical implications, see Chapter XI, (I) (B) (6).

TABLE 147

I. 4-Nitrobenzenesulfonamides
A. Nuclear-substituted 4-Nitrobenzenesulfonamides

R_2	Melting Range	Activities	References
	178°, 180°	+++, ++(S), ±(Cn, Cs, Cw, Pl)	148, 264, 346, 440, 963, 1118, 1195, 1733, 1753, 2441
NO$_2$—			317
NH$_2$—			508

TABLE 148

B. N^1-Substituted 4-Nitrobenzenesulfonamides
1. N^1-Acyclic-4-nitrobenzenesulfonamides

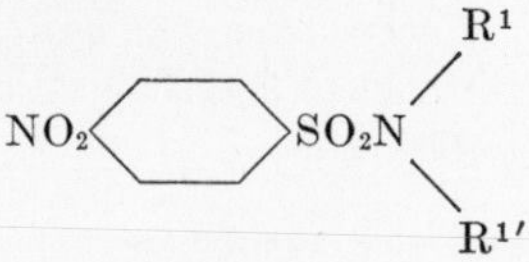

R^1	$R^{1\prime}$	Melting Range	Activities	References
CH_3-		110–1°		105, 963
C_2H_5-		103°		963
C_2H_5-	C_2H_5-			1710
$CH_3(CH_2)_2-$		61°		963
$CH_3(CH_2)_3-$		68°		963, 1710
$CH_3(CH_2)_4-$		59°		963
$CH_3(CH_2)_5-$		67°		963
$CH_3(CH_2)_6-$		71°		963
$CH_3(CH_2)_{16}-$		90.5°	0(S, T)	2260
$HOCH_2CH_2-$		126–7°		103
$CH_3(CH_2)_{10}COOCH_2CH_2-$		72–3.5°		103
$NC-$	$Na-$			9
$HOOCCH_2-$		172.5–4.0°		105
$4-(NO_2)C_6H_4SO_2NH(CH_2)_4-$		201°	0(T)	2260

TABLE 149

2. N^1-Isocyclic-4-nitrobenzenesulfonamides

R^1	Melting Range	Activities	References
C_6H_5-	167–8°		228, 710
$3,5-Cl_2C_6H_3-$	189°		555
$3,5-Br_2C_6H_3-$	172°		555
$4-(NO_2)C_6H_4-$	171–3°	$\pm$(S),0(P, Sa)	968
$3,5-(F_3C)_2C_6H_3-$	138°		555
$4-(HOOCCH_2S)C_6H_4-$	161–2°		1808
$4-(C_2H_5OOCCH_2S)C_6H_4-$	99.5–101°		1808
$4-(HOOC(CH_3)CHS)C_6H_4-$	148–9°		1808
$4-[CH_3(CH_2)_5(C_2H_5OOC)CHS]C_6H_4-$	96–7°		1808
$4-[CH_3(CH_2)_{15}(C_2H_5OOC)CHS]C_6H_4-$	69–71°		1808
$4-(NO_2)C_6H_4SO_2NH$⬡S⬡$-$ 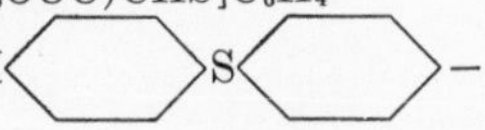			557
$C_6H_5CH(OH)CH_2-$	132.5–3.0°		2370
$4-(CH_3CO)C_6H_4-$	192–4°		352
$4-(HO_2S)C_6H_4-$	146°		228

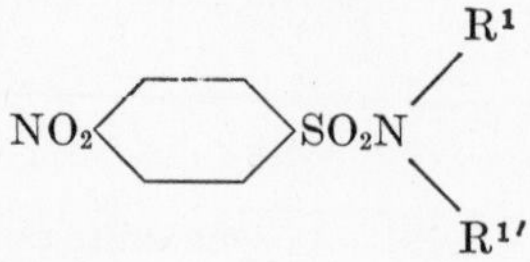

TABLE 149—*(Concluded)*

R^1	Melting Range	Activities	References
4-$(HO_3S)C_6H_4-$			209, 218, 556
4-$(ClO_2S)C_6H_4-$	78°		228
4-$(BrO_2S)C_6H_4-$			209
8-$[4'-(NO_2)C_6H_4SO_2]C_{10}H_6-(1)$	272°		210, 225, 557
3-$(NaO_3SNH)C_6H_4-$			224, 2462
4-$(NaO_3SNH)C_6H_4-$			224, 2462
4-$[4'-(NO_2)C_6H_4SO_2NH]C_6H_4-$	284°D		210, 225, 557

TABLE 150

3. N^1-Heterocyclic-4-nitrobenzenesulfonamides
   a. One N-Atom in the Heterocyclic System

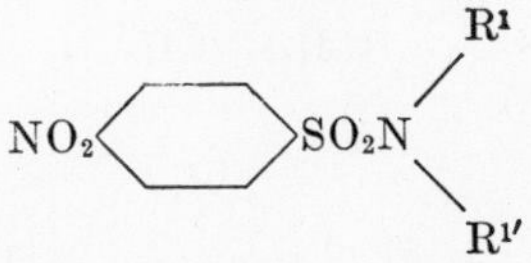

R^1	$R^{1\prime}$	Melting Range	Activities	References
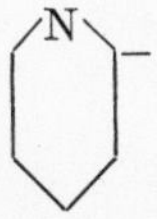		192–3°D [a]	+++(S), 0(I)	11, 58, 105, 334, 341, 486, 542, 658, 1702, 1707
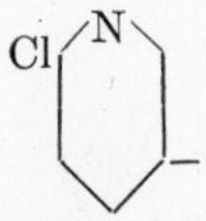				643
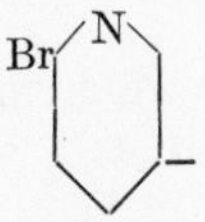				643
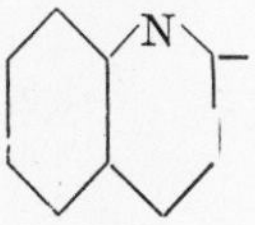				1710
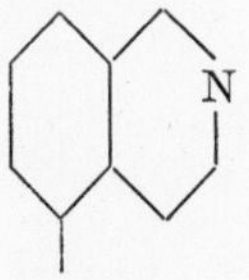		270°D		1239

[a] Nisulfadine.

TABLE 150—(*Concluded*)

R¹	R¹′	Melting Range	Activities	References
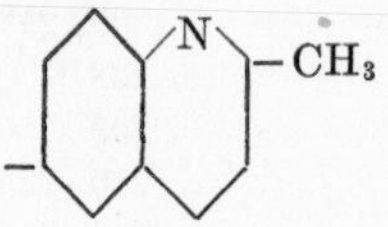				341
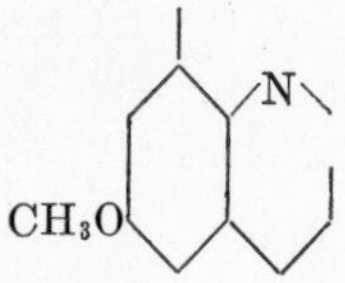		184–5°		344
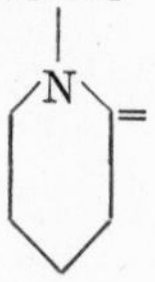 (C₂H₅)₂NCH₂CH₂		133–4°		338
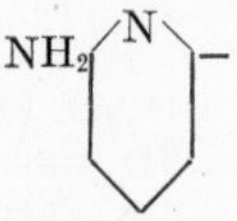 NH₂		228–30°		149

TABLE 151

3. N^1-Heterocyclic-4-nitrobenzenesulfonamides
  b. Two or More N-Atoms in the Heterocyclic System
    1. x-(4′-Nitrophenylsulfonamido)pyrimidines

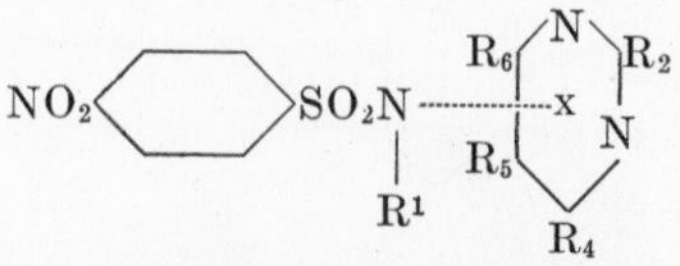

R¹	R₂	R₄	R₅	R₆	Melting Range	Activities	References
	x						647, 1708
	x		Cl–				436, 647
		x					436, 647
Cl–			x				436
CH₃–		x					436
	x	CH₃–			260–1°		493
		x		CH₃–	204.5–6.5°		687
CH₃–		x		CH₃–	201°		1161
	x	CH₃–		CH₃–	220°		1355, 1708
	x	CH₃O–					647
CH₃O–		x					647
C₂H₅O–		x			202°		493
CH₃O–			x				647
CH₃O–		CH₃–	x		222.5–4.5°		687

TABLE 151—(*Concluded*)

R¹	R₂	R₄	R₅	R₆	Melting Range	Activities	References
	x	CH_3-		$HO-$	255–7°		1355
	CH_3O-	CH_3-		x	199–200°		687
	x	CH_3O-		CH_3-	215.5–6.5°		687
	x	CH_3S-		CH_3-	217–22°		687
	x	$HO-$		$HO-$	185°D		1355
	x	CH_3O-		CH_3O-			647
	x	C_2H_5OOC-		$HO-$	210–20°D		1355
	$4\text{-}(NO_2)C_6H_4SO_2NH-$		x				647
CH_3-	x						647

TABLE 152

2. N^1-Heterocyclic-4-nitrobenzenesulfonamides with Three or More N-Atoms in the Heterocyclic System

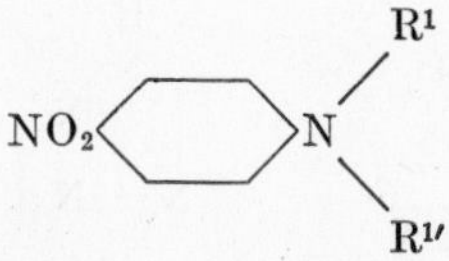

R¹	R¹′	Melting Range	Activities	References
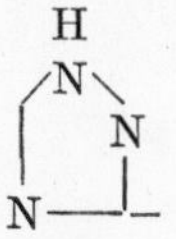		210–11°	+(S), 0(P)	653, 2370
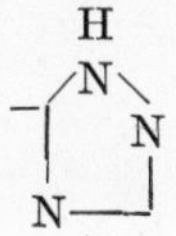		216–8°	0(P)	686
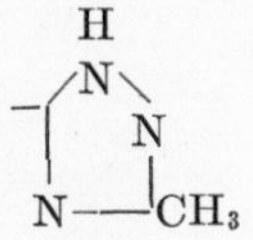		282°D	0(P)	686
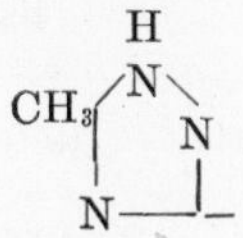		222–2.5°	0(P)	2370
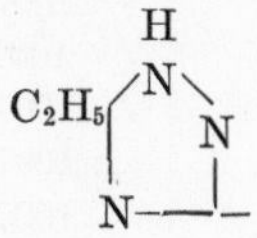		189–90°	+(S), 0(P)	2370

TABLE 152—(Concluded)

R^1	$R^{1'}$	Melting Range	Activities	References
$CH_3(CH_2)_2$ — [heterocyclic structure]		214–4.5°		2370
$(CH_3)_2CH$ — [heterocyclic structure]		210–11°		2370
[heterocyclic structure]		185–6°D	0(S)	16, 434
do	Na—			16
[heterocyclic structure]		236–8°D		731
[heterocyclic structure]				653

TABLE 153

3. N^1-Heterocyclic-4-nitrobenzenesulfonamides
   c. One N-Atom and one O- or S-Atom in the
     Heterocyclic System.
    1. 2-(4-Nitrophenylsulfonimido)-4-thiazolines

R_3	R_5	Melting Range	Activities	References
CH_3—		209°	+++	1007, 2232
C_2H_5—		169–70°		1007, 2232
$CH_3(CH_2)$—		195–7°		1007, 2232
$(CH_3)_2CH$—		163°		1007, 2232
$CH_3(CH_2)_{11}$—		142.5–3.0°	0	1007, 2232
$CH_3(CH_2)_{15}$—		131°	0	1007, 2232

TABLE 153—(*Concluded*)

R_3	R_5	Melting Range	Activities	References
$CH_2=CHCH_2-$		145–6°	+++	1007, 2232
$C_6H_5CH_2-$		210–11°	0	1007
$(C_2H_5)_2NCH_2CH_2-$		165°	0	1007, 2232
C_2H_5-	CH_3-	175°		343

TABLE 154

2. 2-(4-Nitrophenylsulfonamido)thiazoles

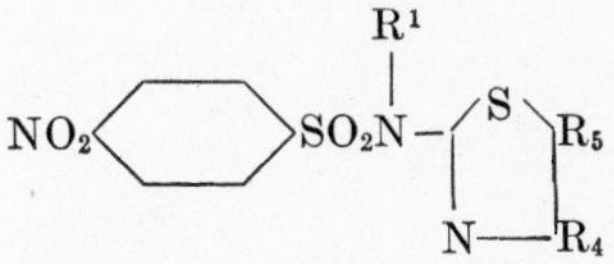

$$NO_2\langle\bigcirc\rangle SO_2N-\overset{R^1}{\underset{N----R_4}{\langle\overset{S}{\underset{}{\rangle}}R_5}}$$

R^1	R_4	R_5	Melting Range	Activities	References
CH_3-			270°, 280–1°D[a]	++, +(P), ++(S)	95, 150, 249, 1702, 1804
					184, 481
	CH_3-		199–200°	+++(S), ±(P)	76, 149, 150, 481, 491, 492, 622
		CH_3-	255°D		343
	C_2H_5-		193–5°		39
	CH_3-	CH_3-	232°D		343
	C_6H_5-			0(I)	658

[a] Nisulfazole.

TABLE 155

3. Miscellaneous N^1-Heterocyclic-4-nitrobenzenesulfonamides with One N- and One O- or S-Atom in the Heterocyclic System

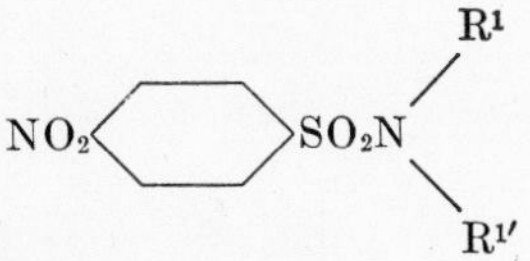

$$NO_2\langle\bigcirc\rangle SO_2N\overset{R^1}{\underset{R^{1'}}{}}$$

R^1	Melting Range	Activities	References
			653, 2492
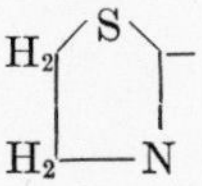			481
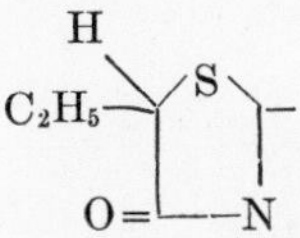	192–3°		371

TABLE 155—(*Concluded*)

R¹	Melting Range	Activities	References
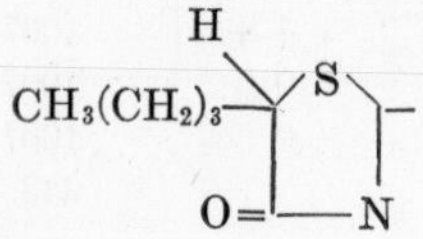 CH₃(CH₂)₃ ... (with H, S, O=, N)	186–7°		371
(ring with S, CN, N)	148°		674
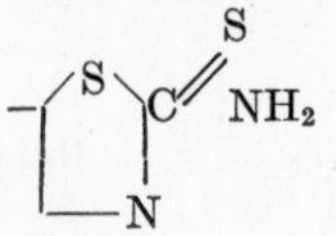 (ring with S, C, NH₂, N)	185°D		674
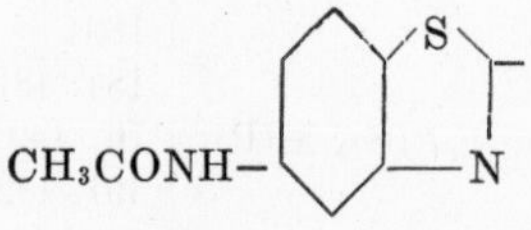 CH₃CONH— (fused ring with S, N)			343

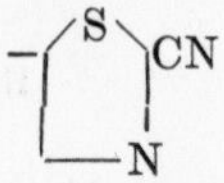

TABLE 156

3. N¹-Heterocyclic-4-nitrobenzenesulfonamides
   d. N¹-Nitrogen a Member of the Heterocyclic System   NO₂⟨ ⟩SO₂N⊃

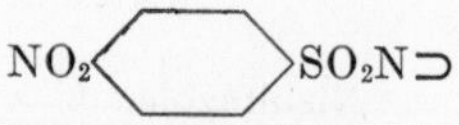

—N⊃	Melting Range	Activities	References
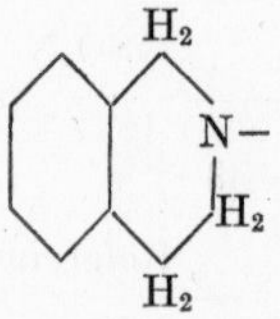 (decalin-type ring, H₂, N—, H₂, H₂)	179°		1239
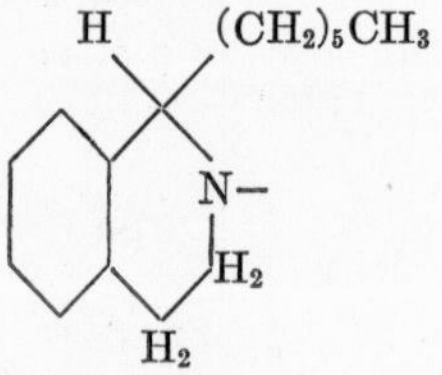 (ring with H, (CH₂)₅CH₃, N—, H₂, H₂)	56–7°		1239
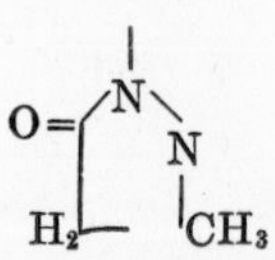 O=⟨N, N, CH₃, H₂⟩	132°		14

TABLE 156—(*Continued*)

$-N\supset$	Melting Range	Activities	References
 H HN=N-N -N	214–5°	0(P)	686
 H HN=N-N -N—CH₃	228–9°	0(P)	686
(phenothiazine ring, N and S)	175–6°		2499
H₂ O =O H₂—N—	197.5–8.0°	++(S), 0(P)	2370
H₂ O =NH H₂—N—	124–6°		2370
H₂ S =O H₂—N—	182–3°	+++(S), 0(P)	1344, 2370
H₂ S =NH H₂—N—	135–7°	−	1344, 2370
H₂ S =NSO₂C₆H₄(NO₂)−4 H₂—N−	268.5–70.5°		1344
H₂ S =O H —N− CH₃	139–41°	++(S), 0(P)	1344, 2370
H₂ S =O H—N− CH₃	133–4.5°		1344

TABLE 156—(*Continued*)

$-N\supset$	Melting Range	Activities	References
H$_2$/S\=NSO$_2$C$_6$H$_4$(NO$_2$)−4 H—|—N− CH$_3$	242–2.5°		1344
H CH$_3$—/O\=O H$_2$—N−	160–161°		2370
H CH$_3$—/O\=NH H$_2$—N−	157–8°		2370
H CH$_3$—/S\=O H$_2$—N−	177°	++(S), 0(P)	1344, 2370
H CH$_3$—/S\=NH H$_2$—N−	114–4.5°	−	1344, 2370
H CH$_3$—/S\=NSO$_2$C$_6$H$_4$(NO$_2$)−4 H$_2$—N−	219.5–20.5°	0(P, S)	1344, 2370
/S\=NCH$_3$ —N−			184
/S\=NSO$_2$C$_6$H$_4$(NO$_2$)−4 −N−	250°D		249
/S\=NSO$_2$C$_6$H$_4$(NO$_2$)−4 CH$_3$—N−	214°		76

TABLE 156—(*Concluded*)

$-N\supset$	Melting Range	Activities	References
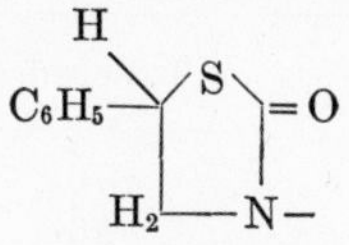 C_6H_5 H S $=O$ H_2 $N-$	165.8–8.0°	$++(S), 0(P)$	1344, 2370
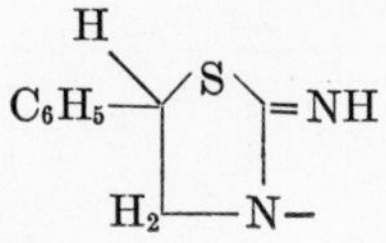 C_6H_5 H S $=NH$ H_2 $N-$	139.5–40.5°		1344
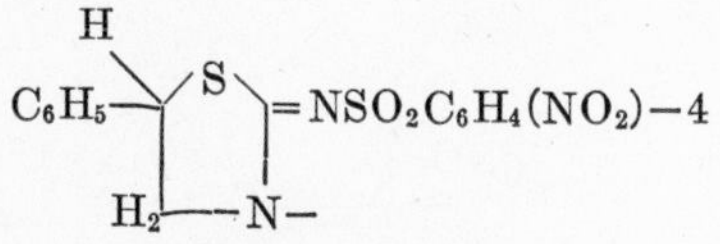 C_6H_5 H S $=NSO_2C_6H_4(NO_2)-4$ H_2 $N-$	215.5–18.0°		1344

TABLE 157

4. N^1-Acyl-4-nitrobenzenesulfonamides

  a. N^1-Acyclic-, Isocyclic- or Heterocyclicacyl-4-nitro-benzenesulfonamides

$$NO_2-C_6H_4-SO_2N\begin{smallmatrix}R^1\\ \\R^{1\prime}\end{smallmatrix}$$

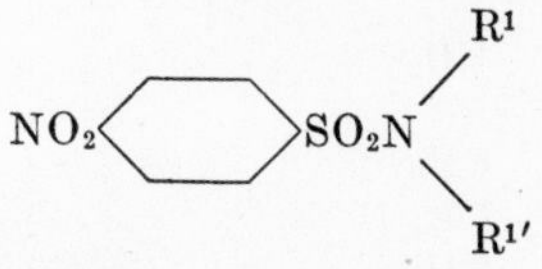

R^1	$R^{1\prime}$	Melting Range	Activities	References
CH_3CO-		192–3°	$0(I)$	165, 247, 658
$ClCH_2CO-$		172–3°		165, 1033
$CH_3CH_2CH_2CO-$		141.5–3.5°		105
$CH_3(CH_2)_{10}CO-$	CH_3-	73.1–4.2°		105
$(CH_3)_2C=CHCO-$		155°		1158
$C_6H_{11}CO-$				165
C_6H_5CO-				105
$2-(CH_3)C_6H_4CO-$		186°		1159
$3-(CH_3)C_6H_4CO-$		126–7°		1159
$4-(CH_3)C_6H_4CO-$		244°		1159
$2,4-(CH_3)_2C_6H_3CO-$		170°		1159
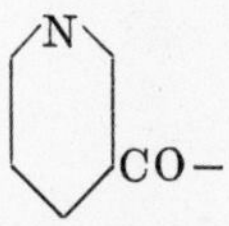 $\begin{smallmatrix}N\\ \\ \quad CO-\end{smallmatrix}$				1862
$(C_2H_5)_2NCOCO-$		157–8°		165
$4-(CH_3O)C_6H_4CO-$		156°		1159
$4-[(CH_3)_2CHS]C_6H_4CO-$		175°		1159
$3-CH_3-4-(CH_3O)C_6H_3CO-$		179°		1159
$4-CH_3-4-(CH_3S)C_6H_3CO-$		185–7°		1159

TABLE 158

b. 4-Nitrophenylsulfonylimido Esters

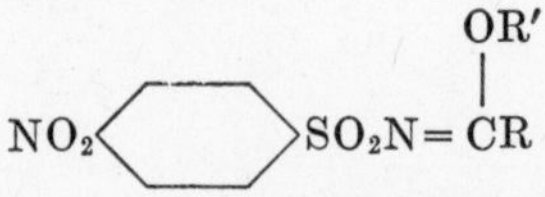

$$NO_2 \langle \bigcirc \rangle SO_2N=CR \; (OR')$$

R	R'	Melting Range	Activities	References
CH_3-	C_2H_5-	87–8°		701
C_6H_5-	do	129–30°		701
do	C_6H_5-	173–4°		701

TABLE 159

c. 4-Nitrophenylsulfonylamidines

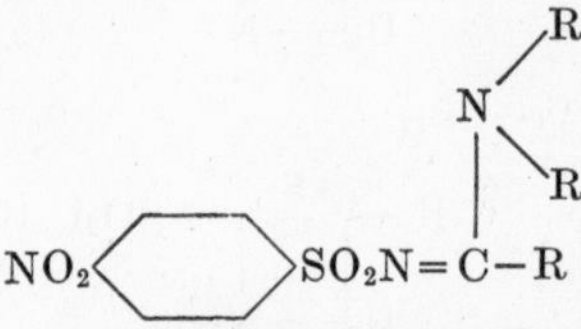

$$NO_2 \langle \bigcirc \rangle SO_2N=C-R \; (N(R')R'')$$

R	R'	R''	Melting Range	Activities	References
CH_3-			190.7–1.3°		165, 1862
CH_3-	CH_3-		152°		165
CH_3-	CH_3-	CH_3-	170°		165
CH_3-	C_2H_5-		100°		165
CH_3-	do	C_2H_5-	133°		165
CH_3-	$CH_2=CHCH_2-$		115–6°		165
CH_3-	do	$CH_2=CHCH_2-$			165
CH_3-	$-(CH_2)_5-$		170°		165
CH_3-	$4-(NO_2)C_6H_4SO_2-$		189–90.7°		1862
C_2H_5-			137°		165
$(CH_3)_2CHCH_2-$			142–4°		165
$(CH_3)_2CH(CH_2)_2-$			247–50°D		1862
$C_6H_{11}-$			188–90°		165
C_6H_5-			159–65°, 180.3–1.0°		165, 701, 1862
do	CH_3-		181.2°D		1862
do	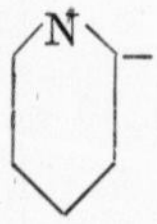 ⟨N⟩-		180–7°D		1862
do	$4-(NO_2)C_6H_4SO_2-$		241.8–2.6°		1862
$4-(CH_3)C_6H_4-$			149.5–60°		1862
do	$4-(NO_2)C_6H_4SO_2-$		213.7–4.9°		1862
$C_6H_5CH_2-$			194.3–5.8°		1862

TABLE 159—(*Concluded*)

R	R′	R″	Melting Range	Activities	References
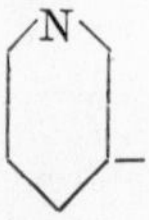			232.5–3.5°		1862
$(CH_3)_2NCH_2-$	CH_3-	CH_3-	143–4°		165
$(C_2H_5)_2NC(=O)-$			137°		165

TABLE 160

4. N^1-Acyl-4-nitrobenzenesulfonamides
   d. Derivatives of Carbonic Acid

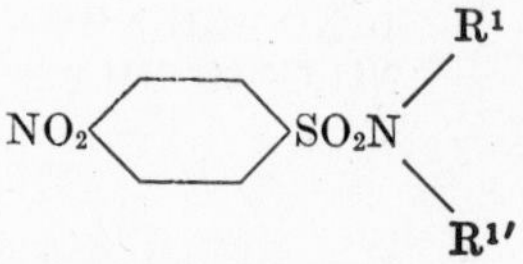

R¹	R¹′	Melting Range	Activities	References
C_2H_5OCO-				166
NH_2CO-		190°D		166
CH_3NHCO-				166
C_2H_5NHCO-		175–6°		166
$(C_2H_5)_2NCO-$				166
$(CH_3)_2CH(CH_2)_2NHCO-$				166
3-$(NO_2)C_6H_4NHCO-$				166
4-$(NO_2)C_6H_4NHCO-$				166
$CH_3OC(=NH)-$				2459
$C_2H_5OC(=NH)-$				2459
$N\equiv C-$			0(En)	9, 1485, 2459
$N\equiv C-$	Na–	286–8°D		9
$NH_2C(=NH)-$			++	17, 1706
$NH_2C(=O)NHC(=NH)-$				646
$NH_2C(=NH)NHC(=NH)-$				20
$C_6H_5NHC(=NH)NHC(=NH)-$		221°		1353
$NH_2C(=S)NHC(=NH)-$				646
$C_2H_5SC(=NH)-$		108–10°		1357
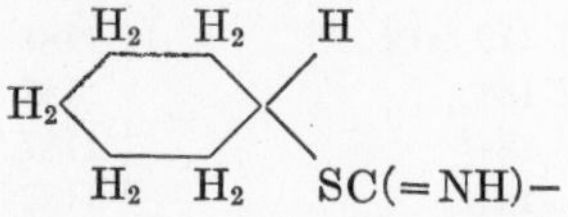		163–5°		1357
$C_6H_5CH_2SC(=NH)-$		172°		1357

TABLE 161

5. N^1-Inorganic Derivatives of 4-Nitrobenzenesulfonamide

R^1	$R^{1\prime}$	Melting Range	Activities	References
HO—		145–9°	++, +(S)	182, 373
4-(NO₂)C₆H₄SO₂—	Na—	250–5°		105
do	CH₃—			105
do	CH₃(CH₂)₁₁—	91–2.5°		105
do	C₆H₅—	264°		701
4-(NO₂)C₆H₄NHSO₂—			0(S)	1427, 1574
NH₂C(=O)NH—				18

TABLE 162

II. Derivatives of Orthanilamide and Metanilamide

    A. Derivatives of Orthanilamide

R^1	R^2	R_3	R_5	Melting Range	Activities	References
					+, ±, 0(S), ±(Sa), 0(En, Pl)	138, 151, 512, 1057, 1485, 1733, 2441
2-(HOOC)C₆H₄—				176.7–178°	±(S)	98, 2441
C₆H₅CHOHCO—				225°		407
	CH₃CO—				0(S)	512
	4-NH₂C₆H₄SO₂—				++(Ec)	1057
			NO₂—	208°		1187
HOCH₂CH₂—			NO₂—	149–50°		1187
	C₆H₅—		NO₂—	168–9°		1187
HOCH₂CH₂—	HOCH₂CH₂—		NO₂—	119–20°		1187
			NH₂—	184°		1187
HOCH₂CH₂—			NH₂—	184°		1187
	C₆H₅—		NH₂—	164°		1187
HOCH₂CH₂—	HOCH₂CH₂—		NH₂—	162–3°		1187
			CH₃—			171
		CH₃—	CH₃—		+(S)	418

TABLE 163

B. Derivatives of Metanilamide
  1. Nuclear-substituted Metanilamides

R₄	R₅	R₆	Melting Range	Activities	References
CH_3-				0(S)	171, 512
CH_3-		CH_3-	187–8°		453
$HO-$			202°	±(P, S, Sa), 0(Ba)	261, 327
CH_3O-				0(M, S)	5
		$HO-$	202°D		2455
	NH_2SO_2-			+(S)	357

TABLE 164

2. N^1-Substituted Metanilamides

R¹	R¹′	Melting Range	Activities	References
			+(Sa), ±, 0(En, Pl, S)	138, 151, 512, 1057, 1485, 1733, 2441
$HOCH_2CH_2-$	$HOCH_2CH_2-$	79–81°	±(S)	105
do			0(P, S)	105, 1057
CH_3CO-		153.5–5.5°	±(P, S)	101, 1057
$CH_3(CH_2)_{12}CO-$		113.5–4.5°		101
$CH_3(CH_2)_{14}CO-$		113.5–4.2°		105
$2\text{-}(HOOC)C_6H_4-$		191.5–3.5°	±(S), 0(P, Pl)	98, 1057, 1733, 2441
$3\text{-}(NH_2)C_6H_4SO_2-$		330°	+(Ec), 0(P, S)	99, 1057

TABLE 165

3. N^3-Substituted Metanilamides

R³	R³′	Melting Range	Activities	References
CH_3CO-		156–7°	0(S)	247, 512
$3\text{-}(NH_2)C_6H_4SO_2-$			0(S)	100, 2441
$4\text{-}(NH_2)C_6H_4SO_2-$			+(P, S)	105, 1057
$HCl\cdot2,4\text{-}(NH_2)_2C_6H_3N=$		198°	+(S)	328

TABLE 166

4. Nuclear-N^1-substituted Metanilamides

Structure: ring with SO_2N bearing R^1 and $R^{1'}$; ring positions R_6, R_2, R_5, NH_2, R_4.

R^1	$R^{1'}$	R_4	R_5	R_6	Melting Range	Activities	References
(piperidine ring, N–)				CH_3-	209°		2463
(piperidine ring, N–)				CH_3-	237–8°		2463
(thiazolidine ring, S, N–)				CH_3-	185°		2463
(CH_3-substituted thiazolidine, S, N–)				CH_3-	238–9°		2463
do	CH_3-			CH_3-			2463
do	C_6H_5-			CH_3-	136–8°		2463
(C_6H_5-substituted thiazolidine, S, N–)				CH_3-	226°		2463
(piperidine ring, N–)		CH_3-		CH_3-	244–5°		453
C_6H_5-		$HO-$			172°		2455
(piperidine ring, N–)		$HO-$			211°		262

TABLE 166—(*Concluded*)

R¹	R¹'	R₄	R₅	R₆	Melting Range	Activities	References
CH₃CHOHCH₂-		CH₃O-			102°	0(M, S)	5
C₆H₅-				HO-	159°		2455
CH₃-	CH₃-		(CH₃)₂NSO₂-		183°		215
			SO₂N(CH₃)₂		158°		2464

(R¹: SO₂N(CH₃)₂ on ring; R₅: NHSO₂- on ring)

TABLE 167

5. Nuclear-N³-substituted Metanilamides

$$\text{SO}_2\text{NH}_2$$

R₆, R₂, R₅, R₄ on ring; -N(R³)(R³')

R³	R³'	R₄	R₅	R₆	Melting Range	Activities	References
CH₃CO-		CH₃-				0(S)	512
HOOC(CH₂)₂CO-				CH₃-		0(C)	1951
HCO-		HO-				0(S)	516
CH₃CO-		HO-				0(S)	512
do		CH₃O-			225.5°	±(M), 0(S)	5
do				HO-	215°		2455
C₂H₅OCH₂CO-		NH₂SO₂-					2464
HCl·2,4-(NH₂)₂C₆H₃N=			NH₂SO₂-		277°D		213

TABLE 168

6. N¹, N³-Substituted Metanilamides

SO₂NHR¹ ; -NHR³

R¹	R³	Melting Range	Activities	References
HOCH₂CH₂-	3-(NH₂)C₆H₄SO₂-	125-7.2°	±(S), 0(P, Pl)	100, 1057, 1733, 2441

TABLE 169

7. Nuclear-N^1,N^3-substituted Metanilamides

General structure: $SO_2N(R^1)(R^{1\prime})$ on a benzene ring bearing R_2, R_6, R_5, R_4, and $N(R^3)(R^{3\prime})$.

R^1	$R^{1\prime}$	R^3	$R^{3\prime}$	R_4	R_5	R_6	Melting Range	Activities	References
pyridyl ring		$4\text{-}(CH_3O)C_6H_4CH=$				CH_3-	225°		2463
do		CH_3CO-				CH_3-	256°		2463
NO_2-phenyl ring		do				CH_3-	234°		2463
pyridyl ring		$4\text{-}(NO_2)C_6H_4CH_2-$	CH_3CO-			CH_3-	266°		2463
do		CH_3CH_2CO-		CH_3COO-		CH_3-	226°		2463
do		C_2H_5OCO-		CH_3O-		CH_3-	251°		2463
do		NH_2CO-		do		CH_3-	260.5-1.0°		453
C_6H_5-		CH_3CO-		do		CH_3-	205°		2455
$HOCH_2CH_2-$		do					152-3°	0(M, S)	5
$CH_3CHOHCH_2-$		do					146-7°	0(M, S)	5
$(CH_3)_2COHCH_2-$		do					125°	±(M), 0(S)	5
C_6H_5-	CH_3-	do			$CH_3-NSO_2-CH_3$		150°		2455
CH_3-		$ClCH_2CO-$				CH_3COO-	186°		2464

CH₃–	CH₃–	CH₃(CH₂)₁₀CO–	do	96°	215
CH₃–	CH₃–	C₂H₅OCH₂CO–	do	152°	2464
CH₃–	CH₃–	C₄H₉NHCH₂CO–	do	107°	2464
CH₃–	CH₃–	Cl–N–CH₂CO–	do	260°	2464
CH₃–	CH₃–	4-NH₂C₆H₄SO₂–	do	181°	2464
CH₃–	CH₃–	NHCOCH₃ / SO₂–	do	174°	2464
CH₃	CH₃–	(structure)	do		215

TABLE 170

III. Acyclic Compounds
 A. Acyclicaminosulfonamides

Compound	Melting Range	Activities	References
$NH_2SO_2NH_2$		0(S, Tt)	1574, 2192
$NH_2SO_2NHCONHSO_2NH_2$		0(S)	1427, 1574
$NH_2CH_2CH_2SO_2NH_2 \cdot HCl$	132.5–3°	0(S)	324, 361, 2263
$C_6H_5CONHCH_2CH_2SO_2NH_2$	165–6°	0(S)	361
$NCH_2CH_2SO_2NH_2$	207–8°	0(S)	361, 2263
$NH_2(CH_2)_3SO_2NH_2 \cdot HCl$	159–60°	0(S)	361, 2263
$NH_2(CH_2)_4SO_2NH_2 \cdot HCl$	127–9°	0(S)	361
$C_6H_5CONH(CH_2)_4SO_2NH_2$	154–5°	0(S)	361

TABLE 171

B. Miscellaneous Acyclicsulfonamides

Compound	Melting Range	Activities	References
$C_2H_5SO_2NHC_6H_4(OC_2H_5)$-4	80.4–81°	0(I, P, S, Sa, Tt)	1574
$C_4H_9SO_2NHC_6H_4(OC_2H_5)$-4	78.2–79.0°	0(P, S, Sa, Tt)	1574
$C_4H_9SO_2NHC(=NH)NH_2$	157–8°		2590
$H_2NO_2S(CH_2)_3SO_2NH_2$		0(S, Tt)	1427, 1574

TABLE 172

C. Analogues of Pantothenic Acid

Compound	Melting Range	Activities	References
$HOCH_2C(CH_3)_2CHOHCONHCH_2CH_2SH$		++(La), −(S)	707
$[HOCH_2C(CH_3)_2CHOHCONHCH_2CH_2]_2S$		+(La), 0(S)	707
$[HOCH_2C(CH_3)_2CHOHCONHCH_2CH_2]_2SO$	143–4°	+(La), 0(S)	707
$[HOCH_2C(CH_3)_2CHOHCONHCH_2CH_2]_2SO_2$	(.2HCl) 226–8°	+(La), 0(S)	707

TABLE 172—(*Concluded*)

Compound	Melting Range	Activities	References
[HOCH$_2$C(CH$_3$)$_2$CHOHCONHCH$_2$CH$_2$S—]$_2$	141–4°	++(La), 0(S)	707
HOCH$_2$CH$_2$CH$_2$CONHCH$_2$CH$_2$COOH			709, 1656
CH$_3$CHOHCH$_2$CH$_2$CONHCH$_2$CH$_2$COOH			709, 1656
HOCH$_2$C(CH$_3$)$_2$CH$_2$CONHCH$_2$CH$_2$COOH			709, 1656
HOCH$_2$C(CH$_3$)$_2$CH=CHCONHCH$_2$CH$_2$COOH			1656
HOCH$_2$C(CH$_3$)$_2$CHOHCH$_2$CONHCH$_2$CH$_2$COOH			1656
HOCH$_2$C(CH$_3$)$_2$CHOHCONHCH$_2$CH$_2$SO$_3$H		+	1656
HOCH$_2$C(CH$_3$)$_2$CHOHCONHCH$_2$CH$_2$SO$_3$Na	a	+(La, P, S), 0 (Ba, Ec, En, Po, pr, Sa, Spd)	479, 709 1485, 1664, 1670
HOCH$_2$C(CH$_3$)$_2$CHOHCONHCH$_2$CH$_2$SO$_2$NH$_2$	b	+, ±(S), 0(P, Sa)	709, 1574, 1656, 1664, 1674
HOCH$_2$C(CH$_3$)$_2$CH(OSO$_2$C$_6$H$_4$CH$_3$)CONHCH$_2$CH$_2$SO$_3$H		0(La)	708
HOCH$_2$C(CH$_3$)$_2$CHOHCH$_2$CONHCH$_2$CH$_2$SO$_3$H	c		709, 1656
HOCH$_2$C(C$_6$H$_5$)$_2$CHOHCONHCH$_2$CH$_2$SO$_3$H		±(La)	708
HOCH$_2$C(CH$_3$)$_2$CHOHCONHCH$_2$CH(C$_6$H$_5$)SO$_3$H		±(La)	708

a Pantoyltaurine.
b Pantoyltauramide.
c Homopantoyltaurine.

TABLE 173

D. Miscellaneous Acyclic Compounds

Compound	Melting Range	Activities	References
CH$_2$=CHCH$_2$OH		0(En, Po)	1485
CH$_3$CO(CH$_2$)$_5$CH$_3$		0(T)	1127
CH$_3$CO(CH$_2$)$_8$CH$_3$		0(T)	1127
CH$_3$COCOCH$_3$		0(I, S, Tt)	1574
CH$_3$COCH$_2$CH$_2$COCH$_3$		0(En, Po)	1485
CH$_3$(CH$_2$)$_{10}$C(=NH)NH$_2$·HCl		0(En, Po)	1485
NH$_2$OC(CH$_2$)$_3$CONH$_2$		0	454
HOOC(CH$_2$)$_4$COOH		0(En, Po)	1485
NH$_2$CONH$_2$	132°	0(I, R)	1574
NH$_2$C(=NH)NHNH$_2$·H$_2$CO$_3$		0(En, Po)	1485
C$_4$H$_9$SCN		0(En, Po)	1485
NH$_2$C(=S)NH$_2$		0(En, Po)	1485
HOOCCH$_2$SCH$_2$SCH$_2$COOH		0(P)	1427, 1574

TABLE 174

IV. Isocyclic Compounds
  A. Isocyclicsulfonamides
    1. 4-Aminoalkylbenzenesulfonamides

$$R_4 \!-\!\!\langle \text{benzene} \rangle\!\!-\! SO_2N \begin{smallmatrix} R^1 \\ R^{1\prime} \end{smallmatrix}$$

R$_4$	R^1	R$^{1\prime}$	Melting Range	Activities	References
NH$_2$CH$_2$—			153°ᵃ	See Table 293	361, 1384, 1443, 1489, 2461, 2523
do	CH$_3$—		100°	++(Cw), 0(H, S, Sa)	1255, 2461
do	CH$_3$—	CH$_3$—	135°		2461
do	C$_2$H$_5$—				2461
do	do	C$_2$H$_5$—			2461
do	CH$_3$(CH$_2$)$_3$—				2461
do	C$_6$H$_5$CH$_2$—				2461
do	[piperidin-N-yl]				2461
do	[piperidin-N-yl]				2461
do	[piperidin-N-yl, N-substituted]				2461
do	CH$_3$[piperazine]CH$_3$		231–2°	+(Cw)	726, 1255
do	[thiazolidin-S,N ring]			+(Cw)	1255, 2461
do	CH$_3$[S–N ring]				2461
do	[bicyclic S–N ring]				2461
do	C$_6$H$_5$[S–N ring]				2461
do	HOCH$_2$CH$_2$—				2461
do	H$_2$N[ring]—				2461
HCl·NH$_2$CH$_2$—			256°, 265°	++(Cw, An), 0(H, S, Sa)	361, 726, 1255, 1443, 2461

ᵃ Homosulfanilamide, Sulfamylon, Marfanil, Mesudin.

TABLE 174—(Continued)

R₄	R¹	R¹′	Melting Range	Activities	References
HCl·NH₂CH₂—	CH₃—		245–7°		726
do	(thiazoline ring S,N)		276–7°		726
C₆H₅CHOHCOOH·NH₂CH₂—			215°		2461
3-HOOC-4-(HO)C₆H₃SO₃H·NH₂CH₂—			252°		2461
CH₃(CH₂)₅CH=NCH₂—			136°		2461
C₆H₅CH=NCH₂—			157°		2461
4-(NO₂)C₆H₄CH=NCH₂—			217°		2461
4-(CH₃)C₆H₄CH=NCH₂—			212°		2461
C₆H₅CH=CHCH=NCH₂—			156°		2461
2-(HO)C₆H₄CH=NCH₂—			162°		2461
4-(CH₃O)C₆H₄CH=NCH₂—			187°		2461
4-HO-3-(CH₃O)C₆H₃CH=NCH₂—			175°		2461
Glucoside of NH₂CH₂—					2461
Galactoside of NH₂CH₂—					2461
Maltoside of NH₂CH₂—					2461
Lactoside of NH₂CH₂—					2461
CH₃CONHCH₂—			177°	0(S)	361, 2461
do	CH₃—		103°		2461
do	CH₃—	CH₃—	125°		2461
do	(pyridine ring)				2461
do	(pyridine ring)				2461
do	(pyridine ring with I)				2461
do	CH₃—, H₂ (thiazolidine ring S,N,H)				2461
do	(thiazoline ring S,N)		169–70°		726, 2461
do	(benzothiazoline ring S,N)				2461
do	C₆H₅—(thiazoline ring S,N)				2461
do	CH₃CONH—(pyridine ring N)				2461
HOOC(CH₂)₂CONHCH₂—			147–9°	+(Cw)	726, 1255

TABLE 174—(*Concluded*)

R_4	R^1	$R^{1'}$	Melting Range	Activities	References
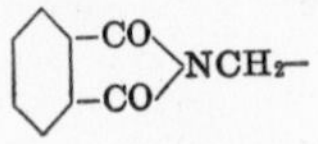 -CO / -CO \NCH$_2$-	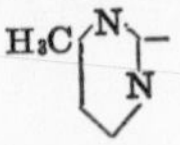 H$_3$C $\diagdown$ N $\diagdown$ N-		233–5°		726
do	 S / N -		207–8°	+(Cw), 0(H, S, Sa)	726, 1255
C$_2$H$_5$OCONHCH$_2$-			143°		2461
4-Cl-2-(HO$_3$S)C$_6$H$_3$CH=NCH$_2$-					2461
C$_6$H$_5$CHCH$_2$CHNHCH$_2$- $\quad\mid\qquad\quad\mid$ NaO$_3$S $\qquad$ SO$_2$Na					2461
4-NH$_2$C$_6$H$_4$SO$_2$NHCH$_2$-			199–201°	+(Cw), 0(H, S, Sa)	726, 1255
			199–201°		726
4-(CH$_3$CONH)C$_6$H$_4$SO$_2$NHCH$_2$-			147.5–9.0°	0(S)	361
NH$_2$CH$_2$CH$_2$-			228–30°	0(S)	361
HCl·NH$_2$CH$_2$CH$_2$-			168–9°	0(S)	361
CH$_3$CONHCH$_2$CH$_2$-				0(S)	361
C$_6$H$_5$CONHCH$_2$CH$_2$-				++(S)	454
HOOC(NH$_2$)CHCH$_2$-					

TABLE 175

2. 4-Aminophenylalkanesulfonamides

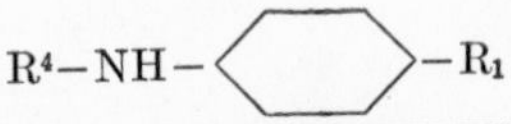

$$R^4-NH-\hexagon-R_1$$

R^4	R_1	Melting Range	Activities	References
	—CH$_2$SO$_2$NH$_2$	168°, 170°, 171–2°	0(S, Tt)	361, 423, 726, 1427, 1574
	—CH$_2$SO$_2$NHC$_6$H$_5$	172–3°		423
	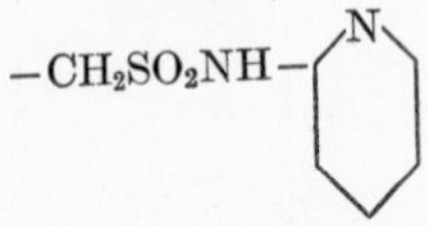 —CH$_2$SO$_2$NH—$\hexagon$N (piperidine)	185–90°		423
	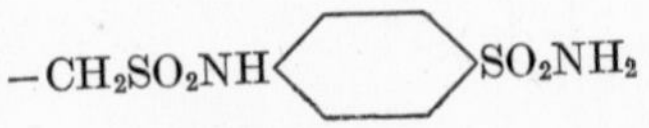 —CH$_2$SO$_2$NH$\hexagon$SO$_2$NH$_2$	162–5°		423
	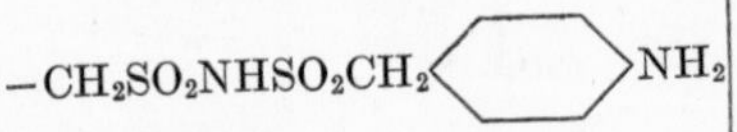 —CH$_2$SO$_2$NHSO$_2$CH$_2\hexagon$NH$_2$	D		423
CH$_3$CO—	—CH$_2$SO$_2$NH$_2$	212°		423
CH$_3$(CH$_2$)$_3$CO—	do	188–9°		423
CH$_3$(CH$_2$)$_4$CO—	do	192–4°		423
C$_6$H$_5$CO—	do	230–1°		423
	—CH$_2$CH$_2$SO$_2$NH$_2$	181–2°	0(S)	361

TABLE 176

3. 4-(Aminoalkyl)phenylalkanesulfonamides

$R_4\langle\ \rangle R_1$

R_4	R_1	Melting Range	Activities	References
NH_2CH_2-	$-CH_2SO_2NH_2$	160.5–2.0°	0(S)	361
$HCl\cdot NH_2CH_2-$	do	278–80°	0(S)	361

TABLE 177

4. Miscellaneous 4-Alkyl(or Substituted Alkyl)benzenesulfon-amides

$R_4\langle\ \rangle SO_2N\begin{smallmatrix}R^1\\R^{1\prime}\end{smallmatrix}$

R_4	R^1	$R^{1\prime}$	Melting Range	Activities	References
CH_3-				$+,\pm,0(S)$	61, 454, 512, 1384, 2441
NO_2CH_2-			141°		2461
CH_3-	C_2H_5-			$\pm(S)$	61
CH_3-	do	C_2H_5-		0(S)	61
CH_3-	C_6H_5-			$\pm(S)$	2441
CH_3-			206–6.5°		2518
CH_3-			146–7°D		2518
CH_3-			215°, 216–7°		249, 2518
CH_3-			132–2.5°		2518
CH_3-			174–5°		2518

TABLE 177—(*Concluded*)

R_4	R^1	$R^{1\prime}$	Melting Range	Activities	References
CH_3-	[N⟩CO– ring structure]		212–3°		476
CH_5-	[N ring ⟩CO– structure]				476
CH_3-	[N ring ... CO– structure]				476
CH_3-	$HO-$			±(S)	182, 330
CH_3-	$Cl-$	$Na-$			1384
$HOOC-$			293°	0(S, Tt)	146, 960, 1427, 1574, 2441
$\overset{O}{\underset{\|}{NH_2\text{-}C-}}$			172°	0(Sa, Tt)	1427, 1574
$N\equiv C-$			169°	0(S, Sa, Tt)	960, 1427, 1574
$N\equiv C-$	CH_3CO-		210°		684
$NH_2(NH=)C-$			251°	+(Cw)	960, 2533
$HCl\cdot NH_2(NH=)C-$			242°ᵃ	++(Rp), 0(Cv, I, L)	659, 767, 960
do	CH_3-			+(Rp)	659
do	$HO-$			+(Rp)	659
$HONH(NH=)C-$				+(Rp)	659
$HCl\cdot HONH(NH=)C-$			ᵇ	++(Rp)	659
$HONH(NH_2CON=)C-$				+(Rp)	659
$HCl\cdot CH_5ONH(HN=)C-$				+(Rp)	659
$C_2H_5ONH(HN=)C-$			157°		960
$HCl\cdot C_6H_5ONH(HN=)C-$			174°	+(Rp)	659, 960
$CH_3ONH(CH_3ON=)C-$				±(Rp)	659
$C_2H_5ONH(C_2H_5ON=)C-$				±(Rp)	659
$C_3H_7ONH(C_3H_7ON=)C-$				±(Rp)	659
$C_2H_5OOCCH_2-$			172°		2461
NH_2OCCH_2-			190°		2461

ᵃ V-147, *p*-sulfamylbenzamidine hydrochloride.
ᵇ V-186, *p*-sulfamylbenzamidoxime hydrochloride.

TABLE 178

5. Miscellaneous Benzenesulfonamides

$$\text{structure with } SO_2N(R^1)(R^{1\prime}) \text{ on benzene ring bearing } R_2, R_3, R_4, R_5, R_6$$

R^1	$R^{1\prime}$	R_2	R_3	R_4	R_5	Melting Range	Activities	References
(piperidino)						171–2°	0(S)	61, 2441 1033
(pyrrolidino)						229–30°, 231–2°		1033, 2518
(CH_3-piperidino)						193–4°		1033
(triazolidine)						132–4°		2518
(thiomorpholino)						172°, 178°		76, 1033, 2180, 2518
(CH_3-thiomorpholino)						161–2°, 240°		76, 492
(thiadiazolidine)						188–9°		1033

TABLE 178—(Continued)

R_1	R_1'	R_2	R_3	R_4	R_5	Melting Range	Activities	References
C_2H_5–[S, N–N ring]						128-30°		2518
[ring]=S, –NCH_3						182-3°		2518
CH_3–[ring]=S, –$NSO_2C_6H_5$						147-8°		76, 492
$NH_2C(=NH)$–						211-2°D	0(S)	2590
$NH_2C(=S)$–						109-10°		1756
$C_2H_5SC(=NH)$–							0(S)	2180
HO–				Cl–		186°	0(S)	182, 331
				Cl–				61, 2441
								341
[pyridine N ring]				Br–		202-3°		2370
[triazole, H–N, N–N]				Br–		224-5°		2370
[triazole, H–N, N–N–CH_3]				Br–		215°		249
[thiazole, S–N]		NO_2–	I–	NO–	I–	149°, 155-268°D	++(S), 0(P, Tt)	346, 713, 1447, 1574
				NO–		>270°D		466
[thiazole, CH_3–S–N]						189-90°	0(P, S)	492

Structure		M.P.	Activity	References
HO—		167-8°, 176-8°	±, 0(S, Sa), ±(P), 0(Ae)	61, 201, 327, 451, 512, 604, 1384, 1574, 2373, 2441, 2454, 2454, 2574
CH₃O— OCH₂CH₂O— [ring] SO₂NH₂	CH₃— / CH₃—	228-9°	0(Te)	2574
O— [ring] NH₂		130-1°	0(L, Lc, P, S, Sa, Y)	964, 968, 1082
OCH₂CH₂O— [ring] SO₂NHCH₃	CH₃— / CH₃—	191-2°	0(Te)	2574
OCH₂CH₂O— [ring] SO₂N(CH₃)₂		198-8.5°	0(Te)	2574
OCH₂CH₂O— [ring] SO₂NHC₂H₅	C₂H₅—	170°	0(Te)	2574
CH₃O— OCH₂CH₂O— [ring] SO₂N(C₂H₅)₂	C₂H₅— / C₂H₅—	51° / 125-5.5°	0(Te)	1712, 2574

TABLE 178—(Continued)

R¹	R¹ᐟ	R²	R³	R₄	R₅	Melting Range	Activities	References
C_3H_7-				OCH_2CH_2O-⟨ring⟩$SO_2NHC_3H_7$		177-8°	0(Te)	2574
	C_3H_7-			OCH_2CH_2O-⟨ring⟩$SO_2N(C_3H_7)_2$		111°	0(Te)	2574
$(CH_3)_2CH-$				OCH_2CH_2O-⟨ring⟩$SO_2NHCH(CH_3)_2$		190°	0(Te)	2574
C_4H_9-				OCH_2CH_2O-⟨ring⟩$SO_2N(C_4H_9)_2$		82-2.5°	0(Te)	2574
$C_8H_{17}-$				OCH_2CH_2O-⟨ring⟩$SO_2N(C_8H_{17})_2$		84°	0(Te)	2574
⟨N-ring⟩				OCH_2CH_2O-⟨ring⟩SO_3H		205°	0(Te)	2574
do	$Na-$			OCH_2CH_2O-⟨ring⟩SO_3Na		D	0(Te)	2574

			Structure			
thiazoline ring			OCH_2CH_2O- ⟨benzene⟩ SO_2NH-(thiazole)	242-3°	0(Te)	2574
do	Na-		OCH_2CH_2O- ⟨benzene⟩ $SO_2N(Na)-$(thiazole)	D	0(Te)	2574
$HOCH_2CH_2-$		$HOCH_2CH_2-$	OCH_2CH_2O- ⟨benzene⟩ $SO_2NHCH_2CH_2OH$	168.5-9°	0(Te)	2574
$HOCH_2CH_2-$		$HOCH_2CH_2-$	OCH_2CH_2O- ⟨benzene⟩ $SO_2N(CH_2CH_2OH)_2$	188-8.5°	0(Te)	2574
		$-CH_2CH_2OCH_2CH_2-$	OCH_2CH_2O- ⟨benzene⟩ $SO_2N(CH_2CH_2)_2O$	246-6.5°	0(Te)	2574
		$-(CH_2)_5-$	OCH_2CH_2O- ⟨benzene⟩ $SO_2N(CH_2)_5$	195°	0(Te)	2574
CH_3CO-			OCH_2CH_2O- ⟨benzene⟩ $SO_2NHCOCH_3$	190-1°	0(Te)	2574

TABLE 178—(Continued)

R^1	$R^{1'}$	R_2	R_3	R_4	R_5	Melting Range	Activities	References
CH_3CO	$Na-$			OCH_2CH_2O- / SO_3NCOCH_3 | Na		D	0(Te)	2574
$HOOCCH_2-$				OCH_2CH_2O- / SO_2NHCH_2COOH		226°	0(Te)	2574
$NaOOCCH_2-$	$Na-$			OCH_2CH_2O- / SO_2NCH_2COONa | Na		D	0(Te)	2574
$^cC_2H_5OOCCH_2-$				OCH_2CH_2O- / $SO_2NHCH_2COOC_2H_5$		150–1°	0(Te)	2574
$(C_2H_5)_2N(CH_2)_3CH(CH_3)-$				OCH_2CH_2O- / $SO_2NHCH(CH_2)_3N(C_2H_5)_2$ | CH_3		93–4[a]	0(Te)	2574

HCl·(C$_2$H$_5$)$_2$N(CH$_2$)$_3$CH— CH$_3$			OCH$_2$CH$_2$O— [ring] SO$_2$ NHCH(CH$_2$)$_3$N(C$_2$H$_5$)$_2$ CH$_3$ HCl		D	0(Te)	2574
C$_2$H$_5$O$_2$S—	Na—		OCH$_2$CH$_2$O— [ring] SO$_2$NHSO$_2$C$_2$H$_5$	NO—	181–2°	0(Te)	2574
do			OCH$_2$CH$_2$O— [ring] SO$_2$NSO$_2$C$_2$H$_5$ Na	NO—	D	0(Te)	2574
[N-ring]			HO—		210°	+(S), ±(P), O(Ae, Sa)	150, 21, 327
			HO—		234°		262
CH$_3$—	CH$_3$—		HS— CH$_3$—	207°			105
C$_6$H$_5$—	CH$_3$—		HO— CH$_3$O—	128°			684
3-ClC$_6$H$_4$—			CH$_3$O— HO—				684
C$_{10}$H$_7$—(2)			HO— HO—				451, 1574, 2373, 2454
CH$_3$—	CH$_3$—	CH$_3$O— HO—	CH$_3$O— HO—	115°			2454
C$_6$H$_5$—		HO— HO—	HO—	225°			2454
3-ClC$_6$H$_4$—		HO— HO—	HO—	177°			2454
C$_{10}$H$_7$—(2)		HO— HO—	HO—	218°			2454

TABLE 178—(Concluded)

R¹	R¹'	R₂	R₃	R₄	R₅	Melting Range	Activities	References
						204°		1720
		NH₂SO₂—	NH₂CO—	O=⟨ ⟩=O		171–3°	0(S)	360 968
		HO—	NH₂SO₂—	O—⟨ ⟩NH₂	HO—	270°	0(S, Tt)	1427, 1574

TABLE 179

6. Naphthalenesulfonamides

R^x	$R^{x'}$	R_1	R_2	R_4	R_5	R_6	R_7	R_8	Melting Range	Activities	References
$NH_2C(=O)-$		x								0(S)	61
			x					$NH_2C(=O)-$			881
		x		NH_2-					206°, 250-1°	0(S)	61, 171, 512, 882, 1222, 1985
C_6H_5-		x		NH_2-					190°		1292
		x		NH_2-							105
		x		NH_2-							105
		x		NH_2-							105
$-(CH_2)_5-$		x		NH_2-							171
		x		NH_2-					156-7°D		105
		x		CH_3CONH-					241°, 247°	±, 0(S)	61, 512, 882
C_6H_5-		x		do					231°		464
		x		NH_2-				NO_2-	213-8°	+(S)	1222
		x		CH_3CONH-				NO_2-			1222
C_6H_5-		x			NH_2-				259-60°		1020
		x			NH_2-				171°		1292
		x			$CONH-$ $|$ CH_3				231-2°		1020
C_6H_5-		x						NH_2-	139-40°		1292, 2274
			x	$H_2O \cdot NH_2-$					131°		881
			x	CH_3CONH-							881
			x		NH_2-						1020
C_6H_5-			x		NH_2-				127-8°		1292
			x		$CONH-$ $|$ CH_3						1020
			x		NH_2-				233.5-5.0°	0(Pr, S)	536, 883
			x		$CONH-$ $|$ CH_3				246-7°	0(S)	536

TABLE 179—(Concluded)

R^x	$R^{x'}$	R_1	R_2	R_4	R_5	R_6	R_7	R_8	Melting Range	Activities	References
C_6H_5-			x					NH_2-			881
			x					NH_2-	146-7°		1292
			x					CONH— CH₃			881
C_6H_5-			x	HO—			CONH— ⬡		125°		1474
do			x	C_6H_5COO-			do		155°		1474

TABLE 180

7. 2'-Substituted Biphenyl-4-sulfonamides

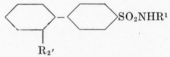

$R_{2'}$

R^1	$R_{2'}$	Melting Range	Activities	References
	NO_2-	203-4°	0(S)	1936
C_6H_5-	NO_2-	155.5-6.5°	0(S)	1940
$C_6H_5CH_2-$	NO_2-	128.5-130°	0(S)	1940
$2-(C_6H_5)C_6H_4-$	NO_2-	161-2°	0(S)	1940
$4-(C_6H_5)C_6H_4-$	NO_2-	164-5°	0(S)	1940
$4-(NH_2SO_2)C_6H_4-$	NO_2-	239.5-240°	0(S)	1940
$2-[4'-(NH_2SO_2)C_6H_4]C_6H_4-$	NO_2-	173-4°	0(S)	1940
	NH_2-	186-7°	0(S)	1936, 1939
C_6H_5-	NH_2-	100-0.5°	0(S)	1940
$C_6H_5CH_2-$	NH_2-	106.5-7.0°	0(S)	1940
$2-(C_6H_5)C_6H_4-$	NH_2-	165-5.5°	0(S)	1940
$4-(C_6H_5)C_6H_4-$	NH_2-	169-70°	0(S)	1940
$4-(NH_2SO_2)C_6H_4-$	NH_2-	197.2-8.2°	0(S)	1940
$2-[4'-(NH_2SO_2)C_6H_4]C_6H_4-$	NH_2-	263-4°	0(S)	1940
	CH_3CONH-	201-2°	0(S)	1936
C_6H_5-	do	163.5-4.5°	0(S)	1940
$C_6H_5CH_2-$	do	161-2°	0(S)	1940
$2-(C_6H_5)C_6H_4-$	do	173.5-5.0°	0(S)	1940
$4-(C_6H_5)C_6H_4-$	do	196.0-6.5°	0(S)	1940
$4-(NH_2SO_2)C_6H_4-$	do	231.5-2.5°	0(S)	1940
$2-[4'-(NH_2SO_2)C_6H_4]C_6H_4-$	do	148.5-150°D	0(S)	1940

TABLE 181

8. 4′-Substituted Biphenyl-4-sulfonamides

$R_4{}' \langle \rangle - \langle \rangle SO_2NHR^1$

R^1	$R_4{}'$	Melting Range	Activities	References
C_6H_5-	NO_2-	228°		119, 181, 1863, 2238
	NO_2-	182–3°		1863, 2238
	NH_2-	259–60°, 266–7°D		119, 181, 527, 1863, 1939, 2238
(cyclohexyl-dimethyl structure)	NH_2-	219°		527
C_6H_5-	NH_2-	186°		527, 1863, 2238
$C_6H_5CH_2-$	NH_2-	184°		527
(biphenyl structure)	NH_3-	216°		527
NH_2SO_2 (biphenyl structure)	NH_2-	277°D		527
	CH_3CONH-	295–6.5°D		181, 527
(cyclohexyl-dimethyl structure)	do	244°		527
C_6H_5-	do	237°		527
$C_6H_5CH_2-$	do	208°		527
(biphenyl structure)	do	250°		527
NH_2SO_2 (biphenyl structure)	do	299°		527

TABLE 182

9. Miscellaneous Isocyclicsulfonamides

Compound	Melting Range	Activities	References
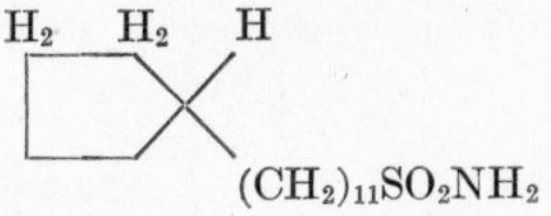 H_2 H_2 H $(CH_2)_{11}SO_2NH_2$	90–2°	±(Le)	673
4-$(NO_2)C_6H_4CH_2SO_2NH_2$		0(S)	1427, 1574
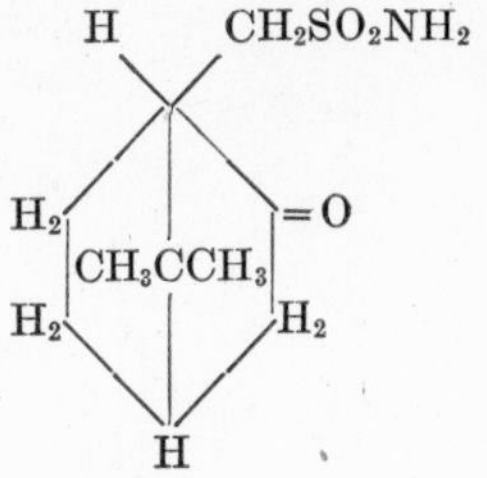 H $CH_2SO_2NH_2$ H_2 $=O$ CH_3CCH_3 H_2 H_2 H		0(S)	173

TABLE 183

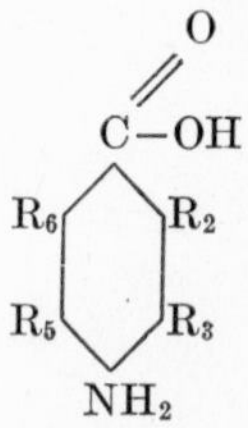

B. Derivatives of 4-Aminobenzoic Acid
  1. Nuclear-substituted

$$\overset{O}{\underset{NH_2}{\overset{\|}{C-OH}}} \quad R_6 \diagup R_2 \quad R_5 \diagdown R_3$$

R_2	R_3	R_5	R_6	Melting Range	Activities[a]	References
					0(En, Pl, Po, S, T)	347, 441, 443, 477, 1485, 1733, 2441
F—				216.0–6.5°	—(Ec)	580, 2632
	F—			215–6°	++(Ec)	580, 2632
Cl—				222°	100–200(Ec), 0(P, S)	580, 1395
	Cl—			225.5–7.0°	++(Ec)	580, 2632
	Cl—	Cl—			±(Ec)	580
Br—					—(Ec)	580
	Br—			214°	700(Ec), 166(S)	580, 1395
	Br—	Br—			0(Ec)	580
I—					—(Ec)	580
	I—				0(Ec)	580
	I—	I—			0(Ec)	580

[a] Figures give antibacterial index = ratio $\dfrac{\text{chemotherapeutic agent}}{\text{PABA}}$.

TABLE 183—(*Concluded*)

R_2	R_3	R_5	R_6	Melting Range	Activities	References
NO_2-					$\pm(Ec)$	580
	NO_2-			292°	0(Ec, P, S)	580, 1395
CH_3-				204°(HCl)	4000(Ec)	580, 1395
	CH_3-			173°	0(Ec), 50(Ec, S)	580, 1395
	CH_3-	CH_3-		254°	0(Ec, P, S)	1395
$HO-$					0(Ec)	580
CH_3O-					$\pm(Ec)$	580
	$HO-$				0(Ec)	580
	CH_3O-			191°	2000–8000(Ec), 80–800(S)	580, 1395
$HOOC-$					0(Ec)	580
	$HOOC-$				$-(Ec)$	580
NH_2-					$++(Ec)$	580
CH_3CONH-				205°	8000(Ec)	1395
	NH_2-				$++(Ec)$	580
NH_2-			NH_2-		0(S)	2441

TABLE 184

B. Derivatives of 4-Aminobenzoic Acid
  2. Carboxy-substituted

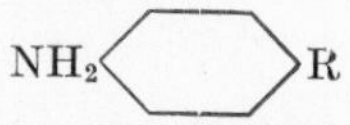

R	Melting Range	Activities	References
CH_3OOC-	112°	0(Spl)	1491
C_2H_5OOC-	92°	0(Spl)	1491
C_4H_9OOC-	56–7°	0(Spl)	1491
$CH_3(CH_2)_{11}OOC-$	81–3°	0(Spl)	1491
$CH_3(CH_2)_{15}OOC-$	86–7°	0(Spl)	1491
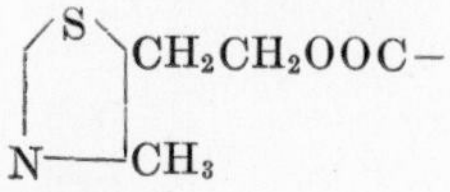	126–7°	0(Spl)	1491
NH_2OC-	178–9°	0(Et, C, P, S)	329, 512, 1491, 1574, 2373, 2441
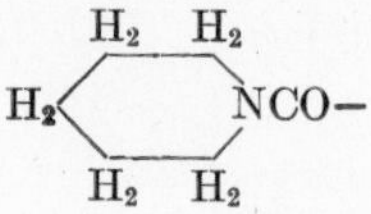		0(T)	1127
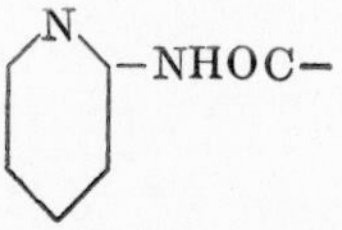	166–7°, 168°		1491, 2632

TABLE 184—(*Concluded*)

R	Melting Range	Activities	References
—NHOC—	240–1°		2632
—NHOC—	257–258°	0(Ec, P, S)	1395, 2632
HOOCCH$_2$NHOC—	197–8°		681
HOOCCH$_2$NHOCCH$_2$NHOC—	226°		681
l-(CH$_3$)$_2$CHCH$_2$(HOOC)CHNHOC—	190°		681
d-(CH$_3$)$_2$CHCH$_2$(HOOC)CHNHOC—	191°		681
d,l-(CH$_3$)$_2$CHCH$_2$(HOOC)CHNHOC—	183°		681
l-HOOCCH$_2$(HOOC)CHNHOC—	180°		681
l-HOOCCH$_2$CH$_2$(HOOC)CHNHOC—	173°	0(Ec, P, S)	681, 1395
d-HOOCCH$_2$CH$_2$(HOOC)CHNHOC—	172°		681
d,l-HOOCCH$_2$CH$_2$(HOOC)CHNHOC—	197°		681
NC—		0(S)	512
NH$_2$C(=S)—	173°	+(Spl)	1491

TABLE 185

B. Derivatives of 4-Aminobenzoic Acid
  3. Amino-substituted

R	R′	Melting Range	Activities	References
CH$_3$—		160°	0(Ec, P, S)	1395
CH$_3$—	CH$_3$—	242°	0(Ec, P, S)	1395
CH$_3$CO—	CH$_3$—	191°	0(Ec, P, S)	1395
NH$_2$C(=O)—			0(Spl)	1491
NH$_2$C(=NH)—		296°	0(Ec, P, S)	1395
NH$_2$C$_6$H$_4$CO—			0(Spl)	1491
HO—				441, 477
4-[(C$_2$H$_5$)$_2$N]C$_6$H$_4$N=		228–30°	0(Ec, P, S)	1395
HOOCC$_6$H$_4$NO=			0(S)	441

TABLE 186

B. Derivatives of 4-Aminobenzoic Acid
  4. Nuclear-carboxy-substituted

R	R_3	Melting Range	Activities[a]	References
NH_2-	CH_3-	125°	333(S), 466(Ec)	1395
CH_3O-	$HO-$		0(S)	2441

[a] Figures give antibacterial index = ratio $\dfrac{\text{chemotherapeutic agent}}{\text{PABA}}$.

TABLE 187

B. Derivatives of 4-Aminobenzoic Acid
  5. Carboxy-amino-substituted

R^1	R^4	Melting Range	Activities	References
CH_3O-	C_2H_5-	138–9°		2645
C_2H_5O-	do	72–3°		2645
H_2N-	do	144–5°		2645
CH_3O-	C_3H_7-	61–2°		2645
C_2H_5O-	do	68–9°		2645
H_2N-	do	137–8°		2645
CH_3O-	C_4H_9-	104–5°		2645
C_2H_5O-	do	68–9°		2645
H_2N-	do	111–2°		2645
CH_3O-	$4-(NO_2)C_6H_4CO-$	244°		1491
CH_3O-	$4-(NH_2)C_6H_4CO-$	235°	0(Spl)	1491
CH_3O-	$4'-[4-(NO_2)C_6H_4CONH]C_6H_4CO-$	365°D	0(Spl)	1491

TABLE 188

C. Derivatives of 4-Nitrobenzoic Acid

R	Melting Range	Activities	References
1. Acyclic Esters			
$HO-$		+(P, S, Sr), ±(H), 0(Pl)	347, 441, 443, 1215, 1733, 1931, 2441
$NaO-$		+(S, Sr), 0(En, Po, T)	347, 1060, 1215, 1485

TABLE 188—(Continued)

R	Melting Range	Activities	References
CH_3O-		±(P, S)	347, 1491
C_2H_5O-		±(P, S)	347
$CH_3(CH_2)_2O-$		+(P), ±(S)	347
$CH_3(CH_2)_3O-$	34–5°	+(P)	347, 1491
$CH_3(CH_2)_5O-$	a	±(P)	347
$C_6H_{13}O-$ "Tertiary"		+(S), 0(P)	1491, 1574
$CH_3(CH_2)_9O-$		±(P)	347
$CH_3(CH_2)_{11}O-$	43–4°		1491
$CH_3(CH_2)_{13}O-$		±(P)	347
$CH_3(CH_2)_{15}O-$	53–5°		1491
$CH_2=CHCH_2O-$		+(P)	347
$CH_2=C(CH_3)(CH_2)_3CH(CH_3)(CH_2)_2O-$		±(S), 0(I, R, Sa)	904, 1574
$CH_3(CH_2)_7CH=CH(CH_2)_8O-$	oil	0(I, R, S)	1574, 2194
$C_{10}H_{17}O-$ (Geranyl)		±(S), 0(Sa)	904, 1574
C_4H_9S-		+(P)	347

2. Isocyclic Esters

R	Melting Range	Activities	References
$C_6H_{11}O-$	51.5–2.5°	+(S), +, 0(P), 0(I, R, Tt)	345, 347, 1446, 1574, 2196
$2-(CH_3)C_6H_{10}O-$		±(P)	347
$4-(CH_3)C_6H_{10}O-$		±, 0(P)	347
$4-(CH_3)C_6H_{10}CH_2(CH_3)_2CO-$		±, 0(P)	347
$C_{10}H_{15}O-$ (2)		0(P)	347
C_6H_5O-		+(P)	347
$2-(NO_2)C_6H_4O-$	138.5–40°	+(S), 0(I, R)	1574, 2194
$3-(NO_2)C_6H_4O-$	174–75°	+(S), 0(I, R)	1574, 2194
$4-(NO_2)C_6H_4O-$	157–59°	+(S), 0(I, P, R)	347, 1574, 2194
$3-(CH_3)C_6H_4O-$		+(P)	347
$4-(CH_3)C_6H_4O-$		+(P)	347
$C_6H_5CH_2O-$		+(P, S)	347
$2-(NO_2)C_6H_4CH_2O-$	114–6°	0(I, R, S)	1574, 2194
$4-(NO_2)C_6H_4CH_2O-$	166–8°	+(S), 0(I, R)	1574, 2194
$C_6H_5CH=CHCH_2O-$	74.5–6.0°	+(S), 0(I, R)	1574, 2194
$C_{10}H_{11}O-$ (2)		0(P)	347
Cholesteryl–		±(P)	347
$C_{10}H_7O-$ (1)		0(P)	347
$C_{10}H_7O-$ (2)		0(P)	347
$2-(HO)C_6H_4O-$	190–4°	0(M, P, S)	2196
$2-(CH_3O)C_6H_4O-$	101–2°	+, ±(P, S), 0(Tt)	345, 347, 1446, 1574
$2-[4'-(NO_2)C_6H_4COO]C_6H_4O-$	252–7°	0(M, P, S)	2196
$3-(HO)C_6H_4O-$	175–7°	0(M, P, S)	2196
$3-[4'-(NO_2)C_6H_4COO]C_6H_4O-$	185–6°	0(M, P, S)	2196
$4-(HO)C_6H_4O-$	190–4°	0(M, P, S)	2196

a Amonal A.

TABLE 188—(Concluded)

R	Melting Range	Activities	References
4-[4'-(NO$_2$)C$_6$H$_4$COO]C$_6$H$_4$O—	252–7°	0(M, P, S)	2196
2,3-(HO)$_2$C$_6$H$_3$O—	193–7°	0(M, P, S)	2196
2,3[4'-(NO$_2$)C$_6$H$_4$COO]$_2$C$_6$H$_3$O—	229–31°	0(M, P, S)	2196

3. Heterocyclic Esters

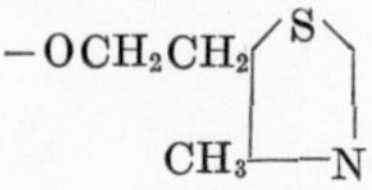 —OCH$_2$CH$_2$ (ring: S, CH$_3$, N)	123°		1491

TABLE 189

C. Derivatives of 4-Nitrobenzoic Acid
4. Miscellaneous Derivatives

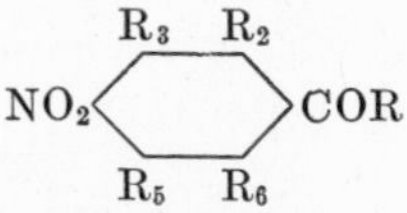

$$NO_2 \underset{R_5 \quad R_6}{\overset{R_3 \quad R_2}{\bigcirc}} COR$$

R$_2$	R$_3$	R$_6$	R	Melting Range	Activities	References
			H$_2$N—		+, −(P), ±(S)	329, 347, 441, 443, 2441
			C$_6$H$_{11}$NH—	203–4°	0(M, P, S)	1574, 2196, 2298
			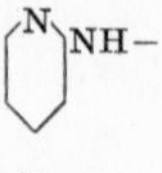 (pyridyl)NH—	223–6°, 244°	0(P, Tt), −(S)	1446, 1491, 1574, 2370, 2632
			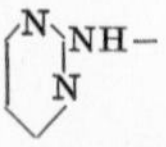 (pyrazinyl)NH—	206.5–7.5°		2632
			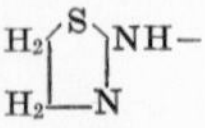 H$_2$(thiazolidine)NH—	211–4°, 243–4°	0(S)	1574, 2370, 2373
			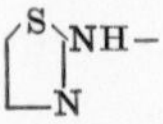 (thiazoline)NH—	297–8°		2632
			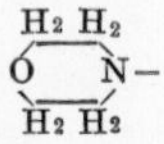 O(morpholine)N—	98°, 101–6°	0(M, S), −(P)	1574, 2217, 2298
			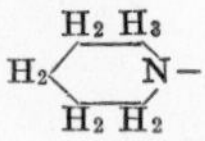 (piperidine)N—	115–8°	0(M, P, S)	2196
			HOOCCH$_2$NH—	129–30°		681
			HOOCCH$_2$NHOCCH$_2$NH—	218°		681
			l-(CH$_3$)$_2$CHCH$_2$CHNH— | COOH			681
			d-(CH$_3$)CHCH$_2$CHNH— | COOH			681

TABLE 189—*Concluded*

R_2	R_3	R_6	R	Melting Range	Activities	References
			$d,l\text{-}(CH_3)_2CHCH_2CHNH-$ COOH	225°		681
			$l\text{-}HOOCCH_2CHNH-$ COOH	151-2°		681
			$l\text{-}HOOCCH_2CH_2CHNH-$ COOH	114-6°		681
			$d\text{-}HOOCCH_2CH_2CHNH-$ COOH	115-7°		681
			$d,l\text{-}HOOCCH_2CH_2CHNH-$ COOH	93-7°		681
			$-N\begin{smallmatrix}H_2 & H_2\end{smallmatrix}N-$ ... $OC\langle\rangle NO_2$	318°	0(M, P, S)	2196
			$4\text{-}NH_2C_6H_4NH-$		0(P)	347
			NH_2NH-		0(S)	441
NO_2-			$HO-$		0(Ec, P, S)	1395
NO_2-		NO_2-	$HO-$		0(S)	441
	CH_3-		$HO-$	216°		1395
$NaOOC-$			CH_3O-		0(S)	347

TABLE 190

D. Derivatives of Sulfanilic Acid

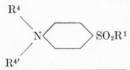

R^4	$R^{4\prime}$	R^1	Melting Range	Activities	References
		$HO-$		+, 0(S), 0(Ca, G), +(L)	48, 61, 151, 512, 1384, 2241, 2654
		C_2H_5O-	78-80°	0	150, 2392
		$5\text{-}NO_2\text{-}2\text{-}NH_2C_6H_3O-$	217-8°D		543
		$4\text{-}NH_2C_6H_4O-$	146°	0	60
		$3\text{-}NO_2\text{-}4\text{-}NH_2C_6H_3O-$	166.5- 7.5°D		543
		N_3-		0(S, Tt)	106, 1427, 1574
CH_3-	CH_3-	$HO-$			1384
	$CH_2=$	$NaO-$		0(S, Tt)	1427, 1574
CH_3CO-		$HO-$		±(P), 0(S)	60, 1427, 1574
do		$2\text{-}NH_2\text{-}5\text{-}(NO_2)C_6H_3O-$	212°(D)		543
do		$2\text{-}CH_3CONH\text{-}5\text{-}(NO_2)C_6H_3O-$	217- 7.5°D		543

TABLE 190—(*Concluded*)

R⁴	R⁴′	R¹	Melting Range	Activities	Reference
CH₃CO		4-(CH₃CONH)C₆H₄O−		0(S)	60, 858
do		3-(NO₂)-4-(NH₂)C₆H₃O−	231-2°D		543
do		3-NO₂-4-(CH₃CONH)C₆H₃O−	211-2°D		543
do		2,5-(NH₂)₂C₆H₃O−	159-60°D		543
do		2,5-(CH₃CONH)₂C₆H₃O−	268°D		543
do		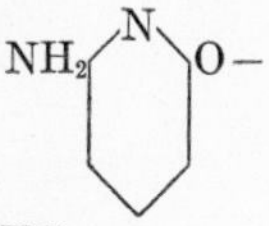 NH₂—[N O−]	148°		410
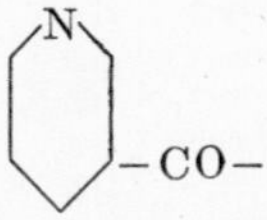 [N —CO−]		HO−	175°	±(P, S), 0(I, Tt)	1574, 2298
NH₂−		HO−			1384
NH₂−		NaO−		±(S), 0(Ca)	48, 61

TABLE 191

E. Ketones

1. Substituted Benzophenones

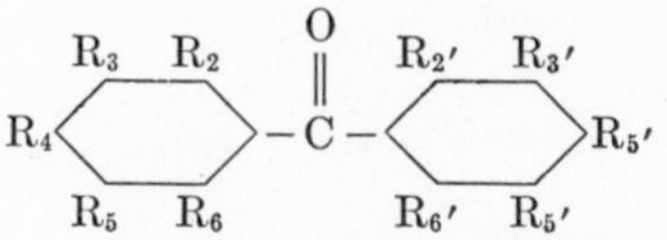

$$R_4 \underset{R_5 \quad R_6}{\overset{R_3 \quad R_2}{\bigcirc}} - \overset{O}{\underset{\|}{C}} - \underset{R_{6'} \quad R_{5'}}{\overset{R_{2'} \quad R_{3'}}{\bigcirc}} R_{5'}$$

R₂	R₃	R₄	R₅	R₂′	R₄′	R₅′	Melting Range	Activities[a]	References
								5(T)	1127
Cl−								2.5(T)	1127
	Cl−							10(T)	1127
		Cl−						2.5(T)	1127
Cl−			Cl−					20(T)	1127
Cl−				Cl−				1(T)	1127
Cl−					Cl−			1(T),0(T)	1064, 1127
		Cl−			Cl−			>20(T)	1127
		Br−			Br−			>20(T)	1127
I−								1.67(T)	1127
		I−						>20(T)	1127
	NO₂−							>20(T)	1127
		NO₂−			NO₂−		189°	0(I, R, S)	441, 1574, 2192

[a] Figures show tuberculostatic concentrations of drugs *in vitro* in mgs. per 100 c.c.

? Question marks show position of substituent uncertain.

TABLE 191—(*Concluded*)

R₂	R₃	R₄	R₅	R₂′	R₄′	R₅′	Melting Range	Activities[a]	References
		CH₃–						1.67(T)	1127
		CH₃–?	Cl–?					1(T)	1127
		CH₃–		Cl–				>20(T)	1127
		C₂H₅–						20(T)	1127
		C₂H₅–?			C₂H₅–?			>20(T)	1127
		(CH₃)₂CH–						>20(T)	1127
		(CH₃)₂CH–?			CH₃–?			>20(T)	1127
(CH₃)₂CH–?		do			(CH₃)₂CH–?			>20(T)	1127
Cl–					C₆H₅–			>20(T)	1127
		HO–						10(T)	1127
		CH₃O–						1.67(T)	1127
		C₂H₅O–						1.25(T)	1127
		C₆H₅CH₂O–						>20(T)	1127
		HOCH₂CH₂O–						20(T)	1127
		CH₃COO–						20(T)	1127
		HOOCCH₂O–						>20(T)	1127
		C₂H₅S–						>20(T)	1127
HO–				HO–				10(T)	1127
CH₃O–				CH₃O–				>20(T)	1127
C₂H₅O–				C₂H₅O–				>20(T)	1127
C₆H₅CH₂O–				C₆H₅CH₂O–				>20(T)	1127
CH₃COO–				CH₃COO–				20(T)	1127
		HO–			HO–			20(T)	1127
		C₆H₅CH₂O–			C₆H₅CH₂O–			>20(T)	1127
		HOOC–						>20(T)	1127
		CH₃OOC–						>20(T)	1127
		C₂H₅OOC–						>20(T)	1127
		CH₃(CH₂)₂OOC–						>20(T)	1127
		CH₃(CH₂)₃OOC–						>20(T)	1127
HOOC–		C₆H₅O–						>20(T)	1127
HOOC–					HO–	Cl–		>20(T)	1127
CH₃(CH₂)₅OOC–					C₆H₅O–			>20(T)	1127
CH₂OOC–					do			>20(T)	1127
CH₂OC₂H₅									
		NH₂–					124°	±(Sp1), 0(I, S)	680, 1574, 2373
		NH₂–			NO₂–		179°	0(S)	441
		NH₂–			NH₂–		236–9,°	+(G, H),	441, 680, 1384
							244–5°	±(S), 0(I, R)	1395, 1491, 1574, 2192
		(CH₃)₂N–			(CH₃)₂N–		173°	+,0(S), +(Sa) 0(I, R)	60, 441, 1574, 2192

TABLE 192

2. Miscellaneous Phenyl Ketones

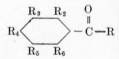

R	R₂	R₄	R₅	Melting Range	Activities[a]	References
CH₃–					>20(T), 0(En, Po)	1127, 1485
CH₃–		Cl–			20(T)	1127
C₂H₅–					20(T)	1127
CH₃(CH₂)₂–					20(T)	1127
do		Cl–			20(T)	1127

[a] Figures show tuberculostatic concentrations of drugs *in vitro* in mgs. per 100 cc.

TABLE 192—(Concluded)

R	R_2	R_4	R_5	Melting Range	Activities[a]	References
$CH_3(CH_2)_3-$					10(T)	1127
$CH_3(CH_2)_4-$					5(T)	1127
$CH_3(CH_2)_5-$					2.5(T)	1127
$CH_3(CH_2)_{10}-$					>20(T)	1127
 [cyclic structure]					10(T)	1127
$C_6H_5CH(OH)-$					0(S)	2441
$4-(NO_2)C_6H_4CH(OH)-$		NO_2-		214°	0(Ec, P, S)	1395
$2-(HO)C_6H_4CO-$	$HO-$			154–5°		1489
$2-(CH_3O)C_6H_4CO-$	$HO-$			124–6°		1489
do	CH_3O-			154–5°		1489
$2-HO-5-BrC_6H_3CO-$	$HO-$		$Br-$	212–3°		1489
$4-(HO)C_6H_4CO-$		$HO-$				1489
CH_2-		NH_2-		106°	0(I, P, S), ±(Spl), 600(S), 33–100(Ec)	680, 1395, 1491, 1574, 2373
$4-(NH_2)C_6H_4CH_2-$					±(Spl)	1490
 [pyridine-like structure]		NH_2-		154–5°, 168°	±(Spl)	1491, 2370
$4-(NH_2)C_6H_4CHOH-$				199°	++(Spl)	1490
$4-(NH_2)C_6H_4CO-$		NH_2-		169°	+++(Spl)	1490, 2488

TABLE 193

F. Quinones

Compound	Melting Range	Activities	References
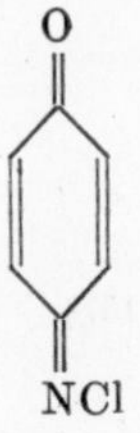 [quinone structure with O and NCl]	75–8°	0(S, Tt), −(P)	1574
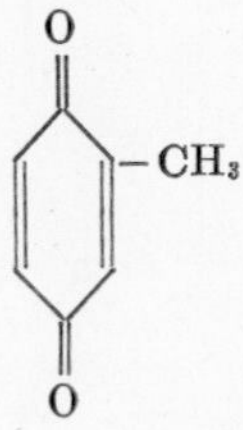 [quinone structure with O, O and CH₃]	65–7°	−(I, S, Sa, Tt)	1574

TABLE 193—(*Concluded*)

Compound	Melting Range	Activities	References
	111–2°	0(S, Sa)	1075, 1574
	203–5°	0(I, S)	1574
	172–4°	0(I, R), −(S)	1446, 1574
		0	2441
	248–50°	0(S, Sa, R)	1574

TABLE 194

G. Isocyclicsulfenamides
  1. 4-Nitrobenzenesulfenamides

$$NO_2\langle\bigcirc\rangle SN-R$$
$$\qquad\qquad\quad R'$$

R	R'	Melting Range	Activities	References
C_2H_5-	C_2H_5-	101–3°	+(S, Sa), ±(P)	968, 1710
$CH_3(CH_2)_3-$		oil		1710
C_6H_5-				1710
$2\text{-}ClC_6H_4-$				1710, 2638
				2638
		170–3°		1707, 1747
				1710
		194–6°		1708, 1748
		215–6°		1708, 1748
		155–60°, 166°		1709, 1747
		176°, 183°		1709
		193°		1747
$NH_2C(=NH)-$				1706

TABLE 195

2. 4-Acetamidobenzenesulfenamides

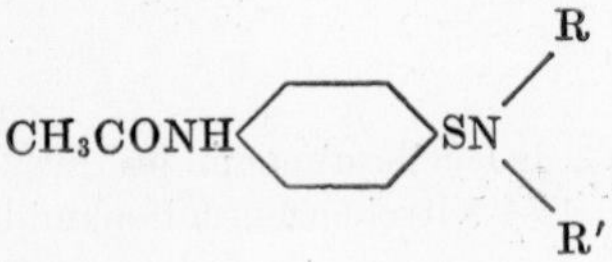

$$CH_3CONH-\!\!\langle\ \rangle\!\!-SN\diagup^{R}_{\diagdown R'}$$

R	R′	Melting Range	Activities	References
C_2H_5-	C_2H_5-	oil		1710
C_6H_5-				1710
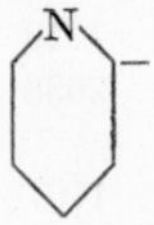 [piperidin-1-yl]				1707, 1747, 2598
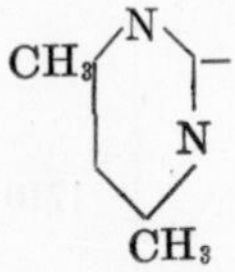 [4-methylpiperazin-1-yl (CH₂ / N–CH₃)]				1708
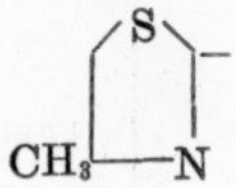 [2-methylthiazolidin-3-yl (S / CH₃—N)]		207°		1709, 2598
do	CH_3CO-	238°		1709
$H_2NC(=NH)-$				1706
$-C(CH_3)=CHSC(=NCOCH_3)-$				1711

TABLE 196

H. Derivatives of Isocyclicsulfinic Acids
  1. 4-Nitrobenzenesulfinamides

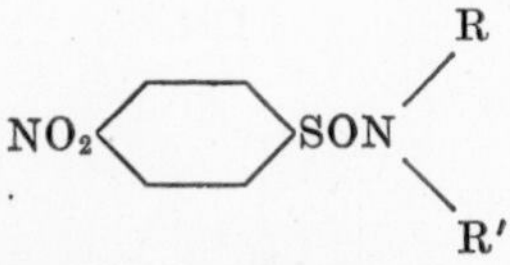

$$NO_2-\!\!\langle\ \rangle\!\!-SON\diagup^{R}_{\diagdown R'}$$

R	R′	Melting Range	Activities	References
CH_3-	CH_3-	149–50°, 164°	–	457, 2370
C_6H_5-		74°		457
		145.5–6.5°		2370
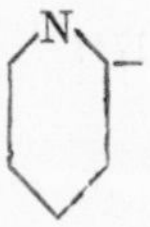 [piperidin-1-yl]		135–6°	–	457, 2370
 [thiazolidin-3-yl (S / N)]		119°, 175.0–5.5°		1804, 2370

TABLE 197

2. Miscellaneous Derivatives of Isocyclicsulfinic Acids

Compound	Melting Range	Activities	References
2-$(NO_2)C_6H_4SONH_2$	150°		457
4-$(NO_2)C_6H_4SO_2H$	140°	+	457, 1550
4-$(NO_2)C_6H_4SOOCH_3$	47°	0(L)	968, 1082
4-$(NO_2)C_6H_4SOOC_2H_5$	49–51°	+(S), ±(Sa), 0(P)	968
4-$(NH_2)C_6H_4SO_2H$	230°D		228, 457, 1384
4-$(NH_2)C_6H_4SONH_2$			457
4-$[CH_3(CH_2)_5NH]C_6H_4SO_2H$	113–6°		373
4-$(CH_3CONH)C_6H_4SO_2H$	145–55°, 153–4°D	+(S), 0(Tt)	60, 156, 457, 1384, 1427, 1574, 1895
4-$(CH_3CONH)C_6H_4SO_2Na$			458
4-$(CH_3CONH)C_6H_4SONH_2$			457
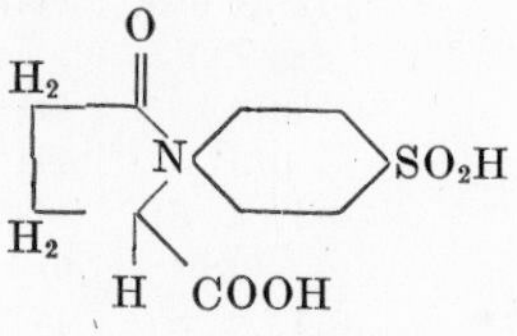	228°	++	60

TABLE 198

I. Isocyclic Selenium Compounds

Compound	Melting Range	Activities	References
4-$(NH_2)C_6H_4SeH$	76–8°		424
4-$(CH_3CONH)C_6H_4SeH$			424
$CH_3CONHC_6H_4SeBr$			424
4-$(NO_2)C_6H_4SeO_2H$			424
$NH_2C_6H_4SeO_2 \cdot \frac{1}{2} Ba$			424
4-$(CH_3CONH)C_6H_4SeO_2Ag$			424
$CH_3CONHC_6H_4SeBr_3$	130–2°D		424
4-$(C_6H_5CONH)C_6H_4SeO_2H$	186°D		424
4-$(NO_2)C_6H_4SeO_3H$	212°		1200
4-$(NO_2)C_6H_4SeO_3K$			424
$NH_2C_6H_4SeO_3H$	178°		1200
4-$(C_6H_5CONH)C_6H_4SeO_3K$			424

TABLE 199

J. Miscellaneous Isocyclicamines

Compound	Melting Range	Activities	References
$C_6H_5NHC_6H_5$	53.0–3.5°	0(I, S, Tt)	1574
$(C_6H_5)_2NNO$		0(S)	441

TABLE 199—(*Continued*)

Compound	Melting Range	Activities	References
$C_6H_5NHCOCH_3$		0(G)	12, 2441, 2654
$C_6H_5NHCSCH_3$		0(S)	2441
$NH_2C(=NH)NHC_6H_5$		0(S)	2441
$C_6H_5NHC(=NH)NHC_6H_5$		0(S)	2441
$C_6H_5NHC(=NC_6H_5)NHC_6H_5$		0(S)	2441
$NH_2C(=S)NHC_6H_5$		0, ±(S)	1756, 2441
$4-(NH_2)C_6H_4F$	187–9° (b.p.)	+(S), 0(I)	1574, 2373
$4-(Cl_3CCONH)C_6H_4F$	90–1°	+(S)	1574, 2373
$4-(NH_2)C_6H_4Cl$	70–2°	+(S), 0(I, Tt)	1574, 2373
$2,4-Cl_2C_6H_3NH_2$	61–3°	0(I, S)	1574, 2373
$4-(NH_2)C_6H_4Br$	62–4°	0(I, S)	1574, 2373
$4-(NH_2)C_6H_4I$	62–3°	0(I, P, S)	1574, 2373
$4-(CH_3CONH)C_6H_4IO$		±(Sa), 0(P, S)	1427, 1574
$4-(CH_3CONH)C_6H_4IO_2$		±(P), 0(S, Sa, Tt)	1427, 1574
$4-(NO)C_6H_4N(CH_3)_2$		0(S)	441
$4-(NO)C_6H_4NHC_6H_5$		0(S)	441
$2-(NO_2)C_6H_4NH_2 \cdot HCl$		0(I, R, S)	1446, 1574
$2-(NO_2)C_6H_4NHCOCH_3$		0(S)	61
$3-(NO_2)C_6H_4NH_2 \cdot HCl$		0(I, R, S)	1446, 1574
$3-(NO_2)C_6H_4NHCOCH_3$		0(S)	61
$4-(NO_2)C_6H_4NH_2$		0(P, S)	347, 1384
$4-(NO_2)C_6H_4NH_2 \cdot HCl$		±(S), 0(I, P, R, Tt)	441, 1427, 1574
$4-(NO_2)C_6H_4NHC_6H_5$		0(S)	441
$4-(NO_2)C_6H_4NHCOCH_3$		0(S)	61, 441
$4-(NO_2)C_6H_4NHN=NC_6H_4(NO_2)-4'$		0(S)	441
$4-(NH_2)C_6H_4CH_3$	42–3°	0(I, S)	1574, 2373
$(C_6H_5CH_2)_2NC(=NH)NH_2 \cdot \frac{1}{2} H_2SO_4$	279°D	0(I, R, Tt)	1574
$(C_6H_5CH_2NH)_2C=NH \cdot HCl$	186°	0(I, R, Tt)	1574
$NH(CH_2)_3N(C_2H_5)_2$ —H H₂ H₂		0(S)	512
$NHCOC_6H_5$		0(T)	1127

TABLE 199—(*Continued*)

Compound	Melting Range	Activities	References
1-[NH$_2$C(=NH)NH]C$_{10}$H$_7$	129–30°	0(I, R, Tt)	1574
NHCH$_2$CH$_2$NH$_2$		0(S)	2441
4-(NH$_2$)C$_6$H$_4$C$_6$H$_5$	53°	0(I, S)	1574, 2373
3-(NH$_2$)C$_6$H$_4$NHCOCH$_3$		0(S)	61
4-(NH$_2$)C$_6$H$_4$NH$_2$		0(S)	512, 2441
4-(NH$_2$)C$_6$H$_4$N(CH$_3$)$_2$		0(S)	2441
4-(NH$_2$)C$_6$H$_4$N(CH$_3$)$_3$Cl			1384
4-(NH$_2$)C$_6$H$_4$NHC$_6$H$_5$		0(S)	2441
4-(NH$_2$)C$_6$H$_4$NHCOCH$_3$	161–2°	0(I, S)	61, 1574, 2373, 2441
1,4(CH$_3$CONH)$_2$C$_6$H$_4$	>295°	+(S), 0(Tt)	1574, 2373
[4-(NH$_2$)C$_6$H$_4$NH]$_2$CO		±(S)	60
1,4[NH$_2$C(=NH)NH]$_2$C$_6$H$_4$	258–9°D	0(I, R, Tt)	1574
4-(NH$_2$)C$_6$H$_4$NHCH$_2$COOH		0(Spl)	1491
4-(NH$_2$)C$_6$H$_4$NHSO$_3$Na		0(S, Tt)	1427, 1574
{4-[NH$_2$C(=NH)NH]C$_6$H$_4$—}$_2$	234–6°D	0(I, P, R, S)	1574
4-(NH$_2$)C$_6$H$_4$CH$_2$C$_6$H$_4$(NH$_2$)—4′	88°	0(S)	60, 1574, 2192
[4-NH$_2$-2-(NO$_2$)C$_6$H$_3$]$_2$CH$_2$		±(S)	60
4-(NH$_2$)C$_6$H$_4$CH=CHC$_6$H$_4$(NH$_2$)—4′		0(Spl)	1490
2,4-(NH$_2$)$_2$C$_6$H$_3$NHC$_6$H$_5$	158°	0(I, R, S)	1574, 2192
2-(HO)C$_6$H$_4$NHCHO	125°	0(I, R, S, Tt)	1446, 1574
2-(HO)C$_6$H$_4$NHCONH$_2$	154°D	0(I, Tt)	1446, 1574
2-(HO)C$_6$H$_4$NHC(=S)NH$_2$	161°	0(I, R, S)	1446, 1574
4-(NH$_2$)C$_6$H$_4$OH	184–6°	±, 0(S), 0(I)	1574, 2373, 2441
4-(NH$_2$)C$_6$H$_4$OCH$_3$	57–8°	0(Et, I, S)	1574, 2373
4-(NH$_2$)C$_6$H$_4$OC$_6$H$_4$(NH$_2$)—4′		0(S)	60
4-(NH$_2$)C$_6$H$_4$SH			1200
		0(I, P, S)	1574, 2192
2-(HCl·NH$_2$)C$_{10}$H$_6$(OH)—1	240–2°D	−(S), 0(I, R)	1075, 1574
4-(HO)C$_{10}$H$_6$(NH$_2$·HCl)—1		−(S)	1574, 2192

TABLE 199—(*Continued*)

Compound	Melting Range	Activities	References
NHCH₂CH₂OH [naphthalene ring with OH]		0(S)	2441
2-(HO)C₁₀H₆(NH₂·HCl)−1		0(I, S), −(P)	1075, 1574
2-(HO)C₁₀H₆(NHCOCH₃)−1	235°D	0(I, R, S)	1075, 1574
2-(HO)C₁₀H₆(NHCONH₂)−1	203–4°D	0(I, R, S)	1075, 1574
CH[N(C₂H₅)₂]CHOHCH₃ [naphthalene ring]		0(S)	512
C₆H₅CH[ring—OCH₃]NH(CH₂)₃N(C₂H₅)₂		0(S)	512
[4-(NH₂)C₆H₄]₂CHOH		0	441
[4-(CH₃)₂NC₆H₄]₂CHOH	94–5°	±(S), 0(I, R, Sa)	441, 1574, 2192
[(CH₃)₂N⟨ring⟩—]₃COH (Gentian Violet)		0(En, Po)	1485
4-(NH₂)C₆H₄CHOHCHOHC₆H₄(NH₂)−4′	244–5°	0(Spl)	1490
4[(CH₃)₂N]C₆H₄CHO		0(Ec, P, S)	1395
[(CH₃)₂N⟨ring⟩—]₂C=NH (Auramine)	136°	0(I, R, S, Tt)	1574
H H₂ H₂ H / ring / NH₂ H₂ H₂ COOH	304–5°	0(Spl)	1491
NH₂ H₂ H₂ H / ring / H H₂ H₂ COOH	486–8°	0(Spl)	1491
4-(NH₂)C₆H₁₀COOC₂H₅	74–5°	−(I, S)	1574, 2373

TABLE 199—(*Continued*)

Compound	Melting Range	Activities	References
4-$(NH_2)C_6H_4CH_2COOH$	199–200°	$\pm$, 0(S), 0(Ec, I, P)	1395, 1574, 2373, 2441
4-$(NH_2)C_6H_4CH(NH_2)COOH$		0(Ec, P, S)	1395
4-$(NH_2)C_6H_4CH = CHCOOH$	174–6°	0(Ec, P, S)	1395
1-$(NH_2)C_{10}H_6(COOH)-4$	195–200°	0(Ec, P, S)	1395
$(C_6H_5)_2C(NH_2)COOH$		0(En, Po)	1485
5-NH_2-2-$(HO)C_6H_3COOH$		0	2441
4-$(HO)C_6H_4CH(NH_2)COOH$		0(En, Po)	1485
2-$(NH_2)C_6H_4SO_3H$			1384
2-$(NH_2)C_6H_4SO_3Na$		+(Ca)	48
2-NH_2-5-$(NO_2)C_6H_3SO_3H$		0(S)	61
3-$(NH_2)C_6H_4SO_3H$		0(S)	61
3-$(NH_2)C_6H_4SO_3Na$		0(Ca)	48
2,5-$(NH_2)C_6H_3SO_3H$		0(S)	2441
		0(S)	2441
SO₃Na / NH₂ (decahydronaphthalene structure)		0, +(S)	61, 2441
SO₃Na / NH₂ (decahydronaphthalene structure)			

TABLE 199—(*Continued*)

Compound	Melting Range	Activities	References
(naphthalene structure) NH₂ / SO₃Na		0(S)	61
[SO₃H / NH₂ ... SO₃−] Al (subscript 3)		0(En)	105, 1485
NH₂—C₆H₄—C₆H₄—NH₂ / HO₃S ... SO₃H		+(S)	2441
HO NH₂ (naphthalene) / HO₃S ... SO₃H		0(S)	2441
4[(CH₃)₂N]C₆H₄P(OH)ONa	162°	0(P, S)	36, 2004
4-(NH₂)C₆H₄PO₃H₂	245°D, 285°	±(Spl)	477, 1491
4-(CH₃CONH)C₆H₄PO₃H₂	229°D	0(Spl)	477, 1491
3-HCl·NH₂-4-(HO)C₆H₃AsO		0(En, Po)	1485
4-(NH₂)C₆H₄AsO₃H₂		0(Ec, P, S)	512, 1384, 1395
4-(NH₂CONH)C₆H₄AsO₃H₂		0(I, R, Tt)	1574
CO(NHC₆H₄AsO₃H₂)₂		0(S)	512
AsO₃H₂ / (ring)—AsO₃H₂ / NH₂		0(S)	512
(naphthalene) AsO₃H₂ / CH₃CONH		0(S)	512
3-NH₂-4-(HOCH₂CH₂)C₆H₃AsO₃H₂		0(En, Po)	1485

TABLE 199—(*Concluded*)

Compound	Melting Range	Activities	References
4-$(NH_2)C_6H_4SbO_3HNa$		0(En, Po)	1485
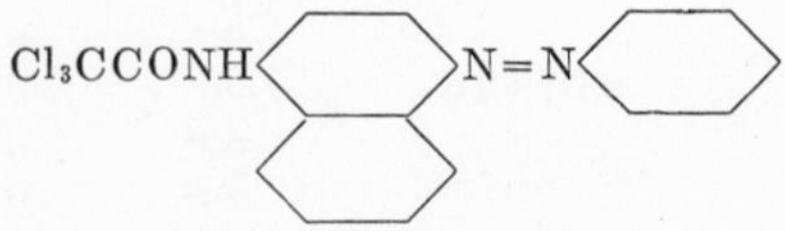 Cl_3CCONH $N=N$	153.5°	0(I, P, S)	1574
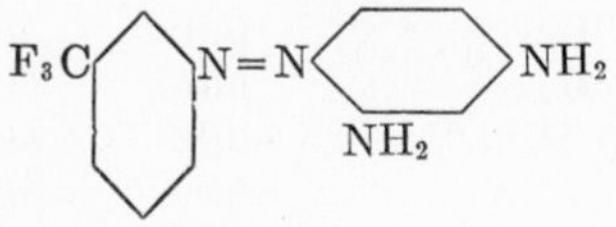 F_3C $N=N$ ... NH_2 / NH_2		0(S)	1427, 1574
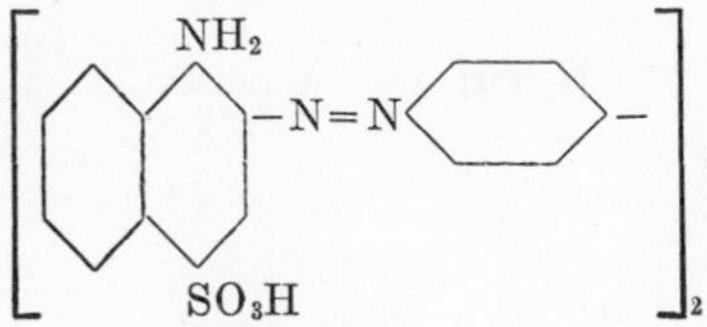 (Congo Red)		0(I, Sa)	1446, 1574
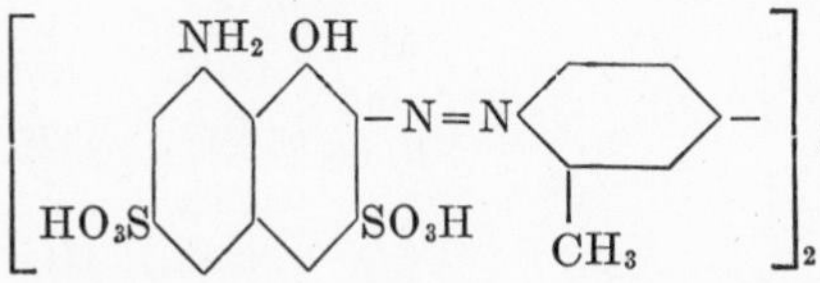 (Trypan blue)		±(Sa), 0(I, Tt)	1447, 1574

TABLE 200

K. Miscellaneous Azo Compounds

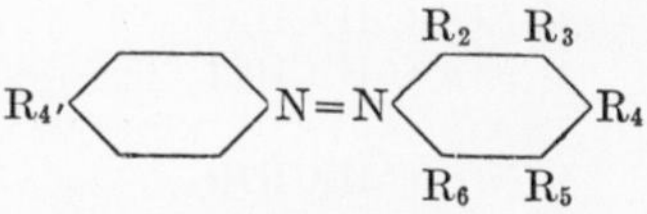

$$R_{4'} \underset{R_6 \quad R_5}{\overset{R_2 \quad R_3}{\bigcirc N=N\bigcirc}} R_4$$

$R_{4'}$	R_2	R_3	R_4	R_5	Activities	References
C_2H_5O-	$HO-$		$HO-$	$CH_3(CH_2)_5-$	0	512
$HOOC-$			$HOOC-$		0	441
NH_2OC-	$HO-$		$HO-$	$CH_3(CH_2)_5-$	0	512
$NC-$	$HO-$		$HO-$	$CH_3(CH_2)_5-$	0	512
$NCCH_2-$	$HO-$		$HO-$	$CH_3(CH_2)_5-$	0	512
HO_3S-			$HO-$		0	512
do	CH_3-		$HO-$		0	512
do		CH_3-	$HO-$		0	512
do	CH_3-		$HO-$	CH_3-	0	512
do	$HO-$	CH_3-		CH_3-	0	512
do	CH_3-		$HO-$	$(CH_3)_2CH-$	0	512

TABLE 200—*(Concluded)*

R_4'	R_2	R_3	R_4	R_5	Activities	References
HO_3S-	$HO-$		$HO-$		0(S)	512
do	CH_3O-		$HO-$		0(S)	512
do		CH_3O-	$HO-$		0(S)	512
do	$HO-$		$HO-$	$CH_3(CH_2)_5-$	0(S)	512
H_2O_3As-			$HO-$		0(S)	512
do	CH_3-		$HO-$		0(S)	512
do		CH_3-	$HO-$		0(S)	512
do	CH_3-		$HO-$	CH_3-	0(S)	512
do	$HO-$	CH_3-		CH_3-	0(S)	512
do	CH_3-		$HO-$	$(CH_3)_2CH-$	0(S)	512
do	$HO-$		$HO-$		0(S)	512
do	CH_3O-		$HO-$		0(S)	512
do		CH_3O-	$HO-$		0(S)	512
do	$HO-$		$HO-$	$CH_3(CH_2)_5-$	0(S)	512

TABLE 201

L. Miscellaneous Isocyclic Compounds

Compound	Melting Range	Activities	References
$1,4-(NO_2)_2C_6H_4$		0(S)	441
$4-(NO_2)C_6H_4Cl$		0(P)	347
$4-(NO_2)C_6H_4CH_3$		$+$, 0(S), $\pm$(P)	347, 441
$4-(NO_2)C_6H_4CH_2Cl$		$\pm$(S)	441
$4-(NO_2)C_6H_4CHCl_2$	43°	$+$(S), 0(I)	1574, 2373
$4-(NO_2)C_6H_4CHBr_2$	80–2°	$+$(S), 0(I)	441, 1574, 2373
$4-(NO_2)C_6H_4C_6H_5$		0(S)	441
$4-(NO_2)C_6H_4C_6H_4(NO_2)-4'$		0(S)	441
$[4-(NO_2)C_6H_4]_2CH_2$		$0, \pm$(S)	60, 441
$[4-(NO_2)C_6H_4]_2CCl_2$	139–40°	$\pm$(S), 0(P)	1574, 2373
trans-$4-(NO_2)C_6H_4CH=CHC_6H_4(NO_2)-4'$		0(S, Tt), $\pm$ (Spl)	1427, 1490, 1574
$4-(NO_2)C_6H_4C\equiv CC_6H_4(NO_2)-4'$		$\pm$(Spl)	1490
$2-(Cl)C_6H_4OCH_2COOH$		0(En, Po)	1485
$4-IC_6H_4OCH_2COOH$		0(S)	512
$2,4,6-I_3C_6H_2OH$			2094
$2,4,6-I_3C_6H_2OCH_2COONa$			2094
$2,4,6-I_3C_6H_2OCH_2CH_2N(C_2H_5)_2 \cdot HCl$			2094

TABLE 201—(*Continued*)

Compound	Melting Range	Activities	References
$2,4,6\text{-}I_3C_6H_2OCH(CH_3)CH_2CH_2N(C_2H_5)_2\cdot HCl$			2094
$2,4,6\text{-}I_3C_6H_2OCH(C_2H_5)CH_2CH_2N(C_2H_5)_2\cdot HCl$			2094
$4\text{-}(NO)C_6H_4OH$		0(S)	443, 2441
$4\text{-}(NO)C_6H_4ONa$		0(S)	441
$3\text{-}(NO_2)C_6H_4OCH_3$		0(S)	441
$4\text{-}(NO_2)C_6H_4OCH_3$		0(S)	441
$4\text{-}(NO_2)C_6H_4OC_6H_4(NO_2)\text{-}4'$		0(S)	441
$2,4\text{-}(NO_2)_2C_6H_3OH$		0(En)	1485
$4\text{-}(NO_2)C_6H_4SH$	77°	±,0(S)	60, 1200
$4\text{-}(NO_2)C_6H_4CH_2OH$		+(S)	347
$2,4\text{-}(CH_3)_2C_6H_3OCH_2COOH$		0(S)	512
$(CH_3)_3CCH_2(CH_3)_2C\langle\bigcirc\rangle OCH_2CH_2OCH_2CH_2N(CH_3)_2$ with Cl and $CH_2C_6H_5$ substituents	a	0(En, Po)	1485
naphthalene-OCH_2COONa		0(En, Po)	1485
$C_6H_5CHOHC_6H_5$		0(En, Po)	1485
$1,2\text{-}(HO)_2C_6H_4$		0(En, S, Tt)	1485, 1574
$1\text{-}[(CH_3)_2NCH_2CH_2O]\text{-}2\text{-}(C_6H_5CH_2O)C_6H_4$		0(S)	512
$1,4\text{-}(HO)_2C_6H_4$		0(S)	2441
$4[(CH_3)_2CH]\text{-}2\text{-}(CH_3O)C_6H_3OH$		0(En, Po)	1485
$2,5(C_5H_{11})_2\text{-}1,4\text{-}(HO)_2C_6H_2$		0(En, Po)	1485
$1,5\text{-}[CH_3(CH_2)_3(CH_3)CH]_2\text{-}2,4\text{-}(HO)_2C_6H_2$		0(En, Po)	1485
$4\text{-}(HO)C_6H_4C_6H_4(OH)\text{-}4'$		±(S)	2441
$4\text{-}(HO)C_6H_4CH=CHC_6H_4(OH)\text{-}4'$		0(En, Po)	1485
$C_6H_6(OSO_3H)_6$		0(I, P, S)	717, 1574

a Phemerol.

TABLE 201—(*Continued*)

Compound	Melting Range	Activities	References
	119°	0(S, Tt)	1574
		0(En, Po)	1485
$C_6H_5CH(NH_2)SO_3H$			324
4-$(NO_2)C_6H_4CHO$		+,±(S)	347, 441
1-[$NaO_3SCH(OH)\cdot$]-4-$(NO_2)C_6H_4$		±(S)	347
		0(T)	1127
$C_6H_5C(=S)C_6H_5$		0(T)	1127
$C_6H_5CH_2COCH_2C_6H_5$		0(T)	1127
		0(T)	1127
C_6H_5COOH		0(En, Po, S)	1485, 2441
$C_6H_5CONH_2$		±(S)	2441
4-$(NO)C_6H_4COOH$		0(S)	441
2-$(NO_2)C_6H_4COOH$		±,0(P, S)	347, 441

TABLE 201—(*Continued*)

Compound	Melting Range	Activities	References
$2\text{-}(NO_2)C_6H_4COOC_6H_{11}$	58–9°	0(S)	1446, 1582
$3\text{-}(NO_2)C_6H_4COOH$		±, 0(P, S), 0(Pl)	347, 441, 1733
$3\text{-}(NO_2)C_6H_4COO(CH_2)_8CH=CH(CH_2)_7CH_3$		+(S)	904, 1574
$3\text{-}(NO_2)C_6H_4COOC_6H_{11}$	110°	0(S)	1446, 1574
$3,5\text{-}(NO_2)_2C_6H_3COOC_6H_{11}$	109–11°	0(M, P, S)	2191
$4\text{-}(CH_3)C_6H_4C(=NH)NH_2\cdot HCl$		+(Cw)	24
$4\text{-}(NO_2)C_6H_4CH_2COOH$		0(S)	441
$2\text{-}(NO_2)C_6H_4CH_2CH_2COOH$		0(S)	347
$C_6H_5CH=CHCOOCH(C_2H_5)C(CH_3)_2CH_2N(CH_3)_2$		0(S)	512
$2\text{-}C_2H_5OOC\text{-}3\text{-}(NO_2)C_6H_3COONa$		0(S)	347

| | | 0(Spl) | 1491 |

| | | 0(Spl) | 1491 |

| $2\text{-}(HO)C_6H_4COOH$ | | | 1489 |
| $2\text{-}(HO)C_6H_4CONHCH_2CHOHCH_3$ | | 0(S, Tt) | 1427, 1574 |

| | | 0(En) | 1485 |

$4\text{-}(HO)C_6H_4COOH$		±(Spl)	1491
$4\text{-}(HO)C_6H_4CH_2COOH$		0(En)	1485
$C_6H_5CHOHCOOH$		0(En, Po)	1485

| | | 0(En, Po) | 1485 |

TABLE 201—(Concluded)

Compound	Melting Range	Activities	References
$C_6H_5SO_3Na$		0(S)	61, 2441
4-$(O_2I)C_6H_4SO_3$ ½ Ca		0(I, R, S, Tt)	1427, 1574
4-$(NO_2)C_6H_4SO_3NH_4$		+(L), 0 (Lc, Y)	1082
4-$(NO_2)C_6H_4SO_3Na$		0(P, S)	347
2-$(HO)C_6H_{10}SO_3Na$		0(S, Tt)	1427, 1574
4-$(HO)C_6H_4SO_3H$		0(S)	2441
4-$(HS)C_6H_4SO_3Na$		0(I, P, R, Tt)	1427, 1574
		0(En, Po)	1485
2-$(HOOC)C_6H_4SO_3H$		0(S)	2441
		0(S)	739, 1574
		0(S)	739, 1574
4-$(NO_2)C_6H_4AsO_3H_2$		0(S)	441
4-$(NH_2SO_2)C_6H_4SbO$			564
4-$[(CH_3)_2NSO_2]C_6H_4SbO$			564
2-Cl-4-$(NH_2SO_2)C_6H_3SbO$			564
2,5$(CH_3)_2$-4-$(NH_2SO_2)C_6H_2SbO$			564
4-$(NH_2SO_2)C_6H_4SbO_3H_2$			564, 2364
4-$[(CH_3)_2NSO_2]C_6H_4SbO_3H_2$			564
2-Cl-4-$(NH_2SO_2)C_6H_3SbO_3H_2$			564
2,5-$(CH_3)_2$-4-$(NH_2SO_2)C_6H_2SbO_3H_2$			564

TABLE 202

V. Heterocyclic Compounds
  A. Heterocyclicsulfonamides
    1. 5-Aminopyridine-2-sulfonamides

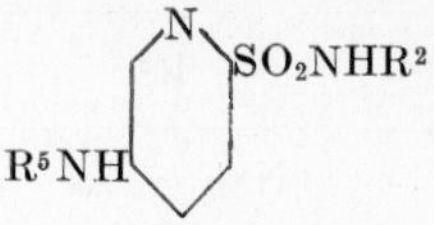

R^5NH —[ring]— SO_2NHR^2

R^2	R^5	Melting Range	Activities	References
C_6H_5-		184–5°	$\pm(S)$	65, 826
		164–5°	$\pm(S)$	65, 826
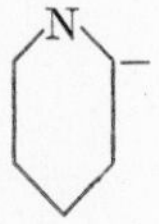 [pyridyl ring]		205–6°	$\pm(S)$	65, 826
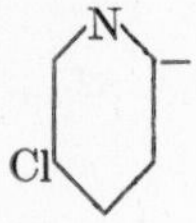 [Cl-pyridyl ring]		221°D		827
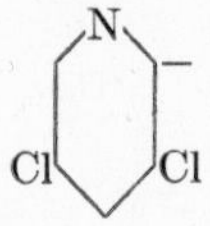 [di-Cl-pyridyl ring]		201°D		827
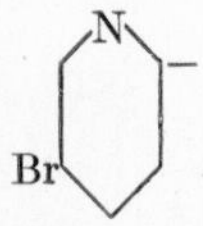 [Br-pyridyl ring]		234°D		827
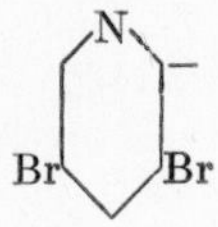 [di-Br-pyridyl ring]		212°D		827
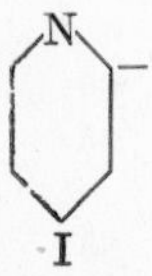 [I-pyridyl ring]		219–20°	$++(S)$	65, 826
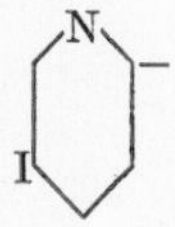 [I-pyridyl ring]		217°D		827
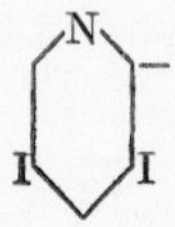 [di-I-pyridyl ring]		229°D		827

TABLE 202—(*Continued*)

R²	R⁵	Melting Range	Activities	References
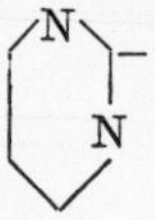		283–5°	±(S)	65, 826
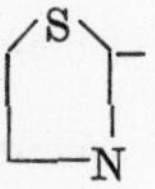		226–7°	±(S)	65, 826
NH=C(NH₂)–		220–1°	±(S)	65, 826
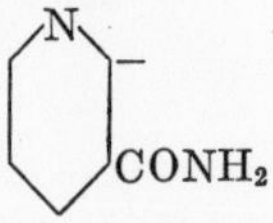		239°D		827
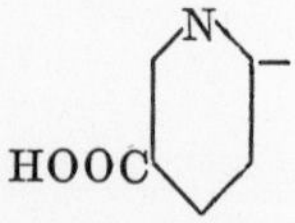		281°D		827
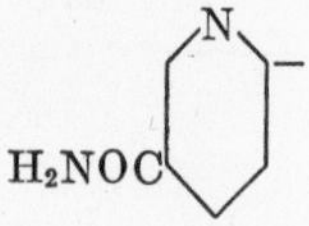		248°D		827
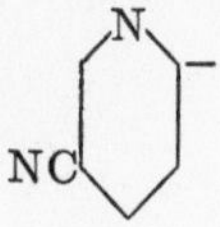		249°D		827
	CH_3CO-	232–3°		65
C_6H_5-	do	213–4°		65
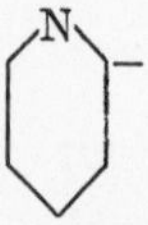	do	231–2°		65
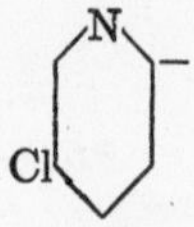	do	237°D		827
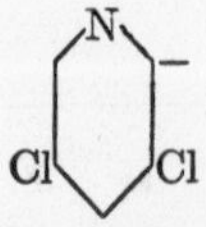	do	215°D		827

TABLE 202—(*Concluded*)

R²	R₅	Melting Range	Activities	References
	CH₃CO—	240°D		827
	do	232°D		827
	do	225–6°		65
	do	221°D		827
	do	247°D		827
	do	231–2°		65
	do	234–5°		65
	do	228–9°		65
	do	287°D		**827**

TABLE 203

2. 2-Aminopyridine-5-sulfonamides

R^5	$R^{5'}$	R^2	$R^{2'}$	Melting Range	Activities	References
				180°		80, 87, 342, 388
CH_3-				140–1°, 147°		80, 342, 1819
CH_3-	CH_3-			157–9°, 164°		80, 1819
C_2H_5-	C_2H_5-			148–9.5°		342, 1819
$CH_3(CH_2)_2-$				114–6°		1819
$CH_2=CHCH_2-$				136–37°		1819
cyclohexyl				129–31°		1819
C_6H_5-				177–8.5°		87, 388
$C_6H_5CH_2-$				143°		342, 515
piperidino				205–6°		80, 342
$-CH_2CH_2OCH_2CH_2-$				178–80°		1819
$-(CH_2)_5-$				160–2°		1819
$HOOCCH_2-$				226–7°D		1819
$2\text{-}(HOOC)C_6H_4-$				250–2°		1819
$4\text{-}(NH_2SO_2)C_6H_4-$				205°		342
NH_2SO_2 piperidino				258°		80, 388
$(CH_3)_2NSO_2$ piperidino						80
$4\text{-}NH_2C_6H_4-$				170°		342
$4\text{-}(CH_3CONH)C_6H_4-$				267–8°		342
		C_2H_5-		189–91°		87
C_2H_5-		C_2H_5-		139–41°		87, 388
		do	C_2H_5-	116–7°		87, 388
		C_4H_9-		121–2°		87, 388
		$CH_2=CHCH_2-$		195–201°		87, 388
		C_6H_5-		181–3°		87, 388
		$C_6H_5CH_2-$		197–201°		87, 388
		$-CH_2CH_2OCH_2CH_2-$				388
$-CH_2CH_2OCH_2CH_2-$		do				388
		CH_3CO-		210°		80
CH_3-		do				80
piperidino		do		256°		80

TABLE 203—(*Concluded*)

R⁵	R⁵′	R²	R²′	Melting Range	Activities	References
$4\text{-}(NH_2SO_2)C_6H_4-$		CH_3CO-		$223°$		80
NH_2SO_2 ⟨N⟩-		do				80
C_6H_5CO-		C_6H_5CO-		$221\text{-}3°$		87, 388
		NH_2⟨N⟩-				87
		NH_2SO_2⟨N⟩$-NH$⟨N⟩-				87

TABLE 204

3. Miscellaneous Pyridinesulfonamides

R₂	R₃	R₄	R₅	Rˣ	Rˣ′	Melting Range	Activities	References
x			NO_2-	⟨N⟩$CONH_2$-		$253°D$		827
x			NO_2-	H_2NOC⟨N⟩-		$260°D$		827
x			NO_2-	NC⟨N⟩-		$251°D$		827
	x			C_6H_5-		$108\text{-}9°$	$\pm(S), 0(Br, Ec, P, Pr, Sa, Tt)$	323, 497, 1036, 1278, 1574, 1743 2013
	x			⟨N⟩-		$145°$		
	x					$231\text{-}2°$	$0(Sa)$	65, 1036
	x			⟨N⟩-		$182°$		2013
	x			$\frac{1}{2}\text{-}Ca\cdot OOCCH_2CH_2-$			$\pm(Sa), 0(P, S)$	1574
	x			$4\text{-}(HOOC)C_6H_4-$		$241°$		2013
	x			$4\text{-}(C_2H_5OOC)C_6H_4-$		$156°$		2013
$Cl-$		x						1535
$Cl-$			x	CH_3-		$175\text{-}6°$		87, 342, 389
								389

TABLE 204—(Concluded)

R₂	R₃	R₄	R₅	Rˣ	Rˣ'	Melting Range	Activities	References
Cl–			x	(4-methylcyclohexyl)				389
Cl–			x	C₆H₅–		149–51°		87, 388, 389
Cl–			x	4-(NO₂)C₆H₄–				389
Cl–			x	C₆H₅CH₂–				515
Cl–			x	(piperidino)		235–6°		88, 342, 389
Cl–			x	–CH₂CH₂OCH₂CH₂–				388, 389
Cl–			x	–(CH₂)₅–		193°D		389
Cl–			x	HOOCCH₂–		116–8°		1819
Cl–			x	C₂H₅OOCCH₂–		193–5°		1819
Cl–			x	2-(HOOC)C₆H₄–		199–200°		342
Cl–			x	4-(NH₂SO₂)C₆H₄–				
Cl–			x	(piperidino, NH₂SO₂)				388, 389
Cl–			x	4-(CH₃CONH)C₆H₄–		225–6°		342
Cl–			x	(Cl-piperidino-SO₂–)	(piperidino)			389
HO–			x			269–71°		88, 389
HO–			x	CH₃–				389
HO–			x	CH₃–	CH₃–	212–4°		389
HO–			x	C₂H₅–	C₂H₅–			88, 389
HO–			x	CH₃(CH₂)₃–				389
HO–			x	CH₂=CHCH₂–		159–61°		88, 389
C₄H₉O–			x	do		67–8°		88
HO–			x	(4-methylcyclohexyl)		169–72°		88, 389
HO–			x	C₆H₅–		210–2°		88, 389
HO–			x	4-(NO₂)C₆H₄–		282°		88, 389
HO–			x	C₆H₅CH₂–		168°		88
HO–			x	(piperidino)		268–9°		1819
C₂H₅O–			x	do		180°		88, 389
HO–			x	–CH₂CH₂OCH₂CH₂–				389
HO–			x	–(CH₂)₅–		236–8°		88, 389
HO–			x	HOOCCH₂–		263–4°		1819
HO–			x	2-(HOOC)C₆H₄–		263°D		1819
HO–			x	(piperidino, NH₂SO₂)		295°		88, 389
HO–			x	4-(NH₂)C₆H₄–		245°		88, 389

TABLE 205

4. Quinolinesulfonamides

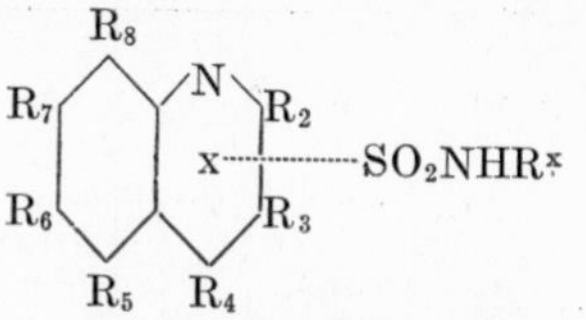

$$R_8,\ R_7,\ R_6,\ R_5,\ R_4,\ R_3,\ R_2\ \text{(quinoline ring)}\quad x\cdots SO_2NHR^x$$

R₂	R₄	R₅	R₆	R₇	R₈	Rˣ	Melting Range	Activities	References
			x				191–2°	0	70, 105, 512, 2356
				x				0	1384
				x		4-(HO₃S)C₆H₄–		0	552
				x		4-(NaO₃S)C₆H₄–		0	552
		NO₂–			x		186–7°	0(I, R, S)	523, 1574
		NO₂–			x	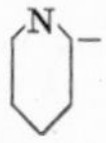 (piperidine ring)	249–50°D		523
CH₃–			x				212–3°		70, 2356
			CH₃–		x		232–3.3°	0(En, I, Po)	105, 892, 1485
HO–	CH₃–		x				316–8°		1799
HO–	CH₃–		x	CH₃–			325–6°		1799
HO–	CH₃–		x		CH₃–		310–2°		1799
CH₃–	NaOOC–		x			Na–		++(S), +(P), ±(Sa), 0(Tt)	1427, 1574
CH₃–	NaNHOC–		x			Na–		0(I, S, R, Tt)	1427, 1574
C₆H₅–	HOOC–		x				• 176°		2512
do	do		x			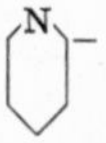 (piperidine ring)	157°		2512
		x		NH₂–			197°	0	507, 1374
		NH₂–	x				261–5.5°D	0(P, S, Sa)	461, 523, 1374, 1574
		NH₂–		x		 (thiazole ring)	260–1°D		523
		x	CH₃O–	NH₂–			280°D		507

TABLE 206

5. 2-Acridinesulfonamides

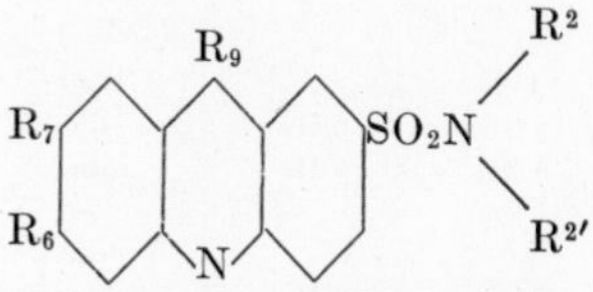

$$R_9,\ R_7,\ R_6\ \text{(acridine ring)}\quad SO_2N\!\begin{smallmatrix}R^2\\R^{2\prime}\end{smallmatrix}$$

R²	R²'	R₆	R₇	R₉	Melting Range	Activities	References
CH₃–	CH₃–	CH₃–	Cl–		182–3°		219
CH₃–	CH₃–		CH₃–	Cl–	208–9°		219
CH₃–	CH₃–		CH₃–	Br–	215–6°		219
C₂H₅–	C₂H₅–		CH₃O–				219

TABLE 206—(Concluded)

R^2	$R^{2\prime}$	R_6	R_7	R_9	Melting Range	Activities	References
			CH_3O-	$Cl-$	>230°D		31
CH_3-	CH_3-		do	$Cl-$	209-10°		219
C_2H_5-	C_2H_5-		do	$Cl-$	188-90°		31, 219
C_6H_5-			do	$Cl-$	207-8°		31
CH_3-	CH_3-		CH_3-	CH_3O-	160-1°		219
CH_3-	CH_3-		CH_3-	C_6H_5O-	221-2°		219
CH_3-	CH_3-		CH_3-	$4-(CH_3)C_6H_4S-$	190-1°		219
CH_3-	CH_3-		CH_3-	NaO_2S-			219
		NH_2-			253°		600
CH_3-	CH_3-	CH_3-		$(C_2H_5)_2NCH_2CHOHCH_2NH-\cdot 2HCl$	236°		219
CH_3-	CH_3-		CH_3-	$(C_2H_5)_2N(CH_2)_2S(CH_2)_3NH-\cdot 2HCl$	105°D		219
CH_3-	CH_3-		CH_3-	$4-(HOCH_2CH_2O)C_6H_4NH-$	199-200°		219
CH_3-	CH_3-		CH_3-	$4-[(C_2H_5)_2NCH_2CH_2O]C_6H_4NH-\cdot 2HCl$	259-60°D		219
CH_3-	CH_3-		CH_3-	$\begin{array}{c}H_2\ \ H_2\\ H_2\diagup\quad \diagdown NCH_2CH_2NH-\\ H_2\ \ H_2\end{array}$	156-7°		219
CH_3-	CH_3-		CH_3-	$4-(NH_2CH_2)C_6H_4NH-\cdot 2HCl$	240-2°		219
CH_3-	CH_3-		CH_3-	$4-(CH_3CONHCH_2)C_6H_4NH-$	129°		219
C_2H_5-	C_2H_5-		CH_3O-	$(C_2H_5)_2NCH_2CH_2NH-$	123°		219
CH_3-	CH_3-		do	$(C_2H_5)_2NCH_2CHOHCH_2NHCH_2CH_2NH-$	156-7°		219
			do	$(C_2H_5)_2N(CH_2)_4NH-$	138°		31
C_6H_5-			do	do	100-5°		31
			do	$(C_2H_5)_2N(CH_2)_3CH(CH_3)NH-$	135°		31
C_2H_5-	C_2H_5-		do	do	105-10°		31
CH_3-	CH_3-		do	$(C_2H_5)_2N(CH_2)_3CH(CH_3)NH-\cdot 2HCl$	239°D		219
CH_3-	CH_3-		CH_3O-	$(C_2H_5)_2NCH_2CHOHCH_2NH-\cdot 2HCl$	231°D		219
C_2H_5-	C_2H_5-		do	do	241°D		219

TABLE 207

6. 3-Acridinesulfonamides

[Structure: acridine ring system with substituents R_9 (top), R_7 and R_6 (left ring), ring nitrogen N (bottom center), and SO_2N bearing R^3 and $R^{3\prime}$ (right).]

R^3	$R^{3\prime}$	R_7	R_9	Melting Range	Activities	References
		CH_3O-	$Cl-$	240°		31
CH_3-	CH_3-	do	$Cl-$	189-90°		219
CH_3-	CH_3-	do	$(C_2H_5)_2NCH_2CHOHCH_2NHCH_2CH_2NH-$			219
		do	$(C_2H_5)_2N(CH_2)_4NH-$	110-5°		31
		do	$(C_2H_5)_2N(CH_2)_3CH(CH_3)NH-$	115-20°		31
CH_3-	CH_3-	do	$(C_2H_5)_2N(CH_2)_3CH(CH_3)NH-\cdot 2HCl$	218-20°D		219

TABLE 208

7. 1-Phenyl-2,3-dimethyl-5-pyrazolone-4-sulfonamides

R^4	R$^{4'}$	Melting Range	Activities	References
		228°, 239°, 260°	±(S), 0(P, Sa)	1413, 2084
CH$_3$—		193°		1413, 2084 2084
C$_2$H$_5$—				
C$_2$H$_5$—	C$_2$H$_5$—	153–4°		1413
C$_6$H$_5$—		203°		1413
		243–4°		1413, 2084
4-(C$_2$H$_5$O)C$_6$H$_4$—		93°		1413
		242°		1413
C$_6$H$_5$CO—		242°D		1413
		165°		2084
4-(H$_2$NO$_2$S)C$_6$H$_4$—		213°		2084

TABLE 208—(*Concluded*)

R^4	$R^{4'}$	Melting Range	Activities	References
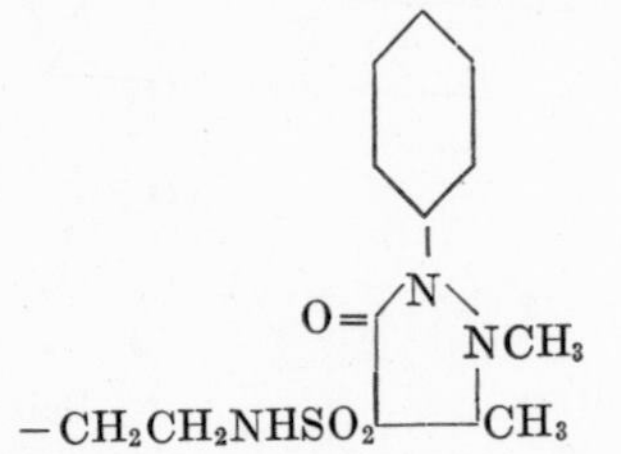		275°		1413

TABLE 209

8. Benzimidazole-5-sulfonamides

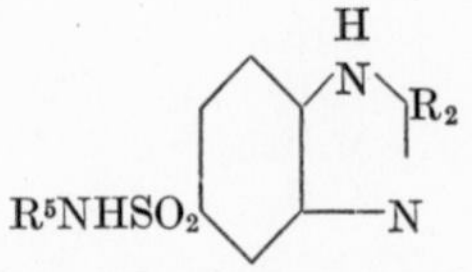

R_2	R^5	Melting Range	Activities	References
		213–4°		623
CH_3-		221°		623
HS–	2-$(HO)C_6H_4-$	265°D		623
HS–	4-$(NH_2)C_6H_4-$	240–2°D		623
HS–	4-$(CH_3CONH)C_6H_4-$			623
$HOCH_2(CHOH)_5-$			0(S, Tt)	1427, 1574

TABLE 210

9. Benzotriazole-5-sulfonamides

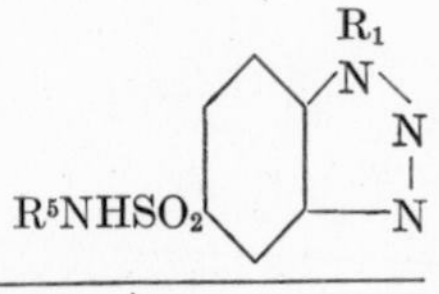

R_1	R^5	Melting Range	Activities	References
		236–7°		623
HO–		222°D		623
HO–	$HOCH_2CH_2-$	168°D		623
HO–	2-$(HO)C_6H_4-$	228°D		623

TABLE 211

10. Isoxazolesulfonamides

$$R_5 \underset{R_4}{\overset{O}{\diagup}} \underset{\quad\overline{}R_3}{\overset{N}{\underset{x}{\diagdown}}} SO_2NHR^x$$

R_3	R_4	R_5	R^x	Melting Range	Activities	References
CH_3-	x		C_6H_5-	64°		415
	x	CH_3-	do	62.5°		415
CH_3-	x	CH_3-		166–7°		415
CH_3-	x	CH_3-	C_6H_5-	122°		415
CH_3-	x	CH_3-	$4\text{-}(NH_2)C_6H_4-$	167°		385
CH_3-	x	CH_3-	$4\text{-}(CH_3CONH)C_6H_4-$	238–40°		385

TABLE 212

11. 2-Aminothiazole-5-sulfonamides

$$R^5HNO_2S \underset{R_4 \quad\overline{} N}{\overset{S}{\diagup\diagdown}} NHR^2$$

R^2	R_4	R^5	Melting Range	Activities	References
	CH_3-		175–6°	0(P)	686
	CH_3-	C_6H_5-	135–6°	0(P)	686
	CH_3-		208–9°	0(P)	686
	CH_3-		241°D	0(P)	686
CH_3CO-	CH_3-		230–1°	0(P)	686
do	CH_3-	C_6H_5-	198–9°	0(P)	686
do	CH_3-		229–30°	0(P)	686
do	CH_3-		235–6.5°	0(P)	686

TABLE 213

12. Benzoxazolone-6-sulfonamides

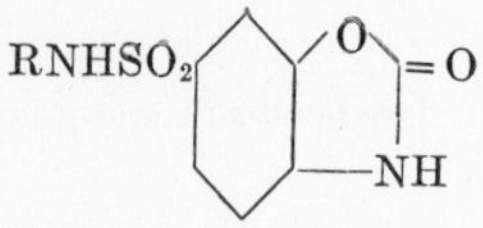

$RNHSO_2$ ... O =O, NH

R	Melting Range	Activities	References
C_6H_5-	269–71°D 215–6°	±(S), 0(P)	469, 640, 1057 469
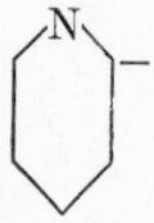	283–95°D		640
			640
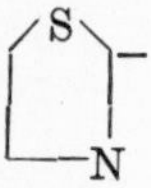			640

TABLE 214

13. 2-Mercaptobenzothiazole-5-sulfonamides

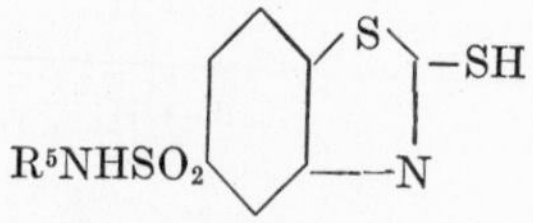

R^5NHSO_2 ... S –SH, N

R^5	Melting Range	Activities	References
$4-ClC_6H_4-$	208–10°D		623
$2-(HO)C_6H_4-$	246–8°D		623
$2-HO-4-(CH_3)C_6H_3-$	218–20°D		623
$4-(CH_3CONH)C_6H_4-$	284–5°D		623

TABLE 215

14. 2-Aminobenzothiazole-6-sulfonamides

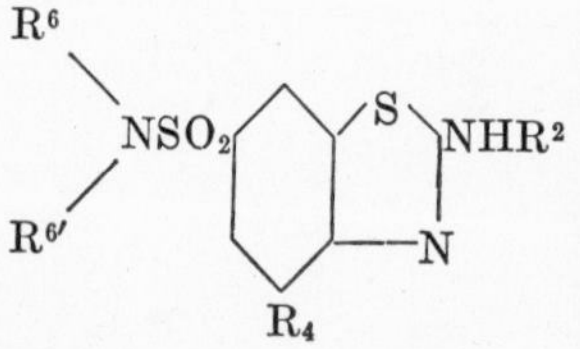

R^6 \ NSO_2 / $R^{6'}$ ... S NHR^2, N, R_4

R^2	R_4	R^6	$R^{6'}$	Melting Range	Activities	References
		CH_3-	CH_3-	278–80° 230°	0(P)	671, 673, 721 1411

TABLE 215—(*Concluded*)

R²	R₄	R⁶	R⁶′	Melting Range	Activities	References
		C_2H_5-	C_2H_5-	197.0–7.5°		1411
		4-$(NO_2)C_6H_4-$		237.5–8°		1411
		4-$(CH_3)C_6H_4-$		206.0–6.5°		1411
		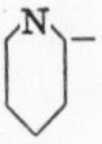		260–2°D		720, 721
		$-(CH_2)_5-$		217–8°		720
		CH_3CO-		265–7°D	0(P)	671, 673
		4-$(NH_2SO_2)C_6H_4-$		246.5°		1411
		4-[4′-$(NH_2)C_6H_4SO_2NH]C_6H_4-$		320°D		1411
$CH_3(CH_2)_{10}CO-$					±(P)	673
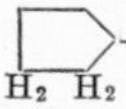 $-(CH_2)_{12}CO-$				217–8°	±, 0(P)	671, 672, 673
	I			232–3°		720

TABLE 216

15. Miscellaneous Heterocyclicsulfonamides

Compound	Melting Range	Activities	References
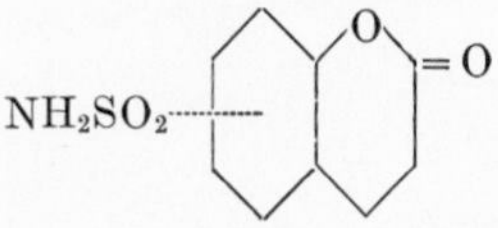		0	173
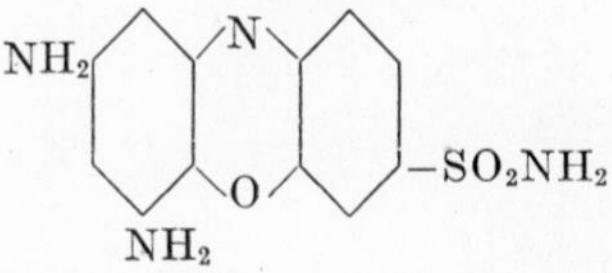		0	512

TABLE 217

B. Miscellaneous Heterocyclic Compounds

Compound	Melting Range	Activities[a]	References
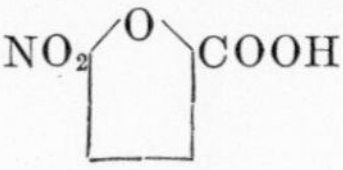	188°	0(Ec, P, S)	1395
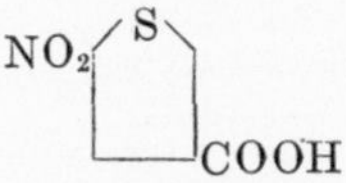	159°	0, 6(S), 11(P), ++(Ec)	1395

[a] Figures give antibacterial index = ratio $\dfrac{\text{chemotherapeutic agent}}{\text{PABA}}$ *in vitro.*

TABLE 217—(*Continued*)

Compound	Melting Range	Activities[a]	References
NO_2 — (thiophene ring) —$CONH_2$	191°	++(Ec), 25(P)	1395
H_2N— (cyclohexane with CH₃) —S—(benzene)—NH_2		0(I, P, R, Tt)	1427, 1574
CH_3CONH— (thiophene ring) —$COCH_3$	279°	20–80(P), ++(Ec)	1395
CH_3CONH— (furan ring, O) —$COOH$	240°	0(Ec, P, S)	1395
$HCl \cdot H_2N$— (thiophene ring) —$CONH_2$		++(Ec), 25(P)	1395
OH (decahydroquinoline) $N \cdot \frac{1}{2} - H_2SO_4$	175–8°	—	1574
OH, I, Cl (quinoline) N	173–8°	0(S)	1574
N (piperidine) $C(=NH)NH_2$	190°	0(Sa, Te)	2497
OH, I (quinoline) N SO_3H		0(S)	1574

TABLE 217—(*Continued*)

Compound	Melting Range	Activities[a]	References
		0(I, Tt), − (S)	1574
	318°	10–100(S), 5(Ec), 0(P)	1395
		0(I, S)	1075, 1574
	250°	0(I, P, S)	1574
(Induline)		0(I)	1574
		0(S, Tt)	1574
		0(S, Tt)	1427, 1574
	180°	0(En, P, Po, S)	1485, 1574 2304

TABLE 217—(*Continued*)

Compound	Melting Range	Activities[a]	References
	106–7°	0(I, P, R, Tt)	1574
	179°	+, 0(S), 0(En, Po, Tt)	105, 1485, 1574, 1756
	220°D	0(S)	1574
		0(S, Tt)	1427, 1574
		0(S, Tt)	1427, 1574
		0(P, Tt)	1427, 1574
		0(I, R, S)	1427, 1574
		0(En, Po)	1485

TABLE 217—(*Concluded*)

Compound	Melting Range	Activities[a]	References
		0(S, Tt)	1427, 1574
		0(S, Tt)	1427, 1574
	256–7°	–	1574
	297°	0(Tt)	1574

Chapter VI

STRUCTURE AND ACTIVITIES OF SULFONES

No attempt has been made in this chapter to list all sulfones. Instead the scope has been restricted to sulfones either tested as chemotherapeutic agents, or closely related structurally to sulfones of demonstrated activity. References to the initial syntheses of many sulfones are lacking in the tables but may be found in references of the papers cited. For nomenclature see Chapter II.

General Pharmacology. Bis(4-aminophenyl) sulfone (which is usually referred to in the literature as 4,4′-diaminodiphenylsulfone) is several times as active as sulfanilamide in experimental infections but, unfortunately, it is many times more toxic so that it is not used in therapy except in the form of N-substituted derivatives. It seems reasonable to assume, however, that most of the activity of such derivatives can be accounted for by the amount of free bis(4-aminophenyl) sulfone liberated from these drugs by the catabolic processes of the host. The evidence rests on the low *in vitro* activities of the compounds, the ability to find diazotizable amine in the blood of animals in the course of studying *in vivo* activities and the fact that none of its derivatives have shown higher potency than bis(4-aminophenyl) sulfone.

While peak activity seems to be found in bis(4-aminophenyl) sulfone, some activity is found in many sulfones of the formula

$$NH_2 \langle \quad \rangle SO_2R,$$

where R may be acyclic, isocyclic or heterocyclic. The amino group may also be substituted or replaced by groups capable of being reconverted to amino by physiological processes.

The activity of most sulfones containing a sulfanilyl or potential sulfanilyl group is antagonized by p-aminobenzoic acid[1384]. This probably means that such sulfones are acting against bacteria by the same fundamental mechanism as sulfanilamide derivatives.

(I) ACYCLIC ISOCYCLIC SULFONES

(A) 4-Aminophenyl Acyclic Sulfones (Tables 218 to 221, p. 347–349)

Synthesis. These compounds may be prepared by treating sodium or silver p-acetamido- or p-nitrobenzenesulfinate with an alkyl halide followed by hydrolysis or reduction.

Pharmacology. The activity of this class of compounds seems to be of a low order but comparatively little information has been published.

(B) Miscellaneous Acyclic Isocyclic Sulfones (Table 222, p. 350)

Pharmacology. Two recently announced sulfones are of considerable theoretical and, perhaps, practical importance. These are 4-(methylsulfonyl)benzamidine hydrochloride (V-187) and 4-(methylsulfonyl)benzylamine hydrochloride (V-335). These compounds possess high bactericidal activity against the clostridia involved in gas gangrene. Unlike sulfones containing a sulfanilyl group, these compounds are not antagonized by PABA[2533].

When given orally to guinea pigs, V-187 was not well absorbed. It was practically all excreted within 5 hours when given intraperitoneally or intramuscularly. It was effective against experimental gas gangrene when injected into the site of infection up to 5 hours after giving 10,000 lethal doses of *Cl. welchii*.

(II) Bis(isocyclic) Sulfones

(A) Symmetrically Substituted Bis(4-Aminophenyl) Sulfones

(1) Nuclear-substituted (Table 223, p. 350)

Pharmacology. Bis(4-aminophenyl) sulfone, which is the parent compound of the series, was discovered to have potent activity against pneumococci by Fourneau, *et al.*[1117] and Buttle, *et al.*[60, 822] at about the same time. The drug has since been studied against many organisms and the results of the *in vivo* tests are listed in Table 294.

As in the derivatives of sulfanilamide, substitution of the nucleus appears to destroy the chemotherapeutic activity but the number of compounds studied is far too few to draw such a conclusion with any degree of certainty.

(2) Nitrogen-substituted

(a) *N-Acyclic* (Table 224, p. 351)

Pharmacology. It seems probable that most of the derivatives which have shown *in vivo* activity are cleaved by body processes to the parent bis(4-aminophenyl sulfone[1384]. Such substituents are known to undergo cleavage when attached to the N^4-position of sulfanilamide and would be expected to undergo the same reactions when attached to bis(4-aminophenyl) sulfone.

"Diasone", the bis(sodium formaldehyde sulfoxalate)derivative of bis(4-aminophenyl) sulfone, has been studied clinically in tuberculosis (see Chapter XII).

(b) *N-Isocyclic or Heterocyclic* (Table 225, p. 352)

Pharmacology. Probably bis[4-(dibenzylamino)phenyl] sulfone owes its lack of *in vivo* activity to failure to reach the blood stream, because in the sulfanilamide series benzyl groups are cleaved by body processes and free bis(4-aminophenyl) sulfone would be expected in the blood if the drug were absorbed. In the case of the *N*-heterocyclic compounds, such groups are probably resistant to catabolic processes and the compounds inactive *per se*.

(c) *N-Nitrogen a Member of a Heterocyclic System* (Table 226, p. 352)

Pharmacology. These compounds, which are imides of dicarboxylic acids, are inactive either through lack of absorption or inability of the host to hydrolyze the imides.

(d) *Anils* (Table 227, p. 353)

Pharmacology. Like the corresponding derivatives of sulfanilamide, the anils of bis(4-aminophenyl) sulfone are cleaved to the parent active substance by body processes but vary in their activity because of differences in rates of absorption or cleavage. A few cases where superior effects of these derivatives have been claimed, when given in 10 to 20 times the dose of bis(4-aminophenyl) sulfone in mouse studies, are probably to be explained by better maintenance of uniform blood levels of the active drug. *In vitro* studies of most of these anils is out of the question because of their insolubility.

(e) *N-Sugar Derivatives* (Table 228, p. 353)

Structure. See discussion of the N^4-sugar derivatives of sulfanilamide (Chapter III, (IV) (E)).

Pharmacology. The sugar derivatives are highly soluble compounds suitable for parenteral administration. They appear to be very rapidly cleaved to bis(4-aminophenyl) sulfone by gastric juice but are less rapidly absorbed and cleaved when given subcutaneously[60].

The digalactoside of bis(4-aminophenyl) sulfone has been used clinically in Europe under the trade name "Tibatin" and claimed to be better tolerated than the parent compound. Like the sulfa drugs, it had no effect on the toxic phase of scarlet fever but was useful in preventing secondary complications[2475, 2643].

Not listed is the compound obtained by reacting bis(4-aminophenyl) sulfone with glucose, then with sodium bisulfite, which is used clinically in this country under the trade name "Promin" and in England as "Promanide". This has been extensively studied in both experimental and clinical tuberculosis with results which make widespread use in tuberculosis of doubtful value (see Chapter XII).

The drug has also been used clinically in leprosy and is said to be the most promising drug so far seen for this use[1045]. While no positive cures were obtained in the two year study, the disease was definitely arrested in a number of cases.

A number of toxic reactions were encountered: Anemia occurred in 46% of the cases. Skin rash occurred in 16% but in two thirds of these patients it was possible to desensitize by giving gradually increasing doses of the drug after the rash had subsided. Nausea was experienced by 35% but only 7% of the patients actually vomited.

Higgins[1304] showed that "Promin" produced severe toxic reactions in growing rats including hyper-irritability, occasional paralysis, anorexia, cyanosis and hypochromic anemia. When the rats were allowed to take a variety of vitamins at will, they increased their intake of thiamine, riboflavine and pyridoxine to six times normal. High intake of these vitamins avoided most of the reactions of the drug.

(f) *N-Acyl* (Table 229, p. 354)

Pharmacology. Many *N*-acyl derivatives of bis(4-aminophenyl) sulfone have been made but again they almost certainly owe any activity to cleavage *in vivo* to bis(4-aminophenyl) sulfone. Variations in activity can be explained by different rates of absorption and hydrolysis.

Bis(4-acetamidophenyl) sulfone was sold in Europe under the name "Rodilone", or "Sulfadiamine". It is not as effective as sulfa drugs, such as sulfathiazole and sulfadiazine, and is more toxic, particularly to the blood cells. According to Buttle, *et al.*[60], it is absorbed slowly when given by mouth and the rate seems independent of the amount given when a certain dose is exceeded. In monkeys, it appeared that the bis(4-aminophenyl) sulfone formed from the diacetyl derivative was eliminated at about the same rate as it was formed so that only traces of diazotizable amine could be detected in the blood; however, the urine contained measurable amounts which produced a chemotherapeutic effect when fed to mice.

"Rodilone" was used in France largely for treatment of gonorrhea[823].

(g) *N-Sulfonyl* (Table 230, p. 357)

Pharmacology. Bis[4-(sulfanilamido)phenyl] sulfone was said to have 1/100th the activity of bis(4-aminophenyl) sulfone, or to be comparable to sulfanilamide[60]. Probably this compound behaves as an N^1-substituted sulfanilamide derivative.

(h) *Azo Derivatives* (Table 231, p. 357)

Pharmacology. By analogy with the azo derivatives of sulfanilamide, these compounds would be expected to be cleaved to bis(4-aminophenyl) sulfone *in vivo.* Lack of activity in some cases may be through poor absorption or resistance to cleavage.
One diazoamino derivative has been described but is not listed. This is:

$$\left[\begin{array}{c} \text{NaO}_3\text{S} \\ \\ \text{NaOOC} \end{array} \bigcirc\text{—NHN=N} \bigcirc\text{—} \right]_2 \text{SO}_2$$

The activity of the compound was not disclosed[2460].

(i) *Miscellaneous N-Inorganic Derivatives* (Table 232, p. 357)

(3) Nuclear-Nitrogen-Substituted (Table 233, p. 358)

(B) Unsymmetrical Bis(4-Aminophenyl) Sulfones with One 4-Aminophenyl Group Substituted

(1) Nuclear-substituted (Table 234, p. 358)

Pharmacology. While substitution in both phenyl groups of bis(4-aminophenyl) sulfone seems to destroy the activity (Table 223), it appears that as long as there is an intact (or potential) sulfanilyl group in the sulfone, activity can be retained. Substitution of one phenyl group with highly ionic groups, such as: —COOH (or its derivatives which are probably hydrolyzed *in vivo*) or —SO₃H, gives inactive compounds. This seems to be rather generally the case in the sulfanilamide derivatives as well. Such groups confer unfavorable absorption-excretion characteristics and may also interfere with penetration of the molecule to the site of action in bacteria (see Chapter XI). Introduction of a sulfamyl group (—SO₂NH₂) ortho to the sulfone linkage on one of the phenyls gives a compound which retains part of the activity of the parent bis(4-aminophenyl) sulfone. In contrast, bis(2-sulfamyl-4-aminophenyl) sulfone (Table 223) was inactive.

(2) Nitrogen-substituted (Tables 235–238, p. 359–361)

Synthesis. Several aldehyde bisulfite derivatives of bis(4-aminophenyl) sulfone have been described in the patent literature[2423] but were not listed in the tables. From cinnamaldehyde by addition of two moles of sodium bisulfite there was obtained the compound:

$$\text{NH}_2\bigcirc\text{SO}_2\bigcirc\text{NHCHCH}_2\text{CH}\bigcirc$$
$$\qquad\qquad\qquad\qquad\quad | \qquad\quad |$$
$$\qquad\qquad\qquad\qquad \text{SO}_3\text{Na} \quad \text{SO}_3\text{Na}$$

Similar derivatives were prepared starting with citral, vanillin, oenanthol, piperonal and 2-methylbutyraldehyde. Some 4,4′-disubstituted derivatives were also prepared.

Pharmacology. These compounds follow in general the comments made on the corresponding $N,N′$-disubstituted derivatives (Tables 224–233). It is a moot point whether two free amino groups are necessary for activity in these compounds. Presence of one acetyl group appears to decrease the *in vivo* activity over the parent compound while the butyryl derivative is highly active. This probably reflects greater speed of hydrolysis of the butyryl group (as has been found in the sulfanilamide series) and would indicate that two free amino groups are essential to high activity.

(C) Unsymmetrical Bis(4-Aminophenyl) Sulfones with Both Nitrogens Substituted

(1) Monoacyl Derivatives (Table 239, p. 361)

Synthesis. One method of synthesizing these compounds is to start with acetylsulfanilyl chloride which is reduced with sodium sulfite to sodium *p*-acetamidobenzenesulfinate. This is then reacted with *p*-bromonitrobenzene to give 4-(4′-nitrophenylsulfonyl)acetanilide. By reduction of the nitro group and introduction of the desired substituent on the free amino group, the final compound can be made. Other acylsulfanilyl chlorides can be used as starting materials or at the stage of 4-(4′-nitrophenylsulfonyl)acetanilide the acetyl can be hydrolyzed and replaced by another acyl group before reduction of the nitro group.

Fairly obvious variations of these methods of making unsymmetrical bis(4-aminophenyl) sulfones will serve to produce most of the compounds in Tables 239–241.

Pharmacology. The few derivatives which have been studied are of the type which might revert to bis(4-aminophenyl) sulfone *in vivo*.

(2) $N,N′$-Diacyl Derivatives (Table 240, p. 362)

Pharmacology. Most of these compounds are active *in vivo*, the variations probably representing varying absorption properties and varying rates of hydrolysis to bis(4-aminophenyl) sulfone. The acyclic, isocyclic and heterocyclic acyl groups, and the derivatives of carbonic acid appear to become increasingly resistant to hydrolysis and to show decreasing activity in that order; however, the evidence for such a deduction is meager and proof awaits some enterprising pharmacologist.

(3) Inorganic Derivatives (Table 241, p. 363)

Synthesis. Jackson[2562] investigated the reaction of phosphorus oxychloride with bis(4-aminophenyl) sulfone and found complex products formed. Under special conditions in pyridine solution a linear compound was formed consisting of three phosphoric acid residues each linked through nitrogen to four molecules of bis(4-aminophenyl) sulfone. When the reaction was run in excess phosphorus oxychloride, a compound of structure,

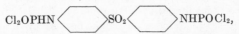

$$Cl_2OPHN\langle\ \ \rangle SO_2\langle\ \ \rangle NHPOCl_2,$$

was formed. When treated with cold sodium bicarbonate, the chlorines were removed and also some of the phosphorus. Some bis(4-aminophenyl) sulfone was recovered and also some 4,4′-bis(sulfanilyl)azoxybenzene. The remainder was a mixture designated as the "N-phosphoryl derivative of 4,4′-diaminodiphenylsulfone".

Pharmacology. This product was studied for its chemotherapeutic properties[2217, 2219] and was found to be from 1/2 to 1/5 as toxic as bis(4-aminophenyl) sulfone. The LD_{50} was about 0.75 Gm./kilo in mice or guinea pigs by subcutaneous injection. These animals tolerated a daily dose of 0.2 to 0.3 Gm./kilo for 2 to 4 weeks. Bacteriostatic tests showed the compound to be as active as sulfadiazine against pneumococcus type I and streptococcus[1685]. *In vivo* tests compared favorably to sulfadiazine also. In experimental tuberculosis in guinea pigs[2217], the compound appeared to be about as active and better tolerated than "Promin."

(D) 4-Aminophenyl Isocyclic Sulfones

(1) Sulfanilyl Group Unsubstituted (Table 242, p. 364)

Pharmacology. The most active of these compounds is 4-(4'-nitrophenylsulfonyl)-aniline where there is the probability of *in vivo* reduction to bis(4-aminophenyl) sulfone. Other members of the group retain only a small fraction of the activity of bis(4-aminophenyl) sulfone. Compounds which are practically inactive result from introduction of ionic groups (HOOC—, HO_3S—) on the second ring. This may be because of adverse absorption-excretion characteristics in the animal or through inability to arrive at the site of action in the bacteria.

(2) Sulfanilyl Group Substituted in the Nucleus (Table 243, p. 365)

Pharmacology. The slight activity reported for 6-(phenylsulfonyl)metanilamide is in need of verification because it is an exception to the usual findings that nuclear substitution of a sulfanilyl group destroys the activity.

(3) Sulfanilyl Group Substituted on Nitrogen (Tables 244–247, p. 365–368)

Pharmacology. The most active compounds in these tables are again those substituted on the nitrogen of the sulfanilyl group with radicals known to be removable *in vivo* and containing a 4-nitro group in the second ring which may be reduced *in vivo* to amino. It thus once more appears probable that these compounds owe their activity largely to the bis(4-aminophenyl) sulfone produced in the body.

Many of the compounds in the class of the 4-(4'-nitrophenylsulfonyl)acylanilines were tested and found active against experimental toxoplasmosis, a disease caused by an intracellular protozoon[740, 1785].

(E) Miscellaneous Symmetrical Bis(isocyclic) Sulfones (Table 248, p. 369)

Pharmacology. The only compound showing high activity in this miscellaneous group was bis(4-nitrophenyl) sulfone. This is probably reduced to bis(4-aminophenyl) sulfone *in vivo*. Even *in vitro* it has been shown that a diazotizable substance is formed[2441], which would seem to account for the *in vitro* activity of the drug.

Bis(4-hydroxyphenyl) sulfone has shown varying results in the hands of different observers *in vivo*. It has appreciable *in vitro* activity[2441] which, however, is not antagonized by PABA[1384].

The slight activity reported for disodium bis(4-carboxyphenyl) sulfone[1057] is an exception to predicted behavior and should be rechecked, particularly to see whether the activity is antagonized by PABA.

(F) **Miscellaneous Unsymmetrical Bis(isocyclic) Sulfones** (Table 249, p. 369)

Pharmacology. The only compound showing slight activity was 4-phenylsulfonyl-nitrobenzene. This by reduction can give a sulfone containing the sulfanilyl radical.

(III) Isocyclic Heterocyclic Sulfones

(A) Sulfanilyl Heterocycles

(1) Sulfanilyl Group Unsubstituted (Table 250, p. 370)

Synthesis. The method most frequently applied to the synthesis of sulfanilyl heterocycles is one of the general methods of sulfone synthesis involving reaction of sodium (or silver) 4-nitro(or acetamido)benzenesulfinate with a haloheterocycle which may contain other groups such as nitro, acetamido, or sulfamyl. The resulting sulfone is then converted by reduction or hydrolysis to the desired product.

The only one of these compounds which has attained possible clinical importance is 2-amino-5-sulfanilylthiazole, or "Promizole", which was first synthesized by Bambas[691, 2495] by a novel method. By reaction of *p*-nitrobenzenesulfenyl chloride with 2 moles of 2-aminothiazole in acetic acid, 2-(4-nitrophenylsulfenamido)thiazole was formed which was rearranged, by addition of acetic anhydride and heating for 16–24 hours at 85–90°C., to give 2-acetamido-5-(*p*-nitrophenylthio)thiazole. This was oxidized to the sulfone with hydrogen peroxide, the acetyl group was hydrolyzed with glacial acetic acid containing concentrated hydrochloric acid and the nitro group was reduced with ammonium chloride and iron at 70–85°.

Pharmacology. "Promizole" has been studied in the chemotherapy of tuberculosis in experimental animals[1062] and clinically[1311]. The compound is only slightly soluble in water (30–40 mg. per 100 cc. at 28–30°C.) and is not appreciably more soluble in the presence of alkalis. In the body, it was conjugated to a form highly soluble in urine[1062]. Like certain of the sulfonamide drugs, when fed for long periods, it caused hyperplasia of the thyroid (goitre). It caused anemia and other blood dyscrasias but none were of a serious nature. The curative effect of "Promizole" in tuberculosis of guinea pigs was slightly inferior to "Promin" when administered at half the standard dosage of "Promin." The drug seemed worthy of further clinical trial but appeared far from being an ideal drug for treatment of tuberculosis.

From an examination of the reported activities of isocyclic heterocyclic sulfones, it appears that the most active compounds are those which are isosteres of bis(4-aminophenyl) sulfone or are convertible thereto by known metabolic processes (reduction, hydrolysis or dealkylation). Such isosteres probably act through the same mechanism of action as bis(4-aminophenyl) sulfone since at least one of them, 5-amino-2-sulfanilylpyridine, has a strong bacteriostatic action *in vivo* and *in vitro* which is antagonized by peptones or PABA[1854].

A compound of theoretical interest is 2-sulfanilyl-5-pyridinesulfonamide which has a low activity *in vivo* but is said to be active *in vitro* and not to have its activity antagonized by PABA[1854].

(2) Sulfanilyl Group Substituted on Nitrogen (Table 251, p. 373)

Pharmacology. These compounds were largely intermediates on the way to the more active compounds of Table 250. The acyl groups are probably removed *in vivo* to give the deacylated drug as the active agent.

(B) **Miscellaneous Isocyclic Heterocyclic Sulfones** (Table 252, p. 374)

Pharmacology. No activity has been reported in this group but certain members would be expected to show some *in vivo* activity as a result of catabolic changes to known active drugs.

(IV) BIS(HETEROCYCLIC) SULFONES (Tables 253–254, p. 375–376)

Pharmacology. These compounds have not shown activity. This is of interest because several are bis isosteres of bis(4-aminophenyl) sulfone. Replacing one 4-amino-phenyl by an isosteric aminoheterocycle lowered but did not destroy the activity (Table 250) while replacing both 4-aminophenyls with heterocyclic isosteres apparently lowered the activity close to the vanishing point.

(V) HETEROCYCLIC SULFONES WITH THE S-ATOM A MEMBER OF THE HETEROCYCLIC SYSTEM (Table 255, p. 376)

Pharmacology. No appreciable activity has so far been found in compounds of this type.

TABLE 218

1. Acyclic Isocyclic Sulfones
   A. 4-Aminophenyl Acyclic Sulfones
      1. Sulfanilyl Group Unsubstituted

NH_2⟨⟩SO_2R

R	Melting Range	Activities	References
CH_3-		$\pm(S)$	152, 220, 484, 1381, 1702
C_2H_5-		$+(S)$	152, 484, 533
$CH_3(CH_2)_2-$		$+(S)$	152, 533, 1381
$(CH_3)_2CH-$		$\pm(S)$	152, 533
$CH_3(CH_2)_3-$		$\pm(S)$	152, 533
$(CH_3)_2CHCH_2-$		$\pm(S)$	152, 533
$CH_3(CH_2)_4-$		$\pm(S), 0(P)$	92, 152, 1702
$(CH_3)_2CH(CH_2)_2-$			533
$CH_3(CH_2)_5-$	172–6°	$0(I, R)$	1574, 2192
$CH_2=CHCH_2-$		$\pm(S)$	152
$HOCH_2CH_2-$		$\pm(S), 0(P)$	92, 1702

TABLE 218—(*Concluded*)

R	Melting Range	Activities	Reference
4-(NH$_2$)C$_6$H$_4$SCH$_2$CH$_2$—			533
4-(NH$_2$)C$_6$H$_4$SO$_2$CH$_2$CH$_2$—		0	152
CH$_3$COCH$_2$—	129–31°	±(S), 0(I, P)	1574, 2373
NaOOCCH$_2$SCH$_2$—			298
NaOOC(CH$_3$)CHSCH$_2$—			298
NaOOCCH$_2$CH$_2$SCH$_2$—			298
2-(NaOOC)C$_6$H$_4$SCH$_2$—			298
NaO$_3$SCH$_2$CH$_2$SCH$_2$—			298
4-(NaSO$_3$)C$_6$H$_4$SCH$_2$—			298
NaOOC(CH$_3$CONH)CHCH$_2$SCH$_2$—			298
NaOOCCH$_2$S(CH$_3$)CH—			298
NaOOCCH$_2$S(CH$_2$=CH)CH—			298
NaOOCCH$_2$—		0	2304
NH$_2$OCCH$_2$—	212–3°D	±(S), 0(I, P)	247, 1381, 1574, 2373
NH$_2$OC(CH$_3$)CH—	179–80°	0	247
NH$_2$OC(C$_6$H$_5$)CH—		0	247

TABLE 219

A. 4-Aminophenyl Acyclic Sulfones
  2. Sulfanilyl Group Substituted in Nucleus

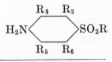

R	R$_3$	Melting Range	Activities	References
CH$_3$—	Cl—	195–6°		220, 221
C$_2$H$_5$—	Cl—	123°		220, 221
C$_3$H$_7$—	Cl—			2460
CH$_3$—	CH$_3$SO$_2$—			484
C$_2$H$_5$—	C$_2$H$_5$SO$_2$—			484
C$_3$H$_7$—	C$_3$H$_7$SO$_2$—			484
CH$_3$(CH$_2$)$_3$—	CH$_3$(CH$_2$)$_3$SO$_2$—			484
C$_2$H$_5$—	C$_6$H$_5$CH$_2$SO$_2$—			484
C$_6$H$_5$CH$_2$—	do			484

TABLE 220

A. 4-Aminophenyl Acyclic Sulfones
  3. Sulfanilyl Group Substituted on Nitrogen

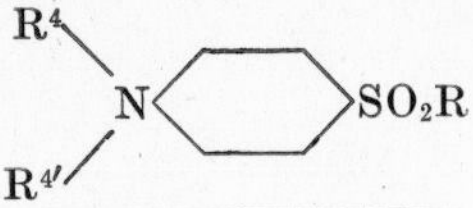

R	R⁴	R⁴′	Melting Range	Activities	References
CH_3-	CH_3-		128–9°		220
CH_3-	CH_3-	CH_3-	167–8°		220
CH_3-	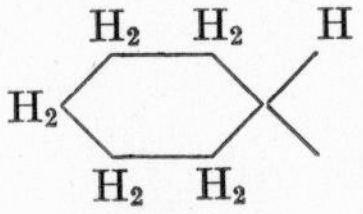 (cyclohexyl structure)		147–8°		220
CH_3-	$C_6H_5CH_2-$		169–70°		220
CH_3-	$-(CH_2)_5-$		116–7°		220
CH_3-	CH_3CO-				858
C_3H_7-	$2\text{-}NaOOC\text{-}5(NaO_3S)C_6H_3NHN=$				2460
$CH_3(CH_2)_{15}-$	CH_3-	CH_3-	70–2°		164, 167
do	C_2H_5-				167
do	do	CH_3-			167
do	do	C_2H_5-			164, 167
do	$C_6H_{11}-$				167
do	$C_6H_5CH_2-$				167
do	$-(CH_2)_5-$				167
$(C_6H_5CO)[CH_3(CH_2)_{15}]CH-$	CH_3-	CH_3-			164, 167
$[(CH_3)_2NC][CH_3(CH_2)_9]CH-$	CH_3-	CH_3-			164
$(C_2H_5)_2NCH_2CH_2-$	CH_3CO-		286°		236

TABLE 221

A. 4-Aminophenyl Acyclic Sulfones
  4. Sulfanilyl Group Substituted in Nucleus and on Nitrogen

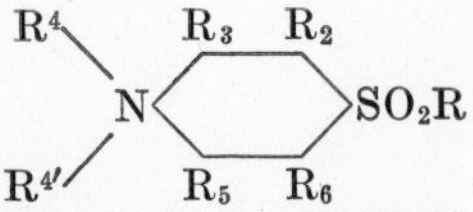

R	R₂	R₃	R⁴	R⁴′	Melting Range	Activities	References
CH_3-	$Cl-$		$HOCH_2-$		79–80°		220
CH_3-		$Cl-$	CH_3-		130°		220
C_3H_7-		$Cl-$	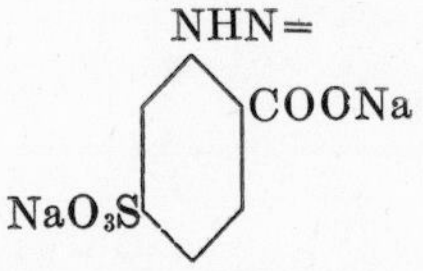 $NHN=$ (structure with COONa, NaO_3S)				2460

349

TABLE 222

B. Miscellaneous Acyclic Isocyclic Sulfones

Compound	Activities	References
$C_6H_5SO_2CH_3$	0(S)	2441
$C_6H_5SO_2C_2H_5$	0(En, Po)	1485
4-$(NO_2)C_6H_4SO_2CH_3$	0(S)	60, 533
4-$(NO_2)C_6H_4SO_2C_2H_5$	0(S)	60, 533
4-$(NO_2)C_6H_4SO_2(CH_2)_2CH_3$	0(S)	60, 533
4-$(NO_2)C_6H_4SO_2CH(CH_3)_2$		533
4-$(NO_2)C_6H_4SO_2(CH_2)_3CH_3$	0(S)	60, 533
4-$(NO_2)C_6H_4SO_2CH_2CH(CH_3)_2$		533
4-$(NO_2)C_6H_4SO_2(CH_2)_2CH(CH_3)_2$		533
4-$(NO_2)C_6H_4SO_2CH_2CH_2SO_2C_6H_4$-$(NO_2)$-4'		533
4-$(NO_2)C_6H_4SO_2CH_2CH_2SO_2CH_2CH_2SO_2C_6H_4$-$(NO_2)$-4'		533
4-$(NO_2)C_6H_4SO_2(CH_2)_3SO_2C_6H_4$-$(NO_2)$-4'		533
4-$(NO_2)C_6H_4CH_2SO_2(CH_2)_3CH_3$		533
4-$(NO_2)C_6H_4SO_2(CH_2)_2CH(CH_3)_2$		533
4-$[H_2NC(=NH)]C_6H_4SO_2CH_3 \cdot HCl$	++(Cn, Cs, Cw), +(S), 0(Rp)	2533
4-$(H_2NCH_2)C_6H_4SO_2CH_3 \cdot HCl$	++(Cw), +(Pa)	2533
4-$(NH_2)C_6H_4CH_2SO_2(CH_2)_3CH_3$		533
4-$(NH_2)C_6H_4CH_2SO_2(CH_2)_2CH(CH_3)_2$		533

TABLE 223

II. Bis(isocyclic) Sulfones
  A. Symmetrically Substituted Bis(4-aminophenyl) Sulfones
    1. Nuclear-substituted

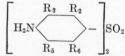

R_2	R_3	Melting Range	Activities	References
		175-6°ᵃ	See Table 294	60, 220, 281, 419, 433, 458, 501, 525, 1077, 1137
	Cl-	180°		220
	NO_2-		±(S)	60
NH_2SO_2-		240°D	0	695

ᵃ Bis(4-aminophenyl) Sulfone.

TABLE 224

A. Symmetrically Substituted Bis(4-aminophenyl) Sulfones
  2. Nitrogen-substituted
    a. *N*-Acyclic

R	R'	Melting Range	Activities	References
CH_3-		179–80°		220
CH_3-	CH_3-	259–60°		220
$CH_3(CH_2)_3-$			±(S)	29
$HOCH_2CH_2-$			−	505
$C_2H_5OCH_2-$	$C_2H_5OCH_2-$		++(S)	460
NaO_2SCH_2-		a	See Table 295	2, 34, 522, 1974
NaO_3SCH_2-			±(S)	34, 35
$NaOOCCH_2SCH_2-$				298
$NaOOCCH_2CH_2SCH_2-$				298
$NaOOCCH(CH_3)SCH_2-$				298
$2\text{-}(NaOOC)C_6H_4SCH_2-$			0(P, Tt)	298, 1574
$NaO_3SCH_2CH_2SCH_2-$				298
$4\text{-}(NaO_3S)C_6H_4SCH_2-$			++(P), 0(I, R, Tt)	298, 1574
$CH_2{=}NCH(COOH)CH_2SCH_2-$				1571
$CH_3CONHCH(COOH)CH_2SCH_2-$				1571
$CH_3CONHCH(COONa)CH_2SCH_2-$			+++(P), ++(S), +(Sa), 0(I, R, Tt)	298, 1571, 1574
$ClCH_2CONHCH(COOH)CH_2SCH_2-$				1571
$BrCH_2CH_2CONHCH(COOH)CH_2SCH_2-$				1571
$C_6H_5CONHCH(COOH)CH_2SCH_2-$				1571
[pyridyl]$CONHCH(COOH)CH_2SCH_2-$				1571
$NaO_3SCH(CH_3)-$				604, 1358
$NaOOCCH_2SCH(CH_3)-$			++(P), 0(Tt)	298, 1574
$NaOOCCH_2SCH(CH{=}CH_2)-$			+(P)	298, 1574
$CH_3CH{=}CHCH(SO_3Na)-$			+++(S), +(P), 0(Dy, I)	1574, 2373
$HOOCCH_2-$			±(P)	1427, 1574

ᵃ Diasone.

TABLE 225

A. Symmetrically Substituted Bis(4-aminophenyl) Sulfones
  2. Nitrogen-substituted
    b. N-Isocyclic or Heterocyclic

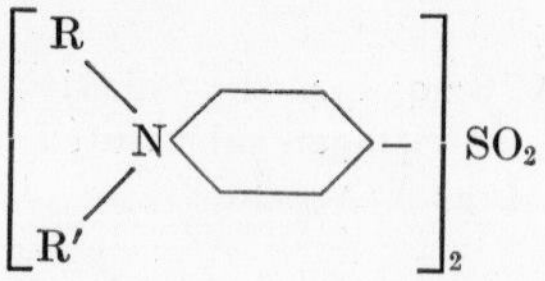

R	R'	Melting Range	Activities	References
$C_6H_5CH_2-$	$C_6H_5CH_2-$	200°	0(S)	60
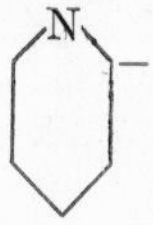		241°	0(S, P)	172
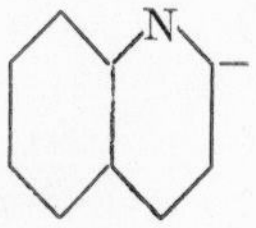		306°	0(S, P)	172
$C_6H_5CHCH_2CH-$ $\quad\mid \qquad\quad \mid$ $NaO_3S \qquad SO_3Na$			++(S)	60, 546

TABLE 226

A. Symmetrically Substituted Bis(4-aminophenyl) Sulfones
  2. Nitrogen-substituted
    c. N-Nitrogen a Member of a Heterocyclic System

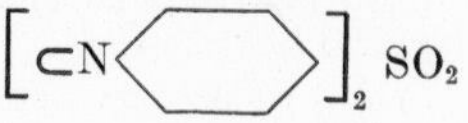

⊂N−	Melting Range	Activities	References
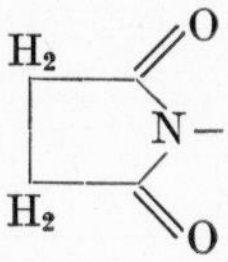	343°	±	1198
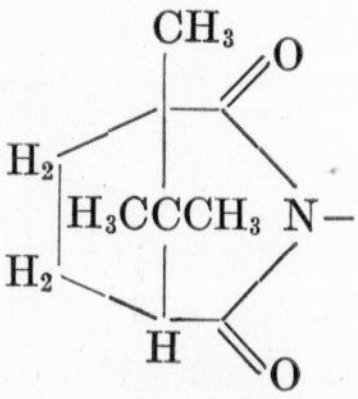	375°		1198
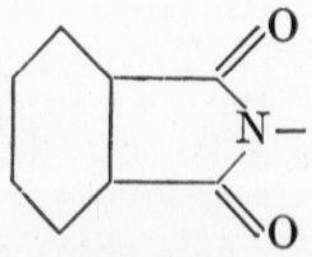	313–315°	0(P, S, Sa)	547, 1198

TABLE 227

A. Symmetrically Substituted Bis(4-aminophenyl) Sulfones
  2. Nitrogen-substituted
    d. Anils

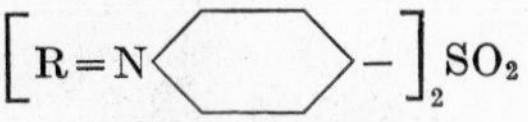

$$\left[R = N \left\langle \underset{}{\bigcirc} \right\rangle - \right]_2 SO_2$$

R	Melting Range	Activities	References
$CH_2=$	260°D	$\pm(P)$, $0(Tt)$, $-$	298, 997, 1571, 1572, 1574
$CH_3CH=$			603
$CH_3CH_2CH=$	246°		229, 603
$CH_3(CH_2)_2CH=$			603
$CH_3(CH_2)_5CH=$			603
$C_6H_5CH=$	214°, 206–7°	$+++(P)$, $0(I)$	229, 1574, 2373
$4\text{-}ClC_6H_4CH=$	233°		229
$C_6H_5CH_2CH=$			603
$4\text{-}(CH_3)C_6H_4CH=$	250°		229, 603
$C_6H_5CH_2CH_2CH=$			603
$C_6H_5CH=CHCH=$	236°, 252°		60, 229, 546, 603
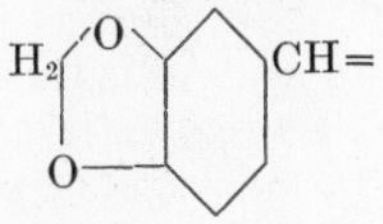	227°		60, 229
$2\text{-}(HO)C_6H_4CH=$	250°		229, 603
$4\text{-}(CH_3O)C_6H_4CH=$	226°		60, 229, 603
$4\text{-}HO\text{-}3\text{-}(CH_3O)C_6H_3CH=$			603
$CH_3C(COOH)=$			299
$CH_3C(COONa)=$			299
$C_2H_5C(COOH)=$			299
$C_3H_7C(COOH)=$			299
$CH_2=CHCH_2C(COOH)=$			299
$2\text{-}(HOOC)C_6H_4CH=$	287°	$+(S)$	60
$C_6H_5CH_2C(COOH)=$			299
$C_6H_5CH_2CH_2C(COOH)=$			299
$2\text{-}(HO_3S)C_6H_4CH=$		$+(P)$	1427, 1574

TABLE 228

A. Symmetrically Substituted Bis(4-aminophenyl) Sulfones
  2. Nitrogen-substituted
    e. *N*-Sugar Derivatives

Sugar	Melting Range	Activities	References
Rhamnose			456
Glucose		$+++(S)$, $+(Ca, L)$, $\pm(An,$ Pp), $0(I, V)$, $++(Tr, P)$	48, 60, 232, 658, 1364, 1646, 1750, 1864, 2150, 2508
Galactose	100°D[a]	$+++$, $++(S)$, $+(Sa)$	2475, 2522, 2554

[a] Tibatin.

TABLE 229

A. Symmetrically Substituted Bis(4-aminophenyl) Sulfones
   2. Nitrogen-substituted
      f. *N*-Acyl

$$\left[RCONH\left\langle\bigcirc\right\rangle - \right]_2 SO_2$$

RCO—	Melting Range	Activities	References
1. Acyclicacyl			
HCO—	148°	+++(S), +(Sa)	29, 152, 392, 973, 1118, 1853
CH₃CO—	140–1°ᵃ	See Table 297	34, 60, 77, 301, 419, 501, 525, 547, 1137
ClCH₂CO—	185–6°	+++(S), +(P), 0(I)	1574, 2373
Cl₂CHCO—	180°D, 100°D	+++(S), +(P)	1574, 1576, 2373
Cl₃CCO—	274–8°, 234–5°	++(S), +(P)	1574, 1576, 2373
CH₃CH₂CO—	221–2°	+++(S), +++, ++(P), +(Pl), 0(C, Dy, Et, I, R, Sa, Tt)	152, 1111, 1118, 1574, 1733, 1853, 2373
CH₃CHClCO—	160–2°	+++(S), +(P), 0(I)	1574, 2373
CH₃CHBrCO—	210–1°	±(P)	1574, 2373
CH₃(CH₂)₂CO—	232–4°	0(P, Sa, Tt)	1574, 1853, 2373
CH₃CHClCHClCO—	230–2°	+(S)	1574, 2373
(CH₃)₂CHCO—	149–51°	+(P), 0(Tt)	1574, 2373
CH₃(CH₂)₄CO—	180–2°	0(P, Tt)	1574, 2373
CH₃(CH₂)₃CHBrCO—	156–8°	+(S), 0(I, P)	1574, 2373
(CH₃)₂CHCH₂CH₂CH(C₂H₅)CO—	155–7°	0(P, Tt)	1574, 2373
CH₃(CH₂)₁₀CO—	148°	0(I, P, R, Tt)	60, 1574, 2373
CH₃(CH₂)₁₂CO—	143–4°	0(P)	60, 1574, 2373
CH₃(CH₂)₁₄CO—	134–6°	0(P)	1574, 2373
CH₃(CH₂)₁₆CO—		0(T)	1593
HOOCCO—	188°D	++(P, S), ±(Sa)	547, 1198
C₂H₅OOCCO—	257°	++(S), ±(P, Sa)	547, 1198
HOOCCH₂CO—	183°D	+(P, S)	547, 1198
HOOCCH₂CH₂CO—	181°, 227°D	++(S)	239, 300, 547, 1198
NaOOCCH₂CH₂CO—		+(S)	300, 2304
HOOC(CH₂)₄CO—			547

ᵃ Rodilone, Sulfadiamine.

TABLE 229—(*Continued*)

RCO—	Melting Range	Activities	References
NaOOC(CH₂)₄CO—		+++(S), ++(P), 0(En, Po)	547, 1198, 1485
C₂H₅OOC(CH₂)₄CO—	139°	+(S)	547, 1198
HOOC(CH₂)₇CO—	134°		547, 1198
CH₃OOC(CH₂)₇CO—	122°		547, 1198
HOOCCH=CHCO—			300, 547
C₂H₅OCH₂CO—	179–80°	+++(S), +(P), 0(I)	1574, 2373
C₄H₉OCH₂CO—		+++(S), 0(I)	1574, 2373
C₆H₅OCH₂CO—	206–8°	+(S), 0(I)	1574, 2373
NaO₃SCH₂CO—	>300°	+(S)	2304
HSCH₂CO—	85–6°	+++(S), +(P), 0(I)	1574, 2373
(CH₃)₃N(Cl)CH₂CO—	>300°	0	695
C₆H₅CH₂NHCH₂CO—			420
(HOCH₂CH₂)₂NCH₂CO—		+(P, S)	1427, 1574
C₆H₅CONHCH(CH₃)CO—		+(P), 0(Tt)	1427, 1574

2. Isocyclicacyl

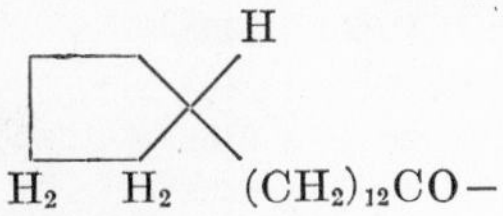		0(T)	1593
(CH₂)₁₂CO—			
C₆H₅CO—	269–71°	0(I, P, R, Tt)	1574, 2373
4-(NO₂)C₆H₄CO—	314–5°, 346°	±(S), 0(P, Sa, Tt)	968, 1574, 2373
C₆H₅CH₂CO—	296–8°	+(P)	1574, 2373
C₆H₅CH=CHCO—	272–3°	0(P, I)	1574, 2373
2-(HOOC)C₆H₄CO—	306–7°	±(S, L), 0(I, Lc, P, R, Sa, Tt, Y)	300, 547, 1082, 1198, 1427, 1574
2-(NH₂OC)C₆H₄CO—		0(P, I, R, Tt)	1427, 1574
2-(NH₂O₂S)C₆H₄CO—		0(P, Tt)	1574, 2373
3-(NaO₃S)C₆H₄CO—			562
3-(FO₂S)C₆H₄CO—	297°D		562
2-HO-6-(NaO₃S)C₁₀H₅CO—(3)			562
4-(H₂N)C₆H₄CO—	300°	0(P, Tt)	1574, 2373

3. Heterocyclicacyl

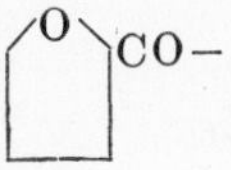		0(I, P, R, Tt)	1574, 2373
	278–9°		

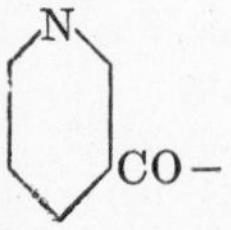		0(P, Tt)	2298

TABLE 229—(Concluded)

RCO—	Melting Range	Activities	References
4. Derivatives of Carbonic Acid			
C_2H_5OCO-	140°D	+(S), 0(I, P, R, Sa, Tt)	1574, 2105, 2373
C_6H_5OCO-	251°D		2468
NH_2CO-	235–6°	++(S), ±(P), 0(I, R, Sa, Tt)	1574, 2373
C_6H_5NHCO-	250–1°D		2468
$HOCH_2(HOCH)_4CH_2NHCO-$			2468
$HOCH_2(HOCH)_4CH_2N(CH_3)CO-$			2468
$HOOCCH_2NHCO-$	197°		2468
CH_3OOCCH_2NHCO-	207–8°		2468
$2-(HOOC)C_6H_4NHCO-$			2468
$3-(HOOC)C_6H_4NHCO-$	>300°D		2468
$3-(NC)C_6H_4NHCO-$	264–5°		2468
$4-(HOOC)C_6H_4NHCO-$			2468
$4-(CH_3OOC)C_6H_4NHCO-$	164°D		2468
$4[3',6'-(NaO_3S)_2-2'-C_{10}H_5NHCO]C_6H_4NHCO-$			2468
$3-(HOOC)C_{10}H_6NHCO-$ (2)	>300°		2468
$3-(CH_3OOC)C_{10}H_6NHCO-$ (2)	181°		2468
$6-(HOOC)C_{10}H_6NHCO-$ (2)	>300°		2468
$6-(CH_3OOC)C_{10}H_6NHCO-$ (2)	239–40°		2468
$3,5-(HOOC)_2C_6H_3NHCO-$	243°D		2468
$3,5-(CH_3OOC)_2C_6H_3NHCO-$	182°		2468
$4-(HO_2S)C_6H_4NHCO-$			2468
$2-(NaO_3S)C_6H_4NHCO-$			2468
$3-(NaO_3S)C_6H_4NHCO-$			2468
$2-Cl-5(NaO_3S)C_6H_3NHCO-$			2468
$2-Cl-5(C_6H_5O_3S)C_6H_3NHCO-$			2468
$4-(NaO_3S)C_6H_4NHCO-$			2468
$3,5-(KO_3S)C_6H_3NHCO-$			2468
$4-(NaO_3S)C_{10}H_6NHCO-$ (1)			2468
$6-(NaO_3S)C_{10}H_6NHCO-$ (1)			2468
$8-(KO_3S)_2C_{10}H_6NHCO-$ (1)			2468
$3,6-(NaO_3S)_2C_{10}H_5NHCO-$ (1)			2468
$4,8-(NaO_3S)_2C_{10}H_5NHCO-$ (1)			2468
$3,6,8-(NaO_3S)_3C_{10}H_4NHCO-$ (1)			2468
$4,6,8-(NaO_3S)_3C_{10}H_4NHCO-$ (1)			2468
$5-(HO_3S)C_{10}H_6NHCO-$ (2)			2468
$6-(NaO_3S)C_{10}H_6NHCO-$ (2)			2468
$7-(NaO_3S)C_{10}H_6NHCO-$ (2)			2468
$8-(NaO_3S)C_{10}H_6NHCO-$ (2)			2468
$3,6-(NaO_3S)_2C_{10}H_5NHCO-$ (2)			2468
$6,8-(NaO_3S)_2C_{10}H_5NHCO-$ (2)			2468
$4,8-(NaO_3S)_2C_{10}H_5NHCO-$ (2)			2468
$3-HO-4-(NaO_3S)C_6H_3NHCO-$			2468
$3-(6'-NaO_3S-2'-C_{10}H_6NHCONH-)C_6H_4NHCO-$			2468
$3-NH_2-4-(HO_3S)C_6H_3NHCO-$			2468
$4-NH_2-3,5-(NaO_3S)_2C_6H_2NHCO-$			2468
$CH_2=CHCH_2NHC(=S)-$	183°		158, 160

TABLE 230

A. Symmetrically Substituted Bis(4-aminophenyl) Sulfones
2. Nitrogen-substituted
   g. N-Sulfonyl
$$\left[RSO_2NH\hspace{-2pt}\left\langle\begin{array}{c}\end{array}\right\rangle \right]_2 SO_2$$

RSO_2-	Melting Range	Activities	References
$4\text{-}(NO_2)C_6H_4SO_2-$			210, 225
$4\text{-}(HO)C_6H_4SO_2-$		$\pm(L)$	1549
$4\text{-}(NH_2)C_6H_4SO_2-$	141–2°D	$++(S)$	60, 77, 152, 210, 225, 1176
$4\text{-}(CH_3CONH)C_6H_4SO_2-$	285°, 292–3°	$+, 0(S), 0(Tt)$	60, 77, 152, 210, 225, 501, 1176, 1427, 1574

TABLE 231

A. Symmetrically Substituted Bis(4-aminophenyl) Sulfones
2. Nitrogen-substituted
   h. Azo Derivatives
$$\left[RN\hspace{-2pt}=\hspace{-2pt}N\hspace{-2pt}\left\langle\begin{array}{c}\end{array}\right\rangle\hspace{-2pt}- \right]_2 SO_2$$

R	Melting Range	Activities	References
$2\text{-}(HO)C_{10}H_6-$ (1)	304°	$0(P, S)$	968
		$0(L, Le, Y)$	1082
$4\text{-}HO\text{-}3\text{-}(HOOC)C_6H_3-$	316°D	$++(P, S), 0(Sa)$	968
$4\text{-}HO\text{-}3\text{-}(NaOOC)C_6H_3-$		$+++(S), 0(Tt)$	1447, 1574
$2\text{-}HO\text{-}8\text{-}(NaO_3S)C_{10}H_5-$ (1)		$0(I, R, S, Tt)$	1447, 1574
$1\text{-}NH_2\text{-}2\text{-}CH_3\text{-}4\text{-}C_{10}H_5-$			2457
$2\text{-}HO\text{-}5\text{-}[HOOCCH(NH_2)CH_2]C_6H_3-$		$+(G), \pm(S)$	405
$1\text{-}NH_2\text{-}4\text{-}(NaO_3S)C_{10}H_5-$ (2)		$+++(S), +(M), 0(I, P, R)$	1447, 1574
$1\text{-}HO\text{-}3,6(NaO_3S)_2\text{-}8\text{-}(NH_2)C_{10}H_3-$ (2)		$+(S), 0(I, R, Tt)$	1447, 1574
$1\text{-}CH_3CONH\text{-}3,6\text{-}(NaO_3S)_2\text{-}8\text{-}(HO)C_{10}H_3-$ (7)			2389
$2\text{-}CH_3CONH\text{-}3,6\text{-}(NaO_3S)_2\text{-}8\text{-}(HO)C_{10}H_3-$ (7)			1529

TABLE 232

A. Symmetrically Substituted Bis(4-aminophenyl) Sulfones
2. Nitrogen-substituted
   i. Miscellaneous N-Inorganic Derivatives
$$\left[RNH\hspace{-2pt}\left\langle\begin{array}{c}\end{array}\right\rangle\hspace{-2pt}- \right]_2 SO_2$$

R	Melting Range	Activities	References
NaO_3SNH-		$0(I, P, R, Tt)$	1427, 1574
Cl_2PO-			193

TABLE 233

A. Symmetrically Substituted Bis(4-aminophenyl) Sulfones
   3. Nuclear-nitrogen-substituted

$$\left[RNH\underset{R_5 \quad R_6}{\overset{R_3 \quad R_2}{\bigcirc}} - \right]_2 SO_2$$

R	R_2	Melting Range	Activities	References
HOOCCH$_2$NHCO—	CH$_3$—	198°		2468
CH$_3$OOCCH$_2$NHCO—	CH$_3$—	208–10°		2468

TABLE 234

II. Bis(isocyclic) Sulfones
   B. Unsymmetrical Bis(4-aminophenyl)
      Sulfones with One 4-Aminophenyl
      Group Substituted
      1. Nuclear-substituted

$$H_2N-\underset{R_5 \quad R_6}{\overset{R_3 \quad R_2}{\bigcirc}} - SO_2 - \bigcirc - NH_2$$

R_2	Melting Range	Activities	References
—COOH	108–13° (alcoholate)	0(S)	433, 630, 1057
—COOC$_2$H$_5$	182–3°	0(S)	433, 630, 1057
—CONH$_2$	264°	0(S)	695
—SO$_3$H	265–7°	0(S)	695, 1895
—SO$_2$NH$_2$	238°, 236°	++, +(S), ++(P), +(Sa), 0(Er, I, Po)	433, 695, 892, 1057, 1485, 1733, 1895
—SO$_2$NH$\left[\text{N}\right]$	214–5°	±(S)	695, 1895
—SO$_2$NHCOCH$_3$	265–7°, 285°	++(Lc), +(S)	695, 1045, 1895
—SO$_2$N(Na)COCH$_3$	>325°D	0(En, I, Po, T)	892, 1060, 1485, 1895
—SO$_2$N(Na)COCH$_2$CH$_3$		0(En, Po)	1485
—SO$_2$NHCO$\left[\text{N}\right]$	247–50°		1895
—NH$_2$	127°	±(S), 0(I, Po)	695, 892

TABLE 235

B. Unsymmetrical Bis(4-aminophenyl)
   Sulfones with One 4-Aminophenyl
   Group Substituted
   2. Nitrogen-substituted
   a. *N*-Acyclic or Heterocyclic

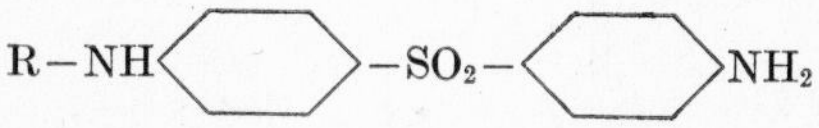

$R-NH\langle\ \rangle-SO_2-\langle\ \rangle NH_2$

R—	Melting Range	Activities	References
CH_3-			199
$CH_3CH_2CH_2-$		$0(En, Po)$	1485
$CH_2=NCH(COOH)CH_2SCH_2-$			1571
$CH_3CONHCH(COOH)CH_2SCH_2-$			1571
$CH_3CONHCH(COONa)CH_2SCH_2-$			1571
$ClCH_2CONHCH(COOH)CH_2SCH_2-$			1571
$BrCH_2CH_2CONHCH(COOH)CH_2SCH_2-$			1571
$C_6H_5CONHCH(COOH)CH_2SCH_2-$			1571
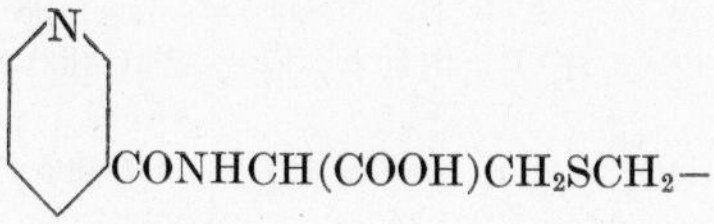 [N-ring]$CONHCH(COOH)CH_2SCH_2-$			1571
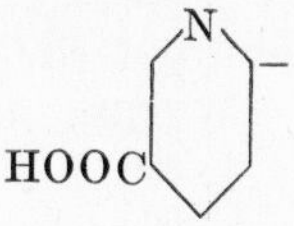 $HOOC$[N-ring]$-$		$\pm(S)$	2219

TABLE 236

b. Monoanils of Bis(4-aminophenyl) Sulfone

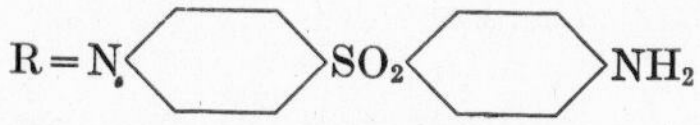

$R=N\langle\ \rangle SO_2\langle\ \rangle NH_2$

R=	Melting Range	Activities	References
$C_6H_5CH=$	232°	$+++(S)$, $0(I)$, $++(P)$	60, 546, 1864
$C_6H_5CH=CHCH=$		$+(P)$, $0(Sa)$	420, 1467
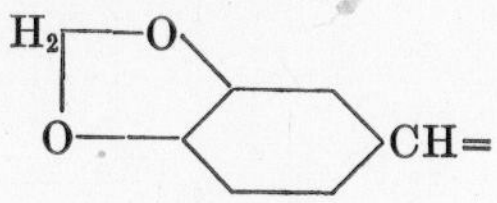 H_2[—O / O—ring]$CH=$	227°, 232°	$+++(S)$	60, 229, 546
$4-(CH_3O)C_6H_4CH=$	228°	$+(Ca)$, $+++(S)$	48, 60, 546
$4-[(CH_3)_2N]C_6H_4CH=$	252°	$+++(S)$	60, 546

TABLE 237

c. *N*-Monoacylbis(4-aminophenyl) Sulfones $\quad$ RCONH⟨⟩SO$_2$⟨⟩NH$_2$

RCO—	Melting Range	Activities	References
1. Acyclicacyl			
HCO—	169°	0(Pv)	237, 238, 2648
CH$_3$CO—	242–3°	++(S), ++, −(P), +(Ec, Pl, Sa), 0(F, Tt)	77, 238, 419, 433, 458, 561, 799, 1057, 1118, 1214, 1574, 1733, 2373, 2467
CH$_3$CH$_2$CO—	200–1°	+(P), 0(Tt)	˙1574, 1576
CH$_3$(CH$_2$)$_2$CO—	192–3°	+++(S), 0(Tt)	1574, 1576
(CH$_3$)$_2$CH(CH$_2$)$_2$CO—	112°		2465
CH$_3$(CH$_2$)$_{10}$CO—		+(T), 0(I, Po)	892, 1060
HOOCCO—	195°D	+(P, S), 0(Sa)	547, 1198
HOOCCH$_2$CH$_2$CO—	130–2°	+(P), 0(I, R, Tt)	239, 300, 1427, 1574
NaOOCCH$_2$CH$_2$CO—	155°D	+(S), 0(En, Po)	300, 695, 1485
HOCH$_2$CH$_2$NH$_3$OOCCH$_2$CH$_2$CO—		0(I, Po)	892
HOOC(CH$_2$)$_4$CO—			239
cis-HOOCCH=CHCO—		+++(S), +(P)	239, 300, 1574, 2373
NaOOCCH=CHCO—			300
NaO$_3$SCH$_2$CO—	>300°	+	695
(CH$_3$)$_3$N(Cl)CH$_2$CO—	150°D	+(P), 0(I, Po)	695, 892
2. Isocyclicacyl			
C$_6$H$_5$CO—	248–9°, 260°	0(P, Tt)	238, 1574, 2373
2-(HOOC)C$_6$H$_4$CO—	176°D	++(S), 0(P, Sa)	300, 547, 1198, 1427, 1574, 2105
2-(NaOOC)C$_6$H$_4$CO—			300
⟨⟩—CO— ⟨⟩—CO—	265°	0(P, S, Sa)	547, 1198, 2105
3. Heterocyclicacyl			
⟨O⟩CO—	215–7°	+(P)	1574, 2373
⟨N⟩CO—	250°	+(P), 0(Tt)	1574, 2298

TABLE 237—(*Concluded*)

RCO—	Melting Range	Activities	References
4. Derivatives of Carbonic Acid			
CH₃OCO—	235°	+++(S), +(P)	1966, 2105
C₂H₅OCO—	228–30°		2105
NH₂CO—	202–3°ᵃ	+(P, S), ±(Ec), +, 0(Cw)	1966, 2105, 2143, 2142, 2145
(CH₃)₂CHNHCO—		+++(S), +(P)	1966
HOOCCH₂NHCO—	228–9°		2105
4-[4'-(NH₂)C₆H₄SO₂]C₆H₄NHCO—	227–8°		2105
6-(NaO₃S)C₁₀H₆NHCO—(2)			2465
NH₂C(=NH)NHC(=NH)—		0(En, Po)	1485

ᵃ Sulfacid.

TABLE 238

d. *N*-Monosulfonylbis(4-aminophenyl) Sulfones RSO₂NH⟨ ⟩—SO₂—⟨ ⟩NH₂

RSO₂—	Melting Range	Activities	References
CH₃(CH₂)₇SO₂—	130°	±(S), 0(P)	15, 433, 1057
C₁₀H₇SO₂—(2)	160–170°	0(P, Tt)	1446, 1574
4-(NH₂)C₆H₄SO₂—	211°	++	15, 433

TABLE 239

II. Bis(isocyclic) Sulfones
  C. Unsymmetrical Bis(4-aminophenyl) Sulfones with Both Nitrogens Substituted
    1. *N*-Monoacyl Derivatives

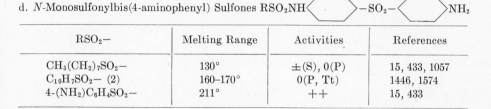

RCONH⟨ ⟩SO₂⟨ ⟩N⟨R' / R''⟩

RCO—	R′	R″	Melting Range	Activities	References
CH₃CO—	NaO₃SCH₂—				561
do	HOOCCH₂SCH₂—			+(P), 0 (I, R, Tt)	1427, 1574
do	4-(HO₃S)C₆H₄SCH₂—			++(S), +(P), ±(Sa)	1427, 1574
do	CH₃CONHCH(COONa)CH₂SCH₂—			+++(S), −(P), 0(I, R, Tt)	1427, 1574
do	CH₃CH₂CH=		130–1°		2466
do	CH₃CH=CHCH=		121–2°D		2466
do	4-(CH₃)C₆H₄CH=		238–9°		2466
do	C₆H₅CH=CHCH=		232–4°		561, 2466
do	4-(CH₃)C₆H₄CH=CHCH=				561, 2466
do	CH₂—O O—⟨ ⟩CH=		219–20°		2466

TABLE 239—(*Concluded*)

RCO—	R′	R″	Melting Range	Activities	References
CH₃CO	Maltose				2466
do	2-(HO)C₆H₄CH=				2466
do	2-(CH₃O)C₆H₄CH=		244–46°		2466
do	4-(CH₃O)C₆H₄CH(SO₃Na)—				561
do	4-(CH₃O)C₆H₄CH=		210–1°		561, 2466
do	4-(CH₃O)C₆H₄CH=CHCH=				561, 2466
do	C₆H₅CH(SO₃Na)CH₂CH(SO₃Na)—				561
CH₃CH₂CO—	NaO₃SCH₂—				561
CH₃(CH₂)₄CO—	CH₂CONHCH(COONa)CH₂SCH₂—			+(P), 0(I, R, Tt)	1427, 1574
C₆H₅CO—	NaO₃SCH₂—				561
C₂H₅OCO—	CH₃—		212–3°		2105

TABLE 240

C. Unsymmetrical Bis(4-aminophenyl)
   Sulfones with Both Nitrogens Substituted
   2. *N,N′*-Diacyl Derivatives

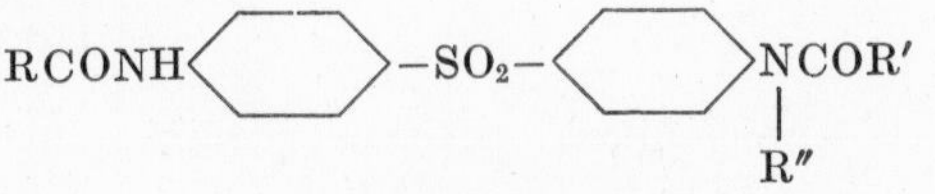

$$RCONH\!\!\bigcirc\!\!-SO_2-\!\!\bigcirc\!\!NCOR'$$
$$\underset{R''}{|}$$

RCO—	R′CO—	R″	Melting Range	Activities	References
a. Acyclicacyl					
CH₃CO—	HCO—		268°		237
ClCH₂CO—	CH₃CO—		214–5°	+++(S), +(P)	2195
Cl₃CCO—	do		268–70°	+++(S), +(P)	2195
Br₃CCO—	do		254–5°		1576
CH₃CH₂CO—	do		229°	+++(S), ++(P)	237, 1577, 2195
do	CH₂ClCO—		201–2°	+++(S), +(P)	2195
CH₃(CH₂)₂CO—	CH₃CO—		223–4°	+++(S), +(P)	237, 1577, 2195
do	ClCH₂CO—		178–9°	+++(S), +(P)	2195
do	CH₃CH₂CO—		201–2°	+++(P, S)	237, 1577, 2195
CH₃(CH₂)₄CO—	CH₃CO—		197–8°	+(P, S)	2195
CH₃(CH₂)₆CO—	do		183–4°	++(P)	1574, 2373
CH₃(CH₂)₈CO—	do		176–8°	+(P)	2195
CH₃(CH₂)₁₀CO—	do		168–70°	+(P)	2195
CH₃(CH₂)₁₂CO—	do		164–5°	+(P)	2195
CH₃(CH₂)₁₄CO—	do		158–60°	+(P)	2195
CH₃(CH₂)₁₆CO—	do		157–62°	+(P, S)	2195
CH₃CH=CHCO—	do		231–2°	+++(S)	2195
HOOCCH₂CH₂CO—	do			+++(S), +(P), 0(Sa)	237, 1427, 1574
do	CH₃CH₂CO—		106–8°	++(S), +(P), 0(I)	1574, 2373
cis-HOOCCH=CHCO—	CH₃CO—		230–1°	++(S), +(P)	2195
do	CH₃CH₂CO—		223–4°	+++(S), +(P)	2195
(HOCH₂CH₂)₂NCH₂CO—	CH₃CO—			+++(S), +(P)	1427, 1574

TABLE 240—(*Concluded*)

RCO—	R'CO—	R''	Melting Range	Activities	References
b. Isocyclicacyl					
C_6H_5CO-	CH_3CO-		212–3°	±(P)	239, 2195
$4-(NO_2)C_6H_4CO-$	do		239–40°	+(S), 0(P)	2195
$C_6H_5CH_2CO-$	do		182–4°	+(P)	1574, 2373
$C_6H_5CH=CHCO-$	do		180–1°	++(S), 0(P)	2195
c. Heterocyclicacyl					
$CO-$	CH_3CO-		240–1°	±(P)	2195
$CO-$	do		282–3°	+(P)	2195
d. Derivatives of Carbonic Acid					
C_2H_5OCO-	CH_3CO-		283°		2015
do	do	CH_3-	187°		2015
do	$2-(HOOC)C_6H_4CO-$				2015
C_6H_5OCO-	CH_3CO-				2465
NH_2CO-	do		256°D	0(P, Tt)	1574, 2015, 2373
do	$2-(HOOC)C_6H_4CO-$				2015
do	$-OC$ $CO-$				2015
do	C_2H_5OCO-				2015
$HOCH_2(CHOH)_4CH_2N(CH_3)CO-$	CH_3CO-				2465
$HOOCCH_2NHCO-$	NH_2CO-		>260°D		2465
$-NHCO$$-NHCO-$ NaO_3S SO_3Na	CH_3CO-				2465
$6-(HOOC)C_{10}H_6NHCO-$ (2)	do		280–1°D		2465
$6-(CH_3OOC)C_{10}H_6NHCO-(2)$	do		230°D		2465
$3,5-(HOOC)_2C_6H_3NHCO-$	do		231–3°D		2465
$3,5-(CH_3OOC)_2C_6H_3NHCO-$	do		240°		2465
$NHCO-$ O_2S $NHCOCH_3$	do		239–40°		2015
$6-(NaO_3S)C_{10}H_6NHCO-2$	do				2465

TABLE 241

C. Unsymmetrical Bis(4-aminophenyl) Sulfones
  with Both Nitrogens Substituted
  3. Inorganic Derivatives

$RN$$SO_2$$NHR''$
  |
  R'

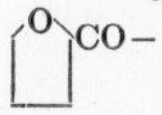

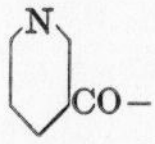

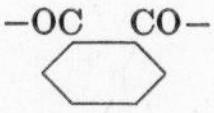

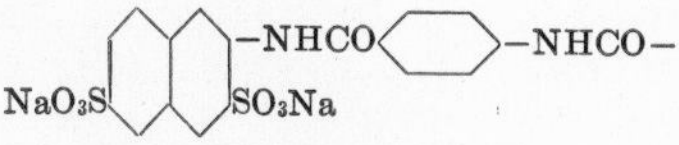

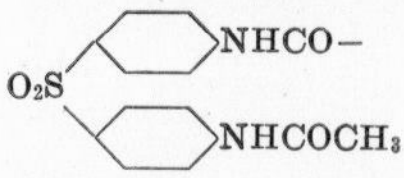

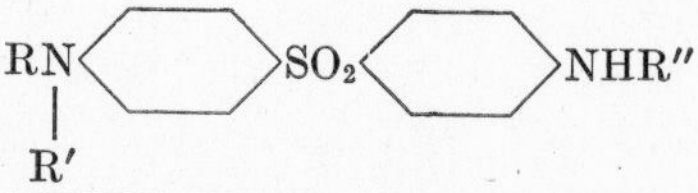

R	R'	R''	Melting Range	Activities	References
$COONa$ $-OH$ $N=$		NH_2CO-			2104

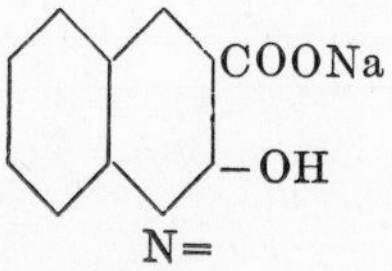

TABLE 241—(*Concluded*)

R	R'	R''	Melting Range	Activities	References
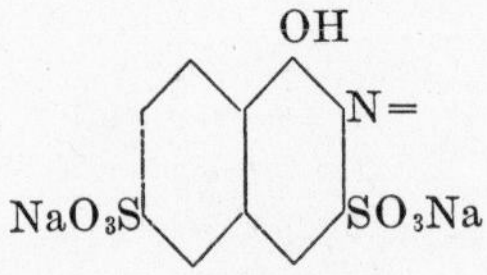		NH_2CO-			2104
		do			2104
		do			2104
		$(HO)_2P(=O)-$		$+++(P, S), ++(T)$	2217, 2219

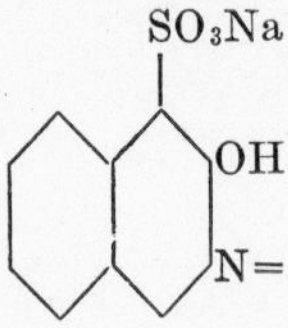

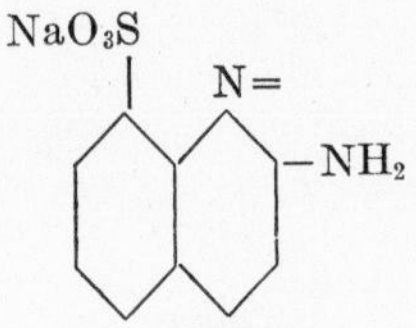

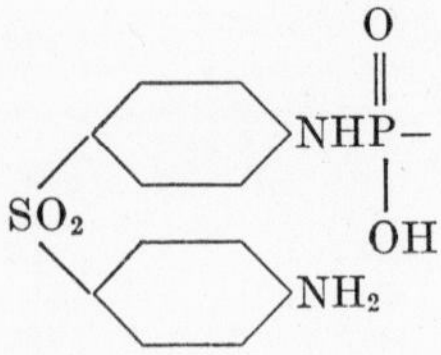

TABLE 242

D. 4-Aminophenyl Isocyclic Sulfones
1. Sulfanilyl Group Unsubstituted

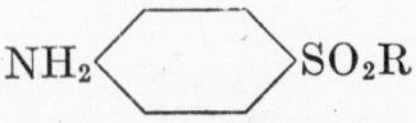

$NH_2$$SO_2R$

R	Melting Range	Activities	References
C_6H_5-	176°	$+(S), 0(I, Po)$	60, 433, 533, 892
$4-(NO_2)C_6H_4-$	171°	$+++(S), +(G, T)$	60, 155, 282, 441, 1118, 1549, 1555, 2217, 2467
$3,4-(NO_2)_2C_6H_3-$			505
$4-(CH_3)C_6H_4-$			1626
$C_6H_5CH_2-$		$\pm(S)$	60, 152, 533, 1702
$4-(HO)C_6H_4-$	193–4°	$++(S), +(T)$	3, 419, 2217
$2,5-(HO)_2C_6H_3-$	180°	$+(Ec, P), \pm(Sa), 0(En, S)$	60, 1057, 1485

TABLE 242—(*Concluded*)

R	Melting Range	Activities	References
2-(HOOC)C$_6$H$_4$–		±(G)	1555
4-(HOOC)C$_6$H$_4$–	271–2°	±(Ec), ±, 0(S)	432, 1057
4-NO$_2$-2-(H$_2$NO$_2$S)C$_6$H$_3$–	236°		1895
4-(HO$_3$S)C$_6$H$_4$–		0(P, Tt)	1427, 1574
4-(NH$_2$SO$_2$)C$_6$H$_4$–			196
4-[(CH$_3$)$_2$NSO$_2$]C$_6$H$_4$–	176–7°		197
3-NO$_2$-4-(NH$_2$O$_2$S)C$_6$H$_3$–	223–5°	±(S)	433
2-(NH$_2$)C$_6$H$_4$–	111°, 117°	±, 0(S)	433, 644, 695
3-(NH$_2$)C$_6$H$_4$–	131°	±, 0(S), 0(I, P, Po)	695, 892, 1057
2,5-(NH$_2$)$_2$C$_6$H$_3$–	150–2°		2397
2-NH$_2$-5-[(CH$_3$)$_2$N]C$_6$H$_3$–	190–2°		2397
4-(NH$_2$)C$_6$H$_3$CH$_2$–			533
2-NH$_2$-5-(HO)C$_6$H$_3$–	212–4°D		2397
2-NH$_2$-4-(NH$_2$O$_2$S)C$_6$H$_3$–	205°	±, 0, (S), 0(Ec, I, P, Po)	695, 892, 1057
3-NH$_2$-4-(NH$_2$O$_2$S)C$_6$H$_3$–	206–7°	0(S)	433

TABLE 243

D. 4-Aminophenyl Isocyclic Sulfones
  2. Sulfanilyl Group Substituted in Nucleus

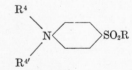

$$NH_2 \underset{R_5 \quad R_6}{\overset{R_3 \quad R_2}{\diagup\!\!\diagdown}} SO_2R$$

R	R$_2$	R$_3$	Melting Point	Activities	References
C$_6$H$_5$–	NH$_2$SO$_2$–	Cl–	197°	+(S)	220, 1626
do					1057
do		NH$_2$–	126°		1626

TABLE 244

D. 4-Aminophenyl Isocyclic Sulfones
  3. Sulfanilyl Group Substituted on Nitrogen
    a. *N*-Acyclic

$$\overset{R^4}{\underset{R^{4\prime}}{\diagup}} N \diagup\!\!\diagdown SO_2R$$

R^4	R$^{4\prime}$	R	Melting Range	Activities	References
CH$_3$–	CH$_3$–	C$_6$H$_5$–	178°		1156
CH$_3$–	CH$_3$–	4-(CH$_3$)C$_6$H$_4$–	212°		727, 1156
NaO$_2$SCH$_2$–		4-(NO$_2$)C$_6$H$_4$–			522
do		4-(HO)C$_6$H$_4$–			3
NaOOCCH$_2$–		do			3
NH$_2$OCCH$_2$–		do			3

TABLE 245

D. 4-Aminophenyl Isocyclic Sulfones
  3. Sulfanilyl Group Substituted on Nitrogen   R⁴CONH〈　〉SO₂R
  b. N-Acyl

R⁴CO-	R	Melting Range	Activities	References
1. Acyclicacyl				
HCO-	4-(NO₂)C₆H₄-	234.2°	+++(To), ++(P)	238, 740, 1788
CH₃CO-	2-(NO₂)C₆H₄-			644
do	4-(NO₂)C₆H₄-	215°, 229-30°	+++(S, To)	13, 155, 238, 419, **441**, 458, 477, 740, 1788, 2467
do	3,4-(NO₂)₂C₆H₃-		-	505
do	2,4,6-(NO₂)₃C₆H₂-	268°		60
do	C₆H₅CH₂-	185°	±	60
do	4-(HO)C₆H₄-	274-5°	++	3, 419
do	4-(CH₃COO)C₆H₄-	171-2°		3, 419
do	2,5-(HO)₂C₆H₃-	282°		60
do	4-NO₂-2-(C₂H₅OOC)C₆H₃-	157-8°		630
do	4-NO₂-2-(NH₂O₂S)C₆H₃-	275°		1895
do	O₂N〈　〉- SO₂NH-[ring]	300°D		1895
do	4-[(CH₃)₂NSO₂]C₆H₄-	208-9°		197
do	4-[4'-(CH₃)C₆H₄CHCH₂CH]C₆H₄- SO₂Na SO₂Na			561
do	4-[4'-(CH₃O)C₆H₄CHCH₂CH]C₆H₄- SO₃Na SO₂Na			561
do	2-(NH₂)C₆H₄-	236°		644
do	4-CH₃CONH-2-(NaO₃S)C₆H₃-			1895
do	4-CH₃CONH-2-(ClO₂S)C₆H₃-			1895
do	4-CH₃CONH-2-(H₂NO₂S)C₆H₃-	275°		1895
do	CH₃CONH〈　〉- SO₂NH-[ring]			1895
do	CH₃CONH〈　〉- SO₂NHCOCH₃	295°		1895
do	CH₃CONH〈　〉- SO₂NHCO-[ring]	170°, 285-90°		1895
ClCH₂CO-	4-(HO)C₆H₄-			3
CH₃CH₂CO-	4-(NO₂)C₆H₄-	190°, 186.4°	+++(To)	740, 1788, 2467
do	4-(HO)C₆H₄-			3
CH₃(CH₂)₂CO-	4-(NO₂)C₆H₄-	186.8°	+++(To)	740, 1788
do	4-(HO)C₆H₄-			3
(CH₃)₂CHCO-	4-(NO₂)C₆H₄-	153°	++(To)	740, 1788
HOOCCO-	do	203.5°D	+(To)	740, 1788
CH₃OOCCO-	do	278-80°D	+(To)	740, 1788

TABLE 245—(*Concluded*)

R⁴CO—	R	Melting Range	Activities	References
HOOCCH₂CH₂CO—	4-(NO₂)C₆H₄—	194°	+(To)	740, 1788
do	4-(HO)C₆H₄—			3
NaOOCCH₂CH₂CO—	do			3
HOOCCH=CHCO—	4-(NO₂)C₆H₄—	214°	+(To)	740, 1788
CH₃OCH₂CO—	do	161°		2467
2. Isocyclicacyl				
C₆H₅CO—	do	226°, 230.8°	++(To)	238, 740, 1788, 2465
C₆H₅CH₂CO—	4-(HO)C₆H₄—			3
4-(CH₃)C₆H₄CH₂CO—	do			3
2-(HOOC)C₆H₄CO—	4-(NO₂)C₆H₄—	255°, 191°, 188°	+(To)	740, 1788, 2105
3. Derivatives of Carbonic Acid				
CH₃OCO—	4-(NO₂)C₆H₄—	226°		2465
C₂H₅OCO—	do	214–5°		2105
C₆H₅CH₂OCO—	do	187–8°		2105
ClCO—	do			2105
NH₂CO—	do	225–6°D		2105
C₆H₅NHCO—	do	129–30–200°		2105
4-[4'-(NO₂)C₆H₄SO₂]C₆H₄NHCO—	do	265°D		2105
HOOCCH₂NHCO—	do	205–208°		2465
C₂H₅OOCCH₂NHCO—	do	228–9°, 212–3°		2105, 2465
4-(HOOC)C₆H₅NHCO—	do	253°D		2105
3,5-(HOOC)₂C₆H₃NHCO—	do	225–6°D		2465
3,5-(CH₃OOC)₂C₆H₃NHCO—	do	245°		2465
4-(NaO₃S)C₆H₄NHCO—	do			2465
5-(NaO₃S)C₁₀H₆NHCO—(2)	do			2465
NH₂C(=S)—	do	160°	+(To)	740, 1788

TABLE 246

D. 4-Aminophenyl Isocyclic Sulfones
  3. Sulfanilyl Group Substituted on Nitrogen   R⁴SO₂NH⟨ ⟩SO₂R
    c. *N*-Sulfonyl

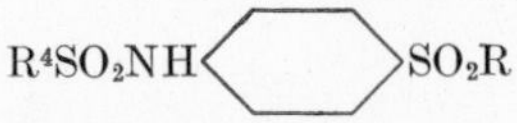

R⁴SO₂—	R	Melting Range	Activities	References
4-(NH₂)C₆H₄SO₂—	4-(NO₂)C₆H₄—	191–2°		1176
do	4-(HO)C₆H₄—			3
4-(CH₃CONH)C₆H₄SO₂—	4-(NO₂)C₆H₄—	279–80°		1176

TABLE 247

D. 4-Aminophenyl Isocyclic Sulfones
  3. Sulfanilyl Group Substituted on Nitrogen $R^4N=N\langle\bigcirc\rangle SO_2R$
    d. Azo Derivatives

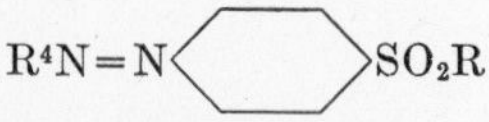

R^4	R	Melting Range	Activities	References
4-HO-3-(HOOC)C_6H_3-	4-(NO_2)C_6H_4-	247°	+(To)	282, 740, 1788
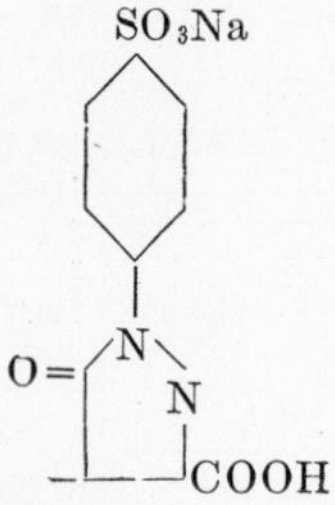	do			282
2-HO-3,6-(HO_3S)$_2C_{10}H_5-$(1)	do		+(F)	282, 288
2-HO-6,8-(HO_3S)$_2C_{10}H_5-$(1)	do			282
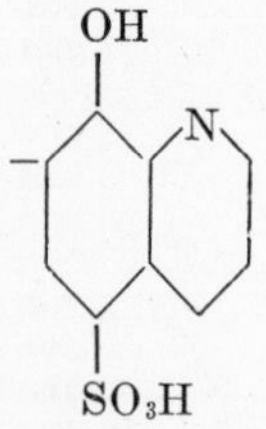	do			282
1,8-(HO)$_2$-3,6-(HO_3S)$_2C_{10}H_4-$	do			282
3,4-(NH_2)$_2C_6H_3-$	do	235°	+(To)	740, 1788
2-HO-4-[(CH_3)$_2$N]C_6H_3-	do			282
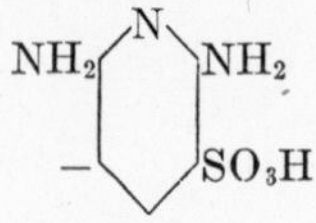	do			282
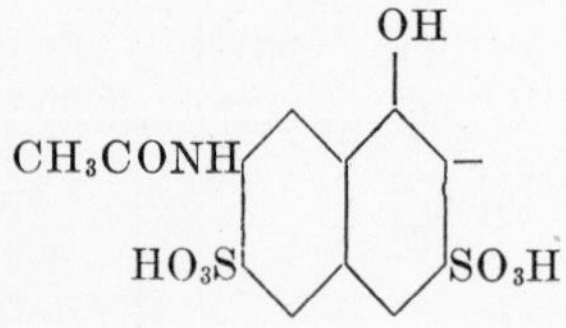	do		+(F)	282, 288
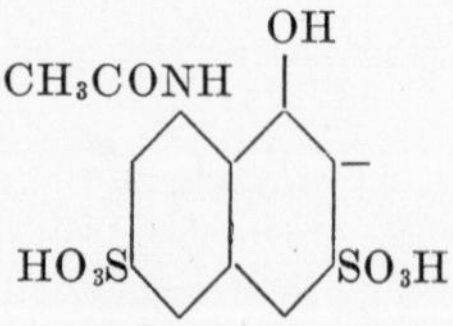	do	a		282, 2590

a "Girard 95."

TABLE 248

E. Miscellaneous Symmetrical Bis(isocyclic) Sulfones $\qquad$ RSO$_2$R

R—	Melting Range	Activities	References
C$_6$H$_5$—		0(Po, I)	892, 2304, 2441
4-(O$_2$I)C$_6$H$_4$—	205°D	±(S), 0 (I, P, R, Tt)	1574, 2373
2-(NO$_2$)C$_6$H$_4$—	179–80°	0(S)	1574, 2373
4-(NO$_2$)C$_6$H$_4$—		++, +++(S), ++(P), ±(L), 0(Ca, I, Lc, Po, Y)	48, 60, 533, 822, 892, 1057, 1082, 1117, 1118, 1137, 2441
2,4-(NO$_2$)$_2$C$_6$H$_3$—		±(S)	60
4-(NO$_2$)C$_6$H$_4$CH$_2$—			533
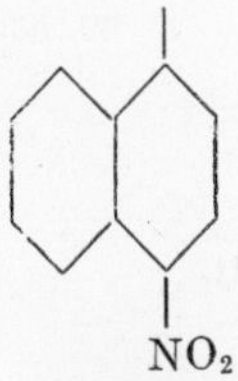	>250°	0(S)	2304
4-(HO)C$_6$H$_4$—		0(L), 0, ±(S)	60, 1384, 1549, 2441
4-(CH$_3$COO)C$_6$H$_4$—		±(S)	285
3-NO$_2$-4-(HO)C$_6$H$_3$—		0(S)	60
4-(HS)C$_6$H$_4$—	90°	0(P)	1574, 2373
4-(NaOOC)C$_6$H$_4$—		+(S), ±(Ec)	1057
4-(NaO$_3$S)C$_6$H$_4$—		0(P, Tt)	1427, 1574
4-(NH$_2$SO$_2$)C$_6$H$_4$—	288°	0(S)	60
2-(NH$_2$)C$_6$H$_4$—	141–3°	0(S)	1574, 2373
3-(NH$_2$)C$_6$H$_4$—		0(S)	2304
4-(NH$_2$)C$_6$H$_4$CH$_2$—	188°	0(S)	533, 2304
3-NH$_2$-4-(HO)C$_6$H$_3$—		0(S)	60

TABLE 249

F. Miscellaneous Unsymmetrical Bis(isocyclic)Sulfones

Compound	Melting Range	Activities	References
4-(NO$_2$)C$_6$H$_4$SO$_2$C$_6$H$_5$		+(S)	60, 533
2,4-(NO$_2$)$_2$C$_6$H$_3$SO$_2$C$_6$H$_5$	157°	0(P)	739, 1574
4-NO$_2$-2-(CH$_3$)C$_6$H$_3$SO$_2$C$_6$H$_4$IO-4′		0(S)	1427, 1574
4-NO$_2$-2-(CH$_3$)C$_6$H$_3$SO$_2$C$_6$H$_4$IO$_2$-4′		0(P, Sa, Tt), −(S)	1427, 1574
C$_6$H$_5$CH$_2$SO$_2$C$_6$H$_4$(NO$_2$)-4			533, 1137
4-(NO$_2$)C$_6$H$_4$CH$_2$SO$_2$C$_6$H$_5$			533
4-(NO$_2$)C$_6$H$_4$CH$_2$SO$_2$C$_6$H$_4$(NO$_2$)-4′		0(S)	60, 533
C$_6$H$_5$C(CH$_3$)$_2$SO$_2$C$_6$H$_4$(NO$_2$)-4			1137
2-(HOOC)C$_6$H$_4$SO$_2$C$_6$H$_3$(NO$_2$)$_2$-2′,4′		0(P)	739, 1574
4-NO$_2$-2-(HO$_3$S)C$_6$H$_3$SO$_2$C$_6$H$_4$(NO$_2$)-4′	285°D		1895

TABLE 249—(*Concluded*)

Compound	Melting Range	Activities	References
4-NO$_2$-2-(ClO$_2$S)C$_6$H$_3$SO$_2$C$_6$H$_4$(NO$_2$)-4′	172°		1895
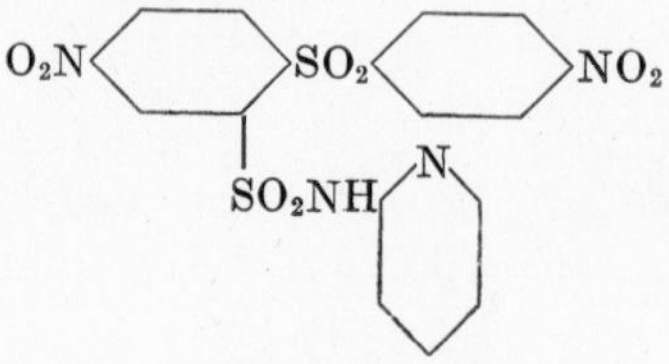	150°		1895
4-(NH$_2$)C$_6$H$_4$CH$_2$SO$_2$C$_6$H$_5$		0(S)	60, 533

TABLE 250

III. Isocyclic Heterocyclic Sulfones
  A. Sulfanilyl Heterocycles
    1. Sulfanilyl Group Unsubstituted

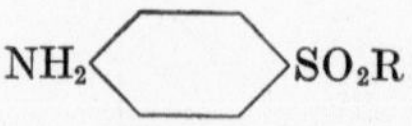

R	Melting Range	Activities	References
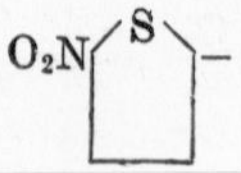	159–62°	+(S)	691
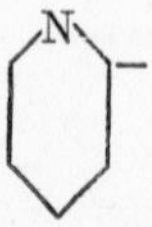	158–60°	+(Ec, S), ±(P)	433, 1057, 1854
		0(P)	1427, 1574
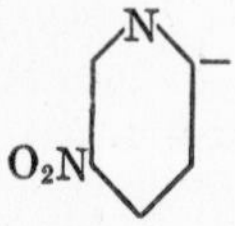	161–3°, 169–71°	++, +, ±(S), +(P)	433, 691, 1057, 1854
	269–71°	+(Ec), 0(P, S)	433

TABLE 250—(*Continued*)

R	Melting Range	Activities	References
	149–51°	+(Ec), 0(P, S)	433, 1057
	159–62°	±(S)	691
	209–10°	++(S)	2495
	165–7°		2495
		±(S)	1854
	186–7°	++, +(P, S), +(Ec), ±(T), 0(En, I, Po)	433, 621, 691, 892, 1057, 1060, 1485, 1854
	224–6°	++, +(S), +, ±(P), 0(I, Po)	691, 892
	295–7°	++, +(S), +, ±(P)	691, 892
	219–21°D[a]	++, +(S), ++(T), +(P)	691, 1062, 1311, 2495

[a] Promizole.

TABLE 250—(*Concluded*)

R	Melting Range	Activities	References
$-$\<thiazole>NHCOCH$_3$	267–9°	++(S)	2495
$-$\<thiazole>NHCOCH=CHCH$_3$			2495
$-$\<thiazole>NHCO\<piperidine N>	246–8°		2495
$-$\<thiazole>NHCOCH$_2$CH$_2$COOH	225–9°	++(S)	2495
$-$\<thiazole>NHCOCH$_2$CH$_2$COONa	225–9°	+(S), ±(P)	691
$-$\<thiazole>NH$_2$ CH$_3$	175–8°	++(S)	2495
$-$\<thiazole>NHCH$_3$ CH$_3$	220–2°	++(S)	2495
$-$\<thiazole>NHCH$_2$CH=CH$_2$ CH$_3$	168–70°		2495
$-$\<thiadiazole>NH$_2$	211–4°	++(S), 0(P)	2495

TABLE 251

A. 4-Aminophenyl Heterocyclic Sulfones
 2. Sulfanilyl Group Substituted on Nitrogen

$$R^4NH\!-\!\langle\ \rangle\!-\!SO_2R$$

R^4	R	Melting Range	Activities	References
CH_3CO-	NO_2 / S ring —	188–90°		691
do	pyridyl (N) —		±(S)	1854
do	pyridyl, NO_2 —		+(S)	1854
do	pyridyl, NH_2SO_2 —		±(S)	1854
do	pyridyl, CH_3CONH —		±(S)	1854
do	quinolinyl (N), NH_2 —	280–2°		691
C_2H_5OCO-	pyridyl, NO_2 —	195°		2105
do	pyridyl, NH_2 —			2105

TABLE 252

B. Miscellaneous Isocyclic Heterocyclic Sulfones   RSO₂R′

R	R′	Melting Range	Activities	References
	4-(NO₂)C₆H₄—		0(P, Tt)	1427, 1574
	C₆H₅—	151–3°	0(S)	552
do	3-(NO₂)C₆H₄—	169–70°		552
do	4-(NO₂)C₆H₄—	217°, 236–42°		552, 691
	do	202–3°		691
	C₆H₅—	180–1°	0(S)	552
do	4-(NO₂)C₆H₄—	237°		552
	C₆H₅—	169–70°	0(S)	552
	do	224°	0(S)	552
	do	268–9°		552

TABLE 252—(*Concluded*)

R	R'	Melting Range	Activities	References
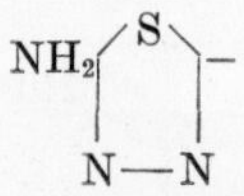 NH$_2$–(thiadiazolyl)–S–	4-(NO$_2$)C$_6$H$_4$–	228–32°		691
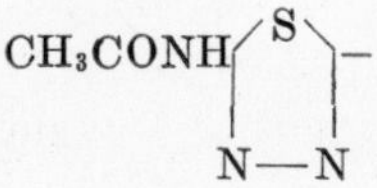 CH$_3$CONH–(thiadiazolyl)–S–	do	250–4°		691

TABLE 253

IV. Bis(heterocyclic)Sulfones   RSO$_2$R

A. Symmetrical Bis(heterocyclic) Sulfones

R	Melting Range	Activities	References
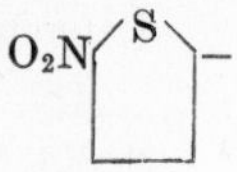 O$_2$N–(thienyl)–	158–60°	±(S), 0(P)	691
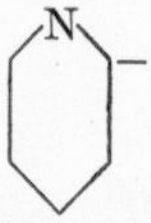 (pyridyl)–	216°	0(P, S)	968
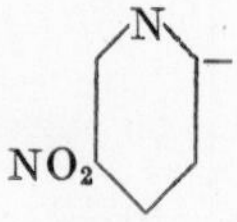 NO$_2$–(pyridyl)–	218.5–20.5°, 222–6°		691, 2300
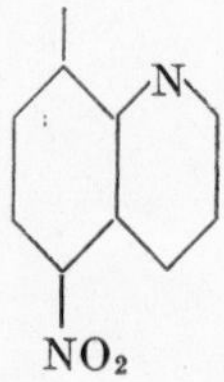 NO$_2$–(quinolyl)–	260°		2300
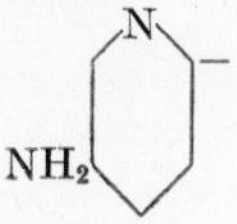 NH$_2$–(pyridyl)–	239–41°	0(P, S)	691, 1574, 2300
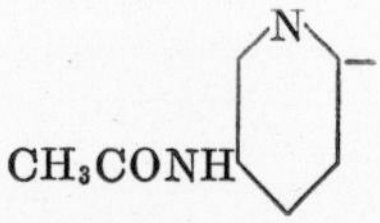 CH$_3$CONH–(pyridyl)–	276–8°	0(I, P, R)	1574, 2300

TABLE 254

B. Unsymmetrical Bis(heterocyclic) Sulfones

Compound	Melting Range	Activities	References
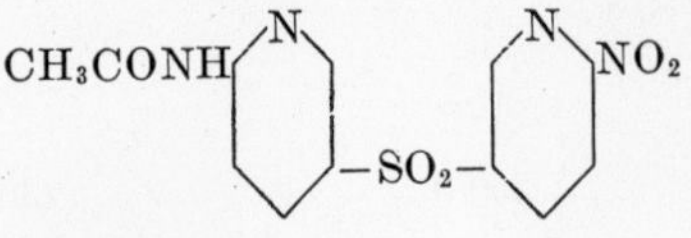			2105
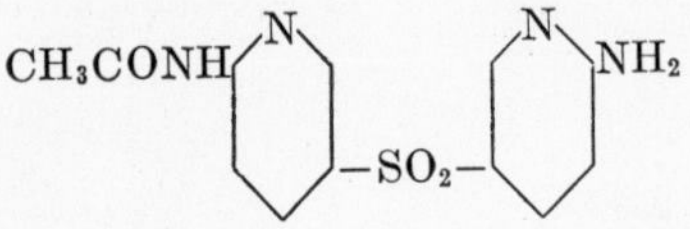			2105

TABLE 255

V. Heterocyclic Sulfones with the S-Atom a Member of the Heterocyclic System

Compound	Melting Range	Activities	References
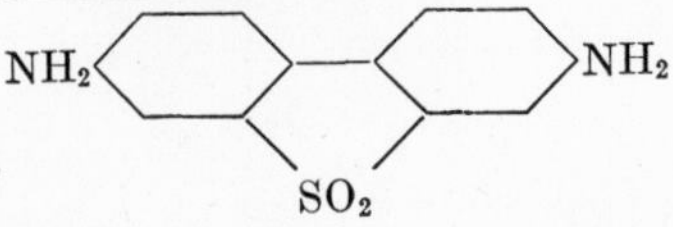		0, −	60, 504, 2441
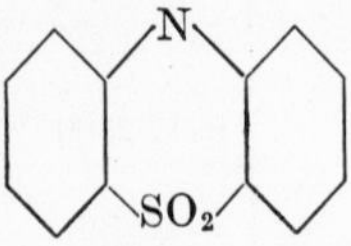		±	505
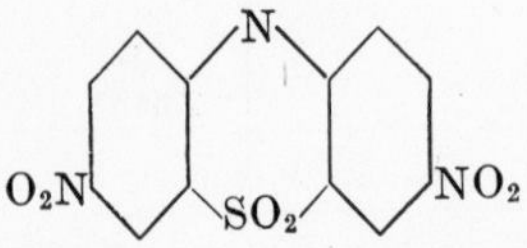		±	505

Chapter VII

STRUCTURE AND ACTIVITIES OF COMPOUNDS RELATED TO THE SULFONES

(I) SULFIDES (Tables 256–265, p. 379–383)

Synthesis. A good starting material for the preparation of a large number of diacyl sulfides is p-(p'-nitrophenylthio)aniline which can be readily obtained by a two stage reaction of sodium sulfide and p-chloronitrobenzene in which sodium p-aminothiophenol is first formed and this reacts with more p-chloronitrobenzene[419].

Pharmacology. The sulfides analogous to the active sulfones have shown disappointing activities both *in vivo* and *in vitro*. Poor agreement on the activity of bis(4-aminophenyl) sulfide is found in the literature but it appears to be much less active than the sulfone. *In vitro* it was active only in relatively high concentrations and its activity could not be reversed by PABA[1384]. It thus seems that the compound may have a different mechanism of action than that of bis(4-aminophenyl) sulfone and is probably not oxidized to the sulfone by bacterial or body enzymes.

(II) SULFOXIDES (Tables 266–267, p. 384–385)

Synthesis. The sulfoxides are usually prepared by oxidation of the sulfide with hydrogen peroxide, care being taken to protect free amino groups by acetylation and avoiding excess peroxide which will lead to further oxidation to the sulfone.

A novel method of preparing bis(4-aminophenyl) sulfoxide is to heat p-acetamidobenzenesulfinamide with aniline and aniline hydrochloride, forming 4-(4'-aminophenylsulfinyl)acetanilide which is readily hydrolyzed to the final product or can be used for the preparation of various unsymmetrical derivatives. Heating p-acetamidobenzenesulfinanilide with aniline and aniline hydrochloride also gives 4-(4'-aminophenylsulfinyl)-acetanilide[2106].

Pharmacology. The sulfoxides appear to lie between the sulfones and sulfides in activity. It is a moot point whether bis(4-aminophenyl) sulfoxide owes its activity to oxidation to bis(4-aminophenyl) sulfone or is active *per se*. Its *in vitro* activity against pneumococci was antagonized by PABA, hence its activity seems to be of the same type as bis(4-aminophenyl) sulfone but it is only 1/32 to 1/14th as potent[1384].

The difference in activity between the optical isomers of p-(phenylsulfinyl)aniline[60] would, if substantiated by further study, rule out the possibility that the activity might be a result of oxidation to the sulfone because oxidation of either optical isomer would give the identical, optically inactive sulfone.

It was noted[60] that although the chemotherapeutic activity of bis(4-aminophenyl) sulfone was considerably lowered by changing to the sulfoxide, the toxicity remained about the same. It was also noted[60] that acetylation had far less effect in reducing the activity of the sulfoxide than of the sulfone.

(III) DISULFIDES (Tables 268, 269, p. 386)

Pharmacology. Bis(4-aminophenyl) disulfide was said to have about 1/25th the activity of bis(4-aminophenyl) sulfone *in vivo*[60] and by others to be inactive[1118]. *In vitro* it was active against pneumococci, hemolytic streptococci, *Strep. viridans*, *Staph. aureus*

377

and *Br. paramelitensis*[1200, 2441]. It had only slight action on *E. coli*, so that its action was the reverse of sulfathiazole which was much more active against *E. coli* than *Staph. aureus*. Also, in contrast to the action of the sulfonamide drugs, its effect was much more rapid and without the lag characteristic of the sulfonamide drugs. PABA was able to antagonize its action only at certain concentrations, above which no amount of PABA was effective and below which growth stimulation took place. It was also noted that, while the molar ratio of a sulfonamide to the PABA required to antagonize its action was 500 or above (depending on the drug and organism), the molar ratio of bis(4-amino-phenyl) disulfide to PABA was 0.2 to 0.5 over the narrow range at which reversal could be produced. Another significant difference was that the action of bis(4-aminophenyl) disulfide was reduced to the vanishing point by presence of whole blood, plasma or serum when tested against any of the above organisms. This would explain its lack of high activity *in vivo*[1200].

Another interesting disulfide is bis(1-phenyl-2,3-dimethyl-5-pyrazolon-4-yl) disulfide which had 1/500th the activity of bis(4-aminophenyl) sulfone *in vivo*[60] and was found active against hemolytic streptococci *in vitro*, less active against pneumococci and inactive against *Strep. viridans*[2441]. It would be interesting to know whether the activity of this compound is antagonized by PABA. One would not predict either activity or its reversal from structural analogies to the active sulfonamide drugs or the sulfones. It may be that the disulfides constitute a class of chemotherapeutic agents distinct from the sulfonamide drugs and active through a different mechanism.

(IV) MISCELLANEOUS DISULFOXIDES (Table 270, p. 387)

Structure. The formulae of the disulfoxides are given with the linkage, $-\overset{\parallel}{\underset{O}{S}}-\overset{\parallel}{\underset{O}{S}}-$, solely for convenience in listing. Actually these are now considered to be better repre-

sented as $-\overset{O}{\underset{\parallel}{\overset{\parallel}{S}}}-S-$ (or $-\overset{O}{\underset{\downarrow}{\overset{\uparrow}{S}}}-S-$) which makes them thio esters of sulfonic acids. [a]

Pharmacology. Bis(4-aminophenyl) disulfoxide was slightly more toxic than bis(4-aminophenyl) sulfone and only 1/100th as active[60]. The oxygen analogue,

$$NH_2\langle\quad\rangle SO_2O\langle\quad\rangle NH_2,$$

was completely inactive[60].

(V) MISCELLANEOUS DISULFONES (Table 271, p. 387)

(VI) COMPOUNDS RELATED TO BIS(4-AMINOPHENYL) SULFONE

(A) Selenium and Tellurium Compounds (Table 272, p. 387)

Pharmacology. Bis(4-aminophenyl) diselenide resembled bis(4-aminophenyl) disulfide in its chemotherapeutic properties *in vitro*. Like the disulfide it was only partially antagonized by PABA[1200].

[a] Gilman, H., "Organic Chemistry", 2nd ed., Vol. I, p. 905ff., John Wiley and Sons, Inc., N. Y. 1943.

Bis(4-acetamidophenyl) ditelluride was quite active but was not antagonized by PABA[1200]. It seems probable that these compounds are acting via a different mechanism than sulfonamide and sulfone drugs.

(B) Phosphorus Compounds (Table 273, p. 388)

Pharmacology. Several of the phosphorus compounds were tested both *in vivo* and *in vitro* for antitubercular activity[477]. The results were not encouraging and seemed definitely inferior to sulfone and sulfonamide drugs.

(C) Arsenic Compounds (Table 274, p. 388)

Pharmacology. These compounds showed very slight protective action *in vivo* but the toxic dose was very close to the therapeutic dose.

TABLE 256

I. Sulfides
  A. Acyclic Isocyclic Sulfides
    1. 4-Aminophenyl Acyclic Sulfides

H_2N⟨ ⟩SR

R	Melting Range	Activities	References
$CH_3(CH_2)_2-$		$\pm$	152
$HOOCCH_2-$	199–200°		1808
$C_2H_5OOCCH_2-$ (HCl)	155–6°		1808
NH_2OCCH_2-	112–3°		247

TABLE 256—(Concluded)

R	Melting Range	Activities	References
HOOC(CH₃)CH—	126–7°		1808
CH₃(CH₂)₅(C₂H₅OOC)CH—	oil		1808
CH₃(CH₂)₇(C₂H₅OOC)CH—	oil		1808
CH₃(CH₂)₉(C₂H₅OOC)CH—	oil		1808
CH₃(CH₂)₁₁(C₂H₅OOC)CH—	oil		1808
CH₃(CH₂)₁₅(C₂H₅OOC)CH—	118°		1808

TABLE 257

2. Miscellaneous Acyclic Isocyclic Sulfides

Compound	Activities	References
4-(NO₂)C₆H₄SCH₂CH₂CH₃	±	152
4-(NO₂)C₆H₄SCH₂COOH		1137

TABLE 258

B. Bis(isocyclic) Sulfides
  1. Bis(4-aminophenyl) Sulfides

R	Melting Range	Activities	References
	108°	++, +, ±(S), +(Ca), ±(P), 0(Ae, Ec, I, R, Sa)	48, 60, 327, 419, 477, 1057, 1118, 1381, 1384, 1466, 1574, 1979, 2192, 2441
NaO₂SCH₂—			2
CH₃CO—	223–4°	+, ±(S), +(Sa), 0(Ae, P)	327, 419, 1057, 1118, 1979
NH₂C(=NH)—	203–4°		783
½ H₂SO₄·NH₂C(=NH)—	>290°	0(I, P, R, S, Tt)	739, 783, 1574
4-(NO₂)C₆H₄SO₂—			210
Cl₂P(O)—			193

TABLE 259

2. Miscellaneous Symmetrical Diphenyl Sulfides   R—S—R

R	Melting Range	Activities	References
2-(NO₂)C₆H₄—	191–2.5°	0(S)	1574, 2373
4-(NO₂)C₆H₄—		+, 0(S), ±(P) 0(Ae, Ca, Sa)	48, 327, 1117
2,4-(NO₂)₂C₆H₃—		±	1117
4-(HO)C₆H₄—		± (S), 0(P)	1057
2-(NH₂)C₆H₄—	84–5°	0(S)	1574, 2373
2-NH₂-5-(CH₃)C₆H₃—			1466

TABLE 260

3. 4-Aminophenyl Isocyclic Sulfides

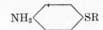

R	Melting Range	Activities	References
2-(NO$_2$)C$_6$H$_4$—	106°	0	1118, 2638
2-(NO$_2$)C$_6$H$_4$—·HCl	225°		2638
4-(NO$_2$)C$_6$H$_4$—	140–1°, 145°	+(S), 0(L, Y, Le)	155, 419, 1082, 1118, 1200, 2638
4-(NO$_2$)C$_6$H$_4$—·HCl	200°		2638
2-NO$_2$-4-ClC$_6$H$_3$—	127–9°		2638
2-NO$_2$-4-ClC$_6$H$_3$—·HCl	215–25°		2638
4-(CH$_3$)C$_6$H$_4$—			1761
2-(NH$_2$)C$_6$H$_4$—		0	1118
4-(CH$_3$CONH)C$_6$H$_4$—			237
4-[CH$_3$(CH$_2$)$_2$CONH]C$_6$H$_4$—			237
4-NH$_2$-2-(SO$_3$H)C$_6$H$_3$—	298°D		1895

TABLE 261

4. 4-(Substituted Amino)phenyl Isocyclic Sulfides　　　R^{4}NH⟨　⟩SR

R$_4$	R	Melting Range	Activities	References
CH$_3$CO—	2-(NO$_2$)C$_6$H$_4$—		0	1118
do	4-(NO$_2$)C$_6$H$_4$—	188°, 198°	+	156, 419, 1118, 2467
CH$_3$CH$_2$CO—	do			2467
do	4-(CH$_3$CONH)C$_6$H$_4$—			237
CH$_3$(CH$_2$)$_2$CO—	do	202°		237
do	4-(CH$_3$CH$_2$CONH)C$_6$H$_4$—	200°		237
CH$_3$OCO—	4-(NO$_2$)C$_6$H$_4$—	157°		2465
C$_2$H$_5$OCO—	do	132–3°		2105
NH$_2$CO—	do	204–5°		2105, 2465
do	4-(C$_2$H$_5$OOCCH$_2$NHCONH)C$_6$H$_4$—	>260°D		2465
HOOCCH$_2$NHCO—	4-(NO$_2$)C$_6$H$_4$—	171°D		2465
C$_2$H$_5$OOCCH$_2$NHCO—	do	201–2°		2465
CH$_3$OCH$_2$CO—	do	142°		2467

TABLE 262

5. Miscellaneous Unsymmetrical Bis(isocyclic) Sulfides

Compound	Melting Range	Activities	References
4-(NO$_2$)C$_6$H$_4$SCH$_2$C$_6$H$_5$		*	1137
4-(NO$_2$)C$_6$H$_4$SC$_6$H$_4$(SO$_2$NH$_2$)—4′			197

TABLE 262—(Concluded)

Compound	Melting Range	Activities	References
4-$(NO_2)C_6H_4SC_6H_4[SO_2N(CH_3)_2]$-4'			197
2-$(NH_2)C_6H_4SC_6H_4(NO_2)$-2'			2638
2-$(NH_2)C_6H_4SC_6H_4(NO_2)$-4'		0	1118
2-$(CH_3CONH)C_6H_4SC_6H_4(NO_2)$-4'		0	1118
4-NH_2-3-$ClC_6H_3SC_6H_4(NO_2)$-4'	127–9°		2638
2-NH_2-3-$(CH_3)C_6H_3SC_6H_4(NO_2)$-2'	108°		2638
2-NH_2-3-$(CH_3)C_6H_3SC_6H_4(NO_2)$-2'·HCl	190°		2638
4-NH_2-3-$(CH_3)C_6H_3SC_6H_4(NO_2)$-2'	101–3°		2638
4-NH_2-3-$(CH_3)C_6H_3SC_6H_3(NO_2)$-2'-Cl-4'	113–5°		2638
4-NH_2-3-$(CH_3)C_6H_3SC_6H_3(NO_2)$-2'-Cl-4'·HCl	215–20°		2638
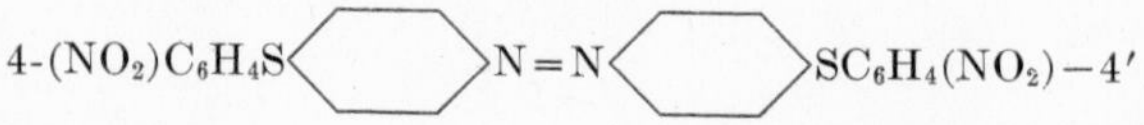 4-$(NO_2)C_6H_4S$⟨ ⟩$N=N$⟨ ⟩$SC_6H_4(NO_2)$—4'			1137

TABLE 263

C. Acyclic Heterocyclic Sulfides   R—S—R'

R	R'	Melting Range	Activities	References
	CH_3—	44–5°		1434
do	$HOOCCH_2$—	270°D	0(S)	1434

TABLE 264

D. Isocyclic Heterocyclic Sulfides   R—S—R'

R	R'	Melting Range	Activities	References
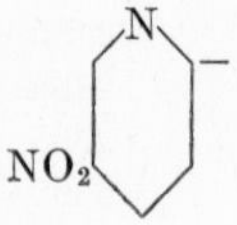	C_6H_5—	121°	0(S)	552
do	4-$(NO_2)C_6H_4$—	126–9°		552, 691
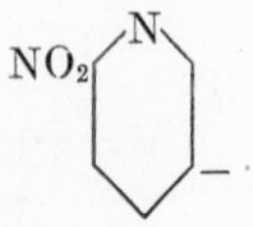	do	112–3°		691

TABLE 264—(*Concluded*)

R	R'	Melting Range	Activities	References
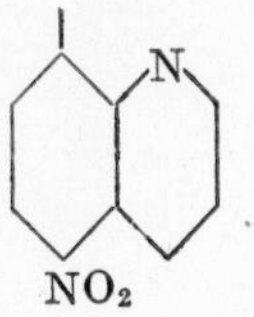 NO₂	C_6H_5-	100°		552
do	$4-(NO_2)C_6H_4-$	223°		552
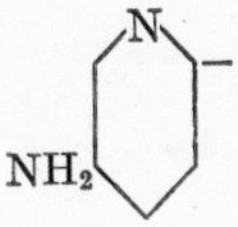 NH₂	C_6H_5-	125–7°	0(S)	552
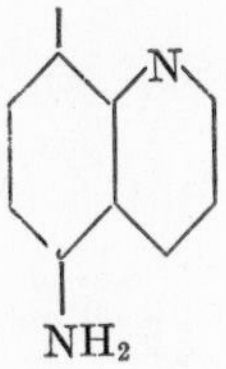 NH₂	do	128°		552
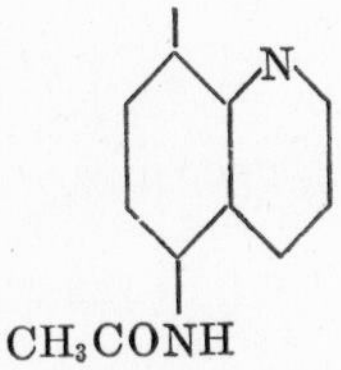 CH₃CONH	do	97–8°		552 .
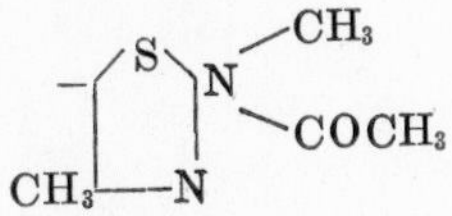	$4-(NO_2)C_6H_4-$	192–4°		2495
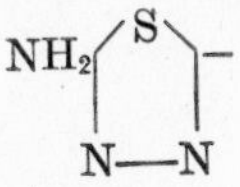	do	196–200°		691

TABLE 265

E. Bis(heterocyclic) Sulfides   R—S—R

R	Melting Range	Activities	References
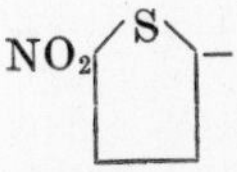	104–6°		691

TABLE 265—*(Concluded)*

R	Melting Range	Activities	References
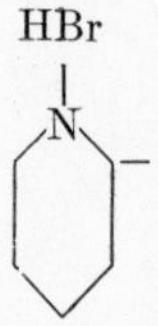 HBr	274°	+(S)	968, 1466
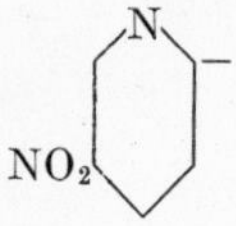 NO₂	132–6°, 136–7°	±(S), 0(P)	691, 1057, 1574, 2300
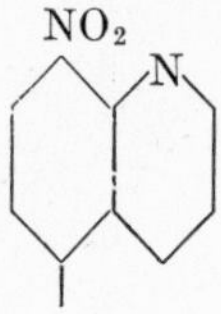 NO₂	288.5–90.5°		2300
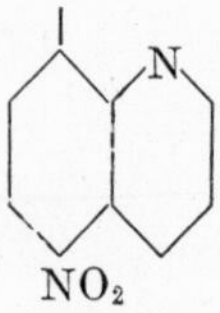 NO₂	280–1°		2300
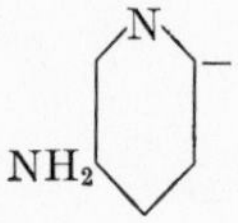 NH₂	130–1.5°	±(S), 0(I, P, R)	1574, 2300
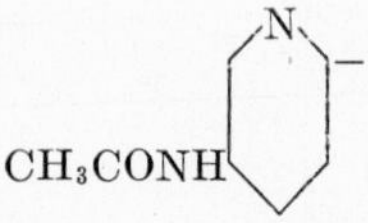 CH₃CONH	265–6.5°	±(S), 0(I, P, R)	1574, 2300

TABLE 266

II. Sulfoxides
  A. Bis(4-aminophenyl) Sulfoxides

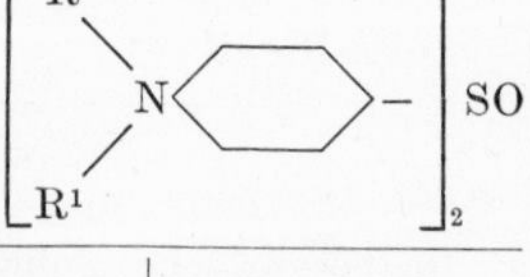

R	R¹	Melting Range	Activities	References
		175°	++, −(S), +(Ca), 0(I, Po)	48, 60, 222, 477, 505, 892, 1118, 1155, 1381, 1384, 1550, 2106, 2441

TABLE 266—(*Concluded*)

R	R¹	Melting Range	Activities	References
CH_3-	CH_3-		$+(S)$	222
NaO_2SCH_2-				522, 2304
$CH_2OH(CHOH)_4CH-$ (Glucose Deriva- $\vert$ SO_3Na tive)				1894
CH_3CO-		278°	$+++, ++(S)$	60, 238, 501, 1118, 1155, 1550, 1556
$NaOOCCH_2CH_2CO-$		>300°	$0(S)$	2304
CH_3OOCCH_2NHCO-		200°		2468
NaO_3SCH_2CO-		>300°	$0(S)$	2304
$Cl_2P(=O)-$				193

TABLE 267

B. Miscellaneous Sulfoxides

RSOR′

R	R′	Melting Range	Activities	References
C_6H_5-	C_6H_5-		$0(S)$	2304
$4-(NO_2)C_6H_4-$	$4-(NO_2)C_6H_4-$		$++(S),$ $0(Ca)$	48, 60, 1118, 1550
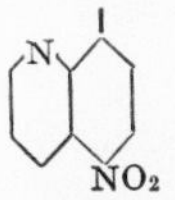	C_6H_5-	145–6°		552
$4-(HO)C_6H_4-$	$4-(HO)C_6H_4-$			1550
$4-(C_2H_5O)C_6H_4-$	$4-(C_2H_5O)C_6H_4-$		$0(I, Po)$	892
$l-4-(NH_2)C_6H_4-$	C_6H_5-	171°	$+(S)$	60
$d,l-4-(NH_2)C_6H_4-$	do	151°	$\pm(S)$	60, 1808
$4-(NH_2)C_6H_4-$	$4-(NO_2)C_6H_4-$	132–4°	$+(G), 0(L)$	155, 1549, 1550, 1555
do	$4-(CH_3)C_6H_4-$	170°		1761, 1808
$4-(CH_3NH)C_6H_4-$	$4-(NO_2)C_6H_4-$		$++(S)$	1550
$4-[(CH_3)_2N]C_6H_4-$	do		$++(S)$	1550
$4-(C_6H_4CH_2NH)C_6H_4-$	do		$++(S)$	1550
$4-(NaO_2SCH_2NH)C_6H_4-$	do			528
$4-[CH_2OH(CHOH)_4CH(SO_3Na)NH]C_6H_4-$ (glucose derivative)	$4-(NH_2)C_6H_4-$			1894
$4-(CH_3CONH)C_6H_4-$	$4-(NO_2)C_6H_4-$	212°	$++(S)$	238, 441, 1550, 1556
do	$4-(NH_2)C_6H_4-$	206°, 207°	$++(S)$	238, 1550, 1556, 2106
$4-(CH_3CH_2CONH)C_6H_4-$	$4-(CH_3CONH)C_6H_4-$	229°		237
$4-(HOOCCH_2CH_2CONH)C_6H_4-$	$4-(NH_2)C_6H_4-$			239
$4-(C_2H_5OCONH)C_6H_4-$	do			2105
do	$4-(CH_3NH)C_6H_4-$	174–5°		2105
do	$4-(CH_3CONH)C_6H_4-$	274°		2105
$4-[4'-(NH_2)C_6H_4SO_2NH]C_6H_4-$	$4-(NO_2)C_6H_4-$	238–9°D		1176
$4-[4'-(CH_3CONH)C_6H_4SO_2NH]C_6H_4-$	do	263–4.5°D		1176
$4-[3'-HOOC-4'-(HO)C_6H_3N=N]C_6H_4-$	$4-(CH_3CONH)C_6H_4-$			2590
$4-[2',4'-(NH_2)_2C_6H_3N=N]C_6H_4-$	do			1556
$4-[2'-HOOC-4',6'-(NH_2)_2C_6H_2N=N]C_6H_4-$	do			1556
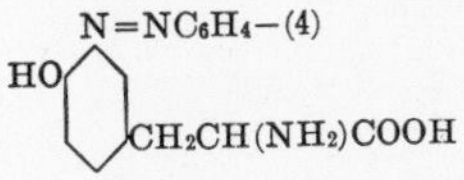	$4-(NO_2)C_6H_4-$		$+(G),$ $\pm(S)$	405

TABLE 268

III. Disulfides
  A. Bis(4-aminophenyl) Disulfides

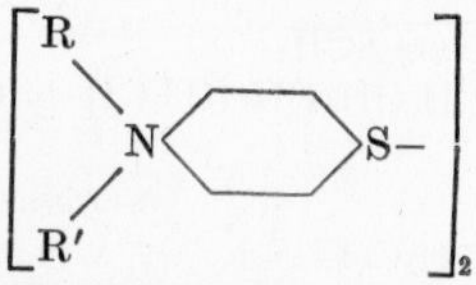

R	R′	Melting Range	Activities	References
		80°	++, 0(S)	60, 1118, 1200, 2441
CH_3-	CH_3-	118°		144
CH_3CO-			0(S)	156, 1118
$NH_2C(=NH)-$		178°		783
$\frac{1}{2}$-$H_2SO_4 \cdot NH_2C(=NH)-$		257–8°	0(I, P, R, S, Tt)	783, 1574

TABLE 269

B. Miscellaneous Disulfides

Compound	Melting Range	Activities	References
$(C_6H_5S-)_2$			1117
$[2\text{-}(NO_2)C_6H_4S-]_2$		0(S)	1117, 1118, 1137
$4\text{-}(NO_2)C_6H_4S-SC_6H_5$		+(S)	1118
$[4\text{-}(NO_2)C_6H_4S-]_2$	182°	+(S), 0(L, Lc, Y)	60, 1082, 1117, 1118, 1200
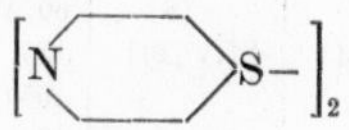	74–5°		1434
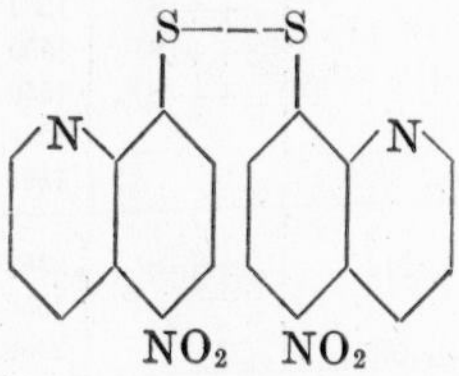	245°, 250–2°D		523, 552
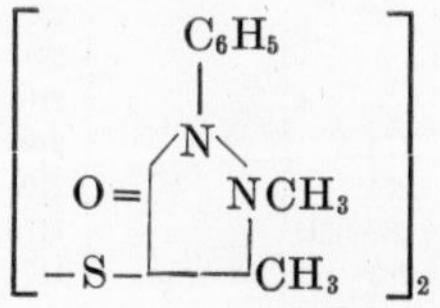		+(S)	60, 2441
$[4\text{-}(NaO_3S)C_6H_4S-]_2$		0(P, Tt)	1427, 1574
$[2\text{-}(NH_2)\text{-}5\text{-}(CH_3)C_6H_3S-]_2$			1466

TABLE 270

IV. Miscellaneous Disulfoxides

Compound	Melting Range	Activities	References
[NH$_2$CH$_2$CH$_2$SO$-$]$_2$			496, 858
[HCl·NH$_2$CH$_2$CH$_2$SO$-$]$_2$	166°D		496
[CH$_3$CH(NH$_2$)CH$_2$SO$-$]$_2$			496
[NH$_2$(CH$_2$)$_3$SO$-$]$_2$			496
[NaO$_3$SC$_6$H$_4$SO$-$]$_2$		0(I, P, R, Tt)	1427, 1574
[4-(NH$_2$)C$_6$H$_4$SO$-$]$_2$		+	60, 725, 858
4-(NO$_2$)C$_6$H$_4$SOSOC$_6$H$_4$[NHC$_6$H$_4-$(NO$_2$)-4']-4"	190°	±(S, 0(P, Sa)	968
4-(CH$_3$CONH)C$_6$H$_4$SOSOC$_6$H$_4$(CH$_3$)-4'			858
[4-(CH$_3$CONH)C$_6$H$_4$SO$-$]$_2$			725, 858

TABLE 271

V. Miscellaneous Disulfones   RSO$_2-$SO$_2$R'

R	R'	Melting Range	Activities	References
4-(NH$_2$)C$_6$H$_4-$	4-(NH$_2$)C$_6$H$_4-$		+(S)	60, 858
4-(CH$_3$CONH)C$_6$H$_4-$	4-(CH$_3$CONH)C$_6$H$_4-$		±, $-$(S), 0(P)	60, 505, 858, 1057

TABLE 272

VI. Compounds Related to Bis(4-aminophenyl) Sulfone

A. Selenium and Tellurium Compounds

Compound	Melting Range	Activities	References
[4-(NO$_2$)C$_6$H$_4-$]$_2$Se	175°		424
[4-NO$_2$C$_6$H$_4-$]$_2$SeO	202°		1742
[4-(NO$_2$)C$_6$H$_4$Se$-$]$_2$	175–6°		424, 1200
[4-(NH$_2$)C$_6$H$_4-$]$_2$Se	117°	0(S)	424, 694, 1742, 2149
[4-(CH$_3$CONH)C$_6$H$_4$]$_2$Se	176°, 216°, 219°		424, 694, 1742
[4-(CH$_3$CONH)C$_6$H$_4$]$_2$SeO		0(S)	2149
[4-(CH$_3$CONH)C$_6$H$_4$]$_2$Se(OH)$_2$	223°	0(S)	694, 2149
[4-(NH$_2$)C$_6$H$_4$Se$-$]$_2$	81°		424, 1200, 1742
[4-(CH$_3$CONH)C$_6$H$_4$Se$-$]$_2$	182°, 204–5°		424, 1200
{4-[CH$_3$(CH$_2$)$_3$CONH]C$_6$H$_4$Se$-$}$_2$	172–3°		424
{4-[CH$_3$(CH$_2$)$_4$CONH]C$_6$H$_4$Se$-$}$_2$	175–7°		424
[4-(C$_6$H$_5$CONH)C$_6$H$_4$Se$-$]$_2$	265–7°		424
[4-(CH$_3$CONH)C$_6$H$_4$Te$-$]$_2$	196–8°		1200

TABLE 273

B. Phosphorus Compounds

Compound	Melting Range	Activities	References
$[4\text{-}NH_2C_6H_4]_2P(=O)OH$		0(T)	477
$\{4\text{-}[(CH_3)_2N]C_6H_4\}_2POH$	165°	++(S), +(P, T)	36, 477, 2004
$\{4\text{-}[(CH_3)_2N]C_6H_4\}_2P(OH)_2$		0(T)	477
$\{4\text{-}[(CH_3)_2N]C_6H_4\}_2P(=O)OH$		±(T)	477
$\{4\text{-}[(CH_3)_2N]C_6H_4\}_3P$	275°	0	36, 2004

TABLE 274

C. Arsenic Compounds

Compound	Melting Range	Activities	References
$4\text{-}(NH_2)C_6H_4As(=O)(OH)C_6H_4(NO_2)\text{-}4'$	239°	±(S)	441
$4\text{-}(CH_3CONH)C_6H_4As(OH)C_6H_4(NO_2)\text{-}4'$		±(S)	441
$\begin{bmatrix} 4\text{-}(CH_3CONH)C_6H_4 \\ \diagdown As- \\ 4'\text{-}(NO_2)C_6H_4 \diagup \end{bmatrix}_2 O$	95–99°	±(S)	441
$4\text{-}(CH_3CONH)C_6H_4As(=O)(OH)C_6H_4(NO_2)\text{-}4'$	258°	±(S)	441
$\{(4\text{-}(NH_2)C_6H_4-]_2As-\}_2O$	85–90°	0(S)	441
$[4\text{-}(NH_2)C_6H_4-]_2As\diagup^{\displaystyle O}_{\diagdown OH}$		0(S)	441, 1175
$\begin{matrix} 4\text{-}(CH_3CONH)C_6H_4 \\ \diagdown As-Cysteine \\ 4'\text{-}(NO_2)C_6H_4 \diagup \end{matrix}$		±(S)	441
$\begin{matrix} 4\text{-}(CH_3CONH)C_6H_4 \\ \diagdown As-Glutathione \\ 4'\text{-}(NO_2)C_6H_4 \diagup \end{matrix}$		±(S)	441
$\begin{bmatrix} 4\text{-}(NH_2)C_6H_4 \\ \diagdown As \\ 4'\text{-}(NO_2)C_6H_4 \diagup \end{bmatrix}_2$		0(S)	441
$\begin{bmatrix} 4\text{-}(CH_3CONH)C_6H_4 \\ \diagdown As- \\ 4'\text{-}(NO_2)C_6H_4 \diagup \end{bmatrix}_2$		0(S)	441

Chapter VIII

EXPERIMENTAL EVALUATION OF CHEMOTHERAPEUTIC ACTIVITY

By Harold J. White

In searching for chemotherapeutic agents we look for compounds which will cure, or at least control, naturally occurring diseases. To be useful, these compounds must exert their effects in a relatively specific manner, so as to avoid permanent injury to the host. The first part of the search consists of finding active compounds and investigating their activity under various experimental conditions. Once a compound has been found to possess potential chemotherapeutic activity, it is subjected to pharmacological study to determine the manner in which it may be employed most effectively and, if its pharmacological properties are such as to indicate that it may be relatively safe, it is then ready for clinical trial. With respect to practical usefulness, it is important to keep in mind that the final evaluation of a drug must be based upon extensive and carefully controlled clinical and field trials. Experimental studies merely provide a basis for a tentative evaluation indicating the degree of probability of achieving the clinical results desired.

The present chapter will be limited to a consideration of some of the factors involved in the experimental evaluation of chemotherapeutic activity, as applied to pathogenic bacteria. However, it is probable that many of the principles upon which the rules of procedure in bacterial chemotherapy are based, are equally applicable to chemotherapeutic problems in general.

(I) Antibacterial Activity Tests

To study drug activity against many infectious agents, such as malarial parasites and most viruses, it is necessary to use *in vivo* methods. On the other hand, both *in vitro* and *in vivo* methods can usually be employed to study antibacterial activity. Irrespective of the method used, the fundamental factors involved are: a) the kind, number and condition of the organisms; b) the concentration and duration of drug at the site of action; and c) environmental factors which may augment or counteract the interaction of drug and parasite.

In experimental studies on the chemotherapy of infectious diseases, we are interested not only in the type of compound which may kill pathogenic organisms directly, but also in the type which may inhibit or weaken the parasites and thus render them susceptible to the destructive and eliminating action of natural defense mechanisms. Consequently, for the preliminary evaluation of antibacterial activity we require methods which will disclose interference with the metabolism and multiplication of the organisms. This calls for methods with which inhibitory and bacteriostatic as well as bactericidal activity can be measured, following relatively prolonged exposure of organisms to the drug.

In the following pages, a procedure for finding active drugs and evaluating their chemotherapeutic potentialities will be discussed. This procedure has been used in the Bacteriology Laboratory, Chemotherapy Division, Stamford Research Laboratories of the American Cyanamid Company. It is realized that the methods referred to are not necessarily superior to many others which might be used. They merely serve as examples. Unfortunately, there are no "standard methods" in chemotherapy.

Preliminary screening *in vitro* is carried out with the objective of finding a few active agents among a large number of unselected compounds using minimum quantities of material and a number of representative pathogenic species. Compounds specifically synthesized for chemotherapeutic testing are investigated in more detail based on analogies to the known activities of drugs of which they may be modifications. All compounds which show relatively high activity *in vitro* are retested for activity in an experimental infection. Any compound which passes this test, by showing significant antibacterial activity in an infected animal, is considered to be a promising lead and it is then subjected, together with as many related compounds as may be available or synthesized, to a thorough study respecting various characteristics which bear upon its possible chemotherapeutic usefulness.

The purpose of a screening test is to find compounds which may lead to the development of a chemotherapeutic agent for a particular disease. Obviously, the more compounds tested, the greater the chance of finding a promising lead. To permit classification of a large number of compounds according to their activity, it is necessary to use a more or less standardized test procedure and a standard drug of reference. From one point of view, it may be considered advisable to screen various compounds with respect to a wide variety of pathogenic species. However, in view of the difficulties often encountered in handling and maintaining bacterial strains in a satisfactory condition for reproducible tests, and in view of the variability in test conditions, it is advisable to limit the number of test organisms in any screening program. For example, it is much simpler and more practicable to screen a thousand compounds against one organism than to screen fifty compounds against twenty organisms, although the total number of tests is the same in each case.

(A) *In Vitro* Tests

The most widely used method for determining the antibacterial activity of drugs consists of cultivating the bacteria in test tubes containing a fluid medium to which the drug has been added. Other methods, such as that employing the slide-cell[900, 901, 1101, 1102] and various modifications of the agar cup plate[2653], have been used to a limited extent. A simple, rapid and apparently very useful agar-streak method for determining antibacterial activity has been recently published by Waksman and Reilly.[a] More specialized methods involving the use of chick embryos[1697, 1805, 2082, 2409, 693, 1035, 1202, 1203]; bone marrow[808, 1872, 1873, 1874, 1875, 1876] and other tissue cultures[1435, 1436] have also been applied to the problem of evaluating chemotherapeutic activity. Direct measurements of the effect of drugs upon cell respiration[805, 996, 2094, 2097], other enzymatic activities of cell metabolism[733, 884, 1392, 1870] and oxidation-reduction potentials in bacterial cultures[1120, 2401] may lead to plausible explanations of the mechanism of drug action, but the practical application of such studies to the problem of chemotherapeutic evaluation may be questioned.

Factors which definitely influence the results of any bacteriostatic test method include the following: species and strain of test organism; composition and pH of medium; inoculum age, size and diluting fluid; the concentrations and stability of drug solutions; temperature and duration of incubation; and finally, the criteria used to determine activity. The various ways in which these factors may affect *in vitro* test results will not be considered in detail here, since they have been discussed rather fully by Henry[1297], Frisk[1135] and MacLeod[2597].

Essential elements of more or less standardized *in vitro* screening tests using typical strains of twenty-seven potentially pathogenic species are outlined in Table 299. A brief

---

[a] Waksman, S. A. and Reilly, H. C., *Ind. Eng. Chem.*, **17**, 556–8 (1945).

discussion of test organisms, media, drug solutions and criteria of bacteriostatic and bactericidal activity follows.

(1) Test Organisms

Satisfactory standardization of test conditions has been obtained for each of the strains listed in Table 299. This has been accomplished by maintaining and transferring stock cultures in a uniform manner, as indicated. In addition, several lyophilized cultures of most of the strains are kept in reserve.

Storage and passage of all stock cultures are carried out on a definite schedule in an attempt to prevent loss of viability and virulence, and to minimize the changes in various characteristics which bacterial strains may otherwise undergo. In this connection, it may be recalled that the terms "culture" and "strain" usually refer to populations of many millions of individual cells. As in any large population, so, too, in a bacterial culture there exists a multitude of individuals which probably vary in many respects. The population, or culture, is usually characterized by the properties of the majority of its individual members. Any environmental change which alters the relative numbers of different individual cells may change the character of the culture. Such changes may be of considerable importance in connection with the susceptibility of a strain to the action of a drug. Even with the utmost care, stock cultures may occasionally lose their virulence, or undergo marked change in their growth characteristics, or possibly in their drug sensitivity, in which case it may be necessary to recover the strain from a lyophilized stock culture.

Test cultures are started by transfer from stock cultures. In most cases, after overnight incubation of the test culture, a 1.0 cc. volume is subcultured into fresh medium in order to obtain a young (5 to 7 hour old) vigorously growing culture for the test inoculum. Test cultures of the rapidly growing avirulent *Mycobacterium* strain 607 are maintained by regular weekly passage in the synthetic medium of Henley and Le Duc. This strain is one of those which on repeated passage occasionally changes in its manner of growth (from a thick dry pellicle to a thin slimy subsurface type of growth). However, the growth characteristics of stock cultures of this strain on solid media appear to be constant. Test cultures of the virulent H37RV strain of *M. tuberculosis* are passed, once a week, in a modified Dubos fluid medium which has been found to be suitable for bacteriostatic tests with this organism. Cultures of the gonococcus strain are kept on chocolate agar slants with passage at 48-hour intervals. Since it is difficult to grow *Pasteurella tularensis* in a fluid medium, this species is maintained and tested on blood cystine agar. The Reiter spirochaete strain is carried and tested in fluid thioglycollate medium to which 10% inactivated rabbit serum and 0.2% liver extract are added.

The smallest inoculum which can be depended upon to yield optimum growth within 48 hours when incubated at 37°C. is used in each bacteriostatic test, with the exception of the mycobacterial tests which require 3 days' and 7 days' incubation for the 607 and H37RV strains, respectively. The inoculum is obtained by suitable dilution of the test culture in the test medium.

A titration for the bacteriostatic endpoint of a standard reference drug is included in all tests. This serves as a control on test conditions, including the susceptibility of the organisms, composition of the medium, and other factors subject to variation, such as technique and incubation temperature.

The reproducibility of bacteriostatic test conditions is indicated in Table 300, in terms of the frequency distribution of bacteriostatic endpoints for standard drugs covering repeated tests over a period of several months.   In view of the fact that these endpoints are measured on a twofold dilution scale, it is evident that with the exception of the hemolytic streptococcus, strain C203, a fair degree of reproducibility can be achieved when care is taken to maintain constant conditions for storage and handling of cultures.

(2) Test Media

Of the many variables which may influence *in vitro* results, it is generally agreed that the composition of the test medium is the factor which often exerts the greatest effect upon drug activity.   This is particularly true of sulfanilamide derivatives, since inhibitors of these compounds appear to be present in the common bacteriological culture media prepared from meat infusions enriched by peptone.   As different batches of infusions and peptones vary widely in their content of sulfonamide antagonists[1690, 1693, 2288, 2291, 2440, 2597], it is practically impossible to obtain constant test conditions for quantitative results with many organisms in media of this type.   Consequently, bacteriostatic test results in different laboratories can not be compared with one another in terms of absolute values. In fact, the effect of variation in test media may be so great as to make it impossible to compare drugs from test to test in the same laboratory, except in terms of activity as related to a standard reference drug.

A further complication is that the test medium may influence drug activity indirectly. Thus, in broth and in blood-broth the activity of a drug against one species (*e.g.*, hemolytic streptococci) may change markedly, while against another species (*e.g.*, pneumococci) in the same media very little change in drug activity may occur.   Finally, the sulfonamide antagonists in a medium may affect one drug more than another[266, 550].

The choice of the bacteriostatic test medium depends largely upon the purpose to be served.   In view of the complex effects obtained with media which contain natural products of unknown chemical composition, it is necessary to use synthetic, or chemically defined, media for exact studies such as those on the mechanism of drug action.   Under these conditions, it is possible to define and, to some extent, control the environment in which the interaction of drug and parasite occurs and thus a satisfactory evaluation of the influence of added factors upon drug action can be made.   Simple media of known chemical composition are available for many species, such as staphylococci and *E. coli*[2253, 1690].   For many strains of the more exacting pathogens, such as Group A hemolytic streptococci and pneumococci, it is sometimes possible to use media which are practically free of sulfonamide antagonists[1135, 1690, 2597].   However, the latter media are relatively complex and, in most cases, contain chemically undefined components.

It would be desirable to test compounds in body fluids in order to simulate, as far as possible, the *in vivo* environment in which chemotherapeutic activity is to be applied. For example, blood or serum may be used for tests with hemolytic streptococci and urine would be an appropriate medium for tests with *Streptococcus fecalis*.   However, it is not practicable to test large numbers of compounds in body fluids because of the technical difficulties involved in sterilization and dilution.

The most commonly used test media are infusion and peptone broths.   As noted above, different batches of these media vary in composition[1546, 2284] especially in their content of sulfonamide antagonists, which makes it practically impossible to compare results of different tests except in terms of relative values.   Simultaneous titration of the activity of a standard reference drug in all tests with media of this kind is necessary, if quantitative comparisons are to be made.

The test media listed in Table 299 have been selected on the basis of ease of handling and also because variation in results with standard drugs fell within reasonable limits, with the exception of the Group A hemolytic streptococcus, strain C203. A more satisfactory test medium for this organism is needed, since its resistance to several sulfanilamide derivatives in the present medium does not agree with the fact that these compounds are highly active against hemolytic streptococci both in experimental and clinical infections. On the other hand, in this same medium which is unsatisfactory for sulfanilamide studies, the high degree of activity of certain pantothenic acid analogues against strain C203 correlates quite well with *in vivo* results. For the study of sulfonamide resistance of hemolytic streptococci, a medium, rather complicated but essentially free of drug antagonists, has been used by Wilson.[a]

In any case, the important thing for preliminary bacteriostatic tests is to use media which will support satisfactory control growth and, at the same time, contain a minimum of drug antagonists. Complete absence of antagonists is not necessary, since test results may be expressed in relative terms.

An example of the influence of test media upon drug activity has been reported by Schmidt[2167] who found that sulfathiazole, sulfadiazine and sulfapyrazine were from ten to one thousand times more active in a synthetic medium than in a beef heart infusion broth, against strains of Friedländer's bacillus. A thousandfold difference in the activity of each of several sulfonamides in different media against strains of *E. coli* has also been demonstrated[550].

In addition to the composition of the test medium, its pH is a factor which may directly, or indirectly, influence the activity of a drug. The pH range for optimal growth of many bacterial species is a fairly narrow one. Furthermore, it has been shown that variation in pH of the culture medium may affect sulfonamide activity directly[802].

(3) Drug Solutions

Each compound is screened for activity starting with a concentration of 128, 64, 32, 16, 8 or 4 mg.%, depending upon its solubility at pH 7.0 to 7.4. Compounds which are insoluble, under test conditions, in a concentration of 4 mg.% are filtered and tested as saturated solutions. In each case, the range of concentrations for titrating bacteriostatic or bactericidal activity covers the appropriate part of a scale graded downward from 128 mg.% by twofold dilution steps. Initially, a stock solution of each compound is made in 0.02 M phosphate buffer (0.016 M $Na_2HPO_4 \cdot 12H_2O$ and 0.004 M $NaH_2PO_4 \cdot H_2O$) with adjustment of the pH to 7.2 as required. In some cases, the use of small amounts of acid or alkali, or solvents, followed by dilution with buffer, may be helpful. In making up test mixtures, 5.0 cc. of buffer solution of drug is added to 5.0 cc. of double strength test medium; 5.0 cc. of this dilution is then serially diluted in 5.0 cc. amounts of single strength medium. After autoclaving, each tube in the various sets of drug concentrations, together with control tubes of medium without drug, is inoculated with 0.2 cc. of diluted test culture. If a compound is known to be unstable to heat, the stock solution is Seitz-filtered and diluted aseptically with sterile test medium.

It is quite important to carry out tests with certain types of compounds in solutions which are sterilized by filtration rather than heat. As examples of compounds which, when tested after autoclaving in alkaline media, give results that may lead to erroneous conclusions, the following may be cited. Certain N^4-substituted sulfanilamide derivatives, including Prontosil, sulfasuxidine and sulfathalidine, and a few N^1-substituted

[a] Wilson, A. T., *Proc. Soc. Exptl. Biol. Med.*, **58**, 130–3 (1945).

derivatives, such as 2-sulfanilamido-5-carboxythiazole and 2-sulfanilamido-5-carboxy-4-methylthiazole, apparently decompose to active compounds.[a]

(4) Antibacterial Activity *in Vitro*

The basic antibacterial effect produced by sulfanilamide derivatives is generally conceded to be an inhibition of bacterial growth[1297]. In a strict interpretation, this would imply inhibition of an increase in the size of individual cells. As commonly employed, however, the term "bacterial growth" refers to bacterial multiplication or increase in population size resulting from both growth and fission of successive crops of cells. This less rigorous definition will be used throughout the present discussion.

The population size of a bacterial culture in a fluid medium can be estimated, in terms of its number of viable units,[b] by means of colony counts using subculture dilution and plating methods. If the population is a large one (about 5,000,000 or more cells per cc., depending upon the species), the total number of cells, both living and dead, can be estimated by means of a microscopic count or by a turbidimetric measurement when turbidity has been calibrated with microscopic counts.

A single turbidity reading merely indicates population size, or total cell mass, at a given point in time. When this is referred to previous absence of turbidity, growth is indicated qualitatively. When a turbidity reading is related to less turbidity at some previous time, growth may be expressed quantitatively in arbitrary units, as measured by inspection or, more precisely, by photometric and photonreflectometric methods[1556]. During the exponential phase of growth, the multiplication rate remains constant and may be determined by plotting the logarithms of viable cell counts, or turbidity measurements, against time.

The overall antibacterial effect of a drug may be described as *inhibitory* when the normal multiplication rate in a culture is depressed; *bacteriostatic* when no multiplication occurs; and *bactericidal* when a decrease in the number of viable units is initiated or accelerated.

When the action of a drug is primarily bactericidal, this can be demonstrated in terms of a culture death rate by plotting viable unit counts against time. Under ordinary test conditions, however, it is extremely difficult to separate the component parts of a population curve in such a way as to permit clear-cut differentiation between inhibitory, bacteriostatic and bactericidal actions, all of which may operate simultaneously.

The end result of any one of these three kinds of drug action may be sterilization of the test system. The criterion for sterility usually consists of failure to obtain growth in subcultures. This should be based upon transfer of an adequate portion of the test mixture to a medium capable of supporting growth of a single viable bacterial unit. Subcultures may sometimes fail to show growth, not because the original test mixture was sterile, but because of continuing inhibition due to the amount of drug carried over in the inoculum. Inactivation of the drug carried over into the subculture may be achieved by simple dilution to a sub-inhibitory level, or by adding a drug antagonist such as *p*-aminobenzoic acid. A check on the suitability of subculture conditions for detecting viability should be made by re-inoculating all negative subculture tubes with a small number of viable bacteria. Any growth resulting from this second inoculum can

---

[a] White, H. J., *et al.*, *J. Pharmacol.*, **85**, 247–57 (1945).

[b] "Viable units" is used here because colony counts do not necessarily represent a corresponding number of individual cells. A colony may develop as a result of planting a single cell, a chain of cells, or a clump of cells.

be interpreted to mean that growth would also have resulted from the amount of test mixture previously subcultured, if it had contained as many viable units.

(a) *Semi-quantitative Methods*

Semi-quantitative methods have been widely used for determining the *in vitro* activity of sulfa drugs. The quantitative part of these methods consists of measuring the minimum concentration of drug required to produce inhibition. The criterion of inhibition is usually the absence of visible signs of growth after bacteria are inoculated into a clear medium containing the drug under test. This is an all or none effect and simply indicates that the inoculated cells did not multiply to an extent sufficient to cloud the medium. For preliminary studies, it would appear to be unnecessary to use more precise criteria of activity.

In the screening tests listed in Table 299, the antibacterial activity of a drug is titrated against a constant inoculum size by using a series of drug concentrations graded in twofold steps. Comparative activity in any one test is based upon the relative amount of each drug required to produce the same qualitative effect. Comparative activity from test to test is related to the activity of a standard drug.

The arbitrarily chosen criterion for activity is the absence of visible growth. Turbidity in the control tubes and in the tubes at the lower end of the range of drug concentrations, coupled with absence of visible growth at the upper end of the range, provide a sharp endpoint for each titration. These inhibitory endpoints are read after 48 hours' incubation, except for a few tests which require a longer period for maximum control growth. Thus, drug activity is measured in terms of the smallest concentration required to prevent visible growth of a bacterial population which, in the absence of drug, would be capable of producing maximum turbidity in the medium used. This endpoint is expressed as the Minimum Effective Concentration (M.E.C.) in milligrams per cent.

The endpoint for a drug in any one test may change with continued incubation. Repeated titrations of a drug under the same test conditions may also show a shift in the activity endpoint (Tables 300 and 301). Therefore, studies on the comparative activity of related compounds require the use of a standard reference drug so that comparisons may be to some extent independent of test conditions. A twofold scale carries an error of the magnitude of plus 100% or minus 50% for a single test. The variation in results from test to test is such that one is probably not justified in attaching significance to less than a fourfold difference in activity ratios (see Table 301, p. 418).

When activity is based upon a qualitative response, as described above, two drugs may have the same activity endpoint and yet may vary widely in their effect upon the inoculated cells. One drug may depress the population growth rate slightly so that at the time of reading the test the cells have multiplied to an extent just short of producing turbidity; another drug may rapidly initiate a death rate with the result that the medium is sterile at the time of reading.

(b) *Quantitative Methods*

Inhibition of bacterial growth can be determined by comparing the increases in population size, or the rates of multiplication, resulting from equivalent inocula in the presence and absence of drug. By measuring the degree of inhibition produced by each of several concentrations of a drug, a dosage-response curve may be derived. Drugs can thus be compared quantitatively in terms of the relative amount of each drug required to produce a fixed amount of inhibition.

Quantitative methods are used for such studies as those on the mechanism of drug action and on the relationship between chemical structure and activity. In this connection, precise measurements have been published on the effect of sulfanilamide derivatives upon the mean bacterial generation time[438], the mean multiplication rate[577, 578, 1457] and in terms of the amount of drug required to hold the increase in population size to a fixed percentage of the increase in a control population for a corresponding period of time[1364].

(B) *In Vivo* Tests

Test tube results may provide much information of theoretical value and they may serve to indicate which compounds merit further study, but they tell us very little about the practical usefulness of a compound as a potential chemotherapeutic agent. Evaluation of chemotherapeutic activity must be carried out *in vivo*.

In a preliminary *in vivo* test the object is simply to find out whether or not a compound is active. Once its activity has been demonstrated in an experimental infection, a drug becomes of considerable interest as a lead for a possible chemotherapeutic agent. It is then compared quantitatively, under a variety of experimental conditions, with related compounds and with known chemotherapeutic agents. Concomitantly, experiments should be carried out in an attempt to elucidate the mechanism of drug action and, if possible, to determine how to enhance the activity. The ultimate objective of the *in vivo* evaluation, in conjunction with pharmacological studies, is to find the compound which is most active and least toxic.

Preliminary test conditions should be such as to favor the antibacterial action of compounds as much as possible, since a compound with slight activity may lead to the development of a valuable drug. Thus, the infecting dose should be the minimum required to establish in animals a type of infection which is both certainly fatal and allows adequate time before death for treatment to take effect; treatment should be initiated at the time of infecting; finally, a compound should not be classified as inactive until a negative result is obtained with its maximum tolerated dose.

The chemotherapeutic activity of sulfanilamide derivatives in a variety of experimental infections has been studied extensively by the following investigators and their associates: Buttle[59—61, 818—823, 900]; Feinstone[138, 139, 141]; Frisk[1134, 1135]; Long[313, 314, 750—757, 1056, 1610—1621]; Marshall[310, 335, 550, 1585, 1725, 1732—1734, 2441]; Powell[1952—1958]; Schmidt[462, 2117—2133]. Extensive studies on the activity of sulfanilamides and sulfones in experimental tuberculosis have been reported by Feldman and his associates[1059—1066] and by Smith and his associates[2217—2219]. The references cited provide illustrations of typical methods of evaluating the activity of drugs *in vivo*. A large number of other references on chemotherapeutic evaluation are given in Tables 275 through 298.

It should be pointed out that a considerable risk of infection may be involved in work with pathogenic bacteria. This is particularly true of infections such as anthrax, brucellosis, tuberculosis and tularemia. Such studies should be carried out only by suitably trained personnel under conditions which reduce the risk to a minimum.

(1) Test Organisms

For standardized test infections, stock cultures are passed through animals on a regular schedule in order to maintain maximum virulence. Passage of streptococcus, pneumococcus, *Pasteurella* and Friedländer cultures through mice is carried out once a week by intraperitoneal injection of 0.5 cc. of diluted stock culture. When the mice appear to be moribund they are sacrificed and heart blood is cultured in blood broth and streaked on a blood agar plate. After this new stock blood broth culture has been incubated for 16 to 18 hours, 1.0 cc. is transferred to 9.0 cc. of fresh broth and allowed to incubate for 6 hours. Thus, a young vigorously growing culture, of recent mouse passage, is used to provide the infecting dose for each *in vivo* test. The new stock culture is refrigerated until the next weekly passage. The 6-hour test culture may contain from 10^8 to 10^9 organisms per cc., depending upon the species. Suitable dilutions are made for the infecting dose, for a virulence titration and for plate counts, in each test.

Mouse virulence of these standard cultures apparently can be maintained to such an extent that one bacterial unit, as determined by plate counts, constitutes a "lethal dose". Over a period of years, stock cultures of the widely used streptococcus strain C203 may occasionally lose their virulence despite regularly repeated passage through animals. To meet this contingency, it is desirable to keep on hand several lyophilized samples of a virulent culture.

The size of the infecting dose is often expressed as a multiple of the so-called "lethal dose" (LD). In each test, this dose is roughly estimated on the basis of a virulence titration. For example, if 0.5 cc. of a 10^{-5} dilution of the test culture is used as the test dose, additional groups of untreated control animals are infected with 0.5 cc. of 10^{-6}, 10^{-7}, 10^{-8} and 10^{-9} dilutions. The number of viable organisms in each dose is estimated by means of colony counts in agar pour plates and thus the smallest number of organisms capable of killing an animal may be estimated. It is at once obvious that the "lethal dose" can be only roughly estimated, since it is an endpoint based upon a response to a single dose and is therefore greatly affected by the number of animals used for its determination.

A simple method of estimating the fifty per cent endpoint in titrating infective agents has been published by Reed and Muench[2009]. The advantages of using the dilution by which half of the animals are affected is that this endpoint is influenced to a minimum extent by small chance variations.

Therapeutic results are influenced by the route of infection. Thus, intraperitoneal inoculation of small doses of strains of type I pneumococcus in mice usually results in a rapidly progressing septicemia terminating in death within about 36 hours. On the other hand, infections produced by subcutaneous inoculation of similar doses usually do not result in death until the fourth or fifth day after infection, thus permitting a longer period of time for drug treatment[42].

One of the most important variables which may influence chemotherapy of experimental infections is the strain of test organism. Drug resistance *in vivo* with many strains of pneumococci has been thoroughly studied by Schmidt and his associates who found that variation from strain to strain within a single type was as great as the variation from type to type[2121].

(2) Test Animals

White mice have been used extensively for evaluating the activity of drugs in experimental infections. These animals are relatively inexpensive and easily handled; they are susceptible to several bacterial species; their small size makes it possible to obtain a great deal of information with small quantities of drug; and, for quantitative studies, statistical control of variation in animal response can easily be achieved by the use of large numbers of mice from reasonably uniform stocks. The value of these animals for studies in bacterial chemotherapy is demonstrated by the fact that the clinical use of

"Prontosil", sulfanilamide, sulfapyridine, sulfathiazole, sulfaguanidine, sulfadiazine, penicillin and streptomycin, each in turn, was originally based to a large extent upon preliminary data from experimental infections in mice.

Satisfactory infections can be obtained in mice by intraperitoneal inoculation of small doses of certain lethal strains of Group A hemolytic streptococci, pneumococci, Friedländer's bacillus, anthrax bacillus, *Erysipelothrix rhusiopathiae* and various *Pasteurella* species (see *in vivo* activity references in Table 298). Mice are also uniformly susceptible to intramuscular injection of spores of several species of *Clostridia*. The use of mice in experimental studies on the chemotherapy of tuberculosis has been reported by Youmans.[a] Infections produced in these animals by intravenous or intraperitoneal inoculation of relatively large doses of certain strains of *M. tuberculosis* would appear to afford an opportunity for preliminary testing of many compounds which are not available in amounts large enough for an adequate trial in the classical guinea pig tuberculosis.

Evaluations of drug treatment in mice infected with certain strains of *Brucella*, *Escherichia coli*, *Eberthella typhosa*, *Hemophilus pertussis*, *Salmonella*, *Shigella*, meningococcus, gonococcus and *Staphylococcus* have also been reported. However, these infections are generally much less satisfactory for drug evaluation purposes, since animals are usually resistant unless a very large infecting dose or mucin enhancement of virulence is used. When an infection is produced by large numbers of bacteria, complications may arise due to bacterial toxins which would be expected to interfere with clear-cut demonstration of drug action. Likewise, mucin may complicate experimental infections by exerting a toxic effect thus interfering with the demonstration of drug action as it might occur under less artificial conditions[550]. In other cases, infections produced by bacteria suspended in mucin may be cured by small doses of a drug which would actually be much less effective against the same bacteria in a naturally susceptible host[2133].

As stated above, there are many obvious advantages connected with the use of the laboratory mouse for a preliminary evaluation of chemotherapeutic activity. Not the least of these advantages is the fact that, under equivalent test conditions, from 5 to 50 times as much drug is required to dose larger animals such as rats, guinea pigs and rabbits. However, for special studies on drugs which are available in relatively large amounts the following experimental infections in larger animals have been used: pneumococci in rats, rabbits and dogs; hemolytic streptococci in guinea pigs and rabbits; staphylococci in rabbits and dogs; *Clostridia* in guinea pigs and dogs; *Brucella* and *Corynebacteria* in guinea pigs; *Mycobacterium tuberculosis* in guinea pigs and rabbits; *Eberthella typhi*, *Pseudomonas aeruginosa* and *Shigella* in rabbits; *Streptococcus viridans* in rats, rabbits and dogs. With the exception of the tuberculosis infection in the guinea pigs and the pneumococcus and hemolytic streptococcus infections in rabbits, it is quite difficult to standardize the majority of these experimental infections to the extent that reproducible results can be obtained and, for this reason, they have not been widely used for evaluation purposes.

(3) Treatment

Once a satisfactory infection has been established in experimental animals, reliable testing of drug activity depends to a large extent upon the manner in which treatment is instituted and carried out. Therapeutic or protective test results may be influenced by the size of drug dose[938, 1364, 1750], the vehicle in which the drug is administered, the route of administration, and the time of initiation, frequency and duration of treatment.

[a] Youmans, G. P., and McCarter, J. C., *Quarterly Bulletin, Northwestern University Medical School*, **19**, 210–11 (1945).

The manner in which drugs are administered depends upon the purpose for which the test is designed.

Comparison of the inherent activity of related drugs requires a dosage schedule which will maintain a more or less constant concentration of drug at the site of action for an adequate period of time. This may be accomplished through frequent dosage by a parenteral route or, more conveniently, with many types of drugs by use of the drug-diet method of treatment[42, 309, 310, 1732, 1733, 1734, 2441]. To determine whether a drug is active or inactive, the animals should be dosed with the maximum tolerated amount for a period of time sufficient to permit measurement of the smallest significant difference in response between treated and untreated animals.

For preliminary trials in typical experimental infections in mice such as those produced by strains of streptococci, pneumococci or *Pasteurella*, drug concentrations of 0.8, 0.2 and 0.05% in the diet may be used. At the normal rate of food intake (about 4 Gm. per mouse per day), 240 Gm. of each of these diets is sufficient for ten mice for six days. Thus, with a total amount of less than 3 Gm. of drug, a preliminary trial is obtained with oral dosage levels of about 1.6, 0.4 and 0.1 Gm. per kilo per day, with ten animals at each level. Mice of 18 to 22 Gm. weight are placed in individual cages and supplied with food cups which are designed to reduce wastage and spillage to a minimum. Drug-diet intakes are then determined semi-quantitatively by calculations based on weight differences in food cup contents for the period of treatment. Drug-diet feeding is carried out for a period of three days prior to infection in order to build up a drug concentration in the blood and tissues and also to provide a basis for eliminating mice whose food intakes may be abnormal because of drug toxicity or inappetence. Mice with suitable food intake values are then infected and continued on a drug-diet for three more days. Dosage is determined by calculating drug intake from diet intake beginning at the time of infection. In these preliminary tests, treatment for three days is sufficient to determine whether or not a drug is active, since control animals usually die within 48 hours after infection. Under these conditions, a significant prolongation of survival time may be readily recognized as evidence of drug activity.

Toxic diets are diluted with normal food and retested. Failure to eat can sometimes be circumvented by the addition of glucose to a concentration of 5% in the diet.

A drug which is active in a preliminary drug-diet test is then compared with a standard reference drug by titration to determine the smallest effective dose. Subsequent tests using other dosage schedules and other routes of administration are made in order to explore its possibilities as a chemotherapeutic agent.

If a chemical or a microbiological method for drug assay is available, activity or inactivity may be correlated with the drug concentration in the blood.

(4) Antibacterial Activity *in Vivo*

The therapeutic response produced by a drug can be evaluated in terms of: permanent cure or complete protection; prolongation of life, or survival over controls; reduction of the degree of infection in susceptible tissues or body fluids as compared with controls. The choice of criteria depends upon the kind of infection and the purpose of the test.

Experimental infections such as the rapidly fatal septicemias in mice provide test conditions under which even a slight degree of drug activity may be detected simply on the basis of a significant difference between the observed and expected survival times. This can be expressed in terms of the mean survival time of animals that die, or as the proportion of survivors to total animals, at an arbitrarily fixed time after infection. Also, in this type of infection indirect evidence of permanent cure or complete protection can be based upon survival of treated animals for a period of time beyond which relapses rarely occur. For example, in the hemolytic streptococcus strain C203 infection, which usually kills all untreated control mice within two days, sulfa drug treated animals that live for twenty-one days are quite unlikely to die from the original infection[309]. For purposes of chemotherapeutic evaluation, survival for twenty-one days may be considered to be presumptive evidence of cure.

To establish that death was caused by the original infection, cultures are made of heart blood from mice dying during the therapeutic and protection experiments.

In the case of chronic infections such as those produced by M. tuberculosis it is customary to compare groups of treated and control animals on the basis of the degree of infection in susceptible tissues. Thus, a significant reduction in the expected amount of infection may be used as evidence indicating that the disease process was retarded by a drug[1060, 1066, 2217].

Direct evidence of permanent cure or complete protection is based upon negative cultures or subinoculations which indicate that the test organisms were eradicated. This is the usual procedure with infections such as those produced by strains of Brucella in guinea pigs.

The purpose of an in vivo test may be to determine: 1) whether or not a compound is active; 2) whether one drug is more active than another; 3) how much more active one drug is than another.

(a) Qualitative Methods

Relatively simple procedures usually suffice for detecting the antibacterial activity of a compound in an experimental infection, since the only criterion necessary is demonstration of a significant prolongation of life or survival over controls. A preliminary test for toxicity is of considerable value as a basis for selection of the therapeutic trial doses. If possible, these doses should cover a range which includes an approximation of the maximum tolerated dose.

Two or more drugs may be compared qualitatively, according to differences in the responses produced by equal doses or by equal concentrations of drug in the blood. For example, it has been reported that in a Staphylococcus infection, a maintained blood concentration of 3.5 mg.% resulted in the survival of 26 out of 30 mice with sulfadiazine, whereas with sulfamerazine only 2 out of 30 mice survived[2133]. Obviously, these results indicate that sulfadiazine was more active than sulfamerazine. However, it is impossible to determine how much more active one drug is than another in experiments of this kind. In fact, in this study, a maintained level of 5.0 mg.% of each drug resulted in only 1.6 times as much survival with sulfadiazine as with sulfamerazine. In addition to the reference cited above, qualitative comparisons based upon equivalent blood levels have been made by Robinson and his associates[2039] and by Frisk.[1135]

A vast number of reports on qualitative comparisons has accumulated in the literature on sulfa drugs. As a rule, the data upon which these comparisons have been based have been obtained by administering the drugs, dose for dose, according to schedules which have varied with each investigator. Considerable variation in drug concentration in the blood must have resulted from the various dosage schedules employed, as well as from differences in absorption and excretion. With many drugs, administration at intervals greater than 6 hours has probably resulted in high concentrations of short duration followed by periods when little or no drug was present in the blood. Although the conclusions of various investigators are in accord in qualitatively indicating the activity of sulfanilamide derivatives, discrepancies in quantitative interpretations indicate that the influence of important variables has been ignored (see tables 275–297, p. 404–411).

(b) *Quantitative Methods*

Evaluation of the chemotherapeutic activity of a compound consists of titrating it against an infection in such a way as to obtain a correlation between dosage (or concentration of drug in the blood or tissues) and a therapeutic response. In this manner, a quantitative comparison of two or more drugs may be made in terms of the estimated dose or concentration of each drug required to produce a fixed response (*e.g.*, 50% survival).

A fundamental study by Litchfield and his associates[309] has established an experimental basis for a method for the quantitative evaluation of the effectiveness of chemotherapeutic agents. In this study, it was demonstrated that the therapeutic effectiveness of sulfanilamide depends upon the maintenance of a more or less constant concentration of drug in the blood by means of frequent dosage for an adequate period of time. The following excerpt illustrates the principles underlying the quantitative character of the general procedure.

[a] "Since Trevan's classical paper on the toxicity of drugs, it has been widely recognized that accurate comparisons with a limited number of animals can be made only at the 50 per cent point of response, in terms of dosage required to obtain this response. Application of these principles to problems in bacterial chemotherapy would appear to depend upon showing that the relationship between dosage and mortality (as expressed by a characteristic curve) which holds for toxicity, applies equally well to conditions under which survival, rather than death, is produced.

"That this relationship does exist is shown by our data which relate both height and duration of blood concentration to per cent survival.

"With a method for maintaining a more or less constant blood concentration of drug during the period of therapy, we have established in this investigation a foundation from which can be derived a method for assessing quantitatively not only the therapeutic effectiveness of a drug under different conditions but also of different drugs under the same conditions.

"The Median Survival Dose (SD_{50}) is obtained from the computed dosage-survival curve. The SD_{50} can be converted into Medial Survival Blood Concentration (SBC_{50}) by a factor which relates blood concentration to dosage. By using a standard reference drug, one obtains a comparative value from the SBC_{50}'s which may be nearly absolute even though the SBC_{50}'s themselves are relative."

A method based upon this study has been applied to the quantitative appraisal of the therapeutic effectiveness of various sulfanilamide derivatives by Marshall and his associates[310, 335, 550, 1585, 1725, 1732–1734, 2441]. The laborious computations involved in the original method have been eliminated, without loss of essential accuracy, by Litchfield in subsequent studies[310, 1583]. Simple graphic methods for estimating the dosage-survival curve (regression of per cent survival in probits on dosage in logarithms) and for calculating errors have been published by Litchfield and Fertig[1583], by Miller and Tainter[b] and by de Beer.[c]

---

[a] Quoted with the permission of the authors and copyright owner.
[b] Miller, L. C., and Tainter, M. L., *Proc. Soc. Exptl. Biol. Med.*, **57**, 261–264 (1944).
[c] de Beer, E. J., *J. Pharmacol.*, **85**, 1–13 (1945).

Statistical treatment of the results of experiments designed to evaluate the chemo-therapeutic activity of drugs is not essential, but may be helpful. For practical purposes, where the observed difference in the activity of two drugs is relatively small (*e.g.*, twofold) it is usually not worthwhile to carry out elaborate experiments in an attempt to assess the significance of the difference until data on toxicity and other pharmacological prop-erties are evaluated. On the other hand, in studies on the relation of chemical structure to activity, it is often desirable to obtain precise evaluation of activity.

An excellent discussion of the variability inherent in bioassay data and the importance of statistical evaluation of this variation has been presented by Burn[a]; a comprehensive review of statistical methods as applied to bio-assay has been published by Bliss and Catell[2501]; and the important question as to how statistical evidence may be used as a basis for making decisions has been considered in detail by Simon[b].

(C) Relation of *in Vitro* to *in Vivo* Activity

In a thorough study of the chemotherapeutic characteristics of several N^1-substituted sulfanilamides Frisk[1135] concluded that, in many cases, the degree of antibacterial activity *in vitro* and *in vivo* corresponded quite well. On the other hand, failure to observe a close correlation between test tube results and therapeutic activity has been emphasized by other investigators[462, 550, 2133, 2167]. When one takes into account all of the factors involved, the following conclusions appear to be justified[2441].

1) Compounds which are *inactive in vitro* are likewise *inactive in vivo*, unless they are changed to an active form in the animal body. An outstanding example of the latter type is Prontosil, which has been shown to owe its *in vivo* activity to decomposition with the release of sulfanilamide[310]. Excessive amounts of drug antagonists in a test medium will, of course, interfere with demonstration of inherent activity *in vitro*.

2) Compounds which are *active in vitro may*, or *may not be active in vivo*. In thera-peutic studies, we deal not only with the action of the drug on the parasite, but also with the action of the drug on the host and the action of the host on the drug. In many cases, failure to carry *in vitro* activity over to the infected animal is probably the result of masking potential therapeutic activity by toxicity. In other cases, compounds which are highly active *in vitro* may be destroyed or changed to inactive products by the host. Other reasons for lack of correlation between *in vitro* and *in vivo* activity may be failure of the drug to reach the site of infection or failure to maintain an effective concentration in the blood and tissues because of poor absorption or rapid excretion. Finally, the presence of excessive concentrations of drug antagonists in the tissues of the host may interfere with the demonstration of *in vivo* activity.

3) Compounds which are active *in vivo* are likewise active *in vitro*. However, among active compounds the relation existing between their *in vivo* and *in vitro* activity is not quantitative.

(II) Experimental Evaluation of Chemotherapeutic Activity Preparatory to Clinical Trial

Before a drug which is intended for use in treating systemic bacterial infections is sub-mitted for preliminary clinical appraisal, an attempt should be made to determine the relationship between blood concentration of the drug and its therapeutic effectiveness in

[a] Burn, J. H., "Biological Standardization", Oxford University Press, London, Hum-phrey Milford, 1937.

[b] Simon, H. A., *J. Am. Statistical Assn.*, **40**, 80–84 (1945).

experimental infections. If possible, bacterial strains which are known to be pathogenic for man should be used for the experimental evaluation. Information of this kind, together with pharmacological data as to the safety of the drug and the dosage-blood concentration relationship in different animal species, provide the clinician with a rational basis for proceeding with trial doses. A comparison of the therapeutic and pharmacological characteristics of a new drug with those of known chemotherapeutic agents also provides the clinician with useful information.

Experimental data illustrating the relationship between dosage and blood concentration of sulfadiazine and its potential therapeutic effectiveness in streptococcal and pneumococcal infections are given in Tables 302-3, p. 419. It is evident from the results in these tables that a maintained blood concentration of drug of about 9 mg.% was required to protect about 95% of the infected animals. Naturally occurring infections would be expected to differ in several respects from those produced artificially. However, the evaluation of activity as indicated helps to provide a reasonable basis upon which to plan the preliminary clinical trial with such a drug. It should be noted that the important experimental value is not dosage, but concentration of drug in the blood. In these experiments, oral dosage of about 0.5 Gm. per kilo per day was needed to maintain 9 mg.% of drug in the blood. In man, however, a similarly effective blood concentration can be maintained with a dosage of only about 0.1 Gm. per kilo per day[2248].

In Tables 302 and 303, both the dose (mg. per kilo per day) and the blood concentration (mg.%) of drug required to protect the average mouse have been estimated according to the procedure of Litchfield and Fertig[1583], as modified by Miller and Tainter.[a] On the basis of these values, it is evident that a slightly higher dose and blood concentration of drug is required to produce a 50% response in the pneumococcus infection.

As an illustration of a quantitative comparison of the activity of two drugs under the same experimental conditions, results for sulfadiazine and sulfathiazole in a *Pasteurella* infection are given in Table 304. A maintained blood concentration of about 2.0 ± 0.2 mg.% was required to obtain 50% survival with either drug. However, about five times as much sulfathiazole as sulfadiazine dosage is required to achieve this effective blood concentration in mice. In this case, the decision as to which would be the more valuable drug for practical use should obviously be based primarily upon such factors as toxicity, dosage required for an effective blood concentration and cost.

(III) Tabulated Summary: Experimental Evaluation of Chemotherapeutic Activity

(A) Experimental Activities of Sulfa Drugs

An evaluation of the chemotherapeutic activity of each of 23 sulfa drugs as reported by different investigators is given in Tables 275-297, p. 404-411.[b] The comparative effectiveness of each drug against different pathogenic organisms is indicated in these tables. It will be noted that in several instances the interpretations of different investigators vary as to the quantitative effectiveness of the same drug against the same organism. However, it is hardly surprising to find that these discrepancies exist in view of the fact that the results are based upon the use of many different kinds of experimental procedures. One variable alone—the strain of test organism—could conceivably account for most of the discrepancies which appear in these tables.

---

[a] Miller, L. C., and Tainter, M. L., *Proc. Soc. Exptl. Biol. Med.*, **57**, 261-264 (1944).

[b] These tables were prepared by Dr. E. H. Northey.

Susceptibility to the action of any sulfanilamide derivative, under identical test conditions, may vary from strain to strain within a single bacterial species as much as it does from species to species. Furthermore, within a serological type, the variation in susceptibility to drug action, from strain to strain, may be as great as the variation from type to type.

The influence of this kind of variation on the results of measurements of drug activity has made it necessary to restrict conclusions to the strains under test. Generalizations as to the effect of a drug on a given species are not justified unless many strains have been examined.

In some instances, enough strains have been compared, under essentially similar test conditions, to permit fairly broad conclusions to be made. Thus, it has been demonstrated that, within the genus *Streptococcus*, the species *S. fecalis*[753, 754, 1293, 1296, 1767, 1833, 1835—1842], is much more resistant to the action of sulfa drugs than the species *S. pyogenes*[679, 749, 1012, 1212, 1415, 1526, 1529, 1566, 1567, 1832, 1835—1836, 1840, 1852, 2242, 2401, 2425, 2438—2439, 2442, 2502]; within the genus *Clostridium*, the species *Cl. perfringens* is more resistant than *Cl. sordelli*[2007, 2259, 2260]; differences among species in the genus *Shigella* have also been demonstrated[335, 1994].

Variation in drug susceptibility from strain to strain, among unselected strains within the same species has been reported for the following: *Brucella abortus*[2359, 2469]; *Diplococcus pneumoniae*[1613, 1631, 2120—22, 2125—6]; *Neisseria gonorrheae*[842, 2136]; *Staphylococcus aureus*[1364, 1513, 2245, 2246, 2253]; *Streptococcus agalactiae*,[1291]; *Streptococcus viridans*[789, 1944, 2303].

Variation in susceptibility to sulfa drugs from strain to strain within a single pneumococcus type has been demonstrated by Schmidt and Hilles[1687, 2121]; strain variation in a single type of Group A hemolytic streptococcus has been reported by Wilson.[a]

Thus, the fact that bacterial species and strains vary in their susceptibility to the action of sulfa drugs undoubtedly accounts for many of the discrepancies in the results of different investigators.

(B) References to Experimental Studies with Sulfonamides

Table 298, p. 412–6, is a guide to the literature on the various test organisms that have been used experimentally in studies of sulfonamide and sulfone drugs.

(C) Illustrative Data

Tables 299–304, p. 416–21, are compiled from data obtained in the Bacteriology Laboratory, Chemotherapy Division, Stamford Research Laboratories of the American Cyanamid Company. The material has been discussed in sections (I) and (II) of this chapter.

[a] Wilson, A. T., *Proc. Soc. Exptl. Biol. Med.*, **58**, 130–3 (1945).

TABLE 275

A. Experimental Activities: 1. Sulfanilamide

Organism	References	Organism	References	Organism	References
0(Aa)	1527	++, +(Ba)	274, 859, 860, 2458	0(Br)	529
±(Ae)	327, 821	±, 0(Bd)	598, 1362	++, 0(Bs)	274, 859, 860
+, ±, 0(An)	938, 1183, 1364, 1750	+(Bm)	274, 859	+, 0(C)	550, 1950, 2437
+(B)	1856	0(Bmu)	1028	+(Ca)	48

TABLE 275—(Concluded)

Organism	References	Organism	References	Organism	References
0(Cd)	1464, 2319	0(I)	443, 658, 1082, 1294, 1864, 1901, 1953	+++, ++(S)	29, 61, 139, 332, 391, 524, 548, 819, 900, 901, 902, 958, 973, 1056, 1552, 1618, 1732, 1734, 1953, 1981, 1991, 2353, 2583
0(Ch)	2203	++, +, ±(L)	252, 643, 658, 697, 829, 1069, 1082, 1549, 1646, 2042, 2572		
±, 0(Cn)	425, 757, 1195, 1277, 1673, 2008, 2083, 2174				
±, 0(Cs)	425, 757, 819, 1195, 1277, 1673, 2008, 2083, 2203	0(Lc)	1082	+, ±(Sa)	61, 93, 139, 332, 327, 351, 799, 818, 819, 914, 1056, 1467
+(Cso)	425, 2008, 2174	+, ±(Le)	1046, 1484, 1931		
+(Csp)	425	++(Lm)	1943		
+, 0(Ct)	757, 1754	0(Lt)	2164	±(Sc)	1527
0(Cv)	443, 668, 1682	++(M)	61, 750, 782, 1056, 1618, 1953, 1964	0(Sd)	1472, 1527
+, ±, 0(Cw)	24, 750, 757, 819, 1195, 1227, 1229, 1277, 1423, 1622, 1673, 2008, 2174, 2175, 2083, 2203			0(Se)	1527
		++(Mp)	2572	0(Sf)	1767
		−(Ne)	678	0(Sp)	1527
		++, +, ±, 0(P)	29, 42, 61, 93, 139, 327, 332, 442, 750, 782, 819, 821, 912, 913, 1056, 1487, 1585, 1734, 1982, 2065, 2121, 2122, 2583	+(Spd)	915, 919, 2320
+, ±(Ec)	263, 550, 578, 719, 914, 1057, 1134, 1472, 1527, 1734, 1950, 2437			+(Ss)	915
				+, 0(Sec)	1527, 1883
0(Em)	598			+, 0(T)	332, 477, 741, 820, 830, 921, 1114, 1207, 2025, 2212, 2222, 2275
0(En)	259, 443, 1485, 1682	0(Pa)	914		
0(Er)	1445, 1943	0(Pc)	890, 1717		
+, ±(Et)	818, 821, 1098, 1472, 1527, 1953	+, ±(Pf)	1011, 1047, 1769		
±, 0(F)	139, 750, 821, 1214, 1472, 2167	+(Pg)	1700	0(Tc)	598
		0(Pi)	889	0(Te)	61, 598, 1472
+(G)	1369, 1699, 2089, 2325	+++, +(Pk)	889, 890, 891	0(Tl)	598
		+, 0(Pl)	535, 890, 1733	0(Tm)	598
0(Gm)	598	0(Pn)	1717	0(To)	2071
±(H)	619, 1931	0(Po)	1419, 1471, 1485, 1682	++(Tr)	2027
0(Hm)	598			+, 0(Ts)	1648, 1696
0(Hp)	937, 1213, 1332	0(Pp)	2090, 2091, 2092	0(Tt)	1877
		+, 0(Pr)	914, 1527	±(Tu)	2309
		±(Ps)	821	0(Tv)	1393
		±, 0(Pv)	1011, 1047, 1717, 1769	0(V)	808, 1465
				+, ±(Vc)	1210, 2002, 2076
		0(R)	803, 1214, 1953	0(Y)	1082

TABLE 276

A. Experimental Activities: 2. Sulfapyridine

Organism	References	Organism	References	Organism	References
0(Aa)	1527	+(Cs)	425, 757, 1195, 1277, 1673, 2008, 2203	+, ±(Et)	1098, 1472, 1527, 1953
+(Ae)	1410	+(Cso)	425, 2008	++, +, ±(F)	139, 575, 750, 1472, 2167
++, ±(An)	938, 1183, 1364, 1750, 2279	+(Csp)	425		
±(B)	1856	+, 0(Ct)	757, 1754, 1755	+++(G)	1302, 1596, 1699, 2325
+, ±(Ba)	274, 1245, 1253, 1433, 1961, 2458	+, 0(Cv)	668		
+(Bd)	1362	+, ±(Cw)	24, 425, 750, 757, 1195, 1227, 1228, 1277, 1423, 1622, 1673, 2008, 2203	++(H)	619, 1930, 1931
++(Bm)	274, 1433, 2458			0(Hp)	937, 1125
+, 0(Br)	529, 1278			0(I)	892, 1082, 1471, 1901, 1953
+, ±(Bs)	274, 1433, 2458	0(Dr)	2344		
++(C)	2227, 2437	+++, ++, +(Ec)	263, 550, 719, 914, 1057, 1134, 1472, 1527, 1734, 1950, 2437, 2583	+++(Ko)	575
+, 0(Cd)	1464, 1818, 2061, 2319			++(Kr)	575
				++, +, 0(L)	252, 658, 829, 1069, 1082, 1678, 2572
0(Ch)	2203	0(En)	259, 1485	0(Le)	1082
±(Cn)	425, 757, 1195, 1277, 1673, 2008	0(Er)	1445, 1943	++(Lm)	1943, 2090
				++(M)	549, 648, 750, 1618, 1678, 1953

TABLE 276—(Concluded)

Organism	References	Organism	References	Organism	References
++(Mp)	2572	0(Pm)	863	++(Sc)	1527
+(Ne)	678	0(Pn)	1717	±(Sd)	1527
++(P)	29, 93, 139, 332, 462,	0(Po)	892, 1471, 1485, 2341	+(Se)	1527
	549, 750, 776, 1111,	+(Pp)	489, 2091, 2092, 2150,	0(Sf)	1767
	1135, 1208, 1209,		2236	±(Sp)	1527
	1282, 1308, 1389,	++, ±(pr)	914, 1527	+(Spd)	915, 919
	1425, 1517, 1585,	0(Pr)	536	+(Ss)	915
	1616, 1632, 1678,	±, 0(Pv)	863, 1882, 2648	±(Ssc)	1527
	1734, 1784, 1953,	0(R)	1574, 1953	+, ±, 0(T)	332, 386, 477, 498,
	1954, 1955, 1980,	0(Rp)	816, 2344		673, 741, 830, 1059,
	1982, 2039, 2117,	+++, ++, +,	93, 139, 332, 549,		1105, 1290, 1407,
	2118, 2120, 2122,	(S)	1057, 1208, 1618,		2212, 2243
	2126, 2258, 2583		1732, 1734, 1953,	++, +(To)	740, 2071
+, 0(Pa)	914, 1399, 1767, 2667		2039, 2441, 2583	+(Tt)	1755
++(Pc)	891, 1717	+(Sa)	139, 332, 755, 758,	±(Tu)	2309
+(Pf)	863		799, 819, 973, 1467,	0(Tv)	574
+++, +(Pk)	861, 891		1953, 1988, 2039,	0(Y)	1082
±(Pl)	1733		2276, 2307		

TABLE 277

A. Experimental Activities: 3. Sulfadiazine

Organism	References	Organism	References	Organism	References
++(A)	1328	++(Et)	1259	++(Pm)	893
++, +(Ae)	1519, 2291, 2639	++, +, ±(F)	139, 1997, 2133, 2167,	+(pn)	1987
++(An)	1183		2291	(Po)	892, 1485
+(B)	1856	+++(G)	608, 1000, 1520, 1878,	+++(Pp)	1594, 1918, 2407
+(Ba)	2469		2089, 2325	++(Pv)	893
±(Bm)	2469	+++(H)	618, 619, 778, 1242,	+++, ++(S)	139, 143, 314, 332,
0(Br)	529		1931		434, 1519, 1734, 1952,
+(Bs)	2469	++(Hp)	778, 1332		1966, 1991, 2039,
+++(C)	550, 2437	0(I)	658, 1901		2133, 2353, 2583
±(Cn)	757, 1674, 2008, 2174,	+++, ++(L)	252, 658, 829, 2034,	++, +(Sa)	139, 314, 332, 421,
	2524		2572		1242, 1467, 1519,
+++(Cs)	757, 2008, 2524	+++(M)	977, 1548, 2322, 2324		1952, 2039, 2133,
++, 0(Cso)	2008, 2174, 2524	++, 0(Mp)	1987, 2572		2603
0(Ct)	757	++(Ne)	678	++(Sc)	2291
+++, +(Cw)	757, 1227, 1228, 1229,	+++, ++,	139, 314, 332, 434,	+(Se)	2291
	1674, 2008, 2174,	+(P)	462, 1057, 1135, 1194,	++(Sf)	1519
	2175, 2524		1242, 1628, 1734,	++(Spd)	2133, 2291
0(Dr)	2277		1952, 1966, 2039,	++(Ss)	2133
+++, ++(Ec)	263, 550, 1057, 1134–		2133, 2353, 2583	+(Ssc)	2291, 2639
	5, 1519, 1734, 1950,	+, ++(Pa)	1519, 2667	±(Sv)	1568
	1966, 2291, 2437,	++(Pf)	893, 2589	++, ±(T)	477, 1060
	2583	++(Pg)	2513	+, ±(Tu)	1996, 2309
0(En)	1485	+++(Pk)	891	+(Tv)	1393
0(Er)	1445	++, +(Pl)	535, 704, 1733	++, ±(Vc)	1210, 2002, 2076

TABLE 278

A. Experimental Activities: 4. Sulfamerazine

Organism	References	Organism	References	Organism	References
+++(C)	1235	+(F)	2133	++(L)	2163, 2572
+++, ++(Ec)	719, 1057, 1135, 1734	+++, ++(H)	619, 1242	+++(M)	1235
0(En)	1485	0(I)	892	++(Mp)	2572

TABLE 278—(*Concluded*)

Organism	References	Organism	References	Organism	References
++, +++(P)	434, 1147, 1235, 1242,	+++, ++(S)	434, 436, 1147, 1235,	+(Spd)	2133
	1645, 1734, 2133		1242, 1734, 2133	+(Ss)	2133
++(Pl)	1733, 2163	++, +(Sa)	1242, 2133	0(Tv)	1393
0(Po)	892, 1485				

TABLE 279
A. Experimental Activities: 5. Sulfamethazine

Organism	References	Organism	References	Organism	References
+++, +(Ec)	719, 1057, 1135	+++(M)	1645	+++, ++,	143, 162, 436, 1057,
0(En)	1485	++(Mp)	2572	+(S)	1574, 2133
++(Ete)	1334	+(Ne)	678	++, +(Sa)	1467, 2133
+(F)	2133	++, +++(P)	162, 436, 1057, 1574,	+(Spd)	2133
++(G)	1645		1628, 2133	+(Ss)	2133
0(I)	892	0(Po)	892	0(Tt)	1574
++(L)	2572	0(R)	1574		

TABLE 280
A. Experimental Activities: 6. Sulfapyrazine

Organism	References	Organism	References	Organism	References
+++(C)	2437	++(M)	706	+(Pp)	2309
++(Dy)	490	+++(P)	462, 490, 1574, 1734,	+++, +(S)	1734, 1978, 2039,
+++(Ec)	719, 1057, 1734, 2309,		1978, 2039, 2066,		2130, 2353
	2437		2353	+++, ++(Sa)	2039
++(F)	2167	++(Pl)	1733	++(Tu)	2309
0(I)	1574	0(Po)	1471		

TABLE 281
A. Experimental Activities: 7. Sulfathiazoline

Organism	References	Organism	References	Organism	References
+++(G)	1369, 1533	0(R)	1574	±(T)	830
++, ±(P)	1977, 1983	++(Sa)	416, 1467, 1977, 1983	0(Tt)	1574
0(Po)	1471				

TABLE 282
A. Experimental Activities: 8. Sulfathiazole

Organism	References	Organism	References	Organism	References
±(Aa)	1527	+++, +(C)	550, 2437	+, 0(Cso)	425, 2008, 2174, 2524
+(Ae)	1410, 2291, 2639	0(Cd)	1464, 2319	+(Csp)	425
++(An)	1183	+, ±(Cn)	425, 757, 1277, 1673,	+(Ct)	757
+(Ba)	2469		1674, 2008, 2174,	+, ±(Cw)	24, 757, 1227, 1228,
±(Bm)	2469		2524		1229, 1277, 1622,
+(Br)	1278	++, +(Cs)	425, 757, 1277, 1673,		1673, 1674, 2008,
+(Bs)	2469		1674, 2008, 2524		2143, 2174, 2524

TABLE 282—(Concluded)

Organism	References	Organism	References	Organism	References
0(Dr)	2277	+++, ++(P)	29, 93, 150, 139, 283,	+++, ++,	29, 93, 139, 283, 314,
+++, ++(Ec)	263, 550, 719, 1057,		314, 332, 462, 517,	+(S)	332, 526, 1057, 1147,
	1134–5, 1734, 1950,		526, 1057, 1111, 1135,		1734, 1966, 2039,
	1966, 2291, 2437,		1147, 1585, 1615,		2353, 2441, 2583
	2583		1628, 1678, 1734,	++(Sa)	139, 283, 314, 332,
0(En)	259, 1485		1966, 1980, 2039,		421, 758, 819, 1057,
0(Er)	1444, 1445		2353, 2583		1467, 1651, 1988,
±(Et)	1472, 1527	+(Pa)	2667		2039, 2307, 2603
+, ±(F)	139, 575, 2167, 2291	0(Pc)	891	++(Sc)	1527, 2291
+++(G)	1302, 1369, 1595,	+(Pcy)	891	±(Sd)	1527
	2089, 2325	+(Pi)	891	+, ±(Se)	1527, 1811, 1812,
+++(H)	619, 1931	+++(Pk)	891		1813, 2291
+(Hp)	1125, 1334	++, +, 0(Pl)	535, 704, 891, 1733	+(Sp)	1527
0(I)	658, 892, 1082, 1901	+(pn)	1987	++(Spd)	915, 917, 919, 2291
++(Ko)	575	0(Po)	892, 1471, 1485	+(Ss)	915
+(Kr)	575	++(Pp)	489, 1594, 1918, 2091,	+, ++(Ssc)	1527, 2291, 2639
++, +, 0(L)	252, 526, 658, 829		2092, 2236	+, ±(T)	142, 477, 690, 830
	1082, 1678, 1987	+, ±(pr)	1527, 2667	±(Tc)	1677
	2043	+, 0(Pv)	1882, 2648	++, +(To)	740, 2071
0(Lc)	1082	0(Rp)	816	+(Tu)	2309
+(Le)	1484			0(Tv)	1393
++(M)	526, 1678			0(V)	658
0(Mp)	1987			++, ±(Vc)	1210, 2002, 2076
+(Ne)	678			0(Y)	1082

TABLE 283

A. Experimental Activities: 9. Sulfamethylthiazole

Organism	References	Organism	References	Organism	References
±(Aa)	1527	++(G)	1595	+++, ++,	758, 1651, 1988, 2307
+(An)	2546	0(I)	892, 1082	+(Sa)	
0(Ba)	2546	++(L)	1069, 1082	++(Sc)	1527
+(Bd)	1362	0(Lc)	1082	±(Sd)	1527
±(Cn)	425, 2008	++(M)	2546	+, ±(Se)	1527, 1811, 1812,
++(Cs)	425, 2008	+++, ++(P)	29, 93, 150, 404, 1135,		1813
+(Cso)	425, 2008		1147, 1363, 2546	+(Sp)	1527
±(Csp)	425	++(Pk)	1896	+(Spd)	915
++, +(Cw)	24, 425, 1365, 1622,	+(Pl)	704	+(Ss)	915
	2008	0(Po)	892, 1485, 2546	+(Ssc)	1527
+++, +(Ec)	1134–5, 1527	+(pr)	1527	0(T)	2546
0(En)	259, 1485	+++(S)	29, 93, 150, 2441	0(Y)	1082
+, ±(Et)	1098, 1527				

TABLE 284

A. Experimental Activities: 10. 2-Sulfanilamido-5-ethyl-1,3,4-thiadiazole, "Globucid"

Organism	References	Organism	References	Organism	References
±(A)	1756	+(Ko)	575	0(Pv)	2653
++, +(Cw)	1453, 2142, 2143	+(Kr)	575	+++(S)	1756
+++, ++(Ec)	1134–5, 1765, 2281	++(P)	1134–5, 1756	+(Sa)	1756
±(Et)	2667	+, ±(Pa)	2281, 2667	+(Sp)	2281
±(F)	575	+(pr)	2281, 2667	+(T)	1756

TABLE 285

A. Experimental Activities: 11. N^1-Acetylsulfanilamide, Sulfacetamide

Organism	References	Organism	References	Organism	References
+(C)	2281, 2437	±(Kr)	575	±(pr)	2667
++, +(Ec)	121, 1057, 1135, 1966, 2437, 2583	+(L)	697	0(Rp)	816
±(F)	575	+, ±(P)	1057, 1574, 1734, 1966, 2583	++, +(S)	115, 982, 1057, 1574, 1734, 1966, 2441, 2583
++, +(G)	711, 1302, 1574, 1699	±(Pa)	2041, 2667		
0(I)	892	0(Pl)	1733	++(Sa)	1057, 1574
±(Ko)	575	0(Po)	892		

TABLE 286

A. Experimental Activities: 12. N^1-(3,4-Dimethylbenzoyl)Sulfanilamide, "Irgafen"

Organism	References	Organism	References	Organism	References
+++, ++(Ec)	1523, 1775, 1966, 1967, 2583	+++, ++(P)	1523, 1606, 1775, 1966, 1967, 2547, 2583	+++, ++(S)	1523, 1775, 1966, 1967, 2583
+, ±(F)	1523, 1775, 1967			++, ±(Sa)	1523, 1775, 1967, 2547
		0(Po)	2547	0(Te)	1523

TABLE 287

A. Experimental Activities: 13. Sulfaguanidine

Organism	References	Organism	References	Organism	References
±, 0(Ae)	46, 1410	++(Ebo)	773	++, +, ±(P)	1057, 1574, 1734
0(B)	1856	++, +(Ec)	719, 1057, 1134–5, 1734, 1950, 2437	+(Pg)	2513
+(Ba)	2469	++(Eh)	1560	+(Pl)	1733
±(Bm)	2469	++(Ema)	1560	0(Po)	892, 1485
+(Bs)	2469	++(Emi)	1560	++, ±(S)	434, 1057, 1147, 1574, 1734, 2441
++, +(C)	335, 1950, 1951, 2437	0(En)	1485	+, ±(Sa)	1057
±, 0(Cn)	757, 2008	0(Ene)	1560	+(Sc)	46
++, 0(Cs)	757, 2008	++(Ep)	1560	0(Se)	46
0(Cso)	2008	++(Et)	1051, 1574	+(Sp)	46
0(Ct)	757	0(Ete)	1560	++(Spd)	1317
+, 0(Cw)	757, 2008	+(Hp)	1332	0(Ss)	1695
0(Dr)	2277	0(I)	658, 892, 1574	0(Tv)	1393
+(Dy)	1574	++, 0(L)	252, 658, 2042	+(Vc)	1210, 2076
++(Ea)	1560	+(Ne)	678		
++(Eb)	1560				

TABLE 288

A. Experimental Activities: 14. N^4-Sulfanilylsulfanilamide, "Disulon", "Diseptal C"

Organism	References	Organism	References	Organism	References
+(Ca)	48	+(L)	697, 698	+++, +(S)	35, 137, 311, 442, 1056, 1057, 1734, 2441
±(Cw)	989	+(Le)	1931		
0(Cv)	443	++(M)	442, 1056		
++(Ec)	719, 1057, 1734	+, ±(P)	311, 1056, 1057, 1734, 2441	+(Sa)	29, 351, 989, 1056, 1057, 1981
0(En)	443				
+(G)	1369, 1699	+(Pl)	1733	±(Sv)	2441
+(H)	1931	0(Po)	892	+(T)	477
0(I)	443, 892				

TABLE 289

A. Experimental Activities: 15. N^1,N^1-Dimethyl-N^4-Sulfanilylsulfanilamide, "Uliron"

Organism	References	Organism	References	Organism	References
±(Bd)	1362	++, +, 0(L)	698, 2572	++, +(S)	311, 989, 1056, 2441
±(Cw)	989	+(M)	311, 1056	+, ±(Sa)	60, 351, 799, 973,
±(Et)	1098	++(Mp)	2572		989, 1056
++, +(G)	711, 1699	0(P)	311, 1056, 1880, 2441	+(Sv)	2441
0(I)	658	0(Pl)	1733	0(T)	1207

TABLE 290

A. Experimental Activities: 16. *"Prontosil"*, *"Prontosil Rubrum"*

Organism	References	Organism	References	Organism	References
0(Ca)	48	+(M)	442	0(Rp)	816, 2344
+, 0(Cv)	443, 668, 1083, 2342	++(Mp)	2572	++, +(S)	61, 116, 328, 442,
0(Dr)	2344	+, ±(P)	442, 1880		901, 973, 987, 991,
0(En)	443	±(Pf)	1769		1225
0(I)	443	+++(Pk)	891	±(Sa)	799, 973
++, ±(L)	286, 698, 2572	0(Pm)	1047	±(Sv)	987
0(Lc)	1083	+, 0(Pv)	1769, 1882	±, 0(T)	741, 972, 1207
0(Lt)	2164				

TABLE 291

A. Experimental Activities: 17. Azosulfamide, "Neoprontosil" ("Prontosil Soluble")

Organism	References	Organism	References	Organism	References
+(Ba)	274	+(G)	1699	0(Po)	1485, 2236
+(Bm)	274	0(I)	443, 1485	0(pr)	2667
0(Bs)	274	0(Ko)	575	0(Pv)	1769, 2648
0(Ca)	48	0(Kr)	575	0(Rp)	816
0(Cd)	1464	±(L)	286, 698	++, +(S)	116, 310, 442, 548,
0(Cv)	442, 2342	++(M)	442		897, 900, 901, 1466,
0(Cw)	1423, 1802	+, ±(P)	42, 442		1981
0(En)	443	0(Pa)	2667	+, ±(Sa)	799, 1467
0(F)	575	±(Pf)	1769	0(T)	1207

TABLE 292

A. Experimental Activities: 18. Succinylsulfathiazole

Organism	References	Organism	References	Organism	References
+++, +(C)	414, 1442, 1918, 1950,	0(Et)	1098	±(S)	1574
	1951, 2437	0(P)	1574	++(Spd)	1317
±(Dy)	1574	±(Pp)	1594, 1918	+(Vc)	1210, 2076
0(Ec)	1057, 1950				

TABLE 293

A. Experimental Activities: 19. 4-Aminomethylbenzenesulfonamide, "Homosulfanilamide", "Marfanil", "Mesudin", "Sulfamylon"

Organism	References	Organism	References	Organism	References
++(An)	992, 1443, 2140	++, +, ±(Cw)	588, 2143, 2145, 2146	++, 0(S)	361, 588, 749, 992,
+(Cd)	992	+(Ec)	749		1255, 1443
++, ±(Cn)	588, 2140, 2146	0(H)	1255	++, 0(Sa)	588, 749, 992, 1255,
++, +(Cs)	588, 1581	+(P)	749, 2135		1581, 2135
				0(T)	2135

TABLE 294

A. Experimental Activities: 20. Bis(4-Aminophenyl) Sulfone

Organism	References	Organism	References	Organism	References
+(An)	1750	++(M)	1056	+++(S)	35, 60, 441, 822,
+(Ca)	48	+++, +(P)	35, 441, 822, 913,		1056, 1118, 1732,
++(Ec)	1057		1056, 1057, 1111,		1979, 2441
±(Et)	822		1118, 1585	++, ±, 0(Sa)	822, 973, 1056, 1467
0(F)	1214	0(Pl)	1733	++(T)	477, 1065, 2217
0(I)	892, 1864	0(Po)	892		

TABLE 295

A. Experimental Activities: 21. "Diasone"

Organism	References	Organism	References	Organism	References
0(Cw)	24	++(P)	35, 1974, 2056	++, +(T)	830, 1063, 1914, 2217
++(M)	2056	+++(S)	35, 1974, 2056		

TABLE 296

A. Experimental Activities: 22. "Promin"

Organism	References	Organism	References	Organism	References
0(Cw)	24	+++, ++(P)	1208	+, ++(T)	142, 477, 498, 667,
0(En)	892	++(Pf)	893		830, 1060, 1066, 1310,
+++(G)	1699	0(Po)	892, 1485		1312, 1635, 1760,
0(I)	1485	++(Pv)	893		2217, 2271, 2273
++(Le)	1045	+++(S)	1208, 2339	+(Tc)	1677

TABLE 297

A. Experimental Activities: 23. Bis(4-Acetamidophenyl) Sulfone, "Rodilone"

Organism	References	Organism	References	Organism	References
0(G)	1555	++, +, ±(P)	35, 912, 913, 1056,	++, +(S)	35, 60, 152, 441, 913,
0(Hp)	1213		1057, 1118, 1574		973, 1056, 1057, 1118,
0(I)	892, 1574	±(Pl)	1733		1574, 1979
+(L)	697	0(Po)	892	±, 0(Sa)	973, 1056, 1574
+(M)	1056	±(Pv)	1011	+(T)	2503
		0(R)	1574	+(To)	477
				0(Tt)	1574

TABLE 298

B. References to Experimental Studies with Sulfonamides
(Grouped by Test Organism Used; Subgrouped by Type of Study)

Bacteria

Actinomyces
  In Vitro Activity: 940, 1756. *In Vivo* Activity: 1328.
Aerobacter aerogenes
  In Vitro Activity: 1293, 1527.
Bacillus anthracis
  In Vivo Activity: 938, 992, 1183, 1443, 2140, 2279, 2546. Synergistic Action: 1364, 1750.
Bacillus subtilis
  In Vitro Activity: 2053.
Brucella abortus
  In Vitro Activity: 859, 860, 1253, 1433. *In Vivo* Activity: 274, 859, 860, 1245, 1253, 1433, 1961, 2458, 2546. Mechanism of Action: 176, 2420, 2469. Synergistic Action: 1768, 2359.
Brucella melitensis
  In Vitro Activity: 260, 859, 1433. *In Vivo* Activity: 274, 859, 1433, 2458. Mechanism of Action: 2469. Synergistic Action: 1768.
Brucella suis
  In Vitro Activity: 860, 1433. *In Vivo* Activity: 274, 860, 1433, 2458. Mechanism of Action: 2469. Synergistic Action: 1768, 2359.
Clostridium histolyticum
  In Vitro Activity: 2259. Synergistic Action: 2203.
Clostridium novyi
  In Vitro Activity: 588, 2259. *In Vivo* Activity: 425, 757, 819, 1195, 1277, 1673, 2008, 2083, 2140, 2146, 2174, 2524, 2533. Mechanism of Action: 2007. Synergistic Action: 1674, 1675.
Clostridium perfringens
  In Vitro Activity: 588, 2259, 2620. *In Vivo* Activity: 24, 425, 750, 757, 819, 838, 989, 992, 1195, 1226, 1227, 1228, 1229, 1255, 1277, 1365, 1423, 1453, 1622, 1673, 1802, 2008, 2083, 2142, 2143, 2145, 2146, 2174, 2175, 2524, 2533. Mechanism of Action: 752, 1581, 2007. Synergistic Action: 1674, 1675, 2203.
Clostridium septicum
  In Vitro Activity: 588, 2259. *In Vivo* Activity: 425, 757, 819, 1195, 1277, 1581, 1673, 2008, 2083, 2146, 2524, 2533. Mechanism of Action: 2007. Synergistic Action: 1674, 1675, 2203.
Clostridium sordelli
  In Vitro Activity: 2259, 2620. *In Vivo* Activity: 425, 2008, 2174, 2524. Mechanism of Action: 2007.
Clostridium tetani
  In Vitro Activity: 2259. *In Vivo* Activity: 757, 1754, 1755.
Coliform bacteria
  In Vitro Activity: 1843. *In Vivo* Activity: 335, 414, 550, 832, 1150, 1235, 1442, 1918, 1945, 1950, 1951, 2227, 2281, 2328, 2437.
Corynebacterium diphtheriae
  In Vitro Activity: 1818. *In Vivo* Activity: 992, 1464, 1818, 2061, 2319. Mechanism of Action: 1694.
Diplococcus pneumoniae
  In Vitro Activity: 327, 462, 679, 749, 789, 808, 1092, 1102, 1135, 1337, 1421, 1526, 1529, 1566, 1567, 1756, 1834, 1873, 1923, 1966, 2010, 2011, 2125, 2441, 2502, 2597. *In Vivo* Ac-

TABLE 298—*(Continued)*

Diplococcus pneumoniae—Continued

tivity: 29, 35, 36, 42, 61, 92, 93, 94, 139, 162, 283, 288, 311, 314, 327, 332, 335, 345, 362, 404, 420, 434, 436, 441, 442, 462, 490, 492, 502, 517, 526, 528, 549, 699, 750, 776, 782, 819, 821, 822, 911, 912, 913, 914, 1056, 1057, 1111, 1118, 1134, 1135, 1147, 1189, 1194, 1208, 1209, 1235, 1242, 1282, 1308, 1363, 1389, 1408, 1463, 1469, 1487, 1517, 1518, 1522, 1523, 1557, 1558, 1574, 1585, 1606, 1615, 1616, 1617, 1618, 1628, 1645, 1678, 1734, 1775, 1824, 1880, 1952, 1953, 1966, 1967, 1974, 1977, 1978, 1979, 1980, 1982, 1983, 2010, 2011, 2039, 2041, 2056, 2065, 2066, 2117, 2118, 2120, 2121, 2122, 2124, 2125, 2133, 2158, 2353, 2546, 2547, 2548, 2583. Mechanism of Action: 329, 330, 593, 1395, 1515, 1632, 1690, 1694, 1763, 1764, 2190, 2289, 2292, 2361. Resistance: 926, 966, 1613, 1631, 1683, 1687, 1691, 1692, 1693, 1814, 2119, 2125, 2126, 2129, 2168, 2351. Synergistic Action: 439, 1211, 1425, 1784, 1892, 1954, 1955, 1957, 2135, 2258, 2261.

Eberthella typhosa

In Vitro Activity: 754, 1527, 1567, 1994, 2152. *In Vivo* Activity: 818, 821, 822, 1051, 1098, 1259, 1472, 1574, 1953, 2408, 2548, 2667.

Erysipelothrix rhusiopathiae

In Vivo Activity: 1444, 1445, 1493.

Escherichia coli

In Vitro Activity: 263, 550, 749, 754, 1057, 1134, 1135, 1293, 1410, 1472, 1519, 1523, 1527, 1567, 1734, 1756, 1775, 1966, 1967, 2133, 2152, 2281, 2296, 2309, 2502. *In Vivo* Activity: 121, 263, 550, 818, 914, 1135, 1410, 1472, 1523, 1734, 1950, 1966, 1967, 2437, 2583. Mechanism of Action: 266, 438, 577, 578, 719, 733, 884, 1395, 1404, 1459, 1561, 1694, 1904, 2000, 2288, 2291. Resistance: 1270. Synergistic Action: 1537, 2112.

Hemophilus influenzae

In Vivo Activity: 1242, 1255, 1930, 1931. Synergistic Action: 618, 619.

Hemophilus pertussis

In Vivo Activity: 937, 1125, 1213, 1214, 1332, 1334. Synergistic Action: 778.

Klebsiella pneumoniae

In Vitro Activity: 575, 1812, 2133, 2167. *In Vivo* Activity: 139, 288, 750, 821, 1214, 1472, 1523, 1775, 1967, 1997, 2133, 2167, 2291. Resistance: 2351.

Klebsiella ozaenae

In Vitro Activity: 575.

Klebsiella rhinoscleroma

In Vitro Activity: 575.

Listerella monocytogenes

In Vivo Activity: 1943, 2090.

Mycobacterium tuberculosis

In Vitro Activity: 90, 477, 689, 1030, 1100, 1113, 1290, 1593, 1598, 1756, 2095, 2096, 2097, 2135, 2212, 2217, 2260, 2272. *In Vivo* Activity: 90, 142, 332, 386, 477, 498, 667, 673, 690, 741, 820, 830, 921, 972, 1055, 1059, 1060, 1061, 1062, 1063, 1065, 1066, 1105, 1114, 1207, 1290, 1310, 1312, 1407, 1598, 1635, 1760, 1806, 1914, 2025, 2097, 2212, 2217, 2222, 2243, 2271, 2273, 2275, 2503, 2546, 2548. Mechanism of Action: 1757, 2094. Synergistic Action: 1776.

Neisseria catarrhalis

Resistance: 2433.

Neisseria gonorrheae

In Vitro Activity: 285, 842, 2136, 2428. *In Vivo* Activity: 285, 608, 692, 693, 711, 840, 894, 1000, 1302, 1369, 1520, 1533, 1555, 1556, 1574, 1595, 1645, 1699, 1782, 1805, 1878, 1956, 2089, 2325. Mechanism of Action: 805, 1694. Resistance: 837, 1133, 1191, 1236, 1266, 1438, 2433.

Neisseria intracellularis

In Vitro Activity: 285, 1212, 1526, 1839. *In Vivo* Activity: 61, 285, 311, 442, 526, 549,

TABLE 298—(*Continued*)

Neisseria intracellularis—Continued
> 706, 750, 977, 1056, 1235, 1408, 1548, 1554, 1616, 1618, 1645, 1678, 1953, 1964, 2056, 2322, 2324, 2546. Mechanism of Action: 1694. Synergistic Action: 439, 648, 781, 782, 1010, 1099. Resistance: 2433.

Neisseria sicca
> Resistance: 2433.

Pasteurella pestis
> *In Vivo* Activity: 489, 1011, 1511, 1594, 1918, 2090, 2091, 2092, 2150, 2236, 2407. Mechanism of Action: 2309.

Pasteurella pseudotuberculosis
> *In Vivo* Activity: 821.

Pasteurella septica
> *In Vivo* Activity: 821.

Pasteurella tularensis
> *In Vitro* Activity: 1996. Mechanism of Action: 2309.

Pseudomonas aeruginosa
> *In Vitro* Activity: 1293, 1519, 1767, 2533. *In Vivo* Activity: 914, 1399, 2041, 2281, 2667. Resistance: 1675.

Proteus ammoniae
> *In Vitro* Activity: 1293.

Proteus morganii
> *In Vitro* Activity: 1843.

Proteus vulgaris
> *In Vitro* Activity: 1527. *In Vivo* Activity: 914, 2281, 2667. Resistance: 1675.

Salmonella enteriditis
> *In Vitro* Activity: 1410, 1527, 1811, 1812, 2291. *In Vivo* Activity: 46, 1410, 1811, 1813.

Salmonella paratyphi
> *In Vitro* Activity: 1527, 1566, 1567, 1994, 2152, 2281. *In Vivo* Activity: 46.

Salmonella pullorum
> *In Vivo* Activity: 696, 2409.

Salmonella schottmülleri
> *In Vitro* Activity: 1527, 1994, 2152, 2291. *In Vivo Activity:* 821, 1883, 2639.

Salmonella suipestifer
> *In Vitro* Activity: 1410, 1527, 2291. *In Vivo* Activity: 46, 1410.

Salmonella typhi-murium
> *In Vitro* Activity: 327, 585, 1410, 1519, 2291. *In Vivo* Activity: 46, 327, 821, 1410, 2639.

Serratia marcescens
> *In Vitro* Activity: 1351.

Shigella alkalescens
> *In Vitro* Activity: 1068. *In Vivo* Activity: 915.

Shigella dispar
> *In Vitro* Activity: 1068.

Shigella paradysenteriae
> *In Vitro* Activity: 335, 585, 1566, 1567, 1994, 2152. *In Vivo* Activity: 915, 917, 919, 1317, 2133, 2291, 2320, 2409. Mechanism of Action: 996. Resistance: 1068.

Shigella shiga
> *In Vitro* Activity: 335, 1994, 2152. *In Vivo* Activity: 1472, 1527.

Shigella sonnei
> *In Vitro* Activity: 335, 1068, 1994. *In Vivo* Activity: 818, 915, 917, 1695, 2697, 2133. Mechanism of Action: 593, 730.

TABLE 298—(Continued)

Staphylococcus aureus

   In Vitro Activity: 327, 588, 679, 714, 749, 754, 838, 839, 1212, 1255, 1276, 1293, 1421, 1523, 1526, 1529, 1566, 1567, 1581, 1756, 1870, 1874, 1876, 1988, 1993, 2030, 2135, 2245, 2246, 2502, 2533. *In Vivo* Activity: 29, 61, 93, 139, 283, 314, 327, 332, 351, 416, 421, 755, 758, 818, 819, 822, 847, 914, 947, 973, 989, 992, 1056, 1057, 1242, 1255, 1276, 1467, 1519, 1574, 1651, 1775, 1925, 1952, 1953, 1967, 1977, 1978, 1981, 1983, 1988, 2039, 2133, 2547, 2603. Mechanism of Action: 593, 802, 1351, 1364, 2170, 2171, 2288, 2361, 2415, 2432. Resistance: 1513, 2253, 2255, 2257, 2351, 2389. Synergistic Action: 736, 799, 1052, 1439, 1675, 1844, 2276, 2307, 2575.

Streptococcus—Group A

   In Vitro Activity: 327, 346, 362, 588, 679, 749, 900, 982, 1012, 1102, 1212, 1232, 1415, 1435, 1436, 1526, 1529, 1566, 1567, 1756, 1832, 1833, 1835, 1836, 1840, 1852, 2062, 2242, 2401, 2425, 2438, 2439, 2442, 2502, 2533. *In Vivo* Activity: 29, 34, 35, 36, 60, 61, 92, 93, 94, 100, 103, 104, 115, 116, 137, 139, 143, 149, 151, 152, 162, 170, 173, 205, 213, 283, 286, 310, 311, 314, 327, 328, 332, 335, 345, 346, 347, 361, 362, 391, 434, 436, 441, 442, 454, 470, 492, 502, 511, 512, 524, 526, 548, 549, 613, 710, 819, 822, 897, 901, 913, 958, 973, 982, 987, 989, 991, 992, 1056, 1057, 1117, 1118, 1147, 1208, 1235, 1242, 1255, 1258, 1269, 1408, 1443, 1463, 1466, 1468, 1469, 1470, 1519, 1522, 1523, 1552, 1553, 1555, 1574, 1584, 1606, 1614, 1616, 1618, 1732, 1734, 1775, 1824, 1849, 1952, 1953, 1966, 1967, 1974, 1978, 1979, 1981, 1991, 2039, 2056, 2130, 2133, 2339, 2353, 2441, 2548, 2583. Mechanism of Action: 473, 569, 748, 752, 854, 1101, 1120, 1139, 1153, 1154, 1180, 1230, 1395, 1404, 1515, 1600, 1601, 1684, 1753, 2093, 2172, 2269, 2352. Resistance: 899, 1672. Synergistic Action: 439, 902, 1267, 1604, 1844.

Streptococcus—Group B

   In Vitro Activity: 754, 1291. Synergistic Action: 2208.

Streptococcus—Group C

   In Vitro Activity: 754. *In Vivo* Activity: 1225, 1406, 2160, 2537.

Streptococcus—Group D

   In Vitro Activity: 753, 754, 1293, 1296, 1767, 1833, 1835, 1836, 1837, 1841, 1842. Mechanism of Action: 593.

Streptococcus—Group G

   In Vitro Activity: 753.

Streptococcus viridans

   In Vitro Activity: 734, 754, 756, 789, 987, 1568, 1875, 2365, 2441. *In Vivo* Activity: 1215, 1437, 1698, 1810. Mechanism of Action: 1785, 2360, 2361. Resistance: 1944, 2303, 2351, 2389.

Vibrio cholerae

   In Vitro Activity: 335, 1210, 2062, 2076. *In Vivo* Activity: 2002.

Rickettsia

In Vivo Activity: 659, 816, 2344.

Viruses

Distemper: 114, 326, 971, 1719, 1937.

Encephalitis (herpes): 1103, 1682.

Encephalitis (St. Louis): 443, 1682, 1845.

Encephalomyelitis (equine): 259.

Fibroma (Shope's): 1682.

Influenza: 89, 443, 659, 886, 892, 1549, 1864, 1901.

Lymphogranuloma venereum: 75, 252, 289, 659, 698, 829, 1081, 1082, 1549, 1646, 1986, 2042, 2043.

Lymphocytic choriomeningitis: 443, 1083, 1549, 1682, 2342.

TABLE 298—(Concluded)

Myxomatosis (rabbits): 1682.
Pleuropneumonia-like organisms: 1084, 2069.
Poliomyelitis: 892, 1419, 1471, 1682, 1845, 2147, 2338, 2341.
Rabies: 1214, 1649, 1803.
Trachoma: 2027.
Vaccinia: 659, 1803.
Yellow fever: 1475.
Bacteriophage: 586, 587, 961 (Fitzgerald, R. J., J. Immunology, in press).

Fungi

151, 975, 976, 1564, 1856, 1857 (Keeney, E. L., *et al.*, Bull. Johns Hopkins Hospital, **75,** 393–409 (1944)).

Spirochaetes

Treponema duttoni: 1362.
Treponema recurrentis: 1278.

TABLE 299

1. Standardized Cultures and Media for Routine Bacteriostatic Tests

	Organism[a]: Genus, Species and Strain	Stock Culture: Medium[b]; Passage	Test Culture: Medium[b]; Incubation	Test Mixture: Medium[b]; Inoculum; Incubation	Reference Standard: Drug; M.E.C.[c] in mg. %
	(1)	(2)	(3)	(4)	(5)
1	Brucella abortus, 19-15A, (L)	Blood agar slant; monthly	TSP broth; 22 hours	TSP broth; 10^{-1}; 48 hours	Sulfathiazole; 128
2	Clostridium histolyticum, H-7C, (L)	Ground meat; monthly	TG broth; 6 hours	T broth; 10^{-5}; 48 hours	Marfanil; 1/2–2
3	Clostridium novyi, N-21B, (L)	Ground meat; monthly	TG broth; 6 hours	TG broth; 10^{-1}; 48 hours	Marfanil; 16–64
4	Clostridium perfringens, BP-6K, (L)	Ground meat; monthly	TG broth; 6 hours	T broth; 10^{-5}; 48 hours	Marfanil; 2–4
5	Clostridium septicum, VS-23, (L)	Ground meat; monthly	TG broth; 18 hours	TG broth; 10^{-1}; 48 hours	Marfanil; 1–4
6	Clostridium tetani, C-710, (L)	Ground meat; monthly	TG broth; 6 hours	T broth; 10^{-3}; 48 hours	Marfanil; 2–8
7	Diplococcus pneumoniae, type I (SV)	TSP-blood broth; mouse passage weekly	TSP-blood broth; 6 hours	TSP broth; 10^{-4}; 48 hours	Sulfathiazole; 1/2–4
8	Eberthella typhi, S-G47	TSP agar slant; semi-monthly	TSP broth; 22 hours	TSP broth 1/2; 10^{-5}; 48 hours	Sulfathiazole; 16–64
9	Erysipelothrix rhusiopathiae, 358, (L)	TSP broth; mouse passage weekly	TSP broth; 6 hours	TSP broth; 10^{-7}; 48 hours	Marfanil; 16
10	Escherichia coli, MacLeod	TSP agar slant; semi-monthly	TSP broth; 22 hours	TSP broth 1/4; 10^{-6}; 48 hours	Sulfathiazole; 1–4
11	Hemophilus pertussis, 32, (L)	Bordet Gengou slant; 3 times a week	Pork infusion broth plus 10% serum; 24 hours	Pork infusion broth; undiluted; 48 hours	Sulfathiazole; 128
12	Klebsiella pneumoniae, B-E, (L)	TSP agar slant; mouse passage weekly	TSP broth; 6 hours	TSP broth 1/16; 10^{-6}; 48 hours	Sulfathiazole; 128
13	Mycobacterium —, ATCC-#607	Steenken-Smith slants; semi-annually	HLD broth; 7 days	HLD broth; 0.025 mg.; 7 days	Bis(4-aminophenyl) Sulfone; 1/8–1/2
14	Mycobacterium tuberculosis, H37RV	Steenken-Smith slants; semi-annually	Modified Dubos medium; 7 days	Modified Dubos fluid medium; 10^{-1}; 14 days	Bis(4-aminophenyl) Sulfone; 1/4–1

TABLE 299—(*Concluded*)

	Organism[a]: Genus, Species and Strain	Stock Culture: Medium[b]; Passage	Test Culture: Medium[b]; Incubation	Test Mixture: Medium[b]; Inoculum; Incubation	Reference Standard: Drug; M.E.C.[c] in mg. %
	(1)	(2)	(3)	(4)	(5)
15	*Neisseria gonorrheae,* 113 (Landy)	Chocolate agar slant; 3 times a week	Pork infusion broth plus 10% serum; 24 hours	Pork infusion broth plus 10% serum; undiluted; 48 hours	Sulfathiazole; 1–2
16	*Neisseria intracellularis,* IIα, 3855, (L)	Chocolate agar slant; 3 times a week	Pork infusion broth with 10% serum; 24 hours	Pork infusion broth with 10% serum; undiluted; 48 hours	Sulfathiazole; 1–4
17	*Pasteurella multocidum,* 310, (L)	Pork infusion broth; mouse passage weekly	Pork infusion broth; 6 hours	Pork infusion broth; 10^{-4}; 48 hours	Sulfathiazole; 1/4–1
18	*Proteus vulgaris,* S-1	TSP agar slant; semi-monthly	TSP broth; 6 hours	TSP broth 1/16; 10^{-5}; 48 hours	Sulfathiazole, 1/64–1/16
19	*Pseudomonas aeruginosa,* ATCC-8689	TSP agar slant; semi-monthly	TSP broth; 6 hours	TSP broth 1/16; 10^{-5}; 48 hours	Sulfathiazole; 2–8
20	*Salmonella schottmülleri,* 5B, (L)	TSP agar slant; semi-monthly	TSP broth; 22 hours	TSP broth 1/2; 10^{-6}; 48 hours	Sulfathiazole; 32–64
21	*Shigella paradysenteriae,* Flexner 5733, (L)	TSP agar slant; semi-monthly	TSP broth; 22 hours	TSP broth 1/2; 10^{-7}; 48 hours	Sulfathiazole; 16–64
22	*Staphylococcus aureus,* Barlow	Blood agar slant; monthly	TSP broth; 6 hours	TSP broth 1/16; 10^{-5}; 48 hours	Sulfathiazole; 8–32
23	*Streptococcus agalactiae,* (Group B), Z53C	Blood agar slant; monthly	TSP blood broth; 6 hours	TSP broth 1/4; 10^{-5}; 48 hours	Sulfathiazole; 2–8
24	*Streptococcus fecalis,* (Group D), Ralston	Blood agar slant; monthly	TSP-blood broth; 6 hours	TSP broth 1/2; 10^{-5}; 48 hours	Marfanil; 16–32
25	*Streptococcus hemolyticus,* (Group A), C203	TSP-blood broth; mouse passage weekly	TSP-blood broth; 6 hours	TSP broth; 10^{-5}; 48 hours	Sulfathiazole; 8–128
26	*Streptococcus viridans,* Moran	Blood agar slant; monthly	TSP-blood broth; 6 hours	TSP broth; 10^{-5}; 48 hours	Sulfathiazole; 1–4
27	*Spirochæta,* Reiter strain, (L)	TG broth with added serum (10%) and liver extract (0.2%); 3 times a week	TG broth with added serum and liver extract; 48 hours	TG broth with added serum and liver extract; undiluted; 72 hours	Neoarsphenamine; 1–4

[a] Organisms: strains numbered 1–6, 9, 11, 12, 16, 17, 20, 21 and 27 were kindly supplied by Lederle Laboratories; strains numbered 13 and 19 were obtained from the American Type Culture Collection; strain 14 was kindly supplied by Dr. L. U. Gardner; strain 15 by Dr. Maurice Landy; strain 23 by Dr. J. C. Kakavas; strains 24 and 26 by Dr. E. Spaulding.

[b] Media: TSP refers to Trypticase Soy Phosphate medium; TG and T refer to thioglycollate fluid medium, with and without added glucose, respectively. These media and the Pork Infusion broth were obtained from the Baltimore Biological Laboratory. HLD refers to the medium of Henley le Duc. The formula for the modified Dubos medium was kindly supplied by Dr. Geoffrey Rake.

[c] M.E.C. = Minimum Effective Concentration. This is the smallest concentration required to prevent visible growth.

TABLE 300

Reproducibility of Bacteriostatic Test Results

Test Organism[a]	Bacteriostatic Endpoint (in mg. %) of Standard Reference Drug[b]										
	128	64	32	16	8	4	2	1	$\frac{1}{2}$	$\frac{1}{4}$	$\frac{1}{8}$
	Number of Tests										
Brucella abortus	11										
Clostridium perfringens						16	4				
Diplococcus pneumoniae						7	41	45	8		
Eberthella typhi		3	2	1							
Erysipelothrix rhusiopathiae				36							
Escherichia coli							5	8	9		
Hemophilus pertussis	6										
Klebsiella pneumoniae	10										
Mycobacterium 607									4	33	14
Neisseria gonorrheae								3	3		
Pasteurella multocidum								5	10	15	
Pseudomonas aeruginosa					7	12	5				
Salmonella schottmülleri		6	1								
Shigella paradysenteriae		5	4	2							
Staphylococcus aureus			6	22	15						
Streptococcus agalactiae						6	5	4			
Streptococcus fecalis			2	6							
Streptococcus hemolyticus	11	9	12	9	6						
Streptococcus viridans						4	7	4			
Spirochaete, Reiter strain						3	11	21			

[a] Test strains and test conditions as indicated in table 299.

[b] Standard Reference Drugs: Marfanil, for tests with strains of *Clostridia*, *Erysipelothrix*, and *Streptococcus fecalis*; Bis(4-aminophenyl) Sulfone for the strain of *Mycobacterium*; Neoarsphenamine for the *Spirochaete* strain; Sulfathiazole for all other test strains.

TABLE 301

Comparative Activity of Sulfanilamide and Sulfathiazole in Repeated Bacteriostatic Tests

Staph. aureus in TSP Broth 1/16			Pneumococcus SVI in TSP Broth			*E. coli* in MacLeod's Synthetic Medium			Dysentery (Flexner) in TSP 1/16		
M.E.C.-mg. %		Ratio ST/SA	M.E.C.-mg. %		Ratio ST/SA	M.E.C.-mg. %		Ratio ST/SA	M.E.C.-mg. %		Ratio ST/SA
ST	SA		ST	SA		ST	SA		ST	SA	
8	64	8	1	16	16	1/16	4	64	1/4	16	64
8	64	8	2	32	16	1/32	4	128	1/8	8	64
8	128	16	1	8	8	1/16	4	64	1/8	8	64
8	128	16	4	16	4	1/16	4	64	1/16	8	128
8	64	8	4	64	16	1/16	4	64	1/16	8	128
8	128	16	4	16	4	1/16	4	64	1/16	4	46
8	64	8	4	64	16	1/32	4	128	1/16	4	64
16	128	8	2	8	4	1/32	2	64	1/8	8	64
8	64	8	1	16	16	1/32	4	128	1/4	16	64
8	64	8	1	16	16	1/32	2	64	1/8	8	64
16	128	8				1/16	8	128	1/8	8	64
8	128	16				1/32	4	128	1/16	4	64
8	128	16				1/32	4	128	1/8	8	64

TABLE 301—(*Concluded*)

Staph. aureus in TSP Broth 1/16			Pneumococcus SVI in TSP Broth			*E. coli* in MacLeod's Synthetic Medium			Dysentery (Flexner) in TSP 1/16		
M.E.C.-mg. %		Ratio ST/SA	M.E.C.-mg. %		Ratio ST/SA	M.E.C.-mg. %		Ratio ST/SA	M.E.C.-mg. %		Ratio ST/SA
ST	SA		ST	SA		ST	SA		ST	SA	
16	128	8				1/32	4	128	1/8	4	32
16	128	8				1/16	4	64	1/16	4	64
16	128	8				1/16	4	64	1/4	8	32
16	128	8				1/16	8	128	1/8	8	64
16	128	8				1/32	2	64	1/8	8	64
8	64	8				1/32	4	128			
8	128	16				1/16	4	64			

ST—Sulfathiazole; SA—Sulfanilamide.

Test strains and media as in table 299.

M.E.C.—Minimum Concentration required to prevent turbidity in 48 hours.

Ratio ST/SA = ratio of activities, i.e., the reciprocal of the ratio of M.E.C.'s.

TABLE 302

Evaluation of the Chemotherapeutic Activity of Sulfadiazine in a Streptococcal Infection in Mice

Organism: *Streptococcus hemolyticus*, Group A, Strain C203.

Mice: CFCW (Carworth Farms); 18–22 Gm.

Infection: Intraperitoneal; 0.5 cc. of a 10^{-5} broth dilution of a 5-hour TSP-blood broth culture; 4000 ± 400 organisms.

Treatment: Drug-diet method; starting 3 days before and ending 3 days after infection.

Per cent Drug in Diet	Dosage		Response		
	Drug Intake mg./kg./day	Blood Conc.[a] mg. %	Survival on 21st Day after Infection		
			Alive/Total Number	Per cent Survival	Mean Time[b]
4/10	800	15.2	20/20	100	—
2/10	450	9.2	57/60	95	9.0
1/10	240	5.3	76/93	82	7.7
1/20	120	3.5	60/97	62	6.1
1/40	58	2.3	41/94	44	5.4
1/80	27	1.5	21/97	22	4.2
1/160	9	1.0	2/30	7	2.8

S.D.$_{50}$[c], 66 ± 9 mg./kg./day; S.B.C.$_{50}$[d], 2.6 ± 0.14 mg. %

Untreated Controls:					
10^{-5} Dose; 4000 ± 400 organisms			0/400	0	1.7
10^{-6} " 400 ± 40 "			11/100	11	2.3
10^{-7} " 40 ± 4 "			15/100	15	2.8

[a] Blood concentrations of drug in the infected animals were determined by the Bratton and Marshall method, as free drug on pooled tail blood samples on the third day after infection.

[b] Mean survival time (in days) of mice that died.

[c] Median Survival Dose.

[d] Median Survival Blood Concentration.

TABLE 303

Evaluation of the Chemotherapeutic Activity of Sulfadiazine in a Pneumococcal Infection in Mice

Organism: *Diplococcus pneumoniae*, type I, strain SVI.
Mice: CFCW (Carworth Farms); 18–22 Gm.
Infection: Intraperitoneal; 0.5 cc. of a 10^{-6} broth dilution of a 5-hour TSP-blood broth culture; 1000 ± 50 organisms.
Treatment: Drug diet method; starting 3 days before and ending 6 days after infection.

| Per cent Drug in Diet | Dosage | | Response | | |
| | Drug Intake mg./kg./day | Blood Conc.[a] mg. % | Survival on 21st Day after Infection | | |
			Alive/Total Number	Per cent Survival	Mean Time[b]
8/10 (toxic)	1400	34.1	11/20	55	3.2
4/10	990	19.6	20/20	100	—
2/10	470	9.1	28/30	94	—
1/10	240	5.2	21/30	70	7.4
1/20	110	3.8	13/30	43	7.1
1/40	54	2.5	7/19	37	7.2
1/80	21	1.5	3/20	15	5.0

S.D.$_{50}$, 115 ± 30 mg./kg./day; S.B.C.$_{50}$, 4.0 ± 0.5 mg. %

Untreated Controls:					
10^{-6} Dose			0/80	0	2.4
10^{-7} "			3/40	8	2.5
10^{-8} "			6/40	15	2.9

[a] Blood concentrations: See Table 302.
[b] Mean survival time (in days) of mice that died.

TABLE 304

Comparison of the Activity of Sulfadiazine and Sulfathiazole in a Pasteurella Infection in Mice

Organism: *Pasteurella multocidum*, strain 310, Lederle.
Mice: CFCW (Carworth Farms); 18–22 Gm.
Infection: Intraperitoneal; 0.5 cc. of a 10^{-7} broth dilution of a 5-hour TSP-blood broth culture; 40 ± 10 organisms.
Treatment: Drug-diet method; starting 3 days before and ending 6 days after infection.

| Per cent Drug in Diet | Dosage | | Response | |
| | Drug Intake mg./kg./day | Blood Conc.[a] mg. % | Survival on 21st Day after Infection | |
			Alive/Total Number	Per cent Survival
		Sulfadiazine		
2/10	510	9.0	19/19	100
1/10	260	5.4	19/19	100
1/20	140	3.7	17/20	85
1/40	50	2.1	10/19	53
1/80	19	1.4	5/20	25
1/160	5	—	2/20	10

TABLE 304—(*Concluded*)

Per cent Drug in Diet	Dosage		Response	
	Drug Intake mg./kg./day	Blood Conc.[a] mg. %	Survival on 21st Day after Infection	
			Alive/Total Number	Per cent Survival
Sulfathiazole				
8/10	2000	7.2	20/20	100
4/10	860	3.7	16/18	89
2/10	380	2.4	13/20	65
1/10	180	1.6	7/18	39
1/20	62	—	2/20	10
1/40	25	—	0/20	0

Sulfadiazine S.D.$_{50}$, 45 ± 10 mg./kg./day; S.B.C.$_{50}$, 2.0 ± 0.2 mg. %

Sulfathiazole S.D.$_{50}$, 250 ± 50 mg./kg./day; S.B.C.$_{50}$, 2.0 ± 0.2 mg. %

Untreated Controls:	0/20	0

[a] Blood concentrations: See Table 302.

Chapter IX

RELATIONSHIP OF STRUCTURE TO CHEMOTHERAPEUTIC ACTIVITY

Chemists and pharmacologists, as a team vitally interested in the development of more potent and safer chemotherapeutic agents, constantly try to draw correlations between chemical structure, therapeutic potency and toxicity of drugs in order to project new syntheses having more than a random chance of accomplishing the desired results. It will be the aim of this chapter to point out some of the generalizations or inferences which may be drawn from the mass of often-conflicting data presented in Chapters III through VIII.

Whether such generalizations serve a uniformly useful purpose is debatable. They tend to over-simplify and to shrink the horizons of research to the point where new fundamental discoveries may be overlooked simply because they do not conform to the established pattern. Especial attention should, therefore, be paid to exceptions of the rules.

Unfortunately, since we are dealing with biological systems which are exceedingly complex and about which we know comparatively little, it is difficult to arrive at a satisfactory basis for correlation of data. For example, if it is found in a single experiment on mice infected with pneumococci, type I, that the treated animals die at about the same rate as the controls, while another group treated with a standard drug survive, we are certainly not justified in concluding that the drug is inactive. The drug may still have activity against this organism and an explanation of the results may lie in one or a combination of factors, such as: (1) The experiment may have been subject to some error which if known would be sufficient explanation. (2) The drug may have been toxic to the mice. (3) The drug may not have reached the site of the infection through lack of absorption or poor distribution to the tissue involved. (4) The drug, though absorbed, may have been excreted so rapidly that an effective concentration was not maintained. (5) The drug may have been destroyed or conjugated by body processes before it could control the infection.

Inactivity against this organism is no positive proof that the drug will be inactive against other organisms or even different strains of the same organism.

Much of the data found in the tables of Chapters III to VII is of the single experiment type. To make generalizations from such data involves use of analogies and suppositions. What follows should, therefore, be viewed with due scientific skepticism.

(I) Summary of Relationships of Structure to Chemotherapeutic Activity

In speaking loosely of chemotherapeutic activity in this field, what is really implied is activity against susceptible strains of β-hemolytic streptococci, commonly the C-203 strain. This is usually accompanied by appreciable activity against susceptible strains and types of pneumococci, gonococci and meningococci. Sulfanilamide-type chemotherapeutic activity means *in vivo* or *in vitro* activity against the above organisms, which is antagonized by p-aminobenzoic acid (see Woods-Fildes Theory, Chapter XI for significance).

(A) Sulfanilamide Derivatives

(1) Nuclear-substituted Sulfanilamides

Nuclear-substituted sulfanilamides are usually inactive.

(2) N^1-Substituted Sulfanilamides

N^1-Substituted derivatives of sulfanilamide include the most potent derivatives so far found.

(a) N^1-Alkylsulfanilamides

N^1-Alkylsulfanilamides show decreased activity with increased length of carbon chain. Introduction of halogen, hydroxyl, or mercaptan groups on the N^1-alkyl does not change the activity appreciably. Introduction of carboxyl, carboxyl derivatives, sulfo or amino groups on the N^1-alkyl destroys the activity almost entirely.

(b) N^1-Isocyclicsulfanilamides

N^1-Isocyclicsulfanilamides show varying degrees of activity but none appears to be appreciably more active than sulfanilamide. Cycloalkyl derivatives are inactive. N^1-Condensed-ring aryl groups, and long chain or polyalkylated N^1-phenyl groups usually give inactive derivatives, probably because of insolubility.

Introduction of halogen, nitro, hydroxyl, alkoxy, amino, sulfanilyl, keto or thio groups on a N^1-phenyl group produces an uncertain effect dependent in part on position of the entering group, or groups, on the ring. No product of clinical importance has been developed of this type as yet. In general, multiple substituents appear to decrease the activity.

Introduction of carboxyl, sulfo or sulfino groups on an N^1-phenyl radical gives adverse absorption-distribution-excretion characteristics and hence low *in vivo* activities.

(c) N^1-Heterocyclicsulfanilamides

N^1-Heterocyclicsulfanilamides include the most potent and useful sulfanilamide derivatives. Peak activities are obtained with two hetero-atoms in the ring such as two nitrogens or a nitrogen and sulfur. Sulfanilamidoheterocycles containing oxygen do not have high activity *in vivo* but may be active *in vitro*. Hydrogenated heterocyclic rings give low activities and derivatives where the N^1-nitrogen is a member of the ring are usually inactive. Substitution of methyl or ethyl groups on the heterocyclic ring may have a beneficial effect, as in the thiadiazole derivatives; a doubtful effect, as in the pyrimidines; or an adverse effect, as in the thiazole and pyridine series. Many of these effects appear to be the result of absorption, distribution, excretion or toxic properties of the drugs in the host rather than large differences in fundamental activities against the bacteria. Substitution of long-chain alkyl, aryl groups or condensed rings on the heterocyclic nucleus results in low activities, probably because of poor absorption of the drugs.

Introduction of halogen on the heterocyclic ring has a variable effect dependent on the nature of the heterocycle and the position of the substituent. Introduction of hydroxyl, carboxy, sulfo, sulfamyl, or other strongly ionic groups destroys the activity. Alkoxy and amino groups have a variable effect.

N^1-Alkyl-N^1-heterocyclicsulfanilamides have very low activities, while the isomeric ring-N-alkylsulfanilimidodihydroheterocycles are considerably more potent than these but are less active than the corresponding non-alkylated N^1-heterocyclicsulfanilamides.

In general, sulfanilamide derivatives where both N^1-positions are substituted, so that the compound cannot ionize, show activities of the order of sulfanilamide or weaker.

The above sulfanilimidoheterocycles are possible exceptions, sulfaguanidine is another possible exception and the compound[2583]

$$NH_2 \langle \quad \rangle SO_2N \langle \quad \rangle OC_2H_5$$
$$\underset{CH(CH_3)_2}{|}$$

is so much of an exception as to need verification.

(d) N^1-Acylsulfanilamides

N^1-Acylsulfanilamides show amazing variations in *in vivo* activities. Most of the derivatives of straight chain aliphatic acids are comparable with sulfanilamide in potency and may be cleaved to this in the body. The methylated benzoic acid derivatives show remarkable effects on the activity, dependent on position isomerism of the methyl groups on the ring. These effects are apparently independent of absorption characteristics and remain unexplained in terms of current theories (Chapter XI). Highest potency was found in N^1-(3,4-dimethylbenzoyl)sulfanilamide. High specificity of action against different organisms was claimed for a number of these derivatives while others were of general high potency[2583].

Sulfanilylamidines have comparatively low activities despite their analogy to sulfanilamidoheterocycles which are highly active.

N^1-Acylsulfanilamides derived from carbonic acid show low activities in general.

N^1-Sulfonylsulfanilamides have very low activities as do almost all N^1-inorganic derivatives.

(3) N^4-Substituted Sulfanilamides

It appears probable that a free amino group in the N^4 position in sulfanilamide derivatives is essential to activity. In a large number of cases, it has been demonstrated that the N^4-substituent of an active compound is removed *in vivo* to produce a diazotizable amine which is presumed (and actually proven in a few cases) to be sulfanilamide. Bacterial catabolism is also capable of removing certain N^4-substituents but is much less general. Many of these compounds thus show *in vivo* activity but are not active *in vitro*.

N^4-Groups known to be removable by animal catabolism are low alkyl, benzyl and substituted benzyl, anil, aldehyde bisulfite and dithionite derivatives, glycosides, acyl and azo groups. N^4-Groups not removable and giving inactive derivatives are long chain alkyl, aryl, heterocyclic, imide, sulfonyl and certain carbonic acid derivatives.

As far as is known, no N^4-substituted sulfanilamide whose activity is completely reversable by PABA is more active *in vivo* than sulfanilamide when activities are compared on the basis of equal concentrations in the blood. Misleading results can be obtained, however, which will show a higher activity for certain of these derivatives in experiments where delayed absorption and cleavage will result in a better-maintained blood level of sulfanilamide from the derivative than from administration of an equivalent amount of sulfanilamide. It is also significant that no N^4-derivative whose activity is reversible by PABA is more active *in vitro* than sulfanilamide.

(4) Complex Sulfanilamide Derivatives

Derivatives in which combinations of the nucleus, N^1- and N^4-positions are substituted, appear to obey the predictions which may be made from the behavior of the corresponding monosubstituted derivatives. Thus, substitution of the nucleus gives comparatively inactive derivatives regardless of what substituents are attached in the N^1 and N^4 positions. Also substitution in the N^4-position by groups which resist cleavage results in inactive drugs. The field is therefore narrowed to N^1,N^4-substituted sulfanilamides where the N^4-group may be removed *in vivo*. Some of these derivatives, such as the 2-(N^4-acylsulfanilamido)thiazoles, have proven to be useful because the active drug. (sulfathiazole) is liberated when and where needed to combat localized infections, as in the intestines.

(B) Compounds Related to Sulfanilamide

1. The 4-nitrobenzenesulfonamides are reduced in the body to the corresponding sulfanilamides, hence may show *in vivo* activity.

2. The isomers of sulfanilamide are inactive except for a few compounds, the low activities of which have not been verified.

3. Acyclic analogues of sulfanilamide are inactive.

4. 4-(Aminomethyl)benzenesulfonamide and some of its N^1-derivatives are highly active *in vitro* but not against systemic infections *in vivo*, either because of adverse absorption-distribution-excretion characteristics, or because the drug is destroyed in the body. This activity is different from that of sulfanilamide because PABA does not antagonize the effect. Certain other derivatives of benzenesulfonamide have shown activity which is not antagonized by PABA but the vast majority of such compounds are inactive.

5. Vinylogues of sulfanilamide such as 2′ and 4′-aminobiphenyl-4-sulfonamides have not shown activity nor have the aminonaphthalenesulfonamides.

6. Various derivatives of *p*-aminobenzoic acid show sulfanilamide type activity which is antagonized by *p*-aminobenzoic acid. Among nuclear-substituted derivatives, both sulfanilamide and antisulfanilamide activity is found. 4-Nitrobenzoic acid and its esters show temporary sulfanilamide-type activity but undergo reduction to PABA which antagonizes the activity. One of these, the *n*-hexyl ester, has been used clinically. This is the only non-sulfonamide (or sulfone) drug having activity similar to sulfanilamide which has reached this stage of development.

7. Ketones derived from *p*-aminobenzoic acid may show slight *in vitro* activity which reaches a maximum in 4,4′-diaminobenzil. Aromatic amines unrelated in any way to *p*-aminobenzoic acid are inactive. Azo derivatives of these are also inactive.

8. Heterocyclic isosteres or analogues of PABA or sulfanilamide show slight activity or may antagonize sulfanilamide-type activity.

(C) Sulfones

An actual or potential sulfanilyl group,

$$\text{NH}_2\text{—}\langle\text{benzene}\rangle\text{—SO}_2\text{—}$$

or an analogue, appears essential to sulfanilamide-type activity in this series, *i.e.*, activity which is antagonized by *p*-aminobenzoic acid.

(1) Acyclic Sulfones

Acyclic sulfones are inactive but sulfanilylalkanes show slight activity when the aliphatic radical is a low alkyl. Two related compounds, 4-(methylsulfonyl)benzamidine hydrochloride and 4-(methylsulfonyl)benzylamine hydrochloride, have been shown to have relatively high potency, but like 4-(aminomethyl)benzenesulfonamide, they act through a different mechanism and are not antagonized by PABA.

(2) Bis(4-Aminophenyl) Sulfones

Bis(4-Aminophenyl) sulfones containing substituents on the amino groups known to be cleaved by the catabolic processes of the host (from studies on sulfanilamide derivatives largely) show varying degrees of activity dependent on absorption, excretion, distribution and rate-of-cleavage characteristics. None of these derivatives has shown greater activity on a blood level basis than bis(4-aminophenyl) sulfone. Such compounds and others which can possibly be converted to bis(4-aminophenyl) sulfone are presumed to owe their activity to the amount of this compound liberated.

(3) Sulfanilylheterocycles

Sulfanilylheterocycles show appreciable activity in some cases, particularly where isosteric with bis(4-aminophenyl) sulfone, but bisheterocyclic sulfones are apparently inactive.

(D) Compounds Related to the Sulfones

(1) Bis(4-Aminophenyl) Sulfide and Bis(4-Aminophenyl) Disulfide

These compounds show activities which are not antagonized, or only partially antagonized, by PABA, hence they probably act through a different mechanism than the sulfone and sulfonamide drugs. The corresponding disulfoxide had only slight activity and was toxic.

(2) Analogues of the Sulfones

Analogues of the sulfones, sulfides, disulfides, etc. where arsenic, phosphorus, selenium or tellurium replaces sulfur, may show activity but, at least in the case of bis(4-aminophenyl) diselenide and ditelluride, this activity is only partially antagonized by PABA.

(II) DISCUSSION OF VARIOUS CORRELATIONS BETWEEN STRUCTURE AND ACTIVITY

An early generalization by Fourneau, et al.[152] claimed the structural unit essential for activity to be:

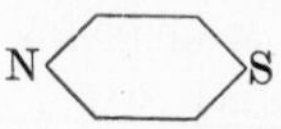

While such a unit is present in many of the active drugs, this generalization is obviously too narrow to account for sulfanilamide-type activity in several compounds which are sulfur-free; however, presence of a nitrogen atom attached directly to a benzene nucleus (or an isosteric heterocycle) appears necessary for sulfanilamide-type activity.

The belief of Frisk[1135], or Green and Bielschowsky[1200], that this nitrogen must be amino (or convertible to amino) appeared to be refuted by the sulfanilamide-type activity of *p*-nitrobenzoic acid. This compound, if converted to *p*-aminobenzoic acid would have exactly the opposite effect, hence it must either be active *per se* or be converted to an unknown active molecule. Recently Martin and Rose[a] have suggested that *p*-nitrobenzoic acid is converted by reduction to *p*-hydroxylaminobenzoic acid and then by rearrangement to 3-hydroxy-4-aminobenzoic acid, which they found had an *in vitro* activity

---

[a] Martin, A. R., and Rose, F. L., *Biochem. J.*, **39**, 91–5 (1945).

one third to one ninth that of sulfanilamide and was slightly active *in vivo*. If this explanation should prove valid, the necessity of a free amino group cannot be adequately contested by other existing evidence and may be accepted as one of the fundamental correlations between constitution and activity.

Jensen and Schmith[1384] stressed that for typical sulfanilamide activity, it was necessary to have para to an amino group, a —SO_2— group, or other group with a high dipole moment but without resonance possibilities ("elektromeren Effekt"). In the case of N^1-substituted sulfanilamide derivatives, they postulated that the activity was increased by introduction of N^1-substituents capable of resonance. The greater the resonance, the greater was the activity, which reached a peak in N^1-heterocyclic sulfanilamides where two hetero-atoms were in the ring. They pointed out that this effect was to a large extent independent of the effect of the resonance on the acid strength of the sulfonamides, since alkylation of such compounds destroyed the acid dissociation, while much of the activity was retained along with the resonating forms. They further stated that the activity of N^1-heterocyclic sulfanilamides was independent of the point of attachment of the sulfanilamido group on the heterocyclic nucleus.

Druey[1007] noted that the highly active sulfa drugs are capable of amino-imino tautomerism and that when such tautomerism is blocked (as by alkylation) the amino form has much lower activity than the imino form. This was verified by Shepherd, *et al.*[2189].

As pointed out by Lauger, Suter and Martin[2583], introduction of N^1-groups capable of resonance, or of amino-imino tautomerism, may give the highest observed activities but presence of such groups is no guarantee of activity.

It would seem that the Bell-Roblin theory is a more comprehensive and satisfying explanation of the influence of N^1-substituents on activity of sulfanilamide derivatives than that offered by Jensen and Schmith or Druey (see Bell-Roblin Theory, Chapter XI).

No correlation of structure and activity nor current theory can explain the anomalous activities of some closely related compounds. Thus, there is no satisfactory explanation of why N^1-(2,5-dimethylbenzoyl)sulfanilamide has a very much lower *in vivo* and *in vitro* activity than the corresponding 3,4-isomer. Such exceptions, thus far, appear to be in the direction of less activity than would be allowable on the basis of the generalization or theory. Since there are many possible explanations why a drug may fail to exhibit its inherent activity, these "negative" exceptions do not refute the theories with the force that a "positive" exception would exert, *i.e.*, the finding that certain compounds were much more active than a theory would predict, would demand modification or abandonment of the theory.

(III) General Conclusions

As defined at the start of this chapter, sulfanilamide-type activity is that which is antagonized by PABA. It, therefore, is of some interest to group compounds of various structures which exhibit sulfanilamide-type activity and also similarly constituted compounds which have shown antibacterial activity that is not antagonized by PABA. This has been done in Tables 305 and 306, p. 431–432.

(A) Classification of Drugs Having Sulfanilamide-Type Activity

From inspection of these tables, it will be observed that compounds exhibiting sulfanilamide-type activity fall into one or more of the following classes, each of which relates the compound structurally to PABA:

1. The compound contains a *p*-aminobenzoyl radical.

2. The compound contains a p-aminophenyl radical attached to an analogue of a carbonyl or carboxyl group (such as —SO_2— or —SO_2NH—).

3. As #2 where there is a potentially free amino group convertible thereto by known metabolic reactions such as hydrolysis, reduction or dealkylation.

4. As #2 where the analogue of a carbonyl or carboxyl group is potential and convertible thereto by known metabolic processes (usually oxidation).

5. As #2 where both the amino group and the analogue of a carbonyl or carboxyl group are potential.

6. The compound is a derivative of PABA.

7. The compound is isosteric with PABA.

8. The compound is isosteric with a compound convertible to PABA by known metabolic processes.

9. As a corollary to these observations, compounds which have none of these structural relationships to PABA are not antagonized by PABA. While they may have antibacterial activity, this is not of the sulfanilamide-type by definition.

Compounds in classes 1, 6, 7 and possibly 8 may either show sulfanilamide-type activity or have an antagonistic action, similar to PABA. In many cases, it is difficult to decide whether to classify the compound as a weak bacterial inhibitor or as a weak antagonist. Several such compounds show effects antagonistic to sulfonamides at low concentrations but become bacterial inhibitors at high concentrations.

(B) Discussion of Exceptions to Generalizations

Apparent exceptions to the above generalizations are arsephenamine and Germanine where a meta relationship seems to be involved. In these cases and some others where weak bacteriostatic activities are exhibited, it remains to be seen whether the effect of PABA is a specific one or whether a non-specific effect is involved such as that observed by Sandground[2631], who found that PABA had a pronounced detoxifying effect on otherwise fatal doses of pentavalent arsenicals (atoxyl, acetarsone, carbarsone, etc.) but that this was not a unique property since the isomers of PABA were also active, as were benzoic, phenylacetic acid, and phenylpropionic acids. No great structural similarity was therefore required for the effect and it appeared to be of a different kind than the relationship between PABA and sulfonamide drugs acting on bacteria. Particularly in those compounds involving arsenic, selenium and tellurium, the action of PABA in antagonizing the bacteriostatic effect, may be of this type. In some of these cases, PABA is able to reverse only part of the bacteriostatic activity.

Compounds which are readily hydrolyzable, oxidizable or reducible to the corresponding active drugs of the sulfanilamide series, or to bis(4-aminophenyl) sulfone, may show little or no activity *in vitro* but most of these are active *in vivo*. It has been shown in many of these cases that an actual conversion to the N^1-substituted sulfanilamide or bis(4-aminophenyl) sulfone takes place in the body. It is, therefore, reasonable to assume that the active agent in these cases is the free N^1-substituted sulfanilamide or bis(4-aminophenyl) sulfone. It would be expected that the activities of these compounds could be antagonized by PABA and this has been observed.

An interesting compound from this point of view is bis(4-aminophenyl) sulfide,

$$\left(NH_2 \diagup \hspace{-0.3em}\bigcirc\hspace{-0.3em}\diagup \right)_2 S$$

which might possibly be oxidized to the active sulfone. This compound is not active in bacteriostatic experiments except at high concentrations (1 in 2500) and its antagonism by PABA is not clear cut, or is absent[719, 1384]. The corresponding sulfoxide is more active and is antagonized by PABA. One might deduce from this that the sulfide is not oxidized to the sulfone while the sulfoxide is so oxidized by the bacteria. No proof of these views is available, however.

Agreement on the effect of PABA on the inhibition produced by p-hydroxylamino-benzenesulfonamide has not been reached. Green and Bielschowski[1199, 1200] and Rosenthal[2055] found PABA unable to reverse its bacteriostatic activity while Jensen and Schmith[1384] found PABA would reverse the *in vitro* activity of both p-hydroxylamino-benzenesulfonamide and 2-(p-hydroxylaminobenzenesulfonamido)thiazole against pneumococcus. Perhaps difference in the time of reading results is an explanation. Bratton, et al.[50] showed that the hydroxylamine derivative was rapidly converted to sulfanilamide in the presence of biological material, hence late reading of results would indicate a reversal by PABA since the agent then present would be sulfanilamide.

Among the compounds not antagonized by PABA (Table 306) are a few which have structural characteristics placing them in classes where if antibacterial activity is exhibited, it might be expected to be antagonized by PABA. Some of these compounds exhibit very weak antibacterial effects and are active only at high concentrations where they may be acting as general protoplasmic poisons, hence the lack of antagonism by PABA may not be significant. Thus 5-nitro-2-furoic acid, which falls in class 8, was bactericidal at 100–400 mg. per 100 cc. and the activity was not antagonized by PABA[1395]. (PABA is also toxic to bacteria at such high concentrations.) In contrast, 5-nitrothiophene-2-carboxylic acid was bacteriostatic at 2.5 to 40 mg. per 100 cc. and was antagonized by PABA.

A more striking anomaly was the high activity of 5-nitrothiophene-2-carboxamide which was antagonized by PABA, while 5-aminothiophene-2-carboxamide was inactive at 1000 mg. per 100 cc.[1395]. A possible explanation would be that the amino compound (known to behave peculiarly in its chemical characteristics) was unable to penetrate to the site of action in bacteria while the corresponding nitro compound did penetrate and was then converted *in situ* to the isostere of PABA.

2-Sulfanilyl-5-pyridinesulfonamide falls in class 2 and might be expected to be antagonized by PABA. The compound is said[1854] to be only slightly active *in vivo* but to be quite active *in vitro* and not antagonized by an equimolecular concentration of PABA. Another compound of class 2 which is not antagonized by PABA is N^1-(3,5-dibromo-phenyl)sulfanilamide. Here the antibacterial activity appears associated with the 3,5-dibromophenyl radical, since other compounds, not derivatives of sulfanilamide, which contain this grouping also show *in vitro* activities of varying degree. It thus appears that these exceptions may represent a new type of chemotherapeutic activity superimposed upon that ascribable to the sulfanilyl group and masking the effect of PABA completely.

H. J. White[a] has verified the inability of PABA to antagonize the action of N^1-(3,5-dibromophenyl)sulfanilamide on Gram-positive organisms but has made the interesting observation that its action on certain Gram-negative organisms, including *E. coli*, is completely antagonized by PABA.

---

[a] H. J. White, unpublished work.

(C) Requirements for Sulfanilamide-Type Activity

That a compound possesses one of the structural relationships to PABA detailed under (A) above appears to be a necessary requirement for sulfanilamide-type activity but is not sufficient because many compounds having the necessary requirements will fail to be active *in vivo* because of insolubility, poor absorption-distribution-excretion characteristics, toxicity or other less obvious defects.

While PABA antagonizes the bacteriostatic action of most sulfanilamide derivatives against most bacteria, this should be regarded as only one phase of the possible actions of these drugs against microorganisms. If the PABA relationship is involved in a fundamental mechanism of action (see Woods-Fildes Theory, Chapter XI), it should be by no means an exclusive mechanism. Thus against certain organisms, a sulfanilamide derivative may show an activity which is only partially antagonized by PABA. This would indicate that probably two mechanisms are active, only one of which involves the sulfanilamide-PABA relationship. Some other part of the molecule may be responsible for the fraction of the total antibacterial activity which is not antagonized by PABA.

(D) Development of New Drugs

It might well be found that such a drug would be effective against organisms which are insensitive to sulfanilamide, the activity arising from the mechanism which was of secondary importance in the effect of the drug on sulfanilamide-sensitive organisms. Further study might then show how this secondary mechanism could be accentuated, perhaps with final elimination of the sulfanilamide part of the molecule. A new type of chemotherapeutic agent would then have been evolved, the transition having been bridged from a sulfanilamide derivative to a drug having a fundamentally new mechanism of action and no longer subject to antagonism by PABA.

Such developments have been noted and more may be expected, but empirical screening of a large number of miscellaneous compounds may be even more fruitful of new chemotherapeutic agents of radically new modes of action, the mechanism of which will only be understood long after the time of their discovery.

TABLE 305

a. Compounds antagonized by PABA

Compounds	References
NH_2⟨⟩SO_2NHR^1 and derivatives convertible thereto in the host or by bacterial metabolism.	473, 569, 577, 680, 1081, 1100, 1122, 1199, 1200, 1271, 1690, 1313, 1364, 1384, 1797, 2477, 2559, 2580, 2590, 2593, 2605
NH_2⟨⟩SO_2⟨⟩NH_2 and derivatives convertible thereto in the host.	680, 1384, 1491, 2272, 2559, 2590
NO_2⟨⟩SO_2⟨⟩$N = NR$	2590
NH_2⟨⟩SO_2R $(R = C_nH_{2n+1})$	1384
NH_2⟨⟩SO_2⟨N⟩NH_2	1854
NH_2⟨⟩SO⟨⟩NH_2	1384
CH_3CONH⟨⟩SO⟨⟩$N = NR$	2590
NH_2⟨⟩SS⟨⟩NH_2 (Partial)	1200
NH_2⟨⟩SO_3H	1313, 1364
NH_2⟨⟩SH	1200
NH_2⟨⟩PO_3H_2	1491
NH_2⟨⟩SbO_3H_2	1797
NH_2⟨⟩AsO_3HNa	1313, 1315, 1904
$HCl \cdot H_2N$ $NH_2 \cdot HCl$ HO⟨⟩$As-As$⟨⟩OH	1797
NH_2⟨⟩$SeSe$⟨⟩NH_2 (Partial)	1200
NO_2⟨⟩$COOR$ $(R = H$ or $C_nH_{2n+1})$	1384, 1435, 1785, 2559, 2605
NH_2⟨⟩$CONH_2$	1313, 1315
NH_2⟨⟩$COCH_3$	680, 1395, 1491
NO_2⟨⟩$COCH_3$	1491

TABLE 305—(*Concluded*)

Compounds	Reference
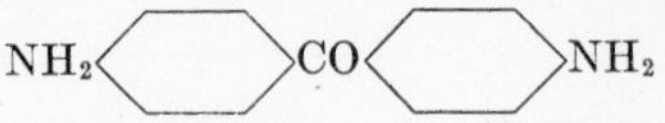 NH_2〈　〉CO〈　〉NH_2	680, 1491
 NH_2〈　〉$COCO$〈　〉NH_2	1490, 1491
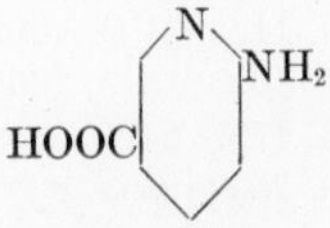 (N, NH_2, HOOC substituted thiazine ring)	1395
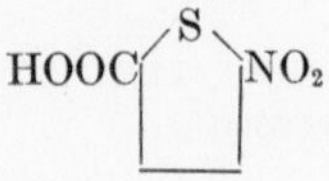 (S, HOOC, NO_2 substituted thiazole ring)	1395
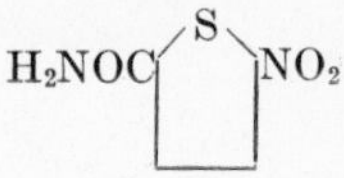 (S, H_2NOC, NO_2 substituted thiazole ring)	1395
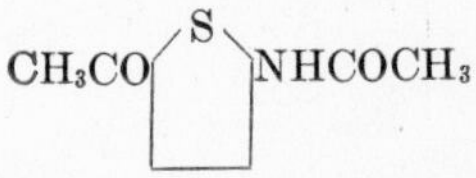 (S, CH_3CO, NHCOCH_3 substituted thiazole ring)	1395
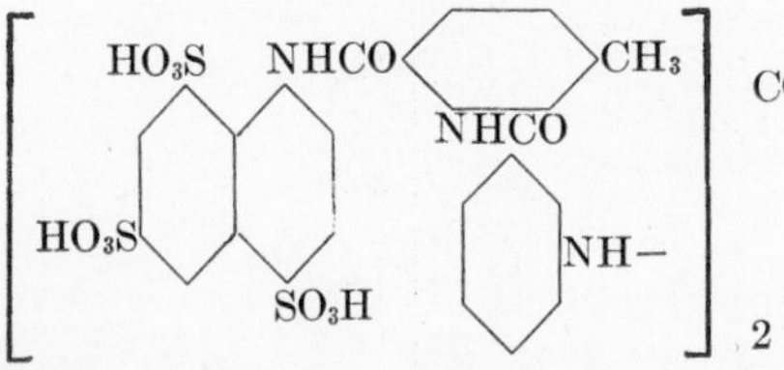 $[HO_3S\ NHCO$〈　〉$CH_3 / NHCO / HO_3S / SO_3H / NH-]_2$ CO　("Germanin")	1797

See also nuclear-substituted derivatives of PABA, Table 183.

TABLE 306

b. Compounds not antagonized by PABA

Compounds	References
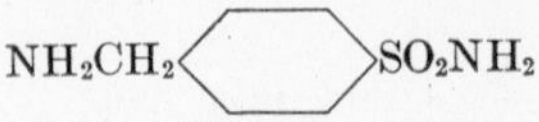 NH_2CH_2〈　〉SO_2NH_2	749, 988, 1384, 1385, 1581, 2135, 2143
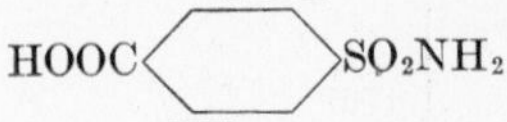 $HOOC$〈　〉SO_2NH_2	1364
 $HCl\ \cdot\ \begin{smallmatrix}NH\\NH_2\end{smallmatrix}C$〈　〉$SO_2NH_2$	659, 2533
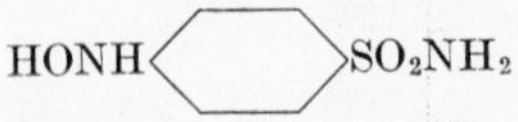 $HONH$〈　〉SO_2NH_2	1199, 1200, 2055
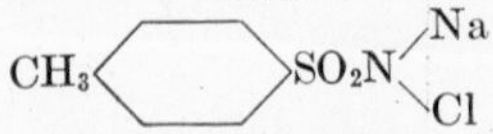 CH_3〈　〉$SO_2N\begin{smallmatrix}Na\\Cl\end{smallmatrix}$	1384
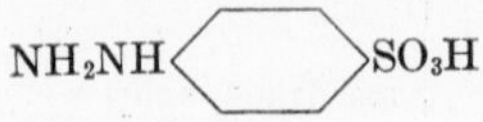 NH_2NH〈　〉SO_3H	1384
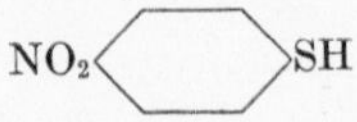 NO_2〈　〉SH	1200

TABLE 306—(*Concluded*)

Compounds	References
$HCl \cdot NH_2CH_2$⟨benzene⟩SO_3CH_3	2533
$HCl \cdot$ $\overset{HN\!\!=}{\underset{H_2N}{C}}$⟨benzene⟩$SO_2CH_3$	2533
HO⟨benzene⟩SO_2⟨benzene⟩OH	1384
NH_2⟨benzene⟩S⟨benzene⟩NH_2	719
NO_2⟨benzene⟩S⟨benzene⟩NH_2	1200
NH_2⟨benzene⟩SO_2⟨$\overset{N-}{\text{benzene}}$⟩$SO_2NH_2$	1854
NO_2⟨benzene⟩SS⟨benzene⟩NO_2	1200
$HO-\overset{NH_2}{\underset{}{⟨benzene⟩}}As\!=\!O$	1904
NO_2⟨benzene⟩SeO_2H	1200
NO_2⟨benzene⟩$SeSe$⟨benzene⟩NO_2	1200
$H_2NCONHNH$⟨benzene⟩	1384
$H_2NCON\!=\!N$⟨benzene⟩	1384
$NO_2\overset{O}{\diagup}COOH$	1395
NH_2⟨benzene⟩SO_2NH⟨$\overset{Br}{\underset{Br}{\text{benzene}}}$⟩	a
⟨benzene⟩SO_2NH⟨$\overset{Br}{\underset{Br}{\text{benzene}}}$⟩	a
Benzoic acid, salicylic acid, sodium thiosalicylate, sulfo-salicylic acid, aniline, phenol, o-cresol, p-nitrophenol, thymol, and resorcinol were not antagonized.	1364, 2559

a Goetchius, G. R. and Lawrence, C. A.; J. Bact. **49**, 575–84 (1945).

Chapter X

PHARMACOLOGY OF SULFONAMIDE AND SULFONE DRUGS

By J. T. Litchfield, Jr.

Stamford Research Labs., American Cyanamid Co., Stamford, Conn.

The pharmacological research which contributes to the cooperative development of a new chemotherapeutic drug of the sulfanilamide type will be the main subject of this chapter. Representative data for important sulfanilamide and sulfone derivatives will be utilized to illustrate various aspects of the discussion. The scope and relation of pharmacology to other biological sciences, as well as the accuracy of measurements of biological responses, will be briefly examined as a preface to the main topic.

(I) General Considerations

Pharmacology has been defined by A. J. Clark[a] as the study of the manner in which the functions of living organisms can be modified by chemical substances. Pathology has been similarly defined as the study of the derangements of the functions of living organisms. Both, therefore, require as their basis, an adequate knowledge of the functions of normal organisms (physiology). The interrelationship of these three biological sciences is illustrated in the diagram below.

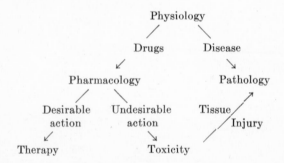

Chemotherapeutic research results from the fusion of common interests of chemistry, pharmacology and either bacteriology or parasitology. The complexity of a chemotherapeutic experiment can be illustrated by the following diagram which shows the interaction of one part on another.

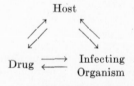

---

[a] Heffter, "Experimentelle Pharmakologie", Ergänzungswerk **4**.

The complexity of biological systems introduces formidable difficulties into studies of drug action. As Clark has pointed out (*ibid.*), the application of the methods of physical chemistry offers an attractive approach to these studies, but it must be remembered in interpreting results, that these methods were never intended for such use. When a physical chemist studies a heterogeneous system, he is careful to choose the simplest one. For example, he prefers to study adsorption by using a polished metal surface rather than pure charcoal because the latter is inconveniently complex. The pharmacologist is forced to use an extremely complex system in studies of drug action and is rarely able to test adequately the hypothesis that the action observed is dependent on any particular physico-chemical process.

A further difficulty inherent in biological data is the low degree of accuracy compared to physico-chemical data. Cause and effect in a biological system are almost always related through a complex chain of physical and chemical events not susceptible to control. Effects, therefore, are difficult to reproduce exactly. Superimposed on this is the considerable error due to variation in cells. As a consequence, any series of biological measurements will show wide dispersion, almost always in excess of $\pm 10\%$ of the average value. For example, it may be possible to determine chemically the concentration of drug in a biological system within 1% but the effect of that concentration may be reproducible only within limits such as 45–55% even under exceptionally favorable circumstances. Furthermore, it usually is particularly difficult to measure accurately effects of less than 10% or more than 90% of the maximum action. Thus, in order merely to observe a 1% incidence of an effect such as survival or death, 100 organisms must be examined, while to establish accurately a 1% incidence several thousand organisms would be required. Biological data, therefore, are often subjected to statistical analysis by methods familiar to physical chemists.

Data regarding effects of a drug can be divided into three types, qualitative, semiquantitative and quantitative. The first type is descriptive only; no measurement of dosage or degree of response is involved. An example of this is a tabulation of the kind of toxic symptoms observed after administration of a drug. Semiquantitative data represent measurement of only one variable. This can be represented by a tabulation of blood concentrations which result in various toxic symptoms. An example of this is the data given by Marshall *et al.*[1729] for sulfanilamide in the dog: 30 mg./100 cc. in the blood, no symptoms; 40 mg./100 cc., excitement, weakness, ataxia; 60–80 mg./100 cc., salivation, vomiting, diarrhea, hyperpnea; over 100 mg./100 cc., rigidity, blindness, coma and complete paralysis. Quantitative data comprise measurement of both dosage and degree of response.

Drug responses which can be measured fall into two classes, 1) graded response (continuous scale) such as change in body weight or degree of movement and 2) all or none response (discontinuous scale) such as survival or death. The first class permits relatively precise measurement of the degree of response to a particular dose in a single animal, as in the case of counting the number of bacteria present in the blood of an infected mouse after treatment with a particular dose of sulfanilamide. Because of the extent to which biological systems vary, measurements are likely to differ widely from animal to animal even though conditions are carefully controlled. In general, it is necessary to average 10–30 replicate measurements to achieve a stable value.

In the case of an all or none response, a single animal is obviously of limited value. In order to convert the all or none scale into a continuous one, it is necessary to make replicate determinations and express the number of positive (or negative) effects as a percentage of the total number of responses; thus after a particular dose of drug, 10 of 30 mice survived or 33%. In general, larger numbers of measurements are required for all or none responses than for graded responses, to achieve equally stable values.

In order to relate size of dose to response, a series of doses must be tested, each on a suitable number of animals. The degree of response is then correlated with size of dose either by plotting the data and drawing a free hand curve or by fitting a curve mathematically. In either case certain values which characterize the relationship between dosage and response are obtained. The values which characterize the relationship in the case of graded response are the mean dose, the mean response and the rate of change in response with change in size of dose; while in the case of all or none responses, the values are: the 50%, *i.e.* the median response, the dose corresponding to this, and the rate of change as in the first case.

By means of these values, quantitative comparison of drugs can be made. A quantitative comparison, however, is meaningful only if it is made by comparing the doses of different drugs which produce the *same* effect. If comparison is made of different responses from the same doses, only qualitative conclusions can be reached, namely, that one drug is more active or more toxic than the other. This can be made clear by considering two examples: 1. The median lethal dose (LD_{50}) of sodium sulfanilamide for mice was found to be 3.0 Gm./kilo, the LD_{50} of sodium sulfapyridine was found to be 1.0 Gm./kilo. The response is the same for both drugs, 50% kill; therefore, the quantitative expression of toxicity is that sulfapyridine is three times as toxic as sulfanilamide for mice. 2. It was found that blood concentrations of 5 mg./100 cc. of sulfanilamide saved 10% and the same concentration of sulfapyridine saved 60% of mice infected with pneumococci. The responses are different so that quantitative expression of activity is not possible. The only conclusion which can be made is that sulfapyridine is more active than sulfanilamide.

For a review of methods used to establish dose-response relationship of drugs the monographs of Burns[a] and Bliss and Cattell[b] should be consulted.

(II) Method of Assay in Body Fluids

Studies of drug action *in vivo* are greatly facilitated if a good analytical method is available; that is, one which is sensitive, accurate and reproducible. If the method is wholly new, or if it is a modification of one well known, it is essential to have data with regard to the ability of the method to recover known amounts of the particular drug. Such recovery experiments must be carried out under conditions which simulate the normal occurrence of the drug in the type of sample being assayed. In addition, the method must be shown to determine the actual drug in question and not altered forms of the drug.

The best analytical method for sulfanilamides, orthanilamides and metanilamides is the procedure of Bratton and Marshall[49]. The basis of the method is diazotization of the aryl amine and coupling with N-naphthylethylenediamine dihydrochloride to form a water-soluble dye which can be estimated colorimetrically. For details of the procedure the original article should be consulted. In their discussion, the authors point out the general utility of the method providing certain precautions are observed. The most important of these are: precipitation of protein at high dilution, or precipitation with alcohol

[a] Burns, J. H., "Biological Standardization", Oxford University Press, London, 1937.
[b] Bliss, C. I., and Cattell, McKeen, *Ann. Rev. Physiol.*, **5,** 479–539 (1943).

in the case of insoluble compounds, addition of alcohol in the event that the final dye is acid-insoluble, and controlled recovery experiments for each new compound.

Because of widespread interest in sulfanilamides, a number of analytical procedures have been devised. The various methods which have been reported for determining concentrations of sulfanilamide derivatives can be classified as gravimetric or volumetric, spectrophotometric and colorimetric. Gravimetric or volumetric methods have very limited application because they can be used only when very high concentrations are present or very large samples can be taken. Aside from isolation and weighing of the drug itself, three other procedures have been used: the condensation of sulfanilamide in acetic acid solution with alcoholic xanthydrol to form a crystalline compound[567], titration of the free aryl amine with nitrous acid (U.S.P. XI), and bromination using bromide-bromate (U.S.P. X). For methods of assay of tablets and powdered drugs, reference should be made to the "New and Non-Official Remedies" and the "U. S. Pharmacopœia."

Sulfanilamide exhibits a strong absorption band in the ultraviolet and this property has been used as the basis for its determination in alcoholic extracts of blood.[a] Direct determination of sulfanilamides in this manner is entirely satisfactory in the case of solutions in water or certain organic solvents and such determinations have been reported by numerous authors[718, 765, 871]. Considerable difficulty is encountered when this method is applied to biological material, in that an excessive and variable background which absorbs strongly in the ultraviolet is encountered. One additional source of error in determinations of sulfanilamides by ultraviolet absorption has been described,[b] namely, a shift in the absorption maxima with change in pH, as well as lowering of the extinction coefficient, when the solutions are strongly acidic. Any determinations of sulfanilamides in biological samples by ultraviolet spectroscopy would appear to require precise control of pH, as well as a special extraction procedure, to eliminate the "blank" if high sensitivity is desired. Even under ideal conditions the sensitivity as indicated by molar extinction coefficients is 1/2 to 1/3 that of the Bratton-Marshall procedure, depending on the particular compound.

Spectroscopic techniques in the visible light range can be applied to any of the procedures in which the sulfanilamide derivative is converted to a dye. Spectrophotometers, such as the Beckman or Coleman instruments, have been widely used for determining sulfanilamides, by the Bratton-Marshall procedure. Greater precision can be attained with these instruments than with those which do not supply monochromatic light. Certain photoelectric colorimeters have been described[c] which, by means of special filter combinations, supply essentially monochromatic light of the same wave length as the point of maximum absorption of the dye formed in the Bratton-Marshall procedure. These instruments offer the same sensitivity and precision as can be attained with direct spectroscopy.

A variety of colorimetric methods has been proposed for sulfanilamide determination. These methods have as a basis the quantitative reaction of the free aryl amino group in a sulfanilamide derivative with other substances to produce a dye. Two types of methods are reported: the first of these is direct coupling with either dimethylaminobenzaldehyde[d] or sodium-β-naphthoquinone-4-sulfonate[2114]. The second type of reaction is one in which the aryl amine is diazotized and coupled. The coupling may be carried out in acid,

[a] Gregerson, M. I., and Painter, E. E., *Am. J. Physiol.*, **123**, 83 (1938).

[b] Robinson, E. J., and Pekrul, L. F., *J. Am. Chem. Soc.*, **67**, 1186–9 (1945).

[c] Rosenfeld, M., *J. Biol. Chem.*, **129**, 179–87 (1939) and the Evelyn instrument.

[d] Kühnau, W. W., *Klin. Wochschr.*, **17**, 116–7 (1938); also Reference[2430].

neutral or alkaline solution, and the selection of coupling agent varies, depending on the conditions. For alkaline coupling either thymol or β-naphthol may be used[153]. For neutral coupling, chromotropic acid[2155] and diphenylamine[a] have been used. For acid coupling, N-naphthylethylenediamine dihydrochloride, as used in the procedure of Bratton and Marshall, appears to be the most satisfactory, although a number of other coupling agents have been used, most of which are the naphthylamine type. For a discussion of these the following references may be consulted[49, 1135].

(III) Development of a New Chemotherapeutic Drug

In Chapter VIII certain procedures were discussed by which the most promising drug of a group may be selected. The drug selected may then be studied further to determine if it merits clinical trial and if so, how it should be tested. If the results of the test in man are favorable, extensive experimental and clinical investigations are undertaken to evaluate the compound with respect to other therapeutic agents. During this period the clinician and the biologist complement each other by pointing out new aspects of the action of the drug which require examination. The results obtained by both investigators coupled with economic considerations form the basis of the decision regarding general clinical use of the new chemotherapeutic agent. The development of a new drug therefore may be divided into two stages, 1) preparatory to clinical trial, and 2) preparatory to general clinical use.

(A) Development Preparatory to Clinical Trial

The first stage of development of a new chemotherapeutic drug can be divided into: 1) chemical studies which characterize the drug; 2) bacteriological studies which evaluate the activity of the drug; and 3) pharmacological studies which examine the fate and toxicity of a drug in order to establish the means for safe and effective trial in man.

(1) Characteristic Properties

From the standpoint of the biologist and the clinician data on the following points are necessary: Formula, molecular weight, analysis (including heavy metals), melting point data; form, appearance, odor, taste, color and stability; solubility data, pH, stability and color of solutions, solubility of salts; method of assay in body fluids.

(2) Evaluation of Antibacterial Activity

See Chapter VIII.

(3) Pharmacological Studies

The pharmacology of a new chemotherapeutic drug is concerned primarily with the simultaneous interaction of drug and host. The action of the host on a drug is termed the metabolism or fate of the drug. The beneficial action of a drug is termed therapy and the deleterious action, toxicity.

(a) *Dosage Schedules*

The *fate of the drug* is of major importance to the problem of establishing a suitable dosage regime for man. It is necessary to investigate first the relation between concentration in the blood and time after administration of the drug (concentration-time curve)

[a] Doble, J. and Geiger, J. C., *J. Lab. Clin. Med.*, **23**, 651–3 (1938).

under various conditions.   By means of concentration-time curves the effect of the following variables should be examined: 1) route of administration (by mouth compared with by injection) and 2) size of dose.   Curves should be obtained for both the mouse and the dog or monkey.

These results help to provide the means for establishing a suitable dosage schedule in man.   Since the mouse is used for studying chemotherapeutic activity, the concentration-time curves obtained in this animal establish an approximate therapeutic concentration of drug in blood.   The studies in the dog or monkey establish the size of dose required to give the same concentration that was therapeutic in the mouse.   The concentration-time curves in dog or monkey show also the time at which additional doses are needed to maintain the therapeutic concentration.   A tentative dosage schedule for man is then set up by assuming that, 1) the therapeutic concentration in man is similar to that in the mouse, and 2) the dosage schedule in man which will maintain therapeutic concentrations is similar to that in the dog or monkey if the difference in body weight is taken into account.

Data from studies on sulfapyridine can be utilized to illustrate this approach.   It was found that doses of 15–20 mg./mouse/24 hours (1.0 Gm./kilo) administered in the diet were effective in a pneumococcus infection.   The therapeutic concentration of sulfapyridine was found by studies of concentration-time curves in mice to be 7–10 mg./100 cc. of blood[1585].   Studies in dogs indicated that sulfapyridine was incompletely absorbed and that 0.2 Gm./kilo by mouth or 0.1 Gm./kilo of sodium salt by injection was necessary to give the therapeutic concentration of 7–10 mg./100 cc.   The curves in dogs indicated also that an additional dose of about 0.05 Gm./kilo would be needed every 6 hours to maintain the therapeutic concentration[1731].

These findings suggest that a suitable dosage schedule in man would be:

	Initial Dose (Gm./kilo)	Maintenance Dose—every 6 hr. (Gm./kilo)
Sulfapyridine by mouth or	0.2	0.05
Sodium sulfapyridine by injection	0.1	0.025

It is of interest to compare this to the dosage schedule given by Spink[2248] after extensive clinical use of this drug.   To maintain concentrations of 5–10 mg./100 cc. he recommends:

	Initial Dose (Gm./kilo)	Maintenance Dose—every 6 hr. (Gm./kilo)
Sulfapyridine by mouth or	0.1	0.05
Sodium sulfapyridine by injection	0.07	0.03

(b) *Excretion Studies*

Two important points regarding excretion should be established in these studies prior to clinical trial; first, the major routes of removal of drug from the blood and, second, the extent to which the drug can be recovered unchanged after administration of a carefully measured dose. The importance of the first point is threefold. Knowledge of the excretory mechanisms can lead 1) to the means of regulating excretion rate; 2) to recognition of individuals to whom the drug should not be given because of impaired excretory mechanisms; and 3) to recognition of a potential site of toxic action of the drug. The second point, recovery of unchanged drug, merits investigation because many drugs are chemically changed in passing through the body. If the alteration of the drug is extensive, the changed drug will require investigation for activity, toxicity and influence on the method of analysis of the drug in body fluids.

(c) *Toxicity Studies*

The object of the toxicity studies prior to clinical trial is to determine 1) if therapeutic doses can be administered to man with reasonable safety, and 2) the nature of the toxic effects produced by the drug. The conventional approach to these problems is to determine the range between the therapeutic dose and the minimal toxic dose. Two kinds of experiments are necessary, 1) *acute toxicity* which examines the range between the initial therapeutic dose and the single dose which produces toxicity; and 2) *subacute toxicity* which examines the range between the therapeutic concentration of drug in the blood and the concentration which causes toxic effects when maintained 2–4 weeks. As before, data should be obtained in two unrelated species such as the mouse or rat and the dog or monkey. If the drug is one which is poorly absorbed after oral administration to animals, the toxicity of the drug should be investigated not only by oral but also by parenteral administration.

The nature of the toxic action of the drug can be determined by careful observation of the symptoms of intoxication and the pathological effects produced.

To illustrate the application of a few of these methods of toxicology some of the reported data on sulfapyridine can be utilized as before. From concentration-time curves of mice given sulfapyridine by mouth the single dose which gave the therapeutic level of 7–10 mg./100 cc. was 0.3 Gm./kilo.[1731]

When large single doses of sulfapyridine were administered orally to mice it was found that 30 Gm./kilo were well tolerated.[a] This would indicate a more than hundredfold margin of safety $(\frac{30}{0.3})$ for mice. When sodium sulfapyridine[1731] was administered similarly,[b] it was found that 2 Gm./kilo was lethal to 50% of the mice and that the margin of safety was only tenfold $(\frac{2.0}{0.2})$. The tenfold margin reflects the inherent toxicity of the sulfapyridine in the blood and tissues; the more than hundredfold margin reflects the fact that the sulfapyridine which has not been absorbed is not very toxic.

The margin of safety for acute doses, on the basis of concentration in the blood was nine- to twelvefold since the acute toxic concentration from 2.0 Gm./kilo was of the order of 90 mg./100 cc.

Sulfapyridine given by mouth to dogs caused no toxic effects. The sodium salt by mouth caused vomiting so that actual dosage was uncertain. Sodium sulfapyridine (0.5 Gm./kilo intravenously) produced concentrations in the blood of 60 mg./100 cc. and was lethal to 2 out of 5 dogs. These data indicate that in dogs the margin of safety on a concentration basis is six- to eightfold. The margin of safety would be only fourfold

---

[a] Baines, E. J., and Wien, R., *Quart. J. Pharmacol.*, **12**, 4–18 (1939).

[b] Use of the soluble sodium salt by mouth is comparable in this case to administration of sulfapyridine parenterally.

if calculated on the basis of concentrations which caused toxic symptoms, *i.e.* 35 mg./ 100 cc.[1731].

From these data one would conclude that concentrations of sulfapyridine in the blood of 30–40 mg./100 cc. would produce severe intoxication and that concentrations of 60 mg./ 100 cc. would be dangerous to life.

The decision to test a new drug in man and the responsibility for it rests with the clinician. The studies preparatory to clinical trial must provide adequate data so that he can decide: 1) if the trial is worthwhile; 2) if it is reasonably safe; and 3) the best conditions under which to test the drug.

(B) Studies Preparatory to General Clinical Use

If the new drug is shown to be effective in man, it should be investigated extensively to evaluate it in comparison with other drugs or methods of therapy. Some of the factors which enter into the potential value of a new drug are, the degree of permissible toxicity, measures available to minimize toxicity and availability of other useful drugs. It is necessary therefore to obtain quantitative data regarding activity, fate and toxicity of the drug compared to a standard drug, if possible. Quantitative studies require strict control of experimental conditions. This control can be achieved in experimental animals much more easily than in man. As a result, it might require thousands of patients to establish facts which can be obtained from a few animal experiments.

Of the many sulfanilamide derivatives which have been examined only a few have merited both extensive experimental investigation and general clinical use. These are given in Table 307, p. 458. Data reported for these drugs will be summarized in the discussion to follow.

(1) Metabolism of Sulfanilamides

With a satisfactory analytical method, a wide variety of studies concerning the fate of the drug can be carried out. The usual procedures are: a) determination of blood or plasma concentration-time curves under various conditions; b) absorption experiments; c) excretion studies, particularly renal clearance and total excretion; d) investigation of the distribution of the drug in the various body fluids and tissues, as well as binding of the drug to body proteins; and e) study of the alteration of the drug in the host with isolation and identification of the altered products, when possible.

(a) *Concentration-Time Curves*

It should be recognized that any concentration-time curve is the result of interaction of various mechanisms for disposing of the drug, such as, absorption, alteration, distribution and excretion[309]. Concentration-time curves are frequently misinterpreted on the basis that they represent the effect of only one or two rather than all the above mechanisms.

A concentration-time curve may demonstrate that absorption of the drug has occurred, but it does not define quantitatively its speed or extent. The curve also may show that removal of the drug has occurred but does not indicate whether such removal is by excretion or alteration, and does not define quantitatively the speed and extent of the removal. Thus, only a limited amount of information can be derived from a single curve.

Curves obtained under different conditions are of considerable value for purposes of comparison. Thus, the relationships can be established between concentration in the blood and such factors as dosage (Figure 1); route of administration (Figure 2); variation between species of animals (Figure 3); and variation between drugs (Figure 4).

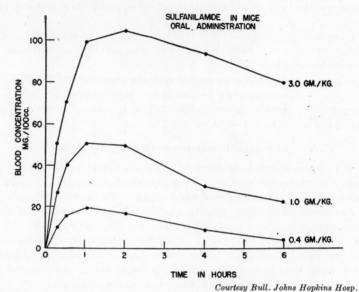

Courtesy Bull. Johns Hopkins Hosp.

FIGURE 1. Relation between blood concentration and dosage. Redrawn from data of Marshall and Cutting[336].

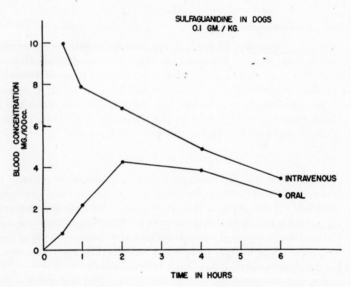

Courtesy Bull. Johns Hopkins Hosp.

FIGURE 2. Relation between blood concentration and route of adminstration. Redrawn from data of Marshall, *et al.*[335].

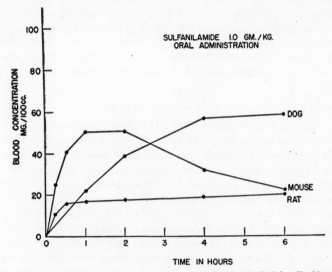

Courtesy Bull. Johns Hopkins Hosp.

FIGURE 3. Relation between blood concentration and species of animal. Redrawn from data of Marshall, *et al.*, *Bull. Johns Hopkins Hosp.*, **63**, 318–27 (1938), and[336].

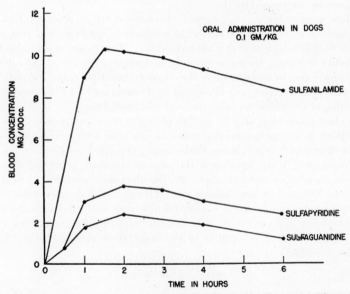

Courtesy Bull. Johns Hopkins Hosp. and J. Pharmacol.

FIGURE 4. Relation between blood concentration and structure of sulfanilamides. Redrawn from data of Marshall, *et al.*[1731] and [335].

It is evident that certain pharmacological characteristics of drugs can be compared qualitatively by means of these curves. A drug which is absorbed rapidly and completely gives an early high peak concentration whereas one which gives a high concentration even after 10–24 hours is excreted very slowly. Van Dyke et al.[a] have used this approach for a comparison of derivatives of sulfadiazine. In Table 308, p. 459, some of these data are reproduced. A somewhat different approach is necessary to obtain quantitative data, however.

(b) Absorption Studies

It is rather difficult to establish the true absorption curve because of the complexity of functions operating on the drug. If distribution and binding were instantaneous, if there were no alteration of the compound, and if there were no excretion, then the blood concentration-time curve would represent primarily the result of absorption. These conditions can be approximated experimentally in the following manner: After the first hour in most experiments the rate of distribution and binding can be assumed to be nearly instantaneous without introducing any serious error. For most sulfanilamides, acetylation and urinary excretion account for essentially all removal of the drug from the body. Urinary excretion can be eliminated experimentally by tying off or removing the kidneys. Acetylation can be eliminated by making the experiment on the dog, the only species of mammal known which does not acetylate sulfanilamides. The concentration-time curve then, in a suitably prepared dog, represents mainly the effect of absorption. If the constant, relating amount of drug in the body to concentration in the plasma, can be established in a previous experiment by intravenous administration of the drug to the same animal (Figure 5) the amount of drug absorbed at any time in the second experiment (Figure 6) can be determined by the relation:

Amount of drug in body = a constant × concentration in plasma. The results obtained in such an experiment are subject to criticism on the basis that they may not be comparable to results obtained in a normal animal. This makes it desirable to examine the absorption of a drug by some alternate procedure. A method for calculating the amount of absorption by integration of the concentration-time curve and data on urinary excretion has been discussed and illustrated by Dominguez and Pomerene[b] who studied the absorption of creatinine in man after oral administration.

Certain other procedures may be used to obtain data on absorption. The amount of drug remaining in the gastrointestinal tract at any time after oral administration of a dose can be determined by sacrificing the animal. The difference between the dose given and the amount left in the intestine is the amount absorbed, providing the drug is not destroyed in the gastrointestinal tract. Similar data on absorption of drug after oral dosage can be obtained by determining the total amount of drug excreted in the feces. Likewise, the total amount of drug excreted in the urine of the dog indicates the amount absorbed providing that nearly complete recovery of drug administered intravenously is possible. When the drug is unstable in the body, these methods do not indicate the true amount absorbed.

(c) Excretion Studies

Quantitative studies on absorption usually require simultaneous determination of excretion of the drug. The latter as an entity, however, is best studied in special experi-

[a] van Dyke, H. B., et al., J. Pharmacol., **83**, 203–12 (1945).
[b] Dominguez, R., and Pomerene, E., Proc. Soc. Exptl. Biol. Med., **60**, 173–81 (1945).

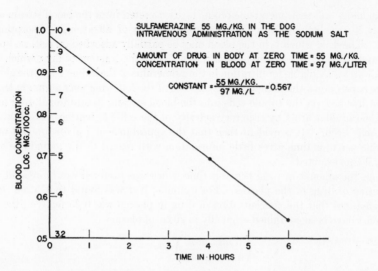

FIGURE 5. Relation between blood concentration and amount of drug in the body. Extrapolation of concentration-time curve to zero time to obtain theoretical initial equilibrium concentration. These data are hypothetical and serve only to illustrate the procedure.

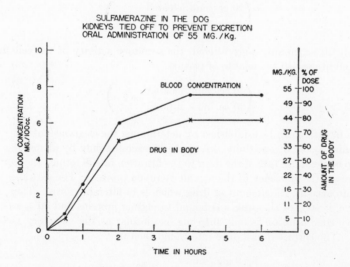

FIGURE 6. Cumulative absorption after oral administration. Lower curve calculated from upper curve using the constant obtained in Figure 5. These data are hypothetical and serve only to illustrate the procedure.

ments. The principal routes of excretion should be established first by qualitative studies on the secretions of the body after administration of the drug. Following this, quantitative study of the indicated secretions should be carried out.

Sulfanilamides and their metabolic products are excreted from the blood stream almost exclusively by the kidneys through a complex process of filtration, reabsorption and secretion. The drug which is in the blood may be partially adsorbed on cells and plasma proteins and partially free in the plasma water. Only the fraction of drug which is free in plasma water is available for filtration in the glomerulus of the kidney. As the glomerular filtrate passes down the kidney tubule any one of the following may occur: 1) the drug may be reabsorbed via the tubule cells into the blood stream; 2) additional drug may be added to the tubular urine by secretory activity of the cells; 3) neither reabsorption nor secretion may occur. It is evident then that the appearance of a given amount of drug in the urine per unit time gives little information with regard to the actual mechanism by which it was excreted.

However, the amount of drug per unit time which was excreted can be related to the concentration of drug in the plasma. For example, if it was found that 5 mg./minute was excreted and that the concentration of drug in plasma was 0.25 mg./cc., the 5 mg. of drug must have been contained originally in 20 cc. of plasma

$$\left(\frac{5 \text{ mg./min.}}{0.25 \text{ mg./cc.}}\right)$$

Accordingly, the *plasma clearance rate* is 20 cc. per minute. In order to find out if the drug has been subjected to reabsorption or secretion it is necessary to know what volume of plasma was filtered during this same period. If 40 cc./minute were filtered then 1/2 of the drug has been reabsorbed

$$\left(\frac{20 \text{ cc./min. cleared}}{40 \text{ cc./min. filtered}} = 0.5\right)$$

while if only 10 cc./minute were filtered, the secretory activity of the cells must have cleared an additional 10 cc./minute of plasma

$$\left(\frac{20 \text{ cc./min. cleared}}{10 \text{ cc./min. filtered}} = 2.0\right).$$

The rate of filtration can be established by determining the clearance rate of a substance such as inulin, xylose or creatinine, known to be excreted only by glomerular filtration.

The ratio of clearance rate of the drug to the filtration rate is termed the *clearance ratio* and it expresses the efficiency of the overall excretion process. The clearance ratio does not take into account the amount of drug which is in filterable form. Thus, in the example above, if 40% of the drug was bound to plasma proteins and 60% was filterable, the effective concentration is only 0.15 mg./cc. insofar as the excretory mechanism is concerned. The corrected clearance rate would then be

$$\frac{5 \text{ mg./min.}}{60 \% \times 0.25 \text{ mg./cc.}} = 33 \text{ cc./min.}$$

The ratio of this corrected clearance rate to the filtration rate is termed the excretion ratio and this ratio characterizes the excretion of the drug. A ratio greater than 1.0 indicates tubular secretion and a ratio less than 1.0, tubular reabsorption of the drug. It should be noted that both the clearance ratio and the excretion ratio can be calculated either on the basis of volumes of plasma per minute or mg. of drug per minute. The numerical values of these ratios will be the same by either method of calculation. In the example which follows the ratios were calculated on the basis of mg. of drug per minute.

Fisher, *et al.*[1097] characterized the excretion of thirty drugs related to sulfanilamide in this manner. A typical experiment and a portion of their discussion is reproduced[a] here to illustrate this type of study.

"An experiment which examines the renal excretion of sulfanilamide: (−45) Min. −800 ml. water by mouth. Creatinine, 200 mg./kilo subcutaneously; sulfanilamide, 75 mg./kilo subcutaneously. (0) Min.-bladder emptied. Four urine collection periods, 15 minutes each. Blood samples taken at middle of each period.

| Period | Plasma (mg./ ml.) | Excretion (mg./ min.) | Glomerular Filtration Rate (mg./ ml.) | Sulfanilamide | | | | | Clearance Ratio | Excretion Ratio |
				Plasma (mg./ ml.)	Plasma Filterable (mg./ ml.)	Filtered (mg./ min.)	Excreted (mg./ min.)	Reabsorbed (mg./ min.)		
1	0.144	6.82	47.4	0.039	0.035	1.66	0.39	1.27	0.21	0.23
2	0.150	6.92	46.1	0.045	0.041	1.89	0.44	1.45	0.21	0.24
3	0.150	7.32	48.7	0.051	0.045	2.19	0.55	1.64	0.23	0.25
Mean			47.0						0.22	0.24

"Glomerular filtration rate is measured following the administration of creatinine, the rate of glomerular filtration in milliliters per minute being equal to the quotient of the milligrams of creatinine excreted per minute and the plasma concentration of creatinine in milligrams per milliliter. Glomerular filtration rate so determined was calculated to be 47.4 ml./min. in the first period of the experiment above. The data on the excretion of sulfanilamide, obtained simultaneously, may be manipulated as follows: The plasma concentration of sulfanilamide during this period was 0.039 mg./ml., 90% of which is in a filterable form. At a glomerular filtration rate of 47.4 ml./min., it may be calculated that 1.66 mg. of sulfanilamide was filtered each minute. However, since the observed excretion accounts for only 0.39 of the 1.66 mg./min. filtered, one must conclude that 1.27 mg./min. of filtered sulfanilamide were reabsorbed in the renal tubules. The calculation throws little light on the mechanism of the reabsorptive process. However, the ratio of the amount excreted to the amount filtered, in this case, 0.23, yields a figure which is characteristic of the excretion of the compound by the average nephron (glomerulus and tubule) under the conditions of the experiment. This ratio, which is designated as the *excretion ratio*, is a useful datum in the study of the renal excretion of a series of related compounds.

"Another ratio which may be calculated from the data and which does not include a correction for the factor of plasma binding, is the sulfanilamide/creatinine *clearance ratio*, in this case 0.21. The latter ratio is important in the definition of the overall renal excretion rate of sulfanilamide but is less useful in indicating the mechanism by which such excretion is accomplished."

Clearance and excretion ratios of some of the important sulfanilamides in both dog

---

[a] Reproduced through the courtesy of the authors and the *Journal of Pharmacology and Experimental Therapeutics*, Williams & Wilkins Company.

and man are given in Table 309, p. 459. These data were assembled from the various reports indicated by the references in the table and since experimental conditions must have varied, between different laboratories, quantitative comparisons should be made with caution. These data illustrate that wide differences occur between ratios of related compounds and that only small differences occur between values for the dog and the corresponding ratios for man. With the exception of sulfacetamide and sulfathiazole all the drugs appear to be reabsorbed by the tubules to some extent.

Earle[2527] discussed the mechanism of reabsorption and pointed out that urea, a small molecule which is passively reabsorbed by a simple diffusion process, had an excretion ratio of 0.6 while sulfamerazine, a much larger molecule, had a ratio of 0.15. This difference as Earle points out is certainly presumptive evidence for active reabsorption on the part of the tubule cell even though he was unable to prove it by using procedures which interfere with this mechanism in the case of other drugs.

These studies on excretion have been emphasized because of their importance to problems such as evaluating quantitatively a new drug, relating structure of drugs to fate in the body, and using chemotherapeutic agents rationally and efficiently. Knowledge of the mechanisms concerned in the excretion of a drug aids in developing measures which modify the process, slowing it or hastening it as desired. Knowledge of these mechanisms leads to an understanding of the toxicity of the drug toward the kidney and to the means for avoiding such toxicity.

(d) Studies on Distribution

The rapid and fairly complete distribution of the sulfanilamides throughout the tissues of the host is responsible to a considerable extent for their effectiveness as therapeutic agents. A drug which does not distribute itself in all of the tissues of the body may possess in vitro activity, and yet be of little value therapeutically because it fails to reach the site of the infection.

The basic procedure for studying distribution is the comparison of the concentration in plasma to that in various tissues. An extensive investigation of the distribution of sulfanilamides was carried out by Fisher, et al.[1097] and one of their experiments is reproduced[a] to illustrate the technique of such studies.

"An experiment which examines the distribution of sulfanilamide in the cat: 9:25—Nembutal, kidneys tied off. 10:00—27.8 mg./kilo sulfanilamide intravenously; body weight = 2.95 kilos. 11:00—Concentration in plasma water = 0.0311 mg./ml. 12:00—Concentration in plasma water = 0.0288 mg./ml. Volume of distribution =

$$\frac{\text{mg. drug in body}}{\text{mg./ml. plasma water}} = \frac{27.8 \times 2.95}{0.0288} = 2840 \text{ ml.}$$

Volume of distribution ml. per Gm. body weight

$$\frac{2840}{2950} = 0.96 \text{ cc./Gm.}$$

[a] Reproduced through the courtesy of the authors and the Journal of Pharmacology and Experimental Therapeutics, Williams & Wilkins Company.

	Tissue or Body Fluid				
	Plasma Water	Red Blood Cells	Muscle	Cere-bro-spinal Fluid	Brain
Concentration mg./100 ml. (or Gm.)	2.88	4.32	3.08	2.11	2.01
Ratio: $\dfrac{\text{Tissue Concentration}}{\text{Plasma Water Concentration}}$	1.00	1.50	1.07	0.73	0.70

These data are derived from an experiment which examines the distribution of sulfanilamide two hours after its intravenous administration. The distribution equilibrium appears to be established at one hour since the plasma concentration at that time is much the same as at the end of the two hour interval. These data indicate that sulfanilamide diffuses readily into all tissues and is localized in the cells of many. This conclusion stems from the finding that the volume of distribution of sulfanilamide (2840 ml.) is in excess of the water content of the body (65% × body weight = 1920 ml.) and that the ratio of sulfanilamide concentration in any tissue to its concentration in plasma water is greater than the water content of the tissue. If sulfanilamide were freely diffusible throughout the body and not specifically localized in any tissue, its volume of distribution would be of the order of 0.65 cc./Gm. body weight, and the tissue to plasma distribution ratios would be considerably lower than those observed and would be similar to the per cent water content of the tissue. If sulfanilamide were largely retained in extracellular fluid it would have a volume of distribution of 0.25–0.30 cc./Gm. and its distribution ratios would be similar to those of sodium or chloride; for example, in the case of muscle, 0.11–0.12."

The technique used by these authors makes possible a more exact definition of distribution characteristics of sulfanilamides than has been possible before. Even though renal excretion is eliminated by tying off the kidneys, the animal is reasonably normal with respect to distribution equilibria for a number of hours. With the compound contained in an essentially closed system, rapid attainment of diffusion equilibrium can be expected and stability of equilibrium concentrations is favored. Thirty compounds related chemically to sulfanilamide were studied by Fisher, *et al.*, using the above technique and the data on some of these are given in Table 310, p. 460.

It can be seen from these data that a change occurred during 24–48 hours in the distribution ratios for the various tissues. The change is most striking in the case of sulfaguanidine and sulfacetamide, and least, in the case of sulfathiazole. Fisher, *et al.*, noted these changes and suggested that in the case of sulfaguanidine and sulfacetamide, the N^1-substituent was removed in the body since the distribution at 48 hours closely resembled that of sulfanilamide. An explanation for the change in the case of the N^1-heterocyclic sulfanilamide derivatives may be found in the observations of Scudi, *et al.* They pointed out that glucuronides of hydroxysulfanilamide, sulfapyridine and sulfathiazole have been isolated from urine and urinary calculi[2157]. They found that after administration to rats of sulfanilamide or various N^1-heterocyclic derivatives, a significant amount of water-soluble metabolites (probably glucuronides or ethereal sulfates of monohydroxy derivatives of the drug) was excreted in the urine.

An additional factor which conditions the distribution ratios given in Table 310 is the degree of plasma binding. Fisher, *et al.*, found the order of magnitude of binding to be the same in the cat as in the dog. If the volume of distribution is calculated on the basis of free or filterable drug in plasma water, the corrected figures given in the B column of Table 310 are obtained. These figures emphasize the localization within or on cells in the case of sulfanilamide, sulfathiazole, and sulfapyridine. The other derivatives are distributed more as if they freely penetrate cell membranes. The pKa's of the compounds in Table 310 do not vary over a wide range and show no correlation with the distribution characteristics of the drugs. In the case of other sulfanilamides studied by Fisher, *et al.*, there was some correlation in that a high pKa was associated with extensive localization of the drug in cells and a low one with restriction of the drug to extracellular fluid.

Table 311, p. 461, shows data on binding of sulfanilamides to plasma protein. It can be seen that binding is more extensive in man than in the dog. The difference between these two species would be even greater if the comparison were made at equal plasma concentrations, because relatively less drug is bound as the concentration increases[953].

Davis[953] suggested the possibility that drug bound to plasma protein was probably unavailable for antibacterial action and that the concentration of filterable drug determined the degree of action. He was unable to test adequately this interesting hypothesis owing to technical difficulties and concluded without giving any data that the protein bound drug was probably inactive. The view that only the filterable drug is available for antibacterial action is reasonable; it is also reasonable to assume that the effective concentration of drug is that in or on the bacterial cell, rather than the concentration of filterable drug in plasma. Reinvestigation of the relative binding to bacteria of various sulfanilamides would be of interest in establishing the correlation between drug concentration in the substrate and drug concentration in and on bacterial cells.

If Davis' hypothesis is true and if concentration of filterable drug determines the degree of antibacterial action *in vivo*, it is of interest to compare the relative amounts of filterable drug which are obtained in various species per unit amount in the body. The figure which expresses this is the ratio:

$$\frac{\text{Concentration in plasma water mg./1.} \times \% \text{ filterable drug}}{\text{Amount of drug in body, mg./kilo}} = \frac{C}{D} \times \% \text{ filterable drug}$$

This figure is the reciprocal of the corrected volume of distribution (Table 310, column B), and expresses the concentration of filterable drug in plasma water per unit of drug in the body (see footnote to Table 310).

These ratios are listed in Table 312, p. 462, for various sulfanilamides in several species. Because of the assumptions made in the calculation of these ratios (see footnote to Table 312), the figures must be regarded as approximations if comparison between species is attempted. The figures for the cat show that the highest concentration of filterable drug per unit amount in the body is obtained with sulfadiazine and the least with sulfathiazole. This is true also for the few drugs examined in the other species excepting the dog. The figures suggest also that higher concentrations are obtained in the rat, monkey and man than in the cat or dog.

Characterization of the distribution of a new drug serves the purpose of demonstrating that it can reach potential sites of infection in effective concentration. Comparison of distribution characteristics between drugs leads to more rational usage by indicating which drug can reach a particular tissue in the highest concentration. Bacterial infections are generally extracellular so that the concentration of drug in extracellular fluid is very important and localization of drug in tissue cells is undesirable. At the same time, a drug which is active *in vivo* can be assumed to be more or less freely diffusible since it could not otherwise reach and penetrate a bacterial cell. From the standpoint of free diffusibility, high concentration in extracellular fluid and a minimum of localization in cells, sulfadiazine and sulfamerazine appear to be the best of the drugs listed in Table 312. However, favorable distribution characteristics mean only that a drug can reach the extracellular fluid which surrounds the bacteria; these characteristics are of value only if the drug has an affinity for and an action against the bacterial cell.

The importance of factors other than concentration in extracellular fluid can be shown best by comparing data on the activity of sulfathiazole and sulfadiazine against *E. coli*[550]. Sulfathiazole was equal to sulfadiazine in activity *in vitro*, where the only protein present was that of the bacteria and where the drug was present in an extracellular fluid—the media. In other words, the concentration of sulfathiazole in the media for a given effect was the same as that of sulfadiazine and this was shown to be true for a variety of conditions in the case of *E. coli*. When these two drugs were compared *in vivo* against the same strain of *E. coli*, they were equally active on the basis of concentrations in whole blood. However, on the basis of concentration in extracellular fluid sulfathiazole would be considerably more active than sulfadiazine. This is shown in Table 313, p. 462, which gives a comparison of the two drugs *in vivo* and *in vitro*. Although the discrepancy between the two kinds of tests is not a great one—twofold—it suggests that the factors other than extracellular fluid concentration play a role in determining the relative activity of these two drugs.

(e) *Alteration of Sulfanilamides*

Sulfanilamides undergo chemical change in passing through the body. The mechanisms of these changes are not well defined. It is probable that these drugs participate in one or more of the many enzyme systems of the body and are chemically changed merely because they have chemical and physical properties allied to substances which normally participate in these systems. The most characteristic change is acetylation of the N^4-nitrogen and this results in loss of activity and in some cases in an increase in toxicity[1731]. Other chemical changes have been noted also. Scudi[468] reported isolation of hydroxy-sulfapyridine and later Weber, *et al.*[a] showed that the hydroxyl group was in the -3- position of the pyridine ring. In addition, they stated that this compound, 2-sulfanilyl-3-hydroxypyridine was active but less so than the parent compound. The available evidence indicates that this compound is excreted partly as such and partly conjugated with glucuronic acid or ethereal sulfate[2156]. Thorpe, *et al.*,[b] report the isolation of glucuronides of hydroxysulfathiazole and hydroxysulfanilamide. In a later paper Scudi, *et al.*[2157] reported additional evidence for the formation in the rat of water-soluble products (glucuronides or ethereal sulfates of monohydroxy derivatives of sulfanilamides), and they estimated that 40% of sulfapyridine; 10–20% of sulfanilamide, sulfathiazole and sulfamerazine; and 4–6% of sulfadiazine and sulfapyrazine, are excreted in this form. They suggested that these products are formed by the liver since liver damage reduced the urinary output of these metabolites. Inasmuch as these metabolites still have the free aryl amino group they are included in the determination of "free" drug by the Bratton-Marshall method. However, since the antibacterial activity of these metabolites is probably less than that of the parent compounds, the interpretation of *in vivo* activity on the basis of concentration in the blood or body fluids is somewhat complicated.

[a] Weber, C. J., *et al.*, *Proc. Soc. Exptl. Biol. Med.*, **53**, 190–2 (1943).
[b] Thorpe, W. V., and Williams, R. T., *Nature*, **146**, 686–7 (1940).

Although it is not possible to estimate the relative amount of these latter metabolites present in the blood stream, considerable information is available regarding the occurrence of the N^4-conjugated derivatives. Frisk[1135] found in man that sulfanilamide and sulfapyridine were most acetylated (50–60% of the drug excreted was in conjugated form and sulfaguanidine, sulfadiazine and sulfathiazole were least conjugated (25–35%). Welch, et al.[2419] found in man that sulfamerazine and sulfamethazine were conjugated somewhat more than sulfadiazine. Hamburger, et al.,[1248] found that sulfapyrazine and sulfadiazine were conjugated to about the same extent. Conjugation of these drugs has been studied experimentally, usually in the rabbit, and the results agree in general with clinical findings as to degree of conjugation; however, quantitative comparison cannot be made.

Sulfanilamides are acetylated in the liver but extrahepatic acetylation may occur also. Deacetylation (and also demethylation of N^4-methylsulfanilamide) have been shown to occur[1724]. Shaffer found in the chicken that extensive deacetylation took place in the kidney and that kidney extracts would rapidly deacetylate sulfanilamides in vitro[2637].

The importance of the degree and kind of change in structure of sulfanilamides lies in the fact that changed sulfanilamides differ from the parent substances in activity and toxicity. New sulfanilamides require investigation in this regard in order to determine if they are changed significantly in the body.

Quantitative studies of absorption, excretion, distribution and alteration of related drugs lead toward the much desired goal of relating chemical structure to fate of the drug in the body. The results obtained in some of the studies to date lend strength to the belief that it may ultimately be possible to synthesize compounds which exert specific actions at specific sites.

(2) Toxicological Studies

An ideal chemotherapeutic agent exerts a minimal effect on the body and a maximal effect on the bacteria. Inasmuch as the ultimate use of a chemotherapeutic drug is in an infected individual, it would seem logical that drug toxicity would be investigated in infected animals as well as in normal animals. However, toxicity studies are customarily undertaken on normal animals mainly because results obtained in a system made up of drug and host are more easily interpreted than those in a system of drug, host and bacteria. In addition the bacterial species concerned may produce a severe infection in mice but little or no infection in the other animals used for toxicity studies. In such a case the more complex system could not be used.

Extremely limited data on toxicity of sulfanilamides for infected animals has been reported. One would expect the toxicity of a drug to be increased in the presence of disease which by itself impairs vital metabolic functions. Partial confirmation of this view was obtained in Marshall's laboratory in experiments on the action of sulfanilamide in mice infected with β hemolytic streptococci, strain C203; however, the data were not published. The observations are given in Table 314, p. 463, along with data previously reported which were part of the same investigation. It can be seen that as the blood concentration of sulfanilamide increases, the survival rate goes to a maximum and then decreases due to toxic effects from the drug. Similar data for sulfadiazine in a pneumococcus infection are given in the second part of the table. These observations were made in the Stamford Laboratories of the American Cyanamid Company by Dr. H. J. White, and confirm the earlier observations. White[a] observed that sulfanilamide at blood concentrations of 10–20 mg.% was severely toxic in dogs infected intraperitoneally with Group C streptococci. Veterinarians have noted toxicity of sulfanilamides in animals under treatment for infections even though blood concentrations were lower than those which cause toxic symptoms in normal animals.[b]

The sulfanilamides which have been used widely in man were studied carefully for toxicity before they came into general use. For the most part each new drug was compared to a predecessor for relative toxicity (acute and chronic) in several species of experimental animals.

(a) Acute Toxicity of Sulfanilamides

Table 315, p. 464, summarizes some data reported for acute toxicity of these drugs. In selecting these, preference was given to comparative studies of two or more drugs. It can be seen that in the case of subcutaneous administration, the drugs do not vary to a great extent in toxicity. The greatest range between LD_{50}'s is roughly sixfold, sulfanilamide being least toxic, sulfathiazole, sulfadiazine and sulfamerazine being twice as toxic, sulfapyridine and sulfamethazine three times as toxic and sulfaguanidine five to six times as toxic. The figures for oral administration are all slightly higher than the corresponding subcutaneous LD_{50}'s. It should be noted that these figures are for the sodium salts of all of the drugs except sulfaguanidine. When the free acids are given to mice only sulfanilamide is sufficiently well absorbed to cause death, and its LD_{50} is about 4 Gm./kilo. The limited data on the dog suggest that this species is more susceptible than the mouse.

The symptoms in mice produced by the different drugs vary from severe depression with sulfanilamide to extreme stimulation with sulfapyridine which suggests that the various drugs kill by affecting different functions. This is also suggested by the fact that the average time to death varies with different drugs. For example, sulfanilamide and sulfadiazine kill in 24–48 hours, sulfapyridine, in 1–6 hours. Because of differences in absorption and excretion of these drugs, LD_{50} values may not reflect inherent toxicity. For this reason, it is useful to determine the concentration in the blood at death. The drugs have been compared on this basis in two ways, 1) determination of the concentration at death after administration of the Median Lethal dose (LD_{50}) and 2) the concentration which is lethal in 2–6 hours regardless of the percentage of mice killed. Table 316, p. 464, presents these comparisons.

The first method compares the drugs on the basis of the median lethal blood concentration (LBC_{50}), that is, the concentration which kills only 50% of the mice. The LBC_{50}, therefore, expresses as a blood concentration, the median lethal dose (LD_{50}). The second method (proposed by Frisk[1135]) compares drugs on the basis of the concentration which kills within 2–6 hours. The fallacy in this latter comparison becomes evident by consideration of the percentage of mice killed by the various concentrations. To take a specific case from Table 316, sulfadiazine at a blood concentration of 80 mg.% killed 100% of 55 mice, some of which died in 2–6 hours while sulfapyridine at a blood concentration of 95 mg.% killed 63% of 82 mice all of which died in 2–6 hours. Since both blood concentrations differ and since both percentage kills differ, there is no common basis for a comparison.

[a] White, H. J., Personal communication.
[b] Morris, M. L., Raritan Animal Hospital, New Brunswick, N. J., Personal communication.

On the basis of the median lethal blood concentration sulfanilamide, sulfadiazine, sulfamerazine and sulfamethazine are least toxic, sulfathiazole and sulfapyridine are about twice as toxic and sulfaguanidine is ten times as toxic. The latter drug, however, was conjugated very extensively and if total drug concentration is considered, sulfaguanidine is about five times as toxic as sulfadiazine.

A larger number of symptoms of acute toxicity can be observed in man than in animals because only objective symptoms can be noted in the latter. Symptoms such as nausea, vomiting, ataxia, depression, restlessness, irritability were found to occur in animals with sulfanilamide or sulfapyridine and these symptoms have been encountered in man with these drugs. Marshall, et al.[1729, 1731] found that concentrations in blood of sulfanilamide or sulfapyridine of 40–50 mg.% depressed renal clearance of the dog temporarily. Concentrations of 10–15 mg.% of acetylsulfapyridine caused a severe depression of renal clearance lasting more than 24 hours. A similar effect was noted in man when large doses of sulfanilamide were given intravenously.

It is important to determine acute toxicity in several different ways so that a valid basis for comparing drugs for toxicity is established. The fact that free acids of the N^1-heterocyclic sulfanilamides administered orally do not produce toxic symptoms does not permit the conclusion that they are non-toxic, but does suggest that large doses of the compounds are very poorly absorbed. When these compounds are administered by other routes and in the form of soluble salts measurable toxicity occurs and a basis for valid comparison is established. Because of differences in absorption and excretion relationships, the lethal dose of a drug will vary from one species to another. The lethal blood concentration is much less dependent on these relationships and is a more direct measure of drug toxicity than the actual dose administered. For these reasons, comparisons between species of the acute toxic effects of a drug should be made on the basis of blood concentration rather than on dosage.

Information of definite value is derived from acute toxicity studies. First, the signs, symptoms and nature of the acute toxic action of the drug are ascertained; second, the inherent acute toxicity of the drug is evaluated; and third, the range between any one dose used in therapy and the acutely toxic dose is established. This information has direct bearing on clinical use, especially in predicting the consequences of overdosage.

(b) Chronic Toxicity

An ideal chronic toxicity study establishes: 1) how well (or poorly) therapeutic doses and concentrations of drug are tolerated in comparison with a standard drug; 2) the maximal tolerated dose and concentration of both the new and the standard drug; and 3) the nature of the toxic effects produced by the drug.

[1] Methods

In these studies the effects from long exposure of the host to therapeutic as well as considerably higher concentrations of drug are examined. The length of exposure studied depends largely on the probable duration of therapy with the drug in man; for example, a drug to be administered to man for not more than two weeks is studied experimentally for 4–12 weeks while a drug to be used for months in man is studied for a year or more in animals.

The animals commonly used comprise two or more representative species such as either the mouse or rat, the guinea pig or rabbit, the dog and the monkey. Pure bred species such as the mouse or rat are widely used in order to decrease biological variation and thereby facilitate the recognition of small differences.

The most important object of these studies is to examine the chronic toxic action of a drug. In order to do this it is almost essential that the animals be in perfect health at the start of the experiment and that environmental factors do not haphazardly influence the results. Under these conditions, deviations from the normal can be attributed to the drug. It is apparent that if the animal is diseased to an unknown degree at the start of the experiment, the interpretation of experimental results is difficult or impossible. This is particularly true in the case of monkeys which almost invariably suffer from tuberculosis and various parasitic infestations (see [2419]).

The drug in question and a standard drug are usually administered according to a schedule which resembles that to be used in man; that is, dosage intervals are selected so that a reasonably constant blood concentration is maintained. In the case of the rat or mouse, the drug-diet method developed by Bieter, et al.[42] offers many advantages over other methods. For other animals the usual procedure is to administer one or more daily doses by means of capsules or by intubation. Ordinarily the drugs are administered by mouth but other routes may be used particularly if the drug is poorly absorbed from the gastrointestinal tract. For example, Schmidt, et al.[2128], found it necessary to use both oral and intravenous administration in the case of sulfadiazine in order to maintain blood concentrations at the desired level. A drug-diet method has been developed for dogs[1951].

The number of animals employed in these long-term studies is necessarily smaller than the number for acute experiments. This difference is compensated to some extent by the type of observations made in a study of chronic toxicity. The animals are examined daily to weekly and a record made of their general appearance, activity, the condition of hair, skin, nose and eyes. Immature animals are weighed daily and mature animals weekly. The food intake is measured, if possible, or the animals are observed during feeding periods in order to discover loss of appetite, a sensitive indicator of beginning toxicity. The blood is examined at frequent intervals to determine concentration of drug, cell counts, hemoglobin and morphology of the cells.

Animals which die during the experiment and the survivors which are sacrificed at the end are carefully examined for pathological changes in the organs and tissues which may be attributed to the drug. This examination is of such fundamental importance in chronic toxicity studies that the pathologist should participate in the entire experiment. Particular emphasis should be placed on the complete gross examination of organs and tissues and microscopic examination should be used to confirm the conclusions reached from gross study.

Certain general considerations are of interest in regard to extending conclusions based on animal experiments to man. These have been discussed by Sollman,[a] Marshall[333, 1729] and van Dyke[2375], and may be summarized as follows:

1. The fate of a drug in humans is unlikely to differ in any important degree from its fate in experimental animals. Thus, one can find abundant evidence in the case of the sulfanilamides that absorption, distribution, alteration and excretion are essentially the same in humans as in animals. Such differences as have been noted are usually quantitative rather than qualitative.

2. Toxicity of drugs is very likely to be greater for humans than for experimental animals. This rather fundamental difference can be attributed to at least two factors.

[a] Sollman, T., "*A Manual of Pharmacology*", 6th ed., p. 55, The W. B. Saunders Co., 1944.

The more specialized functions of humans, particularly those of the central nervous system, favor increased sensitivity to changes in environment. Toxicity of drugs is studied in healthy experimental animals, while in contrast the drugs are administered to diseased or infected humans whose normal functions may be impaired.

In general, relative toxicity (new drug compared to standard) is much the same in man as in experimental animals but absolute toxicity (toxic dose or concentration) often differs in man as compared to other animals.

[2] *Toxic Reactions*

Many toxicity studies of the important sulfanilamide derivatives have been reported. These have been examined recently by van Dyke[2375] whose excellent review summarizes the important aspects of the toxicology of sulfanilamides in clinical use.

A comparison of the toxic reactions noted in man (Table 323) with those observed in experimental animals reveals a striking discrepancy. Severe and acute drug reactions, such as, fever, anemia, leukopenia, dermatitis and hepatitis which are objective in character occur in man but not in experimental animals. (Subjective reactions, such as, psychosis, vertigo, malaise, confusion, headache are difficult or impossible to recognize in animals.) The occurrence of fever, dermatitis and hepatitis could be readily missed in experimental animals because the observations customarily made in chronic toxicity studies would be unlikely to disclose their presence. However, this is hardly the case in regard to the blood picture of experimental animals receiving sulfanilamide derivatives. A number of investigators have found that anemia can be produced in several experimental animals with sulfanilamide and sulfapyridine, but the anemia is rather mild, slow to develop and resembles very little the acute hemolytic crisis that has been observed in man (see references a, b, and c of Table 317). Similarly, anemia and leukopenia have been observed in the rat when deficient diets containing large amounts of a sulfanilamide derivative are fed for several weeks.[a] The causative factor in these experiments appears to be folic and pantothenic acid deficiencies, resulting from inhibition by the sulfanilamide derivative of the bacterial flora which normally synthesize the rat's requirement of these substances. There is no evidence that this anemia or leukopenia in the rat is comparable to acute hemolytic anemia or agranulocytosis in man. It is possible, however, that cases of mild anemia or leukopenia in man represent deficiencies in folic or pantothenic acid resulting from prolonged therapy with a sulfanilamide derivative. Acute hemolytic anemia in man has been shown to be associated with increased fragility of red cells; this does not seem to be true for the anemia in experimental animals[2375].

The group of toxic reactions which have been observed in both animals and man are given in Table 317, p. 465. The relation of anemia in animals to that in man has already been discussed. Cyanosis is an unimportant reaction; it has been shown, however, to be the same in animals as in man[2375]. Nausea and vomiting likewise are the same for both animals and man. This is shown also by the correlation evident between dog, monkey and man.

Renal injury has been the subject of much investigation since the first reports of this reaction in animals and man, and the mechanism has been satisfactorily established[2375]. The injury results from precipitation of poorly soluble drug in the collecting tubules and pelvis of the kidney. The kidney stones thus formed obstruct the outflow of urine and injure the epithelial tissues so that bleeding occurs. Three factors have been shown to

---

[a]Axelrod, A. E., *et al.*, *Arch. Biochem.*, **7**, 91–101 (1945); Daft, F. S., *et al.*, *U. S. Pub. Health Repts.*, **60**, 1201–15 (1945); also References[943, 944, 945, 1150, 2481].

favor the process by which renal injury occurs: a) low solubility of the drug (free or acetylated); b) low pH of the urine; and c) high concentration of drug in the urine.   The means of preventing and treating this complication are now evident because the underlying mechanism is known.

Sulfanilamides cause two kinds of injury to nervous tissue, functional and organic. Severe depression of function of the cerebral cortex was noted first with sulfanilamide[1729] and lesser depression has been found to occur with its derivatives.   The impairment of function leads to increased reflex time and decreased sensory acuity so that individuals receiving therapeutic doses of sulfanilamide should not engage in occupations requiring special skills.   Organic injury to nervous tissue probably represents a different type of action.   Such injury has been noted in both animals and man and may take the form of encephalomyelitis or peripheral neuritis.   Birds have been found particularly susceptible to sulfanilamide derivatives in this respect and have been used by a number of investigators to examine new drugs for this toxic action[735, 2375, 2419].   There appears to be a definite correlation between action of sulfanilamides on nervous tissue of animals and that of man, especially when data on sulfanilamides which have had little clinical use are considered[735].

In considering Table 317 from the standpoint of comparative toxicity of drugs, several points are of interest.   Sulfanilamide and bis(4-aminophenyl) sulfone produce more cyanosis than the other derivatives.   Sulfapyridine and sulfathiazole administered as sodium salts intravenously cause much more nausea and vomiting in dogs than the other derivatives.   Sulfanilamide in large doses causes vomiting but is well tolerated in reasonable dosage by dogs.   In man, sulfapyridine is outstanding for frequency and severity of this reaction.   These three drugs characteristically cause nausea and vomiting in dog, monkey and man in contrast to the others in the table which do not show this reaction to a significant extent.

The anemia-producing property of sulfanilamides and a sulfone in the mouse was studied quantitatively by several investigators who have shown that bis(4-aminophenyl) sulfone is most toxic, and that sulfadiazine and sulfamerazine are much less toxic than sulfanilamide, sulfaguanidine, sulfathiazole and sulfapyridine.   Hemolytic anemia in man is so infrequent that it is difficult to be certain that the drugs differ significantly.   This complication has occurred in man most frequently on a percentage basis with sulfanilamide and sulfapyridine.   Bis(4-aminophenyl) sulfone has been administered to very few patients because severe anemia was encountered.   "Promin" which has been used much more extensively produces anemia rather frequently due to its breakdown to bis(4-aminophenyl) sulfone[1238].

From the standpoint of renal injury there are differences between the drugs.   Renal injury in association with sulfanilamide occurs in conjunction with hemolytic anemia and has been ascribed to precipitation of hemoglobin in the kidney and not to precipitation of drug[2248].   This is in agreement with experimental findings that neither sulfanilamide nor acetylsulfanilamide will cause urolithiasis.   Uroliths of free or acetylated drug have been produced experimentally with all the sulfanilamide derivatives except sulfamethazine. Sulfaguanidine uroliths have been produced only in the dog and only under exceptional conditions[922].   Acetylsulfaguanidine uroliths can be produced in the rabbit as readily as acetylsulfathiazole concretions, by feeding the parent drugs, but in mice, urolithiasis from sulfaguanidine could not be produced[335].   The incidence of renal injury in man corresponds fairly closely with the results in experimental animals, sulfaguanidine and sulfamethazine being least toxic; sulfanilamide and sulfadiazine, intermediate; and sulfathiazole, sulfapyridine, sulfapyrazine, sulfamerazine having the highest incidence of symptoms of renal injury.

Injury to nervous tissue by the sulfanilamides in clinical use appears to be very rare. Cases of this reaction are noted in Table 317 for sulfanilamide, sulfathiazole and sulfapyridine only. In studies on chickens, Bieter, et al.[735] found sulfanilamide to be least injurious to nerves, sulfathiazole most and sulfapyridine intermediate. Welch, et al.[2419] found sulfadiazine, sulfamerazine and sulfamethazine to be about equal to or less injurious than sulfathiazole. However, the overall difference between sulfanilamide and sulfathiazole injury is very small and may not be significant. All of the drugs studied are much less injurious than sulfamethylthiazole, N^4-sulfanilyl-N^1-dimethylsulfanilamide ("Uliron") or sulfaphenylthiazole, the first two of which have shown a high incidence of severe nerve injury in man[735, 2375].

The relation of these toxicity studies in animals to the toxic reaction in man has been emphasized in order to illustrate the basic premise that results of toxicity studies in animals can be extended to man. It is evident also that toxic reactions occur in man which at present cannot be predicted from animal studies. It may be possible to devise experimental techniques to study their occurrence when the nature and mechanism of these unpredictable reactions is better understood.

TABLE 307

Solubilities of Sulfanilamides at 37°C. mg./100 cc.

Drug	Water	Serum	Urine		References
			Solub.	pH	
Sulfanilamide	1500	1970	1500	—	1759, 1717, 877
Sulfacetamide	1100	—	2200	—	
Sulfaguanidine	220	—	220	7.1	335, 1759
Sulfathiazole	96	180–330	80	5.0	1387, 335, 1645
			100	5.4	1759, 705, 885, 877, 1121
			250	7.5	
			500	8.0	
Sulfapyridine	52	61–75	40	5.4	1759, 877, 1387, 335, 1645
			60	7.4	
			90	8.2	
Sulfadiazine	12–15	160	18	5.5	1387, 1121, 705
			110	7.0	1645, 1759, 2126, 877, 1173
			350	7.5	
			400	7.9	
			1200	8.0	
Sulfapyrazine	5.2	—	4	5.5	130, 1248
			59	7.4	
Sulfamerazine	—	—	32	5.5	1173, 2126, 2419
			160	7.5	
			210	8.0	
Sulfamethazine	—	—	60	5.5	1759, 1173, 1645, 2050
			70	6.0	2128, 2126
			120	7.5	
			170	8.0	
N^4-Acetylsulfanilamide	530	—	—	—	1759
N^4-Acetylsulfaguanidine	40	—	50–80	7.1	1759, 335

TABLE 307—(*Concluded*)

Drug	Water	Serum	Urine Solub.	Urine pH	References
N⁴-Acetylsulfathiazole	6	104	10–20	5.4	1759, 335, 885, 1387, 1645
			25–40	7.5	
			265	8.2	
N⁴-Acetylsulfapyridine	16–35	35	11	5.4	1759, 335, 1645
			19	7.1	
			90	8.2	
N⁴-Acetylsulfadiazine	30	125–200	26	5.5	2128, 1759, 2126, 1121
			30	6.0	1173, 1387
			100	7.0	
			200	7.5	
			230	8.0	
N⁴-Acetylsulfapyrazine	5.6	—	8.2	5.5	130, 1248
			136	7.4	
N⁴-Acetylsulfamerazine	—	—	37	5.5	2128, 1173, 2126
			39	6.0	
			110	7.0	
			200	7.5	
			230	8.0	
N⁴-Acetylsulfamethazine	115	—	67	6.0	2128, 2126, 1645, 1759
			88	7.0	1173
			170	7.5	
			215	8.0	

TABLE 308

Absorption and Persistence of Sulfanilamides

Drug	Mouse (Blood)		Monkey (Plasma)	
	2 hrs.	24 hrs.	2 hrs.	24 hrs.
Sulfadiazine*	70	50	50	40
Sulfamerazine	100	100	100	100
Sulfamethazine*	60	40	50	20

* Blood concentrations of sulfadiazine and sulfamethazine in mM/100 cc. expressed as a percentage of the corresponding concentration of sulfamerazine. Each drug administered as a solution of the sodium salt in a dose of .15 mM/kg. of body weight to fasted animals. van Dyke, H. B., *et al.*, *J. Pharmacol.*, **83**, 203–12 (1945), through the courtesy of the *Journal of Pharmacology and Experimental Therapeutics*, Williams & Wilkins Company.

TABLE 309

Excretion of Sulfanilamides

Drug	Dog[a]		Man	
	Clearance Ratio	Excretion Ratio	Clearance Ratio	Excretion Ratio
Sulfanilamide	.27	.30	.27[b]	.34[c]
Sulfaguanidine	.76	.81	.50[b]	.77[c]

Source of figures: [a] (1097). [b] (1135). [c] (1135 and 1170).

TABLE 309—(Concluded)

Drug	Dog[a]		Man	
	Clearance Ratio	Excretion Ratio	Clearance Ratio	Excretion Ratio
Sulfacetamide	1.19	1.37		
Sulfathiazole	.40	1.00	.40[e]	.90[e]
Sulfapyridine	.38	.55	.17[e]	.28[e]
Sulfadiazine	.27	.33	.18[d]	.35[d]
Sulfamerazine	.13	.21	.60[d,e]	.18[d,e]

[d] (2527).

[e] Reinhold, J. G., et al., J. Pharmacol., **83**, 279–87 (1945).

TABLE 310
Distribution in the Cat of Sulfanilamides (1097)

Drug	Time	$\dfrac{T}{C} = \dfrac{\text{Tissue Concentration (mg./kg.)}}{\text{Plasma Water Concentration (mg./l.)}}$								Volume of Distribution* cc./Gm. Body Weight		pKa
		Cerebro-spinal Fluid	Brain	Red Blood Cells	Lung	Liver	Pancreas	Muscle	Nerve	A	B	
Sulfanilamide	2	.68	.73	1.30	1.07	1.37	1.03	1.07	.62	.98	1.10	10.4
	24	.83	.78	1.08	1.06	1.15	1.02	1.06	.94			
Sulfaguanidine	2	.09	.08	.93	1.17	1.29	1.16	.51	.62	.79	.84	—
	48	.30	.48	1.06	1.14	1.19	1.03	1.07	1.00			

* A—Calculated on the basis of total (free and bound) drug in plasma water.

B—Calculated on the basis of free (filterable) drug in plasma water.

C, the concentration of drug in mg./l. of plasma water represents the concentration in plasma, P, corrected for the space occupied by the plasma proteins, that is:

$$C = \frac{P}{.93}$$

V, the volume of distribution represents the following relationship, where D is the dose in mg./kg. and W is the body weight in kg.:

$$V = \frac{DW}{C}$$

The product DW is the amount of drug in the body under the conditions of these experiments and the observed concentration in plasma water, C, is a function of this. The volume of distribution represents literally, the volume of the animal if it consisted only of plasma water. Because this hypothetical volume is dependent on the weight of the animal, it is much more useful to express the volume of distribution with reference to body weight, that is:

$$V = \frac{DW}{CW} = \frac{D}{C} = \frac{\text{Dose in mg./kg.}}{\text{Concentration in mg./l. of plasma water}}.$$

It is then apparent that the ratio D/C expresses the *dose units required to give one concentration unit* of drug in plasma water. The ratio D/C corresponds to the distribution ratio "r" used by Marshall, et al. (J. Pharmacol., **61**, 196–204 (1937)) except that "r" is calculated on the basis of whole blood concentrations. Reproduced through the courtesy of the Authors and the *Journal of Pharmacology and Experimental Therapeutics*, Williams & Wilkins Company.

TABLE 310—(*Concluded*)

Drug	Time	Ratio: $\dfrac{T}{C} = \dfrac{\text{Tissue Concentration (mg./kg.)}}{\text{Plasma Water Concentration (mg./l.)}}$								Volume of Distribution* cc./Gm. Body Weight		pKa
		Cerebro-spinal Fluid	Brain	Red Blood Cells	Lung	Liver	Pancreas	Muscle	Nerve	A	B	
Sulfacetamide	2	.05	.06	.76	.54	.59	.45	.37	.46	.56	.64	5.38
	48	.88	.79	1.09	1.02	1.04	1.05	1.09	.99			
Sulfathiazole	2	.10	.14	.83	.71	1.13	.60	.54	.32	.58	1.40	7.12
	24	.28	.35	.68	.75	1.39	.63	.57	.61			
Sulfapyridine	2	.62	.80	.83	.97	1.33	.93	.91	.68	.82	1.20	8.44
	24	.47	.47	.65	.86	1.09	.74	.60	.57			
Sulfadiazine	2	.31	.21	.53	.60	.63	.44	.45	.38	.46	.55	6.48
	48	.81	.70	.78	.83	.90	.70	.74	.74			
Sulfamerazine	2	.38	.35	.45	.56	.76	.47	.39	.50	.46	.75	7.06
	24	.64	.43	.64	.67	1.22	.66	.59	.55			

TABLE 311
Plasma Binding of Sulfanilamides

Drug	% Bound	
	5 mg. Drug per 100 cc. Plasma	10 mg. Drug per 100 cc. Plasma
	a	b
Sulfanilamide	10	20
Sulfaguanidine	6	25
Sulfacetamide	13	20 [c]
Sulfathiazole	60	75, 55
Sulfapyridine	31	40, 40 [d] [e]
Sulfadiazine	17	56, 25, 32, 32
Sulfapyrazine	—	50, —, —, —
Sulfamerazine	39	84, 59, 63, 57
Sulfamethazine	—	84, —, —, 58

[a] (1097).
[b] (1170).
[c] Reinhold, J. G., *et al.*, *J. Pharmacol.*, **83**, 279–87 (1945).
[d] (2527).
[e] van Dyke, H. B., *et al.*, *J. Pharmacol.*, **83**, 203–12 (1945).

TABLE 312

Filterable Concentration in Plasma Water per Unit Amount in Body of Various
Sulfanilamides*

Drug	Rat	Cat[b]	Dog	Monkey	Man
Sulfanilamide	—	.91	1.00[c]	—	1.6[j]
Sulfaguanidine	—	1.20	.84[d]	—	—
Sulfacetamide	—	1.50	—	—	—
Sulfathiazole	—	.70	—	—	1.1[f,h]
Sulfapyridine	—	.85	.91[e]	—	.95[f]
Sulfadiazine	2.4[a]	1.60	—	2.1[a]	2.2[f,g]
Sulfapyrazine	—	—	—	—	1.4[i]
Sulfamerazine	1.8[a]	1.40	—	1.6[a]	—
Sulfamethazine	1.6[a]	—	—	1.2[a]	—

[a] (2128).
[b] (1097).
[c] Marshall, E. K., Jr., et al., J. Pharmacol., **61,** 196–204 (1937).
[d] (335).
[e] (1731).
[f] **(1135).**
[g] (1912).
[h] (2014).
[i] (1248).
[j] Marshall, E. K., Jr., J. Am. Med. Assoc., **108,** 953 (1937).

* Except for the figures on the cat and dog, the following assumptions were necessary
in the calculations for each drug:
1) the degree of binding in the rat was the same as in the cat and dog;
2) the degree of binding in the monkey was the same as in man;
3) the ratio of plasma concentration to whole blood in the rat and monkey was the
same as in the cat and man, respectively;
4) extrapolation to zero time of the log. concentration-time curve gave the equilibrium
concentration of drug for the dose administered intravenously.   (See figure 5.)

TABLE 313

Activity of Sulfathiazole and Sulfadiazine against E. coli (550)

Drug	In Vitro		In Vivo		
	Minimal Inhibitory Concentration	Activity Ratio[a]	S.B.C.$_{.50}$[b]	SFC$_{50}$[c]	Activity Ratio
Sulfathiazole	2.56 mg. %	1.0	3.6 mg. %	1.7 mg. %	2.3
Sulfadiazine	2.56 mg. %	—	3.3 mg. %	3.9 mg. %	

[a] Activity ratio = $\dfrac{\text{Concentration of Sulfadiazine}}{\text{Concentration of Sulfathiazole}}$.

[b] S.B.C.$_{.50}$ = Concentration in whole blood which produced 50% survival of mice infected with E. coli—(20,000 ± 4000 bacteria in mucin injected intraperitoneally).

[c] SFC$_{50}$ = Concentration of filterable drug in plasma water for S.B.C.$_{.50}$, i.e., concen-

tration of drug in extracellular water. This is calculated by using 1) a factor which converts whole blood to plasma concentration and 2) by correcting plasma binding and space occupied by plasma protein. The calculation was as follows:

$$\text{Sulfathiazole S.B.C.}_{50} \times 1.09 \times \frac{.40}{.93}$$

$$\text{Sulfadiazine S.B.C.}_{50} \times 1.31 \times \frac{.83}{.93}$$

The factors used are derived from data given by Fisher, *et al.*[1097] for the cat and dog and the assumption is made that the relation *between the factors* for the two drugs will be the same in the mouse as in the cat or dog.

TABLE 314

Toxicity in Infected Mice

A. Action of Sulfanilamide in Mice Infected with Streptococci, strain C203. Therapy −1 to +6 Days

% in Diet	Approximate Blood Conc. mg. %	No. of Mice	% Survivals at 30 Days
1/32*	.4	20	5
1/16*	.8	29	52
1/8*	1.8	49	84
1/4*	3.5	30	100
1/2	7	30	93
1	14	30	81
2	25	30	65

* (309) Data for 1/2, 1, and 2% diets obtained in same study but not reported.

(Reproduced through the courtesy of the *Journal of Pharmacology and Experimental Therapeutics*, Williams & Wilkins Company.)

B. Action of Sulfadiazine in Mice Infected with Pneumococci, Type I. Therapy −3 to +6 Days*

% in Diet	Blood Conc. mg. %	No. of Mice	% Survivals at 21 Days
1/80	1.5	20	15
1/40	2.5	20	35
1/20	3.8	20	40
1/10	5	20	70
2/10	9	20	100
4/10	20	20	100
8/10	34	20	55

* Data obtained in the Stamford Laboratories of the American Cyanamid Company.

TABLE 315

Acute Toxicity of Sulfanilamides, Gm./kg.

| Drug | L.D.$_{50}$-Mice | | Approximate Lethal Dose Dog |
	Subcutaneous	Oral	
Sulfanilamide	2.8[a]	3.3[f]	>2[h], *,O
Sulfaguanidine	<.5[b],*,IP	—	>1[b],*,IP
Sulfathiazole	1.7[a]	6.0[g]	
Sulfapyridine	.9[a]	1.7[f]	.5[f],IV
Sulfadiazine	1.3[a]; 1.6[d]	1.8[d]; 2.2[e]	
Sulfapyrazine	.85[e],IV	—	
Sulfamerazine	1.6[d]	3.3[d]; 2.5[e]	
Sulfamethazine	1.1[d]	1.9[d]	

a (1135).   e (2419).
b (335).   f (1731).
c (2039).   g (29).
d (2128).   h (1729).

* Free acid—all other drugs administered as sodium salts. IP = Intraperitoneal; IV = Intravenous; O = Oral.

TABLE 316

Lethal Concentrations of Sulfanilamides in Mice

| Drug | Blood Concentration Lethal to 50% of mice, mg. % | Time of Death Hours | Concentration Lethal in 2–6 Hours mg. % | Mice Killed | |
				No.	%
Sulfanilamide	150[d]	24–48	430[a]	25/25	100
Sulfaguanidine	15[e],*	24–48	130[c]	15/15	100
Sulfathiazole	80[e]	12–24	240[a]	36/40	90
Sulfapyridine	90[d]	1–6	95[a,d]	52/82	63
Sulfadiazine	180[b]	24–48	680[a]	55/55	100
Sulfamerazine	160[b]	2–6	160[b]	38/75	50
Sulfamethazine	120[b]	2–6	120[b]	25/50	50

a (1135).   d (1731).
b (2128).   e (139).
c (335).

* Total drug concentration was 35 mg. %.

TABLE 317

Toxic Reactions to Sulfanilamides

	Cyanosis					Nausea and Vomiting			Anemia					Renal Injury					Nerve Injury	
	Mouse or Rat	Rabbit	Dog	Monkey	Man	Dog	Monkey	Man	Mouse or Rat	Rabbit	Dog	Monkey	Man	Mouse or Rat	Rabbit	Dog	Monkey	Man	Chicken	Man
Sulfanilamide	++	−	−	−	++	+	−	+	+	−	+	+	++	−	−	−	−	+	±	+
Sulfaguanidine	−	−	−	−	−	±	+	−	+	−	−	−	−	−	+	±	−	±	+	−
Sulfathiazole	+	−	−	−	−	++	+	++	+	−	±	+	++	+	+	+	+	++	+	+
Sulfapyridine	−	−	−	±	+	±	−	±	+	−	−	−	±	+	+	+	+	++	±	++
Sulfadiazine	−	−	−		±	−	±	±	±		−	−	±	+	+	+	+	++	±	+
Sulfapyrazine	−	−	−	−	−	−		±	±		−	−	−	+	+	+	+	++	±	−
Sulfamerazine	−	−	−		++	−		±	+		−		+	+	+	+	+	±	±	−
Sulfamethazine	++	−	−	−	±	−		+			−		±	0	+	0	0	±		−
Bis(4-aminophenyl) Sulfone					+			+					++							
Promin					+															

References:

	Cyanosis					Nausea and Vomiting			Anemia					Renal Injury					Nerve Injury	
	Mouse or Rat	Rabbit	Dog	Monkey	Man	Dog	Monkey	Man	Mouse or Rat	Rabbit	Dog	Monkey	Man	Mouse or Rat	Rabbit	Dog	Monkey	Man	Chicken	Man
	a, b	1729	1729	c, d	2248	2128	139	f	1521	1729	2039	c	1238	335	831	1248	2128	h	735	h
	335	1731	1731	139	f	2039	2128	2248	b, a	1731	1729	2128	f	g	335	2128	2419	2248	2419	2375
	139	335	335	2128	h	1729	2419	h	o	335	2128	2419	h	1545	1729	2419	922			2248
	2039	e	2128	2419		335	526			e	2419	922	2248	e	2354	922	2375			
	1521	922	2039	e		922	922			922	922	2337		2375		1729	o			
			1950	922		1731					1953	2039		1729		1731				
			1953			2419								2039						
			922											2128						

a Machella, T. E. and Higgins, G. M., Proc. Staff. Mayo Clin., 14, 183-5 (1939); Am. J. Med. Sci., 199, 157-63 (1940).
b Richardson, A. P., Bull. Johns Hopkins Hosp., 65, 445-55 (1939); J. Pharmacol., 67, 429-36 (1939); 70, 370-7 (1940); 71, 203-9 (1941); 72, 99-111 (1941).
c P'An, S. Y., Chinese Med. J., 56, 111-21 (1939).
d Molitor, H. and Robinson, H. J., Arch. Inter. Pharmacodynamie, 62, 281-94 (1939).
e Rake, G., et al., Am. J. Med. Sci., 200, 353-62 (1940).
f Hawking, F., Brit. Med. J. (1945), 505-9.
g Gross, P., et al., Am. J. Clin. Path., 11, 882-9 (1941).
h Table 323.

++, +, ± denote relative frequency of reaction.
− indicates that the reaction was not observed.
0 indicates that attempts to produce the reaction were unsuccessful.

Chapter XI

THEORIES OF THE MECHANISM OF ACTION OF SULFONAMIDE DRUGS

Chemotherapy with sulfonamide drugs is so new that despite widespread and intensive effort which has built up a considerable literature, there is as yet no universally accepted theory to account for the mechanism of action of these drugs. Instead there are many theories. It would be well for the reader to keep in mind the axiom in general semantics that all theories are at best mere abstractions from reality which are approximately true under special conditions. Theories of the mode of action of chemotherapeutic agents are dealing with such complex phenomena that the special conditions under which they may be approximately true are difficult to define and may differ considerably from reality. In particular, theories based on evidence derived from *in vitro* studies of bacteriostatic action under very special conditions should not be regarded as necessarily valid under the infinitely more complex conditions prevailing in actual chemotherapeutic use of a drug.

It is hoped that the theories presented in this chapter will serve the function of stimulating further work on testing their validity and will open up methods of approach to improved chemotherapeutic agents. The danger in all theories, that they funnel research into narrow channels by closing the mind to other approaches, should be resisted. Theories follow some fundamental discovery and technological improvements may follow the theories, but new fundamental discoveries in the field are usually made by men able to think outside of the prevailing theories or astute enough to recognize phenomena not conforming to the theories.

Before considering the various theories which have been proposed, the generally accepted facts and experimental evidence fundamental to the theories are first reviewed.

(I) Facts Fundamental to a Theory of Action

(A) Summary of the More Important Experimental Findings

The following are a number of experimental findings which must be explained by a satisfactory theory of action of the sulfonamide drugs.

1. The action is largely bacteriostatic, not bactericidal. Bacteria are not usually killed *in vitro* by therapeutic concentrations of the sulfonamides; instead their growth is slowed or stopped. Transfer of bacteria subjected to the action of sulfanilamide for two or three hours to a fresh culture medium free of sulfanilamide results in normal growth of the organism. Growth may also be restored to sulfanilamide-inhibited cultures by addition of sulfonamide antagonists, of which the most potent is *p*-aminobenzoic acid (PABA)[1154, 1415]. The action may be bactericidal on prolonged contact in the presence of blood serum[900], or higher concentrations of drug[1135].

2. There is an appreciable lag before bacteriostatic action of sulfa drugs starts. The resulting growth curve is independent of the time the sulfa drug was added to the culture medium prior to inoculation. In animals, establishment of an adequate blood level of drug before infection does not prevent growth of the organisms for the first few hours[1600, 1632, 1676, 1812].

3. Presence of proteolytic products (peptones) in culture media antagonizes the action of sulfonamide drugs on bacteria[176, 751, 1139, 1271, 1313, 1600, 1601, 1676, 1690, 1812].

4. Leukocytic or phagocytic activity is not stimulated by the drugs, nor is the speed of production, quantity and quality of immune bodies affected;[714, 754, 1092, 1153, 1165, 1212, 1840, 1832, 2010, 2011, 2030, 2535] but these factors are of great importance in clinical cure of infections.

5. The inactivity of the isomers of sulfanilamide (orthanilamide and metanilamide) must be explained, as well as the inability of *o* and *m* isomers of *p*-aminobenzoic acid to antagonize sulfanilamide bacteriostasis. It has been shown that orthanilamide and metanilamide are equally well absorbed by the body and are taken up by bacterial cells equally well, yet all *in vivo* and *in vitro* tests show them to be inactive or nearly so.[140]

6. Bacteria become resistant to the action of the sulfa drugs.

7. Increase of temperature greatly increases the bacteriostatic action of the drugs[2438, 2439, 2587, 2588].

8. At very low concentrations, sulfa drugs may stimulate the growth of bacteria and other cells[176, 1199, 1507, 2535, 2579].

9. The inhibition of growth of many different kinds of cells is brought about by the sulfonamide drugs at various concentrations. In most cases, PABA reverses the inhibition.

These and other findings are considered more in detail below.

(B) Sulfonamide Antagonists

(1) Historical

It was recognized by Lockwood[1600] in 1938 that presence of peptones in culture media had a pronounced antagonistic effect on the bacteriostatic action of sulfanilamide. The importance of this observation to the question of mode of action of the drugs was so apparent that much research was stimulated on the nature of substances which would antagonize sulfonamide action.

McLeod[1690] attempted to find sulfa drug antagonists in various body tissues and fluids. He found them present in fresh muscle, pancreas, and spleen but the amount was greatly increased by autolysis or acid hydrolysis of the tissues. The fresh livers of beef, rabbit and guinea pig were free of antagonists but the autolysate or hydrolysate contained them. Human urine developed antagonists on hydrolysis. Pus always contained considerable quantities.[2504]

In the case of certain bacteria, the antagonist was found in the cells only and in other cases in the supernatant and not in the cells. When pneumococci became fast to sulfapyridine, there was a great increase in the production of antagonist.

Stamp[2269] extracted hemolytic streptococci cells with dilute ammonia and obtained a protein-free extract containing amino acids and other low molecular weight materials which had a powerful antagonistic effect against the *in vitro* inhibition of bacterial growth brought about by sulfapyridine or sulfanilamide. Green[176] obtained similar results. In trying to find the nature of the "P" factor which was a powerful antagonist to sulfanilamide, he tested calcium pantothenate, thiamine, nicotinic acid, beta-alanine, betaindoleacetic acid, pimelic acid, glutamic acid, uracil, cysteine, inositol and biotin. None of these had a similar effect. Woods[569] obtained evidence pointing to *p*-aminobenzoic acid (PABA) as the probable active agent in an extract from yeast, and showed for the first time that synthetic PABA would completely reverse the bacteriostatic activity of sulfanilamide *in vitro* against various bacteria. Selbie[473] and Findlay[1081] showed that

PABA would antagonize the action of sulfonamide drugs *in vivo* as well. Rubbo and Gillespie[447] isolated PABA as its benzoyl derivative while Kuhn and Schwartz[2578] isolated it as the methyl ester from yeast extracts. Blanchard[2500] and others[1665, 2063] have isolated PABA itself from such sources, though usually it appears to be in a combined form in living tissue from which it appears in an active form following hydrolysis. It, therefore, appears probable, but by no means certain, that PABA is the main antagonist of sulfonamide drugs occurring in nature. Other antagonists have been found, but none appears as potent.

Ratner, *et al.*[2619] isolated from 50 kilos of dried yeast about 400 mg. of a peptide of PABA which appeared to consist of PABA linked through the carboxyl group to a chain of 10 to 12 glutamic acid molecules. The amino group was free as shown by diazotization and coupling reactions. The peptide did not antagonize sulfonamides.

(2) *In Vitro* Studies of the Antagonism of PABA and Sulfonamides

Intensive studies by many bacteriologists[447, 577, 1100, 1122, 1199, 1271, 1364, 1690,2477, 2580, 2593, 2605] confirmed the ability of PABA to prevent or reverse the inhibition of growth of most bacteria susceptible to the action of the sulfonamide drugs. These studies were aided by a microbiological method of assay for PABA developed by Landy and Dicken[1510] using *Acetobacter suboxydans* whose growth is a function of added PABA and is very specific for this growth factor. Other bioassays have also been devised[1797, 2607]. It thus became possible to assay culture media employed in *in vitro* testing of the activity of sulfonamide drugs to determine their content of sulfonamide antagonist and to place such testing methods on a more scientific basis. However, as Henry[1297] pointed out in his excellent critical review of the mode of action of sulfonamides, all biological methods of assay are subject to doubt that the growth of the microorganism is actually caused by PABA. Further, there is no assurance that growth-factor activity and sulfonamide-antagonistic activity are necessarily the same, in fact, many powerful growth factors have no effect on sulfonamide inhibition. It nevertheless seems probable that PABA is the most potent single antagonist present in bacterial culture media derived from natural sources. Mirick[1792, 2606] gave supporting evidence by showing that the antagonist produced by pneumococci is rapidly destroyed by a soil bacillus specifically adapted to oxidize PABA.

Lynch and Lockwood[1639] and Spink and Jermsta[2252] showed that growth stimulation and sulfonamide antagonism were dissociated phenomena in the case of the common pathogens. While PABA had a most powerful antagonistic effect on the action of sulfanilamides, it did not stimulate growth. No antagonistic effect[1637, 2063] was shown by *p*-aminophenylacetic acid. It was said to be 10 times as active as PABA as a growth factor for *Cl. acetobutylicum*[2063] but others have found only 0.002% to 0.1% the activity[580, 1508].

Landy and Wyeno[1515] showed that the antagonism of PABA against the action of sulfanilamide, sulfapyridine and sulfathiazole in inhibiting growth of β-hemolytic streptococcus, *Staphylococcus aureus* and pneumococcus was specific. Neither its isomers (*o*- and *m*-aminobenzoic acids), *p*-aminophenylacetic acid nor *p*-aminophenylglycine showed a similar effect (see also [1364]).

Wyss[577, 579] analyzed, mathematically, growth rate studies on *E. coli* grown in a synthetic medium in the presence of sulfanilamide and PABA. He could not demonstrate that PABA had an effect on the growth in the absence of sulfanilamide. However, the data indicated, definitely, that sulfanilamide inhibited growth by competition with PABA and obeyed the law of mass action as shown by the fact that the molar ratio of sulfonamide to PABA required for antagonism was constant over a wide concentration range. These results have been verified by many observers[447, 573, 1200, 1364, 1669, 1812, 2316, 2477].

Fitzgerald and Feinstone[1100] studied the effect of 18 sulfanilamide derivatives on *E. coli* and *M. tuberculosis in vitro* and showed that the relative order of activity of the compounds in bringing about bacteriostasis of the organisms was the same. They also showed that PABA strongly inhibited the action of the sulfonamides against *M. tuberculosis*.

Hirsch[1314] showed that while there is a lag before the bacteriostatic effect of a sulfa drug is exerted, the reversal of this inhibition by PABA is immediate.

(3) *In Vivo* Antagonism of PABA and Sulfonamides

The antagonistic effect of PABA has been demonstrated *in vivo* by a number of workers, usually in mice[1665, 1812, 1976, 2324] against streptococcal, pneumococcal, and meningococcal infections treated with sulfanilamide or its derivatives. The bis(4-aminophenyl) sulfoxides and sulfones are similarly inhibited *in vivo*[2590]. Because PABA is rapidly conjugated or otherwise inactivated in the body[1665], it is usually necessary to give repeated doses to demonstrate its effect[2324]. Fears have been expressed, backed up by some experimental evidence[847, 967, 1418, 1690, 1907, 2063], that local anaesthetics such as procaine, which are derivatives of PABA, should not be used during sulfonamide therapy because of danger to the patient through reversing the effect of the sulfonamide. Local anaesthetics not derived from PABA were without this effect[1418]. It was shown that repeated doses of procaine were necessary to produce an effect and while it was preferable to use other local anaesthetics, a single small injection of procaine could probably be made without adverse effect on an infection being treated by sulfonamides[967], because the liberated PABA was rapidly rendered inert by metabolism of the host.

Substitution of the amino group in local anaesthetics derived from PABA by alkyl or acyl groups was shown to markedly decrease or abolish the antagonism of the compound to the bacteriostatic activity of the common sulfa drugs *in vitro*[2584, 2645] but since *in vivo* studies were not made it is uncertain whether these derivatives can be catabolized to PABA in the host. Based on findings where sulfonamide drugs substituted on the amine group showed activity *in vivo* but not *in vitro* it would appear that removal of such substituents might take place from these local anaesthetics *in vivo* and might give rise to *in vivo* antagonism of sulfonamide drugs.

(4) Action of PABA and Sulfonamides on Other Cells

The antagonism of the effect of sulfonamide drugs by PABA has now been observed on many different types of cells besides bacteria. Sulfanilamide was shown to inhibit the germination of wheat and rice seeds while PABA antagonized this effect[786, 2024]. On oat seedlings, sulfanilamide had a growth retarding effect at a concentration of 0.001 molar which was only partly reversed by PABA[1397]. On some plants, concentrated solutions caused polyploidy, while in very dilute solutions, sulfonamides had a growth stimulating effect[510]. High concentrations of sulfonamides inhibited stem growth of peas and this was reversed by PABA[2444].

The inhibitory effect of 400 mg./kilo/day of sulfanilamide on *Plasmodium gallinaceum* in chickens was completely blocked by 0.25 mg./kilo/day of PABA[1700]. Similar results[2163] were obtained on other malarial parasites and other sulfonamide drugs but PABA had no such effect on atabrine or quinine, indicating that the latter were acting through quite different mechanisms[1733, 2163].

Antagonism of PABA and sulfanilamide has been further demonstrated on such diverse types as the virus of lymphogranuloma venereum[1081] a fungus infection by *Trichophyton purpureum* (Bang)[975]; a fresh water diatom[2443]; *Aspergillus niger*; *Polytomella caeca*, a flagellate,[1638] and yeast[2580].

The effect on lymphogranuloma venereum virus has been disputed[2163].

(5) Failure of PABA to Inhibit Sulfa Drugs

Occasional cases have been described where certain of the sulfonamides have been effective in some measure against particular organisms but the action has not been antagonized by PABA. Thus, Hawking[1278] found sulfapyridine or sulfathiazole effective against *Borrelia recurrentis* infections in mice when fed at a level of 1.5% in the diet. This effect was not reversed by PABA nor by nicotinamide. Other sulfonamide drugs did not suppress the infection nor did pyridine-3-sulfonamide, aminopyridine sulfate or acetylsulfapyridine. It thus appeared that these drugs were acting through a different mechanism than that common to many sulfa drugs against bacteria.

Tamura[2309] noted that while sulfapyrazine, sulfadiazine and sulfathiazole were active *in vitro* against *Pasturella tularense* at concentrations in excess of 5 mg. per 100 cc., the bacteriostasis was not antagonized by PABA. Further, PABA itself inhibited growth at concentrations greater than $M \times 10^{-4}$. *Pasturella pestis* grown on the same medium was inhibited by sulfapyrazine and this effect was antagonized by PABA.

Lawrence and Goetchius[2584] found that PABA had little or no effect in antagonizing the bacteriostatic action of sulfanilamidoindazole on *Brucella melitensis* in contrast to the positive antagonism to sulfathiazole on the same organism. The 3, 5, and 7 isomers were said to behave similarly.

(6) Action of PABA against Drugs Other than Sulfanilamide derivatives

Compounds of many kinds which are antagonized by PABA are listed in Table 305 and are discussed in Chapter IX where it is shown that there is a reasonably close structural similarity between bacteriostatic drugs which are antagonized by PABA and PABA itself. The significance of this will be apparent later in this chapter. It was also shown that bacteriostatic drugs which are not antagonized by PABA usually differ structurally in some important detail. In a few cases, it cannot be predicted whether a compound will act as an inhibitor of bacteria, as an antagonist of sulfanilamide-type activity, or whether it will show both effects dependent on concentration.

(7) Compounds Closely Related to PABA as Sulfonamide Antagonists

Woods[569] in his early study of sulfonamide antagonists gave the following list of compounds and the molar concentration at which they would reverse the inhibition of growth of *Strep. hemolyticus* in the presence of 3.03×10^{-4} M. sulfanilamide.

Compounds which were inactive included *p*-hydroxybenzoic acid, *p*-toluic acid, benzoic acid, benzamide and arsanilic acid.

The antagonistic effects of such compounds as *p*-nitrobenzoic acid, *p*-acetamidobenzoic acid, ethyl *p*-aminobenzoate, procaine, *p*-aminobenzamide, *p*-hydroxylaminobenzoic acid, also *p*-aminobenzaldehyde might be through ability of the bacteria to convert these substances to PABA. However, some nuclear-substituted derivatives of PABA act as weak sulfanilamide antagonists (see Table 183) and conversion of these to PABA by catabolic processes does not seen probable.

Compound	Concentration
PABA	$1.2\text{-}5.7 \times 10^{-8}$ M.
m-Aminobenzoic Acid	0.9×10^{-3}
o-Aminobenzoic Acid	—
p-Nitrobenzoic Acid	1.8×10^{-4}
p-Acetaminobenzoic Acid	1.8×10^{-4}
Ethyl *p*-Aminobenzoate	3.6×10^{-5}
Procaine	5.8×10^{-8}
p-Aminobenzamide	1.4×10^{-6}
2-(*p*-Aminobenzamido)pyridine	0.9×10^{-3}
p-Hydroxylaminobenzoic Acid	5.8×10^{-8}

Ivánovics[1364] found that 20,000 times as much carefully purified *o* or *m*-aminobenzoic acid did not have the antagonistic action of PABA on sulfonamide inhibition of *Staph. aureus*. This might indicate that traces of PABA in the *m*-aminobenzoic acid of Woods were responsible for the slight activity he found.

4-(Aminomethyl)benzoic acid does not inhibit sulfanilamide derivatives, neither does it inhibit "Marfanil"[1384].

(8) Other Sulfonamide Antagonists

The reversal of sulfonamide action is not limited to PABA, although this is still the most potent single antagonist known. Bliss and Long[751] and Kohn and Harris[1271, 1459] demonstrated that sulfanilamide was antagonized by methionine and that a weak antagonistic effect was brought about by combinations of other essential amino acids but not regularly by any single amino acid other than methionine. The effect of methionine was not because it was a growth stimulant; in fact, over 1% concentration of methionine had an antibacterial action which was antagonized to a certain extent by sulfanilamide. Harris and Kohn[183] found that the effect of methionine was enhanced by addition of xanthine and guanine but in the absence of methionine, these purines increased the activity of sulfanilamide. However, this apparently depends on the species of bacteria because adenine, guanine, xanthine and hypoxanthine were able to antagonize sulfonamide bacteriostasis of certain lactic acid bacteria[2226].

Others[266, 1271, 1306, 2288] have demonstrated the antagonistic effect of methionine against sulfanilamide and sulfaguanidine. The *l*-methionine was found to be about ten times as effective as the *d*-form[1271]. Sulfapyridine, sulfathiazole and sulfadiazine bacteriostasis did not appear to be reversed by methionine[2288].

Strauss, *et al.*[2288] found that partially resistant strains of *E. coli* or *Staph. aureus* showed sulfonamide antagonism from presence of methionine, where non-resistant strains did not. Uracil, sodium pyruvate and adenylic acid in combination, but not singly, antagonized the action of sulfaguanidine on *Staph. aureus*. Other possible growth factors including nicotinic acid, thiamine chloride, cocarboxylase, riboflavin and pyridoxine were found not to antagonize sulfathiazole bacteriostasis of *E. coli* or *Staph. aureus* in simple media[422]. The same results were obtained with biotin and sodium pantothenate[1306, 2288]; however, glutamic acid and glutathione were antagonistic to sulfonamides[1306].

Sodium citrate in high concentration (4%) prevented the bacteriostatic action of sulfacetamide on *E. coli* where sodium acetate and sodium lactate did not interfere[1929]. Growth of strains of streptococcus and staphylococcus were inhibited by the 4% sodium citrate but it had no such effect on *E. coli*.

Auhagen[681] recently claimed that p-aminobenzoyl-l-glutamic acid was 8 to 10 times as active as PABA in equimolecular amounts in antagonizing the *in vitro* inhibition of *Streptobacterium plantarum*. The corresponding derivatives of d-glutamic acid, glycine, d- and l-leucine, l-aspartic acid and glycylglycine were inactive. These results were not verified in this country[1395, 2453] where p-aminobenzoyl-l-glutamic acid was found to have only 1/20 the activity of PABA on *Lactobacillus arabinosus* and from 1/400 to 1/8000 the activity with various pathogens. It was suggested that if 0.1% PABA were present as an impurity in the peptide, this would have accounted for the observed activity[2453].

The question of whether PABA is the antagonist chiefly responsible for the activity of peptone is by no means settled. Tabone, Nitti and Mousset[2646] have investigated the question further. They found that if an active peptone was hydrolyzed with HCl, the antagonistic power decreased until only a small part remained. The peptone was found not to couple with diazotized PABA. If diazotized PABA was heated to 100°C., the antagonistic effect was lost but diazotized peptones or peptone hydrolyzates did not lose their effectiveness. When a mixture of diazotized PABA and diazotized peptone or peptone hydrolyzate was heated only part of the activity was destroyed. When yeast autolyzate was diazotized, it lost from a fourth to a half of its antagonistic effectiveness and this was not influenced by addition of PABA to the autolyzate before diazotization. Heating the diazotized mixture destroyed the activity. They, therefore, thought it probable that PABA was the factor in yeast autolyzate responsible for its activity, but that PABA did not account for more than a small fraction of the antagonistic action of peptone.

Eckert[2528] thought tryptophane rather than PABA the source of slight color when peptones were diazotized and coupled. Kohn and Harris[1462] found the bound or unbound PABA in peptone too slight to account for its antagonism. They divided the antagonists present in peptone into two groups, the first of which were equally antagonistic to all sulfonamide drugs. The second group included methionine, serine, glycine, allothreonine (but no other known naturally occurring amino acid), xanthine and guanine[1457]. The second group antagonized sulfapyridine, sulfathiazole and sulfadiazine more than sulfanilamide but antagonism was evident only when the rate of growth was inhibited by more than 65%. The best source of this antagonist was pancreas but it was not a known naturally occurring amino acid, a heat labile protein, or insulin.

Loomis, *et al.*[2592] showed that the antagonistic powers of yeast extract were due to two or more factors. The properties of one of these was similar to PABA. Hirsch[1313] separated the antagonistic substances in yeast extract by precipitation with mercuric chloride, leaving factors which caused growth stimulation but did not have an antagonistic action to the sulfonamide drugs.

Grob[2544] showed that the bacteriostatic activity of sulfathiazole was greatly diminished or even abolished if trypsin was added to the medium because the proteolytic products formed stimulated the growth of bacteria and antagonized the action of sulfathiazole.

Mirick[2606] found an antagonist of sulfonamides produced by a soil bacillus which was not PABA but was not identified.

An isostere of PABA, 2-aminopyrimidine-5-carboxylic acid,

$$H_2N \underset{N}{\overset{N}{\diamondsuit}} COOH$$

was found to have one two-thousandth of the activity of PABA in antagonizing sulfanilamide bacteriostasis of streptococcus[2600]. Isosteres of PABA may be inhibitors or antagonists, apparently, and this is also true of nuclear substituted derivatives of PABA[580, 1395].

(C) Sulfonamide Potentiators or Synergists

A few substances have been found which have the power of increasing the inhibition of bacterial growth produced by sulfonamide drugs. Neter[1831] and Schmelkes and Wyss[2112] showed that addition of a very small amount of Azochloramide to media containing sulfanilamide considerably potentiated the bacteriostatic action of sulfanilamide on *Staph. aureus, Pneumococcus* and *E. coli.* They gave evidence indicating that the action of azochloramide was to inactivate the sulfanilamide inhibitors (PABA). Azochloramide destroyed the immunity of "sulfonamide-fast" strains of *Staph. aureus.* This tended to corroborate McLeod's[1690] contention that some "sulfonamide-fast" strains produce more inhibitor than normal strains. *In vivo* it was difficult to show any benefit from "Azochloramide"-sulfanilamide combinations over "Azochloramide" alone[1844]. Kohn[1457] considered the conclusion that "Azochloramide" acts specifically against sulfonamide antagonists as unwarranted.

"Pyridium" was effective in potentiating the effect of sulfonamides on *E. coli*[1845]. Ethionine and norleucine potentiated the action of the sulfonamides in the absence of methionine or peptone[1271]. Analogues of biotin, and purine and pyrimidine bases were also shown to act synergistically with sulfonamides[2530, 2627]. Purines themselves may act either antagonistically or synergistically with the sulfonamide drugs depending on experimental conditions[183, 1462, 1736, 2226, 2288, 2581].

(D) Action of Sulfonamides on Bacterial Toxins

Levaditi and Vaisman[287] made early investigations of the action of sulfanilamide derivatives and sulfones on endotoxins. They found that orthanilamide and metanilamide had almost as much effect on the endotoxins of the gonococcus and Flexner dysentery organisms as sulfanilamide, in contrast to the antibacterial action of these compounds. Bis(4-hydroxyphenyl) sulfone was more potent than bis(4-aminophenyl) sulfone against the endotoxins, although the hydroxy derivative had low activity against bacteria. The results were verified by some authors[838, 840]; however, others[1212] failed to verify such an antiendotoxic action of sulfanilamides and sulfones.

Zahl, Hutner and Cooper[585, 1347] reviewed work on the possible protective action of the sulfonamides against bacterial toxins and cited the conflicting reports in the literature. Their own work indicated that there was a definite but very limited effect of the clinically used sulfa drugs against endotoxins of certain of the Gram-negative organisms. There was a significant increase in number of mice surviving injections of the endotoxins of *Salmonella typhimurium* and *Shigella paradysenteriae* when large doses of the sulfa drugs were given. The process of immunization was not affected. This detoxifying action was reversed by PABA.

Rake and Hamre[1986] showed that sulfamerazine had no effect on the toxins produced by the lymphogranuloma-psittacosis group of viruses, but was effective on the infections produced by certain viruses of the group.

(E) Specificity of Action of Sulfanilamide Derivatives

One of the questions of fundamental importance in theories of action and in therapeutic use of the sulfa drugs is whether one of the drugs is particularly effective against a certain bacterial organism and another drug is outstanding against a second organism, etc., or whether the drugs differ uniformly in their potency.   If the latter were true there might be one drug which would be best for treating all infections amenable to the sulfa drugs.

There are strong arguments supported by considerable evidence gained from *in vitro* studies to show that there is no specificity in the action of the sulfa drugs; *i.e.*, while there is individual variation in the potency of the various drugs against various organisms the relative order of potency of the drugs is the same regardless of the organism.   On the other hand, many clinicians maintain that such *in vitro* results are not valid evidence and that their pharmacological and clinical results indicate a considerable specificity of action *in vivo*.

Some of the factors which may account for the divergence of results between *in vivo* and *in vitro* testing of the drugs are: 1) Differences in rate of absorption and excretion of the drugs.   Such differences can be eliminated as factors by expressing results in actual blood concentrations of the drugs, as Marshall has done (see below).   2) Differences in distribution of the drugs in the tissues so that locus of the infection affects the results.   3) Presence of sulfonamide inhibitors or potentiating agents in the animal body which may modify the relative activities.   *In vitro* studies show that presence of the chief inhibitor, *p*-aminobenzoic acid, does not change the relative order of activities; however, there are a number of other agents which modify the activity of these drugs and some of these may affect the *in vivo* specificity.

(1) *In Vivo* Specificity

Marshall, *et al.*[1734] after a study of 33 sulfanilamide derivatives for *in vivo* activity against C-203 strain β-hemolytic streptococcus infections, in mice, by the drug-diet method where median survival blood concentrations were measured in comparison with sulfanilamide, found that none of the compounds showed significantly greater therapeutic activity than sulfanilamide.   These compounds included the well known N^1-heterocyclic derivatives which others have claimed to be very much more active than sulfanilamide.   However, they did verify the much greater activity of the N^1-heterocyclic sulfanilamides against pneumococcus infections.   On the basis of this they argued that there was definite specificity in the action of sulfanilamide compounds on various bacterial infections in mice. They found no quantitative relationship between *in vivo* and *in vitro* activities.

Laüger, Suter and Martin[2583] made extensive studies of the *in vivo* activities of many N^1-acylsulfanilamides on experimental streptococcal, pneumococcal and *E. coli* infections in mice.   Drugs were given *per os* in ten doses over a five-day period and survivals were read at the end of ten days.   It was found that a few of the drugs such as N^1-(3,4-dimethylbenzoyl)sulfanilamide and N^1-(4-methylbenzoyl)sulfanilamide were capable of protecting 100% of the mice against any of the three infections.   Other drugs had high activity against streptococci and *E. coli* but none against pneumococci. N^1-Isovalerylsulfanilamide protected 100% against *E. coli* but 0% against streptococci and pneumococci; however, N^1-(4-propylbenzoyl)sulfanilamide protected 100% against streptococci, 0% against pneumococci, and 60% against *E. coli*.   There was thus a high degree of specificity exhibited by many of the compounds.   The only conclusion that could be drawn from the results was that in general compounds which were highly active against pneumococci would show high activity against the other two organisms.

This work, which makes a strong argument for the existence of a high degree of *in vivo* specificity of action, is in need of confirmation since much of it was done on too few experimental animals to be significant. If substantiated it will be of great theoretical and practical importance since it will focus attention on the need for careful study of each drug on each disease.

(2) *In Vitro* Specificity

Wyss, Grubaugh, and Schmelkes[578] on the basis of *in vitro* studies came to the conclusion that the action of sulfonamide drugs was non-specific. They studied the ratio of sulfonamide drug added to a culture medium to the amount of p-aminobenzoic acid (PABA) required to restore growth to $\frac{1}{2}$ maximum and obtained the following data, where an inoculum of one million *E. coli* per cc. was used:

Sulfonamide	mg. %	PABA mg. %	Molar Ratio
Sulfanilamide	200	0.08	2000
"	100	0.05	1600
"	50	0.02	2000
"	25	0.01	2000
Sulfathiazole	10	0.2	27
"	5	0.1	27
"	1	0.02	27
"	3	0.007	23

Thus, "the molar ratios of the antagonists are constant for a wide range of concentrations provided that sufficient excess is employed in order that native sulfonamide inhibitors, present in the inoculum, do not introduce an appreciable error, and provided that the concentration is not so excessive as to affect the physiological properties of the medium significantly".

When the relative efficiency of a series of drugs was measured in terms of their ability to overcome p-aminobenzoic acid, the following data were obtained, using Knight's medium:

Drug	mg %	Staph. aureus			E. coli		
		PABA mg. %	Molar Ratio	Efficiency	PABA mg. %	Molar Ratio Drug /PABA	Efficiency
Sulfanilamide	50	0.0086	4660	1	0.012	3330	1
Sulfaguanidine	50	0.0070	4570	1	0.0081	3960	0.8
Sulfacetamide	5	0.0060	534	9	0.0060	534	6
Sulfapyridine	5	0.0066	416	11	0.0061	450	7
Sulfadiazine	5	0.030	92	51	0.064	43	78
Sulfathiazole	5	0.050	53	88	0.065	41	81

The relative efficiency of the different drugs in overcoming the inhibition of their action by PABA, therefore, holds for different organisms grown in the same culture medium. On making similar tests on a number of different organisms in several different media, further data were obtained showing a nearly constant relative efficiency of two of the drugs:

Organism	Moles SA/PABA	Moles ST/PABA	Efficiency ST/SA
E. coli	2,000	27	74
A. Aerogenes	3,220	45	72
Staph. aureus	4,660	53	88
Ps. aeruginosa	13,330	184	73
Sal. typhimurium	6,650	92	72
L. acidophilus	8,000	133	60
Proteus vulgaris	4,000	55	73

SA = sulfanilamide, ST = sulfathiazole, PABA = p-aminobenzoic acid.

These in vitro results were confirmed by others[578, 1100, 1122, 1135, 1384] using other drugs and other organisms.

Because of the importance of the question of specificity in therapy it is hoped further investigation will be made of the reasons for the differences between in vivo and in vitro results. Further careful studies on the question of in vivo specificity would seem especially worth-while.

(F) Drug Resistance

A common phenomenon observed with bacteria and many other microorganisms, is their ability to become resistant to the action of a drug, so that after a period of growth in the presence of sub-lethal, but gradually increasing concentrations of the drug, the organism ultimately is able to withstand much higher concentrations than originally would have been sufficient to kill or stop growth. It was, therefore, to be expected that bacterial strains would develop on prolonged administration of a sulfonamide drug which would no longer be effectively attacked by the drug. Such resistant strains have now been reported as occurring naturally in many different infections[2132, 2382], particularly where treatment is prolonged (15 days or more) with inadequate dosage to maintain bacteriostasis at the site of the infection. Resistant strains are also produced almost at will in the laboratory by culture of the organisms in the presence of gradually increasing concentrations of the drug either in vitro or in vivo[176, 966, 1441, 1631, 1674, 1692, 2130, 2288, 2384, 2433, 2633]. Resistant strains produced in vitro are resistant in vivo and conversely[2633].

Investigations[1672, 2623] to determine the permanence of sulfonamide resistance have shown that a slight or moderate increase in resistance may be lost but that once resistance is highly developed it is apparently permanent. Highly resistant pneumococci retained their resistance through 200 mouse passages[2633].

The virulence of organisms appears to be independent of their susceptibility to the sulfonamide drugs[1814, 2119].

(1) Specificity of Resistance of Organisms to Different Drugs

Frequently it is found that once an organism has become resistant to one of the potent sulfonamide drugs it is resistant to all the commonly used sulfa drugs. This was found to be the case with various resistant strains of pneumococci[1249, 1631, 2165, 2166].

In contrast to this, strains of Shigella sonnei and Shigella paradysenteriae Flexner, resistant to sulfathiazole and sulfadiazine, were found to have no more resistance to sulfapyrazine than the parent strain. The *sonnei* strains were no more resistant to sulfacet-amide than the parent strain, while the Flexner resistant strain was most resistant to sulfacetamide[920].

Colebrook[899] has also challenged the statement that "an organism which has become resistant to one sulfonamide is correspondingly resistant to all the others". He showed that of 7 strains of hemolytic streptococci which were resistant to sulfanilamide, 6 were still sensitive to sulfathiazole. This evidence is weakened by reason of the much greater potency of sulfathiazole which might mean that though an organism were highly resistant to sulfanilamide it might be only partially resistant to sulfathiazole when compared at equal concentrations.

McIntosh and Selbie[1672] produced resistant strains of streptococcus and staphylococcus by *in vitro* culture in the presence of low concentrations of many different drugs, including sulfathiazole, propamidine, proflavine and penicillin. Organisms made resistant to drugs of one type were usually not resistant to drugs of another type but often resistance to a second drug could be induced, giving rise to double resistance. Resistant bacteria some-times showed high resistance to drugs of a completely dissimilar nature while at times they showed little or no resistance to similar drugs. Bacteria made resistant to sulfanil-amide were susceptible to *p*-aminomethylbenzenesulfonamide (Marfanil). This had pre-viously been noted by others[1384, 1385, 1581, 2135].

Spink, Ferris and Vivino[2249] studied the *in vitro* action of penicillin and sodium sulfa-thiazole on 68 strains of staphylococcus. There was no correlation between the re-sistance to penicillin and that to sodium sulfathiazole. One strain was resistant to both drugs and several strains were highly resistant to penicillin but susceptible to sulfa-thiazole, with the reverse true in several other strains. The results suggested advantage-ous use of combined treatment with sulfathiazole and penicillin in staphylococcal sepsis.

Sulfonamide-fast bacteria were still susceptible to anti-sera[1693].

Bacteria resistant to pantoyltaurine were still sensitive to the sulfonamide drugs and *vice versa*[1666].

(2) Mechanisms for Development of Resistance

Light on the mechanisms by which bacteria become resistant to the sulfonamide drugs resulted from the postulations of the Woods-Fildes theory ((II) (A) in this chapter) which focused attention on the role of PABA.

Ivánovics[1364] obtained evidence that different strains of staphylococci may become re-sistant to sulfonamide drugs through several different mechanisms. He postulated that one of these was by more efficient use of the available PABA in metabolic processes. This seemed the probable explanation for the fact that a strain in which, originally, one mole of PABA antagonized 14 moles of sulfathiazole, changed on becoming resistant so that one mole of PABA was able to antagonize 220 moles of sulfathiazole. Another mechanism of becoming resistant was apparently by increased synthesis of PABA. In some strains both of these mechanisms seemed to be involved in development of re-sistance.

By means of bio-assay methods it was shown that a resistant strain of *Staph. aureus* synthesized about 70 times as much PABA as the parent, susceptible strain. This was sufficient to account for the resistance and confirmed one of the above mechanisms[1513, 2257]. *N. gonorrhoeae*, seemed to become resistant by the same mechanism[1511]. However, in-creased production of PABA could not be demonstrated for resistant strains of *E. coli*,

Shigella dysenteriae, Vibrio cholerae and *D. pneumoniae,* indicating other mechanisms for production of resistance[1513].

Reed, Orr and Reed[2620] investigated the *in vitro* bacteriostatic action of sulfonamide compounds on various species of *Clostridium* and found an inverse relationship between the bacteriostatic action of the drug and the amount of sulfonamide inhibitor produced by the organism. *C. welchii* which produced a large amount of inhibitor was less influenced by sulfonamides than *C. sordelli* which produced but little inhibitor. The order of effectiveness of the drugs was sulfathiazole, sulfadiazine, sulfapyridine, sulfanilamide.

Kirby and Rantz[1438, 1441], whose evidence indicated that strains of bacteria resistant to one sulfa drug were resistant to all such drugs, postulated that resistance was established through an interaction of the organisms and a common structural unit of the sulfa drugs, the *p*-amino group. They also suggested that this interaction might involve the same enzyme system or systems as those concerned in the antagonism of sulfa drugs by PABA.

Harris and Kohn[1270] concluded that the resistance developed by a bacterium depended not only on the medium in which training occurred but also on the medium in which the measure of resistance was made. Since the development of resistance to sulfanilamide did not always parallel that to sulfathiazole, they thought that while the mechanism was similar it was not identical.

Schmidt and Sesler[2130] performed experiments to see whether resistant pneumococci were formed during normal multiplication of a sensitive strain or were produced by some direct action of the sulfa drug on the sensitive organisms. It appeared that the latter mechanism was the important one because pneumococci of increased resistance were formed upon each successive exposure to sulfapyridine. By comparison of the sensitivity of individual pneumococci composing both sensitive and resistant strains they showed that in every instance the organisms that made up the resistant strains were significantly more resistant than any pneumococci in the sensitive strains. They concluded that highly resistant pneumococci are formed as a result of some action of the sulfonamide on the sensitive organism. It was noted, however, that individual pneumococci of either a sensitive or resistant strain varied slightly in their response to the drug so that there is a possibility of developing resistance through a "breeding-out" process. This may accompany the other mechanism.

(3) Clinical Importance of Resistant Organisms

The failures of sulfonamide compounds to cure diseases caused by species of organisms usually susceptible to the drugs must frequently be ascribed to the presence of sulfonamide resistant strains of the organisms. Studies of sulfonamide resistance are therefore of great clinical value.

The question of whether sulfa drug resistant strains of pneumococci occur naturally or become resistant only when treatment is prolonged was studied by Hamburger, *et al.*[1249]. In 168 pneumonia cases no highly resistant strains were found. Moderately resistant strains were found in only 6 instances; the balance, 162, being sensitive to sulfa drugs. Resistant pneumococci developed in 3 cases treated for 47 days or more; of these one became highly resistant. It, therefore, appeared that resistance could be developed by *in vivo* culture of the organisms but that this would be very rarely encountered in treatment of acute diseases because of the time required.

The fear that highly resistant strains of pathogens would be developed by prophylactic use of the sulfonamide drugs for prolonged periods has restrained many physicians from prescribing these drugs for such use.   The results of studies covering over a million cases treated prophylactically with sulfadiazine in the armed forces[888, 1325, 2609, 2655] did not reveal the development of such resistant pathogens, as indicated by the absence of increased streptococcal morbidity over the six months of prophylaxis.   The results were not regarded as a final answer to the question, however[2609].

Schmidt and Sesler[2131] showed that pneumococci can develop a high degree of resistance to the action of penicillin.   Such penicillin resistant strains were still sensitive to the action of the sulfonamides.   Previously it has been shown[1958] that the converse is true, that pneumococci highly resistant to the sulfonamides are still sensitive to penicillin. It is evident that penicillin and the sulfonamides act through different mechanisms.   The clinical importance is evident.   Failure of the sulfonamides to halt an infection will be corrected through use of penicillin and *vice versa*.   There is also the hope that alternate short term treatment with these substances may succeed in curing certain chronic infections where prolonged treatment with one drug has tended to develop resistant organisms.

Spink and Vivino[2253] studied the *in vitro* resistance to sulfathiazole of 57 strains of staphylococci isolated from patients.   Of these, 8 were moderately resistant and 17 were highly resistant.   It was emphasized that because of the localized and inaccessible nature of most staphylococcal infections it is difficult to maintain adequate concentrations of the drugs in contact with the organisms and sulfonamide inhibitors are usually present. Conditions are, therefore, favorable to the development of drug resistance during treatment and this is being encountered with increasing frequency.   While penicillin is effective against sulfonamide resistant staphylococci these organisms may develop *in vitro* resistance to penicillin also.

Carpenter, *et al.*[837] noted an increase from 15 to 59% in incidence of resistant strains of gonococcus within a period of 15 months in which sulfa drugs were used extensively in a locality for control of gonorrhea.   This they attributed to elimination of a number of susceptible strains and to development of resistant strains *in vivo*.

Goodale and Schwab[1192] found that by use of *in vitro* plating it was possible to find whether gonococci were resistant and to predict whether clinical response would be favorable.   Frequently, strains which were resistant to sulfanilamide and sulfapyridine would respond to sulfadiazine, sulfathiazole or sulfamerazine.   In borderline cases sulfamerazine was found definitely weaker in action and sulfadiazine very slightly weaker than sulfathiazole.   Sulfonamide resistant gonorrhea was best treated with penicillin.

A host factor in resistance was postulated by Harkness[1266] who found a strain of gonococci which was susceptible to the sulfonamide drugs *in vitro* but was intractable to treatment with sulfadiazine, sulfanilamide, sulfapyridine, sulfathiazole and sulfamethazine *in vivo*.   He also observed 15 couples in which one or the other of the parties was resistant to treatment although both were almost certainly infected with the same strain of gonococcus.

(G) Bacterial Population *vs* Concentration of Sulfa Drug Required for Bacteriostasis

The majority of investigators[49, 50, 266, 752, 854, 1632, 1676, 2261, 2591] have found that the concentration of drug required to bring about bacteriostasis was roughly proportional to the size of inoculum in experiments *in vitro*.   There is also a widespread and well founded belief among clinicians that severe bacteremias call for higher blood levels of drug than infections with a low bacterial count[313, 929, 1087, 1599, 1759, 2248].   Because the concentration of drug in a culture medium cannot possibly be changed appreciably by a great increase in bacterial population it would appear strange that such a relationship should be found.

Probably high inocula involve the transfer of appreciable amounts of sulfonamide antagonists to the culture medium and thus necessitate higher drug concentrations. In the clinic rapidity of response is of paramount importance and this is favored by higher dosage.

A few investigators[438, 1637, 2504, 2597] have disputed the majority findings. Rose and Fox[438] claimed that the degree of bacteriostasis of E. coli produced by a given concentration of the sulfonamides and PABA in a synthetic culture medium was independent of the size of the inoculum. Their experimental work supported the hypothesis that bacteria possess the ability to undergo only a certain limited number of cell divisions in the presence of a bacteriostatic concentration of a sulfonamide regardless of the size of the inoculum. This explains why bacteriostasis may not be observed when large inocula are employed, because even a small number of cell divisions will bring such cultures into the range of visible turbidity (circa 10,000,000 cells per cc.). They further postulated that a substance necessary for reproduction is present in the bacterial cell. This is synthesized under normal conditions of growth but in the presence of bacteriostatic concentrations of the sulfonamides the synthesis of this substance is prevented and the organism is forced to distribute its original supply in diminished amounts to its progeny. Insufficient quantity of the substance remains in an individual cell, after a certain number of cell divisions, to permit further reproduction.

(H) Effects of Sulfonamide Drugs on Enzymes

Because most theories of the mechanism of action postulate an interference of the sulfonamide drugs with essential bacterial enzymatic processes, studies of the effects of the sulfonamide drugs on the enzymes of bacteria are of particular interest. Such studies are beset with many difficulties not only in experimental technique but in interpretation of results, so that while the work is of the highest importance, no general agreement as to the significance of the experimental results appears to have been reached. This particular field has been more extensively reviewed by Henry[1297] than will be attempted here.

(1) Isolated Enzyme Systems

Most of the searches for specific enzyme inhibitions having the characteristic antibacterial effects of sulfa drugs and their antagonism by PABA have been failures. Thus, Abderhalden[607] was unable to find an effect of various sulfonamide drugs on the action of pepsin, trypsin, and various serum peptidases in vitro.

Zeller[589] found an inhibition of cholinesterase of blood serum by the sulfonamide drugs but a similar inhibition was produced by PABA and other amines so that the effect appeared unrelated to antibacterial action. Collier[2515] found no effect of sulfanilamide on catalase or cytochrome oxidase.

Pulver and Martin[1966] studied the effects of 34 different N^1-acylsulfanilamides on the catalase from blood or E. coli; cholinesterase of blood and diaminoxidase from E. coli or hog kidney and were unable to correlate antibacterial activities with the inhibition of these enzymes.

von Euler and coworkers[2485, 2531] found that sulfonamide drugs and a number of other compounds including PABA, m-aminobenzoic acid, and benzenesulfonic acid would inhibit glucose and lactic acid dehydrogenases but only at much higher concentrations than encountered in therapy. Both sulfonamides and PABA inhibited oxidation of

(1) Statement of Theory

In 1940, Fildes[145] in a now famous paper entitled, "A Rational Approach to Research in Chemotherapy" consolidated and elaborated on these views. He pointed out that bacteria differ considerably in their ability to synthesize various chemicals required for their growth and reproduction. Thus *E. coli* can synthesize all the nitrogenous products they need if supplied with ammonia. Other bacteria need to be supplied with certain amino acids in the substrate, since they are incapable of synthesizing them. Such essential amino acids are "growth factors" for the particular species and strain. *He defined an "essential metabolite" as each stage in any synthesis necessary for growth, without which, either synthesized or supplied from outside, growth cannot occur. A growth factor is thus an essential metabolite which cannot be synthesized.* He pointed out that different strains of the same bacteria may vary considerably in their growth factor requirements.

Fildes postulated that the action of many antibacterial substances may be explained in terms of interference with an essential metabolite. He suggested that the action of oxidizing dyes, such as thionine and methylene blue, which are capable of diffusing into the bacterial cell, may be to oxidize an essential metabolite which the cell requires in a reduced state in order for the enzyme associated with it to function. No growth occurs until the essential metabolite is again reduced. Again, compounds containing —SH groups have been shown to be necessary for growth of staphylococci. Fildes suggested that the action of mercuric ion is to combine with —SH compounds within the cell and interfere with their utilization as essential metabolites. It was shown experimentally that such a combination of Hg and —SH is not in itself inhibitory and that growth stops only when the molecular proportion of mercury exceeds that of the —SH compound. Addition of excess of the essential metabolite restored growth[1078].

In the case of sulfanilamide and its derivatives, he postulated a third type of action— that of competition with the essential metabolite, PABA, for its association with an enzyme necessary to bacterial growth. The structural similarity between sulfanilamide and PABA suggested competition as a possible mode of action. If so, the effect of sulfanilamide should obey the laws of mass action, and this has been experimentally verified.

Fildes further postulated that the sensitivity of an organism to sulfanilamide would depend on how readily it synthesized its requirements of PABA. Inability to synthesize would lead to the most sensitive strains, while resistant strains might well synthesize more than their minimum requirements.

Fildes' mechanism of action has received verification from so many different approaches that it is now the basis of most modern theories of mode of action of sulfa drugs and other chemotherapeutic agents. It is also the springboard for much present day chemotherapeutic research. It was Fildes suggestion that chemotherapeutic research be directed to altering the structure of a known essential metabolite in such a way that the product might block an enzyme system of which the metabolite normally occupied a functional part. Many such metabolite analogues have now been synthesized.

(2) Some Experimental Verifications

Landy, Larkum and Oswald[1512] using a microbiological method of assay claimed to have established PABA as an "essential metabolite" by showing its presence in cultures of species of *Streptococcus, Staphylococcus, Brucella, Corynebacterium, Eberthella, Escherichia,*

Klebsiella, Mycobacterium, Proteus, Salmonella and *Shigella* which were grown on synthetic media free of PABA.

Rubbo and Gillespie[447] established PABA as a growth factor for *Clostridium aceto-butylicum* which was about 10,000 times as active as its ortho- and meta-isomers in stimulating growth. The possibility that PABA occurred in the isomers in sufficient amount to account for their activities was suggested; however, PABA was only 5 times as active as the meta-isomer as an antagonist of sulfonamide drugs on this organism and it is hard to believe that the meta preparation could have contained 20% PABA. Park and Wood[1890] found biotin necessary in order to repeat the work of Rubbo and Gillespie (see also [1508]).

Ivánovics[1364] using very carefully purified *o* and *m*-aminobenzoic acids was unable to find antagonism of sulfonamide drugs at 20,000 times the effective concentration of PABA. The studies were made on strains of *Staph. aureus.*

As pointed out by Henry[1297] no one has yet proved unequivocally that PABA is actually synthesized by various pathogens and that it is in truth an "essential metabolite" for organisms inhibited by the sulfonamide drugs. Such proof will involve growth of the bacteria on media free of PABA and demonstration by chemical isolation and identification that it is present in the growing culture. Mere presence of a diazotizable amine in such cultures is not especially significant and bio-assay methods while indicative, are not conclusive. To date, PABA has been demonstrated in various biological systems including yeasts, but not in pathogens.

(B) Applications and Extensions of the Woods-Fildes Theory

(1) Vitamin Antagonists

Because many of the vitamins were known to be growth factors for bacteria as well as animals and were intimately associated with enzymatic processes, first attempts to apply the Woods-Fildes concepts to the design of new chemotherapeutic agents were aimed at analogues of various vitamins. It had been discovered before Fildes announced his theory that compounds closely related to some of the vitamins had a toxic or anti-vitamin effect on animals, which could be overcome by feeding large quantities of the vitamin. The extensions of these findings to bacterial systems as a verification of the Woods-Fildes theory was quickly accomplished.

(a) *Nicotinic Acid Antagonists*

McIlwain[1662] found that 3-pyridinesulfonamide inhibited the growth of organisms requiring nicotinamide or nicotinic acid. Later[1036, 1796] it was found that this antagonism was not as simple as the relationship between sulfanilamide and PABA. The effect of 3-pyridinesulfonamide on bacteria was nullified by 5-thiazolecarboxylic acid, cozymase, and Fe ion, in addition to nicotinic acid. 5-Thiazolesulfonic acid and 2-(3-pyridylsulf-amyl) pyridine had a weak growth promoting effect on *Staph. aureus.*

3-Pyridinesulfonamide   *Nicotinic acid*

(b) *Pantothenic Acid Antagonists*

Snell[479] and later McIlwain and Hawking[1664, 1670], Kuhn, *et al.*[1493] and Barnett and Robinson[709] showed that pantoyltaurine inhibited organisms unable to synthesize their requirements of pantothenic acid, and that the effect was antagonized by pantothenic acid both *in vitro* and *in vivo*[1658, 1670] but not by PABA, thiamine, riboflavin, nicotinic acid, biotin, inositol, ascorbic acid, uracil, adenine, xanthine, hypoxanthine, guanine, thymine or any of the amino acids[1493].

$$HOCH_2C(CH_3)_2CHOHCONH(CH_2)_2SO_3H$$

Pantoyltaurine

$$HOCH_2C(CH_3)_2CHOHCONH(CH_2)_2COOH$$

Pantothenic acid

β-Aminobutyric acid (but not taurine, hydroacrylic acid or β-alanylglycine) was shown to be an inhibitor of the β-alanine promoted growth of yeast when present in relatively large amounts, and to be antagonized by β-alanine[2610, 2611].

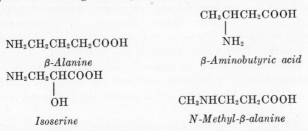

$$NH_2CH_2CH_2CH_2COOH$$

β-Alanine

$$CH_3CHCH_2COOH$$
$$|$$
$$NH_2$$

β-Aminobutyric acid

$$NH_2CH_2CHCOOH$$
$$|$$
$$OH$$

Isoserine

$$CH_3NHCH_2CH_2COOH$$

N-Methyl-β-alanine

Isoserine exhibited a similar, though weaker, effect but *N*-methyl-β-alanine was neither a growth promoter nor an inhibitor for yeast. None of these materials had an inhibitory effect on growth of yeast promoted by pantothenic acid. The difference between these compounds and pantoyltaurine, according to these authors, lies in inhibition of the synthesis of pantothenic acid by these compounds, while pantoyltaurine interferes with the utilization of pantothenic acid.

The results were confirmed in respiration studies on yeast[2552] where the increased respiration brought about by β-alanine was inhibited by β-aminobutyric acid. No inhibition of pantothenic acid-promoted respiration was brought about. As further evidence that β-aminobutyric acid interfered with the synthesis and not the utilization of pantothenic acid it was shown that the ability of β-aminobutyric acid to inhibit the increased respiration induced by β-alanine decreased in proportion to the time delay in adding it to the system. Presumably the β-aminobutyric acid was able to interfere with further synthesis of pantothenic acid but had no effect on the enhanced respiration produced by the pantothenic acid formed before addition of β-aminobutyric acid.

Pollack[2617] found when an alpha methyl group was placed on the β-alanine portion of the pantothenic acid molecule that the compound was inhibitory to the growth of *Lactobacillus casei* and that this effect was antagonized by pantothenic acid.

Ivánovics[2558–2560] showed that the growth of *Staphylococcus aureus* on a synthetic medium was inhibited by 0.001 M. sodium salicylate, but that 5 times this concentration was insufficient to stop growth when 10^{-7} M. pantothenic acid was present. No other biologically important substance investigated showed this specific antagonism. Ivánovics thought the effect of low concentration of salicylate was to inhibit specific enzymes responsible for synthesis of pantothenic acid. In high concentrations it may have had a denaturizing action on bacterial proteins. It was significant that only such bacteria as are able to synthesize pantothenic acid were inhibited by salicylate.

While these findings are of great theoretical importance, they have not proved to be of therapeutic value because it is a practical impossibility to maintain adequate blood concentrations of the readily excreted sulfonic acid analogues of these essential bacterial growth substances. Also, the possible toxic effect through production of deficiency diseases in the host by such administration has to be considered. Snell, *et al.*[2225] claimed to have produced typical pantothenic acid deficiency in rats by prolonged feeding of pantoyltaurine. Wooley and White[571] and Unna[2369] did not confirm this, nor could Wooley and White produce nicotinic acid deficiency in mice through feeding pyridine-3-sulfonic acid, although an earlier report by Wooley, *et al.*[2663] indicated that this was toxic for dogs.

(c) *Thiamine Antagonists*

Wyss[576] showed that the pyridine analogue of thiamine, 2-methyl-4-amino-5-pyrimidyl-methyl(2-methyl-3-β-hydroxyethyl)pyridinium bromide, or "pyrithiamine", inhibited growth of *Staphylococcus aureus* in a molar ratio of about 700 to 1 of thiamine which was essential to its growth. With *E. coli*, the ratio was 20,000 to 1. This compound had no therapeutic possibilities because bacteriostatic concentrations could not be reached safely in the animal body. Pyrithiamine inhibited the usefulness of thiamine to the animal host[2664] and thiamine is an all important agent in the functioning of animal enzyme systems.

Wooley and White[2662, 2665] showed that pyrithiamine inhibited the growth of both microorganisms and animals. Its action was highly selective in that only those organisms which required thiamine for growth were inhibited by pyrithiamine. It was also shown that the insusceptible species did not owe their resistance to the production of thiamine or other antagonists of pyrithiamine. When a resistant strain of *Endomyces vernalis* was developed by cultivation in the presence of pyrithiamine, it was found able to make use of the pyrimidine portion of the pyrithiamine molecule.

Robbins[2624] showed that pyrithiamine inhibited the growth of certain fungi and this was antagonized by thiamine or in some cases by fragments of the thiamine molecule. In certain cases, the pyrimidine part of the molecule was supplied by pyrithiamine and growth could take place since the organism was able to synthesize its requirements of the thiazole portion of the thiamine molecule.

Oxythiamine, prepared from thiamine by replacing the amino group by hydroxy was found to be toxic to rats[2462].

Buchman, *et al.*[2506] showed that the pyrophosphoric acid ester of the thiamine thiazole moiety inhibited the cocarboxylase decarboxylation of pyruvic acid. This was postulated as a competition between the compound and cocarboxylase for the specific protein of carboxylase where the inhibition arises from the inability of the thiazole-moiety-carboxylase-protein combination to function as a decarboxylase.

(d) *Riboflavin Antagonists*

Kuhn, Weygand and Möller[1492] showed that a near relative of riboflavin, in which the ring methyls were replaced with chlorines, was able to inhibit organisms requiring riboflavin in their growth. This inhibition was reversed by riboflavin. Organisms strongly inhibited were *Staph. aureus, Streptobacterium plantarum* and *B. lactis acidi*. Yeast was not inhibited.

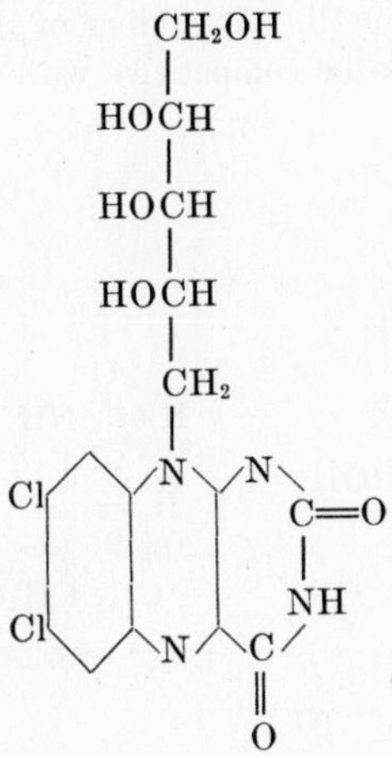

6,7-Dichloro-9(d-1'-ribityl)-isoalloxazine

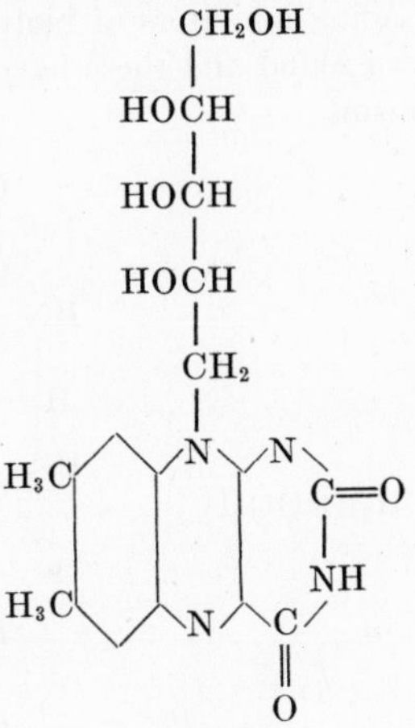

Riboflavin

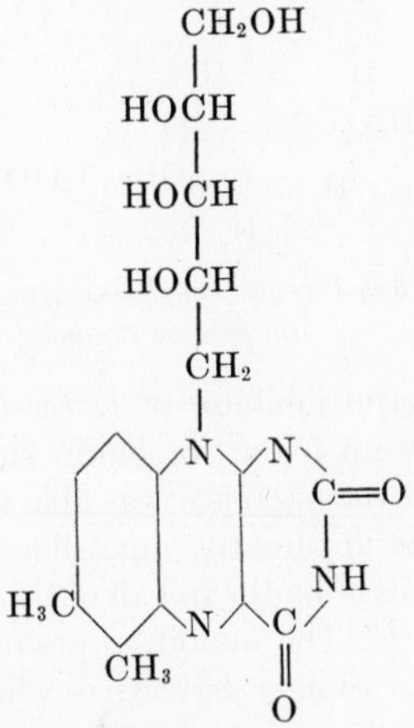

Isoriboflavin

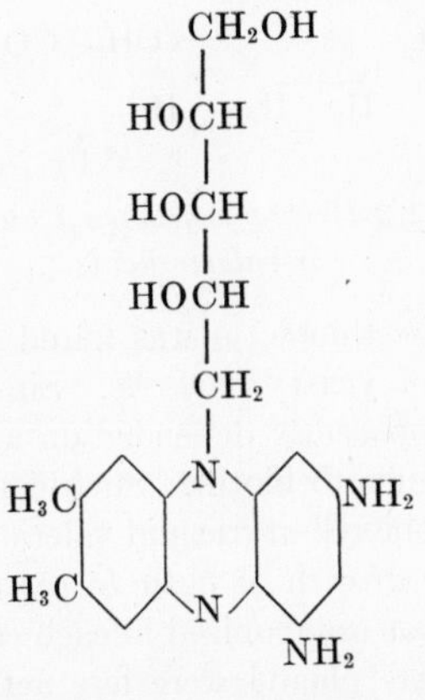

Phenazine analogue of riboflavin

Emerson and Tishler[1027] found that isoriboflavin inhibited the growth of rats and riboflavin reversed this effect. No data on inhibition of growth of microorganisms were presented, but it appeared doubtful if isoriboflavin would have therapeutic possibilities against bacteria because of the importance of riboflavin in human metabolism and the danger of isoriboflavin interfering with body processes.

Woolley[2480] made a diaminophenazine analogue of riboflavin which inhibited the growth of bacteria and was antagonized by riboflavin. It was very readily oxidized, hence of no promise as a chemotherapeutic agent. The corresponding dinitro compound was not inhibitory to bacteria but produced mild riboflavin deficiency in rats which was reversed by large doses of riboflavin.

(e) Biotin Antagonists

The role of biotin as a growth factor for a number of organisms has stimulated investigations on finding inhibitors of biotin-promoted growth. A number of such inhibitors have now been found and these have been shown to be competitive with biotin against certain organisms.

$$
\begin{array}{ccc}
\text{Biotin} & \text{Biotin Sulfone} & \text{Desthiobiotin}
\end{array}
$$

ω-(2,3-Ureylenecyclohexyl)butyric,   ω-(3,4-Ureylenecyclohexyl)butyric,
or valeric acids   or valeric acids

Whereas, desthiobiotin was found to be a powerful inhibitor of *L. casei*, it promoted the growth of yeast[980, 1579, 2520]. Similar results were found for biotin sulfone. These differences apparently depended on whether or not the organism was able to convert the biotin analogues to biotin. Such conversions were apparently impossible in the *omega*-ureylenecyclohexylbutyric and valeric acid analogues of biotin and all of these compounds inhibited the growth of both *L. casei* and yeast[2530]. The inhibition produced by these compounds was antagonized in each case by biotin. Similar derivatives where the carbocyclic ring was phenyl were less active as antibiotin agents. In no case was growth stimulation produced. While the results constituted a verification of the Woods-Fildes theory for the design of antibacterial agents it remains to be seen whether the compounds will prove valuable in therapy.

(2) Amino Acid Antagonists

Gladstone[2542] in 1939, while working with *B. anthracis*, observed some rather complex relationships suggesting antagonisms between certain of the naturally occurring amino acids of similar structure. When valine, leucine or isoleucine was added singly to a mixture of amino acids able to support growth of the organism in their absence, growth was inhibited. However, when these three amino acids were added together, growth was improved and accelerated. The inhibition produced by valine was antagonized by leucine and *vice versa* but inhibition by isoleucine was antagonized only by a combination of valine and leucine. Norleucine and isoleucine were similar in their effects.

Valine and threonine, valine and α-aminobutyric acid, and threonine and serine exhibited similar antagonisms. The inhibition of serine could also be antagonized by a combination of valine and leucine, but not by one alone. Quantitative relationships were found which were not necessarily equimolecular.

$(CH_3)_2CHCH(NH_2)COOH$ $(CH_3)_2CHCH_2CH(NH_2)COOH$

Valine   *Leucine*

$C_2H_5(CH_3)CHCH(NH_2)COOH$

Isoleucine

$CH_3(CH_2)_3CH(NH_2)COOH$ $HOCH_2CH(NH_2)COOH$

Norleucine   *Serine*

$CH_3CH(OH)CH(NH_2)COOH$

Threonine

McIlwain[1663] showed that growth inhibition of certain bacteria could be produced by α-aminosulfonic acid analogues of the naturally occurring α-aminocarboxylic acids and that the α-aminocarboxylic acids would reverse this inhibition, but there was no exact parallel in structure required for this relationship.

Fildes[1079] found 3-indoleacrylic acid competitive with tryptophane; however, there was no quantitative relationship between the two compounds, and addition of tryptophane caused growth despite the presence of 3-indoleacrylic acid. He reasoned that the effect of the compound was to inhibit the synthesis of tryptophane rather than its utilization.

Block and Erlenmeyer[759] made the isosteric 3-(β-naphthyl)-acrylic acid and styrylacetic acid and found them competitive with tryptophan in much the same way. Cinnamic acid had a much weaker action, while hydrocinnamic, benzoic, and fumaric acids had no effect.

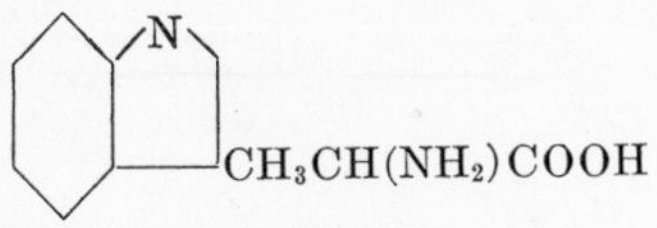

Tryptophane 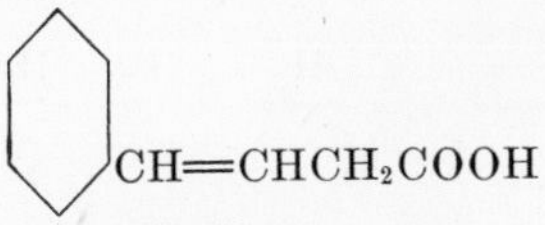   *Styrylacetic acid*

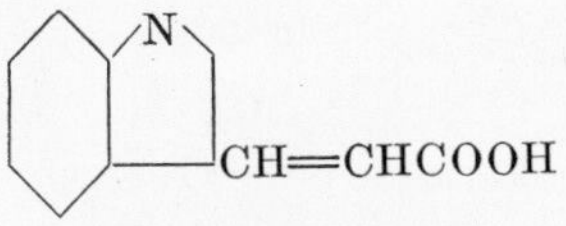

3-Indoleacrylic acid 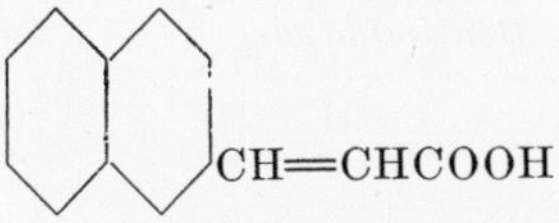   *3-(β-Naphthyl)acrylic acid*

Snell[2641] found that *o*-aminobenzoic acid could substitute for tryptophane in promoting growth of several species of lactic acid bacteria; however, neither orthanilic acid, orthanilamide, nor 2-orthanilamidopyridine inhibited these organisms in contrast to the inhibition produced by the para isomers of these compounds on growth of bacteria requiring *p*-aminobenzoic acid.

Harris and Kohn[1271] found that *E. coli* grown on a synthetic medium was inhibited by ethionine, norvaline and norleucine and that this inhibition could be reversed by methionine.   Dyer[2525] had observed before the advent of the Wood-Fildes theory that ethionine was toxic to rats and that the effect was antagonized by feeding large quantities of methionine.   Roblin, *et al.*[2627] confirmed the work of Harris and Kohn and showed that *dl*-α-amino-γ-methoxybutyric acid (methoxinine), the oxygen analogue of methionine, would inhibit the growth of *E. coli* or *Staph. aureus* grown on a synthetic medium and that this inhibition was reversed by *l*-methionine (but not by *d*-methionine).   A potentiated effect was noted in combination with the sulfonamide drugs where ¼ the minimum effective concentrations of sulfonamide and of methoxinine produced complete bacteriostasis.

Fox, *et al.*[2539] found that gramicidin contained large amounts of the unnatural, *d*-leucine. When this was added to a culture of *Lactobacillus arabinosis* which requires the natural *l*-leucine for growth, inhibition was produced but relatively large quantities of the *d*-leucine were required to produce inhibition as compared to gramicidin.   An equally large concentration of *l*-leucine had no effect on growth.

Doerman[2521] found that a strain of *Neurospora crassa* which required lysine for growth was inhibited by arginine.   Growth was reduced 50% when the molecular ratio was 1 to 1.   When the mole ratio was two arginine to one lysine growth was completely inhibited.   Only the naturally occurring optical isomers of these amino acids were involved in this relationship.

(3) Pyrimidine and Purine Antagonists

Woods[568] found barbituric acid competitive with uracil in bacterial metabolism.

Barbituric acid   Uracil

Benzimidazole   Adenine   Guanine

1-Triazolo[d]pyrimidine   Hypoxanthine   Xanthine

Woolley[2479] reported that benzimidazole had a bacteriostatic action on various bacteria which was reversed by the purine analogues, adenine and guanine, while xanthine and hypoxanthine were ineffective.   Roblin, *et al.*[2627] verified the inhibition of benzimidazole on *E. coli* but could not bring about reversal of the inhibition by other purines or pyrimidines "at concentrations which were not in themselves bacteriostatic".   These authors synthesized a series of analogues of adenine, guanine, hypoxanthine and xanthine in which the imidazole ring of the purine was replaced by the triazole ring, giving rise to a series of 1-triazolo[d]pyrimidines which were tested for antibacterial activity against *E. coli* and *Staph. aureus, in vitro*. The adenine analogue was active at 8 mg. per 100 cc. against *E. coli* but was not effective at 128 mg. per 100 cc. against *Staph. aureus*. The guanine analogue was active against *E. coli* at 64 mg. per 100 cc. and against *Staph. aureus* at 4 mg. per 100 cc. The hypoxanthine and xanthine analogues were less active. The action of the adenine analogue was antagonized by adenine and hypoxanthine but not by guanine, xanthine, uracil, cytosine or thymine. The guanine analogue was antagonized by guanine and xanthine but not by the other purines and pyrimidines.

The guanine analogue showed a synergistic effect with sulfonamide drugs against both *E. coli* and *Staph. aureus*. Sulfonamide-fast organisms were as susceptible to this drug as the parent strains. The results constituted another verification of the Woods-Fildes theory, but the usefulness of the compounds in therapy remains to be demonstrated.

(4) Miscellaneous Antagonisms

McIlwain[1657] reversed the search for verifications of the Woods-Fildes theory by starting with a known, naturally occurring, antibiotic substance and seeking to find the inhibitor or antagonist of its action. Iodinin occurs as a purple pigment with a bronze luster produced by *Chromobacterium iodinum*, which inhibits the growth of certain other bacteria. This has the structure of a dihydroxyphenazine-di-*N*-oxide,

with the exact position of the hydroxyls unknown but 2,3 and 2,5-substitution is excluded.

It was found that about 1×10^{-8} M. iodinin was necessary to prevent growth of *Streptococcus hemolyticus* in a peptone medium. 1,4-, 1,5- and 1,8-dihydroxyanthraquinone were found to neutralize this action at concentrations of 10^{-5} to 10^{-7} M. Such materials are not known to occur in normal blood, but because blood has a weak neutralizing effect on the action of iodinin, McIlwain thought a quinone component of blood might be the antagonist. Vitamin K is a naphthoquinone derivative, and it was found that 2-methyl-1,4-naphthoquinone, part of the Vitamin K molecule, neutralized at a concentration of 2×10^{-6} M.

Further study showed that the antagonistic action of the quinones was not explainable by direct reaction between quinone and iodinin, since the effect takes place only in the presence of the organism and may be followed by a loss of color. Further, the effect was not a growth stimulation by the added quinone. Reduction was postulated as the probable mode of action for the inactivation of iodinin, since it could be brought about by M./100 thiolacetate or M./500 ascorbic acid. These concentrations were high as compared to the antagonistic quinones which were not themselves reducing agents. Other redox systems such as pyocyanine and methylene blue antagonized at 10^{-5} M. and 5×10^{-6} M. respectively.

While McIlvain admitted the evidence was not conclusive, he postulated that iodinin inhibited bacterial systems concerned with quinones. He pointed out the structural similarities between N-oxides of the iodinin type and quinones. Thus the Woods-Fildes theory could at least offer a plausible explanation of the observations.

Kuhn[2577] drew a parallel between the antagonisms of vitamin and antivitamin competing for the specific protein of an enzyme system and the well-known competition of O_2 and CO for hemoglobin. In this case, the toxic agent, CO, has much greater affinity for the protein than does oxygen and it requires high oxygen tension to displace CO from hemoglobin. In the case of most of the antagonisms between chemotherapeutic agent and essential metabolite in bacterial enzyme systems, it requires a high concentration of the chemotherapeutic agent to displace the essential metabolite from the specific protein. However, the structural similarity of O_2 and CO is striking and this may constitute another verification of the Woods-Fildes theory.

There are, of course, many cases of drug antagonisms where there is no structural relationship involved and no thought of an interference with essential metabolites—merely that one drug has an effect opposite to that of another. Pilocarpine and atropine are such an antagonistic pair, one of which counteracts the effect of the other; certainly neither is an essential metabolite nor is any close structural similarity apparent.

It must be admitted, also, that there are cases of antagonism between similarly constituted chemotherapeutic drugs where it is difficult to picture the antagonist as being essential to the metabolism of the parasite. For example, Fischer, *et al.*[2536] found that the leuco base of malachite green antagonized the bacteriostatic action of malachite green on streptococci. The corresponding carbinol base, bisulfite, or hydrosulfite derivatives were all powerful bacteriostatic agents. Browning and Gulbransen (quoted in[2559]) noted that the action of acriflavin on *Nagana* infections was antagonized by parafuchsin.

Such antagonisms have been used by opponents[1297] of the Woods-Fildes theory to claim that the structural similarity of the sulfa drugs and PABA is mere coincidence and does not provide a sound basis for the Woods-Fildes postulations, particularly in the absence of rigorous proof that PABA is actually an "essential metabolite" for pathogenic organisms.

The author is of the opinion that whatever the ultimate fate of the Woods-Fildes theory, it has at least proved highly useful in suggesting many avenues of research for developing chemotherapeutic agents of new types and while no drug of commercial importance has come from these approaches, there are several very promising leads which may yet be fruitful.

(5) Antibacterial Index

After the Woods-Fildes theory seemed well established, McIlwain[1669] defined an "antibacterial index" to express the relationship between a chemotherapeutic agent and its chief antagonist:

$$\text{Antibacterial index} = \frac{C_I}{C_M}$$

C_I = molar concentration of inhibitor just bacteriostatic for a given organism in the presence of a molar concentration, C_M, of the corresponding metabolite. For the case of streptococci, sulfanilamide and PABA, McIlwain found the antistreptococcal index to be 25,000.

He also defined a host index $= \dfrac{C_H}{C_M}$ where C_H = highest molar concentration of drug failing to damage the most susceptible vital tissue of the host in the presence of a molar concentration, C_M, of the essential metabolite.

Then Erlich's "Chemotherapeutic index" $= \dfrac{\text{Host index}}{\text{Antibacterial index}}$

The antibacterial index is a useful expression in rating the relative *in vitro* bacteriostatic activities of different drugs and has been used by many authors both before and after McIlwain gave it a title. The host index will probably not find much application because of the experimental difficulties involved in determination of the respective concentrations of drug and metabolite, *in vivo*, and particularly the critical concentrations "just failing to damage the most susceptible vital tissue of the host." Also in the case of the sulfonamide-PABA antagonism it still remains to be demonstrated that PABA is an "essential metabolite" for humans.

There is good reason to believe that the antibacterial index varies widely with pH of the substrate in the antagonism of the sulfonamide drugs by PABA (see Ionization Theories).

(C) Theory of Kohn and Harris

Kohn and Harris[266, 1271, 1462] accepted the theory of Fildes and Woods but believed the action of the sulfonamides on bacteria and the effects of materials in the substrate were considerably more complex. Provisionally, they[a] "picture the whole process in *E. coli* as follows: The addition of nitrogen in a useful form to cells suspended in salt and glucose increases the respiration per cell. This extra energy production is not inhibited by the sulfonamides; its purpose is to run the syntheses necessary for growth and multiplication. Among the syntheses there is a special group X which requires *p*-aminobenzoic acid as catalyst. The sulfonamides compete with *p*-aminobenzoic acid in these reactions, thereby inhibiting the synthesis of X. Their effectiveness depends upon the bacterial species, and even upon the strain, for reasons not understood and lumped under the term *resistance*. The action of the drugs is not immediately apparent because the cells contain stores of X. The degree of inhibition finally reached depends upon the extent to which the synthesis of X is inhibited, and upon the amounts of X and *p*-aminobenzoic acid in the culture medium. X represents a class of substances a, b, c, d, e. At low concentrations of the drug, the synthesis of a, b, and c may be stopped but not of d and e. Proteose-peptone medium which contains a, b, and c can therefore antagonize low concentrations of the drug; but it cannot antagonize high concentrations which also prevent the synthesis of d and e."

They recognized the possibility that, "some of the sulfonamides may inhibit reactions which others cannot, and which *p*-aminobenzoic acid does not antagonize, as for example, the action of sulfapyridine on the respiration of the dysentery bacillus."

Their data showed that the primary action of the drugs was not one of inhibition of the respiration of the bacterial cells. As the concentration of drug was increased the number of synthetic reactions inhibited by the drug also apparently increased. Sulfanilamide appeared unable to inhibit some of the reactions which were sensitive to sulfapyridine, sulfathiazole and sulfadiazine.

They also obtained evidence[1271] that there were three types of antagonists of the sulfonamides, each acting in a different way: (1) *p*-aminobenzoic acid was active against all concentrations of the sulfonamides; (2) methionine was active against only the lower

[a] Data quoted with the permission of the authors and copyright owner.

concentrations of any sulfonamide; and (3) an unknown substance in proteose-peptone was active against some effect produced only by high concentrations of sulfapyridine, sulfathiazole and sulfadiazine, but not sulfanilamide. This latter compound they designated as *P-2* and showed that it was not a known, naturally occurring amino acid or PABA. Pancreas seemed to be the best source of *P-2* but it was neither insulin nor a protein.

Compounds of the type of methionine they looked upon as secondary antagonists of the sulfonamides and postulated that these compounds are normally synthesized as the result of reactions in which PABA is essential. Sulfonamides inhibit these primary reactions and so prevent the formation of substrates essential to secondary reactions. However, the secondary reactions may be reinstituted by supplying the missing substrates, which thus become secondary antagonists. Certain amino acids and purines in addition to methionine are in this class and many of them work only in concert[1460].

Rantz and Kirby[2000] thought that still another type of antagonist was active through an ability to improve the environment of the organism and thus increase its resistance to the bacteriostatic action of sulfonamides.

(D) Theories Involving Ionization of Sulfonamides

Fox and Rose[1122], Schmelkes, *et al.*[2113] and Cowles[930] called attention to the relationship between the ability of the sulfonamides to ionize as acids and their antibacterial activity. It appeared for a small series of the most active drugs that the ionic form of the drug was the active agent and that the ratio of PABA to ionized drug at concentrations where growth was just restored was approximately constant, whereas the ratio in terms of total concentration of drug varied widely. Thus the molar ratio of PABA to sulfanilamide where growth was restored was 1 to 5000, while with sulfathiazole or sulfadiazine it was 1 to 8. In terms of ionized drugs, the ratio was 1 to 1.4 for sulfanilamide, 1 to 4.9 for sulfathiazole and 1 to 6.4 for sulfadiazine[1122]. Increase in pH of the culture medium favored ionization of the drugs and gave higher antibacterial effects according to Schmelkes[2111].

(1) Theory of Cowles and Brueckner

Cowles[930] and Brueckner[802] found that activity increased with pH of culture medium only up to the point where ionization was about 50% complete. Highly ionized sulfonamides such as sulfadiazine showed an actual drop in activity with increased pH of medium. According to Cowles and Brueckner, when the pH of the medium exceeds the pKa^a of the sulfonamide the drug becomes less active. Brueckner's data supported this notably in the case of sulfadiazine, which was 50% dissociated at pH 6.5 and required a molar concentration of 80×10^{-6} for bacteriostasis, as compared to 99.6% dissociation at pH 8.9 where a molar concentration of 700×10^{-6} was required.

Cowles postulated that the sulfonamides penetrate the bacterial cell wall in the molecular rather than the ionic form, but once inside the bacteria, the ion is the active form in causing bacteriostasis. There is considerable evidence in the literature to support this view, by analogy, from study of other drugs[887, 1024].

Cowle's postulation would also apply to *p*-aminobenzoic acid (PABA). If it is the ion inside the bacteria which is active, then PABA should show a decrease in activity at pH levels higher than its pKa value, because of a deficiency of the molecular form to

[a] pKa = the logarithm of the reciprocal of the acid dissociation constant, K, of the sulfonamide.

penetrate the cell walls. Since the pKa is 4.68, PABA is almost completely ionized at the pH of ordinary cultures. Brueckner[802] was able to show that the activity of PABA in reversing sulfonamide bacteriostasis decreased with increasing pH of the culture medium, based on experiments where just sufficient PABA was added to restore growth to cultures containing four times the minimum bacteriostatic concentration of drug.

Brueckner's data suggesting a decrease in the antagonistic power of PABA with increasing pH have been supported by studies[579] on a mutant of *Neurospora crassa* which requires an exogenous supply of PABA. When this organism was grown at pH levels from 4.0 to 7.0 in the presence of varying amounts of PABA, it was found that the efficiency of the PABA in promoting growth was much greater at pH 4 than at higher pH levels.

The decreasing effectiveness of PABA with increasing pH of culture medium would also explain the observation[2110] that the bacteriostatic activity of N^1-disubstituted sulfanilamide derivatives (which are incapable of ionization) appeared to increase with higher pH of the medium, whereas, it would seem that their activity should be independent of pH since they can exist only in the molecular form (except at very low pH levels not encountered in therapy where the amino group becomes a salt forming group).

Lwoff, *et al.*[1638] found that the action of PABA in reversing the sulfanilamide inhibition of *Polytomella caeca* was 380 times greater at pH 2.25 than at pH 8. This indicated that PABA penetrated the cells much better in the molecular than in the ionized form. This was published in the year preceding Cowles' paper.

Experimental findings that are hard to reconcile with this and other theories involving ionization are presented by Sung and Helmholz[2644] who found that at pH 5.5 in urine in the presence of 64 mg. sulfathiazole per 100 cc., 19 out of 25 strains of *Streptococcus faecalis* were killed, while at double the concentration of sulfathiazole at pH 7.2, none of the twenty-five strains failed to grow. Exactly the opposite results were obtained with *E. coli* where 46 out of 50 strains showed large growth at pH 5.5 in the presence of 50 mg. sulfathiazole per 100 cc. but at pH 7.2 only 6 strains showed growth.

Implications of Theory. The theory predicts that the most active sulfonamide drugs are those which are 50% ionized at the pH of the culture medium. Translated to clinical work, this would mean that the drug should have a pKa of about 7 for use in the tissues. This agrees well with the clinical findings that sulfadiazine (pKa 6.5) and sulfathiazole (pKa 7.1) are the most effective drugs for general use.

Limitations of Theory. The theory is deficient in that it does not explain the activity of such compounds as sulfaguanidine,[a] N^1-dimethylsulfanilamide, or bis(4-aminophenyl) sulfone, which are not known to ionize at pH 7. It must be concluded that the molecular form can also be active. It is also uncertain whether a drug must diffuse into a cell to exert its bacteriostatic effect.

(2) Theory of Bell and Roblin

Bell and Roblin[719] combined the theory of Fildes and the facts of ionization with molecular structure considerations out of which they evolved a theory which permitted for the first time the calculation of approximate *in vitro* activities of new N^1-derivatives of sulfanilamide before synthesis. They stated this theory in its simplest form as follows:

[a] Cowles' value, pKa 11.2, or Brueckner's, pKa 10, for sulfaguanidine is not tenable. The compound does not form a sodium salt as would be expected if it had a pKa value in this range.

"The more negative the —SO₂— group of an N¹-substituted sulfanilamide derivative, the greater is its bacteriostatic power."

They reasoned that for a sulfanilamide derivative to be absorbed into an enzyme system competitively with *p*-aminobenzoic acid, it should resemble the *p*-aminobenzoate ion in its geometrical and electrical characteristics as closely as possible. Since biological processes in mammalian tissues are all buffered at approximately pH 7 and since PABA has been shown to be more than 99% ionized at this pH into a "non-zwitter ion" form[1273], a structure in sulfanilamide derivatives that approximates the *p*-aminobenzoate ion should be the active form. The *p*-aminobenzoate ion at pH 7 consists of a benzene ring bearing an amino group, with a carboxyl ion in the para position consisting of two strongly negative oxygens with a formal electronic charge in resonance between them.

$$
\begin{array}{ccc}
\text{6.7\AA} & & \text{6.9\AA} \\
\text{2.3\AA} & \text{2.4\AA} & \\
\textit{p-Aminobenzoate} & & \textit{Sulfanilamide} \\
\textit{ion} & & \textit{ion}
\end{array}
$$

Bell and Roblin pointed out the similar geometric relationship between the *p*-aminobenzoate ion and a substituted sulfanilamide. In the formulae shown, the hydrogens of the amino groups and the substituted amide nitrogen are out of the plane of the paper. The substituted amide nitrogen is presumed not to play an important part in the geometrical relationship. In order to approximate the electrical state of the carboxyl ion, $—CO_2^-$, the sulfonyl group, $—SO_2—$, must gather an electric charge equivalent to one electron. It is known to be an electron attracting group and since the amide nitrogen has an extra pair of electrons which it is willing to share, the $—SO_2—$ group may be pictured as gathering increased electron density. Bell and Roblin believe that when conditions are such that this electron density becomes a maximum in a substituted sulfanilamide, the compound exhibits the highest bacteriostatic power. They, therefore, searched for a physical property of the sulfonamides which would give a measure of the negativity of the $—SO_2—$ group, and found that the acid dissociation constant of the substituted sulfanilamide gave the desired correlation. The sulfamyl ion, $—SO_2\overline{N}R$, has a formal electronic charge and this means that the $—SO_2—$ group can gather a much higher electron density in the ion than in the unionized molecule. The ion should, therefore, be many times as potent as a bacteriostatic agent, but total activity is the sum of ionic and molecular species.

The effect of the *R* group in modifying activity is as follows: If *R* is an electron attracting group, competition is set up with the $—SO_2—$ group for the electrons of the amide nitrogen, the nitrogen becomes more positive and the amide hydrogen is more free to ionize, *i.e.* the sulfonamide becomes a stronger acid. There are then many more of the highly active ions present, consequently, the total activity of the compound increases. The competition for electrons by the R group means that in the unionized molecule, the electron density about the —SO_2— group decreases. Consequently, the higher the acid dissociation constant of a sulfonamide, the lower is the activity of the *unionized* molecules. Similarly when R has increased in its electron attracting power to the point where the sulfanilamide derivative is highly ionized at the pH of the biological system, further increase means withdrawal of electron density from the —SO_2— group in the ion and activity of the compound will be less. In other words, in a series of substituted sulfanilamides arranged in order of increasing electron attracting power of the R group (or increasing acid dissociation constant) the activity should increase to a maximum and then decline. By measuring the acid dissociation constants of over a hundred N^1-substituted sulfanilamides and correlating with the *in vitro* bacteriostatic activity of the sulfanilamides

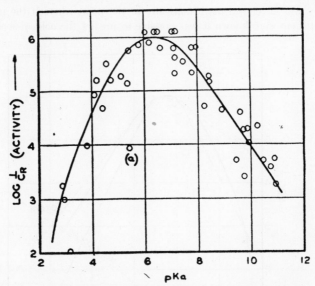

FIGURE 7. Dependence of activity on acid dissociation constants of substituted sulfanilamides.

measured in a synthetic culture medium at pH 7, Bell and Roblin found a remarkable correlation with their deductions. This is shown in Table 318, p. 512, and Figure 7 where representative examples of their data are plotted. In Figure 7 the compounds of greates activity lie at the top of the curve and a well defined maximum in the curve is noted which agrees with the broad outlines of the theory.

The following illustrates with some concrete examples the effect of group substitution: Compound 3 in Table 318 is N^1-methylsulfanilamide which has a very low ionization constant and is of relatively low antibacterial power. By replacing the methyl with a phenyl group which has a higher affinity for electrons, or electronegativity, the nitrogen
$$H$$
of the sulfamyl group —SO_2N—R ,becomes more positive, holds the proton (H^+) less readily and as a result N^1-phenylsulfanilamide ionizes to a greater extent. The increased number of ions is accompanied by a comparable increase in bacteriostatic activity.

The increased ionization is analogous to the increase in acid strength between acetic and benzoic acids except that here the effect of the R group on acidity is transmitted through one more atom (the R is two atoms removed from the ionizing proton in the carboxylic acids, only one atom in the sulfonamides), hence its effect should be more pronounced on the sulfonamides.

R		Ka	R		Ka
CH_3	$\overset{O}{\overset{\|\|}{COH}}$	1.86×10^{-5}	CH_3	$\overset{H}{NSO_2R}$	1.7×10^{-11}
C_6H_5	$\overset{O}{\overset{\|\|}{C\!-\!OH}}$	6.6×10^{-5}	C_6H_5	$\overset{H}{NSO_2R}$	2.5×10^{-10}

The theory was developed mathematically to the point where if the inductive effect of a N^1-substituent were known it was possible to predict the acid dissociation constant

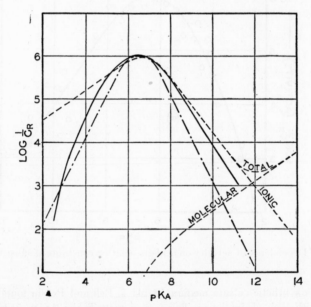

FIGURE 8.   Experimental *vs* theoretical curves relating activity to acid dissociation constants of sulfanilamide derivatives.

———— experimental curve (*from Figure 7*)
- - - - theoretical curve (*Bell-Roblin*)
- · - · theoretical curve (*Cowles-Brueckner*)

of the N^1-substituted sulfonamide and from this to predict the approximate *in vitro* activity of the compound against *E. coli* grown in a synthetic medium.   The calculated activity curves are shown in Figure 8 compared with the experimental curve determined at pH 7.   The point of maximum activity was predicted to shift depending on the pH of the substrate.   Thus if the substrate was at pH 5, a sulfonamide having a pKa of 4.7 should be most active while if the pH of the substrate was 9, a sulfonamide of pKa 8.6

should be most active. This prediction has been verified approximately. Total activity is shown as a combination of molecular and ionic species for drugs of high pKa values. According to the theory, any sulfonamide ion is $10^{4.85}$ times as active as the corresponding molecular form of the drug, hence the contribution of the molecular form to the total activity is negligible for drugs having pKa values lower than 9.

Implications of the Theory.

1) The theory permits the calculation of approximate *in vitro* activities of new N^1-substituted sulfanilamide derivatives from known molecular constants of the substituent groups.

2) It predicts maximum activity of N^1-substituted sulfanilamides when the pKa of the derivative is 6.7 (for substrates at pH 7).

3) It indicates that it is unlikely new sulfanilamide derivatives will be found which are appreciably more active *in vitro* than those in use today if their action is dependent on inhibition of enzyme systems involving PABA.

Limitations of the Theory. The theory is predicted on the assumptions that there is no specificity of action (at least *in vitro*) of sulfanilamide derivatives and that PABA is the chief antagonist of sulfanilamide and its derivatives. Other known antagonists of sulfanilamide are presumed to act through a mechanism involving PABA as an essential metabolite at some stage of the complex processes concerned with growth of bacteria. All of these assumptions are open to argument. It seems probable that heterocyclic derivatives of sulfanilamide are capable of inhibiting other enzyme systems than those involving PABA and the relative importance of these various enzyme systems to bacterial metabolism will vary among different bacteria giving rise to specificity of action both *in vivo* and *in vitro*. There are also a few instances of activity of certain sulfanilamide derivatives against certain organisms where PABA does not antagonize and where a high degree of specificity is apparent.

The studies of Pulver and Martin[1966] and Laüger, Suter and Martin[2583] which showed a high degree of specificity both *in vitro* and *in vivo* are difficult to explain by this or any other current theory. (The *in vivo* results are in need of verification since too few experimental animals were used to be significant.) One of the more striking anomalies pointed out by these authors was the high activity of N^1-(3,4-dimethylbenzoyl)sulfanilamide against *E. coli in vitro* (and similarly against streptococci, pneumococci and *E. coli in vivo* in mice) whereas, the 2,3; 2,4; and 2,5 isomers had little or no activity either *in vivo* or *in vitro*. Because it is difficult to picture any appreciable difference in the acid dissociation constants of these isomers, these results, if verified, would be exceptions to the Bell-Roblin theory.

(3) Further Considerations on Ionization Theories

(a) *Comparison of Cowles-Brueckner and Bell-Roblin Theories*

The author has applied the concepts of Cowles and Brueckner to derive the theoretical curve shown in Figure 8, where a comparison is made with the theoretical and experimental curves of Bell and Roblin relating the *in vitro* activity to the acid dissociation constants of N^1-substituted sulfanilamides. The derivation is as follows:

Postulations. 1) Only the molecular form of the drug penetrates to the site of action. 2) At the site of action (intracellular?) the ion is the active form. 3) The pH at the site of action is unknown but is assumed to be 6 (*E. coli* produces acid in its metabolism). 4) The ions of all sulfonamide drugs are presumed to be equally active.

Let C_R = minimum molar concentration required to produce bacteriostasis of *E. coli* in a synthetic medium buffered at pH 7.

X_0 = fraction of drug ionized in substrate

$1 - X_0$ = molecular form of drug in substrate

X_i = fraction of drug ionized at site of action

k = proportionality constant to adjust to experimental conditions

then $C_R X_i(1 - X_0)$ is proportional to the active fraction of drug reaching the site of action = k

or

$$\log \frac{1}{C_R} = \log X_i(1 - X_0) - \log k$$

From the experimental curve of Bell and Roblin at the point of maximum activity

$$\log \frac{1}{C_R} = 6 \text{ at pKa } 6.7;$$

from which X_i and $1 - X_0$ may be calculated from the relationship,

$$X = \frac{1}{1 + \text{antilog (pKa - pH)}}$$

Substituting these values

$$\log k = 2.7427 - 10$$

The curve is plotted from the expression

$$\log \frac{1}{C_R} = \log X_i(1 - X_0) - (2.7427 - 10)$$

$$= \log X_i(1 - X_0) + 7.2573$$

Inspection of the curves shows that this expression gives better agreement with the experimental curve than the theoretical curve of Bell and Roblin for pKa values less than 6. It appears that a combination of the two theories would give a still better approach to the experimental findings.

(b) *Further Experimental Evidence*

The author is indebted to Dr. Orville Wyss for supplying hitherto unpublished data extending that of Schmelkes[2110, 2111] showing the antibacterial activities of a number of sulfanilamide derivatives at various pH levels of the substrate. Dr. Wyss gives the following description of the experimental method used: "The data below pH 7.0 were obtained with *E. coli* in an asparagine-dextrose-mineral salts medium as described in our earlier papers. The data above pH 7.0 were obtained with a *Strep. fecalis* strain grown on Schumann and Farrel's medium[a] to which we added a small amount of yeast extract

[a] *J. Infectious Diseases*, **69**, 81 (1941).

which had been extracted with acidified ether. At pH 7.0, the data obtained from both organisms checked very well so an average was used.

"Turbidity measurements were made to determine the rate of growth in the log phase. Sufficiently high concentrations of sulfonamides were added to the tubes so that the amount of PABA present in the inoculum or as impurity would be negligible as compared with that added to reverse the sulfonamide action. Closely spaced increments of PABA were added to successive tubes to permit reasonably accurate estimation of that concentration which, in the presence of sulfonamide, would permit growth at a rate one-half that of the control."

Because this datum is the most complete of its nature so far available and offers tests of the various ionization theories, the author has made calculations based on those theories and presents the results in Tables 319 and 320, p. 515–516.

Let X_0^s = fraction ionized in substrate of sulfanilamide derivative

$X_0^p =$ "   •   "   "   "   "   " PABA

$X_1^s =$ "   "   at site of action of sulfonamide

$X_1^p =$ "   "   "   "   "   "   " PABA

C^s = molar concentration of sulfonamide in substrate

$C^p =$ "   "   " PABA   "   "   required to restore growth rate to 50% that of control cultures at the same pH.

Then

$$\frac{C^s}{C^p} = \text{antibacterial index, determined experimentally (Wyss)}$$

$$\frac{C^s X_0^s}{C^p X_0^p} = \text{ratio of ions of sulfonamide to ions of PABA in substrate}$$

where

$$X = \frac{1}{1 + \text{antilog (pKa} - \text{pH)}}$$

If only the molecular forms of the drugs penetrate to the site of action (Cowles-Brueckner) then

$$\frac{C^s(1 - X_0^s)}{C^p(1 - X_0^p)} = \text{ratio of concentration of sulfonamide to concentration of PABA at site}$$

$$\text{of action.}$$

For sulfonamides which are incapable of ionization this becomes

$$\frac{C^s}{C^p(1 - X_0^p)}.$$

Diffusion factors of the sulfonamides and PABA are neglected, as is the concentration of PABA which may be present at the site of action through bacterial synthesis.

If it is the sulfonamide and PABA ions which are active at the site of action, the ratio of these is given by

$$\frac{C^s X_i^s (1 - X_0^s)}{C^p X_i^p (1 - X_0^p)}$$

The pH at the site of action is unknown but since *E. coli* synthesize acid, this pH has been taken as 6 in the calculations.

The data in Tables 319 and 320 seem to support these conclusions:

1) Ionic sulfonamides appear to exert maximum activity $\left(\text{smallest antibacterial index,} \frac{C^s}{C^p}\right)$ at pH levels of substrate approximately equal to the pKa of the sulfonamide. This supports Cowles and Brueckner. The data for sulfacetamide are possible exceptions to this and further highly ionized sulfonamides should be investigated.

2) In contrast to the wide fluctuations in antibacterial index with pH for weakly ionic sulfonamides, the antibacterial index for the respective ions in the substrate,

$$\left(\frac{C^s X_0^s}{C^p X_0^p}\right)$$

is fairly constant for any one drug. This supports all theories claiming that ions are important in the activity but does not appear significant because of the known activity of non-ionizable sulfonamides.

3) The data of Table 320 on non-ionizable sulfonamides appear to support Cowles' contention that only the molecular form of the drugs penetrate to the site of action. In this case, the decreasing ability of PABA to reach the site of action with increased pH is a satisfactory explanation of the experimental fact that the antibacterial index is 20 to 200 times greater at pH 6 than at pH 9. The expression

$$\frac{C^s}{C^p (1 - X_0^p)}$$

which measures the ratio of sulfonamide to PABA at the site of action is reasonably constant for any one drug at varying pH levels, in contrast to the antibacterial index. These data show that the molecular form of the sulfonamides is also active, a factor which is neglected by many ionic theories.

4) Referring to antibacterial indices, at pH 9 sulfapyridine is the most active drug; at pH 7 sulfathiazole is most active and at pH 5.5 or 6.0 sulfadiazine is most active. These facts support both Bell and Roblin and Cowles and Brueckner in their predictions.

5) The fact that the ratio

$$\frac{C^s X_i^s (1 - X_0^s)}{C^p X_i^p (1 - X_0^p)}$$

is not constant for different sulfonamides does not support Cowles that "the influence of the various substituents will be largely, as far as the bacteriostatic activity is concerned, one of changing the ionization constant of the resulting compound and of altering the ease with which it can penetrate the bacterial cell". The fact that this ratio increases with decreasing pKa supports Bell and Roblin that the ions of weakly ionized sulfonamides are more active than those of highly ionized sulfonamides.

(4) Theory of Klotz

Klotz[1454] started with the fundamental postulates of the Woods-Fildes theory that sulfonamides act by blocking an enzyme system essential to the growth of the bacteria and made a mathematical analysis of the various equilibria involved.   His further assumptions were: (1) that a reversible combination between an enzyme and the basic drug molecule or anion was involved in inhibition of bacterial growth; (2) that bacteriostasis results when a certain amount of the sulfonamide-enzyme complex has been formed; and (3) that the bacteriostatic effect of a sulfonamide is antagonized when the concentration of the enzyme-protein—PABA-ion complex reaches a value such that the ratio of this concentration to that of the enzyme-protein—sulfonamide-ion complex is equal to some fixed number.

The equilibria involved are: the dissociation of the sulfonamide as an acid; the combinations of the hydrogen ion and OH-ion with the protein of the enzyme; the protein-sulfonamide ion complex; and similar equilibria for PABA.   Klotz applied the law of mass action to these equilibria and arrived at an expression for the ratio of the concentration of PABA in a substrate to the bacteriostatic concentration of a sulfonamide drug in this substrate in terms of the equilibrium constants, the pH of the substrate and certain constants.

Klotz evaluated the constants based on published data by Bell and Roblin and others. He used the data of Davis and Wood[954] on the binding between sulfonamide drugs and plasma protein which appeared to correlate the acid dissociation constant of the sulfonamide drug with the dissociation constant of the sulfonamide-ion-plasma-protein complex. Klotz made the assumption that this same relationship would hold approximately and be a measure of the binding between the sulfonamide-ion and the protein of the bacterial enzyme.   Gilligan[1170] on investigating more drugs was unable to find any correlation between acid dissociation constant and extent of binding of the drug.   Also, cataphoresis studies[1431] showed that the drugs are bound specifically to plasma albumins and not to globulins, while tissue cells do not bind the drugs appreciably[1170].   It, therefore, seems unjustified to correlate binding between sulfonamides and blood proteins and the similar binding to the specific protein of an enzyme (or enzymes) responsible for growth of bacteria, the nature of which protein is unknown.

Implications of Theory.   The theory gives essentially the same relationship between the acid dissociation constant of a sulfonamide and its bacteriostatic activity as is derived by Bell and Roblin.   The assumptions underlying the constants in the equations are less involved and are somewhat different; however, because essentially the same experimental data is used in evaluation of the constants, the results are very similar.

Limitations of Theory.   The theory predicts more activity than is found experimentally for highly acidic sulfanilamide derivatives.   Klotz believed that inability of anions to penetrate the cell wall of bacteria, as suggested by Cowles, might be the explanation.

As Klotz pointed out "the equations which have been derived may express only a necessary condition for activity but not a sufficient one.   It is quite likely that some compounds combine with the enzyme and, nevertheless, are not chemotherapeutically active.   Thus, Davis and Wood have found that metanilamide and various inactive substituted sulfonamides, as well as active sulfonamides, combine with blood plasma proteins".   The theory, therefore, does not go far enough to enable one to predict active sulfonamide drugs from structural considerations.

This theory does not take into account the activity of undissociated molecules of a sulfonamide drug nor does it account for activity of N^1,N^1-disubstituted sulfanilamides (which cannot ionize) or for activity of sulfones. The theory neglects antagonists other than PABA, although if these were known, the theory might be extended to include them.

(5) Resonance Theory

Kumler and associates[1498, 1497, 1499] proposed a theory which accepted most of the theory of Bell and Roblin but differed in interpretation. Kumler believed that a resonance form[a] of sulfanilamide derivatives in which there is a separation of charge is the active form:

$$\overset{+}{H_2N}=\left\langle\!\!=\!\!\!=\!\!\!=\!\!\right\rangle=\overset{\overset{\displaystyle\bar{O}}{|}}{\underset{\underset{\displaystyle O}{\|}}{S}}-\overset{\displaystyle H}{\underset{}{N}}-R$$

The negative character of the —SO₂—group is made up of such a resonance structure with the ring, plus the inductive effects of the R group and the ionization of the hydrogen on the amide group. Increased negative character of the —SO₂—group increases the contribution of the above form to the total resonance structure of the molecule and thus increases the bacteriostatic activity, according to Kumler's views. He placed emphasis on the coplanar amino group as the main factor affecting activity. Bell and Roblin viewed the —SO₂—group as the chief factor involved in differences of activity between different sulfanilamide derivatives, but also stressed the importance of the p-amino group in the fundamental activity of the drugs.

Kumler and Daniels[1497] pointed out that an —SO₂—group is not active chemically, while an aromatic amino group is highly reactive. A free amino group appears necessary for bacteriostatic activity but a wide variety of substitutions can be made on the amide nitrogen with retention of activity, even though the environment of the —SO₂—group is considerably changed. They explained the inactivity of metanilamide as an inability to form a resonance structure of the above type. Orthanilamide can form an orthoquinone type of structure, but a hydrogen bond is established between the amino and —SO₂—groups so that the amino group is no longer "free". They viewed the inactivity of nuclear substituted derivatives as caused by steric interference with either the coplanar amino group or the —SO₂—group, with consequent reduction in the active resonance form. Structures in which the amino or sulfonamide group appears on a side chain are inactive, because no resonance form can be established similar to the above.

One of the compounds which failed to fall on the activity curve of Bell and Roblin was sulfanilylurea, which showed less activity at pH 7 than was predicted from its pKa. At this pH, it is 97% ionized so the ion is the form chiefly concerned. Kumler and Daniels explained this low activity as caused by a resonance form of the ion in which the charge goes mainly to the urea oxygen rather than to the —SO₂—group:

$$H_2N\left\langle\underset{}{}\right\rangle\overset{\overset{\displaystyle O}{\|}}{\underset{\underset{\displaystyle O}{\|}}{S}}-N=\overset{\overset{\displaystyle O}{\|}}{C}-NH_2$$

---

[a] For background on resonance theory see Pauling, L., "The Nature of the Chemical Bond", 2nd ed., Cornell University Press, Ithaca, New York, 1940.

This means that the —SO_2—group is less negative than normal and the occurrence of resonating forms having the coplanar amino group is greatly reduced with consequent low activity.

In sulfaguanidine, the pKa is so low that it has not been measured, yet the compound is fairly active. Two resonance forms are postulated to explain this:

$$H_2N\text{—}\langle\ \rangle\text{—}\underset{O}{\overset{O}{\underset{\|}{\overset{\|}{S}}}}\text{—}\overset{-}{N}\text{—}\underset{NH_2}{\overset{\overset{+}{NH_2}}{C}} \quad \text{and} \quad H_2N\text{—}\langle\ \rangle\text{—}\underset{O}{\overset{O}{\underset{\|}{\overset{\|}{S}}}}\text{—}\overset{-}{N}\text{—}\underset{\overset{+}{NH_2}}{\overset{NH_2}{C}}$$

A negative charge appears on the amide nitrogen and this increases the negativity of the —SO_2—, which in turn enhances the coplanar amino nitrogen resonance forms.

They also explained the fact that ring N-methylsulfapyridine is a more potent drug than N^1-methylsulfapyridine by stating that in the ring N-methyl compound there is a large contribution from the form:

$$H_2N\text{—}\langle\ \rangle\text{—}\underset{O}{\overset{O}{\underset{\|}{\overset{\|}{S}}}}\text{—}\overset{-}{N}\text{—}\overset{\overset{CH_3}{|}\overset{+}{N}}{}$$

while in the N^1-methyl derivative, the main contribution is from a form which places a positive charge on the amide nitrogen:

$$H_2N\text{—}\langle\ \rangle\text{—}\underset{O}{\overset{O}{\underset{\|}{\overset{\|}{S}}}}\text{—}\overset{\overset{CH_3}{\overset{+}{|}}}{N}=\overset{\overset{-}{N}}{}$$

One of the early bits of evidence in support of Kumler's views was the work of Bradbury and Jordan[777] who studied the effect of sulfanilamide, p-aminobenzoic acid, and related compounds on the electrophoretic mobility of *B. coli*. It was found that sulfanilamide and other active agents behaved similarly to p-aminobenzoic acid, while metanilamide, aniline, benzenesulfonamide, sulfanilic acid and other related but inactive compounds behaved differently. With the active compounds, there was a fluctuation in mobility characterized by two or three well defined maxima, while the inactive compounds showed an initial rapid drop, followed by a nearly constant mobility.

The effects were interpreted as evidence of an association of the polar character of the molecule with its activity. Kumler and Halverstadt's ideas[1498] of polar resonance forms of sulfanilamide and p-aminobenzoic acid were used in the interpretation. It was deduced that the NH_2-group in quaternary resonance form was responsible for association of the drug with the organism and this was a factor in determining activity.

Kumler and Halverstadt[1498] measured dipole moments[a] of sulfanilamide and related compounds from which they calculated that resonance forms of sulfanilamide having a

[a] For other dipole moments of sulfanilamide derivatives, see Jensen and Friediger[1379].

coplanar amino group with separation of charge contributed about 3% to the structure of the molecule. This they regarded as significant.

Kumler and Strait[1499] measured absorption spectra of sulfanilamide and related compounds in acid, neutral and alkaline solution and obtained an apparent higher absorption maximum in alkaline solution. This they thought was evidence in support of their theory and indicated that the resonance form with a separation of charge made a greater contribution in the ion than in the molecule.

Bell, Bone and Roblin[718] attacked these experimental data and showed that if compensation is made for absorption of the NaOH, the extinction coefficient at the absorption maximum of sulfanilamide in N/1 NaOH is within 1.4% of that in N/1 NaCl solution, but is *less* rather than greater. They also pointed out that the resonance form of the *p*-amino group has a positive charge which should make it less basic, since such a charge will oppose addition of a hydrogen ion. However, their experimental data[719] indicated that ionization of the sulfonamide group increased the basic strength of the *p*-amino group. This is further evidence against the assumption that the resonance form with a separation of charge makes a greater contribution in the ion. Since resonance is related to basic strength of the *p*-amino group, it should be possible to correlate bacteriostatic activity with the base constants of the sulfanilamide derivatives. This they were unable to do[719].

Bordwell and Klotz[768] made the further point that if, as Kumler and Daniels suggested, the sulfonamide group is significant for activity only insofar as it affects the amino group, then vinylogs of sulfanilamide of the type

$$\text{NH}_2 \langle \quad \rangle \text{CH}=\text{CHSO}_2\text{NHR}$$

should give rise to the form

$$\text{H}_2\overset{+}{\text{N}} \langle \quad \rangle =\text{CHCH}=\overset{-}{\text{S}}\text{O}_2\text{NHR}$$

and show activity. The parent compound

$$\text{NH}_2 \langle \quad \rangle \text{CH}=\text{CHSO}_2\text{NH}_2$$

was prepared and was practically inactive *in vitro*.

These authors also pointed out that the low activities of sulfanilylurea and 3-sulfanilamido-1,2,4-triazole are not adequately explained by Kumler and Daniels, since the explanations advanced could equally well be applied to N^1-acetylsulfanilamide and sulfadiazine which are highly active.

Limitations of Theory. The hypothesis that the relative bacteriostatic activities of different sulfanilamide derivatives is related to the occurrence of resonance forms of the molecule involving a separation of charge and a coplanar amino group, needs confirmation from further experimental evidence. At present, it present an attractive field for speculation but the utility of the ideas in producing new chemotherapeutic agents remains to be demonstrated.

(III) MISCELLANEOUS THEORIES

(A) The Peroxide-Anticatalase Theory

Shinn, Locke, Mellon and Main in a series of papers[329, 330, 1701, 1763, 2190, 2191] developed the hypothesis that the action of sulfanilamide on certain bacteria was explained by the following: (1) The bacteria in question produced hydrogen peroxide as part of their metabolic processes. (2) Presence of catalase in the tissues of the host destroyed hydrogen peroxide under normal conditions. (3) Sulfanilamide was converted to a derivative which had a powerful anticatalase activity. This was presumed to be the hydroxylamine derivative which was produced by bacterial oxidation. This presumption was suggested by the work of Mayer[1753]. (4) The anticatalase activity in the vicinity of the bacterial cell permitted the accumulation of hydrogen peroxide to levels which were toxic to the bacteria. (5) Inhibition of the growth of anaerobes by sulfanilamide, where production of hydrogen peroxide was obviously a difficult postulation, was suggested to occur through a different mechanism, possibly involving reduction of the sulfonamide group to a toxic sulfide.

Experimental evidence in favor of the above hypothesis was obtained by growing broth cultures of pneumococcus containing glucose and blood in the presence of varying amounts of sulfanilamide and under varying partial pressures of oxygen. It was observed that the inhibition of growth in the presence of 10 mg.% sulfanilamide decreased with oxygen concentration until with 1 to 3% oxygen there was no inhibition. At still lower oxygen concentrations a stimulation of growth was observed but at oxygen levels below 0.04%, inhibition again appeared. Presence of hydrogen peroxide was detected when the oxygen concentration was 10 mg.% or more.

It was shown that N^4-caproyl-N^1-hydroxysulfanilamide[2191] exerted an immediate bacteriostatic effect on blood cultures of pneumococci in contrast to sulfanilamide which had a characteristic lag in its activity. This immediate effect was also shown by o-toluenesulfonhydroxamide and in both cases was transient. This was interpreted as an anticatalase effect of the hydroxamide group. In the case of the sulfanilamide derivative, the transient bacteriostatic effect was succeeded by a second period of activity which was ascribed to the hydrolysis of the caproyl group.

There are a number of discrepancies which do not fit the theory well. Thus sulfathiazole and sulfamethylthiazole which are the most active of the sulfonamides showed only half as high a concentration of H_2O_2 as sulfanilamide and sulfapyridine in in vitro growth studies with type I pneumococcus, while sodium sulfanilylsulfanilate, which has little activity, showed slightly greater concentration of H_2O_2[329].

Long and Bliss[313] pointed out that there was no correlation between the ability of various strains of streptococci to produce peroxide and their sensitivity to sulfanilamide in vitro. It was also shown[1140] that sulfanilamide was effective against strains of streptococci which did not produce peroxide. Also, some peroxide resistant organisms were sensitive to the sulfonamides.

Sevag and Shelburne[2172] could not detect the presence of hydrogen peroxide in a culture of Streptococcus pyogenes, yet the organism was strongly inhibited by the sulfa drugs. Further, they were unable to detect any inhibiting action of p-hydroxylaminobenzenesulfonamide on catalase. Julius and Winkler[1402] also were unable to demonstrate an inhibitory effect of sulfanilamide on the catalase of blood or that produced by bacteria.

Bratton, White and Marshall[50] found p-hydroxylaminobenzenesulfonamide extremely unstable in the presence of blood. This would argue against its formation.

(B) Theory of Sevag, et al.

Sevag, Shelburne, and Mudd[2172, 2173] making use of previous knowledge of enzyme inhibitions[2550] advanced the theory, closely related to that of Woods and Fildes, that drugs which are closely related in structure to all or part of coenzymes may compete with these for the specific proteins (apoenzymes) which when combined with such coenzymes form the enzymes essential to respiratory processes in bacteria. Presence of the drug might displace a coenzyme from its specific protein and form an inactive drug-protein complex, thus inhibiting respiration and growth of bacteria. In the experimental work, sulfapyridine appeared to be competitive with coenzyme I and II and sulfathiazole and sulfadiazine with cocarboxylase. The heterocyclic rings of these sulfa drugs were believed responsible for the competition with similar heterocyclic elements of the coenzymes. It was also postulated that drugs of dissimilar structure may unite with enzyme proteins or enzymes to give inactive "enzyme analogues" or "drug-protein-enzyme" complexes.

Wyss, et al.[581] were of the opinion that this and other attempts to correlate antibacterial activity of sulfa drugs with bacterial respiration were based on faulty evidence, since orthanilamide and metanilamide which are devoid of chemotherapeutic activity have as great an effect on depressing cell respiration as sulfanilamide. Effects of the drugs on growth were not parallel to the effects on respiration.

Sevag, Henry and Richardson[2636] surmounted this objection by the postulation that other proteins are able to compete with the specific proteins of bacterial enzymes for sulfonamide drugs. They pointed out that neopeptone reverses the inhibition of respiration of bacteria caused by sulfonamide drugs and thought their experimental data favored a competitive mechanism rather than the alternative proposal of Lockwood that the neopeptone caused an acceleration of bacterial metabolism. They showed that orthanilamide, metanilamide and sulfanilamide had a similar inhibiting action on the carboxylase activity of *E. coli* in the absence of added protein. However, in the presence of neopeptone or human serum albumin, sulfanilamide retained much of its inhibitory effect but orthanilamide and metanilamide did not inhibit growth. They explained that orthanilamide or metanilamide had high combining power with the added protein, hence was no longer available for combination with the protein of carboxylase and inhibition of this enzyme.

PABA was found to reverse the inhibition of bacterial carboxylases by sulfathiazole.

(C) Theory of Synergism and Antagonism

Johnson, Eyring and Kearns[1392] developed a quantitative theory of synergism and antagonism to explain the observed effects of sulfanilamide derivatives and other drugs on the luminescence of luminescent bacteria. In this case, the effect is known to occur on the light-emitting enzyme-substrate system of the bacteria. The theory and mathematical expressions developed would appear to apply to the inhibition of bacterial growth responsible for the chemotherapeutic uses of the sulfonamide drugs. It is quite clear, however, that the effects on luminescence are independent of the enzyme systems responsible for growth, because addition of PABA, instead of restoring luminescence to bacteria inhibited by sulfanilamide (*i.e.* acting as an antagonist as it does on the inhibition of growth), has an additive effect[a] in further inhibiting luminescence[2566]. Also in contrast to its reversal of the bacteriostatic effects of sulfanilamide, methionine has little or no effect on the inhibition of luminescence brought about by sulfanilamide.

While the problems of bacterial luminescence and bacteriostasis are apparently unrelated, the mathematical analysis of the various equilibria involved is worthy of consideration and adaptation to the interpretation of the complex equilibria between enzyme

---

[a] This is *synergism*, as defined by these authors, in which two drugs have a greater action working together than either has alone. As used by some other authors, this term means an effect greater than expected by the additive effects of the two drugs.

systems responsible for growth and reproduction of bacteria, a sulfonamide drug and the various naturally occurring antagonists and potentiators of its action (including various inert adsorbents of the drugs), when these have been more fully explored. The theory is chiefly of help in interpretation. It is of no special help in the design of new chemotherapeutic agents because it does not include structural considerations.

(D) Postulation of Lee and Foley

Lee and Foley[1538] explained the action of sulfonamides as causing local damage (denaturation) to certain "sulfonamide-receptive parts of the enzyme mosaic". They explained the conjoint action of sulfa drugs with other drugs similarly. The other drugs, if potentiators, become absorbed at other positions and hence increase the effect of the sulfa drugs on the bacterial enzymes; however, if they absorbed at the same site as the sulfonamide drugs, they might protect the enzyme and hence act as inhibitors of sulfa drug activity.

(E) Postulation of Jensen and Schmith

Jensen and Schmith[1384] suggested that p-aminobenzoic acid combined to form an enzyme of the nature,

$$\text{ANH}\langle\ \rangle\text{COB.}$$

The sulfanilamides would then form "pseudoenzymes" of the type

$$\text{ANH}\langle\ \rangle\text{SO}_2\text{NH}_2$$

which would be inactive. The action of p-nitrobenzoic acid as a chemotherapeutic agent could then be explained by formation of a "pseudo-coenzyme",

$$\text{NO}_2\langle\ \rangle\text{COB}$$

which would also be inactive in bacterial metabolic processes necessary for growth.

This view is probably much too narrow to explain the wide variety of bacteriostatic compounds which are antagonized by PABA and does not satisfactorily explain the inactivity of many aniline derivatives or benzoic acid derivatives.

(F) Adsorption Theories

Eyster[1042, 1043] conducted experiments on the adsorption of methylene blue by activated charcoal. Sulfanilamide inhibited the adsorption of the methylene blue and PABA counteracted this inhibition of methylene blue by a competitive mechanism. However, when the concentration of PABA was sufficiently increased it had an additive effect with the sulfanilamide in further inhibiting the adsorption of methylene blue by charcoal.

Hartman and Druey[2553] found that when 1 l. of M./100 sodium p-aminobenzoate was shaken with 50 Gm. of Norite for half an hour, 95% of the PABA was absorbed. When this charcoal was placed in 1 l. of M./100 sodium sulfathiazole, the sulfathiazole displaced the PABA and 200 mg. of PABA were recovered from the filtrate out of the 1300 mg. originally present on the charcoal.

On repetition of the experiment using sulfanilamide, 60 mg. of PABA was recovered. Both authors compared the action in these simple adsorption experiments to effects observed in inhibition of bacteria by the sulfonamide drugs and the reversal of the effect by PABA. Eyster[1042] postulated that sulfanilamide reduced cellular and colloidal adsorption and so prevented nutrition of the cells. PABA antagonized when present in low concentration but when present in large amounts, it added to the inhibition.

(G) Postulations of Henry

Henry[1297] after a thorough review of the experimental evidence and the various theories of sulfonamide mode of action, believed there was ample evidence to show that it is not necessary for an antagonist to be a normal component of the biological system in order to overcome the action of an inhibitor. He thought that this weakened the argument in favor of the Woods-Fildes theory that since PABA antagonizes sulfonamide action competitively, and since PABA is a growth factor for some cells, sulfonamides act by interfering with the metabolism of PABA. He went so far as to class the sulfonamides with narcotics as "indifferent inhibitors".

He believed that normal cell division depends on an unknown but very specific fraction of the total oxidative reactions of the cell and that "indifferent inhibitors" act on that specific set of reactions. He coupled with this view the supposition that antagonists exclude inhibitors from cell catalysts without themselves interfering with the catalytic action.

(IV) Critical Evaluation of Various Theories

The chief benefits to be derived from theories of the mechanism of action of sulfonamide and other chemotherapeutic drugs are: 1) More intelligent use of the drugs as medicinal agents. 2) Stimulation of medical research which will widen the field of usefulness of existing drugs and perhaps suggest drug combinations of increased effectiveness. 3) Aid in the design of new drugs leading to improved or fundamentally new chemotherapeutic agents.

If current theories are examined according to these criteria of their usefulness, it may fairly be said that each has contributed in some measure under items 1) and 2). Thus the Woods-Fildes theory has contributed a considerable body of information about antagonists of sulfonamide action which has armed physicians with the knowledge that tissue breakdown products must be thoroughly removed surgically to obtain much benefit from sulfonamide drugs. It has suggested various combinations of drugs designed to counteract the antagonists while preserving the bacteriostatic effect of the sulfonamide. The theories dealing with ionization of sulfonamide drugs have demonstrated how to make some of the drugs safer to use and have shed light on which of the drugs to employ under special conditions of pH.

When examined according to whether they aid in the design of new chemotherapeutic agents the theories show marked differences. The Woods-Fildes theory and its modifications give a definite program to be followed in the design of new bacteriostatic drugs, i.e., first find a chemical substance which is essential to the metabolism of the particular organism, then synthesize compounds which resemble this essential substance. As a corollary to this might be added the suggestion that the essential metabolite of the bacterium should not be equally or more essential to the metabolism of the host.

In the five years in which much synthetic effort has been directed towards producing metabolite analogues which will be effective chemotherapeutic agents some promising compounds have been obtained but none has proven effective in clinical medicine. It remains to be seen whether this approach will be more productive than others. It may be significant that two drugs for which there are no known metabolite analogues, and which are very potent against anaerobic organisms have been discovered during these five years.   These are:

$$NH_2CH_2\langle\bigcirc\rangle SO_2NH_2 \quad \text{and} \quad \underset{NH}{\overset{NH_2}{C}}\langle\bigcirc\rangle SO_2CH_3$$

The theory of Bell and Roblin is in essence a *post mortem* of the sulfa drugs because it leads to the conclusion that the most active drugs have been synthesized.   It, therefore, leaves little room for promising syntheses in the field except to modify the absorption-distribution-excretion characteristics and toxic properties of the drugs on which it gives no clues in design.

The theories of resonance aside from resting on a meager experimental background do not appear to offer great assistance in synthesis.

The theory of Cowles and Brueckner, based as it is on older experimental work outside of the field of sulfa drugs, would seem to be of some general value in synthesis of chemotherapeutic agents.   It teaches that very strong anionic or cationic groups should not be incorporated into the molecule if penetration of cell walls is important in the activity of the drug.   The prevalence of "zwitterion" types in nature would lead one to balance a strongly cationic group with an appropriately placed anionic group in a molecule designed for systemic use in medicine.

None of the miscellaneous theories appear to help the synthetic chemist but may be of practical importance in suggesting drug combinations and otherwise aiding the pharmacologists and clinicians.

TABLE 318

Effect of Group Substitution on Bacteriostatic Activity
of N^1-Substituted Sulfanilamides

No.	R	Ka	pKa	% Ionized pH 7	Activity $C_R \times 10^5$	Kb $\times 10^{12}$ 1st	Kb $\times 10^{12}$ 2nd
1	$HOCH_2CH_2-$	1.2×10^{-11}	10.92	0.012	50.0	2.0	
2	(morpholinyl) $O\diagup CH_2-$	1.3×10^{-11}	10.88	0.013	20.0	1.8	
3	CH_3-	1.7×10^{-11}	10.77	0.017	30.0	1.6	
4	$H-$	3.7×10^{-11}	10.43	0.04	20.0	2.3	
5	$4\text{-}NH_2C_6H_4-$	0.6×10^{-11}	10.22	0.06	5.0	$>10^{-9}$	0.7
6	$2\text{-}CH_3C_6H_4-$	1.1×10^{-10}	9.96	0.11	10.0	1.1	
7	$4\text{-}CH_3C_6H_4-$	1.5×10^{-10}	9.82	0.15	5.0	1.4	
8	$3\text{-}CH_3C_6H_4-$	1.8×10^{-10}	9.74	0.17	5.0	1.3	
9	H (N ring)	1.9×10^{-10}	9.72	0.19	40.0		
10	C_6H_5-	2.5×10^{-10}	9.60	0.25	3.0	1.4	
11	(ring) NH_2	3.6×10^{-10}	9.44	0.36	20.0	13.5	
12	NH_2 (ring)	1.5×10^{-10}	8.82	1.5	2.0	160	0.8
13	(ring) NH_2	3.4×10^{-9}	8.47	3.4	0.6	10	0.3
14	(N ring)	3.7×10^{-9}	8.43	3.5	0.6	3.8	0.1
15	$3\text{-}(NH_2SO_2)C_6H_4-$	5.9×10^{-9}	8.23	5.3	2.0	1.6	
16	(N ring)	1.3×10^{-8}	7.89	11.4	0.2	10	0.4
17	$4\text{-}(NH_2SO_2)C_6H_4-$	1.4×10^{-8}	7.85	12.4	0.5	0.8	
18	CH_3-N (S ring)	1.6×10^{-8}	7.79	14.0	0.2	2.3	
19	CH_3 / CH_3 (N,N ring)	4.3×10^{-8}	7.37	30.2	0.3	2.3	

TABLE 318—(Continued)

No.	R	Ka	pKa	% Ionized pH 7	Activity $C_R \times 10^5$	$K_b \times 10^{12}$ 1st	2nd
20	(ring, N, Br)	7.1×10^{-8}	7.15	41.7	0.5	0.8	
21	(ring, N, Br)	7.6×10^{-8}	7.12	43.2	0.2	1.0	
22	(ring, S, N)	7.6×10^{-8}	7.12	43.2	0.08	2.3	
23	(ring, N, N, CH₃)	8.7×10^{-8}	7.06	46.5	0.2	1.2	
24	(ring, N, N)	8.7×10^{-8}	7.06	46.5	0.08	3.0	0.2
25	(ring, N, N)	2.4×10^{-7}	6.62	70.8	0.2	0.8	
26	(ring, O, N)	3.2×10^{-7}	6.5	75.8	0.08		
27	(ring, N, N)	3.3×10^{-7}	6.48	77.0	0.08	1.0	
28	(ring, N, N)	6.7×10^{-7}	6.17	87.3	0.1	22	0.2
29	(ring, N, N)	9.1×10^{-7}	6.04	90.3	0.08	0.6	
30	(ring, N, N, Cl)	1.6×10^{-6}	5.80	94.2	0.1		
31	(ring, S, N—N, CH₃)	3.5×10^{-6}	5.45	97.3	0.2	1.6	
32	NH_2CO-	3.8×10^{-6}	5.42	97.5	10.0	0.6	
33	CH_3CO-	4.2×10^{-6}	5.38	98.2	0.7	0.6	
34	NH_2(ring)$CO-$	6.3×10^{-6}	5.20	98.4	0.5	2.7	0.3

TABLE 318—(*Concluded*)

No.	R	Ka	pKa	% Ionized pH 7	Activity $C_R \times 10^5$	Kb × 10¹² 1st	2nd
35	(S, N—N ring)	1.7×10^{-5}	4.77	99.3	0.6	1.4	
36	(N, N, —N ring)	2.2×10^{-5}	4.66	99.5	>80	0.7	
37	C_6H_5CO-	2.7×10^{-5}	4.57	99.6	0.3	0.6	
38	CH_3 (O, N, N ring)	4.0×10^{-5}	4.40	99.7	2.0	0.5	
39	(O, N ring) CH_3	6.3×10^{-5}	4.20	99.8	0.6		
40	(O, N N ring) CH_3	7.9×10^{-5}	4.10	99.9	1.0	0.8	
41	$ClCH_2CO-$	1.6×10^{-4}	3.79	99.92	10.0	0.4	
42	$HOOCCH_2-$	3.0×10^{-4}	3.52	99.96	>90		
43	$C_2H_5SO_2-$	7.9×10^{-4}	3.10	99.99	1000	0.3	
44	$NC-$	1.2×10^{-3}	2.92	99.99	100		
45	$4\text{-}NH_2C_6H_4SO_2-$	1.3×10^{-3}	2.89	99.99	60		

Ka = acid dissociation constant of substituted sulfanilamide.

pKa = logarithm of the reciprocal of the acid dissociation constant.

C_R = minimum molar concentration of drug required to prevent growth of *E. coli* in a synthetic culture medium buffered at pH 7.

Kb = base dissociation constant of substituted sulfanilamide.

TABLE 319

Antibacterial Index *Vs.* pH: Ionizable Sulfonamides

pH	$\dfrac{C^s}{C^p}$	$\dfrac{C^s X_o^s}{C^p X_o^p}$	$\dfrac{C^s(1 - X_o^s)}{C^p(1 - X_o^p)}$	$\dfrac{C^s X_i^s 1(-X_o^s)}{C^p X_i^p(1 - X_o^p)}$
		Sulfanilamide pKa 10.43		
5.5	39,700	.53	3.04×10^5	11.8
6.0	13,440	.52	2.94	11.6
6.5	8,220	.98	5.55	21.3
7.0	2,500	.935	5.25	16.3
8.0	291	1.07	5.8	22.7
9.0	50.6	1.82	9.8	38.1
		Sulfapyridine pKa 8.43		
5.5	1,525	2.06	1.16×10^4	45.1
6.0	650	2.52	1.43	55.5
6.5	210	2.47	1.38	53.5
7.0	123	4.34	2.50	97.0
8.0	45.8	12.4	6.7	260.
9.0	22.9	18.0	9.7	377.
		Sulfathiazole pKa 7.12		
5.5	134	2.89	1.00×10^3	77.
6.0	71	5.45	1.46	112.
6.5	24.8	5.08	1.32	102.
7.0	22.0	9.78	2.19	161.
8.0	34.2	30.1	8.2	632.
9.0	45.7	45.1	11.9	915.
		Sulfadiazine pKa 6.48		
5.5	68.0	12.7	4.8×10^2	121.
6.0	34.0	8.51	5.75	144.
6.5	28.5	14.5	9.5	238.
7.0	67.2	52.0	25.8	630.
8.0	114.0	111.	67.	1660.
9.0	171.0	171.	103.	2570.
		Sulfacetamide pKa 5.38		
5.5	371	243.	12.5×10^2	1035.
6.0	169	143.	7.2	615.
6.5	217	205.	10.3	872.
7.0	158	155.	7.3	630.
8.0	244	244.	9.8	825.
9.0	355	355.	14.	1200.
		PABA pKa 4.68		

TABLE 320

Antibacterial Index *Vs.* pH: Non-ionizable Sulfonamides

pH	$\dfrac{C^s}{C^p}$	$(1 - X_o^p)$	$\dfrac{C^s}{C^p (1 - X_o^p)}$
	N^1-Dimethylsulfanilamide		
6	15,000	.0457	3.2×10^5
7	5,000	.00476	10.5×10^5
8	455	.0005	9.1×10^5
9	200	.00005	40×10^5
	2-(N^1-Methylsulfanilamido)pyrimidine		
6	10,000		2.2×10^5
7	1,500	*ibid.*	3.2×10^5
8	220		4.4×10^5
9	51		10.2×10^5
	1-Methyl-2-sulfanilimidopyridine		
6	3,000		$.65 \times 10^5$
7	500	*ibid.*	1.0×10^5
8	150		3.0×10^5
9	52		10.4×10^5
	2-(N-Methylsulfanilamido)thiazole		
6	6,000		1.3×10^5
7	1,000	*ibid.*	2.0×10^5
8	200		4.0×10^5
9	44		8.8×10^5
	3-Methyl-2-sulfanilimidothiazole		
6	1,000		$.22 \times 10^5$
7	500	*ibid.*	1.0×10^5
8	310		6.2×10^5
9	50		10.0×10^5
	N^1-Acetyl-N^1-methylsulfanilamide		
6	10,000		2.2×10^5
7	6,700	*ibid.*	$14. \times 10^5$
8	1,000		$20. \times 10^5$
9	300		$60. \times 10^5$

Chapter XII

CLINICAL EVALUATION OF SULFONAMIDE DRUGS

(I) General Considerations

The final evaluation of the usefulness of any sulfonamide drug in medicine has not been obtained because new uses are constantly being found, new knowledge of the pharmacological and pathological actions of the drugs is being gained, and medical opinion is gradually changing in the light of a host of medical observations in the field. No adequate evaluation of a new sulfonamide drug is now possible until upwards of 500,000 pounds of the drug have been used. It is not until such widespread use that comparison of small advantages of one drug over another can be made; the incidence of rare toxic reactions of the drug should be noted in a sufficient number of cases to be significant.

It is necessary that those who are engaged in the long experimental approach to launching a new drug have some knowledge of the criteria on which the fruits of their labor will be judged. Such knowledge will help screen out those compounds which will later be found lacking in some essential. It should also help point out medical needs and thus stimulate research to meet such needs. The brief clinical review which follows is for purposes of orientation among those engaged in experimental chemotherapy. It is definitely not a therapeutic guide for the general practitioner nor is it presumed to be of any special value to the clinician outside of giving him ready reference to some of the more recent literature.

(A) Precepts of Chemotherapy

The principles underlying therapeutic use of the sulfonamides, based on best present medical opinion[872, 929, 1759, 2248] may be summarized as follows:

1) Choose a drug of demonstrated high potency against the known or presumed invading organism, which will reach the site of infection in maximum concentration and with least risk of toxic reactions.

2) Give as high doses as is consistent with avoiding serious toxic reactions to the patient. Inadequate chemotherapy may be worse than none because it may lead to development of drug resistant strains of the organism.

3) In treating localized infections remove pus and necrotic tissues because they contain powerful antagonists to the action of sulfonamide drugs.

4) Give the sodium salts of the drugs intravenously where delay of several hours in establishment of adequate blood levels would permit serious spread of the infection, otherwise the oral route should be used if possible.

5) Keep a record of fluid intake and output. Output of urine should be at least 1000 cc. per day when sulfapyridine, sulfathiazole, sulfadiazine, sulfamerazine, sulfamethazine or sulfapyrazine are being given. If this cannot be maintained sulfapyridine should not be given and sodium bicarbonate (or other alkaline salt) sufficient to maintain an alkaline urine (pH 7.0 to 8.0) should be given with the other drugs to prevent crystallization in the kidneys.

6) Question all patients as to previous record of sensitivity to sulfonamide drugs.

Where history of previous drug fever, rash or other idiosyncracy is given administer penicillin or streptomycin.

7) Do not apply a sulfonamide drug topically for more than five days.   Longer use involves risk of sensitization.

8) Stop the drug at appearance of a serious toxic reaction and force fluids to eliminate the drug from the body as rapidly as possible.

9) Avoid exposure to the sun or ultraviolet light while taking a sulfonamide drug.

10) Never give a blood transfusion from a person taking a sulfonamide drug to a patient who is highly sensitive to the drug.

(II) General Infections of the Body Endangering Life

(A) Streptococcal Infections

(1) General Remarks

Bacteria classed as streptococci comprise a very large number of different bacteria, both pathogenic and non-pathogenic, and differing enormously in their sensitivity to the sulfonamide drugs.   The classification by Lancefield is most generally used.   Group A in this system includes 30 or more types and accounts for most of the human pathogenic streptococci.   Group A streptococci are the ones most successfully treated by the sulfonamides, although strains of these can be highly resistant, too.   Group D streptococci are very resistant to the sulfonamides[1999].   *Strep. faecalis* belongs to this group and is important in urinary infections.   Various anaerobic streptococci are also highly resistant and these are encountered in some human infections.   The alpha hemolytic streptococci, which include those producing a green pigment (*Streptococcus viridans*) vary in their susceptibilities.   This accounts for widely differing results by different investigators, each of whom reports work on "Strep. viridans" with the sulfonamides.   Probably there are more resistant alpha than beta hemolytic streptococci.

Sulfadiazine is now recognized as the drug of choice for treating most streptococcal infections[2248], with sulfanilamide second choice because of its greater toxicity.   Marshall, *et al.*[1734] found sulfanilamide unexcelled in antistreptococcal activity in mice when compared on equal blood levels, but since sulfadiazine can be held at higher blood levels with greater safety than sulfanilamide, it produces a better therapeutic result.

(2) Erysipelas

The sulfonamide drugs are specific for erysipelas.   While sulfanilamide has been most used in treatment, sulfadiazine may be the drug of choice because of its lower toxicity[2248].

Deaths from erysipelas occur chiefly in infants.   Gross mortality figures in patients of all ages in groups treated with serum, ultraviolet rays, x-rays, and various local treatments showed 8.66% of 5293 cases[1336, 1827].   This compares with 2.06% of 1067 cases treated with sulfanilamide[1336, 1827, 2198, 2227].

(3) Scarlet Fever

This disease is caused by Group A, beta hemolytic streptococci and at first thought would seem subject to treatment with the sulfonamide drugs.   However, the clinical symptoms are largely the result of an exotoxin and the sulfonamide drugs have little effect on bacterial toxins.   There is good evidence that the drugs are of prophylactic value (see (VI) on Prophylactic Uses) in arresting epidemics of scarlet fever and some further evidence that they are effective in avoiding complications through secondary invaders. The subject is still controversial, however. Spink[2248] considered sulfadiazine of value in addition to convalescent serum or antitoxin and recommended a dose which would maintain a blood concentration of 10 mg. per 100 cc. until the temperature was normal for 48 hours. Benn[724] treated 253 cases of scarlet fever with sulfanilamide and compared with 261 untreated controls. There were no deaths in either group but those treated with sulfanilamide showed 15% incidence of complications as compared with 25.3% in the controls.

Neukirch, *et al.*[1846] treated 1347 new scarlet fever cases with sulfanilamide. The incidence of otitis was lowered from 8.8% to 3.8% and mastoiditis from 3.2% to 1.2%. Incidence of sinusitis and nephritis was not significantly reduced and there was no reduction in myocarditis.

(B) Staphylococcal Infections

Most authors[421, 1247, 1765, 1992, 2248] rate sulfathiazole the drug of choice for treatment of staphylococcal infections of all types, with sulfadiazine and sulfapyridine second and third in effectiveness. Finland[1087, 1090] preferred to employ higher blood levels of sulfadiazine (15 to 20 mgs. per 100 cc.) in staphylococcemias rather than 5 to 10 mgs. per 100 cc. of sulfathiazole, because even at the lower dosage, the higher incidence of toxic reactions with sulfathiazole was a disadvantage.

Norman[1859] described an interesting case of staphylococcal septicemia which failed to respond after 60 Gm. of sulfathiazole had been given, but which responded after changing to sulfadiazine with a drop to normal temperature in 48 hours.

The sulfonamide drugs are not at their best in treating staphylococcal infections and are being displaced by penicillin. Torrey, Julianelle, and McNamee[2345] reviewed the literature to 1941 on treatment of staphylococcal septicemias with the various sulfonamide drugs (except sulfadiazine) and found a record of 83 recoveries in 128 cases. They pointed out that many of these were single case reports of successful use of the drugs and that undoubtedly there were many failures unreported. Their own results (obtained largely on cases referred to them for serum treatment) indicated that the drugs had little or no effect on the course of staphylococcal septicemias. In contrast, Spink, *et al.*[2251] treated 19 cases of staphylococcemia with sulfathiazole and all but one recovered. Some of these had been treated previously with sulfanilamide or sulfapyridine without effect.

(C) Pneumonia

(1) General Remarks

The conquest of pneumonia by the sulfonamide drugs has been their most outstanding contribution to national health. The ten year average pneumonia mortality rate prior to 1938 was 79 per 100,000 which dropped to 32 per 100,000 in 1942; but, as pointed out by Ungerleider, Steinhaus and Gubner[2367], the true measure must take into consideration the incidence of the disease. Analysis of case fatalities showed a drop in mortality from 20.8% in the period 1935 to 1937, to 3.9% from 1939 to June 1, 1942. They estimated that of 52,000,000 gainfully employed persons in the United States no fewer than 25,000 lives were being saved yearly through use of the sulfa drugs in pneumonia. In addition, at least 1,000,000 working days were saved through reduction of lost time from pneumonia from an average of 38 to 27 days per case.

Sulfadiazine[872] or sulfamerazine[1104] are now the drugs of choice for treatment of pneumococcal, Friedländer, or streptococcal pneumonias because of their equal potency and better toleration than sulfapyridine or sulfathiazole. Because delay is dangerous, particularly if the pneumonia is well advanced, the initial dose should be 0.10 Gm. per kilo of body weight of sodium sulfadiazine in 5% solution given intravenously[872, 929, 2248]. If given orally the initial dose is 4.0 Gm. followed by 1.0 Gm. every four hours until the temperature is normal for 72 hours. A blood concentration of 8 to 12 mg. per 100 cc. is considered advisable. Urinary output of at least 1200 cc. per day should also be maintained through sufficient oral intake of liquids or, if necessary, through use of intravenous glucose. If this output cannot be achieved, sufficient sodium bicarbonate should be administered to maintain the urine at pH 7 to 8 so as to avoid kidney complications. Usually 4 Gm. initially, then 2 Gm. of sodium bicarbonate every four hours will accomplish this. Routine use of sodium bicarbonate, regardless of urinary output, provides an extra margin of safety in administration of the drug.

Dowling, et al.[1004] studied the question of dosage of sulfadiazine in pneumonia and found that 6 Gm. initially and 1 Gm. every 4 hours did not save a higher percentage of cases than 2 Gm. initially and 0.5 Gm. every four hours; however at the higher dosage there was a somewhat more rapid response, lower length of stay in the hospital and lower incidence of sequelae. No marked difference in toxic reactions was noted.

(2) Pneumococcal Pneumonia

Flippin, Schwartz and Domm[1109] treated 1,635 cases of pneumococcal pneumonia with sulfapyridine, sulfathiazole and sulfadiazine with an average mortality of 10.6%. This compared with 40.1% mortality in 1,906 cases prior to introduction of the sulfonamide drugs. Their work demonstrated sulfadiazine to be the drug of choice.

Comparative clinical results in treatment of pneumococcal pneumonia are summarized in Table 321, p. 576. Statistics of this kind are of only rough value because no weighting is given for severity of the disease among different population groups. This varies considerably and can shift the gross mortality figures. For example, 72% of the cases reported for sulfapyridine and 85% of the cases for sulfathiazole came from a population group with an untreated mortality rate of 18.65% to 22.5%[770, 2268]; whereas, 26% of the sulfadiazine cases came from a population group with an untreated mortality rate of 40.1%[1109]. The statistics on sulfamerazine, sulfamethazine and sulfapyrazine have too few cases to be very significant. Certainly one is not justified in drawing conclusions as to their relative superiority as compared to each other and sulfadiazine. Sulfanilamide, on the other hand, appears to be definitely inferior to the other drugs.

Comparison of the drugs must take into consideration such factors as relative toxicity, promptness of response to the drug, number of days of hospitalization, etc., in addition to their abilities to save life. It is these factors which make sulfadiazine the drug of choice in comparison to sulfapyridine and sulfathiazole. The newer drugs, sulfamerazine, sulfamethazine, and sulfapyrazine are promising but are not fully evaluated.

Finland, et al.[1092] found that administration of sulfapyridine did not alter the development of antibodies in pneumococcal pneumonia. There was thus the same protection against reinfection in cases cured with sulfapyridine as in cases undergoing spontaneous recovery.

(3) Staphylococcal Pneumonia

Sulfathiazole is considered by many authors to be drug of choice in staphylococcal pneumonia; however, Finland, Peterson and Strauss[1091] found sulfadiazine equally effective and preferred it because of its lower toxicity.

Probably penicillin will be used in this as well as other severe staphylococcal infections because of its greater effectiveness. A combined penicillin-sulfadiazine treatment might be even more effective.

(4) Primary Atypical Pneumonia

This is a virus pneumonia and its course is not altered by the sulfa drugs. Because it is difficult to diagnose, Spink[2247] recommends that sulfadiazine be given to all patients with pneumonia for at least 48 hours. If there has been no improvement and the biological cause of the infection has not been defined he discontinues chemotherapy.

(5) Hemolytic Streptococcal Pneumonia

Browne, *et al.*[798] treated 100 unselected cases of pneumonia in the Canal Zone with sulfadiazine with only one death. Seven of the cases were caused by hemolytic streptococci. The authors concluded that the drug was most efficacious in pneumonia, equally effective in tropical or other climates and was accompanied by fewer drug reactions than sulfathiazole or sulfapyridine. In their experience only one patient developed nausea and vomiting.

Finland, Peterson and Goodwin[1090] treated six cases of streptococcal pneumonia successfully with sulfadiazine.

(6) Friedländer Pneumonia

Hyde and Hyde[1348] found that Friedländer (*Klebsiella pneumoniae*) pneumonia was not helped by chemotherapy to the same degree as pneumococcal pneumonia. Their clinical results, which were at considerable variance with experimental results in mice[139], suggested that sulfapyridine might be superior to sulfadiazine for this use; however, the number of cases was too few to be significant.

(D) Meningitis

(1) Meningococcal Meningitis

One of the most dramatic achievements of the sulfonamide drugs has been the conquering of this fatal and crippling disease which has always become epidemic when men were crowded into army camps in past wars. The recent war was no exception; an outbreak of epidemic proportions occurred during the winter and early spring of 1942–3. Thomas[2322], who reviewed nearly 2000 cases occurring in army camps of seven Southeastern states, gave chemotherapy sole credit for reduction in mortality from 39 per cent in the World War I to less than 3.5 per cent in World War II.

The literature on chemotherapy of meningitis has been covered up to 1942 by the excellent review of Dingle and Finland[977]. At that time, there had been little clinical experience with sulfadiazine against the disease, yet they recommended it as drug of choice, which has been amply justified by subsequent results. (Table 322, p. 576).

Early diagnosis and treatment are very essential as was demonstrated by army experience[2322] where in the first month of the outbreak, the mortality was 12.8%, dropping to 7.3% in the next month, and an average of 2.25% for the next four months. The decrease was attributed to gain of experience by medical personnel in early diagnosis and prompt treatment. Treatment in early, mild cases was an initial dose of 4 Gm. of sulfadiazine followed every four hours by 1 or 1.5 Gm. by mouth. In late and severe cases, an immediate intravenous injection of 5 to 8 Gm. of sodium sulfadiazine (according to the patient's weight) was given in 1000 cc. isotonic saline and was followed by 1000 cc. of 5% glucose intravenously to avoid kidney complications (see section X on toxicity).

Probably these doses were excessive and half would suffice in line with the work of Dowling, et al.[1004] in pneumonia, q.v. The huge doses of sulfadiazine, particularly when given intravenously, produce a high incidence of kidney complications unless very carefully controlled. Many doctors prefer to run this risk rather than be accused of "too little and too late" when dealing with such a grave infection. An initial blood level of 12 to 15 mg per 100 cc. was recommended[872, 2322] as a goal to be achieved, with a maintenance level of 10 to 12 mg. per 100 cc. until the patient was out of danger, then 7 to 10 mg. per 100 cc. or lower until cure was effected. Evidence that lower blood levels suffice was given by Daniels, et al.[948], who treated 112 cases in an army camp with the drug with only one death. Eighty of these had meningitis and 32 meningococcemia. One group of 45 patients was treated with an initial dose of 0.1 Gm. sodium sulfadiazine per kilo of body weight intravenously, followed by one half this dose parenterally every 8 hours until the patient could retain sulfadiazine by mouth, then 1 to 2 Gm. every four hours. This group had an average blood level of drug of 12.9 mg.%. 71% of the group developed microscopic hematuria with 17% having gross hematuria and 6.6% temporary anuria. A second group treated with approximately half the dosage had an average blood level of drug of 8.4 mg.%. Of this group 36% showed microscopic hematuria; none of this group developed gross hematuria or anuria. The recoveries from each group were equally good. This would tend to indicate that more of the drug is commonly administered than is necessary or desirable in view of the incidence of kidney complications at high dosage levels. While high fluid intake (4000 cc. per day) was maintained and urinary output held to a minimum of 1200 cc. per day, there was no control of the alkalinity of the urine, which, if maintained at pH 7 to 7.5 through use of sodium bicarbonate, might have considerably lowered the incidence of urinary complications at the high dosage level.

Hill and Lever[1307] reported a similar series of 68 cases in an army camp where no deaths occurred with sulfadiazine therapy. High dosage of the drug was used, with 5 Gm. sodium sulfadiazine initially and 9 Gm. per day maintenance dose. Average blood concentration of drug was about 11 mg.%. There were 7 cases of macroscopic hematuria and 4 cases of renal colic.

Cheever, et al.[857] reported that after administration of 8 Gm. of sulfadiazine daily to 161 meningococcus carriers over a 72 hour period, all gave negative cultures by the fourth day. While they had no evidence of drug toxicity, they suggested that a smaller dose would be desirable and might have been possible in view of the fact that 12 carriers given 4 Gm. in divided doses during 12 hours gave negative cultures 24 hours later. They pointed out that if an entire army camp were treated simultaneously, an epidemic would be stopped at once, since carriers of the disease would be eliminated.

Fox and Gilbert[1123] called attention to the fact that treatment of meningitis with sulfa drugs has not lowered the incidence of arthritis following the disease.

(2) Friedländer Bacillus Menigitis

This very rare but very fatal disease has been reviewed by Ransmeier and Major[1997] who found but one recovery in 25 cases prior to the advent of chemotherapy. Since then there have been two recoveries out of three cases treated with sulfapyridine, one death on treatment with sulfanilamide, and two recoveries treated with sulfadiazine. The latter is recommended as the drug of choice not only because of its low toxicity, but because animal studies have indicated especially good results on Friedländer infections[139].

(3) Pneumococcal Meningitis

This, up to the advent of the sulfa drugs, was a very fatal disease with only thirty recoveries reported in fifteen years. After advent of sulfanilamide, there were 55 recoveries reported in four years and 88 recoveries with sulfapyridine in $2\frac{1}{2}$ years. Sulfathiazole has been assumed to be inferior to sulfapyridine because of its lower levels in spinal fluid, but this is a debatable conclusion[911, 1318].

Sulfadiazine is definitely the drug of choice for this disease at present. Mortality is 35 to 80% as compared to 99 to 100% prior to the use of sulfa drugs[792]. In experimental infections in dogs a C.S.F. level above 15 mg. sulfadiazine per 100 cc. was necessary for survival[2603].

A recovery was reported for a woman aged 65, treated with sulfamethazine[1881].

(4) Haemophilus Influenzae Meningitis (Pfeiffer's Bacillus)

Sulfadiazine is definitely the drug of choice in treating meningitis caused by this organism[2517]. In experimental studies, Alexander and Leidy[619] confirmed this clinical observation but showed that a combination of sulfadiazine and serum was able to protect mice against one million minimum lethal doses, whereas, singly, neither the drug nor the serum would protect against more than 10,000 minimum lethal doses.

The combination of serum and sulfadiazine has reduced the mortality from 98 to 100%, to 51%[792] in clinical cases.

Sako, Stewart and Fleet[2080] used sulfadiazine in 23 cases of influenzal meningitis among children with death of 6 of the group, all below 8 months of age.

Davies[951] records 20 cases treated with sulfapyridine or sulfanilamide with but four recoveries. Two of these were slow and were believed spontaneous.

(5) Hemolytic Streptococcal Meningitis

The mortality has dropped from about 97% to from 20 to 40% through use of the sulfa drugs[792].

(6) Staphylococcal Meningitis

While sulfathiazole has been recommended as drug of choice for this rare form of meningitis[2253], Pilcher *et al.*[1925, 2603] found that sulfathiazole did not significantly lower the fatality in experimental infections. This they blamed on its low C.S.F. level. Oral sulfadiazine resulted in definitely lower mortality rate and longer survival time in animals dying of the infection. Intracisternal therapy with microcrystalline sulfadiazine gave indefinite results and seemed dangerous.

Penicillin would seem to have the possibility of being more effective than the sulfonamides in treating this disease, but has the disadvantage of not penetrating to the C.S.F. in effective concentrations.

(7) Tubercular Meningitis

Morrow, *et al.*[1806] found "Promin" without effect on 11 cases of tubercular meningitis.

(E) Tuberculosis

The success of the "sulfa" drugs in other fields has stimulated many trials of their effectiveness against tuberculosis, but the nature of the disease makes evaluation of any therapy extremely difficult. No conclusive clinical results have yet been obtained but medical opinion holds that, while the more potent sulfa drugs and sulfones do have an inhibitory effect on the spread of a tubercular infection when given in adequate dosage over long periods, the infection is by no means cured. The toxic properties of the drugs are particularly bad when prolonged administration at high levels is attempted and this must be weighed against their possible beneficial effect in halting the tubercular process. Many authors do not feel that the doubtful benefits justify use of present drugs but think the results are suggestive of much further chemotherapeutic research.

Perhaps more work has been done in clinical tuberculosis with "Promin", "disodium diaminodiphenylsulfone N,N'-didextrose sulfonate", than with other recent chemotherapeutic agents. This has an undeniable effect in slowing the spread of tubercular infections in both experimental animals and human disease. At least when given orally, it is quite probable that the compounds breaks down to give bis(4-aminophenyl) sulfone as the active agent.

Dancey, Schmidt and Wilkie[946] treated with "Promin" 27 patients who were considered to have a poor chance of recovery but whose tubercular lesions were of recent origin and of exudative character. No other treatment except rest was given. The results were not clear cut. They considered the drug to have relatively poor potency against tuberculosis. A wide variety of toxic reactions were encountered which necessitated suspension of treatment in some cases. All patients experienced a fall in hemoglobin and there was attendant cyanosis, headache, weakness and malaise. There was one case of peripheral neuritis and 5 cases of psychosis caused by the drug. One case of drug fever and 5 cases of skin rash were encountered, also two cases of arthralgia.

Heaf, et al.[1285] used "Promin" in 14 cases of pulmonary tuberculosis with indefinite results. In two cases of laryngeal infection, direct application of "Promin" solution gave results suggestive of further trial. Zucher, et al.[599] administered "Promin" by the intravenous drip method but were unable to see any beneficial effect on 12 patients with pulmonary tuberculosis.

Hinshaw, et al.[1312] reported clinical results on 106 patients who had received "Promin" and selected 36 of these which had received adequate dosage for a long enough time. Improvement appeared most marked in patients with "recent lesions of exudative character without extensive destruction of tissue or prominent fibrosis". These 36 patients were reported after two years treatment and the early clinical trends were continued. The authors were unwilling to draw definite conclusions from such a small group, but believed their work "sufficiently suggestive and encouraging to make it urgent that a series of large and fully controlled studies be undertaken to confirm or deny these preliminary impressions". They cautioned against the toxic manifestations of the drug but stated that these were "reversible and controllable and did not appear to have any adverse effect upon the clinical course of tuberculosis".

Edlin, et al.[2559] treated 24 tubercular patients by inhalation of nebulized "Promin" with indeterminate results. Variable blood concentrations of drug were obtained by this method of administration. Barach, et al.[700] administered "Promin" by inhalation of the nebulized spray in guinea pigs and claimed improved results over controls treated with the drug by the oral route. High local concentration without high blood levels and attendant toxicity were thought to be advantages of this method of treatment.

Higgins[1303, 1304, 1305] has studied the blood toxicity of "Promin" in guinea pigs and found a direct toxic effect on the erythrocytes. Other effects were hyperirritability, severe paralysis of the hind limbs, and cyanosis. Vitamins in six times normal dosage largely prevented all but the blood reactions and these were controlled with folic acid. Hall, et al.[1238] have also reported on the blood toxicity of "Promin".

A similar preparation, "Diasone", or disodium [(sulfonyldi-*p*-phenylene)diimino]-dimethanesulfinate, is undergoing clinical trials. Since it, like "Promin", is probably broken down to bis(4-aminophenyl) sulfone in the body, the action and toxicity of the parent compound and derivatives should be similar.

Petter and Prenzlau[1914] studied the results of treating 44 patients for periods in excess of one hundred and twenty days with "Diasone". The dose was 0.33 Gm. with each meal, or 1.0 Gm. per day. The results were: marked improvement, 18%; moderate improvement, 50%; slight improvement, 25%; no change, 2.3% and worse, 4.5%. During chemotherapy of a number of patients, absolute bed rest was not required, nor were collapse measures used. Greatest improvement occurred in the first 60 to 90 days of treatment. The toxic effects of the drug were mild but numerous. Mild to severe nausea occurred in 25% of the patients and 25% complained of nervousness. Headaches occurred in 50%, photophobia in 27%, diplopia in 14% and a slight tremor simulating that of hyperthyroidism occurred in 33%. "None of these symptoms were permanent, unbearable or irreversible". An initial, abrupt fall in hemoglobin content of the blood with partial recovery starting about the third week was noted. No true hemolytic anemia nor significant effect on white cell counts were observed. Drug rash occurred in 1 patient, or 2.3%. Pfuetze and Pyle[1916] have encountered a case of leukocytosis, in which the leukocyte count rose to 19,000 per cu. mm. and 82% were polymorphonuclear leukocytes, after "Diasone" had been administered for three weeks. This was thought to be an idiosyncrasy to the drug.

Pharmacological[1062] and clinical[1311, 1429] trials have been announced of a heterocyclic isostere of bis(4-aminophenyl) sulfone for which the trade name "Promizole" has been given. This has the structure,

$$NH_2 \langle \quad \rangle SO_2 - \overset{S}{\underset{N}{\diagdown}} NH_2 ,$$

and its chemical name is 2-amino-5-sulfanilylthiazole.

This drug was found to exert a favorable influence on the course of experimental tuberculosis in guinea pigs and to be somewhat better than "Promin" in this respect. Prolonged administration produced hyperplasia of the thyroid gland. Some blood dyscrasia was observed but the changes were reversible on withdrawing the drug. Very preliminary clinical results in 56 patients treated at a dosage of 10 to 16 Gm. per day were encouraging. Blood levels at this dosage ranged from 1.5 to 4.2 mg. per 100 cc. and averaged 2.6 mg. per 100 cc. More than 80% of ingested drug appeared in the urine, which was colored pink by a dye formed from the drug. In a case of presumptively diagnosed tubercular meningitis[1429], a cure was obtained in two weeks.

Higgins[1304] found that "Promizole" produced hyperplasia of the thyroid when fed to rats and that they became extremely alopecic. The drug was somewhat less toxic to the erythrocytes than "Promin". Folic acid (vitamin Bc) was effective in overcoming the anemia produced by "Promin" or "Promizole".

Sulfapyridine has been tried in clinical tuberculosis with little or no improvement[1025]. The vomiting which accompanied its use was a deterrent.

Experimental Work on Tuberculosis. Freedlander[1129] investigated the *in vitro* bacteriostatic action of a series of 27 compounds related to benzophenone on *M. tuberculosis* and found that 2,4'-dichlorobenzophenone was active at a dilution of 1–100,000 as compared to "Promin", 1–3000. Whether these results have any clinical significance remains to be seen.

Fitzgerald and Feinstone[1100] investigated a series of 19 sulfa drugs, comparing their *in vitro* bacteriostatic activities on *E. coli* and *M. tuberculosis* with the pKa's of the drugs. They found a close parallel between the bacteriostatic action of the drugs on the two organisms, which bears out the contention of others that *in vitro* there is a lack of specificity in action of the sulfonamide drugs against different organisms (see Chapter XI). Sulfadiazine, sulfathiazole and sulfapyrazine were the most active in these tests.

(F) Bubonic Plague

There is steadily increasing evidence that the more potent sulfa drugs are of definite value in treatment of plague. To be effective, they must be given early in the disease.

Wagle, *et al.*[532] reported 237 cases of plague in India of which 53 were treated with sulfapyridine with a mortality of 24.5% and 32 with sulfathiazole with a mortality of 15.6%. This compared with 82 controls treated only with iodine, with a mortality of 52.4% and 70 cases treated with antiplague serum with a mortality of 28.5%. Mortality in septicaemic cases was 95% in the controls; 43.3% for sulfapyridine treated, and 41.8% for sulfathiazole treated cases.

Plum[1932] treated 91 patients showing buboes with sulfapyridine with recovery of 58. The necessity of early treatment was demonstrated by data which showed 12% mortality on cases treated on the first day increasing to 88% mortality on cases of four or more days' duration.

Patients treated with serum showed a mortality of 70.87% in a large scale trial, while those treated with sulfathiazole showed a 23.33% mortality, which reduced to 14.28% if 24-hour deaths were excluded. Sulfanilamide and sulfapyridine were much inferior to sulfathiazole[2381].

Wayson and McMahon[2407] thought sulfadiazine was the drug of choice and held real therapeutic promise if given before development of generalized bacteremia, based on their studies in guinea pigs.

(III) Intestinal Diseases of Bacillary Origin

(A) Classification of Organisms

Because the organisms responsible for various intestinal diseases are confusing, the main classes are listed on p. 527.[a]

(B) Bacillary Dysentery

The effectiveness of the sulfonamide drugs in treatment of the dysenteries is limited to those of bacillary origin. Protozoal and helminthic dysenteries are not favorably affected and must be treated by other remedies such as emetine, oxyquinoline derivatives, or arsenicals.

---

[a] For more extensive information see Strong, R. P., "Stitt's Diagnosis Prevention and Treatment of Tropical Diseases", 6th Ed., The Blakiston Co., Philadelphia, Pa., 1942.

Many of the organisms causing bacillary dysentery are susceptible to the action of the sulfonamide drugs; however, it is necessary to maintain high levels of the drug in the intestinal contents. This is difficult with drugs which are readily absorbed from the upper intestine, such as sulfanilamide or sulfacetamide, because of the danger of building toxic blood levels. Marshall, *et al.*[335] introduced sulfaguanidine as a solution to this problem and reviewed its use through early 1942[1727]. The drug is sufficiently soluble to give adequate concentrations in intestinal contents but does not build toxic blood levels because it is slowly absorbed and rapidly excreted. The drug was very widely used in the armed forces during World War II.

Disease	Causative Organisms
Bacillary dysentery	*Shigella dysenteriae* (Shiga)
	Shigella paradysenteriae (Flexner, Strong and Hiss types)
	Shigella sonnei (Sonne)
	Shigella ambigua (Schmitz)
Typhoid fever	*Eberthella typhosa*
Paratyphoid fever	*Salmonella paratyphi* (paratyphoid A)
(Food poisoning)	*Salmonella schottmülleri* (paratyphoid B)
	Salmonella enteritidis
	Salmonella aertryche (typhi-murium)
	Salmonella choleraesuis (suipestifer)
Cholera	*Vibrio cholerae*

Hawkins[186] made a study of the concentration of various drugs in the faeces of cats, mice, and men versus the concentrations in blood and urine. Sulfaguanidine reached levels of 300 to 3900 mg./100 Gm. in the faeces with blood levels less than 2 mg./100 cc., but with urinary levels from 22 to 323 mg./100 cc. in humans. Sulfadiazine, sulfathiazole, sulfapyridine, and sulfabenzamide all had levels in the faeces under 100 mg./100 cc. but with blood levels considerably higher than sulfaguanidine.

Bulmer[809], and Bulmer and Priest[810] reported on 4142 cases of bacillary dysentery in the British Army in the Middle East. They found a substantial reduction in hospitalization time among cases treated with sulfaguanidine as compared with untreated control cases. Sulfapyridine was also effective but many patients experienced nausea and vomiting. Sulfanilamide produced no measurable effect on length of hospitalization. Sulfaguanidine caused very few toxic manifestations—there were four rubelliform rashes and one instance of kidney trouble which cleared rapidly. The organisms responsible for these cases were: Flexner 70%, Shiga 19%, Sonne 6%, Schmitz 5%. Six Gm. of sulfaguanidine were given as an initial dose followed by 3 Gm. at four hourly intervals and continued for two or three days after the number of stools had fallen to three daily. A maximum of 350 Gm. was given, with the average about 100 Gm.

Hardy[1262] who made a study of 1500 cases of dysentery caused by Shigella (Flexner, Sonne and Schmitz types) using various sulfonamides, recommended dosage as follows: For all absorbed sulfa drugs (sulfapyrazine, sulfadiazine, sulfamerazine, sulfamethazine, and sulfathiazole) 1 Gm.; sulfaguanidine and succinylsulfathiazole 5 Gm.; and phthalylsulfathiazole 2.5 Gm.; each four times daily. Children between 25 and 75 lb. body weight were to receive one half the adult dosage and infants 0.065 Gm. per lb. of body weight of the absorbed drugs, and proportionately more of the poorly absorbed drugs.   Double these amounts could be given as an initial dose.

Hurevitz[2557] treated 1,120 cases of dysentery in an army overseas hospital with sulfaguanidine or sulfadiazine and obtained prompt results with either drug.   Usually relief was obtained within 24 hours, although the average length of treatment was six and one-half days.   Sulfaguanidine was given in an initial dose of 7 Gm. followed by 3.5 Gm. every 4 hours until the number of stools per day was reduced to five or less, then 3.5 Gm. were given every 8 hours until the stools were normal for four days.   Sulfadiazine dosage was 4 Gm. initially, then 1 Gm. every 4 hours until relief was obtained, then 1 Gm. every 8 hours.

(1) Shigella dysenteriae (Shiga) Dysentery

This is the most severe and fatal form of dysentery.   Fortunately, it is rare in the United States.   It is especially prevalent in tropical countries and in the Near East. Attacks require three to four weeks of hospitalization and in the past have caused severe damage to the colon which became chronically ulcerated in a high percentage of cases.

Sulfaguanidine was highly effective in controlling Shiga dysentery in the British Army of the Middle East as reported by Fairly and Boyd[1049].   In 135 cases, 7 to 8 days' treatment were required before stools were fully formed but improvement was noted quite early.   Gard[1151] reported treating 25 cases of Shiga dysentery in New Guinea.   Average duration of treatment was 13.5 days during which 152 Gm. of sulfaguanidine was given. All patients recovered and no toxic effects of the drug were noted.

(2) Shigella paradysenteriae (Flexner, Strong and Hiss Types) Dysentery

These infections respond very favorably to sulfaguanidine or succinylsulfathiazole.

Page[1884] treated 520 cases of acute bacillary dysentery caused by the Flexner organisms with prompt relief in all but 14 cases which showed continued organisms after 10 days' treatment and were then given a course of sulfadiazine with good results.   The author felt they would have responded equally well to a second course of treatment with sulfaguanidine.   Toxic reactions in the form of drug fever occurred in only 3 cases

Similar results were obtained in 47 cases of Flexner type dysentery treated with sulfaguanidine which cleared in half the time of the 83 controls.   Twenty-one cases treated with sulfanilamide showed increased time to clear the infection.[879]

Sulfaguanidine and succinylsulfathiazole were compared in an outbreak of Flexner dysentery with similar results in reduction of fever, diarrhea, and time required to produce consistently negative stools.[2224]

The number of carriers remaining infective for a month or more was reduced from 57% in the controls to 12% in patients treated with sulfaguanidine[1869].

Cultures were negative after 3 days' treatment with sulfaguanidine of 89 cases of Shigella paradysenteriae in an Army camp.[610]   In 89 untreated controls the organisms disappeared in from 7 to 30 days.   Sulfaguanidine was used on 29 cases who had had the organisms for more than 15 days and stools were negative after treatment for 3 days.

Hoaglund, Harris, and Raile[1317] compared sulfaguanidine (30 cases) and succinylsulfathiazole (15 cases) in treatment of carriers of S. paradysenteriae.   Doses of 5 Gm.

were given 4 times per day for 6 days. All patients were cured. No toxic reactions were observed except that 9 of the patients on succinylsulfathiazole experienced mild or severe anal irritation and 6 complained of mild abdominal pain.

Roberts and Daniels[2032] treated 225 soldiers having dysentéry caused by *Shigella paradysenteriae* Boyd-88 and reported that, succinylsulfathiazole produced no demonstrable effect except in reducing the carrier rate in the bacteriologically proved cases from 18.2% in the untreated group to 2.6% in the group treated with the drug.

Kuhns and Anderson[1494] compared the efficiency of sulfaguanidine and succinylsulfathiazole in treatment of 248 convalescent carriers of *Shigella paradysenteriae* Boyd-88 with 60 untreated controls. All patients were involved in an epidemic occurring in an Army camp. Either drug appeared effective in relieving the carrier state.

Patterson[1898] used sulfadiazine or sulfathiazole and claimed better response in bacillary dysentery than with sulfaguanidine or succinylsulfathiazole.

Fineman and Weiss[2534] in treating over 1,000 cases of bacillary dysentery caused by *S. paradysenteriae* found little difference in control of acute symptoms between use of sulfaguanidine and symptomatic treatment with paregoric and bismuth; however, sulfaguanidine was definitely superior in that patients so treated tolerated a full diet sooner and fewer became carriers of the organism.

(3) Shigella Sonnei (Sonne) Dysentery

The sulfa drugs have been less effective in eradicating this infection than other forms of dysentery. The absorbed sulfonamides such as sulfanilamide, sulfapyridine, sulfadiazine, sulfathiazole, sulfapyrazine and sulfamerazine, have been used in addition to sulfaguanidine, succinylsulfathiazole, and phthalylsulfathiazole. Hardy and Watt[1262] recommended starting treatment with sulfapyrazine, sulfadiazine, sulfamethazine or sulfamerazine (in that order of preference) and later changing to succinylsulfathiazole if the stool continued to be positive after the fourth day. These authors did not recommend sulfanilamide or sulfapyridine. However, Swyer[2306] employed sulfapyridine in 57 cases, with 35 controls, all with Sonne dysentery. Treated cases were bacteriologically clear of the disease in one fourth the time of the controls (5 *vs* 21 days). No relapses in treated cases were observed, but relapses occurred in 6 controls.

In an outbreak of Sonne dysentery in an orphanage involving 83 children, sulfathiazole, sulfadiazine, sulfaguanidine and succinylsulfathiazole were each employed and 90% of the cases cleared in an average of four days. Eight cases which were positive following this treatment were given a second treatment with a different drug. Two required a third course of treatment. No advantage of one drug over another was seen.[1019]

Hailwood[1237] reported rapid cure of 81 cases of Sonne dysentery, including carrier states, with sulfaguanidine in a British Artillery regiment. Osborn and Jones[2614] secured rapid cures in 71 cases of Sonne dysentery but recommended larger doses of sulfaguanidine than usual. They used 30 Gm. of drug in the first 48 hours, then 7.5 Gm. daily.

Brewer[2505] cured 16 Sonne carrier cases with succinylsulfathiazole using a dose of 44 Gm. over 5 days. One case required a second course of treatment.

In contrast to these favorable reports, others[610, 879] have reported no significant difference between cases treated with sulfathiazole or sulfaguanidine and controls.

Experimental. White[2437] evaluated the effectiveness of various sulfanilamide derivatives in treating bacterial infections of the intestinal tract, by their comparative ability to reduce the count of coliform bacteria in the faeces of mice treated by the drug-diet method. The results are summarized in the following table:

Compound	% of Mice Showing Reduction of 100,000-fold or Greater, in Coliform Count
Sulfapyrazine	85
Sulfadiazine	75
Sulfathiazole	60
N^1-Benzoylsulfanilamide	60
Sulfapyridine	45
N^1-Acetylsulfanilamide	40
Sulfaguanidine	30
Sulfanilylarsanilic Acid	25
N^4-Succinylsulfathiazole	25
Sulfanilamide	0
N^1-2-Hydroxyphenylsulfanilamide	0
N^1-3-Hydroxyphenylsulfanilamide	0
N^1-4-Hydroxyphenylsulfanilamide	0
Control diet	0

As part of this work, evidence was obtained which indicated that N^4-succinylsulfathiazole was active solely because of breakdown to sulfathiazole.

It was emphasized that, while data of this kind gave a fairly clear picture of relative potency of the drugs, considerations of toxicity, absorption, excretion, solubility and stability must be taken and that assessment of ultimate usefulness depends on carefully controlled clinical trials.

The results of Poth, et al.[1945, 1948, 1949, 1950] obtained by pharmacological studies in dogs, and from actual clinical trial, showed that N^4-succinylsulfathiazole was much more effective than White's work indicated.

The mechanism of its effectiveness was postulated as follows: In the upper intestine, where absorption of sulfa drugs usually takes place, the N^4-succinylsulfathiazole dissolves in the chyme as a soluble salt, but presence of the strongly ionic succinyl group prevents absorption. In the lower intestine, the succinyl group is gradually cleaved to give an effective concentration of free sulfathiazole, which is the potent bacteriostat. Absorption is poor in the lower intestine so that comparatively little of this sulfathiazole reaches the blood.

Poth's results showed that an average of only 5% of the ingested drug was excreted in human urine, while blood levels rarely exceeded 3 mg./100 cc. The effective dosage was 0.25 Gm. per kilo of body weight initially, followed by 0.25 Gm. per kilo daily.

While sulfapyrazine, sulfadiazine, sulfathiazole and sulfapyridine were all considerably more potent *in vitro* than sulfaguanidine or N^4-succinylsulfathiazole, they were not as useful in combating intestinal infections, because of their toxicity when given in sufficiently large doses.

Recently Poth[1947, 1951] favored N^4-phthalylsulfathiazole over N^4-succinylsulfathiazole because of its greater local bacteriostatic activity (2 to 4 times as great) and lower absorption. About 5% of injested drug appeared in the urine while blood levels did not exceed 2.5 mg. per 100 cc. Concentration of "free", diazotizable drug (presumably sulfathiazole) in the faeces was maintained at 1,250 mg. per 100 cc.

(C) Ulcerative Colitis

The use of the sulfonamide drugs for treatment of ulcerative colitis has given variable results, and is still in a stage of clinical investigation.

Spink[2248] recommended trial of sulfaguanidine or succinylsulfathiazole for 10 to 14 days giving 10 to 15 Gm. per day in four divided doses. Mills and Mackie[1787] studied sulfathiazole, sulfadiazine, and sulfaguanidine in 109 selected cases of ulcerative colitis and obtained improvement in 78%. Sulfadiazine was considered the drug of choice, but it was emphasized that no sulfa drug is specific for the disease and none of the cases were considered *cured* by chemotherapy. Kraemer[1482] treated 16 cases of ulcerative colitis with sulfaguanidine with excellent results in 11 cases, questionable results in 2 cases, and failure in 2 cases. In one case therapy had to be discontinued because of marked suppression of leukocyte formation. Therapy consisted of 6 to 12 Gm. of drug per day for periods of several weeks with an attempt to maintain a concentration of about 500 mg. per 100 Gm. of stool. Five cases of skin rash were encountered.

Major and Douglass[1702] used 2-(*p*-nitrophenylsulfonamido)pyridine ("Nisulfadine") and 2-(*p*-nitrophenylsulfonamido) thiazole ("Nisulfazole") in 5 cases of ulcerative colitis with encouraging results. The thiazole compound was better tolerated.

Rodaniche, *et al.*[2045] followed the changes in intestinal flora of patients undergoing treatment for ulcerative colitis in which sulfaguanidine, sulfathiazole, sulfadiazine and succinylsulfathiazole were used. The bacterial count of the faeces were reduced by each of the drugs and were changed from a predominance of Gram-negative coliform bacilli to Gram-positive cocci, usually streptococci, of which *Strep. faecalis* was most in evidence. Growth of enterococci and streptococci of the viridans group was encouraged because of lack of competition by coliform bacteria.

Poth and Ross[1951] claimed that phthalylsulfathiazole was effective in inducing and maintaining prolonged remissions of the disease.

Bargen[703] thought that a combination of sulfa drugs was more effective than a single drug in ulcerative colitis.

(D) Typhoid

The sulfonamide drugs have not proved outstandingly successful in the treatment of typhoid fever. No large scale clinical trials have been reported because typhoid epidemics have become rare, thanks to modern sanitation.

Hoagland[1316] reported use of sulfathiazole in 20 cases and sulfaguanidine in 10 cases, with 27 untreated controls, all caused by the same strain of *E. typhosa*, in which the drugs did not change the course of the disease, mortality rate, or carrier state. Similar results were reported by Watt and Peterson[2404] and by Hall[1243] using sulfaguanidine.

Hardy[1259] studied use of sulfadiazine in treatment of chronic carriers of *E. typhosa*. The number of such organisms was drastically reduced during treatment, but the infection was not completely eradicated and reappeared in 10 to 14 days after drug treatment. While the results did not justify hope for the chronic carrier, they did suggest that sulfadiazine should be given a thorough clinical trial in acute typhoid fever.

Sulfaguanidine and succinylsulfathiazole are ineffective in treating typhoid carriers[941, 1440, 2086]. Since typhoid fever is not limited to the intestine, chemotherapeutic agents which are absorbed into the blood stream may be desirable.

(E) Paratyphoid

The treatment of Salmonella infections with the sulfa drugs has not been well studied clinically because of the small number of cases available. In this country, *S. aertryche* (typhi-murium) is the most common type and causes a mild gastro-enteritis in 9 cases out of 10.[769]

Bornstein and Strauss[46] studied the *in vitro* effect of sulfaguanidine on 87 different organisms of the Salmonella group. *S. paratyphi A* and *S. choleraesuis* showed marked inhibition but the others showed only slight or no inhibition. These results were confirmed in mice for a few of the organisms. These authors thought that sulfaguanidine might be contraindicated in infections with the resistant members of the Salmonella group because of suppression of the normal coli flora while the pathogens continued to flourish.

McNair Scott, *et al.*[1695] found that sulfaguanidine had no effect on the clinical course of paratyphoid B fever (*S. schottmülleri*), or on the rate of disappearance of the organisms in 40 treated cases, with 48 controls. Treatment for 40 days with sulfaguanidine failed to rid the faeces of this organism in one case[769]. Lowenthal and Corfield[1605], however, were able to eliminate *S. schottmülleri* from a chronic carrier through successive courses of treatment with sulfaguanidine.

(F) Asiatic Cholera

Huang[1340] reported that sulfaguanidine produced dramatic response in 22 patients with severe cholera. Relief was experienced 3 to 4 hours after taking the drug and after eight hours cholera vibrio could no longer be cultured from the stools. Only one of the 22 patients died. This compared with 20 to 60% mortality in other treatments and clinics. Dosage was 3 Gm. initially, then 1 Gm. every two hours for six doses, and 1 Gm. every four hours, thereafter, for one to two days.

Chopra, *et al.*,[862] also reported the successful use of sulfaguanidine in cholera. However, Carruthers[844] failed to show any significant difference between 50 cases of cholera treated with sulfaguanidine and 88 controls. A more extended study is evidently needed to establish the value of the sulfa drugs in Asiatic cholera.

(IV) The Sulfonamides in Otorhinolaryngology

(A) General Remarks

The very frequent infections of the ear, nose and throat have led to widespread application of the sulfonamide drugs in combating these infections. The fact that many of these are localized where there is chance for the accumulation of pus and necrotic tissue containing materials highly antagonistic to the action of the sulfonamides, makes it difficult to cure by drug action alone. Assessment of the value of the drugs in ear, nose and throat infections is difficult and there is, therefore, much medical controversy as to the merits of different methods of applying chemotherapy, or as to the value of any chemotherapeutic treatment. The wide variety of organisms and viruses encountered further complicates the picture because only certain of these are susceptible to the sulfonamide drugs. In the case of virus infections of the nose and throat, the sulfonamides are probably completely inert. Each case in this field thus demands good medical judgement as to the proper use of the drugs together with additional medical or surgical treatment. The only general agreement is that in acute infections where there is danger of spread to the blood stream or spinal fluid of such organisms as the pneumococcus, meningococcus or streptococcus, prompt use of the drugs is life saving.

(B) Systemic Use of the Drugs in Nose and Throat Infections

(1) Tonsillitis and Adenitis

Group A beta hemolytic streptococci are the most common infecting organisms in tonsillitis and adenitis. Results of treatment with the sulfonamides are frequently disappointing because it is difficult to get the drug to the bacteria and antagonists are usually present; however, most authorities recommend use of oral sulfadiazine[872, 929, 1091, 1131, 1942, 2247, 2248] since risk of toxicity in its use is slight and even if the tonsillitis is not materially improved, the danger of complications from spread of the infection will be reduced. Dosage so as to maintain a blood level of 8 to 12 mg. per 100 cc. is recommended[2248].

Finland, *et al.*[1091] treated 28 cases of tonsillitis or peritonsillitis with sulfadiazine and obtained good response attributed to the drug in 25 of these, while in 3 cases the drug was of doubtful benefit.

(2) Pharyngitis

Where there is evidence of "sore throat" caused by beta hemolytic streptococci and the condition is severe enough to cause systemic reactions, oral sulfadiazine is recommended[2248]. This can be supplemented by local use of the sulfonamides (see below).

(3) Common Cold

Most common colds are probably of virus origin and there seems to be general agreement that the sulfonamide drugs have little or no effect on the virus. Since such an infection frequently paves the way for secondary invasion by pneumococci or streptococci which are susceptible to sulfonamide treatment, there is a basis for much medical controversy on whether the drugs should be employed in "colds". It is unquestionably a fact that most general practitioners prescribe sulfadiazine or sulfathiazole for severe colds on the theory that the drugs will do little harm and may prevent dangerous sequelae. There is now a growing feeling that the general practitioner may be right but in the past there have been many warnings that use of the drugs for colds should be discouraged because of the doubtful benefits, the danger of toxic reactions and danger of sensitization of the patient to the drug so that if life endangering sequelae do develop, the drug cannot be used. The latter argument has lost much of its force since it has been shown that sensitization to one drug does not necessarily mean sensitization to all sulfonamide drugs and since penicillin is now available for treatment of severe infections where the patient is sensitive, or the organism is resistant, to the sulfonamide drugs. The real danger lies in uncontrolled self-medication with the drugs for all kinds of inconsequential ills including the "sniffles". Since the law forbids sale of sulfonamide drugs except on prescription, prevention of self-medication rests largely with the physician who should write prescriptions for no more than enough drug to treat the case in hand and make it clear that the prescription is not to be refilled.

Medical authorites[929, 2248] have not recommended general peroral use of the sulfonamides in prophylaxis of complications of the common cold or influenza as yet, because convincing data was not available. The results of extensive prophylactic studies in the armed forces should provide such data. The preliminary results seem outstandingly good (see (VI) on Prophylactic Use of Sulfonamides).

Cecil, Plummer and Smillie[852] reviewed the literature on use of sulfa drugs in treating the common cold and reported their own observations on oral use of sulfadiazine in 48 treated colds with 24 controls, all of which were followed bacteriologically and with adequate clinical observation. They found a striking reduction in the number and variety of organisms in the nasopharynx in the treated cases; however, the duration and course of the uncomplicated colds were not appreciably changed. They believed, on the basis of the bacteriologic findings, that secondary infections might have been prevented in some cases, particularly those in which past history showed severe secondary infections as usual sequelae. Considering the slight, but definite, dangers of toxic reactions of the drug, drug sensitization and development of drug resistant organisms against the dubious benefits of treating the uncomplicated cold, they were opposed to the routine use of sulfadiazine, but favored it for protection against secondary infection in selected cases.

Siegel[2199] reported peroral use of sulfadiazine at first signs of respiratory infection among children in an institution for feebleminded patients. These had shown a previous history of an unusually high susceptibility to acute infections of the respiratory tract and secondary complications. The drug was given for at least four days. The severity of the respiratory illness was favorably modified through use of the drug as measured by reduction in duration of fever and the reduced incidence of secondary infections. Davis[956] treated 162 cases of colds with sulfathiazole and forced fluids; 157 cases with aspirin, alkali, nose drops, an efficient gargle, forced fluids and a cathartic or any combination of a majority of these; and 187 cases treated with a placebo. Results were read after a three day period. Only 7.4% of the sulfathiazole treated cases were unimproved as compared to 25.4% no-improvement cases treated symptomatically.

Livingston[1592] recommended sulfadiazine for acute sinusitis but not to the exclusion of other methods of treatment which should be applied as needed. He pointed to a difficult problem which is occasionally met during the course of treatment with a sulfon-amide drug when the patient develops high fever, headache, nausea and vomiting and decision must be made whether meningitis has developed or drug toxicity. If meningitis, the dosage should be increased while if a toxic reaction, the drug must be withdrawn. Failure at correct diagnosis would place the life of the patient in great jeopardy. This dilemma can now be resolved by changing to penicillin which will continue effective treatment without aggravating the toxic reaction of a sulfonamide drug.

Norris[1860] measured the concentration of sulfadiazine in bronchial secretion as compared with the blood level and obtained an average value of 58%. Combined sulfonamide and bronchoscopic treatment of acquired bronchiectasis resulted in a considerable reduction in daily sputum volume.

Rusk and Ravenswaay[2067] reported use of sulfadiazine in an army camp for treatment of respiratory tract infections. 317 cases treated with an initial dose of 3 Gm. and subse-quent doses of 1 Gm. every four hours showed practically identical results with controls treated with aspirin-phenacetine-caffeine as far as days of fever, average stay in hospital and percentage developing atypical (virus) pneumonia.

Kauvar and Mount[1414] compared results of 75 cases treated symptomatically with 52 comparable cases of upper respiratory infection treated with sulfonamides and could find no special benefit from use of the sulfa drugs.

Appelbaum[2493] treated 50 cases showing chronic bronchial lesions of more than 6 weeks' duration, which had failed to respond to other forms of treatment including peroral sulfonamides, with nebulized solution of 5% sodium sulfathiazole. Definite improve-ment occurred in 43 of the cases. Mutch[2608] discussed the apparatus and experimental background for therapy using nebulized solutions of neutral soluble sulfonamides and antibiotics in bronchial infections.

(C) Local Application of the Sulfonamides in the Upper Respiratory Tract

Sulfanilamide, sulfathiazole and sulfadiazine have been employed locally in the upper respiratory tract in a number of different forms such as by dusting the powder; spraying or instillation of a suspension of the finely divided drug in water or physiological saline; spraying the sodium salt solution of sulfathiazole or sulfadiazine, with or without a vasoconstrictor; application in a nasal jelly; incorporation of the drugs in chewing gum or lozenges; and by spraying a $2\frac{1}{2}\%$ solution of sulfadiazine in 8% triethanolamine. Many favorable publications[796, 856, 986, 1014, 1044, 1070, 1130, 1152, 1166, 1592, 1644, 1723, 1773, 2081, 2200, 2362] have appeared where the duration of the infection was shortened and where complications were fewer in the treated group. However, it is obviously difficult to obtain a clear-cut answer on the effectiveness of a drug in these infections and there is no general agreement on the value of such local treatment.

(1) Local Use in Sinusitis

Fabricant[1044] reviewed the literature on employment of the sulfonamides in nasal and sinus infections. He cautioned against too promiscuous application of the sulfonamides until more adequate pharmacological and clinical evaluations of their effectiveness and relative safety were obtained. He cited the damage to nasal mucosa from use of highly alkaline sodium sulfathiazole solutions and possibility of allergic sensitization to the drugs as deterrents, but believed that the drugs would ultimately be of considerable value, particularly in new forms which take account of nasal physiology.

Turnbull, *et al.*[2362] used a 5% solution of sodium sulfathiazole stabilized with sodium sulfite and containing 0.125% *dl*-desoxyephedrine hydrochloride for treatment of sinusitis and other secondary infections of the common cold in over 1000 cases. The duration appeared to be shortened and the number of cases requiring surgery was considerably decreased. The alkalinity of the solution (pH 8.6 to 8.9) was held to be an advantage, since it promoted ciliary action and gave a high concentration of the active ions of the drug. No nasal irritation was noted.

Merica[1773] applied a 5% solution of sodium sulfathiazole by nasal tamponage in over 300 patients without noting any sloughing of the nasal mucosa but stressed the fact that fresh solutions had to be used since solutions became irritating when allowed to stand several days. Futch, *et al.*[1141] found the solution damaging to the nasal mucosa of rabbits. Hunnicutt[1343] found the solution irritating to the nasal mucosa of mice during the first 3 to 4 days of use after which the irritation subsided during two weeks' application and no permanent damage was found.

Silcox and Schenck[2200] treated 52 patients having acute and chronic sinusitis with a 5% suspension of microcrystalline sulfathiazole in 1.0% paredrine hydrobromide with good results. Salman[2081] treated 75 cases of rhinitis and sinusitis and found the course of the infection shortened with fewer sequelae. No toxic reactions were noted. O'Donnell[1866] noted two cases where severe headache followed use of the preparation.

Marks[1723] used a jelly containing 20 to 50% sulfathiazole for injection into the maxillary sinus for treatment of chronic sinusitis. Approximately two-thirds of the patients responded well. The failures were blamed on chronic inflammatory tissue lining the antrum which the drug did not penetrate.

Brown[796] washed sinuses with saline solution then insufflated with sulfathiazole powder. Treatments were made twice weekly for 4 to 8 weeks. Radical operation was thus avoided in 5 patients with chronic purulent sinusitis.

Lindsay and Judd[1580] after a careful bacteriological study of cases treated locally for sinus infections, came to the conclusion that the treatment did not decrease the duration or severity of the infection.   However, they recommended use of the drugs locally in cases of sinus surgery as an adjunct to adequate blood levels of the drug as a guard against spread of the infection.

(2) Other Local Application of the Sulfonamides in the Upper Respiratory Tract

Dolowitz, *et al.*[986] applied the 2.5% solution of sulfadiazine in 8% ethanolamines as a nasal spray in preventing secondary bacterial infections which commonly follow a cold. The spray was used eight to twelve times daily for the first three days and from five to eight times daily for an additional three days.   Only 9.7% of the treated group showed sinusitis by transillumination as compared to 30% in a control group sprayed with triethanolamine solution not containing sulfadiazine.   No cases of sore throat or laryngitis developed in the treated group as compared with 10% and 2.3% in the control group.

Gertner[1166] recommended sulfathiazole in chewing gum for treatment of throat infections.   Arnett, *et al.*[669, 670] made paraffin blocks for chewing, each containing 0.325 Gm. sulfadiazine.   The concentration in the saliva was measured after 5 min., 30 min., 1 hour and 2 hours and varied from 20.6 to 888 mg. per 100 cc. in different individuals at different times.   The maximum concentration was usually reached after 30 minutes.   Blood levels were less than 1.5 mg. per 100 cc. in each case.   When sulfadiazine was given orally in gelatine capsules, sufficient to give a blood level of 5 to 10 mg. per 100 cc., the sulfadiazine content of the saliva was only 3 to 4 mg. per 100 cc.   Results of clinical studies on throat infections were not published.

MacArthur[1644] described a sulfathiazole nasal jelly used for cold treatment in over 2,000 patients with good results.

Garson[1152] used 8 lozenges per day, each containing 0.065 Gm. sulfanilamide, prophylactically and curatively in combatting a high incidence of tonsillitis in army camps. Prophylactic use cut the incidence from 10% to 2%.

Chapple and Lynch[856] studied the inhalation of a smoke of microcrystalline sulfathiazole, sulfadiazine or sulfapyrazine, both pharmacologically and clinically.   They found rapid absorption into the blood stream and deep penetration into lung, reaching the bronchioles and alveoli.   There were no evidences of drug reaction in 100 patients so treated and no tendency to cough when the particles of drug were below 5 microns in size.   Sulfadiazine had an analgesic effect noted by many patients with pharyngitis or laryngitis.   Duration of symptoms of the respiratory infections were shortened, but a full evaluation of results was not published in the preliminary note.   Freeman[1130] reported application of sulfathiazole powder with a compressed air, powder syringe to 34 cases of acute infection of the pharynx and nasopharynx with production of prompt relief. In this method of application, there was no aspiration into the lung.   Fenton[1070] also reported favorably on sulfathiazole powder applied by a powder blower.   Ebert[1014] treated 92 patients with acute rhinitis by insufflation of sulfathiazole powder with excellent results.   Seventy-nine of these patients had had previous complications from rhinitis and had sought help to prevent recurrence of these complications.   All recovered without incident.   No toxic effects of the drug were noted.

Boissard and Fry[766] using locally applied sulfanilamide powder and Goldman and Patterson[1188] using sulfathiazole powder cured chronic nasal diphtheria carriers.

(D) Otitis Media and Mastoiditis

Use of the sulfonamide drugs in ear infections has considerably reduced the incidence of acute mastoiditis and the necessity of mastoidectomy.   Since a wide variety of organisms may be encountered in such infections and since these vary widely in their susceptibility to the sulfonamides, it is not surprising that there are failures in therapy and disagreements in the literature as to the value of sulfonamide treatment.

DeSanctis, *et al.*[965] reported a ten year experience with 1,992 cases of otitis media and mastoiditis. Patients who did not have sulfonamide treatment of otitis media showed an incidence of mastoiditis of 30%, whereas those treated with sulfonamides showed 9%. In the year 1942, they reported a 3% incidence of mastoiditis in otitis media cases among 60 children, half of whom were treated with sulfathiazole and half with sulfadiazine. The two cases of mastoiditis occurred in the group treated with sulfadiazine. This led them to recommend sulfathiazole as drug of choice.

Bowers[774] as the result of experience gained in 793 cases of acute purulent otitis media, half of which were treated with sulfonamide drugs, drew the conclusions that mastoidectomies could be reduced by about 50% if chemotherapy is given before bone destruction occurs but that it is well to operate if the clinical picture strongly suggests it. He recommended sulfadiazine as drug of choice for intensive use in all complicated cases of mastoiditis.

A number of otologists hold the view expressed by Cirillo[873] that early and promiscous dosage with sulfonamide drugs in ear infections tends to mask the true condition and leads to delay in accurate diagnosis and surgical intervention which increases the mortality. Those holding this view would use sulfonamides only in cases where complications have developed. As pointed out by Connor[908], this "is not a completely rational procedure" since the sulfonamide drugs lose much of their effectiveness when pus is present, as in abscess formation or bone necrosis. He, therefore, advocated giving the drugs in adequate dosage for 5 to 7 days as soon as diagnosis of otitis media was made. He believed that if the drug was to be effective, it would have cured the infection in this time, while longer use entailed increased danger of drug toxicity without much chance of benefit.

All are agreed that signs of septicemia or meningitis should be treated by immediate chemotherapy with sulfadiazine or sulfathiazole.

(E) Sulfa Drugs in Ophthalmology

The sulfonamide drugs have been applied both orally and topically in treatment of various eye infections with satisfactory results. Heath[1286], and Thygeson and Stone[2330] reviewed these uses through 1943.

(1) Blepharitis

Blepharitis (infection of eyelid) responded to frequent applications of sulfathiazole or sulfadiazine ointment in some cases[1286, 2330].

(2) Inclusion Blennorrhea

This conjunctivitis is caused by *Chlamydozoa* which are minute intracellular organisms or virus bodies. Sulfathiazole applied in the form of an ointment brought about rapid healing in 11 of 15 cases and when supplemented by oral use of the drug, the other four cases responded[2330].

Trachoma. (See Virus Diseases.)

(3) Specific Keratitis and Ulcer

This disease of the eye is caused by *Pseudomonas aeruginosa* (*B. pyocyaneous*). Very early treatment with large oral dosage of sulfadiazine was recommended[1286]. Robson and Scott[2041] found that delay of 5 hours after infection of experimental animals before treating with 30% sodium sulfacetamide solution resulted in ulcerated eyes in 7 out of 12 rabbits, while treatment 1 hour after infection prevented ulceration in 11 out of 17 rabbits.   After 12 hours' delay in treatment, 10 out of 12 eyes became ulcerated.

(4) Epidemic Keratoconjunctivitis

This is probably a virus disease.   Conflicting reports on the effectiveness of sulfadiazine and sulfathiazole in treatment have been made[1286, 1323, 2330].

(5) Conjunctivitis, Pneumococcal and Streptococcal

Sulfadiazine or sulfathiazole applied locally in powder form or in ointments has proven effective[907, 2330] particularly when combined with oral therapy with the same drugs. Spink[2248] reported good results from applying sulfadiazine-triethanolamine solution locally.

(6) Staphylococcal Conjunctivitis

Penicillin will probably replace the sulfonamide drugs for these infections because of its much greater effectiveness.

(7) Ophthalmia Neonatorum

Sorsby and Hoffa[2241] compared the value of different sulfonamide drugs for oral treatment of 258 cases of *ophthalmia neonatorum*.   The sulfa drugs appeared much more effective than the classical treatment, particularly in gonococcal ophthalmia.   It was felt that while there was no appreciable difference in the chemotherapeutic action of the four drugs, sulfadiazine, sulfamethazine, sulfathiazole, and sulfapyridine, the poor tolerance to sulfapyridine made it least desirable to use.   In a previous series of 273 cases, 61.9% showed clinical cure in 8 days.   In the present series, 90% of gonococcal cases and 84.3% of non-gonococcal cases were clear in 8 days.   The better response was attributed to somewhat greater dosage.   Recently they have given an initial dose of 0.25 Gm., then 0.125 Gm. at four-hourly intervals and continued 3 days after apparent clinical cure.   Blumberg and Gleich[761] employed sulfathiazole orally in gonorrheal *ophthalmia neonatorum* and found it superior to any other therapy.   Dosage was 1 grain per pound of body weight daily.

Wong[2476] found sulfathiazole superior to sulfanilamide and sulfapyridine for oral treatment of gonorrheal ophthalmia.   Cures in 4 days were effected with sulfathiazole where 8 days were the rule with sulfanilamide.

(V) Sulfa Drugs in Genito-Urinary Infections

(A) Venereal Diseases

(1) Gonorrhea

The sulfonamides have proven outstanding in curing gonorrhea.   The action of sulfathiazole or sulfadiazine has been dramatic.   Clinical cures in more than 80% of the cases were brought about by a dosage of 4 to 6 Gm. per day of the drug, for a two to ten day period.   The earlier treatment started the greater was the rapidity and number of cures. Until recently sulfathiazole has been considered definitely the drug of choice, but sulfadiazine is now given preference by a number of venereologists[608, 1184, 1520, 1739, 1878, 1888, 1971, 2089, 2163] because it provides comparable treatment with lower incidence of toxic reactions, particularly if sufficient sodium bicarbonate to maintain the urine above pH 7 is administered. These two drugs are definitely superior to sulfanilamide, sulfapyridine, Uleron, and sulfacetamide, each of which has been extensively employed in the past against gonorrhea.

Strauss and Grunstein[2294] treated 488 gonorrheal prostitutes with sulfathiazole and secured cures in 90.4% of cases in the first course of treatment. After a second course of treatment this was raised to 98.9%. Mahoney, VanSlyke and Wolcott[1699] treated 360 cases of gonorrhea with 2.0 Gm. of sulfathiazole per day for periods up to 12 days. Gross cure rate was 85.4%. Jefferies and McElligott[1373] treated 567 male cases of acute gonorrhea with sulfathiazole and obtained a cure in 89.5% using a dose of 6 Gm. per day for two days. These results were superior to those achieved with a 5 day course of sulfapyridine.

Heyn[1302] reported the results of very large clinical studies on male gonorrhea in the German Army. His results confirmed those of Miescher[1777, 1779] that two days' intensive treatment with sulfathiazole cured 90% of the cases of gonorrhea. Sulfapyridine, sulfacetamide and "Neouleron" were inferior. Evidence of clinical cure was, first, absence of gonococci in urine, then the urethra was palpated over a straight sound and the prostate, vesicles and Cowper's glands were examined. More slides were then examined and an alcohol test given. After an interval of two days an intravenous injection of gonococcal vaccine was made. After an additional two days and examination of slides and urine the patient was discharged as cured if all these examinations were negative. Examination at end of two weeks was made and relapses in the sulfathiazole series were only 0.5%. Heyn stated that presence of gonococci on the third day was almost certain evidence that the treatment had failed.

Morschhauser[1807] obtained similar results on 731 cases treated with 5 Gm. of sulfathiazole per day for two days with a relapse rate of 5.4%. Preferred dosage was 4 tablets in the morning, 3 at mid-day and 3 in the evening. Pappas[1888] also confirmed Miescher's method of treatment by giving a single dose of 5 to 7 Gm. sulfathiazole to 28 cases of gonorrhea, with cures in 23.

Ferguson, Buckholtz and Gersten[1073] used combined fever therapy and sulfathiazole in treatment of resistant gonococcal infections. Fever of 106° for 7 hours was used. Cures were obtained in 85% of the cases. Because of the drastic nature of this therapy they recommended that it be given only to young and vigorous patients. Sulfadiazine and fever were used by Licht and Dick[1568] on 119 cases of resistant gonorrhea. Penicillin should obviate the need for this type of therapy in the future, in the majority of cases; however, sulfa drugs and fever may be used on cases that are resistant to penicillin[1072].

Drug resistant strains of gonococci are encountered in practice, particularly where the infection is deep-seated and difficult to reach with adequate concentrations of the drugs so that the gonococci gradually develop resistance. Such strains can be transmitted[1913] and offer a public health menace which, fortunately, can now be adequately controlled by penicillin which is highly effective against sulfa drug resistant gonococci.

Campbell[836] reported that, whereas, previous experience in the British Army had indicated cures of 70 to 75% by a two day treatment using a total of 10 Gm. of sulfathiazole, the gonorrhea contracted in Sicily and Italy appeared much more resistant to chemotherapy and less than 25% of cases responded to this treatment. Increased treatment using 25 to 30 Gm. sulfathiazole in 4 to 5 days still resulted in less than 50% cures, but promising results were being obtained with penicillin therapy.

Oard, et al.[1865] recommended combined therapy with sulfathiazole and penicillin in gonorrheal urethritis.   In 232 patients so treated there appeared to be an enhanced effect over either drug alone.

Strauss, et al.[2295] reported a one-day treatment of chronic gonorrhea in women with a cure rate between 86 and 90%.   No significant difference in results were obtained following 8 Gm. sulfathiazole, 8 or 6 Gm. sulfadiazine.   Failures were four times greater in white than in colored patients.   The authors did not advocate general use of the one-day treatment and thought it should be restricted to hospitalized patients where time was at a premium.

Schmither and Lenhoff[2634] used a dose of 30 Gm. urea along with a sulfonamide drug to treat sulfa resistant cases of gonorrhea and obtained about 50% cure of these cases. Penicillin now makes this and other treatments of sulfa resistant gonorrheal cases obsolete.

(2) Chancroid

This venereal disease, caused by *Hemophilus ducreyi*, responds well to a combination of oral and local treatment with the sulfonamides.   Open lesions are treated by local applications of powder or ointment, but buboes are never incised.   Greenblatt[1205] called sulfanilamide, sulfadiazine and sulfathiazole specific for the disease, but rated sulfathiazole as drug of choice.   The dose was 2 to 4 Gm. daily for 7 to 12 days.   Combes, et al.[905] in a study of minimum effective dosage of sulfathiazole in 97 cases, recommended an initial dose of 2 Gm. followed by 1 Gm. every six hours.   In simple chancroid, cures were effected in 5 days with a total dosage of 21 Gm. of the drug; when buboes were present, 7 days and 29 Gm. of drug were required.

Trautman and Emenhiser[2348] treated 109 cases of chancroid with sulfanilamide and compared results with 109 controls given other treatment.   Total days in hospital for the two groups were 1,759 and 4,217, respectively.

(3) Lymphopathia Venerea (Lymphogranuloma Venereum)

This venereal disease is caused by a filterable virus, yet responds reasonably well to sulfa drugs.   This apparent exception to the lack of effectiveness of these drugs in most virus diseases is still a disputed point.   Some authors maintain that the drugs have no direct virucidal action but work against secondary invaders or merely attenuate the virulence of the virus.   Sulfadiazine appears to be the drug of choice based on experimental work[252, 658, 1759] (see Virus Diseases, (VII) (A)) with sulfathiazole and sulfapyridine next.

(4) Syphilis

The sulfa drugs have no effect on *Treponema pallidum*, the spirochete of syphilis, but may help control secondary invaders in certain conditions.

(B) Prophylactic Use of Sulfa Drugs against Gonorrhea and Chancroid

Sulfathiazole has been used extensively in the armed forces as a prophylactic against gonorrhea and chancroid, with excellent results.   Loveless and Denton[1629] reduced the incidence of gonorrhea in a regiment of negro troops from 170 to 8 per 1,000 per year through giving 2 Gm. of sulfathiazole on return to camp and 2 Gm. the following morning. Incidence of chancroid dropped concomitantly from 52 to 6 per 1,000 per year.   Arthur and Dermon[676] studied prophylactic use of sulfathiazole given to negro soldiers in doses of 3, 2 and 1 Gm. on the day following return to camp from exposures that were almost certain to be infected.   Controls showed an incidence of 109 infections per 1,000 contacts while the treated group showed an incidence of 30 per 1,000. Keet[1416] obtained similar results with an incidence of gonorrhea infections of 8 per 1,000 contacts in the group treated with 1 Gm. of sulfathiazole within 12 hours of contact. This compared with an incidence of 26 per 1,000 in the controls. Chancroid was nil in the treated group and 10 per 1,000 in the controls.

Reque and Bergsma[2017] gave a single 3 Gm. dose of sulfathiazole, prophylactically, as soon as possible after exposure, to 1,482 soldiers with development of but one case of gonorrhea. In another group of 3,555 who used other prophylactic measures in addition, there were two failures. Of the total 3 Gm. doses given (5,037) there was an incidence of toxic reactions of 3.8%, none of which incapacitated the soldier for more than 24 hours. Gooch and Gorby[1190] treated soldiers after 5,902 exposures with four different plans of prophylaxis using sulfathiazole and other agents. A total dose of 2 Gm. sulfathiazole appeared to be as effective as twice this amount.

(C) Miscellaneous Urinary Infections

Infections of the urinary tract occur with a wide variety of organisms besides those responsible for venereal disease. The more common of these are *E. coli, Streptococcus viridans, Streptococcus faecalis, Aerobacter aerogenes, Staphylococcus albus and aureus, Proteus ammoniae, Proteus vulgaris, Pseudomonas aeruginosa* and various beta (hemolytic) streptococci and gamma (nonhemolytic) streptococci. The sulfa drugs are effective against many of these but in varying degree. Variations in strain differ in their susceptibility as much or more than the different species. These facts make it impossible to establish any optimum urinary concentration of drug applicable to all such infections. Sulfathiazole is rated drug of choice by most clinicians[1294, 2248] for the majority of these infections, with sulfadiazine second choice. Since urinary concentration of drug is an important factor it may be that more extensive use of sodium bicarbonate to promote urinary excretion of sulfadiazine will ultimately make it drug of choice, because of its lower toxicity. However, higher urinary concentration may be offset by the effect of increase in pH of urine on the bacteriostatic activity of the drugs in certain infections.

In the case of *Streptococcus faecalis*, Helmholz[1295] found that at pH 5, 10 mg. per 100 cc. of sulfathiazole would stop growth. At pH 5.5 the concentration had to be raised to 30 mg. per 100 cc. and at pH 6.0 there was practically no effect. Sulfadiazine at concentrations up to 300 mg. per 100 cc. at pH 6.5 did not inhibit growth of the organism. *Streptococcus faecalis* is perhaps the most troublesome urinary infection to combat with the sulfa drugs.

Helmholz and Sung[2644] in further study of the effect of pH, verified the work on *Strep. faecalis* by showing at pH 5.5 that 19 out of 25 strains were inhibited by 64 mg. sulfathiazole per 100 cc. while at pH 7.2 all strains grew in the presence of twice this concentration of drug. Exactly opposite results were obtained on *E. coli* where 46 out of 50 strains showed large growth at pH 5.5 in the presence of 50 mg. sulfathiazole per 100 cc. while at pH 7.0 only six strains showed growth. This work would indicate the importance of bacteriological identification of the infecting organism in treating urinary infections so that conditions least favorable to growth of the bacteria may be controlled during treatment.

Kidney infections must be treated with extreme care if sulfathiazole or sulfadiazine is used because of the danger of kidney stoppage. Many clinicians prefer to use the less potent but more soluble drugs such as sulfanilamide and sulfacetamide in such cases.

Greene, *et al.*[1206] observed that there was little correlation between urinary concentration of sulfadiazine and its curative effect. Cures at urinary levels as low as 62 mg./ 100 cc. and failures at 208 mg. per 100 cc. were noted. They noted fewer toxic reactions among patients treated with sulfadiazine but thought it slightly less effective than sulfa-thiazole. A wide variety of organisms was encountered in the 44 cases reported. La Towsky[1519] reported 100 cases of urinary infections treated with sulfadiazine with gen-erally favorable results. Helmholz[1294] studied the action of sulfathiazole, sulfadiazine, sulfapyridine, sulfacetamide and sulfanilamide on 38 strains of *E. coli* and found their effectiveness to decline in that order. Sulfadiazine and sulfathiazole were essentially the same in potency at moderate concentrations, but at 0.5 mg. per 100 cc., sulfathiazole appeared more active. Neter[1838] obtained similar results and was able to cure a case of pyelitis resistant to sulfanilamide through use of sulfadiazine. Alyea and Parrish[628] obtained cures with sulfadiazine of two cases resistant to sulfathiazole.

Neter[1845] claimed that combinations of pyridium with sulfanilamide, sulfapyridine or sulfadiazine had greater bacteriostatic activity against *E. coli* than could be explained by additive effect of the components.

Welebir and Barnes[2426] treated 200 cases of cystitis with sulfacetamide with recoveries in 85.5% of the cases. They were able to cure a number of patients who were intolerant to sulfanilamide or sulfathiazole, or who had not responded to these drugs. As a result of their work they were convinced of the clinical superiority of sulfacetamide in treating bacillary infections of the urinary tract.

Young, et al.[584] found sulfacetamide more active than sulfanilamide when tested *in vitro* in urine against *Strep. faecalis*, *E. coli*, *Aerobacter* and *Proteus*. In 15 patients with urinary infections by these organisms they cured 7 through use of the drug.

(VI) Prophylactic Use of Sulfonamides

The use of the sulfonamide drugs in preventive medicine is constantly increasing. It has proven highly effective in controlling epidemics of bacillary diseases such as menin-gitis, dysentery, and scarlet fever. It has also had great success in prophylaxis of gonor-rhea and chancroid (*q.v.*). The armed forces provided unique conditions for testing the prophylactic value of drugs and publications from this source constitute the best clinical evidence of the effectiveness of these drugs.

The prophylactic value of the sulfa drugs in wounds, burns and surgery has been well investigated during the recent war and is discussed elsewhere under these subjects.

(A) Meningitis

Rapid control of epidemics of meningococcic meningitis through prophylactic use of sulfadiazine was demonstrated by Kuhns, et al.[1495]. In a group of 15,000 soldiers given 2 to 3 Gm. of sulfadiazine per day for three days there was an incidence of only two cases of meningitis as compared with 40 cases in 18,800 untreated controls. The meningo-coccus carrier rate was lowered in the treated group from 36% to 4% while the control group showed an increase to 56.5%. No serious toxic reactions were encountered and the men continued basic training.

Painton[2615] gave 5 Gm. of sulfadiazine over a period of 18 to 19 hours to 18,000 trainees in an army camp, all on a single day, to arrest an epidemic of meningitis. No further cases of meningitis were encountered and no cases of scarlet fever developed. Further, the incidence of all upper respiratory infections was reduced by approximately 50% for nine days following administration of the drug. Unexpectedly, the incidence of measles and mumps was also reduced for one week following the drug. The only reactions noted were six cases of skin rash, of which only one was severe.

(B) Respiratory Infections

Coburn[888] made a preliminary report on the prophylactic use of sulfadiazine in prevention of respiratory tract bacterial infections among 30,000 naval trainees. This was part of a larger program involving 250,000 men carried out between December, 1943, and April, 1944. The results showed that 1.0 Gm. or even 0.5 Gm. of sulfadiazine daily, given continuously, was highly effective in checking a streptococcic epidemic, whether at the onset or after it had become well advanced. About 85% of susceptible recruits were protected from implantation with bacterial respiratory pathogens.

In contrast to the effectiveness of a short course of sulfadiazine prophylaxis in arresting an outbreak of meningococcic infection by eliminating the organisms from carriers, streptococcic outbreaks required continuous prophylaxis for a considerable period, since the throat flora of carriers was not materially changed. Presence of sulfadiazine in the mucous lining of the respiratory tract "prevents implantation of hemolytic streptococci but does not modify the streptococcus flora already implanted".

Holbrook[1325] obtained similar results among 40,000 air force personnel, with adequate controls for comparison. His results showed a 50 to 75% reduction in incidence of respiratory diseases during the period of sulfadiazine prophylaxis which extended to 3 months in some cases. He estimated that sulfadiazine prophylaxis might save 50 to 75% of the loss of fourteen million days in the hospital in one year because of common respiratory diseases among an army of seven million troops.

Warren[2655] published similar results on 6,000 trainees. The complete report on 600,000 naval trainees[2609] duplicated the findings of the preliminary report.

(C) Rheumatic Fever

It is estimated that over a million persons have had rheumatic fever and that 40,000 of them die each year in the United States from rheumatic heart disease[2321]. While the sulfonamides seem to have little effect during an acute attack of the disease[1178, 1331] there is now a considerable body of evidence[2209] to show that when given prophylactically over long periods they will do much to prevent rheumatic recurrences. Thomas[2321] reviewed the use of sulfanilamide for this purpose to 1942 and recommended that small daily doses be given to all children for at least five years after an attack of rheumatic fever during the season of greatest susceptibility to respiratory infections. She pointed out that the cost of this treatment would be far less than that of caring for such patients as cardiac invalids.

In a still more recent review[2647] (Oct., 1944) she found reports from civilian sources extending over a seven year period covering 815 "patient seasons" treated prophylactically with sulfanilamide with but 8 recrudescences of rheumatic fever, giving an incidence of less than 1% as compared to from 10 to 35% incidence among control groups. In view of the very extensive work (see below) on prophylactic use of sulfadiazine in the armed forces she recommended that all patients who have recovered from the acute stages of rheumatic fever should start taking sulfadiazine at a rate of 0.5 Gm. per day for a three week period, then at a rate of 1.0 Gm. per day *every day for the next five years*, or longer, interrupting the schedule only if the patient develops sensitivity to the drug. Such sensitivity is unlikely to occur after the first three weeks.

Prophylactic treatment with sulfadiazine has been carried out on an impressive scale in the armed forces. Holbrook[1325] in a preliminary article reported on one phase of a program which embraced 40 Army Air Force hospitals representing 25,000 beds and 800,000 troops. Treated and control groups were approximately the same size and were as nearly identical as possible, epidemiologically. Several different courses of treatment with sulfadiazine were given. In a group of 5,000 troops, 4 Gm. sulfadiazine given over a 48 hour period produced a demonstrable but brief drop in hospital admissions for respiratory disease. When in a like group this was increased to 6 Gm. given over a period of 3 days the hospital admissions were reduced by about 75% for a period of twelve days. The best procedure appeared to be a daily dose of 1 Gm. sulfadiazine which produced the same drop and maintained a low incidence of respiratory infections as long as the drug was continued (22 days in this experiment). Experience at two other bases showed almost equally good results from daily use of 0.5 Gm. sulfadiazine. While no final data were published, the statement was made that the available statistics showed that reduction in rheumatic fever paralleled the reduction in respiratory diseases and streptococcic infections.

Coburn[888], in reporting part of a study on prophylaxis with sulfadiazine among 250,000 naval trainees, observed that incidence of rheumatic fever among treated personnel was only 15% that of controls, in the 30,000 cases reported. The full report[2609] summarized by Thomas[2647] confirmed these results. In one training center incidence of rheumatic fever among treated personnel was only 7% that of controls.

(D) Bacillary Dysentery

Prophylactic use of sulfaguanidine at a dosage of 0.5 Gm., three times per day, promptly arrested an epidemic of bacillary dysentery among children in an institution, after segregation and sanitary precautions had failed[2152]. No toxic reactions were seen. An outbreak in a hospital ward was controlled through prophylactic use of sulfaguanidine at a dosage of 0.05 Gm. per kilo. every 4 hours for the first day, then every eight hours for two days. None of 118 patients so treated developed the disease[1634].

Hardy and Watt[1262] reported prophylactic use, or "mass therapy," with sulfadiazine in 1 Gm. doses, twice daily, in groups totaling 1,646 heavily infected personnel. Clinical cases practically disappeared and the prevalence of Flexner organisms declined with striking rapidity.

(E) Scarlet Fever

An epidemic of scarlet fever caused by group A, type 19, hemolytic streptococci among personnel of a U. S. naval station was effectively brought under control by giving 1 Gm. of sulfadiazine per day, either as a single dose, or as two 0.5 Gm. doses at 8:00 A.M. and 4:00 P.M.[2402]. The drop in incidence of new cases was dramatic. It was also noted that the average of daily sick calls for respiratory complaints was halved during the period of prophylaxis which extended for 32 days. Toxic reactions were negligible. There were three cases of drug rash, giving an incidence of less than one per cent. No gastro-intestinal disturbances were seen. These results were essentially repeated in another epidemic of the same kind in an army camp in Ontario[1053].

Coburn[888] reported treating 2,500 recruits in a naval training station prophylactically with 1 Gm. sulfadiazine daily. Incidence of scarlet fever caused by group A, type 19, hemolytic streptococci declined in two weeks to 0.75 per 1,000 while the incidence increased over the same period among 2,500 untreated controls to 6.5 per 1,000.

(F) Drug Resistant Organisms in Prophylaxis

One of the deterrents to a program of prolonged administration of the drugs in low dosage has been the fear of cultivating sulfonamide resistant strains of pathogenic organisms in the patients. The comparative ease with which such resistant strains can be developed *in vitro* (see Drug Resistance, Chapter XI) and the well demonstrated occurrence of resistant strains in clinical practice, strengthened this fear.

Julianelle and Siegel[1401] made an extensive bacteriological and clinical study of the effects of continuous administration of 1 to 2 Gm. sulfadiazine per day over a period of four months to a group of 30 children using an equal number as controls. There were transient mild toxic symptoms in two cases, otherwise no ill effects from the prolonged treatment. Throat cultures were taken periodically from both groups and no significant difference in total number of organisms was noted between treated and control groups. There was a considerable change in types of organisms, however. The Gram-negative cocci (Neisseriae) decreased markedly during the first month, then increased. These were found to be sulfadiazine resistant. Similar changes occurred in the pneumococci population; only two types persisted and these were sulfadiazine resistant. Within a short time these sulfadiazine resistant strains had spread to the control group of children who were housed in the same cottage.

Siegel[2199] who continued these studies over a two year period on the same group of children found that response to the drug in subsequent periods of therapy was equally good. This would indicate that production of drug resistant strains was not a serious problem.

Holbrook[1325] and Coburn[888] in their mass prophylactic studies with sulfadiazine in the armed forces found no evidence of the production of resistant strains of respiratory pathogens. While they did not believe the question was settled with certainty, they observed equally good response to a second period of prophylaxis as to the first. Further, those who had received prophylaxis and then developed an acute illness, responded as well to therapeutic use of the drug as those who had not previously received sulfadiazine.

Even if dangerous pathogens, resistant to the sulfonamide drugs, were developed by prophylactic use of the drugs, these organisms would not constitute a serious public health problem because penicillin could be used to control them.

(G) Drug Toxicity in Prophylaxis

The fears of many that widespread use of sulfonamide drugs prophylactically would gradually result in sensitization of a large section of the population to these drugs and preclude later use in serious illnesses, seem to be allayed by reports from the armed forces on very extensive prophylactic studies using sulfadiazine, where no such mass sensitization was observed. Thus Holbrook[1325] reported use of 1 Gm. sulfadiazine daily in 40,000 troops for periods up to three months. Repeated periods of prophylaxis on the same group failed to show increased sensitivity. No deaths from drug reactions were encountered. Only 13 individuals out of the 40,000 lost time from duty through drug reactions. Mild reactions, not involving lost time, were seen in only 33 additional cases. No renal complications and no neutrophilic leukopenia occurred. Holbrook quoted results at another air base where 4 Gm. sulfadiazine given over 24 hours to 18,000 recruits resulted in a similar low incidence of reactions. In another 25,000 troops receiving 2 Gm. sulfadiazine in a single dose there were no deaths but 13 cases of severe skin rashes and 15 additional mild skin reactions occurred. All of the severe skin rashes were among individuals who were subsequently found to have had a history of previous reaction to the sulfonamide drugs.

Coburn[888] reported an incidence of 0.2 to 0.7% of mild dermal sensitivity among 30,000 naval trainees treated prophylactically with sulfadiazine. About half of these reactors were placed back on the prophylactic program when later found insensitive to the drug. No increased incidence of reactions was seen on reinstitution of prophylaxis after a lapse of one to four weeks. The indications were that sensitization did not result from sulfadiazine prophylaxis *per se*, but that a small percentage of persons have an idiosyncrasy to the drug. Dangerous reactions occurred in 0.01% of individuals and involved about equal incidence of exfoliative dermatitis and granulocytopenia. One death occurred.

(VII) MINOR OR UNCERTAIN APPLICATIONS OF THE SULFA DRUGS

(A) Virus Diseases

The sulfonamide drugs have been disappointing in their action on virus diseases. Some medical opinion holds that the drugs have no direct viricidal activity but prevent or cure secondary invasion by bacteria. The majority opinion is that there is a viricidal effect on a few viruses, among which are those causing lymphopathia venereum, trachoma and molluscum contagiosum in humans; mouse pneumonitis and neurolymphomatosis (fowl paralysis) in chickens (see veterinary uses). It is generally agreed than these drugs have no direct effect against the viruses responsible for such human diseases as influenza, mumps, measles, smallpox, atypical pneumonia, poliomyelitis, rabies, encephalomyelitis, psittacosis and dengue. In some of these diseases, the drugs may be effective in prophylaxis against, or cure of, complications brought about by secondary bacterial infections, but such uses are still largely experimental.

(1) Lymphopathia (Lymphogranuloma) Venereum

This venereal disease of virus origin has been treated with a number of different sulfonamide drugs in both experimental and clinical infections. The results are by no means as striking and conclusive as in many of the bacterial diseases, yet there seems to be little doubt that the more potent sulfa drugs such as sulfathiazole and sulfadiazine have a decided effect on this virus. There remains a question of whether the drugs ever completely free the patient of the virus even though most of his clinical symptoms are apparently cured.

The work of Jones, Rake, and McKee[252] in which the virus was grown in eggs and inoculated into mice showed that the drugs would protect a majority of the mice from death from the acute infection, yet the virus appeared to persist in many of the mice for long periods. Rodaniche[2043] obtained similar results. The virus continued to grow in the brains of mice but in contrast to the controls was not recoverable from the spleens. The antagonistic effect of PABA, first noted by Findlay[1081] on the viricidal effect of sulfanilamide was confirmed for the action of sulfathiazole. The descending order of activity for the various drugs in these experimental infections was sulfadiazine, sulfathiazole, sulfaguanidine, sulfanilamide and sulfapyridine. Sodium sulfanilylsulfanilate has been claimed effective in the clinical disease on prolonged treatment[187, 1069]. Penicillin had no effect on lymphopathia venereum[658].

(2) Trachoma

This virus infection of the eyes appears to respond well to oral, local or combined treatment with the sulfonamides. Sulfanilamide appears to be most frequently prescribed but the other drugs seem as effective.

Richards, Forster, and Thygeson[2027] reported remarkable improvement or complete disappearance of trachoma in twelve Indian children treated with sulfanilamide. Treatment was prolonged; four and a half months were required to effect cures in several cases. Two of the children served as controls and showed no improvement until they too were treated. Gallager[1144] gave sulfanilamide internally for a ten day course of treatment. Supplementing this he applied sulfanilamide in Ringer's solution, locally, for 1 to 3 months with generally successful results in 199 cases of active trachoma. Lee and Rottenstein[1536] treated 95 patients with sulfanilamide with good results. The drug was given orally to 75 of these and intramuscularly in oil suspension to 20 patients. Cosgrove[923] treated 206 cases with oral or local sulfanilamide or both, and reported excellent results from either method of administration. Local use was attended by fewer toxic reactions. Cosgrove and Handley[924] treated 1,866 cases and 73% responded.

In spite of the favorable response it is still uncertain whether the action of sulfa drugs is against trachoma virus *per se* or merely against secondary invading organisms.

(3) Mumps and Measles

Haerem[1233] reported treatment with sulfanilamide, sulfapyridine and sulfathiazole of 500 cases of mumps and 400 cases of measles in an army hospital. In neither disease did the sulfa drugs give improved results over symptomatic treatment of control cases, as measured by length of illness, days of fever, or incidence of orchitis. Swyer[2305] reported similar results in 324 children using sulfanilamide and sulfapyridine, with 869 controls. However, he recommended their use in combating complications caused by secondary invaders. Fatality rate from measles-pneumonia was cut from 30% to 11.2% through use of the drugs. Litvak, Sands and Gible[1558] also recommended use of sulfathiazole or sulfadiazine in combatting secondary invaders. They found no effect on encephalitis complicating measles.

(4) Smallpox

Most authors agree that the sulfonamides have no effect on the virus of smallpox, yet there is some evidence[927, 1547] to show that use of the drugs greatly reduces the suppurative stage or abolishes it completely. Further, incidence of complications by sulfonamide sensitive organisms, such as conjunctivitis or pneumonia are lessened. These factors may justify use of the drugs, but much more evidence is needed. Leishman[1547] found sulfapyridine ineffective, but used sulfathiazole in twelve major cases, with results suggestive of further trial. Wilkinson[2449] reviewed 103 cases treated with sulfanilamide and found no evidence that the drug had an effect on the virus, but thought it useful in decreasing the number of lesions, in avoiding septic complications, and in reducing scarring.

(5) Experimental Virus Infections

Rake, Jones, and Nigg[1987] showed that while either sulfadiazine or sulfathiazole was very effective on mouse pneumonitis, neither drug had any effect on meningo-pneumonitis. Extensive investigations of the Lilly Research Laboratories[1574] failed to disclose compounds effective against the viruses of influenza or rabies. Andrews, King and Van den Ende[658] studied 115 miscellaneous compounds including 11 of the well known sulfa drugs and found none effective against influenza A or vaccinia viruses. Kramer, Geer, and Szabel[1485] studied several hundred compounds without success in experimental poliomyelitis and encephalomyelitis. Cavanagh[850] reported no effect of sulfa drugs in dengue. Coggeshall and Maier[892] also failed to find a drug effective against influenza or poliomyelitis.   Koprowski and Lennette[1475] found sulfapyridine and sulfathiazole ineffective in experimental yellow fever virus infections.   No effect of the sulfa drugs against feline pneumonitis was found[1254].

(B) Protozoal Diseases

These diseases, caused by one celled animal parasites, vary in their response to treatment with the sulfa drugs.   Among the failures are giardiasis, amoebic dysentery and leishmaniasis.   Diseases where there is good evidence of a direct action on the protozoa are malaria and coccidiosis.   Diseases in which the action is questionable or against commensal organisms are toxoplasmosis and *Trichomonas vaginalis* vaginitis.

(1) Malaria

The use of sulfonamide compounds in treatment of malaria had been studied sporadically with but little success prior to capture of the world's chief source of quinine by the Japanese early in 1942.   Intensive search for new antimalarials was inaugurated at that time.   The sulfonamides have been restudied; however, the results of large field tests have not been revealed.   It is only from such studies that final evaluation of the usefulness of a new antimalarial can be made, since experimental infections vary widely in their susceptibilities to the drugs and there is frequently a lack of effect in the human disease by drugs that were very promising against bird malaria.

The three main organisms of human malaria are: 1) *P. vivax* giving rise to tertian malaria characterized by recurrence of paroxysms at 48 hour intervals.   This is used therapeutically for treatment of neurosyphilitics.   2) *P. malariae* which causes quartan malaria with paroxysms every 72 hours.   This is a mild form of the disease but is sometimes most difficult to cure.   It occurs comparatively rarely.   3) *P. falciparum* which gives rise to great variability in the type of malaria.   It is the organism of aestivoautumnal or malignant tertian malaria.   This is especially severe and fatal in tropical countries and is the most prevalent form in these regions, but is rare in the temperate zone.

Coggeshall[890] showed in 1938 that sulfanilamide would sterilize the blood of monkeys infected with *P. knowlesi*.   This was encouraging but unfortunately the drug had little or no effect on the plasmodia of human malaria.

Later Coggeshall, *et al.*[893] published the results of use of "Promin" in 17 cases, of which 12 were caused by *P. vivax* and 5 by *P. falciparum*.   In the *P. vivax* cases, the parasites disappeared in an average of 3-3/8 days in eight of the cases but persisted in four cases. All the *P. falciparum* cases responded to the drug but gametocytes persisted in one case for 10 days.

Sulfadiazine was studied in 7 *P. vivax* infections with one failure, in 5 *P. falciparum* infections with two failures and in one *P. malariae* case.   Of the cases which were cured, the plasmodia disappeared in from 1 to 5 days.   The conclusion was that the sulfonamides should be regarded merely as important substitutes for quinine and atabrine and should not be given in preference.

Coggeshall[890] showed that the effect of sulfanilamide was so specific to *Plasmodium knowlesi* infections in monkeys that when monkeys were infected with a mixture of this parasite and *P. inui* and treated, the *P. knowlesi* infection was eliminated leaving *P. inui*.

Chopra, Hayter, and Sen[863] studied use of sulfapyridine in a small group of patients (12) with encouraging results.   It appeared to destroy both sexual and asexual forms of *Plasmodium vivax*, but only the asexual form of *Plasmodium falciparum*.

Johnson[1390] has recently published results of the use of sulfadiazine in eradicating

P. malariae from the blood of 13 neurosyphilitic patients. The dose was 4 Gm. per day (after the first day during which larger doses were given to build up the blood level). Treatment varied from 4 to 8 days. There were three relapses which were cured by a second course of the drug. On the basis of his limited number of cases, Johnson believed sulfadiazine to be an effective antimalarial which deserved much wider clinical trial.

Coggeshall, *et al.*[2514] showed that sulfadiazine and sulfapyrazine were particulary effective in ridding young chickens of certain exoerythrocytic stages of *Plasmodium gallinaceum* malaria, or would prevent their appearance when given prophylactically, where atabrine and quinine had no effect. Such forms have not been identified in human malaria so the importance of these results is questionable except that they give another lead in study of malarial chemotherapy.

Lieshman and Kelsall[2589] tried sulfadiazine on 54 cases of malaria and found that it was slower in repressive action than quinine or atabrine. Relapses occurred in 75% of patients within four weeks although on completion of the course of treatment no parasites were found in the blood.

(2) Mechanism of Action in Malaria

Maier and Riley[1700] for *P. gallinaceum*; Marshall, Litchfield and White[1733] and later Seeler, Graessle, and Dusenberry[2136] for *P. lophurae* showed that PABA inhibited the action of sulfonamides on these malarial parasites. It thus appears that, at least in certain stages of the life cycle, protozoa respond to the same mechanism of action of sulfonamide drugs as do the bacteria.

Coggeshall and Maier[891] studied the action of several sulfa drugs in the *in vitro* respiration of various plasmodia. There appeared to be no uniform correlation between the inhibition of respiration of the plasmodia and the curative effect of the drug *in vivo*. Thus sulfadiazine had no effect on the respiration of *Plasmodium knowlesi* but was very effective in curing monkeys infected with the parasite.

(3) Toxoplasmosis

Sabin and Warren[2071] found that sulfathiazole and sulfapyridine, when given in large doses to rabbits or mice infected with toxoplasma (an intracellular protozoon), prevented development of the disease as long as the drug was given but was curative in only a small proportion of the cases This was in spite of a lack of activity against the organisms *in vitro*. Sulfanilamide was not effective either *in vitro* or *in vivo*. Atabrine, quinine, and a number of similar drugs were active *in vitro* but were not active *in vivo*. Weinman and Berne[2414] found it possible to cure acute toxoplasmosis in mice through use of sulfapyridine or sodium sulfadiazine; sulfathiazole was less effective. All mice were shown to be carriers of virulent toxoplasmas in the brain. Biocca[740] found 4-(p-nitrophenylsulfonyl)-formanilide to be several times as active as sulfathiazole against toxoplasmosis in mice.

(4) Trichomonas Vaginalis

Greenblatt[1204] reported successful use of sulfathiazole or sodium sulfadiazine powder applied by insufflation in *Trichomonas vaginalis* vaginitis. Apparently the action was against commensal bacteria and not against the trichomonads *per se*, since the organisms remained motile in a test tube containing vaginal secretions, normal saline, and sulfathiazole for over 19 hours. When moniliasis occurred concurrently with the trichomoniasis, sulfathiazole was ineffective. Finley and Shaffer[1094] treated 23 cases of *trichomonas vaginalis* vaginitis with sulfanilamide powder (which they considered superior to sulfathiazole). Symptoms stopped immediately, but there were 6 recurrences.

(5) Giardiasis

Sulfanilamide had no effect on *Giardia muris*[598].

(6) Coccidiosis

(See Veterinary Uses.)

(C) Fungus Diseases

The sulfonamides have little or no fungistatic properties. Noojin and Callaway[1856] studied the *in vitro* activity of the common sulfa drugs on *Blastomyces dermatitidis* and found that high concentrations of drug were required to stop growth. In the case of sulfadiazine, which was most effective, this was 125 mg. per 100 cc. Sulfathiazole was ineffective at twice this concentration. They suggested possible value from wet dressings of sulfadiazine on cutaneous blastomycosis.

(1) Epidermophytosis (Athlete's Foot)

In epidermophytosis (athlete's foot) conflicting statements of effectiveness are found in the literature. It seems probable that the drugs are effective in inhibiting secondary invaders but have little effect on the fungus itself. Dimond and Thompson[976] found sulfanilamide fungistatic but not fungicidal on *Trichophyton purpureum* and *Trichophyton gypseum* at a concentration of 100 mg. per 100 cc. or greater in the absence of sulfanilamide antagonists. When antagonists were present the lag in growth was extended but the growth rate was not retarded after the lag phase. Other sulfonamide drugs were ineffective. They concluded that the drugs would have little effectiveness as specific therapy for these infections but might show improvement in cases having secondary pyogenic infections. Lewis and Hopper[1564] tested the *in vitro* effect of sulfanilamide, sulfapyridine, sulfathiazole, sulfadiazine and their sodium salts on *M. albicans* and found no inhibition but claimed that all had some retardation on growth of *Trichophyton gypseum*. Rademacher[1972] treated athlete's foot with sulfathiazole-talc powder in 38 cases and 37 cases with sodium sulfathiazole powder. The 44 cases resistant to these treatments were treated with 10% sulfathiazole in 2% salicylic acid ointment and 33 were cured.

(2) Actinomycosis

This disease, caused by the ray fungus, has been successfully treated by various of the sulfonamide drugs but treatment is in many cases prolonged and must frequently be accompanied by surgery or x-rays. Since the disease is comparatively rare there have been no really adequate clinical evaluations of the drugs.

Dorling and Eckhoff[998] obtained four cures using sulfanilamide and sulfapyridine in five cases of abdominal actinomycosis. Since the abdominal disease is almost uniformly fatal the results appeared significant. Five cures using sulfanilamide for actinomycosis of the jaw, lungs and abdomen were reported[722, 984].

Lyons, Owen and Ayers[1642] used sulfathiazole and sulfadiazine over 1 to 7 months with successful results when accompanied by surgery. McCloy[1647] treated actinomycosis of the tongue first with potassium iodide and when iodism developed continued with sulfapyridine to a successful cure. Ladd and Bill[1505] successfully treated a case of actinomycosis of the chest which spread to the abdomen, using sulfadiazine. The temperature was normal after five days and remained normal. The drug was continued for six weeks. Hollenbeck and Turnoff[1328] treated facial actinomycosis with sulfadiazine. The lesions showed a pure culture of the fungus. This was some evidence that the drug had a fungistatic effect and did not merely act on secondary bacterial invaders as had been suggested[664].

(3) Coccidioidomycosis

The sulfones and sulfa drugs have no effect on this disease[2586, 2519] but may help in control of secondary infections.

(D) Rickettsial Diseases

The sulfonamide drugs have not proven effective against Rickettsial parasites responsible for such diseases as typhus fever (louse borne), Rocky Mountain spotted fever (tick borne) and Q-fever.

(1) Typhus Fever

There is general agreement that the usual sulfonamide drugs have no effect on the course of typhus fever[994, 2344, 2393, 2471].

Walther[2393] reported some action by "Rubiazole" and Wohlrab[2471] found slight or questionable effect from an undisclosed azo-sulfonamide designated as Be 1034, which showed slightly more effect than Rubiazole. Bury[816] found no effect of the sulfa drugs on the progress of typhus fever or its mortality but thought the drugs useful in combating complications through secondary infections.

Andrews, *et al.*[659] reported successful treatment of experimental typhus fever in mice with the compounds:

p-sulfamylbenzamidine hydrochloride,

and

p-sulfamylbenzamidoxine hydrochloride,

While these results were not translatable into typhus infections of guinea pigs or human typhus fever, they were the first promising lead in chemotherapy of a rickettsial disease and may stimulate further search.

(2) Q-Fever

Zemp[590] found sulfadiazine ineffective against Q-fever in one case.

(3) Rocky Mountain Spotted Fever

Steinhaus and Parker[2277] found sulfadiazine, sulfathiazole and sulfaguanidine without effect on experimental spotted fever in guinea pigs. Topping[2344] found Prontosil and sulfapyridine also ineffective.

(E) Local Use in Dermatology

Cole[896] has reviewed the local uses of the sulfonamide drugs in treating various skin. infections. Débridement and cleanliness are prerequisite to successful treatment since the drugs must come into contact with the organisms, and drug action is strongly inhibited by presence of pus. Aside from direct use of the powdered drugs, the best vehicle for application is considered to be an oil-in-water emulsion rather than a grease base, since the latter does not mix with serum and may coat over an underlying infection, providing anaerobic conditions where the infection may grow.

Each of the sulfonamide drugs has been used for local application but sulfanilamide and sulfathiazole are used most extensively. Sulfathiazole must be used with caution because of the danger of sensitization (see section on toxicity). Sulfaguanidine is said to be dangerous when used on a raw surface[1941].

The results from treatment of impetigo, ecthyma, chancroid and pyococcic infections are excellent, but Cole believes that except for chancroidal infections it is questionable whether the sulfa drugs should be used unless other forms of therapy have been tried unsuccessfully. In any case, their use should be restricted to five days or less, to cut down danger of sensitization.

Harris[1274] treated impetigo with topically applied paste of microcrystalline sulfathiazole and was able to cure the lesions in 24 hours. Bigger and Hodgson[737] confirmed the greater rapidity of cure of microcrystalline sulfathiazole over ordinary powder, although more than 24 hours was required to effect a cure in their experience. Pijoan, et al.[1922] treated impetigo by first softening the scabs with hydrogen peroxide and removing, then applying several coats of a solution of sulfadiazine and methylcellulose in 50% acetone. Usually one treatment sufficed. This had the advantage of not requiring bandages and so being more acceptable to the patients.

Schlesinger and Martin[2108] preferred oral therapy with sulfathiazole or sulfadiazine for treatment of impetigo. Cures in four to five days usually resulted.

(F) Miscellaneous Uses

(1) Anthrax

The sulfonamide compounds have proven fairly effective in controlling anthrax infections. Gold[1183] reviewed the literature to 1942 on the use of the drugs in this infection and included 42 cases treated by himself. He rated sulfapyridine as most effective followed by sulfathiazole and sulfadiazine but preferred sulfathiazole to sulfapyridine because of its lower toxicity.

(2) Brucellosis (Undulant Fever)

Spink[2248] reported successful use of sulfadiazine or sulfanilamide in treatment of *Brucella abortus* infections where the disease was of fairly recent origin, but obtained disappointing results in patients with chronic brucellosis of six months' duration or more. The opinion was expressed that failure to differentiate between acute and chronic cases accounted for some of the controversy in the literature on the value of sulfonamide drugs in brucellosis.

Sarvis[2088] reported three cases of undulant fever successfully treated with sulfaguanidine.

Several authors have reported no effect from use of the sulfonamide drugs in brucellosis[1565, 2469].

(3) Infectious Mononucleosis

This disease whose etiology is unknown has been observed by Hoffman, Lees, and Comroe[1320] to respond well to sulfathiazole therapy in twelve cases. Contratto[909] observed no improvement with sulfadiazine therapy in a small number of cases.

(4) Subacute Bacterial Endocarditis

Lichtman[293] reviewed current results in treatment of this fatal disease. Sulfa drug therapy had been disappointing; however, he believed that the small number of recoveries justified continued use of the drugs. Thus of 489 treated cases 4% recovered. Of 215 cases treated with sulfa drugs, plus heparin or fever therapy, 8.5% recovered. This was compared with an estimated 1% incidence of spontaneous recovery. Galbreath and Hull[1143] treated 42 cases with sulfanilamide, sulfapyridine or sulfathiazole and all died. Dick[970] gave massive doses of sodium sulfadiazine intravenously and claimed to have cured a case of subacute bacterial endocarditis. Hull, *et al.*[1342] who tried this therapy on four cases, reported failure in each case.

(5) Tularemia

Reports[1015, 1231, 1394, 1625, 1751, 2026, 2221, 2412, 2429] of the use of sulfa drugs in treatment of tularemia have not been too encouraging. In an *in vitro* study Tamura[2309] showed that sulfapyrazine was the only drug which completely inhibited *Pasturella tularense* at as low a concentration as 5 mg. per 100 cc. Sulfadiazine and sulfathiazole were decreasingly effective in that order, while sulfanilamide, sulfapyridine, sulfaguanidine and Neoprontosil were inactive at 20 mg. per 100 cc. Tamura believed sulfapyrazine to be the only sulfa drug worthy of clinical trial.

(6) Vincent's Angina

Linton[1582] reported successful results from two days' use of sulfathiazole in treating Vincent's infection in the tonsils of soldiers returning from the South Pacific. A dose of 0.5 Gm. was given every two hours by allowing a tablet to dissolve on the tongue. While only four cases were reported, the results on these suggested that sulfathiazole was beneficial.

(7) Ludwig's Angina

Sulfadiazine or sulfathiazole are recommended[2450] as adjuncts to other treatment including surgery.

(8) Helminthic Diseases

Sulfanilamide was found to have little or no effect on experimental trichinosis in rats[1648, 1696].

(9) Leprosy

Faget, *et al.*[1045] found that "Promin" had a definite effect in arresting the progress of leprosy in a considerable number of cases when administered over long periods.

The drug has been approved by the U. S. Food and Drug Administration specifically for the treatment of leprosy.

(VIII) Wound and Surgical Applications of Sulfonamides

(A) Wounds

(1) General Considerations

The sulfonamide drugs were employed very extensively in World War II for local and systemic use in wound prophylaxis. Each United States soldier or sailor carried a shaker envelope containing 5 Gm. of granular, sterile sulfanilamide with instructions to sift the drug into the wound as soon as possible. He also carried a packet of 0.5 Gm. sulfadiazine tablets and was instructed to take all eight of these, with much water, immediately after the wound was incurred. Sulfanilamide crystals were used to "frost" the wound at every dressing or surgical operation. It was recommended that in wounds closed by primary suturing (rarely a safe procedure) 0.05 Gm. of crystalline sulfanilamide be applied per square inch of wound surface and in contaminated, or infected wounds, double this amount. Not more than 10 Gm. were to be applied locally in any 24 hour period, however. Thorough débridement and careful surgical treatment were prerequisites, because necrotic tissue and pus contain sulfonamide inhibitors.[906, 1488, 1611] Sulfonamide drugs for local application must be sterile, since it has been demonstrated that tetanus will develop if spores are introduced into wounds with sulfanilamide[1016, 2421].

(2) Value of Local Application of Sulfa Drugs in Prophylaxis of Wounds

Assessment of the value of this extensive use of sulfonamide drugs in prophylaxis of wounds is difficult and no final evaluation has been made. Most authors agree that such application has done much to lower the fatalities from wounds[906, 1076, 1426, 1488, 1741, 1759]. Pulvertaft[1968] cautioned against too much enthusiasm, since he found to his surprise that comparative statistics between wound experience at the close of the first World War and experience in the British Army of World War II showed little difference. Wound sepsis was apparently not an important cause of mortality. He cited a mortality rate of 0.5% from all causes in 10,000 cases in 1918 and since some of this was because of gas gangrene (with a fatality rate of 25%) not much was left over for wound sepsis as a cause of death. He stated that the sulfonamides have not prevented wound infection. "sepsis is all but universal, and few die of it now; the condition was apparently identical in 1918". He pointed out that the evaluation of the treatment cannot be made in terms of mortality statistics alone, but must be based on how long the patient was invalided and how the wound behaved. Wounds treated by the closed plaster cast treatment, he pointed out, frequently suppurated profusely for long periods and caused a great deal of misery and discomfort to the patient. The patient rarely died but his restoration to normal health was problematical.

MacLennan[1689] found that the incidence of gas gangrene was 0.32% of all wounded and the case mortality 50% in the Middle East theatre of the recent war. This compared with an incidence of 0.36%, in much more heavily infected terrain, with a mortality of 25% during 1917 and 1918. Thus, despite widespread use of the sulfonamide drugs and antisera, gas gangrene prevention and treatment had not notably advanced in 25 years. Surgery remained the only effective treatment of gas gangrene.

Meleney[1762] reviewed the results on 1500 wound cases and found no evidence that local use of sulfanilamide or sulfadiazine cut down the incidence of local infections; however, he believed that spread of such infections had been minimized.

Admiral Sheldon[2186] also cast doubt on the value of locally applied sulfonamides, but cited the low death rate (much less than 1%) of wounded personnel evacuated from the

Solomon Islands. However, he was positive of the value of internally administered sulfa drugs in preventing general sepsis, which is what kills. He also reported general agreement as to the value of locally applied sulfonamides in wounds of the skull, chest, and abdomen, but expressed the view that their value in these cases may well be due to the absorptive capacities of these cavities.

Pulvertaft and Mackenzie[1969] proposed the local use of succinylsulfathiazole for prophylaxis and healing of wounds on the theory that high local concentration could be obtained without systemic absorption of the drug. Results in 8 cases in which a 20% lanolin cream was used as medium indicated quick control of Gram-positive flora and acceleration of healing.

Schmelkes[2111] believed the local application of sulfanilamide buffered with calcium carbonate to pH 8.8 was worthy of trial on the theoretical basis that the increased ionization of sulfanilamide at this pH would make it more effective against bacteria. Preliminary clinical observations were favorable.

Key[1426] preferred a mixture of 2 parts of sulfanilamide and 1 part of sulfathiazole for local application in his surgical cases. Usually 5 Gm. sufficed and no more than 10 Gm. of the mixture was ever used. He found no difference in results from particle sizes ranging from fine powder to coarse crystals, but was careful to distribute the drug evenly through use of a sterile salt shaker.

(3) Combinations of Sulfa Drugs and Other Agents in Local Treatment

The use of urea-sulfonamide combinations for local treatment of wounds has been claimed to be highly effective, because the urea increases the solubility of the sulfonamides and has a strong lytic and deodorant action which tends to help keep the wound clean[1327, 1350, 1868, 2357].

Tsuchiya, *et al.*[2317, 2357] claimed that urea had an effect on sulfonamide inhibitors present in wounds and further that it was capable of overcoming resistance to the action of the sulfonamides. This was disputed by Kirby[1439] whose experiments indicated that urea was itself bacteriostatic in high concentrations but that in low concentrations it did not counteract sulfonamide inhibitors nor potentiate the action of the sulfonamides against resistant organisms. Lee, *et al.*[1537] supported Tsuchiya, *et al.*, in their claims of a synergistic effect of urea and claimed thiourea and guanidine to be even more effective.

Olson, *et al.*[1868] showed that urea promoted granulation but seriously retarded epithelization. Pfister[1915] described a dusting powder for wound use called "Sufortan", consisting of 20 parts of sulfapyridine, 70 parts of urea and 10 parts of a urea-formaldehyde resin. Dingwall[979] recommended a mixture of 9.5% urea, 5.0% disodium phosphate, 75% sulfanilamide, 10% calcium carbonate, 0.1% "Azochloramid," 0.2% granulating agent and 0.2% sodium tetradecyl sulfate. This was made into granules with a particle size between 40 and 80 mesh. Opinions were that wounds cleared up quickly without evidence of tissue injury or caking of the powder in the wounds.

Goldberger[1185] and Neter[1831] have studied the use of "Azochloramid" and sulfanilamide in wounds and localized infections. It was claimed that a potentiation occurred, probably because the "Azochloramid" oxidized the sulfonamide inhibitors present in necrotic material. Skelton[2208] verified the potentiation *in vitro* against *Streptococcus agalatiae* but "Azochloramid" failed to show increased effect over sulfanilamide alone in treatment of bovine mastitis.

Chambers, *et al.*,[853] recommended local application in wounds and surgery of microcrystalline sulfathiazole, prepared by low temperature neutralization of a solution of the sodium salt while agitating violently by a high speed agitator or by an ultrasonic vibrator. The resulting slurry, which was the consistency of thick cream, could be employed directly, or the material could be filtered, dried and used as a powder. It was claimed that sulfathiazole in this form had a much higher rate of solution and would tend to keep tissue adjacent to it near saturation concentration. The tendency to lump or cake in the wound was definitely less than with other powders.

Klepser[1452] could find no evidence that sulfanilamide interfered with the normal healing process except that it mechanically prevented contact of the edges of the wound. He thought its use in clean operative wounds unnecessary but recommended use where contamination was evident. Throckmorton[2329] investigated the tissue reactions produced by intraperitoneal application of the sulfonamides. Sulfanilamide produced little response because it was absorbed rapidly. Sulfapyridine produced a severe reaction in which masses of the drug were walled off before they could be absorbed. Sulfadiazine produced a somewhat similar effect. Sulfathiazole and sulfamerazine behaved as non-irritating foreign bodies. Similar results were obtained by others[939, 947]. Throckmorton considered sulfathiazole as drug of choice for intraperitoneal use. Zintel[596] found that while sulfanilamide did not delay healing of experimental wounds, either macrocrystalline or microcrystalline sulfathiazole delayed healing. The latter had less retarding action on attaining normal strength of scar tissue.

Perhaps the greatest value of locally applied sulfonamides in war wounds was in lengthening the time between wounding and thorough surgical débridement without correspondingly greater risk of serious infection[611].

Sulfathiazole should never be applied locally in brain surgery because it has caused epileptic convulsions[1371, 1758, 1925, 1926, 2403]. Sulfanilamide and sulfadiazine did not produce these effects[2403]; however, none of the sulfonamides should be applied in the immediate vicinity of nerve trunks[1759]. Other toxic reactions from local use of the drugs correspond with those observed from systemic dosage, as would be expected, since the drugs are absorbed into the blood stream when applied locally. For this reason excessive amounts of the drugs should never be given locally.

In osteomyelitis, locally applied sulfathiazole[2346] has been recommended for routine use after surgery. A few successful cures have also been reported where oral sulfathiazole was employed without surgery[1338, 1995].

Kenney[2571] analyzed 3,176 cases of acute hemotogenous osteomyelitis. Whereas the mortality was 23% before the advent of chemotherapy it was then 3.5%. He ascribed this advance to early bone decompression which is now possible because the sulfonamides control the septicaemia.

(4) Gas Gangrene—Experimental Work

Apparently the sulfonamide drugs have not proven effective in the field in preventing gas gangrene[1689, 1968]. There has been much experimental work in animals (chiefly guinea-pigs) on the various *Clostridia* responsible for the disease. The sulfa drugs if given before or at infection will prevent deaths from gas gangrene. However, they appear to have little or no effect on the progress of the infection once gas gangrene has started, and delay of even an hour in administration of the drug after infection materially increases the mortality.

Rosenthal[2055] has studied the *in vitro* effect of various sulfanilamide derivatives and related compounds on six species of Clostridia (*histolyticum, welchii, tetani, septicum, novyi, sporogenes*). The commercial sulfa drugs and bis(4-aminophenyl) sulfone were feebly active against all but *Cl. septicum*. The medium was beef infusion broth containing 2% neo-peptone and hence contained known sulfonamide inhibitors. In contrast to the failure of the aminosulfonamides, 4-nitrobenzenesulfonamide, 2-(4-nitrophenyl-sulfonamido)thiazole and 4-(4-nitrophenylsulfonyl)aniline inhibited growth at dilutions of about 1 to 10,000 and the action was not reversed by addition of PABA. 3-Nitro-benzenesulfonamide was equally active. It remained to be seen whether the nitro compounds would retain their activity on living tissue and whether one of these would prove useful for local chemotherapy of wounds.

Hac, *et al.*[1228, 1229] studied the effect of sulfa drugs in the diet on protection of mice infected with *Clostridium welchii* and obtained results showing increasing effectiveness of the drugs in the order: sulfanilamide, sulfapyridine, sulfathiazole, and sulfadiazine. However, the tissue at the site of injection became necrotic and sloughed off even though the mice survived. Penicillin was much more effective than the sulfa drugs but it, too, had to be given at the time of inoculation for best results.

McIntosh and Selbie[1674] compared various drugs by local treatment of anaerobic infections in mice one hour after infection. Sulfathiazole failed to save any of the mice infected with *Cl. welchii*, but was the most effective drug against *Cl. septicum*. Penicillin was outstandingly good against *Cl. welchii*, protecting 78% of the mice. Sulfadiazine was less effective than sulfathiazole. Against *Cl. oedematiens* penicillin produced some prolongation of life but all mice died within three days under any drug treatment. These same authors[1675] claimed that a mixture of one part proflavine with 99 parts sulfathiazole gave very superior results in treatment and prophylaxis of wound infections as shown both in experimental animals and in clinical trials.

Bliss, Long and Smith[757] reviewed the literature on experimental gas gangrene treatment with the sulfonamides and found many conflicting results. Their own work, in which mice were infected in the thigh muscles, then treated either by drug in the diet or by local injection, showed sulfadiazine to be effective against *Cl. welchii* and *Cl. septique* while sulfathiazole and sulfapyridine were much less effective and sulfanilamide and sulfaguanidine were inactive. None of the sulfonamides were effective against *Cl. oedematiens* (*Cl. novyi*). Against *Cl. tetani* sulfathiazole was moderately effective and the other sulfonamides inactive. Zinc peroxide applied locally was most effective against the latter two organisms but inactive against *Cl. welchii*. Others[825, 2083] obtained essentially similar results.

Reed and Orr[2007, 2008] found that *Cl. welchii*, *Cl. septicum*, and *Cl. novyi* responded in decreasing order to chemotherapy in experimental guinea pigs, but that chemotherapy was ineffective against *Cl. sordelli*. They gave the following order of increasing effectiveness of the sulfa drugs: sulfanilamide, sulfacetamide, sulfaguanidine, sulfapyridine, sulfamethylthiazole, sulfadiazine and sulfathiazole. They found a combination of oral and local treatment to work best.

"Marfanil", or *p*-(aminomethyl)benzenesulfonamide, homosulfanilamide,

$$NH_2CH_2-\left\langle\ \right\rangle-SO_2NH_2,$$

was claimed by Domagk, Shreus and others[988, 990, 992, 2145] to be active against gas gangrene organisms. As employed in the Germany Army it was mixed with sulfanilamide or sulfathiazole. A salt of "Marfanil" with naphthalenedisulfonic acid was also used.

Link[1581] found that *in vitro* bacteriostatic experiments using "Marfanil" were not inhibited by PABA and that a sulfathiazole resistant strain of staphylococci remained sensitive to "Marfanil". This suggested that "Marfanil" acted through a different mechanism than ordinary sulfonamide drugs. Experiments designed to check these results *in vivo* using guinea pigs infected with *Cl. septicum* demonstrated that the effect *was* neutralized by PABA. This discrepancy was not explained, but perhaps the toxicity of PABA was the cause of increased deaths in the animals.

Mitchell, Rees and Robinson[1793] reported that "Marfanil" gave them results in infected wounds which were superior to all other sulfonamide drugs applied locally. They predicted that it will be used in combination with penicillin. They quoted a statement from a report by Fleming: "Marfanil" is a much weaker bacteriostatic agent on the test streptococcus than sulfathiazole, but is not inhibited by PABA or pus".

Ivánovics, *et al.*[1363] found sulfamethylthiazole, applied locally, superior to all other treatment in experimental gas gangrene of guinea pigs where a mixed infection was produced with contaminated earth.

(B) Burns

(1) General Remarks

World War II with its high incidence of burn casualties stimulated much clinical research designed to improve methods of treatment. Many of these were tried under field conditions and found unsuited. The most notable advances were in better systemic treatment of severe burns. Blood plasma saved many lives by overcoming shock and the loss of blood volume through "weeping" burns. The widespread employment of the sulfonamide drugs, both systemically and locally, has probably played a part in preventing death from generalized infections resulting from contaminated burns. Such prophylactic chemotherapy was generally recommended with sulfadiazine as drug of choice for internal use.

The sulfonamide drugs have also been applied locally to burns in a great many forms, ranging from the dry powders to sprays of suspensions or solutions of the drugs, various ointments and "preformed eschar" containing the drugs. Much medical controversy exists as to the relative merits of these and other local treatments of burns. This subject was authoritatively reviewed by the Council on Industrial Health and Council on Pharmacy and Chemistry of the American Medical Association[928]. The most notable trend seemed to be away from tannic acid and to the pressure dressings advocated by Allen and Koch[624] who considered a burn as the equivalent of a wound and treated it accordingly.

(2) Pickrell Treatment of Burns

Pickrell[1920] treated burns by spraying the burned area after cleaning, with 2.5% sulfadiazine in 8% triethanolamine solution, every hour for the first 24 hours, then every two hours for the second day and every 3 hours for the third day. A thin pliable eschar was formed in 24 to 36 hours. No additional dressings were applied and the patient was maintained in a heat cradle when the burn was extensive. Because the drug was absorbed into the blood stream, little, if any, sulfadiazine was given by mouth and the blood level of drug was watched to avoid an excessively high level when treating extensive burns. In 32 cases involving second and third degree burns varying from 10 to 45% of the body surface, results were good[2059]. Others have used the method with success[611, 1124, 1251, 1265].

The method did not find much favor in military medicine because of the frequent attention required. About a fourth of the patients complained of a burning sensation when being sprayed[1774].

(3) Membranes Impregnated with Sulfa Drugs

Various sulfa drugs have been incorporated into plasticized methylcellulose film. These have been applied as dressings to burns and wounds. The film is light and strong and as it slowly dissolves it liberates the sulfa drug which helps prevent infection. Pickrell[1921] described such a film prepared by spraying a glass surface with a solution of 3% sulfadiazine, 2.5% methyl cellulose, 3% triethanolamine and 0.5% sorbitol in 50% alcohol or acetone as the solvent. The film could be sterilized by dry heat. The solution could also be applied as a spray directly on the skin, but for this purpose, the alcohol or acetone was omitted and the film was dried with a warm air blower[903]. For greater strength, the methylcellulose film was formed in fine mesh rayon, nylon, or silk[876].

Andrus and Dingwall[660] used a methylcellulose film containing 20% sulfanilamide and 10% sodium sulfacetamide buffered to pH 9. Andrus, *et al.*[661] used a similar film containing sulfanilamide and "Azochloramid."

Gelatin base films have also been tried with variable success[903, 2623].

(C) Abdominal Surgery

The hope of sterilizing the intestinal tract through preoperative dosage with the sulfa drugs so as to permit aseptic surgery of the bowel was raised, but failed in accomplishment[1096]; however, the number of coliform organisms could be remarkably decreased through use of sulfaguanidine or succinylsulfathiazole[1945]. With the latter drug the number of *E. coli* per Gm. of feces could be reduced to less than 1000 in 93 per cent of patients treated for 7 days. Poth[1945] considered that use of the drug had reduced the incidence of bacterial infection following resections of the large bowel, and shortened the period of hospitalization. A dosage of 0.5 Gm. per kilo. of body weight was given the first day and half this thereafter in six equal doses at 4 hour intervals. This was continued until the *E. coli* count in the feces had dropped below 1,000 per Gm. before operation. The drug was continued postoperatively as soon as the patient could tolerate liquids.

Stafford, *et al.*[2267] found the intraperitoneal and systemic use of the sulfa drugs of value in treatment of a large number of cases of peritonitis following acute perforative appendicitis. Morbidity and mortality were both reduced. Sulfanilamide in crystalline form was applied in 10 Gm. doses sprinkled into the peritoneal cavity and onto the abdominal wound. Microcrystalline sulfathiazole was employed intraperitoneally in one third of the cases during 1942. Anglem and Clute[663] used sulfanilamide intraperitoneally in 75 surgical operations requiring the opening and closure of hollow viscera within the peritoneal cavity. No other chemotherapy was given and no deaths from peritonitis occurred. Jonas[1396] treated 61 patients with perforated appendix with sulfathiazole given orally or intravenously. No drug was used intraperitoneally since he felt such practice made it difficult to control toxic reactions. There were two deaths in this series, or 3.28% mortality, as compared to a mortality rate of 10.02% in 479 similar cases in the preceeding 8 years. Similar treatment in another series reduced the mortality from 7.89% to 2.2%[2405]. In 27 cases of peritonitis accompanying appendectomies treated with 8 Gm. sulfanilamide intraperitoneally and 2 Gm. in the skin layer, no deaths occurred[2334]. Local use of sulfathiazole in transurethral prostatic resections lessened the postoperative febrile reactions and number of complications[2297].

Walter and Cole[2391] preferred to insert 6 Gm. of sulfadiazine rather than 10 Gm. of sulfanilamide intraperitoneally based on their comparative study of the drugs in 62 cases each, where the incidence of wound infection was 4% with sulfadiazine and 14% with sulfanilamide. Ogilvie[1867] made a suspension of sulfadiazine in gelatine and saline which was run into the abdomen through a rubber tube after operation for abdominal wounds. He claimed this the only satisfactory drug because sulfanilamide was absorbed too rapidly, while sulfapyridine and sulfathiazole tended to form cakes which were in evidence at post-mortem examination. Sulfadiazine, given as described, produced remarkably few adhesions and had disappeared in cases coming to post-mortem examination. The advantages for this route of administration were that an adequate concentration of drug was assured at the seat of trouble for at least 48 hours, during the time when the oral route was unusable and the intravenous one was required for other fluids. Debenham[959] also described use of sulfadiazine given by catheter through the operative wound in 11 cases of bowel perforation from battle wounds. Nine of the 11 lived.

Mueller and Thompson[1809] employed intraperitoneal sulfanilamide in 133 cases of acute appendicitis where there was danger of contamination and peritonitis. None of these patients died. Jackson and Coller[1367] used sulfanilamide in 62 cases involving operations on the stomach and intestines. They found the drug to be absorbed very rapidly and cautioned against use of more than 5 Gm. locally, particularly if the drug were given orally at the same time, since they encountered toxic hepatitis in several of their patients.

Kaufman, and Mersheimer[1409] used sulfanilamide or sulfathiazole intraperitoneally in 412 appendectomy cases with a gross mortality of 2.4%. They recommended oral administration to supplement the locally applied drugs.

(IX) Sulfa Drugs in Veterinary Medicine

(A) General Considerations

The sulfa drugs have been studied extensively in animal diseases and their success has been roughly parallel to infections with the same or similar organisms in humans. Since economic factors are of paramount importance in treatment of farm animals, the use of the more expensive sulfa drugs has been restricted to valuable animals where the cost of treatment could be justified. It can be anticipated that veterinary applications will expand enormously when the drugs are available in large quantities at very low prices.

The various animals differ considerably in their absorption, degree of acetylation and excretion of the drugs, so that general statements as to dosage, which will bring about a given blood level of active drug, cannot be made. Alstrom[626] found that considerably larger doses of sulfanilamide were required in cattle than in horses to secure a given blood level. Horses showed 12 to 20% of the total sulfanilamide in the blood as acetylsulfanilamide. Cattle showed still higher acetylation, while dogs showed no acetylation. Zipkin, et al.[597] found 37% conjugated sulfanilamide in the blood of cows and 69% conjugation in the milk.

Klein[1449] recommended 7.5 Gm. of sulfanilamide per 100 lb. of body weight as an initial dose in horses, to be followed by 25 Gm. every 8 hours. The dose in cattle was 6 to 10 Gm. per 100 lb. at 8-hourly intervals. In dogs he recommended 0.1 Gm. per lb. of body weight daily in six portions, together with sufficient sodium bicarbonate to prevent acidosis.

Sulfapyridine, sulfathiazole and sulfadiazine have been administered successfully in calf pneumonia[2327]. Various streptococcal infections are usually treated with sulfanilamide[1197]. These belong to Lancefield groups B, C, and G[2265].

(B) Bovine Mastitis

The oral use of the sulfa drugs (sulfanilamide, sulfathiazole, and sulfadiazine) has not proven effective in treating streptococcic or staphylococcic mastitis, according to Schlotthauer[2109]. When treatment is continued for a week or more the cows get indigestion, probably because the sulfa drug changes the bacterial flora in the rumen. Intravenous administration gave no better results. Direct injection of a suspension of sulfanilamide into the udder has been employed for some time and is effective. A homogenized 35% suspension of sulfanilamide in oil is recommended[1403, 1885, 1886, 2109].

Skelton[2208] tried a combination of "Azochloramid" and sulfanilamide but found that if given in sufficiently high concentration to be effective against the Group B streptococci, severe tissue damage resulted.

(C) Distemper in Dogs

This disease is caused by a filterable virus and most authorities are agreed[326, 971, 1782, 1937] that the sulfa drugs have no effect on the virus. Secondary invaders and bacterial infections having similar symptoms are, however, successfully treated. This has led to much confusion in the literature as to the effectiveness of these drugs on distemper[114, 1197, 1719].

(D) Brucellosis in Cattle

Live, Stubbs and Gardiner[1590] studied use of sulfathiazole and sulfapyridine in cows whose milk was contaminated with *Brucella abortus*. Doses were given as high as possible without serious toxic reactions. While there was reduction in the bacterial count during treatment, the infection was not cured and the milk again contained the organisms after drugs were stopped.

(E) Infectious Coryza in Chickens

Sulfathiazole in high doses, consisting of 1.5 Gm. morning and night, with 0.5 Gm. at noon, to a total of 7 Gm. was able to effect complete recovery in chickens who were not in an advanced stage of the disease[1250]. Prophylactic dosage at a rate of 7 oz. of sulfathiazole per 100 lb. feed cut the incidence of "colds" from 90% to 20%[1288].

(F) Neurolymphomatosis (Fowl Paralysis)

Asplin[678] reported excellent results in the treatment of fowl paralysis in young chicks with sulfadiazine. Of 138 chicks inoculated with 18 strains of virus and treated with sulfadiazine in the food at a level of 7.3 to 22 Gm. per kilo of food, none showed macroscopic lesions, in contrast to 117 control infected and untreated chicks, 101 of which showed gross lesions on post-mortem examination. Other drugs were effective and Asplin lists them in decreasing order as sulfadiazine, sulfamethazine, sulfathiazole, sulfapyridine and sulfaguanidine. Sulfanilamide proved too toxic in effective dosage. The action of the drugs was reversed by PABA.

This remarkable result and particularly its reversal by PABA is in such contrast to usual results in attempted chemotherapy of virus diseases, as to need verification.

(G) Intestinal Diseases in Animals

(1) Calf Scours

Thorp[2327] gave sulfaguanidine in 57 cases of calf scours with loss of 6 calves. Succinylsulfathiazole was given in 27 cases with death of 3 calves. Herriott[1299] gave succinylsulfathiazole prophylactically during an epidemic of severe scours and was able to prevent its appearance. When administered after symptoms had developed, 13 out of 16 calves were saved, but two of the deaths were in calves that were in critical condition before treatment started.

Wise and Anderson[2470] also employed sulfaguanidine successfully and recommended its use prophylactically in new born calves.

Thorp, *et al.*[2328] reported beneficial results from administration of succinylsulfathiazole and phthalylsulfathiazole to calves with infectious calf scours.

(2) Pullorum Disease in Turkeys

Bankowski[696] found sulfaguanidine and sulfathiazole ineffective against acute pullorum disease in turkeys.

(3) Infectious Enteritis in Swine

Sulfaguanidine has been used successfully to check infectious enteritis in swine, a disease that is usually caused by organisms of the Salmonella group. It was found effective in experimental infections with *S. choleraesuis*[955]. In a field study, dosage of sulfaguanidine was 0.165 to 0.33 Gm. per kilo daily, divided between morning and evening. Four to five days sufficed to check diarrhea but the drug was continued for three or four days longer before releasing the animals[1422]. Among treated animals recovery was 69% while among controls only 16% recovered. In another series recovery was 92% among treated pigs. (See also[834].)

(4) Coccidiosis in Chickens

Horton-Smith and Taylor[1334] showed that 2% sulfamethazine in the mash, or saturated solution in the drinking water, would prevent development of symptoms of cecal coccidiosis in chickens infected with *Eimeria tenella*. Hawkins[1280] verified this by reducing the mortality from 84% to 24% by use of a saturated solution of the drug as drinking water for the infected chickens. Treatment was not started until 96 hours after infection.

Farr and Allen[1051] showed that 2% sulfaguanidine in the feed would also prevent infection with *Eimeria tenella* but that 3 to 5% fed to infected chickens did not effect recovery, although it lowered the oöcyst count. Beach[715] secured similar results. Allen and Farr[625] found 0.5% sulfaguanidine in the diet of chickens was of prophylactic value and did not interfere with acquirement of an effective resistance to the disease. (See also [2211].)

(5) Coccidiosis in Animals

The use of various sulfa drugs greatly reduces the oöcyst count in lambs, rabbits or calves but does not completely eradicate the infection in most cases[773, 791, 1281]. When treatment is begun after clinical symptoms have appeared, results are no better than in control animals, but when given prophylactically before infection, a high percentage is protected[864, 1116].

(H) Surgical Use in Animals

Sulfanilamide has been employed for wound prophylaxis and to prevent infection following surgery, in all domestic animals. The material is dusted into the wound or crystals are sprinkled on. In other cases an ointment containing the drug is applied. These applications are similar to those in human surgery (*q.v.*).

(I) Toxic Effects in Animals

The toxic effects of the drugs as encountered in human therapy are also found in animals. The most serious of these is kidney damage through crystallization of the drugs.

(X) CLINICAL TOXICITIES

(A) General Remarks

(1) Classification of Toxic Reactions and Definitions

The manifestations of toxic reactions to the sulfonamide drugs are numerous and important for the attending physician to recognize. The importance is reflected in statistics by Sutliff, *et al.*[2301] indicating that sulfa drugs caused one death in 2,571 deaths from all causes, or one death in 685 pneumonia deaths in New York City for 1941. Many such deaths must be charged to carelessness or lack of knowledge on the part of the doctor in charge. Probably the situation has improved now through introduction of the less toxic drugs, sulfadiazine and sulfamerazine, and through increased knowledge of the proper use of all sulfa drugs.

It is comforting to know that the ratio of lives saved to deaths caused by the sulfa drugs was roughly 200 to 1, according to Sutliff. It is unfortunate that these drugs were heralded as "miracle" drugs which killed bacteria without harm to the patient, in early lay publications. The same statements are now being made for penicillin and streptomycin. Many drugs go through the history of initial enthusiastic acclaim for their curative properties, followed by some sad experiences with toxic reactions associated with misuse of the drugs or from use in drug-sensitive patients. It is, of course, foolish to speak of non-toxic drugs, particularly those used in chemotherapy, which are bound to be toxic for both host and parasite. The best that can be done is to provide drugs with as high a therapeutic index as possible and penicillin is perhaps closer to the ideal in this respect than any other chemotherapeutic agent.

Toxicities are classified and discussed in what follows according to the parts of the body affected.

(B) General Effects on the Whole Body

(1) Drug Fever

The occurrence of fever as a toxic response to the sulfa drugs is often difficult to dissociate from fever accompanying the infection being treated. When it occurs late in the course of treatment after the high temperature accompanying the disease has subsided, it is reasonably certain that the reaction is one of sensitization to the drug. This is confirmed if the fever disappears on withholding the drug and reappears when given at a later date.

Boyd and Pratten[783] have studied the common sulfa drugs with the exception of sulfadiazine and found that sulfapyridine is the only one with an antipyretic effect on fever artificially induced in animals with peptone. Sulfanilamide, "Promin" and sulfacetamide showed varying degrees of pyrexia in normal animals. Such reactions do not correspond with clinically observed "drug fever" which occurs with all the sulfa drugs, but less with sulfadiazine than any of the others.

(C) Toxic Reactions to the Blood

(1) Hemolytic Anemia

In order to get experimental evidence, Latven and Welch[1521] fed high amounts of drug to mice and measured the average blood level of drug which produced a 50% incidence of hemolytic anemia.   They found 2.8 mg. per 100 cc. for sulfapyridine; 33 mg. per 100 cc. for sulfadiazine and 31 mg. per 100 cc. for sulfamerazine.

Moeschlin[1794] studied a number of drugs fed at high dosage levels to mice and found that sulfanilamide was much more toxic to erythrocytes than the other drugs.   Sulfapyridine was next and sulfathiazole least toxic.   Other drugs such as "Prontosil", "Uleron" and sulfamethylthiazole were intermediate in toxicity.

Higgins[1304] found that "Promin" and "Promizole" caused a high incidence of hypochromic anemia in rats but folic acid (vitamin Bc) was able to prevent its appearance or cure the anemia after it had been induced.

(2) Agranulocytosis

Damage to the bone marrow with resulting loss of white blood cells responsible for defense against infections has been one of the severe toxic reactions ascribed to most of the sulfonamide drugs.   It is more common in the case of sulfapyridine than sulfathiazole and particularly sulfadiazine.   Nixon, Eckert and Holmes[1855], while not denying that the drug might on occasion cause agranulocytosis, advocated that sulfadiazine therapy be continued in cases of severe agranulocytosis so as to counteract bacterial sepsis during a period of temporary bone marrow depression and until return of normal white cell defense of the body.   They gave three case histories of severe agranulocytosis, occurring during treatment with sulfadiazine, which were successfully treated with large doses of sulfadiazine.   In each case, there was a period where no polymorphonuclear leukocytes were observable in the blood smears, but subsequent recovery to a normal blood picture occurred.

Park[1893] noted that neutropenia (which culminates in agranulocytosis) bears the characteristics of an allergy.   Such cases usually develop after the drugs have been given a week or longer.   Since most infections which are going to respond to a sulfa drug, do so within a week, he advised continuing the drug only this long and thereby avoiding the serious consequences of sensitizing the patient to the drug.   Spicer, Daft, Sebrell and Ashburn[2244], and Daft and Sebrell[945] found that granulocytopenia and leukopenia produced in rats by feeding purified diets and sulfa drugs, could be cured by liver or liver extracts and by crystalline folic acid.

It would seem preferable to treat agranulocytosis occurring during sulfa drug treatment, with penicillin rather than risk further sensitivity reactions.   Agranulocytosis has responded well to penicillin in a small number of cases[2640].

(3) Cyanosis

Cyanosis was seen rather frequently in patients with large doses of sulfanilamide, but very rarely in patients treated with sulfathiazole or sulfadiazine.

(4) Thrombopenic Purpurea

This toxic reaction, which frequently culminates in fatal hemorrhage, is fortunately of very rare occurrence.   No statistics on the incidence of the reaction are possible but there have been occasional case reports.   Judging from these, sulfathiazole is the most frequent offender but all the common sulfa drugs have been implicated.   There seems to be little correlation between the amount of drug given and the occurrence of the reaction. Kracke and Townsend[1481] reported a fatal case resulting from 10 Gm. sulfathiazole given in a two day period.   They found only ten cases reported in the literature up to 1943; two from sulfanilamide, five from sulfapyridine and three from sulfathiazole, to which they added two more from sulfathiazole. There is some evidence to suggest that the effect is brought about by a sensitization. Subsequent administration of very small doses of the drug may then cause complete disappearance of blood platelets.

(D) Toxic Effects on the Nervous System

Little[1587] reviewed the literature to 1942 on toxicity of the sulfonamide drugs to the nervous system. His conclusions that sulfanilamide was least toxic to the nervous system and "some of the newer derivatives" most toxic, does not stand in good agreement with facts since he included sulfadiazine which appears to be considerably less toxic to the nervous system than its predecessors, sulfathiazole, sulfapyridine and sulfanilamide.

(1) Temporary Disturbances

Sulfanilamide causes a very high incidence of such toxic reactions to the central nervous system as headache, dizziness, ringing in the ears, depression, mental confusion and optic disturbances. These are very rare with sulfadiazine. Peripheral neuritis is extremely rare with either drug[745].

(2) Peripheral Neuritis

One of the serious toxic reactions of the sulfonamide drugs, which is fortunately of rare occurrence, is damage to the peripheral nerves causing such manifestations as numbness and tingling in the fingers, wrist-drop, foot-drop, deafness and sciatica.

Bieter, et al.[735] studied a number of sulfonamide drugs in chickens in an attempt to correlate experimental nerve damage with the clinical findings. No very exact parallel was found, but actual damage to peripheral nerves was produced in the chickens and demonstrated by pathological study. As a result of this study, the compounds were arranged in the following ascending order of toxicity: sulfanilamide, sulfapyridine, sulfathiazole, sulfamethylthiazole, N^4-sulfanilyl-N^1,N^1-dimethylsulfanilamide ("Uleron"), and sulfaphenylthiazole. High levels of the drugs were demonstrated in the peripheral nerves, particularly the sciatic nerve.

Sulfathiazole was shown to be dangerous when applied locally to the brain, where it caused death by epileptic convulsions[1371, 1758, 1925, 1926, 2403]. It also caused sciatica when applied locally near the sciatic nerve. Other sulfonamides in current use do not have these effects[2403] except in very high concentrations, or in the form of their sodium salts[1371]. Intravenous sodium sulfathiazole produced convulsions at a level of 88 mg.% in the blood, while sodium sulfadiazine did not produce convulsions at 107 mg.% free and 260 mg.% total drug in the blood[1371]. Although the sodium salts of sulfapyridine and sulfadiazine produced a pronounced effect on the electroencephalogram in experimental animals, the free drugs were without this effect except for sulfathiazole[784]. The sodium salt of sulfapyridine when injected intramuscularly produced nerve palsies if close to nerve trunks[1022].

Sulfamethylthiazole, while it appeared to be of equal or greater potency than sulfathiazole in curing infections, was suddenly withdrawn from further clinical trial in this country when it became evident that it caused about a 2% incidence of peripheral neuritis among patients treated with it[794]. Although the drug was banned in this country its clinical use continued in Europe. Gsell[1216] reported two cases of polyneuritis among 50 pneumonia patients treated with the drug. One patient had received 43 Gm., the other 19 Gm. of sulfamethylthiazole. In another series 2 out of 151 patients developed polyneuritis from the drug[2546]. Gsell[1216] stated that in therapeutic doses only "Uleron" and sulfamethylthiazole produce these effects, but that in very high doses any of the drugs may do so.

In the case of sulfadiazine, the incidence of peripheral neuritis following its use is extremely low. Blankenhorn[745] noted an incidence of 6 cases of multiple peripheral neuritis among 600 cases treated with sulfonamide drugs including sulfadiazine, or an incidence of 1%. This was compared with an incidence of 0.85% among general admissions not treated with sulfa drugs. It was further noted that alcoholism or deficiency states may have contributed. Also of interest was the fact that of 8 cases of mild peripheral neuritis occurring spontaneously and subsequently treated with sulfonamide drugs, only one became worse under treatment.

Since the action of sulfonamide drugs on the intestinal flora results in inhibition of those organisms which normally synthesize part of the body requirements of B vitamins and other essential factors, there may be danger of producing avitaminosis when sulfa drugs are given over long periods. This has been demonstrated in rats by several groups of workers[743, 943, 945, 1476, 1569, 1851, 2416, 2576]. Avitaminosis may possibly be a factor in nervous disorders ascribed to the sulfonamides.

(3) Psychoses

Mental disturbances caused by the sulfa drugs are very difficult to distinguish from similar effects caused by the disease being treated. Such effects do occur, particularly with sulfanilamide, where the patient may become disoriented, suffer from severe headache, show mental depression or simulate alcoholic intoxication. For this reason, ambulatory patients taking sulfanilamide should never be allowed to drive a car or operate machinery where they could do serious harm through onset of mental disturbances of this kind.

Sulfathiazole and sulfadiazine[2060] are said not to cause mental disturbances or to interfere with the performance of heavy manual or mental work when used prophylactically. When sulfadiazine was given prophylactically to healthy men, no differences in eye-hand coordination and reaction times were observed[1960]. In rats sulfapyridine and sulfathiazole were depressants while sulfadiazine, even in massive doses, stimulated muscular performance[1653].

(4) Encephalopathy

Applebaum and Nelson[665] noted four cases of encephalopathy among 141 cases of meningitis treated with sulfadiazine. This they ascribed to the effect of the drug, but admit that it was difficult to differentiate from the effects of the disease. The patients became stuporous or progressed to deep coma but "occasionally there were delirium, hallucinations or convulsions".

(E) Toxic Action on the Kidney

(1) Mechanical Blockage

The most serious toxic effects of the more potent sulfa drugs involve damage to the kidney. With drugs of low solubility, such as sulfapyridine, sulfathiazole, sulfadiazine and sulfamerazine, this involves crystallization of the drug or its acetyl derivative in the collecting tubules or elsewhere in the kidney. The first evidence of damage is commonly the appearance of blood in the urine which may be so slight as to be detectable only by microscopic examination (microscopic hematuria) or readily seen (gross hematuria).

This may be followed by partial stoppage of the flow of urine (oliguria) and accumulation of nitrogen waste products in the blood (azotemia). With further crystallization of the drug, complete stoppage of urine flow results (anuria) and death is caused by uremic poisoning unless the flow of urine is restored by emergency treatment. Flank pain associated with renal colic is another manifestation of severe kidney damage from the drugs.

Gross hematuria is a danger sign that calls for stoppage of the drug while if the more serious complications ensue, emergency treatment must be instituted.

In the case of sulfanilamide, the solubility of both it and its acetyl derivative is sufficient so that there have been few, if any, cases of precipitation in the kidney from administration of therapeutic doses. Sulfapyridine, on the other hand, has a bad record in this respect. Coupled with other toxic reactions, there is no longer much justification for its medical use, now that better drugs are available. The only safe way to give sulfapyridine is to maintain such a large urinary output that the solubility of the drug in the urine will not be exceeded. This may be difficult especially in the tropics where comparatively little urine is excreted because of excessive sweating.

(a) *Alkalization as a Preventive Measure*

In Chapter XI, the degree of ionization of the various sulfonamides is discussed. It will be evident that when the pH of the medium exceeds the pKa of the drug, a rapidly increasing amount of the drug is ionized. Since the salts (or ions) of the sulfonamides are enormously more soluble than the molecular form, this means that the solubility of the drug increases considerably when the pH is above the pKa of the drug.

Climenko, Barlow, and Wright[885]; Fox and Rose[1122]; and Fox, Jensen and Mudge[1121] brought these facts to the attention of clinicians. They pointed out that sulfanilamide and sulfapyridine are such weak acids that it is not possible to materially increase their solubility in urine through increase of pH. They showed in the case of sulfathiazole and sulfadiazine, however, that administration of sodium bicarbonate, so as to maintain an alkaline urine, will prevent crystallization of these drugs in the kidney.

Jensen[1386] studied these effects experimentally in dogs; he found that while sulfanilamide and sulfapyridine had less than a twofold increase in solubility in changing from unbuffered water to urine at pH 7.4; sulfathiazole increased in solubility 3.6-fold and sulfadiazine 35-fold.

Robinson, Seigel and Graessle[2039] showed that sulfapyrazine caused a greater incidence of kidney concretions in rats than did sulfadiazine. This might be expected in view of its lower solubility. However, when sodium bicarbonate was incorporated in the diet so as to maintain the urinary pH above 7.0, no crystallization took place.

Peterson, Goodwin, and Finland made an extensive investigation of the urinary excretion of sulfadiazine[1910]. They found a urine flow in excess of 50 cc. per hour adequate in normal individuals for excretion of the usual dosage of sulfadiazine, *i.e.*, 1 Gm. every four hours. Great increase in urinary output, as high as 1200 cc. per hr., did not materially increase sulfadiazine excretion, nor did intravenous administration of 50% glucose, nor administration of large amounts of urea by mouth. Intravenous saline did not produce a rapid increase in output of either urine or drug. The best way of markedly increasing the output of drug was to give large doses of sodium bicarbonate sufficient to make the urine highly alkaline (pH above 7.5). This was suggested as a means of quickly eliminating the drug in the management of drug rashes, fevers, or blood disorders. On the other hand, if high blood levels are desirable, an acid urine as obtained through administration of ammonium chloride might be a preferable means to the end rather than increased intake of drug.

For combating hematuria, oliguria or other renal complications, they recommended greatly increasing the volume of urine and lowering the concentration of drug in it by intravenous injection of large volumes of 5 or 10% glucose solution. This could be supplemented by ingestion of large volumes of water, if well tolerated. By preventing reabsorption of water and concentrating the drug in the urine beyond its solubility, deposition would be prevented, yet the drug would not be flushed out of the blood stream.

Fox, et al.[1121] prevented renal obstruction in two patients given 25 and 30 Gm. sodium sulfadiazine in one intravenous dose, by preliminary large doses of sodium bicarbonate. Urinary level of sulfadiazine rose as high as 788 mg. per 100 cc. without crystal formation when the pH was above 7.5.

Gilligan, Garb and Plummer[1172] studied the effect of administering sufficient sodium bicarbonate to maintain urinary alkalinity in patients receiving sulfadiazine. They found that before use of sodium bicarbonate 4.8% of the patients developed mild to severe renal complications and 30% crystalluria, but of 350 patients receiving 6 Gm. sulfadiazine orally per day whose urine was kept neutral or alkaline, none developed crystalluria and there was no evidence of renal irritation or urinary tract obstruction attributable to the drug. The amount of sodium bicarbonate necessary to achieve this result varied with different individuals from 10 to 20 Gm. per day. They recommended for routine use an initial dose of 6 Gm. to be taken with the first dose of sulfadiazine followed by 2.6 Gm. (40 grains) of sodium bicarbonate at four hour intervals, and continued 24 hours after sulfadiazine is stopped. Alkalinity of the urine should be checked with litmus or nitrazine paper and additional sodium bicarbonate given, if the paper does not turn blue. Daily volume of urine should be 1500 cc. or more.

These authors pointed out that, whereas, the solubility of acetylsulfadiazine increases from 20mg. per 100 cc. at pH 5.5 to 512 mg. per 100 cc. at pH 7.5, acetylsulfathiazole shows only an increase from 7 mg. to 28 mg. per 100 cc. at the respective pH levels. Alkali therapy is, therefore, less effective in combating the urinary complications attendant with use of sulfathiazole. Solubility of acetylsulfapyridine increases only from 33 to 37 mg. per 100 cc. over the same pH range and sodium bicarbonate has proven to be ineffective in preventing renal complications from sulfapyridine.

Barnes and Kawaichi[705] stressed the importance of maintaining alkalinity of the urine and assuring sufficient volume when giving sulfathiazole or sulfadiazine. They stated that there is an unexplained higher incidence of urinary concretions from these drugs among the Oriental races as compared with the white race.

Gilligan, Dingwall, and McDermott[1171] recommended alkalization of the urine by giving 500–1500 cc. of M./6 sodium lactate intravenously during prophylactic therapy with sodium sulfadiazine in patients undergoing gastric or intestinal resections. The sodium sulfadiazine was preferably given with the sodium lactate solution. When the pH of the urine was above 7.0, only 2% of 265 specimens showed crystalluria, as compared with 56% of 76 acid urines.

Trevett and Blackman[2354] made an experimental investigation in rabbits to find the source of hematuria from administration of sulfathiazole. Hemorrhages were found in the renal pelves, ureters, or bladder and were apparently caused by crystals penetrating the mucosa. No evidence was found of injury to the glomeruli. Hematuria was less prevalent in rabbits having an alkaline urine than in those with an acid urine.

Potassium bicarbonate because of its combined diuretic and alkalizing effect was used successfully on pneumonia patients with severe heart damage who were undergoing treatment with sulfadiazine[2612].

(2) Kidney Damage of Non-Mechanical Types

Murphy, *et al.*[1817] pointed out that kidney damage by mechanical stoppage through crystallization of the drugs, while the most common, was by no means the only toxic effect of the drugs on the kidney. They classified these other toxic lesions as "(a) simple tubular degeneration; (b) necrotic tubular degeneration; and (c) glomerular changes." In some cases these changes accompanied mechanical obstructions.

Clinical and pathological data were presented on 14 cases, of whom 13 died and were studied post-mortem. Sulfathiazole had been employed in six of these cases, sulfadiazine in three, sulfanilamide in three, sulfacetamide and sulfathiazole in one, and sulfathiazole and sulfadiazine in one. There seemed to be no correlation between total dosage and the injury; dosage resulting in fatality varied between 0.6 Gm. and 41 Gm.

(F) Toxic Action on the Liver

Peterson, Deutsch and Finland[1906] reviewed the literature on reported liver damage caused by the sulfonamide drugs. While they did not deny that these drugs have caused damage to the livers of sensitive individuals, they believe that most of the reported liver damage has been associated with the disease rather than with the drug—particularly in the case of sulfadiazine and sulfathiazole. They deliberately treated 37 patients suffering from various types of liver damage with sulfadiazine and sulfathiazole Where there was acute hepatitis associated with a bacterial infection, the liver function improved as the drug cured the infection. In cases of chronic hepatitis, the improvement was not as dramatic but neither was the hepatitis aggravated by the drug. Other common toxic effects of these drugs were more frequent in patients suffering from portal cirrhosis and were twice as frequent with sulfathiazole as with sulfadiazine. This was probably the result of lowered ability of the liver to detoxify the drugs. They concluded that the presence of liver damage was no bar to the administration of these drugs and that sulfadiazine was the drug of choice.

Leach and Forbes[284, 1532] expected to find an accentuation of liver necrosis from combined administration of sulfa drugs and carbon tetrachloride or chloroform. Instead, they found that the sulfa drugs (sulfanilamide, sulfapyridine, and sulfathiazole) actually protected rats against otherwise fatal liver necrosis caused by CCl_4 or $CHCl_3$! Sulfanilic acid failed to protect.

(G) Toxic Action on the Heart

French[1132] stated that he was able to produce interstitial myocarditis in experimental mice, rats, and rabbits from "Neoprontosil", sulfanilamide, and the sodium salts of sulfapyridine and sulfathiazole. The frequency of the effect was increased by size of dose and duration of treatment. Similar findings on autopsy of humans were noted.

(H) Skin Reactions

(1) Classification

The allergic sensitization of patients to the sulfonamide drugs has been noted with each drug, but seems most common with sulfathiazole. When given orally, skin reactions of various kinds may appear and the highest incidence of reactions seems to occur between the fifth and eighth day of administration. These reactions vary in severity from mild erythematous or morbilliform eruptions to maculopapular, erythema multiforme, vesicular, bulbous, urticarial, exfoliative and purpuric[2383]. The latter two are frequently fatal.

Such skin manifestations are usually acompanied by other toxic reactions such as drug fever and chills, but either may occur independently of the other. Soon after a patient has recovered from a rash, exposure to the sun will frequently cause a severe recurrence. Such photosensitivity is most common with sulfanilamide, sulfapyridine and sulfathiazole sensitivity. It appears to be gradually lost over a three month period, while the original sensitivity to administration of the drug is retained for long periods[1039].

Sensitization is also commonly caused by contact of the drugs with the skin for prolonged periods such as by the application of sulfonamide ointments to skin infection. Such sensitizations may be so severe as to prevent therapeutic use of the drugs for a blood stream infection at a later date[2315]. The eruption may start at the site of application and remain more or less localized or it may extend over the whole body. Frequently the eruption resembles the skin disease being treated. The incidence is about 1.0%[1591].

Appearance of rash is usually considered a warning to discontinue the drug immediately, yet if the disease being treated has not had time to respond adequately to the drug, the physician may be confronted with a dilemma of whether to risk the life of the patient by withholding the drug, or risk fatal poisoning by continuing the drug. Erskine[1040] states that if the condition is one of "8th-day allergic sensitivity", if Werner's test is positive, and it is desirable to continue medication, he does so in full dosage. If further treatment of the disease is not necessary, he still continues the drug, but in half the dose, for two or three days so as to desensitize the patient (see below).

Weiner[2413] differentiates types of skin reactions: *Dermatitis medicamentosa* is the kind of sensitivity developed by oral administration or by absorption into the blood stream from topically applied drug. In this type of sensitivity negative patch tests are to be expected, but positive with passive transfer reactions (Prausnitz-Kustner). In *dermativis venenata*, or contact dermatitis from topical application of the drug, patch tests should be positive. Weiner believes that considerable confusion exists among medical men, other than dermatologists, as to these differences in type of sensitivity. He believes that a clearer conception of the processes involved would be of value in management of clinical cases.

Miescher[1778] discussed at length the various types of sensitivity to sulfathiazole and pointed out reactions that seemed to distinguish the action of sulfathiazole from that of other sulfa drugs. The *nodosal exanthemata* from sulfathiazole appeared more often from treatment of some diseases than others. Four out of 26 cases of meningitis treated with sulfathiazole showed the reaction while only 1 in 1,000 cases of gonorrhea was noticed. The reaction appears commonly on the third or fourth day of treatment and may regress under continued treatment. It does not usually recur on subsequent treatment with the drug. Miescher suggested that the sulfathiazole may act as an activator of other toxic or allergic substances which tend to produce the nodules. Shaffer, et al.[2177] have reached similar conclusions.

A further observation that has a bearing on this subject arose in the course of the Navy prophylactic study using sulfadiazine where it was found that the incidence of mild dermal reactions was four times as great among new recruits who were being immunized to typhoid, tetanus, etc. as among seasoned personnel[2647].

It was also observed in this study[2609] that a few patients with severe dermal reactions seemed to have sulfadiazine fixed in the tissues as indicated by the recovery of the drug from bullae in the skin and in considerable amounts from the blood and urine several days after injection of the last dose. These patients apparently handled sulfadiazine in an abnormal manner and became sensitized, however, about half of the group having dermal reactions were able to continue prophylaxis after withholding the drug for two weeks.

(2) Test for Hypersensitivity

Leftwich[1542] described an intradermal test which demonstrated hypersensitivity to the sulfonamide drugs. It has been applied to cases showing drug fever or *dermatitis medicamentosa* but its usefulness in contact dermatitis sensitivity remains to be seen. Leftwich reasoned that since the sensitivity was very similar to serum sickness, it was probably caused by a combination of the drug with serum protein such as had been demonstrated to occur by Davis[953]. The sulfonamide may act as a hapten, which when attached to a plasma protein, may sensitize the patient specifically for that drug. He reasoned that such an antigenic substance was in the blood of an individual who had received a sulfa drug for several days whether or not signs of sensitivity had appeared. To test the hypothesis, blood was withdrawn from a patient who had received sulfathiazole for 7 days and who showed 4 mg. per 100 cc. sulfathiazole in the whole blood. The serum was injected intradermally into 4 patients who had shown definite signs of hypersensitivity to sulfathiazole. A typical allergic wheal was formed in each case.

A thorough study was then made using sera from patients receiving sulfanilamide, sulfathiazole, sulfamerazine and sulfadiazine who had received the drug long enough so that their blood cultures were negative for the original infecting organisms. As controls, serums from the same patients were used which were taken either before the sulfa drug was started or during convalescence when the blood was free of drug. Test and control serums (0.5 cc.) were injected intracutaneously into the flexor surface of the forearm using tuberculin syringes. The size of the wheal and diameter of the erythema were measured immediately and at intervals of 5 minutes for 20 minutes. When negative (and in control subjects) the increase in wheal size was only 1 to 2 mm. to a total diameter of 7 or 8 mm. Any redness was slight and no more than 20 mm. in diameter. Positive tests showed an immediate increase in diameter of wheal to 12 to 18 mm. with intense erythema 30 to 40 mm. in diameter. The maximum reaction occurred in 15 minutes and all traces had disappeared in 90 minutes. A difference in size between control and test wheal of at least 4 mm. in diameter was the criterion for positivity.

Of 30 definitely hypersensitive patients 18 were sensitive to sulfathiazole alone, 3 to sulfanilamide alone, 2 to sulfadiazine alone, and 4 to sulfamerazine alone. One was sensitive to sulfapyridine and sulfathiazole, one to sulfanilamide and sulfathiazole and one to sulfadiazine and sulfathiazole. The especially high incidence of sensitivity to sulfathiazole, Leftwich thinks, may be the result of its greater protein binding power. (This, if true, would mean that sulfamerazine should show a greater incidence of sensitivity than sulfathiazole because 84% is bound as against 75% for sulfathiazole; however, this does not seem borne out by clinical experience to date. While protein binding power may be a factor, it would seem that the thiazole ring is inherently more toxic than the pyrimidine ring.)

The low percentage of cases where the patient was sensitized to more than one drug differs from many loose statements in the literature to the effect that if a patient becomes sensitized to one sulfa drug he is usually sensitive to them all.

Leftwich noted one case of sensitivity to sulfamerazine, alone, in a group of 11 individuals who had never received a sulfa drug in any form. This individual had not had an allergic disease but every member of her family had a history of hay fever, asthma, or urticaria. Possibly this had a bearing on the false positive skin reaction.

Jackson[2561] reported difficulty in duplicating the work of Leftwich. Apparently more work is required to establish the test so that it can be generally applied.

Park[1892] investigated 40 cases of internal or eczematous allergy, induced by a sulfonamide drug, by skin tests and oral medication with other sulfonamides, sulfanilic acid and procaine. Twenty-four of the forty cases reacted only to the individual drug to which they were initially sensitized. Those individuals who were sensitive to more than one sulfa drug were allergic to all such drugs tested and sulfanilic acid. Sixteen cases were of this type. Fourteen of this group were tested with procaine and seven were allergic.

(3) Incidence of Skin Reactions

The incidence of contact dermatitis from topically applied sulfathiazole depends considerably on the type of infection being treated and the duration of treatment. It appears particularly high among allergic individuals and the drug should never be applied to patients with chronic eczema or psoriasis. In general civilian practice the incidence was 12 in 1,000 cases[1591], 12 in 218[949], 5 in 115[1786] and 2 in 86[2040] all from topical use of sulfathiazole. The average incidence therefore appears to be 2.2%.

The incidence of *dermatitis medicamentosa* from oral sulfathiazole appears to be about 5%, but again much depends on size of dosage and length of treatment. This compares with 1.46% of 9228 cases from the literature treated with sulfadiazine and 3.1% of 966 cases treated with sulfamerazine. The incidence of toxic rash from sulfaguanidine is very low when ordinary doses are given. Smith[2215] who used a massive dosage totaling 142 grams of the drug in a ten day course of treatment designed to eliminate *Sh. dysenteriae* (*Flexner*) from 44 carriers, found that 21 of the patients developed a maculopapular rash between the eighth and tenth day. Blood levels were 10 to 15 mg. per 100 cc., which are unusually high for sulfaguanidine. The sensitization was specific for sulfaguanidine; rash was not produced by sulfathiazole, sulfadiazine, or sulfanilamide.

(a) *Readministration of Drug*

The incidence of toxic fever and rash was claimed by Lyons and Balberor[1643] to reach 36% of 53 patients receiving a second course of treatment with sulfathiazole. Fortunately, others do not corroborate these results. Leftwich[1542] reported that a compilation, by Nelson from the records of Johns Hopkins Hospital, showed an incidence of 11.2% of febrile or cutaneous toxic reactions among 964 patients given their first administration of sulfathiazole, while of 133 patients who showed no toxic effects of the first course of treatment only 10.4% developed toxic reactions of this type to a second course of treatment with the drug. Fink and Wilson[1085] found no increased reactions among children given a second course of either sulfathiazole or sulfadiazine.

Talbot and Adcock[2308] noted an increased incidence in fever and rash among a small group of patients given a second course of sulfadiazine. Finland[1090] in study of a larger group did not verify this. Plummer and Wheeler[1936] found a slight increase from 8.0% to 11.5%.

Dowling and Lepper[1005] found that the incidence of fever after a second course of sulfathiazole increased to 16.7% as compared to 8.1% without previous administration of sulfa drugs. With sulfadiazine the corresponding percentages were 7.4% and 4.3%, and with sulfapyridine 9.1% and 3.6%. Since the incidence of fever on a second course of treatment where a different drug was used was no greater than on initial treatment, these authors advised changing to a different drug for a second course of chemotherapy.

Greene, *et al.*[1206] described clinical results in which 55 patients treated with sulfathiazole without the appearance of toxic reactions were retreated after a 9 to 10 day interval. Six toxic reactions were observed of which three were of a febrile type. This was approximately the same incidence as in 300 first administrations in which there were 30 toxic reactions. They, therefore, felt that readministration of the drug was no more dangerous then initial use. They also were led to believe that the majority of toxic reactions are not necessarily manifestations of hypersensitivity.

(4) Permanence of Sensitivity

Persons who have shown dermal sensitivity to a sulfonamide drug may retain this sensitivity for a long time. Reports have frequently been made[1039] of severe dermal reactions occurring from readministration of the drug a year or more after a drug rash was first experienced. Leftwich[1542] noted sensitivity to sulfanilamide in a patient exhibiting fever and rash from its use five years previously, but who had not received sulfa drugs in any form since that time. Not all persons retain their sensitivity, since in the extensive prophylactic studies using sulfadiazine in the Navy[2609] it was found that about half of the trainees who exhibited a mild dermal sensitivity were able to continue prophylaxis after a 2 week recess.

(5) Desensitization

The process of desensitization is still very much in the experimental stage and should not be attempted by the inept. Tate and Klorfajn[2315] reported that they successfully desensitized fourteen patients who were highly sensitive to topically applied sulfanilamide (as proved by positive patch tests) by giving the drug orally, 1 Gm. three times daily for an 8-day period. The severe dermatitis and fever, which appeared initially, gradually subsided and when the rash had disappeared, patch tests were negative and continued so for 4½ months at least.

The process of densensitization, while it appeared effective in the relatively small number of cases cited, is rough on the patient since not only is he subjected to the discomfort of a skin rash but may react with a high fever, deafness, visual disturbances mental confusion and blood changes. It would appear also that Tate and Klorfajn did not insufficiently emphasize the danger of agranulocytosis in such treatment although they recommended checking the leukocyte count. They also warned of danger of exposure to sunlight during desensitization.

They developed a plausible hypothesis to explain the process of epidermal sensitization and desensitization but since it is in need of much more experimental verification it will not be discussed.

Erskine[1040] used a similar scheme to desensitize patients showing "8th day allergic sensitivity," as noted above.

Park[1893] also claimed successful desensitization in a number of patients. In cases of sensitivity to orally administered drug in which the first sign was a rise in temperature he recommended starting with 0.1 Gm. of drug given orally four to five times daily. On successive days the dose was doubled until a mild allergic response was produced or until 1.0 Gm. per dose was being given on the fourth or fifth day. The dose was then held steady until the symptoms subsided. The average case required six weeks to desensitize.

In more sensitive cases it was necessary to start with much smaller doses. In the most sensitive the starting dose was 0.005 Gm. and nine weeks were required to work up to a 1 Gm. dose. In eczemas such high sensitivity appears to be the rule.

Apparently, from the case history given, it was customary to stop the drug in these highly sensitive cases until the reaction which had been induced subsided before continuing with the desensitization process.

The question of the permanence of the desensitization remains to be answered. In the case cited, mild reactions to full doses of the sensitizing drug were observed nine months and one year after desensitization.

(I) Toxic Reactions to the Eyes

(1) Visual Disturbances

Wagener[2386] has reviewed the literature to early 943 on the toxic effect of various sulfonamides on the eyes. Sulfanilamide, in particular, but also sulfapyridine, caused blurred vision (myopia) in a number of patients.

Depth perception seems to be adversely affected by prophylactic doses of sulfathiazole or sulfadiazine and makes it questionable whether men such as pilots, locomotive engineers, motorists and precision workers should be allowed to continue in active work when taking the drugs[2021]. In very rare cases optic neuritis may occur with temporary blindness. Most of the effects of the drugs on the eyes are transitory and clear up rapidly when the drug is stopped.

(2) Conjunctivitis

Sulfathiazole causes about a 1% incidence of conjunctivitis. This is probably an allergic reaction and is often associated with skin rash. This reaction is extremely rare with other sulfa drugs.

(J) Detoxification

Since there is some evidence that administration of sulfonamide compounds will interfere with synthesis of vitamins by the intestinal flora and further indications that there may be interference with utilization of certain of these in the enzymatic functions of the body, there have been several attempts to demonstrate the ability of the vitamins and essential amino acids to counteract some of the toxic manifestations of the sulfonamides. Martin, et al.[337, 2400] claimed to have secured a significant reduction in acute toxicities of sulfanilamide, sulfapyridine, and sulfathiazole through use of such agents as cystine, aminoacetic acid, calcium glucuronate and ascorbic acid. It was further claimed that this reduction in toxicity did not effect the therapeutic efficiency of the drug. Others[2569] were unable to show that ascorbic acid had any effect on the acute toxicity of sulfanilamide in guinea pigs.

Higgins[1304] has demonstrated in rats that increased vitamin intake and particularly of vitamin B_c (folic acid) will prevent or cure the anemias and other blood dyscrasias produced by "Promin" and "Promizole". Similar results have been obtained in counteracting the widespread toxic reactions in rats receiving sulfaguanidine or succinylsulfathiazole[682, 2545].

Strauss and Finland[2290] found that PABA had no effect on the course of sulfonamide rashes or fevers. It was shown,[2576] however, that PABA would alleviate the vitamin K deficiency produced in rats by prolonged feeding of sulfadiazine. This was apparently because PABA antagonized the sulfonamide inhibition of intestinal flora responsible for synthesis of vitamin K.

Chamelin and Funk[2510] found the acute toxicity of sulfanilamide for rats lowered by simultaneous administration of liver extract.

(K) Clinical Incidence of Toxic Reactions to Sulfonamide Drugs

Table 323, p. 577 gives a compilation from many sources of the clinical incidence of toxic reactions to various sulfonamide drugs when administered by the oral route in therapeutic doses. Because various clinicians differ materially in their reading and recording of toxic reactions and because toxic reactions of the drugs are frequently difficult to dissociate from effects of the disease being treated, there are wide discrepancies between different observers as to the incidence of toxic reactions and particularly those which occur rarely. In many publications no mention is made of these rarer toxic reactions. It is then questionable whether the reactions were absent or were overlooked by the observer. In other cases the clinician has probably attributed toxic reactions to the drug which were actually caused by the disease or has picked several occurrences of a particular toxic reaction out of a small group of cases and has arrived at a ficticiously high incidence. The true incidence of toxicity probably lies somewhere between the percentage obtained by dividing the total number of observed reactions by the total cases studied by all observers and the higher percentage obtained by dividing the total number of observed reactions by the total case histories of those authors reporting such reactions. This has been done and accounts for the range given in the table.

No range is shown for toxic reactions such as skin rash and drug fever because practically all observers report the incidence of these common reactions. In the case of a rare reaction such as cyanosis (rare for all the drugs except sulfanilamide) the one case reported for sulfadiazine in a series of 69, gives an incidence of 1.45%. This is, obviously, a distorted picture and the true incidence lies somewhere between this value and 0.01% which is obtained by dividing the one recorded case of cyanosis by 10,525, the total number of cases receiving sulfadiazine observed for toxic reactions of any kind. On the other hand, cyanosis resulting from administration of sulfanilamide probably has an incidence closer to 20.22% than to the lower level shown because mild cyanosis was accepted as of such common occurrence as to be unworthy of mention in publications.

Some of the outstanding differences between the toxic reactions of the various drugs which seem worthy of comment are:

1) Sulfadiazine seems to be generally less toxic than any other sulfa drug employed for systemic therapy with the possible exception of sulfamethazine, on which too few cases are recorded to be highly significant.

2) Despite the lower dosage recommended for sulfamerazine the incidence of toxic reactions appears to be significantly higher than for sulfadiazine.

3) Incidence of sensitivity reactions (drug fever, conjunctivitis, and skin rash) appears greatest with sulfathiazole.

4) The high incidence of kidney involvement by sulfapyrazine, of nausea with sulfapyridine and sulfathiazole, and of cyanosis and vertigo with sulfanilamide are toxic reactions characteristic of these drugs. Edema seems peculiar to sulfamethazine.

5) It should not be inferred because a toxic reaction is unlisted or given a zero incidence that it is unreported for a particular drug. Individual case reports of such reactions were ignored because of lack of information on the total number of cases in which the single reaction was observed.

TABLE 321

a. Comparative Clinical Results Pneumococcal Pneumonia

Drug	No. Cases	Gross Mortality		References
		No.	%	
Sulfadiazine	1,755	174	9.91	770, 798, 1001, 1034, 1090, 1093, 1106, 1109, 2176
Sulfamerazine	466	32	6.9	651, 1002, 1106, 1107, 1235, 1242
Sulfamethazine	432	22	5.1	1002, 1375, 1626, 1645, 1766, 1803, 1902
Sulfanilamide	622	138	22.2	1959 and others not listed
Sulfapyrazine	40	0	0	706, 2066
Sulfapyridine	17,025	1,626	9.55	656, 770, 992, 993, 1001, 1089, 1091, 1109, 1766, 1803, 1899, 1959, 2047, 2107, 2383, 2388
Sulfathiazole	10,303	961	9.32	770, 833, 1001, 1089, 1109, 1959, 2268, 2388, 2461

TABLE 322

a. Comparative Clinical Results
   Meningococcal Meningitis

Drug	No. Cases	Gross Mortality		References
		No.	%	
Sulfadiazine	2518	81	3.21	665, 948, 978, 1058, 1090, 1307, 1548, 2314, 2376
Sulfamerazine	347	20	5.8	651, 1002, 1107, 1157, 1235, 1548, 2613
Sulfamethazine	51	4	7.8	1002, 1375, 1645
Sulfapyridine	985	78	7.92	770, 804, 1268, 2239, 2451

TABLE 323

k. Clinical Incidence of Toxic Reactions to Sulfonamide Drugs

Toxic Reaction	Succinyl-Sulfathiazole Cases	%	Sulfadiazine Cases	%	Sulfaguanidine Cases	%	Sulfamerazine Cases	%	Sulfamethazine Cases	%	Sulfanilamide Cases	%	Sulfapyrazine Cases	%	Sulfapyridine Cases	%	Sulfathiazole Cases	%
Fever	374	0.54	9820	1.55	1029	2.14	1483	3.98	540	2.04	3627	4.89–5.11	539	1.47–1.67	6313	2.28–2.78	5008	4.74–4.98
Thrombocytopenic Purpura			3906	0.02–0.05			200	0.07–0.50			114	0.026–0.88						
Hemolytic Anemia			2483	0.02–0.08	1017	0	564	0.21–0.53	217	0	2147	1.08–1.92	154	0	5441	0.94–1.32	2641	0.15–0.32
Leukopenia			9438	1.37	1017	0	1435	2.35–2.44	389	1.13–1.80	1214	0.61–1.92	517	0.33–0.39	5304	1.58–2.28	4350	1.08–1.30
Agranulocytosis			2240	0.05–0.22	1017	0	159	0	275	0	1300	0.026–0.079	259	0	2537	0.18–0.55	1344	0.04–0.15
Cyanosis			69	0.01–1.45					361	0.16–0.28	717	3.84–20.22	149	0	854	0.53–4.81		
Peripheral Neuritis			660	0			555	0	231	0	300	0.026–0.33	380	0	608	0.03–0.33	1582	0.11–0.38
Psychoses	350	0.57	1804	0.41–2.38			1197	0.81–1.01	376	0.16–0.27	100	0.052–2.00	412	0.32–0.49	3345	1.84–4.22	2533	0.68–1.42
Arthralgia	250	0.27–0.40	1357	0.01–0.07			678	0.47–1.03					132	0				
Nausea and Vomiting			4911	1.03–2.20	600	0.09–0.17	1416	3.04	582	1.55	603	0.90–5.67	539	0.33–0.37	4792	25.1–40.2	3774	7.54–10.50
Vertigo											300	2.20–27.67						
Encephalopathy	100	0	1498	0.05–0.33			1083	0.95–1.29	169	0.32–1.18			614	1.47	1424	0.39–2.12	716	0.15–1.12
Hematuria Gross	20	0	4098	0.37–0.95	711	0.38–0.56	878	3.38–5.70	236	0.16–0.42			482	41.9–53.4	4804	3.08–4.92	3532	4.15–6.20
Hematuria Microscopic			10067	2.06	826	0.09–0.12	735	1.01–2.04	621	0.48			539	1.8–2.04	6215	1.76–2.17	4466	1.06–1.26
Oliguria, Azotemia, Anuria			9134	0.75							214	0.11–1.87						
Skin Rash	374	0.54	10525	1.49	1061	2.82	1483	3.58	598	2.04	3783	2.62	539	0.16–0.18	7675	2.11	5256	4.26
Photosensitivity			1357	0.02–0.15														
Hepatitis	100	0.27–1.00	3480	0.03–0.09			278	0.06–0.36	68	0	1617	0.24–0.55	132	0	869	0.04–0.35	1968	0.06–0.15
Conjunctivitis													132	0	200	0	3088	0.66–1.13
Yellow Vision																		
Edema			660	0.02–0.32					77	0.48–3.89								
Leukocytosis																		
References	880, 1945, 2223		665, 948, 1001, 1004, 1006, 1034, 1090, 1093, 1109, 1307, 1548, 1610, 1803, 1933, 1936		809, 811, 933, 1884, 2215, 2223		651, 874, 1002, 1106, 1107, 1235, 1242, 1548, 2613		1002, 1375, 1627, 1645, 1650, 1766, 1803, 1902		797, 1234, 1610, 2198, 2201		706, 1109, 2064, 2066, 2358, 2649, 2652		656, 711, 797, 1001, 1006, 1089, 1108, 1109, 1506, 1596, 1610, 1803, 1848, 1899, 2047, 2213		1001, 1002, 1006, 1089, 1108, 1109, 1610, 1959, 2250, 2383, 2652	

The following journals have been searched through the date of issue indicated:

American Journal of the Medical Sciences, The...................... Dec., 1944
American Review of Tuberculosis, The............................ Dec., 1944
Annals of Internal Medicine..................................... Dec., 1944
Archives of Biochemistry.. Dec., 1944
Archives of Internal Medicine................................... Nov., 1944

Bacteriological Reviews... Dec., 1944
Berichte der deutschen chemischen Gesellschaft...................... Nov., 1943
Biochemical Journal..Vol. 38, #2, 1944
British Chemical and Physiological Abstracts..................... Oct., 1944
British Medical Journal... Dec. 16, 1944
Bulletin of the Johns Hopkins Hospital.......................... Nov., 1944
Bulletin of War Medicine.. Sept., 1944

Chemical Abstracts.. Nov. 20, 1944
Chemical Reviews.. Oct., 1944

Helvetica Chimica Acta.. Nov., 1941

Journal of the American Chemical Society........................ Dec., 1944
Journal of the American Medical Association..................... Dec. 23, 1944
Journal of the American Pharmaceutical Association.............. Dec., 1944
Journal of the American Veterinary Medical Association.......... Dec., 1944
Journal of Bacteriology... Nov., 1944
Journal of Biological Chemistry, The............................ Dec., 1944
Journal of the Chemical Society (London)........................ Oct., 1944
Journal of Clinical Investigation, The.......................... Nov., 1944
Journal of the Franklin Institute............................... Dec., 1944
Journal of Industrial and Engineering Chemistry................. Dec., 1944
Journal of Laboratory and Clinical Medicine, The................ Dec., 1944
Journal of Organic Chemistry, The............................... Sept., 1944
Journal of Pharmacology and Experimental Therapeutics, The...... Oct., 1944
Journal für praktische Chemie .... May, 1943
Journal of the Society of Chemical Industry (Chemistry and Industry).... Dec. 9, 1944

Lancet, The... Dec. 23, 1944

Nature.. Dec. 16, 1944

Proceedings of the Society of Experimental Biology and Medicine........ Dec., 1944
Proceedings of the Staff Meetings of the Mayo Clinic................... Dec. 13, 1944

Recueil des travaux chimiques des Pays-Bas...................... May, 1941

Science... Dec. 29, 1944

U. S. Public Health Reports..................................... Dec. 29, 1944

Veterinary Medicine... Jan., 1945

War Medicine.. Dec., 1944

References

Largely Chemical

1 Abbott Laboratories (Raiziss, G. W., Clemence, L. W., and Kremens, A. J.): U. S. 2,229,127 (Jan. 21, 1941).
2 —— (Raiziss, G. W., Clemence, L. W., and Freifelder, M.): U. S. 2,256,575 (Sept. 23, 1941).
3 —— (Raiziss, G. W., and Clemence, L. W.): U. S. 2,248,283 (July 8, 1941).
4 Adams, R., Long, P. H., and Jeanes, A.: *J. Am. Chem. Soc.*, **61**, 2346 (1939).
5 ——, ——, and Johanson, A. J.: *Ibid.*, 2342 (1939).
6 Aktien-Ges. vorm. B. Siegfried: Swiss 198,137 (Sept. 1, 1938); *Chem. Abst.*, **33**, 3530.
7 ——: Swiss 199,674-5 (Nov. 16, 1938); *Chem. Abst.*, **33**, 3536.
8 Alba Pharmaceutical Co. (Klarer, J.): U. S. 2,247,913 (July 1, 1941).
9 American Cyanamid Co. (Anderson, G. W., and Roblin, R. O., Jr.): U. S. 2,259,721 (Oct. 21, 1941); Brit. 551,122 (Mar. 11, 1943).
10 —— (Climenko, D. R.): U. S. 2,238,973 (Apr. 22, 1941).
11 —— (Northey, E. H., and Hultquist, M. E.): U. S. 2,245,292 (June 10, 1941).
12 —— (Roblin, R. O., Jr.): U. S. 2,254,191 (Aug. 26, 1941).
13 —— (Roblin, R. O., Jr., and Williams, J. H.): U. S. 2,227,400 (Dec. 31, 1940).
14 —— (Williams, J. H.): U. S. 2,243,324 (May 27, 1941).
15 —— (Williams, J. H.): U. S. 2,240,383 (Apr. 29, 1941).
16 —— (Winnek, P. S.): U. S. 2,209,243 (July 23, 1940).
17 —— (Winnek, P. S.): U. S. 2,218,490 (Oct. 15, 1940); U. S. 2,229,784 (Jan. 28, 1941); U. S. 2,233,569 (Mar. 4, 1941); Brit. 554,526 (Aug. 5, 1943); Brit. 553,996.
18 —— (Winnek, P. S.): U. S. 2,336,907 (Dec. 14, 1943).
19 —— (Winnek, P. S.): U. S. 2,230,875 (Feb. 4, 1941).
20 —— (Winnek, P. S.): U. S. 2,295,884 (Sept. 15, 1942).
21 Amorosa, M.: *Ann. chim. farm.*, May, **1940**, 54-69; *Chem. Abst.*, **34**, 7910.
22 Amundsen, L. H., and Malentacchi, L. A.: *Science*, **93**, 286 (1941).
23 Ardley, D. G.: *Lancet*, **1941, 2**, 625-8.
24 Armstrong, A. R., and Rae, M. V.: *Can. Med. Assoc. J.*, **45**, 116-8 (1941); *Brit. Chem. Abst.*, **1941, 3**, 908.
25 Backer, H. J., and de Jonge, J.: *Rec. trav. chim.*, **60**, 495-501 (1941).
26 ——, and Grevenstuk, A. B.: *Ibid.*, **60**, 502-4 (1941).
27 Baggesgaard-Rasmussen, H.: *Arch. Pharm. Chem.*, **46**, 127 (1939); *J. Am. Pharm. Assoc.*, **29**, 110 (1940).
28 Banks, C. K., and Hamilton, C. S.: *J. Am. Chem. Soc.*, **62**, 1859-60 (1940).
29 Barlow, O. W., and Homburger, E.: *Proc. Soc. Exptl. Biol. Med.*, **42**, 792-7 (1939); *ibid.*, **43**, 317-323 (1940).
30 Basu, U. P., and Das-Gupta, P. K.: *J. Indian Chem. Soc.*, **16**, 301-4 (1939); *Chem. Abst.*, **34**, 1021.
31 ——, and ——: *J. Indian Chem. Soc.*, **16**, 100-6 (1939); *Chem. Abst.*, **33**, 5852.
32 ——, and ——: *J. Indian Chem. Soc.*, **18**, 167-8 (1941); *Chem. Abst.*, **36**, 754.
33 Bauer, H.: *J. Am. Chem. Soc.*, **61**, 613-16 (1939).
34 ——: *Ibid.*, 617-18 (1939).
35 ——, and Rosenthal, S. M.: *U. S. Pub. Health Repts.*, **53**, 40-9 (1938).
36 ——, and ——: *Ibid.*, **54**, 2093-5 (1939).
37 Bayer and Co.: Ger. 226,239-40; *Frdl.*, **10**, 806-7.
38 Behari, B., and Ghosh, B. N.: *Calcutta Med. J.*, **34**, 275-84 (1938); *Chem. Abst.*, **33**, 9448.
39 Bergeim, F. H., Coy, N. H., and Lott, W. A.: *J. Am. Chem. Soc.*, **62**, 1873-4 (1940).
40 Bergmann, F., and Haskelberg, L.: *Ibid.*, **63**, 2243-5 (1941); U. S. 2,308,640 (Jan. 19, 1943).
41 Berlin, E., Laudon, J., and Sjögren, B.: *Svensk, Kem. Tid.*, **53**, 372-4 (1941); *Chem. Abst.*, **36**, 1595.
42 Bieter, R. N., Larson, W. P., Levine, M., and Cranston, E. M.: *Proc. Soc. Exptl. Biol. Med.*, **41**, 202 (1939); *J. Pharmacol.*, **68**, 252-8 (1940).
43 Bobranski, B.: *Arch. Pharm.*, **277**, 75-86 (1939); *Chem. Abstr.*, **33**, 5377.
44 Bobranski, B. R., and Ecker, I. M.: *J. Appl. Chem. (U.S.S.R.)*, **13**, 1637-41 (1940); *Chem. Abst.*, **35**, 3986.
45 Boots Pure Drug Co. Ltd. (Pyman, F. L., and Cohen, A.): Brit. 519,136 (Mar. 18, 1940).

46 Bornstein, S., and Strauss, L.: *Proc. Soc. Exptl. Biol. Med.*, **47**, 112–115 (1941).
47 Bost, R. W., and Starnes, C. F.: *J. Am. Chem. Soc.*, **63**, 1885–6 (1941).
48 Boyland, E.: *Biochem. J.*, **32**, 1207–13 (1938).
49 Bratton, A. C., and Marshall, E. K., Jr.: *J. Biol. Chem.*, **128**, 537–50 (1939).
50 ——, White, H. J., and Marshall, E. K., Jr.: *Proc. Soc. Exptl. Biol. Med.*, **42**, 847–53 (1939).
51 Braun, C. E., and Towle, J. L.: *J. Am. Chem. Soc.*, **63**, 3523 (1941).
52 ——, ——, and Nichols, S. H., Jr.: *J. Org. Chem.*, **7**, 19–23 (1942).
53 Braun, J. V., and Rudolph, W.: *Ber.*, **74B**, 264–72 (1941); *Chem. Abst.*, **35**, 2892.
54 British Colloids, Ltd. (Jones, J. I. M., and Balaban, I. E.): Brit. 538,354 (July 31, 1941).
55 —— (Jones, J. I. M., and Haines, R. T. M.): Brit. 538,302 (July 29, 1941).
56 Browning, C. H.: *Brit. Med. J.*, **1939**, 265–9 (Aug. 5, 1939).
57 Burger, A., Modlin, L. R., Jr., Krahler, S. E., and Bass, K., Jr.: *Proc. Virginia Acad. Sci.*, 1940–41 in *Virginia J. Sci.*, **2**, 191 (1941); *Chem. Abst.*, **36**, 2080.
58 Burton, H., McLeod, J. W., McLeod, T. S., and Mayr-Harting, A.: *Brit. J. Exptl. Path.*, **21**, 288–302 (1940).
59 Buttle, G. A. H.: *Brit. Med. J.*, **1939**, 269–73 (Aug. 5, 1939); *Chem. Abst.*, **33**, 7884.
60 ——, Dewing, T., Foster, G. E., Gray, W. H., Smith, S., and Stephenson, D.: *Biochem. J.*, **32**, 1101–1110 (1938).
61 ——, Gray, W. H., and Stephenson, D.: *Lancet*, **1936**, 1286.
62 Calco Chemical Co. (Hultquist, M. E.): U. S. 2,142,847 (Jan. 3, 1939).
63 —— (Northey, E. H.): U. S. 2,133,787 (Oct. 18, 1938).
64 —— (Northey, E. H.): U. S. 2,154,248 (Apr. 11, 1939).
65 Caldwell, W. T., and Kornfeld, E. C.: *J. Am. Chem. Soc.*, **64**, 1695–8 (1942).
66 ——, ——, and Donnell, C. K.: *Ibid.*, **63**, 2188–90 (1941).
67 Cantoni, G., and de Caro, L.: *Boll. soc. ital. biol. sper.*, **13**, 722–31 (1938); *Chem. Abst.*, **32**, 9265.
68 Cass, W. E.: *J. Am. Chem. Soc.*, **62**, 3255–6 (1940).
69 Cavallini, G., Cornet, F., and Carissimi, M.: *Chimica e industria (Italy)*, **22**, 510–12 (1940); *Chem. Abst.*, **35**, 2892.
70 Chelintsev, G. V., and Zakotin, V. M.: *J. Gen. Chem. (U.S.S.R.)*, **11**, 729–30 (1941); *Chem. Abst.*, **36**, 477.
71 Chemisch-Pharmazeutische A-G. Bad Homburg: Brit. 502,786 (Mar. 24, 1939); *Brit. Chem. Abst.*, **1939B**, 804.
72 Cherntsov, O. M., and Drosdov, N. S.: *J. Gen. Chem. (U.S.S.R)*, **9**, 1435–40 (1939); *Chem. Abst.*, **34**, 1668.
73 Chinoin Gyogyszer es Vegyeszeti Termekek Gyara R. T. (Földi, Z.): Brit. 500,674 (Feb. 14, 1939); Brit. 503,271 (Apr. 4, 1939). Ger. 716,089 (Nov. 20, 1941); Ger. 712,162 (Sept. 18, 1941); U. S. 2,331,573 (Oct. 12, 1943); U. S. 2,338,106 (Jan. 4, 1944) to Alien Property Custodian.
74 ——: Fr. 837,468 (Feb. 10, 1939); Brit. 505,312 (May 9, 1939); *Chem. Abst.*, **33**, 7315, 7963; Ger. 702,284 (Jan. 9, 1941); *Chem. Abst.*, **35**, 8211.
75 ——: Fr. 837,468 (Feb. 10, 1939).
76 —— (Földi, Z., Konig, R., and Demjen, I.): Brit. 542,160 (Jan. 22, 1942); Belg. 438,838; *Chem. Abst.*, **36**, 3192; U. S. 334,990 (Apr. 20, 1943) to Alien Property Custodian.
77 ——: Hung. 121,910 (Nov. 2, 1939); *Chem. Abst.*, **34**, 1336.
78 ——: Hung. 122,450 (Dec. 15, 1939).
79 ——: Hung. 123,881 (June 15, 1940); *Chem. Abst.*, **34**, 7860; Brit. 544,215 (Apr. 2, 1942).
80 ——: Hung. 124,130 (July 15, 1940); *Chem. Abst.*, **34**, 7297.
81 ——: Hung. 127,731 (Aug. 16, 1941); *Chem. Abst.*, **36**, 2270.
82 ——: Hung. 127,837 (Sept. 1, 1941).
83 Choudhury, A. K., and Basu, U.: *Science and Culture*, **2**, 653 (1937).
84 ——, Das-Gupta, P., and Basu, U.: *J. Indian. Chem. Soc.*, **14**, 733–5 (1937).
85 Chraszczewska, A., and Dobrowolski, C.: *Roczniki Chem.*, **17**, 411–22 (1937); *Chem. Abst.*, **32**, 1674.
86 ——, and Sztabzyb, R.: *Roczniki Chem.*, **18**, 439–42 (1938); *Chem. Abst.*, **33**, 3774.
87 Cilag, Chemisches Industrielles Laboratorium A. G. (Naegeli, C.): U. S. 2,170,209 (Aug. 22, 1939); *Chem. Abst.*, **34**, 1134.
88 —— (Naegeli, C.): U. S. 2,211,702 (Aug. 13, 1940).
89 Climenko, D. R.: *J. Pharmacol.*, **69**, 165 (1940).
——, Crossley, M. L., and Northey, E. H.: *Ibid.*, **67**, 201–11 (1939).
90 ——, and Schmidt, R. L.: *Proc. Soc. Exptl. Biol. Med.*, **43**, 622–7 (1940).
91 Cocker, W.: *J. Chem. Soc.*, **1940**, 1574–6.

92   Cooper, F. B., Gross, P., and Lewis, M.: *J. Chemotherapy*, **15**, 31–5 (1938); *Chem. Abst.*, **33**, 1390.
93   ——, ——, and ——: *Proc. Soc. Exptl. Biol. Med.*, **42**, 421–5 (1939).
94   ——, ——, and ——: *Ibid.*, **43**, 491–4 (1940).
95   ——, ——, and ——: *Ibid.*, **47**, 508–13 (1941).
96   Cox, E. H.: *J. Am. Chem. Soc.*, **62**, 743–4 (1940).
97   Craig, J. J., and Cass, W. E.: *Ibid.*, **64**, 783–4 (1942).
98   Crossley, M. L., Northey, E. H., and Hultquist, M. E.: *Ibid.*, **60**, 2217–22 (1938).
99   ——, ——, and ——: *Ibid.*, 2222–4 (1938).
100   ——, ——, and ——: *Ibid.*, 2225–7 (1938).
101   ——, ——, and ——: *Ibid.*, **61**, 2950–5 (1939).
102   ——, ——, and ——: *Ibid.*, **62**, 372–4 (1940).
103   ——, ——, and ——: *Ibid.*, 532–4 (1940).
104   ——, ——, and ——: *Ibid.*, 1415–16 (1940).
105   ——, ——, and ——: Unpublished work.
106   Curtius, T., and Stoll, W.: *J. prakt. Chem.*, **112**, 120–137 (1926).
107   Daniels, T. C., and Iwamoto, H.: *J. Am. Chem. Soc.*, **62**, 741–2 (1940).
108   ——, and ——: *Ibid.*, **63**, 257–8 (1941).
109   Das-Gupta, S. J.: *J. Indian Chem. Soc.*, **16**, 364–8 (1939); *Chem. Abst.*, **34**, 2379.
110   ——: *Ibid.*, **18**, 25–28 (1941); *Chem. Abst.*, **36**, 92.
111   Davidson, A. M. M., and Reade, T. H.: *J. Chem. Soc.*, **1939**, 1701–3.
112   De, S. P., and Basu, U. P.: *Indian J. Med. Research*, **26**, 537–40 (1938); *Chem. Abst.*, **33**, 6961.
113   Dewing, T., and Smith, S.: *Nature*, **148**, 24 (1941).
114   Dochez, A. R., and Slanetz, C. A.: *Science*, **87**, 142–3 (1938).
115   Dohrn, M., and Diedrich, P.: *Münch. med. Wochschr.*, **85**, 2017–18 (1938).
116   Domagk, G.: *Klin. Wochschr.*, **15**, 1585–90 (1936).
117   ——: *Deut. med. Wochschr.*, **66**, 203–5 (1940).
118   Donley-Evans and Co. (Vogenthaler, C. A.): U. S. 2,252,822 (Aug. 19, 1941).
119   Donnell, C. K., Dietz, J. H., and Caldwell, W. T.: *J. Am. Chem. Soc.*, **63**, 1161–2 (1941).
120   Donovick, R., and Henderson, E.: *J. Pharm.*, **73**, 170–2 (1941).
121   ——, and ——: *Ibid.*, 173–5 (1941).
122   Drozdov, N. S., and Stavrovskaja, V. I.: *Compt. rend. Acad. Sci. (U.S.S.R.)*, **1939**, 61–3; *Chem. Abst.*, **33**, 8914.
123   ——, and ——: *J. Gen. Chem. (U.S.S.R.)*, **9**, 1642–6 (1939); *Chem. Abst.*, **34**, 3703.
124   Duegan, B. S., Narang, K. S., and Ray, J. N.: *J. Chem. Soc.*, **1939**, 476–8.
125   Dyson, G. M.: Brit. 517,682 (Feb. 6, 1940); *Chem. Abst.*, **35**, 7117.
126   Ebert, J. (The Farastan Co.): Personal communication, Apr. 18, 1940.
127   Egger, I., Iván Gyogyszergyaros, Dr.: Hung. 123,532 (Apr. 15, 1940); *Chem. Abst.*, **34**, 4866; Hung. 127,284 (July 1, 1941); *Chem. Abst.*, **35**, 8214.
128   ——, ——: Hung. 127,081 (June 16, 1941).
129   Eldahl, A.: *Ugesk. f. laeger*, **101**, 486–8 (1939).
130   Ellingson, R. C.: *J. Am. Chem. Soc.*, **63**, 2524–5 (1941).
131   Ensworth, H., Liebman, J., Lockhart, M. C., and Plummer, N.: *Ann. Internal Med.*, **15**, 52–62 (1941).
132   Etablissements Mouneyrat & Cie: Fr. 839,711 (Apr. 11, 1939); *Chem. Abst.*, **33**, 7963.
133   Farastan Co. (Ebert, J.): U. S. 2,143,829 (Jan. 10, 1939); U. S. 2,182,075 (Dec. 5, 1939).
134   —— (Ebert, J.): U. S. 2,223,937 (Dec. 3, 1940); *Chem. Abst.*, **35**, 1936.
135   —— (Ebert, J.): U. S. 2,235,145 (Mar. 18, 1941); *Chem. Abst.*, **35**, 4160.
136   —— (Ebert, J.): U. S. 2,237,342 (Apr. 8, 1941); *Chem. Abst.*, **35**, 4552.
137   Feinstone, W. H. (American Cyanamid Company): Personal communication (Apr. 24, 1940).
138   ——, Williams, R. D., and Florestano, H. J.: *Proc. Soc. Exptl. Biol. Med.*, **49**, 234–8 (1942).
139   ——, ——, Wolff, R. T., Huntington, E., and Crossley, M. L.: *Bull. Johns Hopkins Hosp.*, **67**, 427–56 (1940).
140   ——, ——, and Florestano, H. J.: *J. Bact.*, **43**, 75 (1942).
141   ——, Wolff, R., and Williams, R. D.: *Ibid.*, **39**, 47–8 (1940).
142   Feldman, W. H., Hinshaw, H. C., and Moses, H. E.: *Am. Rev. Tuberc.*, **45**, 303–333 (1942); *Proc. Staff Mayo Clin.*, **15**, 695–99 (1940); *ibid.*, **16**, 187–90 (1941).
143   Fellows, E. J.: *Proc. Soc. Exptl. Biol. Med.*, **48**, 680–4 (1941).
144   Fichter, E., and Tamm, W.: *Ber.*, **43**, 3032–8 (1910).
145   Fildes, P.: *Lancet*, **1940**, **1**, 955–7.

146 Fischer, A.: *Arch. intern. pharmacodynamie*, **56**, 131–45 (1937).
147 Fischer, Paul: *Ber.*, **24**, 3788 (1891).
148 Flynn, L. M., and Kohl, M. F. F.: *Proc. Soc. Exptl. Biol. Med.*, **47**, 466–69 (1941).
149 Fosbinder, R. J., and Walter, L. A.: *J. Am. Chem. Soc.*, **61**, 2032–3 (1939).
150 ——, and ——: Personal communication (Apr. 20, 1940) (Pharmacological testing by Mellon and Cooper, Western Pennsylvania Hospital).
151 Fourneau, J., Tréfouël, J., Tréfouël, Mme. J., Nitti, F., and Bovet, D.: *Compt. rend. soc. biol.*, **122**, 258–9 (1936); *ibid.*, 652–4 (1936).
152 ——, ——, ——, ——, and ——: *Ibid.*, **127**, 393–7 (1938); *Bull. acad. méd.*, **118**, 210 (1937).
153 Fuller, A. T.: *Lancet*, **1937, 1,** 194–8.
154 Fuchs, W.: *Monatsh.*, **36**, 124–5 (1915).
155 Gabel, Y. O., and Grinberg, F. L.: *J. Appl. Chem. (U.S.S.R.)*, **12**, 1481–4 (in French 1484) (1939); *Chem. Abst.*, **34**, 6244.
156 ——, and Shpanion, A. L.: *J. Appl. Chem. (U.S.S.R.)*, **12**, 1485–9 (in French 1489) (1939); *Chem. Abst.*, **34**, 6244.
157 Gaind, K. M., Sehgal, R. P., and Ray, J. N.: *J. Indian Chem. Soc.*, **18**, 209–12 (1941); *Chem. Abst.*, **36**, 754.
158 Ganapathi, K.: *J. Indian Chem. Soc.*, **15**, 525–31 (1938); *Current Sci.*, **6**, 608–9 (1938); *Chem. Abst.*, **32**, 8382.
159 ——: *Indian J. Med. Research*, **27**, 971–8 (1940); *Chem. Abst.*, **35**, 1871.
160 ——: *Proc. Indian Acad. Sci.*, **11A**, 298–31 (1940); *Chem. Abst.*, **34**, 6243.
161 ——: *Proc. Indian Acad. Sci.*, **12A**, 274–83 (1940); *Chem. Abst.*, **35**, 1772.
162 ——: *Current Sci.*, **9**, 457–8 (1940); *Brit. Chem. Abst.*, **1941, A2,** 109; *Proc. Indian Acad. Sci.*, **13A**, 386–9 (1941).
163 ——, and Nandi, B. K.: *Current Sci.*, **9**, 67–8 (1940); *Brit. Chem. Abst.*, **1940, A2,** 261.
164 Geigy, J. R., A.-G.: Brit. 508,148 (June 27, 1939); *Chem. Abst.*, **34**, 1102.
165 —— (Martin, H., and Hirt, R.): U. S. 2,337,909 (Dec. 28, 1943); *Brit. Chem. Abst.*, **1941, B3,** 344.
166 ——: Brit. 538,884 (Aug. 20, 1941); *Brit. Chem. Abst.*, **1941, B3,** 343.
167 —— (Martin, H., and Hirt, R.): Swiss 200,667 (Jan. 16, 1939); *Chem. Abst.*, **33**, 8859; U. S. 2,207,021 (July 9, 1940).
168 Gelmo, P.: *J. prakt. Chem.*, **77** (2), 369–71 (1908).
169 Gilman, H., and Stuckwisch, C. G.: *J. Am. Chem. Soc.*, **63**, 2844–5 (1941).
170 Goissedet, P., Despois, R., Gailliot, P., and Mayer, R. L.: *Compt. rend. soc. biol.*, **121**, 1082–4 (1936).
171 Goldirev, L. N., and Postovski, I. J.: *J. Applied Chem. (U.S.S.R.)*, **11**, 316 (1938).
172 Gray, W. H.: *J. Chem. Soc.*, **1939**, 1202.
173 ——, Buttle, G. A. H., and Stephenson, D.: *Biochem. J.*, **31**, 724 (1937).
174 Green, A. G., and Coplans, M.: *Chemistry & Industry*, **59**, 793–4 (1940).
175 ——, and ——: Brit. 524,011 (July 29, 1940); *Chem. Abst.*, **35**, 7118; U. S. 2,214,527 (Sept. 10, 1940).
176 Green, H. N.: *Brit. J. Exptl. Path.*, **21**, 38–64 (1940).
177 Grove, F. C., and Keenan, G. L.: *J. Am. Chem. Soc.*, **63**, 97–9 (1941); **65**, 2479 (1943).
178 Gueioult, A., and Cariage, J. L.: *Paris medicien*, **29**, 201 (1939).
179 Hager, G. P., Starkey, E. B., and Chapman, C. W.: *J. Am. Pharm. Assoc.*, **30**, 65–8 (1941).
180 Halpern, B. N., and Mayer, R. L.: *Presse méd.*, **45**, 747–9 (1937).
181 Halverstadt, I. F., and Kumler, W. D.: *J. Am. Chem. Soc.*, **63**, 624–5 (1941).
182 Hampil, B., Webster, G. W., and Moore, M. L.: *J. Pharmacol.*, **71**, 52–8 (1941).
183 Harris, J. S., and Kohn, H. I.: *J. Biol. Chem.*, **141**, 989–90 (1941).
184 Hartmann, M., and Druey, J.: *Helv. Chim. Acta*, **24**, 536–8 (1941).
185 Haslewood, G. A. D.: *Biochem. J.*, **35**, 1307–10 (1941).
186 Hawking, F.: *Lancet*, **1942, 1,** 290–1; *ibid.*, **2**, 507–10.
187 Hebb, A., Sullivan, S. G., and Felton, L. D.: *U. S. Pub. Health Repts.*, **54**, 1750–69 (1939).
188 Heidelberger, M., and Jacobs, W. A.: *J. Am. Chem. Soc.*, **41**, 2145 (1919).
189 Henderson, E. (Schering Corporation): Personal communication (Apr. 17, 1940).
190 Höber, R.: *Proc. Soc. Exptl. Biol. Med.*, **49**, 87–90 (1942).
191 Hoffman—La Roche, Inc. (Warnat, K.): U. S. 2,305,751 (Dec. 22, 1942); Fr. 856,339 (June 11, 1940); Swiss 213,196 (Apr. 16, 1941) and 206,549; *Chem. Abst.*, **36**, 4673.
192 —— (Warnat, K.): U. S. 2,287,155 (June 23, 1942); Belg. 435,311 (July 31, 1939); Brit. 527,548 (Oct. 10, 1940); *Chem. Abst.*, **35**, 7120; Can. 401,354 (Dec. 9, 1941); *Chem. Abst.*, **36**, 1736; Fr. 853,666 (Nov. 26, 1940); *Chem. Abst.*, **36**, 2688; Swiss 211,297 (Dec. 2, 1940); Swiss 214,335 (July 16, 1941); Ger. 713,079 (Oct. 9, 1941); Ger. 721,667 (May 7, 1942); *Chem. Abst.*, **37**, 5079; Ger. 735,695 (Apr. 15, 1943); *Chem. Abst.*, **38**, 2665.

193 —— (Warnat, K.): U. S. 2,287,154 (June 23, 1942); Brit. 531,590 (Jan. 7, 1941); *Chem. Abst.*, **35**, 8213.

194 —— (Warnat, K.): Brit. 534,150 (Feb. 28, 1941); *Chem. Abst.*, **36**, 1142; Swiss 213,500 (June 3, 1941); *Chem. Abst.*, **36**, 4974; U. S. 2,316,908 (Apr. 20, 1943).

195 ——: Swiss 205,019 (Aug. 16, 1939); *Chem. Abst.*, **35**, 2160.

196 ——: Swiss 200,845 (Jan. 16, 1939); *Chem. Abst.*, **33**, 8924.

197 ——: Swiss 206,925, addition to 200,845 (Dec. 1, 1939); *Chem. Abst.*, **34**, 7543.

198 ——: Swiss 206,549 (Nov. 16, 1939); *Chem. Abst.*, **35**, 3036.

199 ——: Swiss 208,882 (June 1, 1940); *Chem. Abst.*, **35**, 3652.

200 ——: Ger. 666,431 (Oct. 19, 1938); *Chem. Abst.*, **33**, 2287.

201 —— (Warnat, K.): U. S. 2,192,490 (Mar. 5, 1940); Brit. 480,486 (Feb. 23, 1938); Swiss 191,673; 194,681–5; 194,885; 195,177; 195,466; 199,682–6; 199,910.

202 —— (Warnat, K.): U. S. 2,245,539 (June 10, 1941); Brit. 530,902 (July 5, 1939); *Brit. Chem. Abst.*, **1941, B3**, 78; *Chem. Abst.*, **35**, 6070; Ger. 713,079; 726,739; 720,740; 727,473; Swiss 213,147 (Apr. 16, 1941).

203 ——: Ger. 666,431 (Oct. 19, 1938); *Chem. Abst.*, **33**, 2287.

204 Hoyt, F. W., and Gilman, H.: *Proc. Iowa Acad. Sci.*, **47**, 262 (1940); *Chem. Abst.*, **35**, 7197.

205 Hykes, O. V., Hykes, D. E., and Rerabek, J.: *Compt. rend. soc. biol.*, **126**, 635 (1938).

206 I. G. Farbenindustrie A.-G.: Brit. 458,417 (Dec. 18, 1936).

207 ——: Brit. 487,233 (July 14, 1938).

208 ——: Brit. 491,925 (Sept. 9, 1938).

209 ——: Brit. 500,118 (Jan. 30, 1929); *Chem. Abst.*, **33**, 5598; *Brit. Chem. Abst.*, **1939, B**, 551.

210 —— (Mietzsch, F., and Klarer, J.): Brit. 502,173 (Mar. 10, 1939); *Chem. Abst.*, **33**, 6529; U. S. 2,280,497 (Apr. 21, 1942) to Winthrop Chemical Co.

211 —— (Behnish, R., Mietzsch, F., and Klarer, J.): Brit. 474,423 (Oct. 28, 1937); Fr. 820,546 (Nov. 13, 1937); U. S. 2,169,971 (Aug. 15, 1939) to Winthrop Chemical Co.; Ger. 725,537 (Aug. 13, 1942).

212 —— (Clingestein, H., and Dobmaier, K.): Ger. 573,047 (Nov. 12, 1931); U. S. 2,019,844 (Nov. 5, 1935).

213 —— (Mietzsch, F., and Klarer, J.): Ger. 607,537 (Jan. 2, 1935); Brit. 430,580 (June 21, 1935); Fr. 766,081; U. S. 2,085,037 (June 29, 1937) to Winthrop Chemical Co.

214 —— (Mietzsch, F., and Klarer, J.): Ger. 610,320 (Mar. 7, 1935); Brit. 430,580 (June 21, 1935); Fr. 766,081; U. S. 2,113,597 (Apr. 12, 1939) to Winthrop Chemical Co.; U. S. 2,148,705 (Feb. 28, 1939) to Winthrop Chemical Co.

215 —— (Mietzsch, F., and Klarer, J.): Ger. 638,701 (Nov. 21, 1936); Fr. 788,679 (Oct. 14, 1935); U. S. 2,123,634 (July 12, 1938) to Winthrop Chemical Co.; U. S. 2,148,910 (Feb. 28, 1939) to Winthrop Chemical Co.

216 —— (Mietzsch, F., and Klarer, J.): Brit. 470,462 (Aug. 11, 1937); Fr. 816,988 (Aug. 21, 1937); Ger. 681,684 (Sept. 7, 1939); U. S. 2,335,599 (Nov. 30, 1943) to Winthrop Chemical Co.

217 —— (Mietzsch, F., and Klarer, J.): Brit. 470,461 (Aug. 11, 1937); Brit. 482,576 (Mar. 28, 1938); Fr. 817,034 (Aug. 24, 1937); Ger. 681,685 (Sept. 7, 1939); Ger. 736,661 (May 13, 1943); *Chem. Abst.*, **38**, 2968.

218 —— (Mietzsch, F., and Klarer, J.): Brit. 486,421 (May 29, 1938); Brit. 486,497 (May 30, 1938); Fr. 830,754 (Aug. 9, 1938).

219 —— (Mietzsch, F., Maus, H., and Klarer, J.): Ger. 642,758 (July 13, 1936); *Frdl.*, **23**, 541; Brit. 466,505 (May 28, 1937).

220 ——: Brit. 490,043 (Aug. 9, 1938); *Chem. Abst.*, **33**, 644; Brit. 506,227 (May 24, 1939); *Chem. Abst.*, **33**, 9328; Fr. 829,926 (July 11, 1938); *Chem. Abst.*, **33**, 1760.

221 ——: Brit. 507,378 (June 14, 1939); *Chem. Abst.*, **34**, 636.

222 ——: Brit. 509,415 (July 13, 1939) addition to Brit. 506,227; *Chem. Abst.*, **34**, 3764.

223 ——: Brit. 513,242 (Oct. 6, 1939) addition to Brit. 480,059; *Chem. Abst.*, **35**, 1808.

224 ——: Brit. 518,903 (Mar. 11, 1940); *Chem. Abst.*, **35**, 8213; *Brit. Chem. Abst.*, **B**, 403, 1940.

225 ——: Fr. 841,694 (May 24, 1939); *Chem. Abst.*, **34**, 4393.

226 ——: Fr. 843,418 (July 3, 1939); Ger. 681,686 (Sept. 7, 1939).

227 ——: Fr. 843,558 (July 5, 1939); *Chem. Abst.*, **34**, 6945.

228 —— (Pöhls, P.): Ger. 710,678 (Aug. 7, 1941); U. S. 2,282,769 (May 12, 1942) to Winthrop Chemical Co.

229 —— (Behnisch, R., and Pöhls, P.): Fr. 845,532 (Aug. 25, 1939); *Chem. Abst.*, **35**, 1184; U. S. 2,339,318 (Jan. 18, 1944) to Winthrop Chemical Co.

230 —— (Klarer, J., and Mietzsch, F.): Ger. 690,195 (Mar. 28, 1940); *Chem. Abst.*, **35**, 4041.

231 —— (Mietzsch, F., and Klarer, J.): Ger. 693,922 (June 27, 1940) addition to Ger. 692,325; *Chem. Abst.*, **35**, 4783; (see Brit. 480,059 and 513,242).

232 —— (Behnisch, R.): Ger. 694,679 (July 11, 1940).
233 —— (Mietzsch, F., and Klarer, J.): Ger. 694,946 (July 18, 1940); *Chem. Abst.*, **35**, 5258.
234 —— (Mietzsch, F., Behnisch, R., and Klarer, J.): Ger. 696,973 (Sept. 5, 1940); *Chem. Abst.*, **35**, 5915; (see Brit. 513,242).
235 —— (Behnisch, R., and Pöhls, P.): Ger. 700,801 (Nov. 28, 1940); *Chem. Abst.*, **35**, 7658.
236 —— (Ufer, H.): Ger. 702,064 (Jan. 2, 1941); *Chem. Abst.*, **36**, 98.
237 Imperial Chemical Industries, Ltd. (Ellingsworth, S., and Rose, F. L.): Brit. 517,421 (Jan. 30, 1940); *Chem. Abst.*, **35**, 6973.
238 —— (Ellingsworth, S., and Rose, F. L.): Brit. 517,457 (Jan. 30, 1940); *Chem. Abst.*, **35**, 7118.
239 —— (Rose, F. L.): Brit. 533,565 (Feb. 17, 1941); *Chem. Abst.*, **36**, 1045; *Brit. Chem. Abst.*, **1941, B3**, 132.
240 Itai, Y., Ojüna, S., and Yasawa, T.: *J. Pharm. Soc. Japan*, **57**, 592-7 (1927); *Chem. Abst.*, **31**, 6210.
241 Ivanovics, G.: *Orvosi Hetilap*, **84**, 139-40 (1940); *Chem. Abst.*, **34**, 4454.
242 Jacobs, W. A., and Heidelberger, M.: *J. Am. Chem. Soc.*, **39**, 2418-43 (1917).
243 James, G. V.: *Analyst*, **65**, 206-15 (1940); *Chem. Abst.*, **34**, 4227.
244 ——: *Biochem. J.*, **34**, 636-47 (1940).
245 ——, and Fuller, A. T.: *Ibid.*, 648-56 (1940).
246 Jensen, K. A.: *Helv. Chim. Acta*, **24**, 1249-50 (1941).
247 ——, and Lundquist, F.: *Dansk Tids. Farm.*, **14**, 129-33 (1940); *Chem. Abst.*, **35**, 3987 (in German).
248 ——, and ——: *Dansk Tids. Farm.*, **14**, 208-14 (1940); *Chem. Abst.*, **35**, 2483 (German summary).
249 ——, and Thorsteinson, T.: *Dansk Tids. Farm.*, **15**, 41-77 (1941); *Chem. Abst.*, **35**, 5109 (German summary).
250 Johnson, F. H., and Moore, K.: *Proc. Soc. Exptl. Biol. Med.*, **48**, 323-5 (1941).
251 Joiner, R. R., and Spoerri, P. E.: *J. Am. Chem. Soc.*, **63**, 1929-30 (1941).
252 Jones, H. P., Rake, G., and McKee, C. M.: *Proc. Soc. Exptl. Biol. Med.*, **48**, 318-23 (1941).
253 Juneja, G. L., Narang, K. S., and Ray, J. N.: *J. Indian Chem. Soc.*, **17**, 495-8 (1940); *Chem. Abst.*, **35**, 2147.
254 Kamlet, J.: Meetings of the American Chemical Society in Rochester, New York, Sept., 1937, and in Baltimore, Maryland, Apr., 1939.
255 ——: Personal communication (Apr. 18, 1940).
256 ——: U. S. 2,111,913 (Mar. 22, 1938).
257 ——, and Rosenthal, L.: U. S. 2,309,248 (Jan. 26, 1943).
258 Keefer, C. S.: *Med. Clin. N. America*, **23**, 1133-48 (1939); *Chem. Abst.*, **34**, 166.
259 Kempf, J. E., and Soule, M. H.: *Proc. Soc. Exptl. Biol. Med.*, **44**, 107-10 (1940).
260 Kempner, W., Wise, B., and Schlayer, C.: *Am. J. Med. Sci.*, **200**, 484-92 (1940).
261 Kermack, W. O., Spragg, W. T., and Tebrich, W.: *J. Chem. Soc.*, **1939**, 608-10.
262 ——, and Tebrich, W.: *Ibid.*, **1940**, 202-5.
263 Klinefelter, H. F.: *Bull. Johns Hopkins Hosp.*, **67**, 365 (1940); *Proc. Soc. Exptl. Biol. Med.*, **46**, 591-3 (1941).
264 Kohl, M. F. F., and Flynn, L. M.: *Proc. Soc. Exptl. Biol. Med.*, **44**, 455-7 (1940); *ibid.*, **47**, 470-3 (1941).
265 Kohlbach, D.: *Arhiv. Hem. Farm.*, **11**, 99-123 (1937); *Chem. Abst.*, **33**, 2897.
266 Kohn, H. I., and Harris, J. S.: *J. Pharmacol.*, **73**, 343-61 (1941).
267 Kolloff, H. G.: *J. Am. Chem. Soc.*, **60**, 950-51 (1938).
268 ——, and Hunter, J. H.: *Ibid.*, **62**, 158-60 (1940).
269 ——, and ——: Personal communication (Apr. 9, 1940).
270 ——, and ——: *J. Am. Chem. Soc.*, **62**, 1646-9 (1940).
271 ——, and ——: *Ibid.*, 3355-7 (1940).
272 ——, and ——: *Ibid.*, **63**, 490-2 (1941).
273 Kolmer, J. A.: *Arch. Internal Med.*, **65**, 671-743 (1940).
274 ——, and Rule, A. M.: *J. Pharmacol.*, **68**, 406-12 (1940).
275 Kuhn, R., and Birkofer, L.: *Ber.*, **71B**, 621-33 (1938).
276 Kumler, W. D.: Personal communication (Apr. 30, 1940).
277 ——: *J. Am. Chem. Soc.*, **62**, 2560-1 (1940).
278 Kuroyanagi, S.: *J. Pharm. Soc. Japan*, **60**, 301-8 (in German 176-7) (1940); *Chem. Abst.* **35**, 7944.
279 ——, and Kawai, H.: *J. Pharm. Soc. Japan*, **60**, 481-7, Abst. (in English) 183-4 (1940); *Chem. Abst.*, **35**, 7945.
280 "Labopharma" Dr. J. Riesenberg & Co., G. m. b. H. (Weindling, I., and Riesenberg, J.): Ger. 695,034 (July 18, 1940); *Chem. Abst.*, **35**, 5258.

281 Laboratoires français de chimotherapie (Girard, A.): Fr. 844,220 (July 20, 1939); *Chem. Abst.*, **34**, 7543.
282 —— (Girard, A.): U. S. 2,256,261 (Sept. 16, 1941).
283 Laudon, J., and Sjogren, B.: *Svensk. Kem. Tid.*, **52**, 64–7 (1940); *Chem. Abst.*, **34**, 4734.
284 Leach, B. E., and Forbes, J. C.: *Proc. Soc. Exptl. Biol. Med.*, **48**, 361–3 (1941).
285 Levaditi, C., Girard, A., and Vaisman, A.: *Compt. rend. soc. biol.*, **127**, 19–21 (1938); *ibid.*, **128**, 305–7 (1938).
286 ——, and Vaisman, A.: *Presse méd.*, **43**, 2097–2102 (1935).
287 ——, and ——: *Compt. rend. soc. biol.*, **131**, 33–5 (1939).
288 ——, ——, and Krassnoff, D.: *Bull. acad. méd.*, **121**, 730–50 (1939); *Ann. Inst. Pasteur*, **62**, 36–80 (1939).
289 ——, ——, and Reinie, L.: *Compt. rend. soc. biol.*, **131**, 403 (1939).
290 Lever Bros. Co. (Anderson, C. N.): U. S. 2,135,553 (Nov. 8, 1938).
291 Lewis, R., and Tager, M.: *Yale J. Biol. Med.*, **13**, 111–5 (1940); *Chem. Abst.*, **35**, 198.
292 Liaci, L.: *Arch. farmacol. sper.*, **68**, 155–62 (1939); *Chem. Abst.*, **34**, 1392.
293 Lichtman, S. S.: *Ann. Internal Med.*, **19**, 787–94 (1943).
294 Lilly, E., and Co. (Fortune, W. B.): U. S. 2,208,096 (July 16, 1940).
295 —— (Kharasch, M. S.): U. S. 2,191,432 (Feb. 20, 1940); Brit. 500,607 (Feb. 13, 1939); *Chem. Abst.*, **33**, 6000.
296 —— (Kharasch, M. S., and Reinmuth, O.): U. S. 2,097,414 (Oct. 26, 1937); Brit. 506,431 (May 30, 1939).
297 —— (Kharasch, M. S., and Reinmuth, O.): U. S. 2,097,415 (Oct. 26, 1937); Brit. 512,460 (Sept. 18, 1939).
298 —— (Kharasch, M. S., and Reinmuth, O.): U. S. 2,224,156 (Dec. 10, 1940); Brit. 549,985; *Brit. Chem. Abst.*, **1943**, **B3**, 63.
299 —— (Kharasch, M. S., and Reinmuth, O.): U. S. 2,254,872 (Sept. 2, 1941).
300 —— (Kharasch, M. S., and Reinmuth, O.): U. S. 2,268,754 (Jan. 6, 1942).
301 —— (Kleiderer, E. C., and Shonle, H. A.): U. S. 2,117,251 (May 10, 1938).
302 —— (Kleiderer, E. C., and Van Arendonk, A. M.): U. S. 2,260,626 (Oct. 28, 1941).
303 —— (Powell, H. M.): U. S. 2,145,799 (Jan. 31, 1939).
304 —— (Shonle, H. A.): U. S. 2,268,780 (Jan. 6, 1942).
305 —— (Stuart, E. H.): U. S. 2,117,260 (May 10, 1938).
306 —— (Stuart, E. H.): U. S. 2,145,800 (Jan. 21, 1939).
307 —— (Stuart, E. H.): U. S. 2,186,773 (Jan. 9, 1940).
308 —— (Stuart, E. H.): U. S. 2,254,877 (Sept. 2, 1941).
309 Litchfield, J. T., White, H. J., and Marshall, E. K., Jr.; *J. Pharmacol.*, **67**, 437–53 (1939).
310 ——, ——, and ——: *Ibid.*, **72**, 291–7 (1941).
311 Long, P. H.: Personal communication (Apr. 12, 1940).
312 ——: *Sigma Xi Quart.*, **29**, 149–69 (1941).
313 ——, and Bliss, E. A.: "Clinical and Experimental Use of Sulfanilamide, Sulfapyridine and Allied Compounds," The Macmillan Co., New York, 1939.
314 ——, ——, and Ott, E.: *Bull. Johns Hopkins Hosp.*, **69**, 297–302 (1941).
315 Lott, W. A. (E. R. Squibb and Sons): Personal communication (Apr. 18, 1940).
316 ——, and Bergeim, F. H.: *J. Am. Chem. Soc.*, **61**, 3593–5 (1939).
317 Loudon, J. D., and Shulman, N.: *J. Chem. Soc.*, **1938**, 1618–21.
318 Lurie, S. I.: *J. Gen. Chem. (U.S.S.R.)*, **10**, 1909–14 (1940); *Chem. Abst.*, **35**, 4022; *Brit. Chem. Abst.*, **1941**, **A2**, 379.
319 ——, Fedorova, A. I., and Volkova, E. D.: *J. Gen. Chem. (U.S.S.R.)*, **11**, 739–44 (1941); *Chem. Abst.*, **36**, 1013.
320 ——, Kuleshova, M. G., and Kochetkov, N. K.: *J. Gen. Chem. (U.S.S.R.)*, **9**, 1933–8 (1939); *Chem. Abst.*, **34**, 4387.
321 ——, Starobogatov, O. I., and Nikitskaya, E. S.: *J. Gen. Chem. (U.S.S.R.)*, **11**, 545–9 (1941); *Chem. Abst.*, **35**, 6938.
322 Lustig, O., and Katschner, E.: *Monatsh.*, **48**, 87–98 (1927).
323 McIlwain, H.: *Nature*, **146**, 653–4 (1940); *Chem. Abst.*, **35**, 1127.
324 ——: *J. Chem. Soc.*, **1941**, 75–7.
325 ——: *Lancet*, **1942**, **1**, 412–5.
326 MacIntyre, A. B., and Montgomery, R. F.: *Brit. Med. J.*, **1938**, **1**, 875.
327 McLeod, M.: *Biochem. J.*, **32**, 1770–4 (1938).
328 Magidson, O. Y., and Rubstov, M. V.: *J. Gen. Chem. (U.S.S.R.)*, **10**, 756–68 (1940); *Chem. Abst.*, **35**, 2483.
329 Main, E. R., Shinn, L. E., and Mellon, R. R.: *Proc. Soc. Exptl. Biol. Med.*, **42**, 115–8 (1939).
330 ——, ——, and ——: *Ibid.*, **43**, 593–8 (1940).

331   Mangini, A.: *Boll. sci. facolta, chim. ind. Bologna,* **1940,** No. 4, 127–9; 143–7; *Chem. Abst.,* **34,** 7286; *ibid.,* **37,** 617–9.
332   Marchant, C., Lucas, C. C., McClelland, L., and Greey, P. H.: *Can. J. Research,* **20B,** 5–16 (1942).
333   Marshall, E. K., Jr.: *Science,* **91,** 345–50 (1940).
334   ——, Bratton, A. C., and Litchfield, J. T., Jr.: *Ibid.,* **88,** 597–9 (1938).
335   ——, ——, White, H. J., and Litchfield, J. T., Jr.: *Bull. Johns Hopkins Hosp.,* **67,** 163–88 (1940).
336   ——, and Cutting, W. C.: *Bull. Johns Hopkins Hosp.,* **63,** 328–36 (1938).
337   Martin, G. J., Fisher, C. V., and Thompson, M. R.: *Arch. Internal Med.,* **69,** 662–9 (1942).
338   May and Baker Ltd. (Ashley, J. N.): Brit. 537,291 (June 17, 1941); *Chem. Abst.,* **36,** 1334.
339   —— (Ewins, A. J., and Ashley, J. N.): Brit. 521,821 (May 31, 1940); *Chem. Abst.,* **36,** 872.
340   —— (Ewins, A. J., and Newbery, G.): Brit. 486,449 (Jan. 2, 1938).
341   —— (Ewins, A. J., and Phillips, M. A.): Brit. 512,145 (Aug. 30, 1939); Brit. 530,187 (Dec. 6, 1940); U. S. 2,259,222 (Oct. 14, 1941); U. S. 2,275,354 (Mar. 3, 1942); U. S. 2,312,032 (Feb. 23, 1943); U. S. 2,335,221 (Nov. 23, 1943); Ger. 737,796 (June 17, 1943).
342   —— (Ewins, A. J., Phillips, M. A., and Newbery, G.): Brit. 516,288 (Dec. 29, 1939); *Chem. Abst.,* **35,** 5910.
343   —— (Newbery, G., and Viaud, P.): Brit. 517,272 (Jan. 25, 1940); Fr. 855,538 (May 14, 1940) to Rhône Poulene; U. S. 2,362,087 (Nov. 7, 1944).
344   —— (Phillips, M. A.): Brit. 531,957 (Jan. 15, 1941).
345   Mayer, R. L., and Oechslin, C.: *Compt. rend. soc. biol.,* **130,** 211–4 (1939).
346   ——, and ——: *Compt. rend.,* **205,** 181–2 (1937).
347   ——, and ——: *Arch. intern. pharmacodynamie,* **62,** 211–30 (1939).
348   Mazza, F. P., and Migliardi, C.: *Atti accad. Lincei, Classe sci. fis., mat. nat.,* **28,** 152–7 (1938); *Chem. Abst.,* **33,** 9300.
349   ——, and ——: *Atti accad. Lincei, Classe sci. fis., mat. nat.,* **29,** 80–3 (1939); *Chem. Abst.,* **34,** 3360.
350   Mellon, R. R., Gross, P., and Cooper, F. B.: "Sulfanilamide Therapy of Bacterial Infections," Charles C. Thomas, Springfield, Illinois, 1939.
351   ——, Shinn, L. F., and McBroom, J.: *Proc. Soc. Exptl. Biol. Med.,* **37,** 563–5 (1937).
352   Merck, E.: U. S. 2,289,761 (July 14, 1942); Fr. 847,244 (Oct. 5, 1939); *Chem. Abst.,* **35,** 5513.
353   Merrell, Wm. S., Co. (Shelton, R. S.): U. S. 2,262,779 (Nov. 18, 1941).
354   Meyer, F.: Brit. 519,661 (Apr. 2, 1940); *Chem. Abst.,* **36,** 98.
355   ——: U. S. 2,208,641 (July 23, 1940); *Chem. Abst.,* **35,** 281.
356   ——, and Schreiber, Eva: U. S. 2,141,843 (Dec. 27, 1938).
357   Mietzsch, F.: *Ber.,* **71A,** 15–28 (1938).
358   Migliardi, C.: *Ricerca Sci.,* **12,** 1056–8 (1941); *Chem. Abst.,* **36,** 1022.
359   Militzer, W., Smith, E., and Evans, E.: *J. Am. Chem. Soc.,* **63,** 436 (1941); *Chem. Abst.,* **35,** 2121.
360   Miller, E., Rock, H. J., and Moore, M. L.: *J. Am. Chem. Soc.,* **61,** 1198–200 (1939).
361   ——, Sprague, J. M., Kissinger, L. W., and McBurney, L. F.: *Ibid.,* **62,** 2099–2102 (1940).
362   Miura, K.: *Japan J. Med. Sci. IV Pharmacol.,* **12,** 209–35 (1940).
363   Möller, H.: *Arch. Exptl. Path. Pharmacol.,* **192,** 708–14 (1939).
364   Molitor, H., and Robinson, H.: *J. Pharmacol.,* **65,** 405–23 (1939).
365   Monsanto Chemical Co. (Dvornikoff, M. N.): U. S. 2,240,496 (May 6, 1941); *Chem. Abst.,* **36,** 5258.
366   —— (Mares, J. R.): U. S. 2,236,825 (Apr. 1, 1941); *Chem. Abst.,* **35,** 4393.
367   Monti, L.: *Gazz. chim. ital.,* **69,** 749–52 (1939); *Chem. Abst.,* **34,** 4739.
368   ——, and Felici, L.: *Gazz. chim. ital.,* **70,** 375–80 (1940); *Chem. Abst.,* **35,** 3241.
369   ——, and Simonetti, A.: *Gazz. chim. ital.,* **70,** 369–74 (1940); *Chem. Abst.,* **35,** 3241.
370   Moore, M. L. (Sharp and Dohme Co.): Personal communication (Apr. 19, 1940).
371   ——, and Miller, C. S.: *J. Am. Chem. Soc.,* **63,** 2781–4 (1941).
372   ——, and ——: *Ibid.,* **64,** 1572–6 (1942).
373   ——, ——, and Miller, E.: *Ibid.,* **62,** 2097–9 (1940).
374   ——, and Miller, E.: U. S. 2,260,632 (Oct. 28, 1941); Brit. 546,076 (July 23, 1942).
375   Morren, H., and Lehmann, R.: *pharm. Belg.,* **21,** 953 (1939); *Chem. Abst.,* **34,** 4389.
376   Morris, C. J. O.: *Biochem. J.,* **35,** 952–9 (1941).
377   Mossini, A.: *Boll. chim.-farm.,* **78,** 429–31 (1939); *Chem. Abst.,* **33,** 9300.
378   ——: *Ann. chim. farm.,* Dec., **1939,** 47–53; *Chem. Abst.,* **34,** 2175.

379 ———: *Boll. soc. ital. biol. sper.*, **14**, 387–9 (1939); *Chem. Abst.*, **34**, 2810.
380 ———: *Ateneo parmense*, **11**, 237–41 (1939); *Chem. Abst.*, **34**, 7870.
381 ———: *Ateneo parmense*, **11**, 470–2 (1939); *Chem. Abst.*, **34**, 3879.
382 ———: *Ann. chim. farm.*, May, **1940**, 24–34; *Chem. Abst.*, **34**, 7916.
383 Mouneyrat, A.: Fr. 849,504 (Nov. 25, 1939); *Chem. Abst.*, **35**, 6979.
384 ———: Fr. 850,553 (Dec. 20, 1939); *Chem. Abst.*, **36**, 1736.
385 Musante, C.: *Gazz. chim. ital.*, **71**, 565–73 (1941); *Chem. Abst.*, **36**, 7023.
386 Muschenheim, C., Forkner, C. E., and Duerschner, D. R.: *Proc. Soc. Exptl. Biol. Med.*, **45**, 556–9 (1940).
387 Mutch, N.: *Brit. Med. J.*, **1941**, **2**, 502–7.
388 Naegeli, C., Kündig, W., and Brandenburger, H.: *Helv. Chim. Acta*, **21**, 1746–56 (1938).
389 ———, ———, and ———: *Ibid.*, **22**, 912–25 (1939).
390 Nepera Chemical Co. (Tisza, E. T., Duesal, B. F., and Friedman, H. L.: U. S. 2,202,933 (June 5, 1940).
391 Nitti, F., and Bovet, D.: *Compt. rend.*, **202**, 1221–3(1936).
392 ———, ———, Tréfouël, Mme. J., Tréfouël, J.: *Ann. Inst. Pasteur*, **61**, 811–12 (1938).
393 Novelli, A.: *Anales assoc. quim. argentina*, **28**, 87–90 (1940); *Chem. Abst.*, **34**, 6621.
394 ———: *Ciencia*, **1**, 260 (1940); *Chem. Abst.*, **34**, 7903.
395 N. V. Orgachemia (Salomon, A.): U. S. 2,322,974 (June 24, 1943) to Alien Property Custodian; Fr. 843,429 (July 3, 1939); Brit. 517,919 (Feb. 13, 1940); Ger. 732,136 (Jan. 28, 1943); *Chem. Abst.*, **34**, 6771.
396 ——— (Salomon, A.): Fr. 845,317 (Aug. 18, 1939); U. S. 2,309,870 (June 29, 1943) to Alien Property Custodian; Ger. 734,957 (Apr. 1, 1943); Brit. 520,707 (May 1, 1940); *Chem. Abst.*, **36**, 624; *Brit. Chem. Abst.*, **1940**, **B**, 566.
397 ——— (Salomon, A.): Dutch 50,705 (July 15, 1941); *Chem. Abst.*, **36**, 4292.
398 ——— (Salomon, A.): Dutch 47,894 (Feb. 15, 1940); *Chem. Abst.*, **34**, 8185.
399 ——— (Salomon, A.): Dutch 48,377 (Apr. 15, 1940); *Chem. Abst.*, **34**, 8183.
400 Ockerblad, N. F., and Carlson, H. E.: *J. Urol.*, **41**, 801–7 (1939).
401 Oneto, J. F., and Way, E. L.: *J. Am. Chem. Soc.*, **61**, 2105–6 (1939); *ibid.*, **62**, 2157–8 (1940).
402 ———, and ———: *Ibid.*, **63**, 762 (1941).
403 ———, and ———: *Ibid.*, 3068–70 (1941).
404 Ozeki, H.: *Kitasato Arch. Exptl. Med.*, **18**, 135–44 (1941); *Chem. Abst.*, **36**, 2018.
405 Passedouet, H., and Vaisman, A.: *Compt. rend. soc. biol.*, **130**, 130–2 (1939).
406 Perez, M.: *Boll. soc. ital. biol. sper.*, **14**, 536–8 (1939); *Chem. Abst.*, **34**, 1392.
407 Perotti, A., and Mezzadra, A.: *Ann. chim. applicata*, **30**, 307–18 (1940); *Chem. Abst.*, **35**, 1773.
408 Phillips, M. A.: *Nature*, **148**, 409 (1941).
409 ———: *J. Chem. Soc.*, **1941**, 9–15.
410 ———: *Ibid.*, 291–3.
411 Plaskon, Co. (Simons, J. K.): U. S. 2,237,372 (Apr. 8, 1941).
412 Pollak, J., Pollak, R., Riesz, E., and Wittels, A. E.: *Monatsh.*, **58**, 118 (1931).
413 Polyakova, I. M., and Kirsanov, A. N.: *J. Appl. Chem. (U.S.S.R.)*, **13**, 1215–19 (in French 1219) (1940); *Chem. Abst.*, **35**, 2145.
414 Poth, E. J., and Knotts, F. L.: *Proc. Soc. Exptl. Biol. Med.*, **48**, 129–30 (1941).
415 Quilico, A., and Justoni, R.: *Gazz. chim. ital.*, **70**, 1–11 (1940); *Chem. Abst.*, **34**, 2843.
416 Raiziss, G. W., and Clemence, L. W.: *J. Am. Chem. Soc.*, **63**, 3124–6 (1941).
417 ———, ———, and Freifelder, M.: *Ibid.*, 2739–40 (1941).
418 ———, Severac, M., and Moetsch, J. C.: Meeting of the American Chemical Society in Rochester, New York, Sept., 1937.
419 ———, ———, ———, and ———: *J. Am. Chem. Soc.*, **61**, 2763–5 (1939).
420 ———, Kolmer, J. A., and Rule, A. M.: *J. Infectious Diseases*, **66**, 138–43(1940); *Chem. Abst.*, **34**, 5175.
421 Rammelkamp, C. H., and Jewell, M. L.: *Proc. Soc. Exptl. Biol. Med.*, **48**, 27–33 (1941).
422 Rantz, L. A.: *Proc. Soc. Exptl. Biol. Med.*, **49**, 137–40 (1942).
423 Rao, P. L. N.: *J. Indian Chem. Soc.*, **17**, 227–33 (1940); *Chem. Abst.*, **34**, 6356.
424 ———: *J. Indian Chem. Soc.*, **18**, 1–6 (1941); *Chem. Abst.*, **35**, 7945.
425 Reed, G. B., and Orr, J. H.: *Lancet*, **1941**, **1**, 376–9.
426 Renfrew, A. G., and Butler, C. L.: *J. Am. Chem. Soc.*, **62**, 3304–5 (1940).
427 Research Corporation (Daniels, T. C.): U. S. 2,192,828 (Mar. 5, 1940).
428 Richter Gedeon Vegyeszeti Gyár R. T.: Hung. 120,724 (June 1, 1939).
429 ———: Hung. 124,475 (Sept. 2, 1940), addition to 120,724; *Chem. Abst.*, **35**, 4919.
430 Riedel, J. D.-de Haen, E., A.-G. (Boedecker, F., and Heymons, A.): Brit. 529,274 (Nov. 18, 1940); U. S. 2,256,274 (Sept. 16, 1941).
431 Rimington, C., and Hemmings, A. W.: *Biochem. J.*, **33**, 960–977 (1939).

432 Roblin, R. O., Jr.: Personal communication (Sept. 15, 1939); (Dec. 2, 1942).
433 ——, Williams, J. H., and Anderson, G. W.: *J. Am. Chem. Soc.*, **63**, 1930–4 (1941).
434 ——, ——, Winnek, P. S., and English, J. P.: *Ibid.*, **62**, 2002–5 (1940).
435 ——, and Winnek, P. S.: *Ibid.*, 1999–2002 (1940).
436 ——, ——, and English, J. P.: *Ibid.*, **64**, 567–70 (1942).
437 Robson, J. M., and Wallace, A. B.: *Brit. Med. J.*, **1941**, **1**, 469.
438 Rose, H. M., and Fox, C. L., Jr.: *Science*, **95**, 412–3 (1942); *J. Clin. Invest.*, **21**, 628
      (1942).
439 Rosenthal, S. M.: *J. Am. Med. Assoc.*, **113**, 1710–14 (1939).
440 ——, and Bauer, H.: Personal communication (Apr. 13, 1940).
441 ——, ——, and Elvove, E.: *U. S. Pub. Health Repts.*, **54**, 1317–36 (1939).
442 ——, ——, and Branham, S. E.: *Ibid.*, **52**, 662–71 (1937).
443 ——, Wooley, J. G., and Bauer, H.: *Ibid.*, 1211–7 (1937).
444 Rosicky, J.: Fr. 843,415 (July 3, 1939); *Chem. Abst.*, **34**, 6770.
445 ——, and Ostreil, J.: *Prakticky lékar (médecin praticien)*, **17**, 41 and 69 (1937).
446 Rotondaro, F. A.: *J. Am. Pharm. Assoc.*, **30**, 161–6 (1941).
447 Rubbo, S. D., and Gillespie, J. M.: *Lancet*, **1942**, **1**, 36–8; *Nature*, **146**, 838–9 (1940).
448 Rubtzov, M. V.: *J. Gen. Chem. (U.S.S.R.)*, **10**, 831–43 (1940); *Brit. Chem. Abst.*, **1941**,
      A2, 61; *Chem. Abst.*, **35**, 2483.
449 Saccardi, P., and Frulla, M.: *Chim. ind. agr. biol.*, **17**, 144–5 (1941); *Chem. Abst.*, **35**,
      5472.
450 Sakai, T., and Yamamoto, S.: *J. Pharm. Soc. Japan*, **58**, 683–6 (1938); *Chem. Abst.*,
      34, 86.
451 Sammons, H. G., Shelswell, J., and Williams, R. T.: *Biochem. J.*, **35**, 557–63 (1941).
452 Sausville, J. W., and Spoerri, P. E.: *J. Am. Chem. Soc.*, **63**, 3153–4 (1941); *Chem.
      Abst.*, **36**, 425.
453 Savitskii, A. Y., and Rodimovskaya, E. I.: *J. Gen. Chem. (U.S.S.R.)*, **10**, 2091–4
      (1940); *Chem. Abst.*, **35**, 3988.
454 Schaffer, C. W.: *Proc. Soc. Exptl. Biol. Med.*, **37**, 648–50 (1938).
455 Schalm, O. W.: *J. Am. Vet. Med. Assoc.*, **97**, 20–27 (1940).
456 Schering, A.-G.: Fr. 842,726 (June 19, 1939); *Chem. Abst.*, **34**, 5857.
457 Schering Corp. (Vonkennel, J., and Kimmig, J.): U. S. 2,316,825 (Apr. 20, 1943);
      Brit. 509,804 (July 21, 1939); Fr. 842,073 (June 26, 1939).
458 —— (Tschesche, R., and Bohle, K.): U. S. 2,331,009 (Oct. 5, 1943); Brit. 510,127
      (July 27, 1939); *Chem. Abst.*, **34**, 4079; Ger. 735,560 (Apr. 15, 1943); *Chem. Abst.*,
      38, 2668.
459 Schering A.-G. (Dohrn, M., and Diedrich, P.): Swiss 114,936 (Feb. 2, 1938).
460 —— (Tschesche, R., and Bohle, K.): Ger. 704,017 (Feb. 20, 1941); *Chem. Abst.*, **36**,
      1143.
461 Schering Corp. (Dohrn, M., and Diedrich, P.): U. S. 2,323,651 (July 6, 1943); Brit.
      502,559 (Mar. 15, 1939); Ger. 716,667 (Dec. 14, 1941) to Schering-Kahlbaum A.-G.
462 Schmidt, L. H., Ruegsegger, J. M., Sesler, C. L., and Hamburger, M., Jr.: *J. Pharma-
      col.*, **73**, 468–73 (1941).
463 Schmith, K.: *Dansk Tids. Farm.*, **14**, 215–18 (German summary) (1940); *Chem. Abst.*,
      35, 2609.
464 Schroeter, G.: *Ber.*, **39**, 1559–70 (1906).
465 Schurman, I.: *J. Assoc. Official Agr. Chemists*, **24**, 810–14 (1941); *Chem. Abst.*, **36**, 618.
466 Scudi, J. V.: *J. Am. Chem. Soc.*, **59**, 1480–3 (1937).
467 ——: *Ind. Eng. Chem., Anal. Ed.*, **10**, 346–7 (1938).
468 ——: *Science*, **91**, 486 (1940); *Proc. Soc. Exptl. Biol. Med.*, **56**, 197–9 (1944).
469 ——, and Buhs, R. P.: *J. Am. Chem. Soc.*, **63**, 879–80 (1941).
470 ——, and Graessle, O.: *Proc. Soc. Exptl. Biol. Med.*, **46**, 364–9 (1941).
471 ——, Ratish, H. O., and Bullowa, J. G. M.: *J. Am. Chem. Soc.*, **61**, 2554–5 (1939).
472 Seikel, M. K.: *Ibid.*, **62**, 1214–6 (1940).
473 Selbie, F. R.: *Brit. J. Exptl. Path.*, **21**, 90–3 (1940).
474 Shank, R. E., Maxwell, R. W., and Bozalis, G. S.: *J. Am. Med. Assoc.*, **117**, 2238–40
      (1941).
475 Shapiro, D., and Bergmann, F.: *J. Org. Chem.*, **6**, 774–9 (1941).
476 S. M. A. Corp. (Fohring, W. O., Szabo, L. J., and Landy, M.): U. S. 2,270,201 (Jan.
      13, 1942).
477 Smith, M. I., Emmart, E. W., and Westfall, B. B.: *J. Pharmacol.*, **74**, 163–74 (1942).
478 Smyth, H. F., and Carpenter, C. P.: *Science*, **87**, 350 (1938).
479 Snell, E. E.: *J. Biol. Chem.*, **139**, 979 (1941); *ibid.*, **141**, 121–8 (1941).
480 Société pour l'industrie chimique à Bâle: Fr. 848,175 (Oct. 24, 1939); *Chem. Abst.*, **35**,
      5512.

481 ——: Swiss 210,425 (Oct. 1, 1940); Swiss 210,429 (Sept. 16, 1940); Swiss 210,775–94 (Oct. 16, 1940); *Chem. Abst.*, **35**, 5514–6.
482 ——: Brit. 531,167 (Dec. 30, 1940); *Chem. Abst.*, **35**, 7978.
483 ——: Brit. 533,495 (Feb. 14, 1941); *Chem. Abst.*, **36**, 1050; *Brit. Chem. Abst.*, **1941, B2**, 133.
484 —— (Felix, F., Von Capeller, R., and Sallmann, R.): U. S. 2,221,915 (Nov. 19, 1940); Swiss 199,651–3 (Nov. 16, 1938); Fr. 818,727 (Aug. 16, 1937); 822,226 (Dec. 23, 1937); Ger. 725,072 (July 30, 1942).
485 Société des usines chimiques Rhône-Poulene: Brit. 462,765 (Mar. 16, 1937); Fr. 815,502 (July 13, 1937).
486 ——: Fr. 846,191 (Sept. 11, 1939); *Chem. Abst.*, **35**, 1184.
487 —— (Despois, R. L.): Ger. 704,447 (Feb. 27, 1941); U. S. 2,262,544 (Nov. 11, 1941); Brit. 487,378 (Jan. 15, 1938); Fr. 831,366 (Sept. 1, 1938).
488 —— (Despois, R. L., and Goissedet, P. E. C.): Brit. 465,914 (May 19, 1937); Brit. 483,945 (Apr. 28, 1938); Fr. 812,053 (Apr. 29, 1937); Fr. 849,121 (Nov. 7, 1938); U. S. 2,111,768 (Mar. 22, 1938); Ger. 682,238 (Sept. 21, 1939).
489 Sokhey, S. S., and Dikshit, B. B.: *Lancet*, **1940, 1**, 1040–2.
490 Spies, T. D., Ruegsegger, J. M., and Hamburger, M.: *Southern Med. J.*, **34**, 446 (1941).
491 Sprague, J. M. (Sharpe and Dohme Co.): Personal communication (Apr. 19, 1940).
492 ——, and Kissinger, L. W.: *J. Am. Chem. Soc.*, **63**, 578–81 (1941).
493 ——, ——, and Lincoln, R. M.: *Ibid.*, 3028–30 (1941).
494 ——, McBurney, L. F., and Kissinger, L. W.: *Ibid.*, **62**, 1714–6 (1940).
495 Squibb, E. R., and Sons (Christiansen, W. G.): U. S. 2,161,407 (June 6, 1939).
496 —— (Christiansen, W. G., and Dolliver, M. A.): U. S. 2,242,236 (May 20, 1941).
497 Steffenoni, S.: *Arch. farmacol. sper.*, **72**, 44–62 (1941).
498 Steinbach, M. M., and Duca, C. J.: *Proc. Soc. Exptl. Biol. Med.*, **44**, 133–5 (1940); *ibid.*, **49**, 460–4 (1942).
499 Stern, S., and Taub, A.: *J. Am. Pharm. Assoc.*, **28**, 1032–6 (1939).
500 Stuart, E. H., Powell, A. M., Rose, C. L., and Bibbins, F. E.: *Ibid.*, 90–5 (1939).
501 Sugasawa, S., and Sakurai, K.: *J. Pharm. Soc. Japan*, **60**, 22–4, Abstracts (in English) 1–3 (1940); *Chem. Abst.*, **34**, 3704.
502 Suter, C. M., and Weston, A. W.: *J. Am. Chem. Soc.*, **62**, 604–6 (1940).
503 Süto-Nagy, G. de, and Johnson, T. B.: *Ibid.*, **63**, 3234–5 (1941).
504 Sweet, L. A. (Parke-Davis and Co.): Personal communication (Nov. 3, 1939).
505 Tabern, D. L. (Abbott Laboratories): Personal communication (Apr. 20, 1940).
506 Tappi, G., and Migliardi, C.: *Ricerca sci.*, **12**, 1058–60 (1941); *Chem. Abst.*, **36**, 1023.
507 ——, and ——: *Ricerca sci.*, **12**, 1061–5 (1941); *Chem. Abst.*, **36**, 1023.
508 Thorpe, W. V., Williams, R. T., and Shelswell, J.: *Biochem. J.*, **35**, 52–60, 61–5 (1941).
509 Tobie, W. C., Williams, R. D., and Robinson, E. J.: *Science*, **93**, 349–50 (1941).
510 Traub, H. P.: *J. Heredity*, **32**, 157–9 (1941); *Chem. Abst.*, **35**, 5935.
511 Trefouel, J., Trefouel, Mme. J., Nitti, F., and Bovet, D.: *Compt. rend. soc. biol.*, **120**, 756 (1935).
512 ——, ——, ——, and ——: *Ann. inst. Pasteur*, **58**, 30–47 (1937).
513 ——, ——, ——, ——, and Hamon, V.: *Ibid.*, **61**, 812–3 (1938).
514 Tscherntzov, O. M., and Drozdov, N. S.: *J. Gen. Chem. (U.S.S.R.)*, **9**, 1373–5 (1939); *Brit. Chem. Abst.*, **1939, A2**, 562.
515 Tschitschibabin, A. F., and Vialatout, M.: *Bull. Soc. chim.*, **6** (5), 736–9 (1939).
516 Tuda, K., Itikawa, A., and So, D.: *J. Pharm. Soc. Japan*, **59**, 213–5 (in German, 155–8) (1939); *Chem. Abst.*, **33**, 8201.
517 ——, and Suzuki, K.: *J. Pharm. Soc. Japan*, **59**, 224–8 (1939); *Chem. Abst.*, **34**, 7407.
518 Turpeinen, L., and Kallio, O. M. Y.: *Soumen Kemistilehte*, **14B**, 8–9 (1941); *Chem. Abst.*, **36**, 426.
519 Tutiya, H., and Ōmori, S.: *Japan. J. Med. Sci. XIII Dermatol. Urol.*, **2**, 113–29 (1940); *Chem. Abst.*, **35**, 8105.
520 Tyobei Takeda Co. (Yosida, M.): Jap. 132,943 (Oct. 30, 1939); *Chem. Abst.*, **34**, 8183.
521 Tyōbei Takeda Syōten K. K.: Jap. 133,931 (Dec. 20, 1939); *Chem. Abst.*, **35**, 4919.
522 United States Government (Rosenthal, S. M., and Bauer, H.): U. S. 2,234,981 (Mar. 18, 1941); *Chem. Abst.*, **35**, 4160.
523 Urist, H., and Jenkins, G. L.: *J. Am. Chem. Soc.*, **63**, 2943–4 (1941).
524 Vacirca, F.: *Boll. sez. ital. soc. intern. microbiol.*, **11**, 16–9 (1939); *Chem. Abst.*, **33**, 7673; *Boll. ist. sieroterap. milan.*, **18**, 81–93 (1939); *Chem. Abst.*, **33**, 5509.
525 Van Arendonk, A. M., and Kleiderer, E. C.: *J. Am. Chem. Soc.*, **62**, 3521–2 (1940); *Chem. Abst.*, **35**, 1036.
526 Van Dyke, H. B., Greep, R. O., Rake, G., and McKee, C. M.: *Proc. Soc. Exptl. Biol. Med.*, **42**, 410–16 (1939).

527 Van Meter, C. T., Bianculli, J. A., and Lowy, A.: *J. Am. Chem. Soc.*, **62**, 3146–8 (1940).
—, and Lowy, A.: *Ibid.*, **63**, 1330–1 (1941); *Chem. Abst.*, **35**, 4358.
528 Von Seemann, C., and Lucas, C. C.: *Can. J. Research*, **19B**, 291–5 (1941); *Chem. Abst.*, **36**, 1305.
529 Vargas, L., and Zozaya, J.: *Rev. Inst. Salubridad enfermedadestrop (Mex.)*, **2**, 303–10 (1941); *Chem. Abst.*, **37**, 1189.
530 Vargha, L.: *Magyar Biol. Kutatóintézet Munka*, **11**, 372–4 (1939); *Chem. Abst.*, **34**, 3703.
531 Vorozhtsov, M. N., Jr.: *J. Gen. Chem. (U.S.S.R.)*, **10**, 435–31 (1940); *Chem. Abst.*, **35**, 3989.
532 Wagle, D. M., Sokhey, S. S., Dikshit, B. B., and Ganapathi, K.: *Indian Med. Gaz.*, **76**, 29–32 (1941).
533 Waldron, W. R., and Reid, E. E.: *J. Am. Chem. Soc.*, **45**, 2399–417 (1923).
534 Walker, H. A., and Van Dyke, H. B.: *J. Pharmacol.*, **71**, 138–50 (1941).
535 —, and —: *Proc. Soc. Exptl. Biol. Med.*, **48**, 368–72 (1941).
536 Walker, J.: *J. Chem. Soc.*, **1940**, 686–92.
537 —: *Ibid.*, 1304–7.
538 Wander Gyógyszerés Tápszergyár, R. T.: Hung. 122,625 (Jan. 2, 1940); *Chem. Abst.*, **34**, 1686.
539 —: Hung. 124,141 (July 15, 1940); *Chem. Abst.*, **34**, 7543.
540 Ward Blenkinsop and Co., Ltd. (Weisner, B. P. H., and Katschner, E.): Brit. 536,216 (May 7, 1941); *Chem. Abst.*, **36**, 1332; U. S. 2,284,461 (May 26, 1942); *Brit. Chem. Abst.*, **1941, B3**, 216.
541 Watanabe, A.: *Naturwissenschaften*, **29**, 116 (1941); *Chem. Abst.*, **36**, 695.
542 Weber, C. J., Lalich, J. J., and Major, R. H.: *Proc. Soc. Exptl. Biol. Med.*, **48**, 616–9 (1941).
543 Webster, G. L., and Gershon, S. D.: *J. Am. Chem. Soc.*, **63**, 1927–9 (1941).
544 —, and Powers, L. D.: *Ibid.*, **60**, 1553–5 (1938).
545 Wedum, A. G.: *Proc. Soc. Exptl. Biol. Med.*, **45**, 218–9 (1940).
546 Wellcome Foundation Ltd. (Henry, T. A., and Gray, W. H.): Brit. 491,265 (Aug. 30, 1938); *Chem. Abst.*, **33**, 1104.
547 — (Henry, T. A., Gray, W. H., and Platt, B. C.): Brit. 531,571 (Jan. 7, 1941); *Chem. Abst.*, **35**, 8214; *Brit. Chem. Abst.*, **1941, B3**, 79.
548 Whitby, L. E. H.: *Lancet*, **1937, 1**, 1517–9.
549 —: *Ibid.*, **1938, 1**, 1210–2.
550 White, H. J., Litchfield, J. T., Jr., and Marshall, E. K., Jr.: *J. Pharmacol.*, **73**, 104–18 (1941).
551 Wiesner, B. P. H., and Katschner, E.: Brit. 536,369 (May 13, 1941); *Chem. Abst.*, **36**, 1735.
552 Winter, H. C., and Reinhart, F. E.: *J. Am. Chem. Soc.*, **62**, 3508–10 (1940).
553 Winterbottom, R.: *Ibid.*, 160–1 (1940).
554 Winthrop Chemical Co. (Mietzsch, F., Behnisch, R., and Klarer, J.): U. S. 2,132,178 (Oct. 4, 1938); U. S. 2,276,664 (Mar. 17, 1942).
555 — (Behnisch, R., Klarer, J., and Mietzsch, F.): U. S. 2,248,911 (July 8, 1941); Ger. 734,565 (Mar. 25, 1943) to I. G. Farbenindustrie A.-G.
556 — (Behnisch, R., Klarer, J., and Mietzsch, F.): U. S. 2,270,676 (Jan. 20, 1942).
557 — (Mietzsch, F., and Klarer, J.): U. S. 2,022,921 (Dec. 3, 1935).
558 — (Klingel, H., and MacLennan, W. C.): U. S. 2,167,719 (Aug. 1, 1939); Brit. 526,747 (Sept. 25, 1940).
559 — (Mietzsch, F., Klarer, J., and Behnisch, R.): Can. 402,835 (Feb. 10, 1942).
560 — (Mietzsch, F., and Klarer, J.): U. S. 2,202,219 (May 28, 1940); *Chem. Abst.*, **34**, 6771; Ger. 681,686 (Sept. 28, 1939) to I. G. Farbenindustrie.
561 — (Pohls, P., and Behnisch, R.): U. S. 2,267,748 (Dec. 30, 1941); Ger. 708,465 (June 12, 1941).
562 — (Pohls, P., and Mietzsch, F.): U. S. 2,213,805 (Sept. 3, 1940).
563 — (Pohls, P., and Mietzsch, F.): U. S. 2,218,030 (Oct. 15, 1940).
564 — (Schmidt, H.): U. S. 2,215,430 (Sept. 17, 1940); Fr. 845,098 (Aug. 10, 1939) to I. G. Farbenindustrie, A. G.; Brit. 487,233 (July 14, 1938).
565 Woelm, M.: Brit. 490,350 (Jan. 18, 1938); Fr. 831,300 (Aug. 29, 1938).
566 —, Firma: Ger. 702,730 (Jan. 23, 1931); *Chem. Abst.*, **35**, 8213.
567 Wood, F. C.: *Nature*, **136**, 837 (1935); *Chem. Abst.*, **30**, 692.
568 Woods, D. D.: *Biochem. J.*, **36**, 3–4 (1942).
569 —: *Brit. J. Exptl. Path.*, **21**, 74–90 (1940).
570 Woolley, D. W., and Krampitz, L. O.: *J. Exptl. Med.*, **78**, 333–9 (1943).
571 —, and White, A. G. C.: *Proc. Soc. Exptl. Biol. Med.*, **52**, 106–8 (1943).
572 Work, T. S.: *J. Chem. Soc.*, **1942**, 426–9.

573 Wright, C. I., and Lillie, R. D.: *U. S. Pub. Health Repts.*, **58,** 1242–50 (1943).
574 Wruble, M.: *J. Am. Pharm. Assoc.*, **32,** 80–2 (1943).
575 Wurm, K., and Hsiä, Y. D.: *Z. Immunitäts,* **101,** 81–101 (1942); *Chem. Abst.*, **38,** 1799.
576 Wyss, O.: *J. Bact.*, **46,** 483–4 (1943).
577 ——: *Proc. Soc. Exptl. Biol. Med.*, **48,** 122–6 (1941).
578 ——, Grubaugh, K. K., and Schmelkes, F. C.: *Ibid.*, **49,** 618–21 (1942).
579 ——, Lilly, V. G., and Leonian, L. H.: *Science,* **99,** 18–9 (1944).
580 ——, Rubin, M., and Strandskov, F. B.: *Proc. Soc. Exptl. Biol. Med.,* **52,** 155–8 (1943).
581 ——, Strandskov, F. B., and Schmelkes, F. C.: *Science,* **96,** 236–7 (1942).
582 Wyss-Chodat, F., and Paillard, R.: *Compt. rend. Soc. Phys. Hist. Nat. Genéve,* **56,** 50–3 (in *Arch. Sci. Phys. Nat.*, **21,** July–Aug., 1939); *Chem. Abst.*, **34,** 4225.
583 Yannet, H., Deutsch, J. V., and Lieberman, R.: *Yale J. Biol. Med.*, **16,** 443–50 (1944).
584 Young, H. A., Hill, J. H., Jewett, H. S., and Satterthwaite, R. W.: *J. Urol.*, **45,** 903–28 (1941).
585 Zahl, P. A., Hutner, S. H., and Cooper, F. S.: *Proc. Soc. Exptl. Biol. Med.*, **55,** 4–7 (1944).
586 Zaytzeff-Jern, H., and Meleney, F. L.: *J. Lab. Clin. Med.*, **24,** 1017–26 (1939).
587 ——, and ——: *Ibid.*, **26,** 1756–67 (1941).
588 Zeissler, J.: *Klin. Wochschr.*, **22,** 441–2 (1943); *Bull. War Med.*, **4,** 322–3 (1944).
589 Zeller, E. A.: *Helv. Chim. Acta.*, **25,** 216–29 (1942); *Chem. Abst.*, **36,** 5190.
590 Zemp, F. E.: *J. Am. Med. Assoc.*, **121,** 828–30 (1943).
591 Zide, H. A., and Davis, I.: *War Med.*, **2,** 455–9 (1942).
592 Ziegler, W. M.: *J. Am. Chem. Soc.*, **63,** 2946–8 (1941).
593 Zimmerman, A., and Pike, R. M.: *J. Bact.*, **45,** 522 (1943).
594 Zinnermann, K.: *J. Path. Bact.*, **50,** 243–50 (1940).
595 Ziegler, W. M.: *J. Am. Chem. Soc.*, **66,** 744–5 (1944)
596 Zintel, H. A.: *Ann. Surg.*, **119,** 949–53 (1944).
597 Zipkin, I., Anderson, A. K., and Thorp, W. T. S.: *Am. J. Vet. Res.*, **3,** 329–35 (1942).
598 Zurett, S., and Culbertson, J. T.: *J. Parasitol.*, **26,** 235–6 (1940).
599 Zucker, G., Pinner, M., and Hyman, H. T.: *Am. Rev. Tuberc.*, **46,** 277–84 (1942).

Supplementary References

Largely Clinical

600 Aarons, E., and Albert, A.: *J. Chem. Soc.*, **1942,** 183.
601 Abbott Laboratories (Moore, E. E.): U. S. 2,342,957 (Feb. 29, 1944).
602 —— (Raiziss, G. W.): U. S. 2,300,702 (Nov. 3, 1942).
603 —— (Raiziss, G. W.): U. S. 2,336,501 (Dec. 14, 1943).
604 ——: Personal communication from E. H. Volwiler (Jan. 8, 1943).
605 —— (Raiziss, G. W., Clemence, L. W., Severac, M., and Moetsch, J. C.): U. S. 2,302,955 (Nov. 24, 1942).
606 ——: Brit. 548,314; *Brit. Chem. Abst.*, **1943, B3,** 21.
607 Abderhalden, R.: *Fermentforschung,* **16,** 435–40 (1942); *Chem. Abst.*, **37,** 2396 (1943).
608 Adair, F. L., and Hac, L. R.: *New Engl. J. Med.*, **227,** 465–9 (1942).
609 Adams, F. R.: *J. Am. Dental Assoc.*, **30,** 58–68 (1943).
610 Adams, J. W., and Atwood, R. T.: *War Med.*, **5,** 14–20 (1944).
611 Adams, W. M., and Crawford, J. K.: *Southern Surgeon,* **11,** 324–40 (1942).
612 Adamson, D. W.: *J. Chem. Soc.*, **1943,** 39–40.
613 Adolph, P. E., and Lockwood, J. S.: *Arch. Otolaryngol.*, **27,** 535–51 (1938).
614 Aguirre, R. C., Calcarami, J. R., Giraldes, D. A., and Berisso, H. M.: *Semana Med.*, **49,** 621–50 (1942); *J. Am. Med. Assoc.*, **119,** 982 (1942).
615 Aktiebolaget Astra Apotekarnes Kemiska Fabriker: Belg. 438,457 (Mar. 27, 1940); *Chem. Abst.*, **36,** 2868; Austral. 112,885 (Apr. 8, 1941); *Chem. Abst.*, **36,** 3188.
616 Albert, A.: *Lancet,* **1942,** 633.
617 ——: *Med. J. Australia,* **1,** 245–8 (1944).
618 Alexander, H. E.: *Am. J. Diseases Children,* **66,** 160–71 (1943).
619 ——, and Leidy, G.: *J. Pediat.*, **23,** 640–55 (1943).
620 Alexander, H. H., Jr.: *Ind. Med.*, **12,** 434–6 (1943).
621 Alien Property Custodian (Dohrn, M., and Laubereau, O.): U. S. 371,412 (Dec. 23, 1940).
622 —— (Földi, Z., Gerecs, A., Demjén, I., and König, R.): U. S. 342,190; 387,978-9-80 (Apr. 20, 1943); U. S. 2,332,906 (Oct. 26, 1943).

623 Allen, C. F. H., Bell, A., and Wilson, C. V.: *J. Am. Chem. Soc.*, **66**, 835–7 (1944).
624 Allen, H. S., and Koch, S. L.: *Surg. Gynecol. Obstet.*, **74**, 598–603 (1942).
625 Allen, R. W., and Farr, M. M.: *Poultry Sci.*, **21**, 464 (1942).
626 Alstrom, I.: *Skand. Veterinar-Tids.*, **31**, 662 (1942); *ibid.*, **32**, 105–7 (1932).
627 Alture-Werber, E.: *J. Bact.*, **47**, 399–400 (1944).
628 Alyea, E. P., and Parrish, A. A.: *Southern Med. J.*, **36**, 719–23 (1943).
629 Ambrose, A. M., Griswold, R. A., Hamilton, J. E.: *Am. J. Med. Sci.*, **205**, 376–83 (1943).
630 American Cyanamid Co. (Anderson, G. W.): Brit. 555,314 (Sept. 16, 1943); U. S. 2,336,210 (Dec. 7, 1943).
631 —— (Anderson, G. W.): U. S. 2,357,249 (Aug. 29, 1944).
632 —— (Crossley, M. L., Feinstone, W. H., and Lee, J. W.): Brit. 557,447–8.
633 —— (Faith, H. E., and Winnek P. S.): U. S. 2,357,181 (Aug. 29, 1944).
634 —— (Hultquist, M. E., and Crossley, M. L.): U. S. 2,328,455 (Aug. 31, 1943).
635 —— (Hultquist, M. E., and Kuh, E.): U. S. 2,268,033 (Dec. 30, 1947); Brit. 559,455 (May 24, 1941).
636 —— (Kuh, E.): U. S. 2,269,274 (Jan. 6, 1942).
637 —— (Northey, E. H.): U. S. 2,254,186 (Aug. 26, 1941); Brit. 552,101 (Mar. 23, 1943).
638 —— (Northey, E. H., and Dhein, L. H.): U. S. 2,322,196 (June 15, 1943).
639 —— (Northey, E. H., and Hultquist, M. E.): U. S. 2,258,162 (Oct. 7, 1941).
640 —— (Roblin, R. O., Jr.): U. S. 2,333,445 (Nov. 2, 1943).
641 —— (Roblin, R. O., Jr., and Anderson, G. W.): U. S. 2,357,268 (Aug. 29, 1944).
642 —— (Roblin, R. O., Jr., and English, J. P.): U. S. 2,309,739; Brit. 548,422 (Oct. 9, 1942).
643 —— (Roblin, R. O., Jr., and Winnek, P. S.): U. S. 2,295,867 (Sept. 15, 1942).
644 —— (Williams, J. H.): U. S. 2,336,445 (Dec. 7, 1943).
645 —— (Winnek, P. S.): U. S. 2,301,000 (Nov. 3, 1942); Brit. 553,217 (May 12, 1943).
646 —— (Winnek, P. S.): U. S. 2,303,972 (Dec. 1, 1942).
647 —— (Winnek, P. S., and Roblin, R. O., Jr.): Brit. 555,865 (July 15, 1943); *Brit. Chem. Abst.*, **1944**, B3, 18; Brit. 557,447–8 (Dec. 16, 1943); Fr. 870,224 (Dec. 5, 1941).
648 Amies, C. R.: *Lancet*, **1940, 1**, 999–1000.
649 Amoroso, M.: *Gazz. chim. ital.*, **71**, 343–50 (1941); *Chem. Abst.*, **36**, 7009.
650 Anderson, U.: *Ugeskriftlaeger*, **105**, 177–8 (1943); *Chem. Zentr.*, **1943, 1**, 1906.
651 Anderson, D. G., Oliver, C. S., Keefer, C. S.: *New Engl. J. Med.*, **230**, 369–79 (1944).
652 Anderson, E. G., Pilgrim, F. J., and Elvehjem, C. A.: *Proc. Soc. Exptl. Biol. Med.*, **55**, 39–41 (1944).
653 Anderson, G. W., Faith, H. E., Marson, H. W., Winnek, P. S., and Roblin, R. O., Jr.: *J. Am. Chem. Soc.*, **64**, 2902–5 (1942).
654 Anderson, K., and Snow, J. S.: *Amer. J. Path.*, **16**, 269–75 (1940).
655 Anderson, T.: *Lancet*, **1939, 2**, 257–60.
656 ——, Cooper, E. D., Cairns, J. G., and Brown, J. P.: *Lancet*, **1939, 2**, 776–8.
657 Anderson, T. T., Schmith, K., Søbye, P.: *Ugeskr. Laeger*, **104**, 215–21 (1942); *Chem. Abst.*, **37**, 3506.
658 Andrewes, C. H., King, H., and van den Ende, M.: *J. Path. Bact.*, **55**, 173–81 (1943).
659 ——, ——, ——, and Walker, J.: *Lancet*, **1944, 2**, 777–81.
660 Andrus, W. DeW., and Dingwall, J. A., 3rd.: *Ann. Surg.*, **119**, 694–9 (1944).
661 ——, Nickel, W. F., and Schmelkes, F. C.: *Arch. Surg.*, **46**, 1–8 (1943).
662 Angevine, D. M.: *War Med.*, **3**, 186–93 (1943).
663 Anglem, T. J., and Clute, H. M.: *New Engl. J. Med.*, **229**, 432–4 (1943).
664 Anonymous: *Lancet*, **1944, 1**, 764–5.
665 Appelbaum, E., and Nelson, J.: *Am. J. Med. Sci.*, **207**, 492–507 (1944).
666 Archer, N., and Singer, E.: *Brit. Med. J.*, **1943, 1**, 286.
667 Armstrong, A. R., Rae, M. V., Lucas, C. C., and Greey, P. H.: *Am. Rev. Tuberc.*, **50**, 160–2 (1944).
668 Armstrong, C.: *Military Surgeon*, **91**, 129–46 (1942).
669 Arnett, J. H.: *Am. J. Med. Sci.*, **205**, 6–8 (1943).
670 ——, Spink, W. W., Boynton, R., and Agnew, S.: *Proc. Soc. Exptl. Biol. Med.*, **52**, 54–6 (1943).
671 Arnold, H.: *Arch. Pharm.*, **279**, 181–6 (1941); *Chem. Abst.*, **38**, 2325.
672 ——: *Ber.*, **75B**, 87–93 (1942).
673 ——, Helmert, E., Mobus, Th., Prigge, R., Rauen, H., and Warner-Jauregg, Th.: *Ber.*, **75B**, 369–78 (1942).
674 Arnold, M. H. M., and Scaife, C. W.: *J. Chem. Soc.*, **1944**, 103–4.
675 Arreguine, V.: *Anales asoc. quim. argentina*, **31**, 38–47 (1943); *Chem. Abst.*, **37**, 6595.

676 Arthur, R. D., and Dermon, H.: *Am. J. Syphilis, Gonorrhea and Venereal Diseases*, **27**, 261–6 (1943).
677 Ashburn, L. L., Daft, F. S., Endicott, K. M., and Sebrell, W. H.: *U. S. Pub. Health Repts.*, **57**, 1883–91 (1942).
678 Asplin, F. D.: *Nature*, **153**, 253 (1944).
679 Atwell, R. J., Sexton, R. P., and Poston, M. A.: *J. Lab. Clin. Med.*, **28**, 1620–3 (1943).
680 Auhagen, E.: *Z. physiol. Chem.*, **274**, 48–54 (1942); *Chem. Abst.*, **37**, 5100.
681 ——: *Ibid.*, **277**, 197–204 (1943).
682 Axelrod, A. E., Grosse, P., Bosse, M. D., and Swingle, K. F:: *J. Biol. Chem.*, **148**, 721–2 (1943).
683 Backeberg, O. G., and Marais, J. L. C.: *J. Chem. Soc.*, **1942**, 758.
684 ——, and Marais, J. L. C.: *Ibid.*, **1943**, 78–79.
685 Backer, H. J., and deJonge, J.: *Rec. trav. chim.*, **61**, 403–6 (1942); *Chem. Abst.*, **38**, 2327.
686 ——, and ——: *Rec. trav. chim.*, **62**, 158–66 (1943); *Chem. Abst.*, **38**, 2938.
687 ——, and Grevenstuk, A. B.: *Rec. trav. chim.*, **61**, 291–8 (1942); *Chem. Abst.*, **38**, 2326.
688 Bair, H. L.: *Med. Clinics N. America*, **28**, 789–97 (1944).
689 Ballon, H. C., and Guernon, A.: *Am. Rev. Tuberc.*, **45**, 212–216 (1942).
690 ——, ——, and Simon, M. A.: *Ibid.*, 217–28 (1942).
691 Bambas, L. L.: Div. of Medicinal Chemistry, ACS, Memphis, Tenn., Apr. 1942; *J. Am. Chem. Soc.*, **67**, 668–70 (1945).
692 Bang, F. B.: *Am. J. Syphilis*, **27**, 716–32 (1943).
693 ——, and Bang, B. G.: *Proc. Soc. Exptl. Biol. Med.*, **46**, 527–30 (1941); *J. Urol.*, **46**, 427–30 (1941).
694 Banks, C. K., and Hamilton, C. S.: *J. Am. Chem. Soc.*, **61**, 2306 (1939).
695 ——, and Tullar, B. F.: Div. of Medicinal Chemistry, ACS, St. Louis, Mo., Apr., 1941.
696 Bankowski, R. A.: *Cornell Vet.*, **33**, 312–4 (1943).
697 Bär, F.: *Klin. Wochschr.*, **17**, 588–90 (1938).
698 ——: *Z. Immunitäts.*, **97**, 344–65 (1940).
699 Barach, A. L., and Molomut, N.: *J. Lab. Clin. Med.*, **26**, 1915–7 (1941).
700 ——, Molomut, N., and Soroka, M.: *Am. Rev. Tuberc.*, **46**, 268–76 (1942).
701 Barber, H. J.: *J. Chem. Soc.*, **1943**, 101–4.
702 Barber, M., Dible, J. D., and Haslewood, F. A. D.: *Proc. Biochem. Soc.; Biochem. J.*, **37**, vi (1943).
703 Bargen, J. A.: *Med. Clinics N. America*, **28**, 811–24 (1944).
704 Barlow, O. W.: *J. Clin. Investigation*, **21**, 647–8 (1942).
705 Barnes, R. W., and Kawaichi, G. K.: *J. Urol.*, **49**, 324–30 (1943).
706 Barnett, H. L., Perley, A. M., Forbes, G. B., and Goldring, D.: *Am. J. Med. Sci.*, **206**, 599–610 (1943).
707 Barnett, J. W.: *J. Chem. Soc.*, **1944**, 5–8.
708 ——, Dupre, D. J., Holloway, B. J., and Robinson, F. A.: *J. Chem. Soc.*, **1944**, 94–6.
709 ——, and Robinson, F. A.: *Biochem. J.*, **36**, 357–67 (1942).
710 Basu, U. P., and De, S. P.: *Indian J. Med. Res.*, **26**, 537–40 (1938).
711 Batchelor, R. C. L., *et al.*: *Brit. Med. J.*, **1938**, **2**, 1142–5; *ibid.*, **1940**, **1**, 961–6.
712 Bauer, H.: *J. Am. Chem. Soc.*, **63**, 2137–8 (1941).
713 ——, and Rosenthal, S. M.: *Ibid.*, **66**, 611–4 (1944).
714 Bayliss, M.: *Proc. Soc. Exptl. Biol. Med.*, **44**, 525–9 (1940).
715 Beach, J. R.: *Vet. Med.*, **38**, 147 (1943).
716 Behrens, E.: *Zentr. Bact. I, Orig.*, **141**, 385–97 (1938).
717 Behrens, O. K., Eli Lilly & Co.: Unpublished (see Reference 1574).
718 Bell, P. H., Bone, J. F., and Roblin, R. O., Jr.: *J. Am. Chem. Soc.*, **66**, 847 (1944).
719 ——, and Roblin, R. O., Jr.: *Ibid.*, **64**, 2905–17 (1942); *Ann. N. Y. Acad. Sci.*, **44**, 449–54 (1943).
720 Bellavita, V.: *Ricerca Sci.*, **13**, 140–1, 226–8 (1942); *Chem. Abst.*, **37**, 6653; *ibid.*, **38**, 339.
721 ——: *Ricerca Sci.*, **13**, 328–30 (1942); *Chem. Abst.*, **38**, 340.
722 Benbow, E. P., Smith, D. T., and Grimson, K. S.: *Am. Rev. Tuberc.*, **49**, 395–407 (1944).
723 Benesch, R., Barron, N. S., and Mawson, C. A.: *Nature*, **153**, 138–9 (1944).
724 Benn, E. C.: *Brit. Med. J.*, **1939**, **2**, 644–6.
725 Bere, C. M., and Smiles, S.: *J. Chem. Soc.*, **1924**, 2359–63.
726 Bergeim, F. H., and Braker, W.: *J. Am. Chem. Soc.*, **66**, 1459–60 (1944).
727 Bergel, F., and Doring, H.: *Ber.*, **61B**, 844–5 (1928).
728 Bergmann, E., Haskelberg, L., and Bergmann, F.: *J. Am. Chem. Soc.*, **63**, 2247 (1941).
729 Bergmann, F., and Schapiro, D.: *J. Org. Chem.*, **7**, 419–23 (1942).

730   Berkman, S., and Koser, S. A.: *J. Infectious Diseases*, **73**, 57–64 (1943).
731   Berlin, E., and Sjögren, B.: *Svensk. Kem. Tid.*, **53**, 457–9 (1941); *Chem. Abst.*, **37**, 3744.
732   Bernheim, F.: *J. Pharmacol.*, **71**, 344–8 (1941).
733   ——: *Science*, **98**, 223 (1943).
734   Bierman, W., Schwartzman, G., and Rosenberg, S. I.: *J. Lab. Clin. Med.*, **29**, 454–61 (1944).
735   Bieter, R. N., Baker, A. B., Beaton, J. G., Shaffer, J. M., Seery, T. M., and Orr, B.A.: *J. Am. Med. Assoc.*, **116**, 2231–6 (1941).
736   Bigger, J. W.: *Lancet*, **1944, 2**, 142–5.
737   ——, and Hodgson, G. A.: *Lancet*, **1944, 2**, 78–80.
738   Billington, M. B.: *Brit. Med. J.*, **1944, 1**, 326.
739   Billman, J. H.: Unpublished work (see Reference 1574).
740   Biocca, E.: *Arq. Biol. (Sao Paulo)*, **27**, 7–10; 63–4 (1943).
741   Birkhaug, K. E.: *Proc. Soc. Exptl. Biol. Med.*, **42**, 270–5, 275–7 (1939).
742   Bjørneboe, J.: *Norges Apotekerforen. Tids.*, **51**, 25–8 (1943); *Chem. Abst.*, **38**, 4691.
743   Black, S., Overman, R. S., Elvehjem, C. A., and Link, K. P.: *J. Biol. Chem.*, **145**, 137–43 (1942).
744   Blahd, M., Frank, I., and Saphir, O.: *Arch. Path.*, **27**, 424–32 (1939).
745   Blankenhorn, M. A.: *Ann. Internal Med.*, **20**, 423–30 (1944).
746   Blattner, R. J., Heys, F. N., and Hartman, A. F.: *Arch. Path.*, **36**, 262 (1943).
747   Bliss, C. I.: *Quart. J. Pharm. Pharmacol.*, **11**, 192–215 (1938).
748   Bliss, E. A.: *Bull. Johns Hopkins Hosp.*, **60**, 140–53 (1937).
749   ——, and Deitz, H. C.: *Proc. Soc. Am. Bact.; J. Bact.*, **47**, 449 (1944).
750   ——, Feinstone, W. H., Garrett, A. W., and Long, P. H.: *Proc. Soc. Exptl. Biol. Med.*, **40**, 619–21 (1939).
751   ——, and Long, P. H.: *Bull. Johns Hopkins Hosp.*, **69**, 14–38 (1941).
752   ——, and ——: *J. Am. Med. Assoc.*, **109**, 1524–28 (1937).
753   ——, and ——: *New Engl. J. Med.*, **217**, 18–21 (1937).
754   ——, and ——: *Proc. Soc. Exptl. Biol. Med.*, **39**, 483–5 (1938).
755   ——, and ——: *Ibid.*, **40**, 32–4 (1939).
756   ——, ——, and Feinstone, W. H.: *Southern Med. J.*, **31**, 303–8 (1938).
757   ——, ——, and Smith, D. G.: *War Med.*, **1**, 799–810 (1941).
758   ——, and Ott, E.: *Proc. Soc. Exptl. Biol. Med.*, **43**, 706–9 (1940).
759   Bloch, H., and Erlenmeyer, H.: *Helv. Chim. Acta*, **25**, 694–7 (1942); *ibid.*, **25**, 1063–6 (1942); *Chem. Abst.*, **37**, 152; *Chem. Abst.*, **37**, 1460.
760   Blum, J.: *Schweiz. Arch. Tierheilk.*, **85**, 152–60 (1943); *Chem. Abst.*, **38**, 4697.
761   Blumberg, M. L., and Gleich, M.: *J. Am. Med. Assoc.*, **123**, 132–4 (1943).
762   Boehringer, C. F., and Soehne G. M. B. H. (Rabald, E.): Ger. 726,989 (Sept. 17, 1942).
763   Bogen, E.: *U. S. Naval Med. Bull.*, **41**, 1135–8 (1943).
764   Bograchov, E.: *J. Am. Chem. Soc.*, **65**, 1652–3 (1943).
765   Bohme, H., and Wagner, J.: *Arch. Pharm.*, **280**, 255–67 (1942); *Fette u. Siefen*, **49**, 785–7 (1942); *Chem. Abst.*, **37**, 6411.
766   Boissard, J. M., and Fry, R. M.: *Lancet*, **1942, 1**, 610–4.
767   Boots Pure Drug Co. Ltd.: Brit. 544,836 (May 28, 1942).
768   Bordwell, F. G., and Klotz, I. M.: *J. Am. Chem. Soc.*, **66**, 660–1 (1944).
769   Bornstein, S., and Schwarz, H.: *Am. J. Med. Sci.*, **204**, 546–50 (1942).
770   Bortz, E. L.: *J. Am. Med. Assoc.*, **121**, 107–13 (1943).
771   Bose, A. N.: *Indian Med. Gaz.*, **77**, 657–9 (1942); *Chem. Abst.*, **37**, 2078.
772   Bost, R. W.: Source of compounds tested by Eli Lilly & Co. (see Reference 1574).
773   Boughton, D. C., and Davis, L. R.: *Am. J. Vet. Res.*, **4**, 150–4 (1943); *ibid.*, 66–72 (1943).
774   Bowers, W. C.: *Eye, Ear, Nose and Throat Monthly*, **22**, 293–300 (1943).
775   Boyd, E. M., and Pratten, J. S.: *Am. J. Med. Sci.*, **204**, 715–8 (1942).
776   Bracken, M. M., Johnston, J. M., Crum, G. E., Patrick, D. R., Permar, H. H., and Maclachlan, W. W. G.: *J. Pharmacol.*, **68**, 259–66 (1940).
777   Bradbury, F. R., and Jordan, D. O.: *Biochem. J.*, **36**, 1–7 (1942); *ibid.*, **36**, 287–93 (1942).
778   Bradford, W. L., Brooks, A. M., and Katsampes, C. P.: *Yale J. Biol. Med.*, **16**, 434–42 (1944).
779   Brady, D., Bauer, R., and Yonkman, F. F.: *J. Am. Pharm. Assoc.*, **32**, 142–3 (1943).
780   Branch, G. E. K., and Calvin, M.: "The Theory of Organic Chemistry," Prentice-Hall, Inc., New York, N. Y., 1941.
781   Branham, S. E.: *U. S. Pub. Health Repts.*, **55**, 12–25 (1940).
782   ——, and Rosenthal, S. M.: *U. S. Pub. Health Repts.*, **52**, 685–95 (1937).

783 Braun, C. E., and Ludwig, B. J.: *J. Org. Chem.*, **3**, 16–25 (1938).
784 Brenner, C., and Cohen, S.: *J. Am. Med. Assoc.*, **123**, 948–9 (1943).
785 Brewer, A. E.: *Brit. Med. J.*, **1943, 1,** 36–40.
786 Brian, P. W.: *Nature*, **153,** 83 (1944).
787 British Drug Houses Ltd. (Skrimshire, G. E. H.): Brit. 540,032 (Oct. 2, 1941).
788 British Schering Research Laboratories (Hay, D. H., and Beynon, J. H.): Brit.
    588,017 (Jan. 14, 1944); *Brit. Chem. Abst.*, **1944, B3,** 73.
789 Britton, C. J. C.: *Brit. J. Exptl. Path.*, **19,** 140–3 (1938).
790 Brooke, W. S., and Day, R.: *Bull. Johns Hopkins Hosp.*, **74,** 285–7 (1944).
791 Brose, C. P.: *N. Y. State Dept. Health Ann. Rept. Div. Lab. & Res.*, **1941,** 40; *Chem.*
    Abst., **36,** 5896.
792 Brown, A. E.: *Kentucky Med. J.*, **42,** 75–80 (1944).
793 ——, *Med. Clinics N. America*, **28,** 869–81 (1944).
794 ——, and Herrell, W. E.: *Am. J. Med. Sci.*, **200,** 618–31 (1940).
795 Brown, J. H., and Schaub, I. G.: *Ibid.*, **208,** 385–9 (1944).
796 Brown, L. A.: *Ann. Otol. Rhin. Laryngol.*, **51,** 611–14 (1942).
797 Brown, W. H., Thornton, W. B., and Wilson, J. S.: *J. Am. Med. Assoc.*, **114,** 1605–11
    (1940).
798 Browne, S. M., Marvin, H. P., and Smith, E. R.: *Diseases of Chest*, **9,** 297–301 (1943).
799 Browning, P.: *J. Path. Bact.*, **50,** 431–8 (1940).
800 Brownlee, G., Copp, F. C., Duffin, W. M., and Tonkin, I. M.: *Biochem. J.*, **37,** 572–7
    (1943).
801 ——, and Tonkin, I. M.: *Nature*, **148,** 167–8 (1941); *Trop. Diseases Bull.*, **39,** 35–6
    (1942); *Chem. Abst.*, **36,** 5555.
802 Brueckner, A. H.: *Yale J. Biol. Med.*, **15,** 813–21 (1943).
803 Bruni, A., and Buda, L.: *Settim. Med.*, **27,** 1131–3 (1939).
804 Bryant, J., and Fairman, H. D.: *Lancet*, **1939, 1,** 923–6.
805 Bucca, M. A.: *J. Bact.*, **46,** 151–66 (1943).
806 Buddingh, G. J.: *J. Exptl. Med.*, **80,** 59–64 (1944).
807 Bukantz, S. C., and Abernethy, T. J.: *Proc. Soc. Exptl. Biol. Med.*, **47,** 94–7 (1941).
808 Bullowa, J. G. M., Osgood, E. E., Bukantz, S. C., and Brownlee, I. E.: *Am. J. Med.*
    Sci., **199,** 364–80 (1940).
809 Bulmer, E.: *Trans. Roy. Soc. Trop. Med. Hyg.*, **37,** 225–42 (1944); *Brit. Med. J.*, **1943,**
    1, 374; *ibid.*, **1944, 1,** 569.
810 ——, and Priest, W. M.: *Lancet*, **1943, 2,** 69–71.
811 Bunting, J. J., and Levan, N. E.: *J. Am. Med. Assoc.*, **125,** 773–4 (1944).
812 Burger, A.: Personal communication (Dec. 16, 1942).
813 Burton, H.: *Chemistry & Industry*, **1941,** 449; *Chem. Abst.*, **35,** 6937.
814 ——, McLeod, J. W., Mayr-Harting, A., and Walker, N.: *J. Path. Bact.*, **54,** 407–19
    (1942).
815 ——, and Walker, N.: *J. Chem. Soc.*, **1943,** 656–7.
816 Bury, K. J.: *Klin. Wochschr.*, **21,** 709–10 (1942); *Chem. Abst.*, **37,** 3825.
817 Butler, G. C., Lozinski, E., and Odell, A. D.: Brit. 559,775; *Brit. Chem. Abst.*, **1944,**
    B3, 118.
818 Buttle, G. A. H.: *Lancet*, **1937, 2,** 1076–7.
819 ——: *Ibid.*, **1940, 1,** 890–2.
820 ——, and Parish, H. J.: *Brit. Med. J.*, **1938, 2,** 776–7.
821 ——, ——, McLeod, M., and Stephenson, D.: *Lancet*, **1937, 1,** 681–4.
822 ——, Stephenson, D., Smith, S., Dewing, T., and Foster, G. E.: *Lancet*, **1937, 1,**
    1331–4.
823 ——: *Trans. Roy. Soc. Trop. Med. Hyg.*, **33,** 141–68 (1939).
824 Calamari, J. A., Hubata, R., and Roth, P. B.: *Ind. Eng. Chem., Anal. Ed.*, **14,** 534–5
    (1942).
825 Caldwell, G. A., and Cox, F. J.: *Southern Med. J.*, **35,** 789–98 (1942).
826 Caldwell, W. T., and Fellows, E. J.: Personal communication (Dec. 31, 1942).
827 ——, Tyson, F. T., and Lauer, L.: *J. Am. Chem. Soc.*, **66,** 1479–84 (1944).
828 Calkins, H. E., and Bond, G. C.: *Proc. Soc. Exptl. Biol. Med.*, **56,** 46 (1944).
829 Callomon, F. T., and Brown, H.: *Am. J. Syphilis, Gonorrhea and Venereal Diseases*,
    27, 590–600 (1943).
830 ——, and Groskin, L.: *Am. Rev. Tuberc.*, **47,** 97–106 (1943).
831 ——, and Linton, L. G.: *J. Lab. Clin. Med.*, **29,** 574–84 (1944).
832 ——, and Raiziss, G. W.: *J. Pharmacol.*, **79,** 200–7 (1943).
833 Callomon, V. B., and Goodpastor, W. E.: *Ann. Internal Med.*, **14,** 1024–31 (1940).
834 Cameron, H. S.: *Cornell Vet.*, **38,** 1 (1942).
835 Camponovo, L. E.: *Prensa méd. argent.*, **29,** 1769–82 (1942).
836 Campbell, D. G.: *Brit. Med. J.*, **1944, 2,** 44.

837 Carpenter, C. M., Ackerman, H., Winchester, M. E., and Whittle, F.: *Am. J. Pub. Health*, **34**, 250–4 (1944).
838 ——, and Barbour, G. M.: *Proc. Soc. Exptl. Biol. Med.*, **41**, 255–9, 354–7 (1939).
839 ——, ——, and Hawley, P. L.: *J. Pediat.*, **14**, 116 (1939).
840 ——, Hawley, P. L., and Barbour, G. M.: *Science*, **88**, 530–1 (1938).
841 ——, Stokinger, H. E., and Charles, R. L.: *J. Pharmacol.*, In Press.
842 ——, and Wingate, H. F.: *J. Bact.*, **41**, 473–8 (1941).
843 Carrara, G., and Monzini, G.: *Chimica e industria (Italy)*, **23**, 391–2 (1941); *Chem. Abst.*, **36**, 6510.
844 Carruthers, L. B.: *Trans. Roy. Soc. Trop. Med. Hyg.*, **36**, 89–93 (1942).
845 Carryer, H. M., and Osterberg, A. E.: *J. Lab. Clin. Med.*, **28**, 110–12 (1942).
846 Case, W. E.: *J. Am. Chem. Soc.*, **64**, 785–7 (1942).
847 Casten, D., Fried, J. J., and Hallman, F. E.: *Surg. Gynecol. Obstet.*, **76**, 726–8 (1943).
848 Cavallini, G., and Carrissimi, M.: *Chimica e industria (Italy)*, **24**, 201–3 (1942); *Chem. Atst.*, **38**, 3629.
849 ——, and Saccarello, A.: *Chimica e industria (Italy)*, **24**, 425–6 (1942); *Chem. Abst.*, **38**, 4257.
850 Cavanagh, J. R.: *War Med.*, **4**, 549–55 (1943).
851 Cecil, R. L., Angevine, D. M., and Rothbard, S.: *Am. J. Med. Sci.*, **198**, 463–75 (1939).
852 ——, Plummer, H., and Smillie, W. G.: *J. Am. Med. Assoc.*, **124**, 8–14 (1944).
853 Chambers, L. A., Harris, T. N., Schumann, F., and Ferguson, L. K.: *Ibid.*, **119**, 324–7 (1942).
854 Chandler, C. A., and Janeway, C. A.: *Proc. Soc. Exptl. Biol. Med.*, **40**, 179–84 (1939).
855 ——, and Taussig, H. B.: *Bull. Johns Hopkins Hosp.*, **72**, 42–53 (1943).
856 Chapple, C. C., and Lynch, H. M.: *Am. J. Med. Sci.*, **207**, 488–92 (1944).
857 Cheever, F. S., Breeze, B. B., and Upham, H. C.: *Ann. Internal Med.*, **19**, 602–8 (1943).
858 Child, R., and Smiles, S.: *J. Chem. Soc.*, **1926**, 2696–702.
859 Chinn, B. D.: *J. Infectious Diseases*, **64**, 78–82 (1939).
860 ——: *Proc. Soc. Exptl. Biol. Med.*, **38**, 732–4 (1938).
861 Chopra, R. N., and Das Gupta, B. M.: *Indian Med. Gaz.*, **73**, 395–6 (1938); *ibid.*, **74**, 201–2 (1939); *Chem. Abst.*, **32**, 9268.
862 ——, de Monte, A. J. H., Gupta, S. K., and Chatterji, B. C.: *Indian Med. Gaz.*, **76**, 712–13 (1941).
863 ——, Hayter, R. T. M., and Sen, B.: *Ibid.*, **74**, 658–60 (1939).
864 Christiansen, J. F., and Foster, A. O.: *Vet. Med.*, **38**, 144–7 (1943).
865 Christiansen, W. J.: *J. Am. Chem. Soc.*, **63**, 632 (1942).
866 Chu, E. J., Shen, Z., Chien, T., and Tuan, T. S.: *Ibid.*, **66**, 651 (1944).
867 Churg, J., and Lehr, D.: *Am. J. Med. Sci.*, **202**, 687–91 (1941).
868 Cilag, Chemisches Industrielles Laboratorium A.-G.: Swiss 212,060 and 212,062 (Jan. 16, 1941); 214,352 (July 16, 1941); *Chem. Abst.*, **36**, 3632, 4975, 5960.
869 ——: Swiss 213,150 and 213,151 (Apr. 16, 1941).
870 ——: Swiss 213,815 and 213,816 (June 3, 1941); *Chem. Abst.*, **36**, 4974.
871 Ciminera, J. L., and Wilcox, P. W.: *J. Am. Pharm. Assoc.*, **33**, 85–90 (1944).
872 Circular Letter No. 17 (Feb. 23, 1942), Office of the Surgeon General, United States Army, Washington, D. C.: *War Med.*, **2**, 466–81 (1942).
873 Cirillo, A. A.: *Arch. Otolaryngol.*, **36**, 541–7 (1942).
874 Clark, J. K., Flippin, H. F., and Murphy, F. D.: *Am. J. Med. Sci.*, **205**, 846–51 (1943).
875 ——, Murphy, F. D., and Flippin, H. F.: *J. Lab. Clin. Med.*, **28**, 1828–34 (1943).
876 Clark, W. G., Strakosch, E. A., and Leven, L. N.: *Journal-Lancet*, **62**, 455–6 (1942).
877 ——, ——, and Levitan, N. I.: *J. Lab. Clin. Med.*, **28**, 188–9 (1942).
878 ——, ——, and Nordlum, C.: *Proc. Soc. Exptl. Biol. Med.*, **50**, 43–8 (1942).
879 Clay, A. C.: *Brit. Med. J.*, **1943**, **2**, 35–6.
880 Clay, R. C., and Pickrell, K. L.: *J. Am. Med. Assoc.*, **123**, 203–4 (1943).
881 Cleve, P. T.: *Ber.*, **21**, 3272 (1888).
882 ——: *Ibid.*, **23**, 961 (1890).
883 ——: *Of. SV*, **1893**, 331; *Beil.*, **XIV**, 749.
884 Clifton, C. E., and Loewinger, I. E.: *Proc. Soc. Exptl. Biol. Med.*, **52**, 225–7 (1943).
885 Climenko, D. R., Barlow, O. W., and Wright, A. W.: *Arch. Path.*, **32**, 889–94 (1941).
886 ——, Crossley, M. L., and Northey, E. H.: *J. Am. Med. Assoc.*, **110**, 2099–100 (1938).
887 Clowes, G. H. A., Keltch, A. K., and Krahl, M. E.: *J. Pharmacol.*, **68**, 312–29 (1940).
888 Coburn, A. F.: *J. Am. Med. Assoc.*, **126**, 88–93 (1944).
889 Coggeshall, L. T.: *J. Bact.*, **39**, 30–1 (1940); *J. Exptl. Med.*, **71**, 13–20 (1940).
890 ——: *Proc. Soc. Exptl. Biol. Med.*, **38**, 768–73 (1938); *Am. J. Trop. Med.*, **18**, 715–21 (1938).
891 ——, and Maier, J.: *J. Infectious Diseases*, **69**, 108–13 (1941).

892 ——, and ——: *J. Pharmacol.*, **76,** 161–6 (1942).
893 ——, ——, and Best, C. A.: *J. Am. Med. Assoc.*, **117,** 1077–81 (1941).
894 Cohn, A., and Peizer, L. R.: *J. Infectious Diseases*, **63,** 77–80 (1938).
895 Cokkinis, A. J., and McElligott, G. L. M.: *Lancet*, **1938, 2,** 355–62.
896 Cole, H. N.: *J. Am. Med. Assoc.*, **123,** 411–7 (1943).
897 Colebrook, L.: *Lancet*, **1936, 1,** 1280–90.
898 ——: *Lancet*, **1942, 1,** 761.
899 ——: *Lancet*, **1943, 2,** 207.
900 ——, Buttle, G. A. H., and O'Meara, R. A. Q.: *Lancet*, **1936, 2,** 1323–6.
901 ——, and Kenny, M.: *Lancet*, **1936, 1,** 1279–86.
902 ——, and Maxted, W. R.: *Lancet*, **1940, 1,** 21–3.
903 Collings, G. H., Jr.: *Ind. Med.*, **12,** 301–3 (1943).
904 Collins, C. J., Eli Lilly & Co.: Unpublished (see Reference 1574).
905 Combes, F. C., Canizares, O., and Landy, S.: *Am. J. Syphilis*, **27,** 700–2 (1943).
906 Committee on Chemotherapy and Other Agents and the Committee on Surgery of the Division of Medical Sciences of the National Research Council: *Bull. War Med.*, **2,** 488–96 (1942).
907 Connell, E. S., and Trowbridge, B. C.: *Arch. Ophthalmol.*, **27,** 705–6 (1942).
908 Connor, C. E.: *Minnesota Med.*, **26,** 257–63 (1943).
909 Contratto, A. W.: *Arch. Intern. Med.*, **73,** 449–59 (1944).
910 Cooke, W. T.: *Lancet*, **1941, 2,** 510–12.
911 Cooper, F. B., Gross, P., and Hagan, M. L.: *J. Clin. Investigation*, **21,** 281–6 (1942).
912 ——, Gross, P., and Lewis, M.: *Am. J. Med. Sci.*, **196,** 343–7 (1938); *ibid.*, **197,** 609–17 (1939).
913 ——, ——, and ——: *Proc. Soc. Exptl. Biol. Med.*, **38,** 375–7, 835–6 (1938).
914 ——, ——, and ——: *Ibid.*, **40,** 34–6, 37–8 (1939).
915 Cooper, M. L., and Keller, H. M.: *J. Am. Med. Assoc.*, **116,** 2529 (1941).
916 ——, and ——: *J. Bact.*, **45,** 26–7 (1943).
917 ——, and ——: *J. Pediat.*, **18,** 458–68 (1941).
918 ——, and ——: *Proc. Soc. Exptl. Biol. Med.*, **50,** 148–52 (1942).
919 ——, and ——: *Ibid.*, **45,** 111–4 (1940).
920 ——, and ——: *Ibid.*, **52,** 92–5 (1943).
921 Corper, H. J., Cohn, M. L., and Bower, C.: *Am. Rev. Tuberc.*, **40,** 452–66 (1939).
922 Corwin, W. C.: *Bull. Johns Hopkins Hosp.*, **69,** 39–52 (1941).
923 Cosgrove, K. W.: *Am. J. Ophthalmol.*, **23,** 911 (1940); *J. Am. Med. Assoc.*, **115,** 1225–6 (1940).
924 ——, and Hundley, L. K.: *Southern Med. J.*, **35,** 43–8 (1942).
925 Costantino, G., and Callerio, C.: *Biochim. terap. sper.*, **30,** 25–35 (1943); *Chem. Abst.*, **38,** 4690.
926 Cotler, H. V., Kirchner, M. T., and Romano, M.: *Proc. Soc. Exptl. Biol. Med.*, **46,** 241–4 (1941).
927 Cottrell, J. D., and Knights, H. T.: *J. Royal Army Med. Corp.*, **81,** 7–15 (1943).
928 Council on Industrial Health and Council on Pharmacy and Chemistry of the American Medical Association: *J. Am. Med. Assoc.*, **125,** 969–73 (1944).
929 Council on Pharmacy and Chemistry of the American Medical Association: "New and Nonofficial Remedies, 1944," American Medical Association, Chicago, 1944.
930 Cowles, P. B.: *Yale J. Biol. Med.*, **14,** 599–604 (1942).
931 Cox, E. H.: *J. Am. Chem. Soc.*, **64,** 2225–6 (1942).
932 ——: *J. Org. Chem.*, **7,** 307–8 (1942).
933 Crafton, J. W., and Diggle, G.: *Lancet*, **1944, 1,** 367–8.
934 Crawford, J. H.: *Lancet*, **1943, 1,** 787.
935 Crippa, G. B., and Maffei, S.: *Gazz. chim. ital.*, **72,** 97–9 (1942); *Brit. Chem. Abst.*, **1943, A2,** 141.
936 Crowe, M.: *Brit. Med. J.*, **1943, 2,** 214.
937 Cruickshank, J. C.: *Lancet*, **1938, 2,** 310–11.
938 ——: *Ibid.*, **1939, 2,** 681–4.
939 Crutcher, R. R., Daniel, R. A., Jr., and Billings, E. T.: *Ann. Surg.*, **117,** 677–85 (1943).
940 Cutting, W. C., and Gerhardt, L. P.: *Science*, **94,** 568–9 (1941).
941 ——, and Robson, G. B.: *J. Am. Med. Assoc.*, **118,** 1447–9 (1942).
942 ——, and Sultan, E. H.: *Ann. Intern. Med.*, **16,** 708–15 (1942).
943 Daft, F. S., Ashburn, L. L., and Sebrell, W. H.: *Science*, **96,** 321–2 (1942).
944 ——, Endicott, K. M., Ashburn, L. L., and Sebrell, W. H.: *Proc. Soc. Exptl. Biol. Med.*, **53,** 130–1 (1943).
945 ——, and Sebrell, W. H.: *U. S. Pub. Health Repts.*, **58,** 1542–5 (1943).
946 Dancey, R. J., Schmidt, R. H., Jr., and Wilkie, J. M.: *Am. Rev. Tuberc.*, **49,** 510–34 (1944).

947 Daniel, R. A., Jr., Billings, F. T., and Crutcher, R. R.: *Ann. Surg.*, **117**, 670–7 (1943).
948 Daniels, W. B., Solomon, S., Jaquette, W. H., Jr.: *J. Am. Med. Assoc.*, **123**, 1–9 (1943).
949 Darke, R. A.: *J. Am. Med. Assoc.*, **124**, 403–4 (1944).
950 Davenport, H. W.: *Yale J. Biol. Med.*, **14**, 589–97 (1942).
951 Davies, J. N. P.: *Lancet*, **1943**, **1**, 553–6.
952 Davis, B. D.: *New Engl. J. Med.*, **230**, 734–8 (1944).
953 ———: *Science*, **95**, 78 (1942); *J. Clin. Investigation*, **22**, 753–62 (1943).
954 ———, and Wood, W. B., Jr.: *Proc. Soc. Exptl. Biol. Med.*, **51**, 283–5 (1942).
955 Davis, G. K., Hale, E. B., and Freeman, V. A.: *J. Animal Sci.*, **2**, 138–45 (1943).
956 Davis, H. J.: *Ind. Med.*, **12**, 426–7 (1943).
957 Day, H. G., Wakim, K. G., Krider, M. M., and O'Banion, E. E.: *J. Nutrition*, **26**, 585–600 (1943).
958 De, S. P., and Basu, U. P.: *Indian J. Med. Research*, **25**, 465–70 (1937).
959 Debenham, R. K.: *Brit. Med. J.*, **1943**, **2**, 223–7.
960 Delaby, R., and Harispe, J. V.: *Bull. soc. chim.*, **10**, 580–4 (1943); *Chem. Abst.*, **38**, 4572.
961 Delbrück, M., and Luria, S. E.: *J. Bact.*, **46**, 574–5 (1943).
962 Deliwala, O. V., Ganapathi, K., and Shirsat, M. V.: *Proc. Indian Acad. Sci.*, **18A**, 360–3 (1943); *Chem. Abst.*, **38**, 4573.
963 Demeny, L.: *Rec. trav. chim.*, **48**, 1145–54 (1929).
964 Dermer, V. H., and Dermer, O. C.: *J. Am. Chem. Soc.*, **64**, 3056–7 (1942).
965 DeSanctis, A. G., Larkin, V. deP., and Gougelman, W. A.: *J. Am. Med. Assoc.*, **120**, 1087–93 (1942).
966 Dettwiler, H. A., and Schmidt, L. H.: *J. Bact. Proc.*, **40**, 160–1 (1940).
967 deWaal, H. L., Kanaar, A. C., and McNaughton, J.: *Lancet*, **1942**, **2**, 724–7.
968 Dewing, T., Gray, W. H., Platt, B. C., and Stephenson, D.: *J. Chem. Soc.*, **1942** 239–44.
969 Dharmendra, and Bose, R.: *Ind. J. Med. Res.*, **31**, 133–136 (1943).
970 Dick, G. F.: *J. Am. Med. Assoc.*, **120**, 24–5 (1942).
971 Dickerson, V., and Whitney, L. F.: *Proc. Soc. Exptl. Biol. Med.*, **38**, 263–4 (1938).
972 Dietrich, H. F.: *Am. Rev. Tuberc.*, **38**, 388–92 (1938).
973 Digonnet, L.: *Compt. rend. soc. biol.*, **130**, 409, 543, 627–30 (1939).
974 DiMaio, M., and Bird, C. E.: *New Engl. J. Med.*, **228**, 390–1 (1943).
975 Dimond, N. S.: *Science*, **94**, 420–1 (1941).
976 ———, and Thompson, K. W.: *J. Investigative Dermatol.*, **5**, 397–402 (1942).
977 Dingle, J. H., and Finland, M.: *War Med.*, **2**, 1–58 (1942).
978 ———, Thomas, L., and Morton, A. R.: *J. Am. Med. Assoc.*, **116**, 2666–8 (1941).
979 Dingwall, J. A., 3rd.: *Am. J. Surg.*, **64**, 323–7 (1944).
980 Dittmer, K., Melville, D. B., and du Vigneaud, V.: *Science*, **99**, 203–5 (1944).
981 Divinskii, A., and Vorobéva, E.: *Compt. rend. acad. sci. U.S.S.R.*, **36**, 203–5 (1942); *Chem. Abst.*, **37**, 2722.
982 Djin, H. Y.: *Z. Immunitäts.*, **98**, 220–52 (1940).
983 Doak, G. O., Steinman, H. G., and Eagle, H.: *J. Am. Chem. Soc.*, **62**, 3012–3 (1940).
984 Dobson, L., Holman, E., and Cutting, W. C.: *J. Am. Med. Assoc.*, **116**, 272–5 (1941).
985 Dodge, K. G., Baldwin, J. S., and Weber, M. W.: *J. Pediat.*, **24**, 483–501 (1944).
986 Dolowitz, D. A., Loch, W. E., Haines, H. L., Ward, A. T., Jr., and Pickrell, K. L.: *J. Am. Med. Assoc.*, **123**, 534–6 (1943).
987 Domagk, G.: *Deut. Med. Wochschr.*, **61**, 250–73 (1935).
988 ———: *Ibid.*, **69**, 379–85 (1943); *Bull. War Med.*, **4**, 300 (1944).
989 ———: *Klin. Wochschr.*, **16**, 1412–18 (1937).
990 ———: *Ibid.*, **21**, 448 (1942); *Chem. Abst.*, **36**, 5895.
991 ———: *Z. Klin. Med.*, **132**, 775–801 (1937).
992 ———: *Z. physiol. Chem.*, **274**, 55–65 (1942); *Chem. Abst.*, **37**, 6741.
993 Don, C. S. D., et al.: *Lancet*, **1940**, **1**, 311–14.
994 Donald, C., and Barker, P. B.: *Brit. Med. J.*, **1942**, **2**, 333–5.
995 Dorfman, A., and Koser, S. A.: *J. Infectious Diseases*, **71**, 241–52 (1942); *Chem. Abst.* **37**, 3469.
996 ———, Rice, L., Koser, S. A., and Saunders, F.: *Proc. Soc. Exptl. Biol. Med.*, **45**, 750–3 (1940).
997 Döring, L.: *Med. Klin.*, **37**, 354–6 (1941); *Chem. Abst.*, **38**, 2735.
998 Dorling, G. C., and Eckhoff, N. L.: *Lancet*, **1940**, **2**, 707–8.
999 Dosa, A.: *Acta Dermato-Venereol*, **22**, 315–19 (1941); *Chem. Abst.*, **37**, 679.
1000 Douglas, R. G., Davis, I. F., and Shandorf, J. F.: *Am. J. Obstet. Gynecol.*, **44**, 1026–47 (1942).
1001 Dowling, H. F.: *Med. Ann. Distr. Columbia*, **10**, 463–7 (1941).
1002 ———: *Ibid.*, **12**, 468–71 (1943).

1003 ——, Dumoff-Stanley, E., Lepper, M. H., and Sweet, L. K.: *J. Am. Med. Assoc.*, **125**, 103–5 (1944).
1004 ——, Hartman, C. R., Feldman, H. A., and Jenkins, F. A.: *Am. J. Med. Sci.*, **205**, 197–203 (1943).
1005 ——, and Lepper, M. H.: *Ibid.*, **207**, 349–53 (1944).
1006 ——, and ——: *J. Am. Med. Assoc.*, **121**, 1190–4 (1943).
1007 Druey, J.: *Helv. Chim. Acta.*, **24**, 226–33E (1941).
1008 ——, and Oesterheld, G.: *Ibid.*, **25**, 753–60 (1942); *Chem. Abst.*, **37**, 150.
1009 Dubos, R. J., Straus, J. H., and Pierce, C.: *J. Exptl. Med.*, **78**, 161–8 (1943).
1010 Dunarric de la Riviere, R., Roux, E., and Cheve, J.: *Bull. acad. med.*, **122**, 159–63 (1939).
1011 Durand, P.: *Arch. inst. Pasteur di Tunis*, **28**, 83–94, 96–106 (1939); *Bull. soc. path. exot.*, **32**, 286–90 (1939).
1012 Dyson, C. B.: *J. Path. Bact.*, **47**, 641–2 (1938).
1013 Earle, K. V.: *Lancet*, **1939, 2**, 1265–6.
1014 Ebert, E.: *Arch. Otolaryngol.*, **38**, 324–7 (1943).
1015 Eckstein, A. W.: *Rhode Island Med. J.*, **24**, 84–90 (1941).
1016 Editorial: *Pharm. J.*, **148**, 192 (1942).
1017 Eddy, B. E.: *U. S. Public Health Repts.*, **59**, 485–99 (1944).
1018 Einsel, I. H., Nixon, E. N., Gitman, L., and Rogoff, J. M.: *Gastroenterology*, **1**, 882–91 (1943).
1019 Eisenoff, H. M., and Goldstein, H.: *J. Am. Med. Assoc.*, **123**, 624–6 (1943).
1020 Ekbom, A.: *Ber.*, **23**, 1118–24 (1890).
1021 Eckstrand, T.: *Svensk Kem. Tid.*, **54**, 257–62 (1942).
1022 Elkington, J. St. C.: *Lancet*, **1942, 2**, 425–6.
1023 Ellis-Foster Co. (John B. Rust): U. S. 2,310,038 (Feb. 2, 1943).
1024 Ellisor, L. D., and Richardson, C. R.: *J. Cellular Comp. Physiol.*, **11**, 377–81 (1938).
1025 Ellman, D., Lawrence, J. S., and Cumings, J. M.: *Tubercle, London*, **22**, 296–302 (1941); *J. Am. Med. Assoc.*, **119**, 451 (1942).
1026 Elvidge, W. F.: *Quart. J. Pharm. Pharmacol.*, **14**, 134–48 (1941).
1027 Emerson, G. A., and Tishler, M.: *Proc. Soc. Exptl. Biol. Med.*, **55**, 184–5 (1944).
1028 Emery, F. E.: *Proc. Soc. Exptl. Biol. Med.*, **44**, 56–7 (1940).
1029 Emmart, E. W., and Smith, M. I.: *U. S. Pub. Health Repts.*, **56**, 1277–86 (1941).
1030 ——, and Smith, M. I.: *Proc. Soc. Exptl. Biol. Med.*, **51**, 320–4 (1942).
1031 Endicott, K. M., Kornberg, A., and Daft, F. S.: *U. S. Pub. Health Repts.*, **59**, 49–54 (1944).
1032 Englis, D. T., and Skoog, D. A.: *Ind. Eng. Chem., Anal. Ed.*, **15**, 748–9 (1943).
1033 English, J. P., Chappell, D., Bell, P. H., and Roblin, R. O., Jr.: *J. Am. Chem. Soc.*, **64**, 2516 (1942).
1034 Ensworth, H. K., Kalkstein, M., Barefoot, S. W., Liebmann, J., and Plummer, N.: *Am. J. Med. Sci.*, **204**, 179–85 (1942).
1035 Epstein, J. A., Foley, E. J., and Lee, S. W.: *J. Bact.*, **47**, 573–4 (1944).
1036 Erlenmeyer, H., Block, H., and Kiefer, H.: *Helv. Chim. Acta.*, **25**, 1066–72 (1942); *Chem. Abst.*, **37**, 1460.
1037 ——, and Würgler, W.: *Helv. Chim. Acta.*, **25**, 249–52 (1942).
1038 Ershoff, B. H., and McWilliams, H. B.: *Proc. Soc. Exptl. Biol. Med.*, **54**, 277–8 (1943).
1039 Erskine, D.: *Brit. J. Vener. Diseases*, **15**, 260–8 (1939).
1040 ——: *Lancet*, **1943, 1**, 382; *ibid.*, **1942, 2**, 568–9.
1041 Euler, H. V., Ahlström, L., and Hasselquist, H.: *Arkiv, Kemi, Mineral. Geol.*, **15B**, No. 21, 8 pp. (1942); *Chem. Abst.*, **37**, 5115.
1042 Eyster, H. C.: *J. Cellular Comp. Physiol.*, **21**, 191–8 (1943).
1043 ——: *Science*, **96**, 140 (1942).
1044 Fabricant, N. D.: *Am. J. Med. Sci.*, **206**, 546–53 (1943).
1045 Faget, M. H., *et al.*: *U. S. Pub. Health Repts.*, **58**, 1729–41 (1943).
1046 ——, Johansen, F. A., and Ross, H.: *Ibid.*, **57**, 1892–9 (1942).
1047 ——, Palmer, M. R., and Sherwood, R. O.: *Ibid.*, **53**, 1364–6 (1938).
1048 Failey, R. B., Jr., Anderson, R. C., Henderson, F. G., and Chen, K. K.: *J. Pharmacol.*, **78**, 366–71 (1943).
1049 Fairley, N. H., and Boyd, J. S. K.: *Brit. Med. J.*, **1942, 2**, 673–5.
1050 Farinaud, M. E., and Ragiot, C.: *Bull. soc. path. exot.*, **31**, 907–10 (1938).
1051 Farr, M. M., and Allen, R. W.: *J. Am. Vet. Med. Assoc.*, **100**, 47–51 (1942).
1052 Farrell, L. N.: *Brit. J. Exp. Path.*, **21**, 302–10 (1940).
1053 Feasby, W. R., and Bynoe, E. T.: *War Med.*, **5**, 207–15 (1944).
1054 Featherston, W. P.: *Am. Rev. Tuberc.*, **49**, 449–50 (1944).
1055 Feinstone, W. H.: *Ibid.*, **46**, 101–4 (1942).

1056 ——, Bliss, E. A., Ott, E., and Long, P. H.: *Bull. Johns Hopkins Hosp.*, **62**, 565–92 (1938).
1057 ——, and Coworkers: American Cyanamid Co., Personal communication (Apr. 14, 1943).
1058 Feldman, H. A., Sweet, L. K., and Dowling, H. F.: *War Med.*, **2**, 995–1007 (1942).
1059 Feldman, W. H., and Hinshaw, H. C.: *Am. Rev. Tuberc.*, **41**, 732–50 (1940).
1060 ——, and ——: *Am. J. Clin. Path.*, **13**, 144–7 (1943).
1061 ——, and ——: *Am. Rev. Tuberc.*, **48**, 255–9 (1943).
1062 ——, ——, and Mann, F. C.: *Proc. Staff Mayo Clin.*, **19**, 25–33 (1944); *Am. Rev. Tuberc.*, **50**, 418–40 (1944).
1063 ——, ——, and Moses, H. E.: *Arch. Path.*, **36**, 64–73 (1943).
1064 ——, ——, and ——: *Proc. Soc. Exptl. Biol. Med.*, **54**, 60–2 (1943).
1065 ——, ——, and ——: *Am. J. Med. Sci.*, **207**, 290–305 (1944).
1066 ——, Mann, F. C., and Hinshaw, H. C.: *Am. Rev. Tuberc.*, **46**, 187–95 (1942); *Am. J. Path.*, **18**, 750–1 (1942).
1067 Feldt, R. H.: *Am. J. Med. Sci.*, **207**, 483–8 (1944).
1068 Felsenfeld, O.: *J. Bact.*, **45**, 25–6 (1943).
1069 Felton, L. D., Hebb, A., and Oliphant, J. W.: *Proc. 8th Am. Sci. Congr.*, **6**, "Pub. Health and Med.," 449–58 (1942).
1070 Fenton, R. A.: *Arch. Otolaryngol.*, **37**, 491–5 (1943).
1071 Feofilaktov, V. V.: *Bull. acad. sci. U.R.S.S. Classe sci. chim.*, **1941**, 521–30; *Chem. Abst.*, **37**, 2348.
1072 Ferguson, C., and Buckholtz, M.: *J. Am. Med. Assoc.*, **125**, 22–3 (1944).
1073 ——, ——, and Gersten, S.: *Am. J. Med. Sci.*, **204**, 685–8 (1942); *Venereal Disease Inform.*, **23**, 377–9 (1942).
1074 Ferguson, F. F., Holmes, J. R., and Lavor, E.: *J. Elisha Mitchell Sci. Soc.*, **58**, 1, 53–9 (1942); *Biol. Abst.*, Sec. C, **17**, 13945 (1943).
1075 Ferguson, J. W., Eli Lilly and Co.: Unpublished (see Reference 1574).
1076 Ferguson, L. K., Brown, R. B., Nicholson, J. T., and Stedman, H. E.: *U. S. Naval Med. Bull.*, **41**, 299–305 (1943).
1077 Ferry, C. W., Buck, J. S., and Baltzly, R.: *Org. Syntheses*, **22**, 31–4 (1942).
1078 Fildes, P.: *Brit. J. Exptl. Path.*, **21**, 67–73 (1940).
1079 ——: *Brit. J. Exptl. Path.*, **22**, 293–8 (1941).
1080 Findlay, G. M.: *Biol. J.*, **36**, 1–7 (1942).
1081 ——: *Brit. J. Exptl. Path.*, **21**, 356–60 (1940).
1082 ——: *Lancet*, **1940**, **2**, 682–3.
1083 ——, and MacCallum, F. O.: *Brit. Med. J.*, **1938**, **1**, 875.
1084 ——, Mackenzie, R. D., and MacCallum, F. O.: *Brit. J. Exptl. Path.*, **21**, 13–22 (1940).
1085 Fink, H. W., and Wilson, J. L.: *J. Pediat.*, **22**, 513–17 (1943).
1086 Finkelstein, S.: *J. Am. Chem. Soc.*, **66**, 407–8 (1944).
1087 Finland, M.: *Conn. State Med. J.*, **7**, 92–100 (1943).
1088 ——, Lowell, F. C., Spring, W. C., Jr., and Taylor, F. H. L.: *Ann. Intern. Med.*, **13**, 1105–20 (1940).
1089 ——, ——, and Strauss, E.: *Ibid.*, **14**, 1184–98 (1941).
1090 ——, Peterson, O. L., and Goodwin, R. A., Jr.: *Ibid.*, **17**, 920–34 (1942).
1091 ——, ——, and Strauss, E.: *Arch. Intern. Med.*, **70**, 183–205 (1942).
1092 ——, Spring, W. C., Jr., and Lowell, F. C.: *J. Clin. Investigation*, **18**, 483 (1939); *ibid.*, **19**, 178–99 (1940).
1093 ——, Strauss, E., and Peterson, O. L.: *J. Am. Med. Assoc.*, **116**, 2641–7 (1941).
1094 Finley, R. K., and Shafer, J. M.: *Ohio State Med. J.*, **39**, 924–5 (1943).
1095 Firma B. Fragner: Ger. 735,415 (Apr. 8, 1943); *Chem. Abst.*, **38**, 2668.
1096 Firor, W. M.: *Ann. Surg.*, **115**, 829–32 (1942).
1097 Fisher, S. H., Troast, L., Waterhouse, A., and Shannon, J. A.: *J. Pharmacol.*, **79**, 373–91 (1943).
1098 Fisk, R. T.: *J. Infectious Diseases*, **68**, 20–3 (1941).
1099 ——, and Blakely, L.: *Am. J. Hyg.*, **33**, 9–16 (1941).
1100 Fitzgerald, R. J., and Feinstone, W. H.: *Proc. Soc. Exptl. Biol. Med.*, **52**, 27–30 (1943).
1101 Fleming, A.: *J. Path. Bact.*, **50**, 69–81 (1940).
1102 ——: *Lancet*, **1938**, **2**, 74–8 564–7.
1103 Flexner, J., Chassin, M. R., and Wright, I. S.: *J. Infectious Diseases*, **66**, 30–2 (1940).
1104 Flippin, H. F.: *Penn. Med. J.*, **47**, 492–3 (1944).
1105 ——, Forrester, J. S., and Fitz-Hugh, T., Jr.: *Am. Rev. Tuberc.*, **42**, 821–3 (1940).
1106 ——, Gefter, W. I., Domm, A. H., and Clark, J. H.: *Am. J. Med. Sci.*, **206**, 216–21 (1943).
1107 ——, Reinhold, J. G., and Gefter, W. I.: *Med. Clin. North Am.*, **27**, 1447–62 (1943).
1108 ——, ——, and Schwartz, L.: *J. Am. Med. Assoc.*, **116**, 683–90 (1941).

1109 ——, Schwartz, L., and Domm, A. H.: *Ibid.*, **121**, 230–7 (1943).
1110 Florey, H. W.: *Brit. Med. J.*, **1944, 2**, 169–71.
1111 Fogas, M.: *J. Bact.*, **40**, 149 (1940).
1112 Fohlen, G. M.: *J. Am. Pharm. Assoc.*, **33**, 33–41 (1944).
1113 Follis, R. H., Jr.: *Am. Rev. Tuberc.*, **41**, 117–9 (1940).
1114 ——, and Rich, A. R.: *Bull. Johns Hopkins Hosp.*, **65**, 466–83 (1939).
1115 Forbes, J. C., and Evans, E. I.: *War Med.*, **4**, 418–21 (1943).
       Wash. D. C., **8**, 33–8 (1941); *Chem. Abst.*, **35**, 8106.
1116 Foster, A. O., Christensen, J. E., and Habermann, R. T., *Proc. Helminthol. Soc. Wash.
       D. C.*, **8**, 33–8 (1941); *Chem. Abst.*, **35**, 8106.
1117 Fourneau, E., Trefouel, J., Nitti, F., Bovet, D., and Trefouel, Mme. J.: *Compt. rend.
       acad. sci.*, **204**, 1763 (1937); *ibid.*, **205**, 299–300 (1937).
1118 ——, ——, Trefouel, Mme. J., Nitti, F., and Bovet, D.: *Bull. acad. med.*, **118**, 210–217
       (1937).
1119 Fox, C. L., Jr.: *J. Am. Med. Assoc.*, **122**, 891 (1943).
1120 ——, German, B., and Janeway, C. A.: *Proc. Soc. Exptl. Biol. Med.*, **40**, 184–9 (1939).
1121 ——, Jenson, J. O., and Mudge, H. G.: *J. Am. Med. Assoc.*, **121**, 1147–50 (1943).
1122 ——, and Rose, H. M.: *Proc. Soc. Exptl. Biol. Med.*, **50**, 142–5 (1942).
1123 Fox, M. J., and Gilbert, J.: *Am. J. Med. Sci.*, **208**, 63–9 (1944).
1124 Fox, T. A.: *U. S. Naval Med. Bull.*, **40**, 557–70 (1942).
1125 Frank, W. P., Patton, E. F., and Hamilton, P. M.: *J. Pediatrics*, **20**, 720–22 (1942).
1126 Franklin, A. L., and Chaikoff, I. L.: *J. Biol. Chem.*, **148**, 719–20 (1942).
1127 Freedlander, B. L.: *Am. Rev. Tuberc.*, **49**, 543–8 (1944).
1128 ——: *Calif. West. Med.*, **61**, 85 (1944).
1129 ——: *Proc. Soc. Exptl. Biol. Med.*, **51**, 153–6 (1942).
1130 Freeman, M. S.: *Arch. Otolaryngol.*, **37**, 496–501 (1943); *J. Am. Med. Assoc.*, **122**, 967
       (1943).
1131 Freis, E. D.: *J. Am. Med. Assoc.*, **126**, 93–4 (1944).
1132 French, A. J.: *Proc. Soc. Exptl. Biol. Med.*, **48**, 1–3 (1941).
1133 Frisch, A. W.: *Am. J. Syphilis, Gonorrhea and Venereal Diseases*, **28**, 397–405 (1944).
1134 Frisk, A. R.: *Acta Med. Scand.*, **110**, 337–58 (1942); *Chem. Abst.*, **38**, 395.
1135 ——: *Acta Med. Scand.*, Suppl. **142**, 1–199 (1943); *Chem. Abst.*, **38**, 4692.
1136 Frist, T. F.: *War Med.*, **5**, 150–4 (1944).
1137 Fromm, E., and Wittmann, J.: *Ber.*, **41**, 2264–73 (1908).
1138 Fuller, A. T.: *Lancet*, **1942, 1**, 760–1.
1139 ——, Colebrook, L., and Maxted, W. R.: *J. Path. Bact.*, **51**, 105–25 (1940).
1140 ——, and Maxted, W. R.: *Brit. J. Exp. Path.*, **20**, 177–81 (1939).
1141 Futch, C. E., Rosenvold, L. K., and Stewart, C. E.: *J. Am. Med. Assoc.*, **119**, 7–8
       (1942).
1142 Galat, A.: *Ind. Eng. Chem.*, **36**, 192 (1944).
1143 Galbreath, W. R., and Hull, E.: *Ann. Intern. Med.*, **18**, 201–3 (1943).
1144 Gallaher, C.: *J. Oklahoma State Med. Assoc.*, **36**, 185–91 (1943).
1145 Ganapathi, K.: *Proc. Indian Acad. Sci.*, **18A**, 355–9 (1943); *Chem. Abst.*, **38**, 4572.
1146 ——, Deliwala, C. V., and Shirsat, M. V.: *Proc. Indian Acad. Sci.*, **16A**, 115–26, 126–8
       (1942); *Chem. Abst.*, **37**, 1403.
1147 ——, and Rao, R. S.: *Proc. Indian Acad. Sci.*, **14B**, 427–36 (1941).
1148 ——, Shirsat, M. V., and Deliwala, C. V.: *Ibid.*, **14A**, 630–5 (1941); *Chem. Abst.*, **36**,
       4102.
1149 Gandhi, R. C., and Venkataraman, K.: *J. Indian Chem. Soc., Ind. & News Ed.*, **5**,
       89–101 (1942); *Chem. Abst.*, **37**, 2189.
1150 Gant, O. K., Ransone, B., McCoy, E., and Elvehjem, C. A.: *Proc. Soc. Exptl. Biol.
       Med.*, **52**, 276–9 (1943).
1151 Gard, J. J.: *Med. J. Australia*, **2**, 188–90 (1943).
1152 Garson, P.: *Brit. Med. J.*, **1943, 2**, 452–4.
1153 Gay, F. P., and Clark, A. R.: *J. Exptl. Med.*, **66**, 535–48 (1937).
1154 ——, Clark, A. R., Street, J. A., and Miles, D. W.: *J. Exptl. Med.*, **69**, 607–24 (1939).
1155 Gazdar, M., and Smiles, S.: *J. Chem. Soc.*, **1908**, 1833–6.
1156 Gebauer-Fulneg, E., and Schwartz, P.: *Ber.*, **61B**, 1307–8 (1928).
1157 Gefter, W. I., Rose, S. B., Domm, A. H., and Flippin, H. F.: *Am. J. Med. Sci.*, **206**,
       211–6 (1943).
1158 Geigy, J. R., A.-G.: Brit. 547,966 (Oct. 15, 1942); *Brit. Chem. Abst.*, **1943**, B3, 21.
1159 ——: Brit. 560,661 (May 11, 1944).
1160 ——: Swiss 210,833; *Chem. Abst.*, **35**, 5654; Swiss 213,552, 213,558 (May 16, **1941**);
       Chem. Abst., **36**, 4975.
1161 —— (Gysin, H.): U. S. 2,351,333 (June 13, 1944); Brit. 553,205 (June 10, 1943); *Brit.
       Chem. Abst.*, **1943**, B3, 193.

1162 Gelarie, A. J.: *J. Lab. Clin. Med.*, **29**, 532–3 (1944).
1163 General Aniline and Film Corp. (Orthner, L., Balle, G., and Schild, H.): U. S. 2,349,912 (May 30, 1944).
1164 General Electric Co. (D'Alelio, G. F.): U. S. 2,312,691–2; 2,312,698 (Mar. 2, 1943).
1165 Gershenfeld, L., and Silver, M. J.: *Am. J. Pharm.*, **116**, 4–13 (1944).
1166 Gertner, J.: *J. Am. Med. Assoc.*, **122**, 1204 (1943).
1167 Gessler, C. N.: *Southern Med. J.*, **37**, 365–72 (1944).
1168 Gessner, O., Hasemeyer, H. W., and Barz, E.: *Arch. Dermatol. Syphilis*, **181**, 129–38 (1940).
1169 Giacomello, G., and Riverso, P.: *Gazz. chim. ital.*, **71**, 209–15 (1941); *Chem. Abst.*, **36**, 2768.
1170 Gilligan, D. R.: *J. Pharmacol.*, **79**, 320–8 (1943).
1171 ——, Dingwall, J. A., 3rd., and McDermott, W.: *Ann. Intern. Med.*, **20**, 604–18 (1944).
1172 ——, Garb, S., and Plummer, N.: *J. Am. Med. Assoc.*, **122**, 1160–5 (1943).
1173 ——, and Plummer, N.: *Proc. Soc. Exptl. Biol. Med.*, **53**, 142–5 (1943).
1174 Gilman, H., and Stuckwisch, C. G.: *J. Am. Chem. Soc.*, **65**, 1461–4 (1943).
1175 Gilta, G.: *Bull. Soc. Chim. Belg.*, **48**, 444–6 (1939); *Chem. Abst.*, **34**, 2342.
1176 Giovambattista, N.: *Rev. facultad. cienc. quim.*, **16**, 217–26 (1941); *Chem. Abst.*, **36**, 6147.
1177 Girard, A., Ray, A., and Richard, G.: *Nature* **140**, 283 (1937).
1178 Glazebrook, A. J., and Thompson, S.: *J. Hygiene*, **42**, 20–2 (1942).
1179 Glen, W. L., and Robinson, R.: *J. Chem. Soc.*, **1943**, 557–61.
1180 Gley, P., and Girard, A.: *Presse Med.*, **45**, 1291–2 (1937).
1181 Goetchius, G. R., and Lawrence, C. A.: *J. Lab. Clin. Med.*, **29**, 134–8 (1944).
1182 Goissedet, P. E. C., and Despois, R. L.: U. S. 2,309,841 (Feb. 2, 1943) to Alien Property Custodian.
1183 Gold, H.: *Arch. Intern. Med.*, **70**, 785–821 (1942).
1184 ——: *Bull. N. Y. Acad. Med.*, **19**, 132–50 (1943).
1185 Goldberger, H. A.: *Am. J. Surgery*, **56**, 353–74 (1942).
1186 Golden, B. I.: *Ibid.*, **62**, 235–40 (1943).
1187 Goldfarb, A. R., and Berk, B.: *J. Am. Chem. Soc.*, **65**, 738–9 (1943).
1188 Goldman, J., and Patterson, W. H.: *Brit. Med. J.*, **1942, 1**, 641.
1189 Goldstein, D. H., and Graef, I.: *Arch. Path.*, **30**, 701–20 (1940).
1190 Gooch, J. O., and Gorby, A. L.: *Military Surgeon*, **94**, 339–44 (1944).
1191 Goodale, W. T., Gould, R. G., Schwab, L., and Winter, V. G.: *J. Am. Med. Assoc.*, **123**, 547–9 (1943).
1192 ——, and Schwab, L.: *J. Clin. Investigation*, **23**, 217–23 (1944).
1193 Goodman, L., and Gilman, A.: "The Pharmacological Basis of Therapeutics," The Macmillan Co., New York, 1941.
1194 Goodwin, R. A., Peterson, O. L., and Finland, M.: *Proc. Soc. Exptl. Biol. Med.*, **51**, 262–5 (1942).
1195 Gordon, J., and McLeod, J. W.: *Lancet*, **1941, 1**, 407–9.
1196 Gough, N.: *Lancet*, **1943, 2**, 571–2.
1197 Gould, G. N.: *Vet. Record*, **55**, 107 (1943).
1198 Gray, W. H., and Platt, B. C.: *J. Chem. Soc.*, **1942**, 42–5.
1199 Green, H. N., and Bielschowsky, F.: *Brit. J. Exptl. Path.*, **23**, 1–13 (1942).
1200 ——, and Bielschowsky, F.: *Brit. J. Exptl. Path.*, **23**, 13–26 (1942).
1201 Green, R. C., Steckel, M. L., and Michener, J. M.: *Military Surgeon*, **93**, 399–405 (1943).
1202 Green, T. W.: *J. Infectious Diseases*, **74**, 37–40 (1944).
1203 ——, and Birkeland, J. M.: *J. Infectious Diseases*, **74**, 32–6 (1944).
1204 Greenblatt, R. B.: *J. Med. Assoc. Georgia*, **31**, 172–3 (1942).
1205 ——: *Vener. Diseases Inform.*, Supp. No. **19**, 1–43 (1943).
1206 Greene, L. F., Pool, T. L., and Cook, E. N.: *Proc. Staff Mayo Clin.*, **17**, 510–11 (1942)
1207 Greey, P. H., Boddington, G. D. M., and Little, M. H.: *Proc. Soc. Exptl. Biol. Med.*, **40**, 418–22 (1939).
1208 ——, MacLaren, D. B., and Lucas, C. C.: *Can. Med. Assoc. J.*, **40**, 319–24 (1939).
1209 Gregg, L. A., Loosli, C. G., and Hamburger, M. J.: *J. Clin. Investigation*, **19**, 257–65 (1940); *Proc. Soc. Exptl. Biol. Med.*, **41**, 459–62 (1939).
1210 Griffitts, J. J.: *U. S. Pub. Health Repts.*, **57**, 814–8 (1942).
1211 Gross, P., Cooper, F. B., and Lewis, M.: *Am. J. Med. Sci.*, **198**, 66–73 (1939).
1212 ——, ——, and ——: *J. Infectious Diseases*, **63**, 245–50 (1938); *Proc. Soc. Exptl. Biol. Med.*, **38**, 275–9 (1938).
1213 ——, ——, and ——: *Proc. Soc. Exptl. Biol. Med.*, **38**, 407 (1938).
1214 ——, ——, and ——: *Ibid.*, **39**, 12–3 (1938); *ibid.*, **40**, 649–50 (1939).
1215 Gruhzit, O. M.: *Arch. Path.*, **29**, 732 (1940).

1216   Gsell, O.: *Schweiz. med. Wochschr.*, **71**, 1576–7 (1942); *Chem. Abst.*, **37**, 3182.
1217   Guha, P. C., and Dokras, V. M.: *Current Sci.*, **12**, 119–20 (1943); *Brit. Chem. Abst.*, **1943, A2**, 335.
1218   ——, and Das Gupta, V. M.: *Current Sci.*, **12**, 120 (1943).
1219   ——, and Handu, K. L.: *Ibid.*, 150 (1943); *Chem. Abst.*, **37**, 6671.
1220   ——, and Roy, A. N.: *Current Sci.*, **12**, 150 (1943); *Chem. Abst.*, **37**, 6653.
1221   Gundrum, L. K.: *Arch. Otolaryngology*, **37**, 209–18 (1943).
1222   Gvirtsman, R. P.: *Ukrain, Gosudarst. Inst. Eksptl. Farm. (Kharkov) Konsul' tatsionnge Materialy*, **1939**, 267–8; *Chem. Abst.*, **36**, 3167.
1223   Haack, E.: U. S. 2,312,404 (Mar. 2, 1943) to Alien Property Custodian.
1224   ——: Alien Property Custodian Serial No. 369,118 (Apr. 20, 1943).
1225   Habs, H., and Roper, E.: *Z. Immunitäts.*, **91**, 360–5 (1937).
1226   Hac, L. R.: *J. Infectious Diseases*, **74**, 161–72 (1944).
1227   ——, and Eilert, M. L.: *Ibid.*, **73**, 167–72 (1943).
1228   ——, ——, and Adair, F. L.: *Proc. Soc. Exptl. Biol. Med.*, **51**, 108–10 (1942); *J. Infectious Diseases*, **73**, 167–72 (1943).
1229   ——, and Hubert, A. C.: *Proc. Soc. Exptl. Biol. Med.*, **53**, 58–60 (1943); *J. Infectious Diseases*, **74**, 150–60 (1944).
1230   Hadley, F. P., and Hadley, P.: *Proc. Soc. Exptl. Biol. Med.*, **43**, 102–4 (1940).
1231   Hadley, H. G.: *Virginia Med. Monthly*, **67**, 115 (1940).
1232   Hadley, P., and Hadley, F.: *J. Infectious Diseases*, **68**, 246–63 (1941).
1233   Haerem, A. T.: *Military Surgeon*, **92**, 306–9 (1943).
1234   Hageman, P. O., and Blake, F. G.: *Am. J. Med. Sci.*, **195**, 163–74 (1938).
1235   ——, Harford, C. G., Sorbin, S. S., and Ahrens, R. E.: *J. Am. Med. Assoc.*, **123**, 325–9 (1943).
1236   Hagerman, G.: *Acta Path. Microbiol. Scand.*, Suppl. **46**, 1–108 (1942); *Chem. Abst.*, **37**, 6693.
1237   Hailwood, J. G.: *Brit. Med. J.*, **1944, 1**, 806–7.
1238   Hall, B. E., Pfuetze, K., Hinshaw, H. C., and Feldman, W. H.: *Proc. Staff Mayo Clin.*, **17**, 24–7 (1942); *J. Clin. Investigation*, **21**, 632 (1942).
1239   Hall, G. E.: Thesis Yale University, 1942; Personal communication from Prof. A. J. Hill.
1240   Hall, J. F., Jr.: *J. Lab. Clin. Med.*, **27**, 1218–22 (1942).
1241   Hall, L. T., Thompson, J., Wyrens, R. J., Harris, A. M., and Wilder, V.: *Ann. Intern. Med.*, **17**, 835–41 (1942).
1242   Hall, W. H., and Spink, W. W.: *J. Am. Med. Assoc.*, **123**, 125–31 (1943).
1243   Hall, W. M.: *New Orleans Med. Surg. J.*, **94**, 283–4 (1941).
1244   Hallay, L. I.: *Virginia Med. Monthly*, **69**, 334 (1942).
1245   Hamaan, E. E., and Huddleson, I. F.: *Proc. Soc. Exptl. Biol. Med.*, **42**, 555–6 (1939).
1246   Hamburger, M., and Robertson, O. W.: *J. Exptl. Med.*, **72**, 261–4 (1940).
1247   ——, and Ruegsegger, J. M.: *Ann. Intern. Med.*, **14**, 1137–54 (1941).
1248   ——, ——, Brookens, N. L., and Eakin, E.: *Am. J. Med. Sci.*, **204**, 186–93 (1942).
1249   ——, Schmidt, L. H., Sesler, C. L., Ruegsegger, J. M., and Grupen, E. S.: *J. Infectious Diseases*, **73**, 12–30 (1943); *J. Clin. Investigation*, **21**, 628–9 (1942).
1250   Hamilton, C. M.: *J. Am. Vet. Med. Assoc.*, **103**, 144–6 (1943).
1251   Hamilton, J. E.: *Am. J. Surg.*, **58**, 350–64 (1942).
1252   Hamilton, W. F., George, M. F., Jr., Simon, E., and Turnbull, F. M.: *J. Am. Pharm. Assoc. Sci. Ed.*, **33**, 142–4 (1944).
1253   Hammann, E. E., and Huddleson, I. F.: *Proc. Soc. Exptl. Biol. Med.*, **42**, 555–6 (1939).
1254   Hamre, D. M., and Rake, G.: *J. Infectious Diseases*, **74**, 206–11 (1944).
1255   ——, Walker, H. A., Dunham, W. B., Van Dyke, H. B., and Rake, G.: *Proc. Soc. Exptl. Biol. Med.*, **55**, 170–3 (1944).
1256   Hansen, A. E., Platou, R. V., and Dwan, P. F.: *Am. J. Diseases Children*, **64**, 963–76 (1942).
1257   Hansen, L., and Kreidler, Wm. A.: *J. Infectious Diseases*, **70**, 208–20 (1942); *Chem. Abst.*, **37**, 181.
1258   ——, and ——: *J. Lab. Clin. Med.*, **25**, 1246–59 (1940).
1259   Hardy, A. V.: *U. S. Pub. Health Repts.*, **58**, 833–9 (1943).
1260   ——, Burns, W., and DeCapito, T.: *U. S. Pub. Health Repts.*, **58**, 689–93 (1943).
1261   ——, and Cummins, S. D.: *U. S. Pub. Health Repts.*, **58**, 693–6 (1943).
1262   ——, and Watt, J.: *Am. J. Pub. Health*, **34**, 503–9 (1944); *ibid.*, *J. Am. Med. Assoc.*, **124**, 1173–9 (1944).
1263   ——, ——, and Peterson, J.: *U. S. Pub. Health Repts.*, **57**, 529–35 (1942).
1264   Hare, R., and Clark, E. M.: *War Med.*, **4**, 140–51 (1943).
1265   Harkins, H. N.: *Illinois Med. J.*, **84**, 103–6 (1943).
1266   Harkness, A. H.: *Lancet*, **1943, 2**, 116.

1267 Harned, B. K., Miller, R. E., Wiener, M., and Watts, N. P.: *Proc. Soc. Exptl. Biol Med.*, **55**, 234–5 (1944).
1268 Harries, G. E.: *Brit. Med. J.*, **1942, 2**, 423–5.
1269 Harris, A. H., and Miller, J. K.: *J. Bact.*, **41**, 495–509 (1941).
1270 Harris, J. S., and Kohn, H. I.: *J. Immunol.*, **46**, 189–94 (1943).
1271 ——, and Kohn, H. I.: *J. Pharmacol.*, **73**, 383–400 (1941).
1272 ——, and ——: *Ibid.*, **78**, 56–64 (1943).
1273 Harris, L. J.: *Proc. Roy. Soc. (London)*, **97B**, 364 (1925); *ibid.*, **104B**, 412 (1929); *Biochem. J.*, **24**, 1080–97 (1930).
1274 Harris, T. N.: *J. Am. Med. Assoc.*, **121**, 403–5 (1943).
1275 ——, Sommer, H. E., and Chapple, C. C.: *Am. J. Med. Sci.*, **205**, 1–6 (1943).
1276 Hartmann, F. W.: *J. Bact.*, **47**, 259–71 (1944).
1277 Hawking, F.: *Brit. Med. J.*, **1941, 1**, 263–8.
1278 ——: *Brit. J. Exptl. Path.*, **25**, 63–7 (1944).
1279 ——: *J. Path. Bact.*, **55**, 41–52 (1943).
1280 Hawkins, P. A.: *Vet. Med.*, **39**, 251 (1944); *Poultry Sci.*, **22**, 459 (1943).
1281 ——, Cole, C. L., and Thorp, F., Jr.: *Vet. Med.*, **38**, 337–9 (1943).
1282 Havens, W. P., Hansen, L. P., and Kramer, C. G.: *Proc. Soc. Exptl. Biol. Med.*, **42**, 408–10 (1939).
1283 Hayden, R.: *Am. J. Surgery*, **60**, 161–81 (1943).
1284 ——: *N. Y. State J. Med.*, **43**, 1213–9 (1943).
1285 Heaf, F. R. G., Hurford, J. V., Eiser, A., and Franklin, L. M.: *Lancet*, **1943, 1**, 702–4.
1286 Heath, P.: *J. Am. Med. Assoc.*, **124**, 152–4 (1944).
1287 Hegler, C.: *Deut. med. Wochschr.*, **69**, 390–4 (1943).
1288 Heiman, V.: *Vet. Med.*, **38**, 26–8 (1943).
1289 Heinemann, M.: *J. Clin. Investigation*, **22**, 29–32 (1943).
1290 Heise, F. H., and Steenken, W., Jr.: *Am. Rev. Tuberc.*, **42**, 801–4 (1940).
1291 Heishman, J. O., and Miller, W. T.: *J. Am. Vet. Med. Assoc.*, **96**, 176–9 (1940).
1292 Heller, K.: *J. prakt. chem.*, **121**, (2) 193–203 (1929).
1293 Helmholz, H. F. and Barson, N.: *Proc. Staff Mayo Clin.*, **15**, 651–66 (1940).
1294 ——: *Ibid.*, **17**, 529–33 (1942); *Am. J. Diseases Children*, **65**, 399–411 (1943).
1295 ——: *Wisconsin Med. J.*, **41**, 472–6 (1942).
1296 ——, and Nichols, H.: *Proc. Staff Mayo Clin.*, **18**, 481–7 (1943).
1297 Henry, R. J.: *Bacteriological Reviews*, **7**, 175–262 (1943).
1298 Hepburn, J. S., Paxson, N. F., and Rogers, A. N.: *Arch. Pediat.*, **59**, 413–8 (1942).
1299 Herriott, H. W.: *J. Am. Vet. Med. Assoc.*, **102**, 261–3 (1943).
1300 Herrold, R. D.: "Chemotherapy of Gonococcic Infections," C. V. Mosby Co., St. Louis, 1943.
1301 Heubner, W.: *Deut. med. Wochschr.*, **69**, 385–90 (1943).
1302 Heyn, W.: *Deut. Militärarzt.*, **7**, 322–31 (1942); *Bull. War Med.*, **3**, 340–1 (1943).
1303 Higgins, G. M.: *Am. J. Med. Sci.*, **205**, 834–41 (1943); *ibid.*, **207**, 239–47 (1944).
1304 ——: *Proc. Staff Mayo Clin.*, **19**, 202–3 (1944); *ibid.*, 329–35 (1944); *Am. J. Clin. Path.*, **14**, 278–83 (1944); *ibid.*, **13**, 28–33 (1943).
1305 ——, and Feldman, W. H.: *Am. Rev. Tuberc.*, **49**, 179–84 (1944).
1306 Hill, J. H., and Mann, E. F.: *J. Urol.*, **47**, 522–30 (1942).
1307 Hill, L. W., and Lever, H. S.: *J. Am. Med. Assoc.*, **123**, 9–13 (1943).
1308 Hilles, C., and Schmidt, L. H.: *Proc. Soc. Exptl. Biol. Med.*, **40**, 73–7 (1939).
1309 Hinshaw, H. C.: *Proc. Staff Mayo Clin.*, **14**, 769–72 (1939).
1310 ——, and Feldman, W. H.: *J. Am. Med. Assoc.*, **117**, 1066–8 (1941).
1311 ——, ——, and Pfuetze, K. H.: *Proc. Mayo Clin.*, **19**, 33–6 (1944).
1312 ——, Pfuetze, K. H., and Feldman, W. H.: *Am. Rev. Tuberc.*, **47**, 26–34 (1943); *ibid.*, **50**, 52–7 (1944).
1313 Hirsch, J.: *Compt. rend. ann. arch. soc. Turque des Sci. Phys. Nat.*, **10**, 1–123 (1942).
1314 ——: *J. Immunol.*, **48**, 199–201 (1944).
1315 ——: *Science*, **96**, 139–40 (1942).
1316 Hoagland, R. J.: *J. Am. Med. Assoc.*, **122**, 653–6 (1943).
1317 Hoagland, R. J., Harris, F. H., and Raile, R. B.: *War Med.*, **4**, 400–3 (1943).
1318 Hodes, H. L., Smith, M. H. D., and Ickes, H. J.: *J. Am. Med. Assoc.*, **121**, 1334–7 (1943).
1319 Hodgson, A. R., and Robinson, J. R.: *Lancet*, **1942, 2**, 392–4.
1320 Hoffman, H. T., Lees, H. D., and Comroe, B. I.: *Am. J. Med. Sci.*, **203**, 731–6 (1942).
1321 Hoffmann-LaRoche & Co., A.-G.: Swiss 214,737 (Aug. 1, 1941); *Chem. Abst.*, **37**, 1229.
1322 —— (John Lee): U. S. 2,339,787–8 (Jan. 25, 1944).
1323 Hogan, M. J., and Crawford, J. W.: *War Med.*, **2**, 984–94 (1942).
1324 Högger, D.: *Schweiz. med. Wochschr.*, **71**, 8–10; 901–4 (1941); *Chem. Abst.*, **37**, 6345.
1325 Holbrook, W. P.: *J. Am. Med. Assoc.*, **126**, 84–7 (1944).

1326 Holbourn, A. H. S., and Pattle, R. E.: *J. Lab. Clin. Med.*, **28**, 1028–33 (1943).
1327 Holder, H. G., and MacKay, E. M.: *Military Surg.*, **90**, 509–18 (1942); *Surgery*, **13**, 677–82 (1943).
1328 Hollenbeck, W. F., and Turnoff, D.: *J. Am. Med. Assoc.*, **123**, 1115–6 (1943).
1329 Holliman, F. G., and Mann, F. G.: *J. Chem. Soc.*, **1942**, 737–41.
1330 Hoogewerff, S., and VanDorp, W. A.: *Rec. trav. chim.*, **8**, 173–201 (1889).
1331 Hopkins, W. A.: *Ann. Rheumatic Diseases*, **2**, 233–46 (1941); *J. Am. Med. Assoc.*, **119**, 451 (1942).
1332 Hornibrook, J. W.: *U. S. Pub. Health Repts.*, **57**, 535–7 (1942).
1333 ——, and Ashburn, L. L.: *Ibid.*, **54**, 439–44 (1939).
1334 Horton-Smith, C., and Taylor, E. L.: *Vet. Record*, **54**, 516 (1942); *ibid.*, **55**, 109–10.
1335 Howard, M. E.: *Arch. Path.*, **29**, 733 (1940).
1336 Hoyne, A. L., Wolf, A. A., and Prim, L.: *J. Am. Med. Assoc.*, **113**, 2279–81 (1939).
1337 Hoyt, R. E., and Levine, M.: *Proc. Soc. Exptl. Biol. Med.*, **40**, 465–7 (1939).
1338 Hoyt, W. A., Davis, A. E., and Van Buren, G.: *J. Am. Med. Assoc.*, **117**, 2043–50 (1941).
1339 **Hrad,** O.: *Deut. med. Wochschr.*, **67**, 1147–50 (1941); *Bull. War Med.*, **3**, 542–3 (1943).
1340 Huang, J.: *J. Am. Med. Assoc.*, **125**, 23–4 (1944).
1341 Hubata, R.: *War Med.*, **5**, 56–7 (1944).
1342 Hull, E., Bayley, R. H., and Holoubek, A. B.: *J. Am. Med. Assoc.*, **122**, 928–30 (1943).
1343 Hunnicutt, L. G.: *Arch. Otolaryngol.*, **36**, 837–42 (1942).
1344 Hunter, J. H., and Kolloff, H. G.: *J. Am. Chem. Soc.*, **65**, 156–9 (1943).
1345 Hunter, R. F.: *Chemistry & Industry*, **1943**, 118–21.
1346 Hurst, H.: *Nature*, **152**, 292 (1943).
1347 Hutner, S. H., and Zahl, P. A.: *Science*, **96**, 563–4 (1942).
1348 Hyde, L., and Hyde, B.: *Am. J. Med. Sci.*, **205**, 660–75 (1943).
1349 Hydronaphthene Corporation (Hentrich, W., Kirstahler, A., and Kaiser, W.): U. S. 2,318,556 (May 4, 1943).
1350 Ilfield, F. W.: *Surg. Gynecol. Obstet.*, **76**, 427–37 (1943).
1351 Illenyi, A.: *Biochem. Z.*, **311**, 19–23, 24–8 (1943); *Chem. Abst.*, **37**, 2409.
1352 Imler, A. E.: *Am. J. Surg.*, **56**, 469–70 (1942).
1353 Imperial Chemical Industries Ltd. (Rose, F. L.): Brit. 550,538 (Feb. 11, 1943); *Brit. Chem. Abst.*, **1943, B3,** 88.
1354 —— (Haworth, E., and Rose, F. L.): Brit. 551,524 (Mar. 25, 1943); *Brit. Chem. Abst.*, **1943, B2,** 174.
1355 —— (Haworth, E., and Rose, F. L.): Brit. 552,887 (Apr. 29, 1943).
1356 —— (Haworth, E., and Rose, F. L.): Brit. 556,425 (Nov. 4, 1943); *Brit. Chem. Abst.*, **1944, B3,** 17; U. S. 2,359,912 (Oct. 10, 1944).
1357 —— (Haworth, E., Rose, F. L., and Swain, G.): Brit. 554,975 (**Aug. 26, 1943**); *Brit. Chem. Abst.*, **1943, B3,** 279.
1358 —— (Rose, F. L.): Brit. 556,901 (Nov. 25, 1943); *Brit. Chem. Abst.*, **1944, B3,** 33.
1359 Irie, Tōse: *Bull. Inst. Phys. Chem. Research (Tokyo)*, **20**, 150–86 (1941); *Chem. Abst.*, **36**, 2881.
1360 Irreverre, F., and Sullivan, M. X.: *J. Am. Chem. Soc.*, **64**, 1488–9 (1942); *Chem. Abst.*, **36**, 4485.
1361 ——, and ——: *J. Am. Chem. Soc.*, **64**, 2230–1 (1942).
1362 Ishii, M., Shigeya, S., and Tsuda, K.: *Jap. J. Exptl. Med.*, **19**, 5–9 (1941).
1363 Ivanovics, G.: *J. Path. Bact.*, **51**, 91–6 (1941).
1364 ——: *Z. Immunitäts.*, **96**, 252–4 (1939); *ibid.*, **101**, 58–80 (1942).
1365 ——, Gieszer, G. N., Eollos, Z., and Diczfalussy, E.: *Klin. Wochschr.*, **21**, 1096–1100 (1942); *Chem. Abst.*, **38**, 2733.
1366 Jackson, E. L.: *J. Am. Chem. Soc.*, **64**, 1371–4 (1942); *Chem. Abst.*, **36**, 4485.
1367 Jackson, H., and Coller, F. A.: *J. Am. Med. Assoc.*, **118**, 194–200 (1942).
1368 Jacobs, M. H.: *Dental Survey*, **19**, 59–60 (1943).
1369 Jacoby, A., Baron, I. J., and Ollswang, A. H.: *Am. J. Syphilis, Gonorrhea and Venereal Diseases*, **26**, 305–8 (1942).
1370 Janbon, M., Lazergues, P., and Métropolitanski: *Presse méd.*, **51**, No. 437 (1943); *Chem. Abst.*, **38**, 1029.
1371 Jasper, H., Cone, W., Pudenz, R. H., and Bennett, T.: *Surg. Gynecol. Obstet.*, **76**, 599–611 (1943); *Trans. Am. Neurol. Assoc.*, **69**, 109–12 (1943).
1372 Jawetz, E., and Meyer, K. F.: *Am. J. Path.*, **20**, 457–70 (1944).
1373 Jefferiss, F. J. G., and McElligott, G. L. M.: *Lancet*, **1943, 1,** 65–6.
1374 Jenkins, G. L., Purdue University: Personal communication (Nov. 30, 1942**).
1375 Jennings, P. A., and Patterson, W. H.: *Lancet*, **1942, 2,** 308–9.
1376 Jensen, K. A.: *Dansk Tids. Farm.*, **15**, 299–304 (1941); *Chem. Abst.*, **36**, 5793.
1377 ——: *Dansk Tids. Farm.*, **16**, 1–10 (1942); *Chem. Abst.*, **37**, 4375.

1378 ——, Falkenberg, P., Thorsteinsson, T., and Lauridsen, M.: *Dansk Tids. Farm.*, **16**, 141–53 (1942); *Chem. Abst.*, **38**, 3263.
1379 ——, and Friediger, A.: *Dansk Tids. Farm.*, **16**, 280–4 (1942); *Chem. Abst.*, **38**, 3629.
1380 ——, and Hansen, O. R.: *Rec. trav. chim.*, **62**, 658–60 (1943).
1381 ——, and Kjaer, A.: *Dansk Tids. Farm.*, **16**, 110–8 (1942); *Chem. Atst.*, **38**, 2326.
1382 ——, Possing, B., and Schmith, K.: *Dansk Tids. Farm.*, **15**, 191–7 (1941); *Chem. Abst.*, **38**, 1482.
1383 ——, and Schmith, K.: *Dansk Tids. Farm.*, **15**, 197–9 (1941); *Chem. Abst.*, **38**, 1483.
1384 ——, and Schmith, K.: *Z. Immunitäts.*, **102**, 261–98 (1942).
1385 ——, Schmith, K., and Brandt, P.: *Klin. Wochschr.*, **21**, 1042 (1942); *Chem. Abst.*, **38**, 2681.
1386 Jensen, O. J.: *Am. J. Med. Sci.*, **206**, 746–56 (1943).
1387 ——, and Fox, C. L., Jr.: *J. Urol.*, **49**, 334–9 (1943).
1388 Jerchel, D.: *Ber.*, **75B**, 75–81 (1941); *Brit. Chem. Abst.*, **1942, A2**, 289; *Chem. Abst.*, **36**, 7023.
1389 Johannsen, M. W., and St. George, A. V.: *Am. J. Clin. Path.*, **9**, 414–20 (1939).
1390 Johnson, C. E., Jr.: *Am. J. Med. Sci.*, **206**, 327–335 (1943).
1391 Johnson, F. H.: *Science*, **95**, 104–5 (1942).
1392 ——, Eyring, H. B., and Kearns, W.: *Arch. Biochem.*, **3**, 1–31 (1943); *J. Bact.*, **46**, 110 (1943).
1393 Johnson, G., and Trussell, R. E.: *Proc. Soc. Exptl. Biol. Med.*, **54**, 245–9 (1943).
1394 Johnson, J. M.: *J. Am. Med. Assoc.*, **115**, 1360 (1940).
1395 Johnson, O. H., Green, D. E., and Pauli, R.: *J. Biol. Chem.*, **153**, 37–47 (1944).
1396 Jonas, A. F., Jr.: *Am. J. Surgery*, **57**, 112–13 (1942).
1397 Jones, R. F.: *Nature*, **153**, 379 (1944).
1398 Joshua, J. O.: *Vet. Record*, **55**, 149 (1943).
1399 Joy, H. H.: *Proc. Soc. Exptl. Biol. Med.*, **45**, 709–10 (1940).
1400 Julianelle, L. A.: *J. Immunol.*, **48**, 155–61 (1944).
1401 ——, and Siegel, M.: *City of N. Y. Dept. Health Quart. Bull.*, **11**, 53–4 (1943).
1402 Julius, H. W., and Winkler, K. C.: *Antonie van Leeuwenhoek J. Microbiol. Serol.*, **7**, 153–68 (1941); *ibid.*, **7**, 25–31 (1941); *Chem. Abst.*, **37**, 5439; *ibid.*, **38**, 4643.
1403 Kavakas, J. C., Palmer, C. C., Hay, J. R., and Biddle, E. S.: *Am. J. Vet. Res.*, **3**, 274–84 (1942).
1404 Kalmanson, G. M.: *J. Bact.*, **40**, 817–22 (1940).
1405 Kaplan, H., and Lindwall, H. G.: *J. Am. Chem. Soc.*, **65**, 927–8 (1943).
1406 Karel, L., Grubb, T. C., and Chapman, C. W.: *J. Infectious Diseases*, **69**, 125–30 (1941).
1407 Karlson, A. G., and Feldman, W. H.: *Am. Rev. Tuberc.*, **42**, 146–50 (1940).
1408 Karr, N., Murayama, F., Finnegan, J., and Leake, C. D.: *J. Pharmacol.*, **69**, 291 (1940).
1409 Kaufman, L. R., and Mersheimer, W. L.: *Am. J. Surg.*, **65**, 393–400 (1944).
1410 Kauffmann, F., and Schmidt, K.: *Acta Path. Microbiol. Scand.*, **20**, 1 (1943).
1411 Kaufmann, H. P., and Buchmann, H. J.: *Arch. Pharm.*, **279**, 194–209 (1941); *Chem. Abst.*, **38**, 2324.
1412 ——, and Huang, L. S.: *Ber.*, **75B**, 1214–36 (1942); *Brit. Chem. Abst.*, **1943, A2**, 174.
1413 ——, and Steinhoff, F.: *Arch. Pharm.*, **278**, 437–42 (1940); *Chem. Abst.*, **36**, 2553.
1414 Kauvar, A. J., and Mount, F. R.: *J. Kansas Med. Soc.*, **44**, 290–3 (1943).
1415 Keefer, C. S., and Rantz, L. A.: *Arch. Intern. Med.*, **63**, 957–73 (1939).
1416 Keet, E. E., Jr.: *Am. J. Syphilis, Gonorrhea and Venereal Diseases*, **28**, 315–19 (1944).
1417 Keilin, D., and Mann, T.: *Nature*, **146**, 164–5 (1940).
1418 Keltch, A. K., Baker, L. A., Krahl, M. E., and Clowes, G. H. A.: *Proc. Soc. Exptl. Biol. Med.*, **47**, 533–8 (1941).
1419 Kelson, S. R.: *Ibid.*, **36**, 718–20 (1937).
1420 Kempf, A. H., and Nungester, W. J.: *Ibid.*, **43**, 627–8 (1940).
1421 Kempner, W., Schlayer, C., and Summers, P.: *Am. J. Med. Sci.*, **203**, 172–7 (1942).
1422 Kernkamp, H. C. H., and Roepke, M. H.: *Proc. Soc. Exptl. Biol. Med.*, **50**, 268–9 (1942); *Vet. Med.*, **37**, 397 (1942); *Am. J. Vet. Res.*, **4**, 3–14 (1943).
1423 Kendrick, D. B., Jr.: *J. Clin. Investigation*, **18**, 593–6 (1939).
1424 Kent, E. M., and Graham, E. A.: *J. Thoracic Surg.*, **11**, 198–202 (1941).
1425 Kepl, M., and Gunn, F. D.: *Proc. Soc. Exptl. Biol. Med.*, **40**, 529–32 (1939); *ibid.*, **41**, 457–9 (1939).
1426 Key, J. A.: *J. Am. Med. Assoc.*, **122**, 1003–6 (1943).
1427 Kharasch, M. S., and Reinmuth, O.: Unpublished work (see Reference 1574).
1428 Kienle, R. H., and Sayward, J. M.: *J. Am. Chem. Soc.*, **64**, 2464–8 (1942).
1429 Kieth, H. M.: *Proc. Staff Mayo Clin.*, **19**, 36–7 (1944).

1430 Kimmig, J.: *Klin. Wochschr.*, **22**, 31–4 (1943); *Chem. Abst.*, **38**, 4002.
1431 ——, and Weselmann, H.: *Arch. Dermatol.*, **182**, 436–51 (1941); *Klin. Wochschr.*, **21**, 675 (1942); *Chem. Abst.*, **38**, 2109.
1432 ——, and ——: *Klin. Wochschr.*, **20**, 235–7 (1941).
1433 King, E. S., and Lucas, M.: *J. Lab. Clin. Med.*, **26**, 616–21 (1941).
1434 King, H., and Ware, L. L.: *J. Chem. Soc.*, **1939**, 873–7.
1435 King, J. T., and Henschel, A. F.: *Proc. Soc. Exptl. Biol. Med.*, **41**, 208–9 (1939); *ibid.*, **44**, 268–70 (1940); *ibid.*, **47**, 400–2 (1941).
1436 ——, and Green, B. S.: *J. Am. Med. Assoc.*, **113**, 1704–9 (1939); *Proc. Soc. Exptl. Biol. Med.*, **38**, 810–2 (1938).
1437 Kinsella, R., and Muether, R.: *Arch. Intern. Med.*, **62**, 247–70 (1938).
1438 Kirby, W. M. M.: *Proc. Soc. Exptl. Biol. Med.*, **52**, 175–6 (1943).
1439 ——: *Ibid.*, **53**, 109–11 (1943).
1440 ——, and Rantz, L. A.: *J. Am. Med. Assoc.*, **119**, 615–8 (1942).
1441 ——, and Rantz, L. A.: *J. Exptl. Med.*, **77**, 29–39 (1943).
1442 Kirchof, A. C., Racely, C. A., Thompson, A. I., and David, N. A.: *Western J. Surg. Obstet. Gynecol.*, **51**, 419–26 (1943).
1443 Klarer, J.: *Klin. Wochschr.*, **20**, 1250 (1941); *Chem. Abst.*, **37**, 5704.
1444 Klauder, J. V., Kramer, D. W., and Nicholas, L.: *J. Am. Med. Assoc.*, **122**, 938 (1943).
1445 ——, and Rule, A. M.: *Arch. Dermatol. Syphilol.*, **49**, 27 (1944).
1446 Kleiderer, E. C., Eli Lilly & Co.: Unpublished work (see Reference 1574).
1447 ——, and Shonle, H. A.: *J. Am. Chem. Soc.*, In Press.
1448 ——, and Wayne, W., Eli Lilly & Co.: Unpublished work (see Reference 1574).
1449 Klein, L. A.: "Sulfanilamide in Veterinary Practice," *Veterinary Extension Bull.*, No. **86**, University Pennsylvania (Mar. 31, 1942); *J. Am. Vet. Med. Assoc.*, **101**, 38 (1942).
1450 Klein, M., and Sorsby, A.: *Brit. J. Ophthalmol.*, **27**, 241–54 (1943); *Chem. Abst.*, **37**, 4801.
1451 Klemme, C. J., and Beals, E. L.: *J. Org. Chem.*, **8**, 448–55 (1943).
1452 Klepser, R. G.: *Med. Ann. Dist. Columbia*, **11**, 211–13 (1942).
1453 Klöse, F., and Schröer, W.: *Zentr. f. Bakt. I Abt. orig.*, **149**, **1**, 15 (1942); *Deutsch. Med. Wochschr.*, **68**, 681–4 (1942); *Bull. War Med.*, **3**, 191, 311.
1454 Klotz, I. M.: *Science*, **98**, 62–3 (1943); *J. Am. Chem. Soc.*, **66**, 459–64 (1944).
1455 Knight, C. A.: *J. Exptl. Med.*, **79**, 487–96 (1944).
1456 Knouf, E. G., Mitchell, W. G., and Hamilton, P. M.: *J. Am. Med. Assoc.*, **119**, 687–91 (1942).
1457 Kohn, H. I.: *Ann. N. Y. Acad. Sci.*, **44**, 503–24 (1943).
1458 ——: *Fed. Proc. Am. Soc. Exptl. Biol.*, **2**, 26 (1943).
1459 ——, and Harris, J. S.: *Am. J. Physiol.*, **133**, 354 (1941).
1460 ——, and ——: *Fed. Proc. Am. Soc. Exptl. Biol.*, **1**, 47 (1942).
1461 ——, and ——: *J. Bact.*, **44**, 717–8 (1942).
1462 ——, and ——: *J. Pharmacol.*, **77**, 1–16 (1943).
1463 Kolmer, J. A.: *Arch. Otolaryngol.*, **27**, 519–34 (1938).
1464 ——: *Proc. Soc. Exptl. Biol. Med.*, **48**, 390–1 (1941).
1465 ——, and Brown, H.: *Ibid.*, 138–40 (1941).
1466 ——, ——, and Raiziss, G. W.: *J. Pharmacol.*, **61**, 253–71 (1937).
1467 ——, ——, and Rule, A. M.: *Arch. Intern. Med.*, **69**, 636–42 (1942).
1468 ——, ——, and ——: *J. Lab. Clin. Med.*, **24**, 164–77 (1938).
1469 ——, Raiziss, G. W., and ——: *Proc. Soc. Exptl. Biol. Med.*, **39**, 95–8, 581–4 (1938); *J. Lab. Clin. Med.*, **24**, 779–95 (1939).
1470 ——, and Rule, A. M.: *J. Lab. Clin. Med.*, **22**, 1007–105 (1937).
1471 ——, and ——: *Ibid.*, **27**, 1166–8 (1942).
1472 ——, and ——: *Proc. Soc. Exptl. Biol. Med.*, **40**, 23–4, 77–9, 615–19; *ibid.*, **42**, 305–7, 307–9 (1939); *ibid.*, **48**, 388–90 (1941).
1473 ——, ——, and Groskin, L.: *J. Lab. Clin. Med.*, **27**, 1043–6 (1942).
1474 Konig, W., and Haller, H.: *J. Prakt. Chem.*, **101**, 38–57 (1920).
1475 Koprowski, H., and Lennette, E. H.: *Am. J. Hyg.*, **40**, 1–24 (1944).
1476 Kornberg, A., Daft, F. S., and Sebrell, W. H.: *U. S. Pub. Health Repts.*, **59**, 832–43 (1944); *Science*, **98**, 20–2 (1943).
1477 Kornblith, B. A., Jacoby, A., and Chargin, L.: *J. Am. Med. Assoc.*, **117**, 2150–3 (1941).
1478 Koser, S. A., Dorfman, A., and Berkman, S.: *J. Bact.*, **45**, 23 (1943).
1479 ——, and Wright, M. H.: *J. Infectious Diseases*, **71**, 86–8 (1942).
1480 Kracke, R. R.: *Am. J. Clin. Path.*, **14**, 191–9 (1944).
1481 ——, and Townsend, E. W.: *J. Am. Med. Assoc.*, **122**, 169–72 (1943).
1482 Kraemer, M.: *Am. J. Digestive Diseases*, **9**, 356–7 (1942).

1483 Krahl, M. E., Keltch, A. K., and Clowes, G. H. A.: *J. Pharmacol.*, **68**, 330–50 (1940).
1484 Krakower, C., Morales-Otero, P., and Axtmayer, J. H.: *J. Infectious Diseases*, **72**, 1–10 (1943).
1485 Kramer, S. D., Geer, H. A., and Szobel, D. A.: *J. Bact.*, **45**, 87 (1943); *J. Immunol.*, **49**, 273–314 (1944).
1486 ——, and Mack, W. N.: *U. S. Pub. Health Repts.*, **56**, 581–7 (1941).
1487 Kreidler, W. A.: *Proc. Soc. Exptl. Biol. Med.*, **37**, 146–9 (1937).
1488 Krueger, R.: *Deut. med. Wochschr.*, **69**, 417–20 (1943); *Bull. War Med.*, **4**, 321–2 (1944).
1489 Kuhn, R., Birkofer, L., and Möller, E. F.: *Ber.*, **76B**, 900–4 (1943).
1490 ——, Möller, E. F., and Wendt, G.: *Ibid.*, 405–12 (1943).
1491 ——, ——, ——, and Beinert, H.: *Ibid.*, **75B**, 711–9 (1942).
1492 ——, Weygand, F., and Möller, E. F.: *Ibid.*, **76B**, 1044–51 (1943).
1493 ——, Wieland, Th., and ——: *Ibid.*, **74B**, 1605 (1941).
1494 Kuhns, D. M., and Anderson, T. G.: *Am. J. Pub. Health*, **34**, 750–5 (1944).
1495 ——, and Feldman, H. A.: *Ibid.*, **33**, 1461–5 (1943); *Bull. War Med.*, **4**, 653 (1944).
1496 ——, Nelson, C. T., Feldman, H. A., and Kuhn, L. R.: *J. Am. Med. Assoc.*, **123**, 335–9 (1943).
1497 Kumler, W. D., and Daniels, T. C.: *J. Am. Chem. Soc.*, **65**, 2190–6 (1943).
1498 ——, and Halverstadt, I. F.: *Ibid.*, **63**, 2182–7 (1941).
1499 ——, and Strait, L. A.: *Ibid.*, **65**, 2349–54 (1943).
1500 Kuttner, A. G., and Reyersbach, G.: *J. Clin. Investigation*, **22**, 77–85 (1943); *N. Y. State J. Med.*, **43**, 1941 (1943).
1501 Kwartler, C. E., and Lucas, P.: *J. Am. Chem. Soc.*, **65**, 354–5 (1943).
1502 ——, and ——: *Ibid.*, 1804–6 (1943).
1503 ——, Winthrop Chemical Co.: Personal communication (Mar. 13, 1943).
1504 "Labopharma" Laboschin G. m.b. H. (Weindling, I., and Riesenberg, J.): Ger. 683,866 (Oct. 26, 1939); *Chem. Abst.*, **36**, 4289.
1505 Ladd, W. E., and Bill, A. H., Jr.: *New Engl. J. Med.*, **229**, 748–50 (1943).
1506 Laird, S. M.: *Lancet*, **1942, 1**, 463–4.
1507 Lamanna, C., and Shapiro, I. M.: *J. Bact.*, **45**, 385–94 (1943).
1508 Lampen, J. O., and Peterson, W. H.: *Arch. Biochem.*, **2**, 443–9 (1943).
1509 *Lancet*, **1943, 1**, 821: List of trade names.
1510 Landy, M., and Dicken, D. M.: *J. Biol. Chem.*, **146**, 109–14 (1942).
1511 ——, and Gerstung, R. B.: *J. Bact.*, **47**, 448 (1944).
1512 ——, Larkum, N. W., and Oswald, E. J.: *Proc. Soc. Exptl. Biol. Med.*, **52**, 338–41 (1943); *J. Bact.*, **45**, 24–5 (1943).
1513 ——, ——, ——, and Streightoff, F.: *Science*, **97**, 265–7 (1943).
1514 ——, and Oswald, E. J.: *J. Lab. Clin. Med.*, **28**, 743–5 (1943).
1515 ——, and Wyeno, J.: *Proc. Soc. Exptl. Biol. Med.*, **46**, 59–62 (1941).
1516 LaRosa, W. V.: *Ibid.*, **53**, 98–100 (1943).
1517 Larson, W. P., Bieter, R. N., and Levine, M.: *Ibid.*, **40**, 703 (1939).
1518 ——, ——, ——, and McLimans, W. F.: *Ibid.*, **42**, 649–51 (1939).
1519 LaTowsky, L. W.: *J. Urol.*, **50**, 625–31 (1943).
1520 ——, Knight, F., Uhle, C. A. W., and Baker, R. B.: *J. Lab. Clin. Med.*, **27**, 1001–6 (1942).
1521 Latven, A. R., and Welch, A. D.: *Am. J. Med. Sci.*, **206**, 805 (1943); *J. Pharmacol.*, **81**, 301–6 (1944).
1522 ——, and ——: *Fed. Proc. Am. Soc. Exptl. Biol.*, **3**, 78 (1944).
1523 Läuger, P., Martin, H., Pulver, R., and Suter, R.: *Schweiz. med. Wochschr.*, **73**, 399–408 (1943); *Bull. War Med.*, **4**, 48 (1943); *Chem. Abst.*, **38**, 5304.
1524 Lavor, E. M., and Ferguson, F. F.: *J. Elisha Mitchell Sci. Soc.*, **58, 2**, 163–9 (1942); *Biol. Abst.*, Sec. C., **17**, 13960 (1943).
1525 Lawrence, C. A.: *J. Bact.*, **47**, 452 (1944).
1526 ——: *Proc. Soc. Exptl. Biol. Med.*, **43**, 92 (1940).
1527 ——: *Ibid.*, **44**, 162–5 (1940).
1528 ——: *Ibid.*, **52**, 90–1 (1943).
1529 ——, and Klingel, H.: *Ibid.*, 129–30 (1943); *J. Bact.*, **45**, 23, 521 (1943).
1530 Lawson, G. McL.: *Ibid.*, **44**, 145–6 (1942).
1531 Lazarus, A. S., and Meyer, K. F.: *Ibid.*, **38**, 121 (1939).
1532 Leach, B. E., Forbes, J. C., and Williams, G. Z.: *Proc. Soc. Exptl. Biol. Med.*, **51**, 47–8 (1942).
1533 Leberman, P. R., and Alexander, R.: *Am. J. Syphilis, Gonorrhea and Venereal Diseases*, **27**, 187–92 (1943).
1534 Lederle Laboratories (Lockhart, M. C.): Can. 406,835–6 (Aug. 18, 1942); *Chem. Abst.*, **36**, 3755.
1535 —— (Tiesler, A. E.): U. S. 2,349,060 (May 16, 1944).

1536 Lee, O. S., and Rottenstein, H.: *J. Am. Med. Assoc.*, **115,** 107–12 (1940).
1537 Lee, S. W., Epstein, J. A., and Foley, E. J.: *Proc. Soc. Exptl. Biol. Med.*, **54,** 105–8 (1943).
1538 ——, and Foley, E. J.: *J. Am. Pharm. Assoc.*, **33,** 82–5 (1944).
1539 ——, and Hannay, N. B.: *Ind. Eng. Chem., Anal. Ed.*, **15,** 763 (1943).
1540 ——, ——, and Hand, W. C.: *Ibid.*, 403 (1943).
1541 ——, ——, and ——: *Science*, **97,** 359–60 (1943).
1542 Leftwich, W. B.: *Bull. Johns Hopkins Hosp.*, **74,** 26–48 (1944).
1543 Lehr, B., Antopol, W., Churg, J., and Sprinz, H.: *Proc. Soc. Exptl. Biol. Med.*, **45,** 15–20 (1940).
1544 Lehr, D.: *Bull. N. Y. Med. College, Flower and Fifth Ave. Hospital*, **6,** 70–7 (1943).
1545 ——: *Proc. Soc. Exptl. Biol. Med.*, **56,** 82–6 (1944).
1546 Leifson, E.: *Bull. Johns Hopkins Hosp.*, **72,** 179–99 (1943).
1547 Leishman, A. W. D.: *J. Roy. Army Med. Corps*, **82,** 58–62 (1944).
1548 Lepper, M. H., Sweet, L. K., and Dowling, H. F.: *J. Am. Med. Assoc.*, **123,** 134–8 (1943).
1549 Levaditi, C.: *Compt. rend. soc. biol.*, **127,** 958–60; **128,** 138–40, 875–7; **129,** 490–2 (1938).
1550 ——, Girard, A., Vaismann, A., Ray, A., and Richard, G.: *Compt. rend. acad. sci.*, **205,** 1018–20 (1937).
1551 ——, and Reinie, L.: *Compt. rend. soc. biol.*, **127,** 1179–80 (1938).
1552 ——, and Vaisman, A.: *Compt. rend. acad. sci.*, **200,** 1694–6 (1935).
1553 ——, and ——: *Compt. rend. soc. biol.*, **119,** 946–9 (1935); *ibid.*, **120,** 1077–9 (1935); *ibid.*, **121,** 803–5 (1936).
1554 ——, and ——: *Ibid.*, **125,** 604–6 (1937).
1555 ——, and ——: *Ibid.*, **127,** 1428–30 (1938); *Chem. Abst.*, **32,** 5918; *ibid.*, **128,** 476–8 (1938).
1556 ——, and ——: *Presse med.*, 1731–3 (Sept. 29, 1937).
1557 ——, ——, and Krassnoff, D.: *Bull. acad. med.*, **119,** 553–76 (1938).
1558 ——, ——, and ——: *Compt. rend. soc. biol.*, **127,** 22–5 (1938).
1559 ——, ——, and Reinie, L.: *Ann. Inst. Pasteur*, **61,** 635–61 (1938).
1560 Levine, P. P.: *Cornell Vet.*, **32,** 430–9 (1942); *Chem. Abst.*, **37,** 685; *J. Parasitol.*, **29,** 362–3 (1943).
1561 Levitan, N. I., Kolthoff, I. M., Clark, W. G., and Tenenberg, D. J.: *J. Am. Chem. Soc.*, **65,** 2265–8 (1943).
1562 Levy, J. G., Holder, E. C., and Bullowa, J. G. M.: *Am. J. Digestive Diseases*, **9,** 237–9 (1942).
1563 Lewenstein, M. J.: Brit. 542,319 (Jan. 29, 1942); *Chem. Abst.*, **36,** 3808.
1564 Lewis, G. M., and Hopper, M. E.: *Arch. Dermatol. Syphilol.*, **44,** 1101–3 (1941).
1565 Leys, D. G.: *Brit. Med. J.*, **1943, 1,** 187–9; *Vet. J.*, **99,** 119–25 (1943).
1566 Libby, R. L.: *J. Bact.*, **40,** 733–45 (1940).
1567 ——, and Joyner, A. L.: *J. Infectious Diseases*, **67,** 67–9 (1940).
1568 Licht, S., and Dick, V.: *Arch. Phys. Therapy*, **25,** 207 (1944); *War Med.*, **5,** 405 (1944).
1569 Light, R. F., Cracas, L. J., Olcott, C. T., and Frey, C. N.: *J. Nutrition*, **24,** 427–35 (1942); *Chem. Abst.*, **37,** 1160.
1570 Lilly, Eli and Co. (Kharasch, M. S., and Reinmuth, O.): U. S. 2,300,676 (Nov. 3, 1942); Brit. 553,164 (May 11, 1943).
1571 —— (Kharasch, M. S., and Reinmuth, O.): U. S. 2,300,677 (Nov. 3, 1942); Brit. 550,011; *Brit. Chem. Abst.*, **1943, B3,** 63.
1572 —— (Kharasch, M. S., and Reinmuth, O.): U. S. 2,300,678 (Nov. 3, 1942).
1573 —— (Kharasch, M. S., and Reinmuth, O.): U. S. 2,303,698 (Dec. 1, 1942); Brit. 550,040; *Brit. Chem. Abst.*, **1943, B3,** 63.
1574 ——: Personal communication from H. M. Powell, H. A. Shonle, and W. A. Jamieson (Feb. 4 to Mar. 15, 1943).
1575 —— (Shonle, H. A.): U. S. 2,297,079 (Sept. 29, 1942).
1576 —— (Shonle, H. A., and VanArendonk, A. M.): U. S. 2,323,573 (July 6, 1943); U. S. 2,333,394 (Nov. 2, 1943).
1577 —— (Shonle, H. A., and VanArendonk, A. M.): U. S. 2,325,344 (July 27, 1943).
1578 —— (VanArendonk, A. M., and Shonle, H. A.): U. S. patent applied for (see Reference 1574).
1579 Lilly, V. G., and Leonian, L. H.: *Science*, **99,** 205–6 (1944).
1580 Lindsay, J. R., and Judd, D. K.: *Trans. Am. Acad. Ophthalmol. and Otolaryngol.*, **47,** 431–41 (1943).
1581 Link, T.: *Klin. Wochschr.*, **22,** 364–6 (1943); *Bull. War Med.*, **4,** 240 (1943).
1582 Linton, C. S.: *J. Am. Med. Assoc.*, **123,** 341 (1943).
1583 Litchfield, J. T., Jr., and Fertig, J. W.: *Bull. Johns Hopkins Hosp.*, **69,** 276–86 (1941).
1584 ——, White, H. J., and Marshall, E. K., Jr.: *J. Pharmacol.*, **66,** 23 (1939).

1585 ——, ——, and ——: *Ibid.*, **69**, 166–70 (1940).
1586 Little, P. A.: *J. Immunol.*, **47**, 97–109 (1943).
1587 Little, S. C.: *J. Am. Med. Assoc.*, **119**, 467–74 (1942).
1588 Litvak, A. K., Sands, I. J., and Gibel, H.: *Am. J. Diseases Children*, **65**, 265–95 (1943).
1589 Liu, P. Y., Zia, S. H., and Chung, H. L.: *Proc. Soc. Exptl. Biol. Med.*, **37**, 17–8 (1937).
1590 Live, I., Stubbs, E. L., and Gardiner, M. R., Jr.: *Am. J. Vet. Res.*, **4**, 276–86 (1943); *North Am. Vet.*, **24**, 661 (1943).
1591 Livingood, C. S., and Pillsbury, D. M.: *J. Am. Med. Assoc.*, **121**, 406–8 (1943).
1592 Livingston, G. S.: *J. Pediat.*, **24**, 363–8 (1944).
1593 Lloyd, J. B., and Middlebrook, G.: *Am. Rev. Tuberc.*, **49**, 539–42 (1944).
1594 Lloyd, P. R., and Barnes, L. N.: *J. Franklin Inst.*, **235**, 94–7 (1943).
1595 Lloyd, V. E., and Erskine, D.: *Lancet*, **1940, 2**, 186–7.
1596 ——, Erskine, D., and Johnson, A. G.: *Lancet*, **1938, 2**, 1160–3.
1597 Lo, C. P., and Chu, L. J.: *J. Am. Chem. Soc.*, **66**, 660 (1944).
1598 Locke, A., Locke, R. B., and Schlesinger, H.: *Proc. Soc. Exptl. Biol. Med.*, **44**, 519–22 (1940).
1599 Lockwood, J. S.: *Ann. N. Y. Acad. Sci.*, **44**, 525–38 (1943).
1600 ——: *J. Am. Med. Assoc.*, **111**, 2259–64 (1938).
1601 ——, and Lynch, H. M.: *J. Bact.*, **38**, 244 (1939); *J. Am. Med. Assoc.*, **114**, 935–40 (1940).
1602 ——, and Robinson, H. J.: *J. Pharmacol.*, **68**, 201–15 (1940).
1603 Loennecken: *Norsk. Mag. Laegevidenskap.*, **99**, 1353–7 (1938).
1604 Loewenthal, H.: *Lancet*, **1939, 1**, 197–9; *Proc. Roy. Soc. Med.*, **32**, 349–58 (1939).
1605 ——, and Corfield, W. F.: *Brit. Med. J.*, **1943, 2**, 105–6.
1606 Löffler, W.: *Schweiz. med. Wochschr.*, **73**, 567–75 (1943).
1607 ——, and Hegglin, R.: *Ibid.*, **72**, 7–9 (1942); *Chem. Abst.*, **36**, 6244.
1608 Löhe, H.: *Deut. med. Wochschr.*, **69**, 394–6 (1943); *Bull. War Med.*, **4**, 239 (1943).
1609 Long, L., Jr., and Burger, A.: *J. Am. Chem. Soc.*, **63**, 1586–9 (1941).
1610 Long, P. H.: *Connecticut State Med. J.*, **7**, 6–10 (1943).
1611 ——: *J. Am. Med. Assoc.*, **121**, 303–6 (1943).
1612 ——: *Lancet*, **1942, 2**, 322.
1613 ——, and Bliss, E. A.: *Ann. Intern. Med.*, **13**, 232–7 (1939).
1614 ——, and ——: *J. Am. Med. Assoc.*, **108**, 32–7 (1937).
1615 ——, and ——: *Proc. Soc. Exptl. Biol. Med.*, **43**, 324–7 (1940).
1616 ——, and ——: *Southern Med. J.*, **30**, 479–87 (1937).
1617 ——, ——, and Feinstone, W. H.: *J. Am. Med. Assoc.*, **112**, 115–21 (1939).
1618 ——, ——, and ——: *Penn. Med. J.*, **42**, 483–91 (1939).
1619 ——, and Feinstone, W. H.: *Proc. Soc. Exptl. Biol. Med.*, **39**, 486–91 (1938).
1620 ——, and Haviland, J. W.: *Ann. Intern. Med.*, **14**, 1043–9 (1940).
1621 ——, Haviland, J. W., and Edwards, L. B.: *Proc. Soc. Exptl. Biol. Med.*, **43**, 328–32 (1940).
1622 Longacre, A. B., and Honold, E.: *Ibid.*, **46**, 9–13 (1941).
1623 Loomis, T. A., Hubbard, R. S., and Koepf, G. F.: *Am. J. Physiol.*, **139**, 197–201 (1943).
1624 ——, Koepf, G. F., and Hubbard, R. S.: *Am. J. Physiol.*, **141**, 158 (1944).
1625 Loria, F. L.: *Am. J. Med. Sci.*, **202**, 803–8 (1941).
1626 Loudon, J. D.: *J. Chem. Soc.*, **1939**, 902–6.
1627 Loughlin, E. H., Bennett, R. H., and Flanagan, M. E.: *J. Lab. Clin. Med.*, **25**, 569–73 (1944).
1628 ——, ——, ——, and Spitz, S. H.: *Ibid.*, **28**, 1455–68 (1943); *ibid.*, **29**, 921–35 (1944); *Am. J. Med. Sci.*, **205**, 223–9 (1943).
1629 Loveless, J. A., and Denton, W.: *J. Am. Med. Assoc.*, **121**, 827–8 (1943).
1630 Loving, W. L.: *Am. J. Trop. Med.*, **23**, 593 (1943).
1631 Lowell, F. C., Strauss, E., and Finland, M.: *Ann. Intern. Med.*, **14**, 1001–23 (1940).
1632 ——, Strauss, E., and Finland, M.: *J. Immunol.*, **40**, 311–23 (1941).
1633 Lubowe, I. I., and Somerville, W. T.: *U. S.* 2,330,828 (Oct. 5, 1943).
1634 Lucchesi, P. F., and Gildersleeve, N.: *J. Pediat.*, **22**, 319–24 (1943).
1635 Lurie, M. B., and Stokes, J., Jr.: *J. Bact.*, **45**, 194–5 (1943).
1636 Lushbaugh, C. C., and Cannon, P. R.: *J. Infectious Diseases*, **71**, 33–9 (1942).
1637 Lwoff, A., Nitti, F., and Trefouel, Mme. J.: *Ann. inst. Pasteur*, **67**, 173–85 (1941).
1638 ——, ——, and Hamon, V.: *Ibid.*, 9–36 (1941).
1639 Lynch, H. M., and Lockwood, J. S.: *J. Immunol.*, **42**, 435–43 (1941).
1640 Lynn, D., Bergh, G. S., and Spink, W. W.: *Surgery*, **13**, 447–9 (1943).
1641 Lyon, G. M.: *West Virginia Med. J.*, **37**, 25–8, 54–66 (1941).
1642 Lyons, C., Owen, C. R., and Ayers, W. B.: *Surgery*, **14**, 99–104 (1943).
1643 Lyons, R. H., and Balberor, H.: *J. Am. Med. Assoc.*, **118**, 955–8 (1942).
1644 MacArthur, R. S.: *Clin. Med.*, **50**, 132 (1943).
1645 Macartney, D. W., Smith, G. S., Luxton, R. W., Ramsey, W. A., and Goldman, J.: *Lancet*, **1942, 1**, 639–41.

1646 MacCallum, F. O., and Findlay, G. M.: *Lancet*, **1938, 2,** 136–8.
1647 McCloy, A.: *Brit. Med. J.*, **1943, 2,** 106.
1648 McCoy, O. R.: *Proc. Soc. Exptl. Biol. Med.*, **38,** 461–2 (1938).
1649 McCrea, F. D.: *Am. J. Physiol.*, **126,** 569–70 (1939).
1650 McDermott, W., Gilligan, D. R., Wheeler, C., and Plummer, N.: *N. Y. State J. Med.*, **44,** 394–7 (1944).
1651 MacDonald, A.: *Lancet*, **1940, 1,** 1157–9.
1652 McElroy, J.: *Cellular Comp. Physiol.*, **23,** 109–12 (1944).
1653 Macht, D. I.: *Exptl. Med. Surg.*, **1,** 260–72, 415 (1943).
1654 ——: *Proc. Soc. Exptl. Biol. Med.*, **49,** 694–6 (1942).
1655 McIllwain, H.: *Biochem. J.*, **36,** 1–7 (1942).
1656 ——: *Ibid.*, 417–26 (1942).
1657 ——: *Ibid.*, **37,** 265–71 (1943); *J. Chem. Soc.*, **1943,** 322–5.
1658 ——: *Biochem. J.*, **38,** 97–105 (1944.)
1659 ——: *Proc. Biochem. Soc.*, **36,** vi (1942).
1660 ——: *Ibid.*, **37,** xii (1943).
1661 ——: *Ibid.*, **38,** xxxiv–xxxv (1944).
1662 ——: *Brit. J. Exptl. Path.*, **21,** 136–47 (1940).
1663 ——: *Ibid.*, **22,** 148–55 (1941).
1664 ——: *Ibid.*, **23,** 95–102 (1942).
1665 ——: *Ibid.*, 265–71 (1942).
1666 ——: *Ibid.*, **24,** 203–12, 212–7 (1943).
1667 ——: *Nature*, **151,** 270–3 (1943).
1668 ——: *Ibid.*, **153,** 300–4 (1944).
1669 ——: *Science*, **95,** 509–11 (1942).
1670 ——, and Hawking, F.: *Lancet*, **1943, 1,** 449–51.
1671 ——, and Hughes, D. E.: *Biochem. J.*, **38,** 187–95 (1944).
1672 McIntosh, J., and Selbie, F. R.: *Brit. J. Exptl. Path.*, **24,** 246–52 (1943).
1673 ——, and ——: *Lancet*, **1940, 1,** 240–2.
1674 ——, and ——: *Ibid.*, **1943, 1,** 793–5; *ibid.*, **1943, 2,** 224–5.
1675 ——, and ——: *Ibid.*, **1944, 1,** 591–3.
1676 ——, and Whitby, L. E. H.: *Ibid.*, **1939, 1,** 431–5.
1677 McIvor, B., Anderson, H. H., Luduena, F. P., and Leake, C. D.: *Fed. Proc. Am. Soc. Exptl. Biol.*, **1,** 160 (1942).
1678 McKee, C. M., Rake, G., Greep, R. O., and VanDyke, H. B.: *Proc. Soc. Exptl. Biol. Med.*, **42,** 417–21 (1939).
1679 McKee, G. M., Hermann, F., Baer, R. L., and Sulzberger, M. B.: *J. Lab. Clin. Med.*, **28,** 1642–9 (1943).
1680 ——, Herman, F., Baer, R. L., and Sulzberger, M. B.: *Science*, **98,** 66–8 (1943).
1681 McKennis, H. J.: *J. Am. Chem. Soc.*, **63,** 631 (1941).
1682 McKinley, E. B., Meck, J. S., and Acree, E. G.: *Science*, **87,** 43–4 (1938); *J. Infectious Diseases*, **64,** 36–42 (1939).
1683 McKinney, R. A., and Mellon, R. R.: *J. Infectious Diseases*, **68,** 233–45 (1941).
1684 ——, and ——: *Proc. Soc. Exptl. Biol. Med.*, **37,** 333–6 (1937).
1685 McKinstry, D. W., and Reading, E. H.: *J. Franklin Inst.*, **237,** 422–31 (1944).
1686 Maclean, B.: *Lancet*, **1944, 1,** 452.
1687 MacLean, I. H., Rogers, K. B., and Fleming, A.: *Lancet*, **1939, 1,** 562–8.
1688 MacLean, I. W., Jr., Beard, D., Taylor, A. R., Sharp, D. G., Beard, J. W., Feller, A. E., and Dingle, J. H.: *J. Immunol.*, **48,** 305–16 (1944).
1689 MacLennan, J. D.: *Lancet*, **1943, 2,** 123–6.
1690 MacLeod, C. M.: *J. Exptl. Med.*, **72,** 217–32 (1940).
1691 ——: *Proc. Soc. Exptl. Biol. Med.*, **41,** 215–18 (1939); *J. Am. Med. Assoc.*, **113,** 1405–10 (1939).
1692 ——, and Daddi, G.: *Proc. Soc. Exptl. Biol. Med.*, **41,** 69–71 (1939); *J. Clin. Investigation*, **18,** 493 (1939).
1693 ——, and Mirick, G. S.: *Am. J. Pub. Health*, **31,** 34–8 (1941).
1694 McLeod, J. W., Mayr-Harting, A., and Walker, N.: *Brit. J. Exptl. Path.*, **25,** 27–37 (1944).
1695 McNair Scott, T. F., Beeson, P. B., and Hawley, W. L.: *Lancet*, **1943, 1,** 487–90.
1696 McNaught, J. B., Beard, R. R., and DeEds, F.: *Proc. Soc. Exptl. Biol. Med.*, **41,** 17–20 (1939).
1697 MacNeal, W. J., Blevins, A., and Pacis, M.: *J. Bact.*, **46,** 111 (1943).
1698 ——, Spence, M. J., and Blevins, A.: *N. Y. State J. Med.*, **44,** 603–5 (1944).
1699 Mahoney, J. F., VanSlyke, C. J., and Wolcott, R. R.: *Proc. 8th Am. Sci. Cong.*, **6,** Pub. Health Med. 459–65 (1942); *Chem. Abst.*, **37,** 1197 (1943); *Venereal Disease Information*, **22,** 425–31 (1941).
1700 Maier, J., and Riley, E : *Proc. Soc. Exptl. Biol. Med.*, **50,** 152–4 (1942).
1701 Main, E. R., Shinn, L. E., and Mellon, R. R.: *Ibid.*, **39,** 272–6 (1938).

1702 Major, R. H., and Douglas, H. L.: *J. Kansas Med. Soc.*, **43**, 287–8 (1942).
1703 Mallinckrodt Chemical Works, Ltd. (Leitch, L. C., and Brickman, L.): U. S. 2,230,962 (Feb. 4, 1941).
1704 —— (Leitch, L. C., and Brickman, L.): U. S. 2,339,083 (Jan. 11, 1944).
1705 Manchester Oxide Co., Ltd. (Bann, B., and Krug, P.): Brit. 552,885 (Apr. 29, 1943).
1706 —— (Bann, B., Krug, P., Wheeler, D. E., Taylor, W., and Gladding, G.): Brit. 551,205 (Mar. 11, 1943).
1707 —— (Bann, B., Krug, P., Wheeler, D. E., Taylor, W., and Gladding, G.): Brit. 551,206 (Mar. 11, 1943).
1708 —— (Bann, B., Krug, P., Wheeler, D. E., Taylor, W., and Gladding, G.): Brit. 551,207 (Mar. 11, 1943).
1709 —— (Bann, B., Krug, P., Wheeler, D. E., Taylor, W., and Gladding, G.): Brit. 551,681 (Apr. 1, 1943).
1710 —— (Bann, B., Krug, P., Wheeler, D. E., Taylor, W., and Gladding, G.): Brit. 553,269 (May 14, 1943); *Brit. Chem. Abst.*, **1943**, **B2**, 243.
1711 —— (Bann, B., Krug, P., Wheeler, D. E., Taylor, W., and Gladding, G.): Brit. 559,384–5; *Brit. Chem. Abst.*, **1944**, **B2**, 131.
1712 —— (Clayton, J. H., and Bann, B.): Brit. 546,277–8; 546,301 (July 7, 1942); *Chem. Abst.*, **37**, 3103–4.
1713 Mangini, A.: *Atti accad. Italia. Rend. classe sci. fis. mat. nat.*, **1** (7), 452–8 (1940); *ibid.*, **1**, 554–7 (1940); *Chem. Abst.*, **37**, 98; *ibid.*, 352.
1714 ——, and Colonna, M.: *Boll. sci. facoltá. chim. ind. Bologna*, **1940**, 316; *Chem. Abst.*, **37**, 6653.
1715 ——, and Filomeni, M.: *Boll. sci. facoltá chim. ind. Bologna*, **3**, 23–4 (1942); *Chem. Abst.*, **37**, 4465.
1716 Mann, F. G., and Watson, J.: *J. Chem. Soc.*, **1943**, 606–9.
1717 Manwell, R. D., Counts, E., and Coulston, F.: *Proc. Soc. Exptl. Biol. Med.*, **46**, 523–5 (1941).
1718 Mao, Shou-Pai: *Natl. Med. J. China*, **27**, 410–5 (1941); *Chem. Abst.*, **37**, 79.
1719 Marcus, P. M., and Necheles, H.: *Proc. Soc. Exptl. Biol. Med.*, **38**, 385–7 (1938).
1720 Marini-Bettolo, G. B.: *Gazzetta*, **71**, 627–35 (1941); *Brit. Chem. Abst.*, **1943**, **A2**, 88.
1721 Marinkovitch, R.: *Lancet*, **1941**, **1**, 144–5.
1722 Markoff, N.: *Schweiz. med. Wochschr.*, **71**, 904–7 (1941); *Bull. War Med.*, **3**, 296–7 (1943).
1723 Marks, R. F.: *Arch. Otolaryngol.*, **35**, 794–8 (1942).
1724 Marshall, E. K., Jr.: *Ann. Rev. Physiol.*, **3**, 643–70 (1941).
1725 ——: *Bull. N. Y. Acad. Sci.*, **16**, 723–31 (1940).
1726 ——: *Physiol. Rev.*, **22**, 190–204 (1942).
1727 ——: *The Mississippi Doctor*, 4–9 (June, 1942).
1728 ——: *U. Penn. Bicentennial Conference*, "Chemotherapy," 1–8 (1941).
1729 ——, Cutting, W. C., and Emerson, K., Jr.: *J. Am. Med. Assoc.*, **110**, 252–7 (1938).
1730 ——, ——, and ——: *Science*, **85**, 202–3 (1937).
1731 ——, and Litchfield, J. T., Jr.: *J. Pharmacol.*, **67**, 454–75 (1939).
1732 ——, ——, and White, H. J.: *Ibid.*, **69**, 89–102 (1940).
1733 ——, ——, and ——: *Ibid.*, **75**, 89–104 (1942).
1734 ——, ——, ——, Bratton, A. C., and Shepherd, R. G.: *Ibid.*, **76**, 226–34 (1942).
1735 Martin, G. J.: *Proc. Soc. Exptl. Biol. Med.*, **51**, 56–9 (1942).
1736 ——, and Fisher, C. V.: *J. Biol. Chem.*, **144**, 289–90 (1942).
1737 ——, and ——: *J. Lab. Clin. Med.*, **29**, 383–9 (1944).
1738 ——, and Rennebaum, E. H.: *J. Biol. Chem.*, **151**, 417–26 (1943).
1739 Mascall, W. N.: *Brit. Med. J.*, May 16, 1942, 622.
1740 Mashkovskiĭ, M. C.: *Farmatsiya*, **1941**, No. 2, 35–7; *Chem. Abst.*, **37**, 2514; *ibid.*, **38**, 1800.
1741 Matthews, D. N.: *Lancet*, **1942**, **2**, 271–5; *Ann. Surg.*, **113**, 910–4 (1941).
1742 Matti, J.: *Bull. soc. chim.*, **7**, 617–21 (1940); *Chem. Abst.*, **36**, 2850.
1743 ——, Nitti, F., Morel, M., and Lwoff, A.: *Ann. inst. Pasteur*, **67**, 240–3 (1941); *Chem. Abst.*, **36**, 7134.
1744 Mattis, P. A., and Benson, W. M.: *Federation Proc.*, **3**, 80 (1944).
1745 ——, Benson, W. M., and Koelle, E. S.: *J. Pharmacol.*, **81**, 116–32 (1944).
1746 Mawson, C. A.: *Biochem. J.*, **36**, 845–7 (1942).
1747 May & Baker, Ltd. (Barber, H. J.): Brit. 550,446 (Feb. 4, 1943).
1748 —— (Barber, H. J.): Brit. 557,055 (Dec. 2, 1943); *Brit. Chem. Abst.*, **1944**, **B3**, 34.
1749 —— (Ewins, A. J., and Phillips, M. A.): U. S. 2,293,811 (Aug. 25, 1942).
1750 May, H. B., and Buck, S. C.: *Lancet*, **1939**, **2**, 685–6.
1751 May, L. M.: *Ann. Intern. Med.*, **15**, 320–3 (1941).
1752 Mayer, R. L.: *Biol. Med.*, **27**, Supplement 45–73 (1937); *ibid.*, 74–107.

1753 ——: *Bull. acad. med.*, **117**, 727–35 (1937).
1754 ——: *Ibid.*, **120**, 277–85 (1938).
1755 ——: *Compt. rend. soc. biol.*, **130**, 1560–2 (1939); *Chem. Abst.*, **33**, 6954 (1939).
1756 ——: *Rev. médicale France*, Nov.–Dec. **1941**, 3–19; *Chem. Abst.*, **36**, 5199.
1757 ——: *Science*, **98**, 203–4 (1943).
1758 Meacham, W. F., Angelucci, R., Benz, F., and Pilcher, C.: *Arch. Neurol. Psychiat.*, **50**, 633–758 (1943).
1759 Medical Research Council, War Memorandum No. 10, "The Medical Use of Sulphon-amides," His Majesty's Stationery Office, London (1943).
1760 Medlar, E. M., and Sasano, K. T.: *Am. Rev. Tuberc.*, **47**, 618–24 (1943).
1761 Meister Lucius & Bruning: Ger. 269,799 (Oct. 13, 1912); *Frdl.*, **11**, 380.
1762 Meleney, F. L.: *Ann. Surg.*, **118**, 171–86 (1943).
1763 Mellon, R. R., Locke, A. P., and Shinn, L. E.: *Am. J. Med. Sci.*, **199**, 749–59 (1940).
1764 ——, and McKinney, R. A.: *Proc. Soc. Exptl. Biol. Med.*, **42**, 677–9 (1939).
1765 Melton, G.: *Lancet*, **1941, 1**, 274–7; *ibid.*, **1942, 2**, 522–3.
1766 ——: *Ibid.*, **1944, 1**, 277–8.
1767 ——, and Beck, A.: *Ibid.*, **1939, 1**, 867–9.
1768 Menefee, E. E., and Poston, M. A.: *J. Bact.*, **37**, 269–76 (1939).
1769 Menk, W., and Mohr, W.: *Arch. Schiffs-u. Tropen-Hyg.*, **43**, 117–25 (1939).
1770 Mentzer, Ch., Buu-Hoi, and Cagniant, P.: *Bull. soc. chim.*, **10**, 141–5 (1943); *Chem. Abst.*, **38**, 3963.
1771 Merck and Company (Kamlet, J.): U. S. 2,295,481 (Sept. 8, 1942); Brit. 539,893 (Mar. 29, 1941).
1772 —— (Kamlet, J.): U. S. 2,305,260 (Dec. 15, 1942).
1773 Merica, F. W.: *J. Am. Med. Assoc.*, **119**, 286–7 (1942).
1774 Meyer, K. A., and Gradman, R.: *Surg. Gynecol. Obstet.*, **76**, 584–6 (1943).
1775 Michaud, L.: *Schweiz. med. Wochschr.*, **73**, 575–80 (1943).
1776 Middlebrook, G., and Lloyd, J. B.: *Am. Rev. Tuberc.*, **49**, 535–42 (1944).
1777 Miescher, G.: *Schweiz. med. Wochschr.*, **70**, 621–7; 891 (1940).
1778 ——: *Ibid.*, **73**, 521–31 (1943); *Bull. War Med.*, **4**, 493–4 (1944).
1779 ——, and Schnetz, A.: *Ibid.*, **71**, 175–9 (1940).
1780 Mietzsch, F.: *Z. Physiol. Chem.*, **274**, 19–26 (1942); *Chem. Abst.*, **37**, 5488.
1781 Migliardi, C., and Tappi, G.: *Arch. sci. biol.*, **27**, 164–9 (1941); *Chem. Abst.*, **38**, 2022.
1782 Millar, J. A. S.: *North Am. Vet.*, **24**, 24–8 (1943).
1783 Miller, C. P., and Hawk, W. D.: *Arch. Path.*, **28**, 764 (1939).
1784 Miller, J. K.: *J. Bact.*, **37**, 228 (1939).
1785 ——: *J. Pharmacol.*, **71**, 14–19 (1941).
1786 Miller, J. L.: *Arch. Dermatol. Syphilol.*, **46**, 379–85 (1942).
1787 Mills, M. A., and Machie, T. T.: *Am. J. Digestive Diseases*, **10**, 55–9 (1943).
1788 Mingoja, Q., and Berti, F.: *Arg. Biol. (Sao Paulo)*, **27**, 4–7 55–63 (1943).
1789 Mininni-Montesano, N.: *Biochem. terap. sper.*, **27**, 377–84 (1940); *Chem. Abst.*, **38**, 1567.
1790 Minlon, H., and Lo, C. P.: *J. Chinese Chem. Soc.*, **9**, 61–5 (1942); *Brit. Chem. Abst.*, **1943, A2**, 259.
1791 ——, Lo, C. P., and Chu, L. J. Y.: *J. Chinese Chem. Soc.*, **9**, 57–60 (1942); *Brit. Chem. Abst.*, **1943, A2**, 260.
1792 Mirick, G. S.: *J. Clin. Investigation*, **21**, 628 (1942).
1793 Mitchell, G. A. G., Rees, W. S., and Robinson, C. N.: *Lancet*, **1944, 1**, 627–9.
1794 Moeschlin, S.: *Schweiz. med. Wochschr.*, **71**, 789–92 (1941).
1795 Moir, R. A.: *Lancet*, **1943, 1**, 556–7.
1796 Möller, E. F., and Birkofer, L.: *Ber.*, **75B**, 1108–26 (1942); *Chem. Abst.*, **37**, 5105.
1797 ——, and Schwartz, K.: *Ber.*, **74B**, 1612–16 (1941); *Chem. Abst.*, **37**, 356.
1798 Monsanto Chemical Co. (Kyrides, L. P.): U. S. 2,330,223 (Sept. 28, 1943); Brit. 557,289.
1799 Monti, L., and Palmieri: *Gazzetta*, **71**, 662–7 (1941); *Chem. Abst.*, **37**, 128 (1943).
1800 Monto, R. W.: *J. Michigan State Med. Soc.*, **41**, 569 (1942).
1801 Moore, M.: *J. Bact.*, **39**, 110 (1940); *Science*, **89**, 514–15 (1939).
1802 Morales-Otero, D., and Gonzalez, L. M.: *Proc. Soc. Exptl. Biol. Med.*, **44**, 532–4 (1940).
1803 Morgan, T. N., and Wylie-Smith, R.: *Lancet*, **1943, 2**, 731–3.
1804 Morren, H., and Lehmann, R.: *J. pharm. Belg.*, **1**, 127–8 (1942); *Chem. Abst.*, **38**, 3263.
1805 Morrow, G., and Berry, G. P.: *J. Bact.*, **38**, 280–1 (1938).
1806 Morrow, W. J., Epstein, H. C., and Toomey, J. A.: *J. Pediat.*, **24**, 623–6 (1944).
1807 Morschäuser, B.: *Deut. Militararst.*, **7**, 381–22 (1942); *Bull. War Med.*, **3**, 341 (1943).
1808 Mount, L. G.: Thesis Yale University (1940). Personal communication from Prof. A. J. Hill.

1809 Mueller, R. S., and Thompson, J. E.: *J. Am. Med. Assoc.*, **118,** 189–93 (1942).
1810 Muether, R. O., and Kinsella, R. A.: *Ibid.*, **110,** 603–4 (1938).
1811 Muir, R. D., Shemleffer, V. J., and Jones, L. R.: *J. Bact.*, **41,** 84 (1941).
1812 ——, ——, and ——: *Ibid.*, **44,** 95–110 (1942).
1813 ——, ——, and ——: *Proc. Soc. Exptl. Biol. Med.*, **45,** 31–3 (1940).
1814 Mulder, J., Berg, R., van den, and Eimers, G.: *J. Am. Med. Assoc.*, **114,** 2156 (1940).
1815 Muller, O.: *Schweiz. Arch. Tierheilk.*, **84,** 13–24 (1942); *Chem. Abst.*, **37,** 3833.
1816 Murphy, F. D., Clark, J. K., and Flippin, H. F.: *Am. J. Med. Sci.*, **205,** 717–26 (1943).
1817 ——, Kuzma, J. F., Polley, T. Z., and Grill, J.: *Arch. Intern. Med.*, **73,** 433–43 (1944).
1818 Murray, J. F.: *S. African J. Med. Sci.*, **5,** 110–6 (1940); *Chem. Abst.*, **35,** 2172 (1941).
1819 Naegeli, C., Kündig, W., and Suter, H.: *Helv. Chem. Acta,* **25,** 1485–98 (1942); *Chem. Abst.*, **37,** 5949.
1820 Nagell, H.: *Med. Welt.*, **13,** 221–2 (1939).
1821 Nagler, F. P. O.: *Australian J. Exp. Biol. Med. Sci.*, **22,** 29–35 (1944).
1822 ——: *Med. J. Australia,* **1942, 1,** 281–3.
1823 Nandi, B. K., and Ganapathi, K.: *Current Sci.*, **9,** 177 (1940); *Brit. Chem. Abst.*, **1940, A2,** 261.
1824 Nathan, A. H., Hunter, J. H., and Kolloff, H. G.: *J. Am. Chem. Soc.*, **65,** 949–50 (1943).
1825 Neal, J. B., Applebaum, E., and Jackson, H. W.: *J. Am. Med. Assoc.*, **115,** 2055–8 (1940).
1826 Nelson, C. T., and Spink, W. W.: *Am. J. Med. Sci.*, **206,** 315–22 (1943).
1827 Nelson, J., Rinzler, H., and Kelsey, M. P.: *J. Am. Med. Assoc.*, **112,** 1044–5 (1939).
1828 Nepera Chemical Co.: Brit. 547,976 (Oct. 15, 1942); *Brit. Chem. Abst.*, **1943, B3,** 21.
1829 —— (Tisza, E. T., and Duesel, B. F.): U. S. 2,307,650 (Jan. 5, 1943).
1830 —— (Tisza, E. T., Duesel, B. F., and Friedman, H. L.): U. S. 2,332,615 (Oct. 26, 1943).
1831 Neter, E.: *Am. J. Surg.*, **58,** 69–72 (1942); *Proc. Soc. Exptl. Biol. Med.*, **47,** 303–5 (1941); *J. Pharmacol.*, **74,** 52–60 (1942).
1832 ——: *Arch. Path.*, **26,** 1082–3 (1938).
1833 ——: *J. Bact.*, **36,** 669–75 (1938).
1834 ——: *J. Infectious Diseases,* **67,** 84–7 (1940).
1835 ——: *Ibid.*, **68,** 278–84 (1941).
1836 ——: *J. Lab. Clin. Med.*, **24,** 650–3 (1939).
1837 ——: *J. Urol.*, **45,** 240–8 (1941).
1838 ——: *Ibid.*, **46,** 95–100 (1941).
1839 ——: *Proc. Soc. Exptl. Biol. Med.*, **39,** 84–6 (1938).
1840 ——: *Ibid.*, **41,** 62–5 (1939).
1841 ——: *Ibid.*, **42,** 668–72 (1939).
1842 ——: *Ibid.*, **43,** 774–6 (1940).
1843 ——, and Clark, P.: *Ibid.*, **56,** 34–5 (1944); *J. Urol.*, **51,** 101–9 (1944).
1844 ——, Hubbard, R. S., and Lamberti, T. G.: *Am. J. Surg.*, **60,** 227–31 (1944).
1845 ——, and Loomis, T. A.: *Urol. Cutaneous Rev.*, **45,** 295–7 (1941); *Chem. Abst.*, **36,** 2582.
1846 Neukirch, F., Zahle, V., and Baumgarten, I.: *Acta Med. Skand.*, **113,** 11–42 (1943); *Chem. Abst.*, **38,** 4317.
1847 Neumann, F. W., Krider, M. M., and Day, H. G.: *Proc. Soc. Exptl. Biol. Med.*, **52,** 257–60 (1943).
1848 Newcomer, W., and Frame, E. M.: *U. S. Naval Med. Bull.*, **41,** 966–72 (1943).
1849 Newman, H. C.: *J. Immunol.*, **38,** 377–82 (1940).
1850 Nielson, E., and Black, A.: *Proc. Soc. Exptl. Biol. Med.*, **55,** 14–6 (1944).
1851 ——, and Elvehjem, C. A.: *J. Biol. Chem.*, **145,** 713–14 (1942).
1852 Nitti, F., Bovet, D., and Depierre, F.: *Compt. rend. soc. biol.*, **124,** 16–8 (1937).
1853 ——, ——, and Hamon, V.: *Ibid.*, **128,** 26–8 (1938); *Chem. Abst.*, **32,** 6332.
1854 ——, and Matti, J.: *Compt. rend. soc. biol.*, **136,** 401–2 (1942); *Chem. Abst.*, **37,** 4089.
1855 Nixon, N., Eckert, J. F., and Holmes, K. B.: *Am. J. Med. Sci.*, **206,** 713–21 (1943).
1856 Noojin, R. O., and Callaway, J. L.: *Arch. Dermatol. Syphilol.*, **47,** 620–6 (1943).
1857 ——, ——, and Schulze, W.: *Am. J. Syphilis, Gonorrhea and Venereal Diseases,* **27,** 601–6 (1943).
1858 Nordmark-Werke, G. M. B. H. (Loop, W.): Ger. 706,695 (Apr. 30, 1941); *Chem. Abst.*, **37,** 2016.
1859 Norman, H. B.: *Brit. Med. J.*, **1944, 1,** 183.
1860 Norris, C. M.: *J. Am. Med. Assoc.*, **123,** 667–70 (1943).
1861 Northey, E. H.: *Ind. Eng. Chem.*, **35,** 829–36 (1943).
1862 ——, Pierce, A. E., and Kertesz, D. J.: *J. Am. Chem. Soc.*, **64,** 2763–5 (1942).
1863 Novelli, A., and Somaglino, J. C.: *Ibid.*, **63,** 854–5 (1941).
1864 Oakley, G. L.: *Brit. Med. J.*, **1938, 1,** 895–6.

1865 Oard, H. C., Jordan, E. V., Nimaroff, M., and Phelan, W. J.: *J. Am. Med. Assoc.*, **125**, 323–5 (1944).
1866 O'Donnell, M. C.: *Ibid.*, **122**, 298 (1943).
1867 Ogilvie, W. H.: *Surg. Gynecol. Obstet.*, **78**, 225–38 (1944).
1868 Olson, M., Slider, E., Clark, W. G., and MacDonald, R.: *Proc. Soc. Exptl. Biol. Med.*, **49**, 396–9 (1942).
1869 Opper, L., and Hale, V.: *J. Am. Med. Assoc.*, **119**, 1489–91 (1942).
1870 Ordal, E. J., and Halvorson, H. O.: *J. Bact.*, **40**, 148–9 (1940).
1871 Osgood, E. E.: *Can. Med. Assoc. J.*, **50**, 1–8 (1944).
1872 ——: *J. Lab. Clin. Med.*, **24**, 954–62 (1939).
1873 ——, and Brownlee, I. E.: *J. Clin. Investigation*, **17**, 502 (1938).
1874 ——, and ——: *J. Pediat.*, **17**, 740–6 (1940).
1875 ——, ——, and Joski, J.: *Am. J. Med. Sci.*, **200**, 596–603 (1940).
1876 ——, Joski, J., and Brownlee, I. E.: *Surg. Gynecol. Obstet.*, **71**, 445–9 (1940).
1877 ——, and Powell, H. M.: *Proc. Soc. Exptl. Biol. Med.*, **39**, 37–40 (1938).
1878 Osmond, T. E.: *Brit. Med. J.*, **1943, 2**, 72–4.
1879 Osterberg, G.: *Ugeskrift Laeger*, **104**, 835–9 (1942); *Chem. Abst.*, **38**, 2390.
1880 Osterholz, E.: *Zentr. Bakt.*, **142**, 293–303 (1938).
1881 Pakenham-Walsh, R.: *Lancet*, **1943, 1**, 649–50.
1882 ——, and Rennie, A. T.: *Ibid.*, **1940, 2**, 485.
1883 Page, G. B.: *Lancet*, **1942, 1**, 154.
1884 Page, S. G.: *Virginia Med. Monthly*, **70**, 561–9 (1943); *Bull. U. S. Army Med. Dept.*, **72**, 52–61 (1944).
1885 Palmer, C. C.: *North Am. Vet.*, **23**, 776–9 (1942).
1886 ——, and Kakavas, J. C.: *Ibid.*, **25**, 348–9 (1944).
1887 Pan, Shih-Yi: *Proc. Soc. Exptl. Biol. Med.*, **49**, 385–6 (1942).
1888 Pappas, J. P.: *Military Surgeon*, **90**, 662–7 (1942); *ibid.*, **91**, 681–4 (1943); *Bull. War Med.*, **3**, 517 (1943).
1889 Parfentjev, I. A., and Collins, S. W., Jr.: *J. Immunol.*, **38**, 137–41 (1940).
1890 Park, C. R., and Wood, W. B., Jr.: *Bull. Johns Hopkins Hosp.*, **70**, 19–25 (1942).
1891 Park, J. H., Jr.: *J. Pediat.*, **23**, 326 (1943).
1892 Park, R. G.: *Brit. Med. J.*, **1944, 1**, 781–3.
1893 ——: *Lancet*, **1944, 1**, 401–3; *Brit. Med. J.*, **1944, 2**, 816–7.
1894 Parke Davis and Company (Tillitson, E. W.): U. S. 2,287,071 (June 23, 1942); Brit. 532,893 (Feb. 3, 1941); *Chem. Abst.*, **36**, 1044.
1895 —— (Tullar, B. F.): Brit. 553,601 (May 28, 1943); *Brit. Chem. Abst.*, **1943, B2**, 225; U. S. 2,358,365–6 (Sept. 19, 1944).
1896 Patel, B. V.: *Current Sci.*, **11**, 187 (1942); *Brit. Chem. Abst.*, **1942, A3**, 840.
1897 ——: *Current Sci.*, **12**, 153 (1943); *Chem. Abst.*, **37**, 6740 (1943).
1898 Patterson, W. B.: *Hawaii Med. J.*, **3**, 222–5 (1944).
1899 Pepper, D. S., Flippin, H. F., Schwartz, L., and Lockwood, J. S.: *Am. J. Med. Sci.*, **198**, 22–35 (1939).
1900 Perlman, H. H., Brown, H., and Raiziss, G. W.: *Amer. Rev. Tuberc.*, **44**, 83–91 (1941).
1901 Personnel of Naval Laboratory Research Unit No. 1: *Science*, **98**, 348–9 (1943).
1902 Peters, B. A., and Easby, M. L.: *Brit. Med. J.*, 230–1 (Aug. 21, 1943).
1903 Peters, J. T.: *J. Amer. Med. Assoc.*, **124**, 31–3 (1944).
1904 Peters, L.: *J. Pharmacol.*, **79**, 32–6 (1943).
1905 ——, Beyer, K. H., and Patch, E. A.: *Fed. Proc.*, 3 and 36 (1944).
1906 Peterson, O. L., Deutsch, M. D., and Finland, M.: *Arch. Intern. Med.*, **72**, 594–612 (1943).
1907 ——, and Finland, M.: *Am. J. Med. Sci.*, **207**, 166–75 (1944).
1908 ——, and ——: *J. Clin. Investigation*, **21**, 629 (1942).
1909 ——, ——, and Ballou, A. M.: *Am. J. Med. Sci.*, **204**, 581–8 (1942).
1910 ——, Goodwin, R. A., Jr., and Finland, M.: *J. Clin. Investigation*, **22**, 659–72 (1943).
1911 ——, and Finland, M.: *Am. J. Med. Sci.*, **202**, 757–72 (1941).
1912 ——, Strauss, E., Taylor, F. H. C., and Finland, M.: *Ibid.*, **201**, 357–67 (1941).
1913 Petro, J.: *Lancet*, **1943, 1**, 35–8.
1914 Petter, C. K., and Prenzlau, W. S.: *Am. Rev. Tuberc.*, **49**, 308–22 (1944); *Illinois Med. J.*, **85**, 188–97 (1944).
1915 Pfister, W.: *Munch. med. Wochschr.*, **90**, 345–7 (1943); *Chem. Abst.*, **38**, 3020–1.
1916 Pfuetze, K. H., and Pyle, M. M.: *J. Am. Med. Assoc.*, **125**, 354–5 (1944).
1917 Phillips, R. F., and Frank, V. S.: *J. Org. Chem.*, **9**, 9–12 (1944).
1918 Phillips, R. L., and Barnes, L. H.: *J. Franklin Inst.*, **235**, 94–7 (1943).
1919 Pick, E. P., Brooks, G. W., and Unna, L.: *J. Pharmacol.*, **81**, 133–41 (1944).
1920 Pickrell, K. L.: *Bull. Johns Hopkins Hosp.*, **69**, 217–21 (1941).
1921 ——: *Ibid.*, **71**, 304–6 (1942).

1922 Pijoan, M., Worman, F., and Pijoan, J.: Southwestern Med., **27**, 118–20 (1943).
1923 Pike, R. M., and Foster, A. Z.: J. Bact., **47**, 97–105 (1944).
1924 ——, and Mackenzie, G. M.: Ibid., **40**, 171–95 (1940).
1925 Pilcher, C.: Ann. Surg., **119**, 509–17 (1944).
1926 ——, Angelucci, R., and Meacham, W. F.: J. Am. Med. Assoc., **119**, 927 (1942).
1927 ——, and Meacham, W. F.: J. Am. Med. Assoc., **123**, 330–32 (1943).
1928 Pillsbury, N. R., and Wassersug, J. D.: New Engl. J. Med., **230**, 72–4 (1944).
1929 Pinck, B. D., Morton, G. L., and Mattice, M. R.: J. Lab. Clin. Med., **29**, 462–3 (1944).
1930 Pittman, M.: U. S. Pub. Health Repts., **54**, 1769–75 (1939).
1931 ——: Ibid., **57**, 1899–1910 (1942).
1932 Plum, D.: East African Med. J., **19**, 3–9 (1942); War Med., **2**, 880 (1942).
1933 Plummer, N.: New York State J. Med., **43**, 425–33 (1943).
1934 ——, and Ensworth, H. K.: J. Am. Med. Asscc., **113**, 1847–54 (1939).
1935 ——, and ——: Proc. Soc. Exptl. Biol. Med., **45**, 734–8 (1940).
1936 ——, and Wheeler, C.: Am. J. Med. Sci., **207**, 175–84 (1944).
1937 Plummer, P. J. G., Mitchell, C. A., and Walker, R. V. L.: Can. J. Comparative Med., **2**, 139–41 (1938).
1938 Popkin, A. H.: J. Am. Chem. Soc., **65**, 2043–5 (1943).
1939 ——, and McVea, G. B.: Ibid., **66**, 796–8 (1944).
1940 ——, and Perretta, G. M.: Ibid., **65**, 2046–8 (1943).
1941 Porritt, A. E.: Military Surgeon, **94**, 227–8 (1944); Brit. J. Surgery, **31**, 208–21 (1944).
1942 Porter, C. T.: Trans. Am. Acad. Ophthalmol. Otolaryngol., **46**, 273–8 (1942).
1943 Porter, J. R., and Hale, W. M.: Proc. Soc. Exptl. Biol. Med., **42**, 47–50 (1939).
1944 Poston, M. A., and Orgain, E. S.: Am. J. Med. Sci., **203**, 577–80 (1942).
1945 Poth, E. J.: J. Am. Med. Assoc., **120**, 265–8 (1942).
1946 ——: Surg. Gynecol. Obstet., **78**, 373–80 (1944).
1947 ——: Texas State J. of Med., **39**, 369–72 (1943).
1948 ——, Chenoweth, B. M., and Knotts, F. L.: J. Lab. Clin. Med., **28**, 162–7 (1942).
1949 ——, and Knotts, F. L.: Arch. Surg., **44**, 208–222 (1942).
1950 ——, ——, Lee, J. T., and Inui, F.: Ibid., 187–207 (1942).
1951 ——, and Ross, C. A.: Fed. Proc., **2**, 89 (1943); Texas Repts. Biol. Med., **1**, 345–70 (1943); J. Lab. Clin. Med., **29**, 785–808 (1944); Proc. Soc. Exptl. Biol. Med., **57**, 322–7 (1944).
1952 Powell, H. M., and Chen, K. K.: J. Ind. State Med. Assoc., **34**, 602–8 (1941); Chem. Abst., **36**, 2017.
1953 ——, and ——: J. Pharmacol., **67**, 79–100 (1939).
1954 ——, and Jamieson, W. A.: Arch. Path., **28**, 755–6 (1939).
1955 ——, and ——: J. Immunol., **36**, 459–65 (1939).
1956 ——, and ——: J. Ind. State Med. Assoc., **35**, 361–2 (1942).
1957 ——, and ——: Proc. Soc. Exptl. Biol. Med., **41**, 281–3 (1939).
1958 ——, and ——: Ibid., **49**, 387–9 (1942).
1959 Price, A. E., and Myers, G. B.: Arch. Intern. Med., **70**, 558–66 (1942).
1960 ——, and Pedulla, J. C.: J. Am. Med. Assoc., **125**, 105–7 (1944).
1961 Priestley, F. W.: Vet. Record, **52**, 3 (1940).
1962 Proescher, F.: Personal communication (Dec. 14, 1943).
1963 ——, and Sycheff, V. M.: J. Pharmacol., **69**, 298 (1940).
1964 Proom, H.: Lancet, **1937, 1**, 16–8.
1965 Puhr, L.: Schweiz. med. Wochschr., **72**, 761–3 (1942); Chem. Abst., **38**, 4697.
1966 Pulver, R., and Martin, H.: Arch. exptl. Path. Pharmakol., **201**, 491–501 (1943).
1967 ——, and Suter, R.: Schweiz. med. Wochschr., **73**, 403–8 (1943); Bull. War Med., **4**, 48 (1943).
1968 Pulvertaft, R. J. V.: Lancet, **1943, 2**, 1–2.
1969 ——, and MacKenzie, D. H.: Ibid., 379–84.
1970 Quin, D. C., and Robinson, R.: J. Chem. Soc., **1943**, 555–6.
1971 Quinby, W. C.: New Engl. J. Med., **229**, 972–4 (1943).
1972 Rademacher, C. J.: Military Surgeon, **90**, 431–4 (1942).
1973 Ragno, M., and Solarino, C.: Gazz. chim. ital., **71**, 235–52 (1941); Chem. Abst., **36**, 2849.
1974 Raiziss, G. W.: Science, **98**, 350 (1943).
1975 ——, and Freifelder, M.: J. Am. Chem. Soc., **64**, 2340–2 (1942).
1976 ——, Severac, M., and Moetsch, J. C.: J. Am. Pharm. Assoc. (Sci. Ed.), **31**, 198–200 (1942).
1977 ——, ——, and ——: J. Lab. Clin. Med., **27**, 1276–9 (1942).
1978 ——, ——, and ——: Ibid., **28**, 1580–5 (1943).
1979 ——, ——, ——, and Clemence, L. W.: Proc. Soc. Exptl. Biol. Med., **39**, 339–44 (1938); ibid., **42**, 12–17 (1939).

1980 ——, ——, and ——: *Ibid.*, **46**, 361–3 (1941).
1981 ——, ——, ——, and Clemence, L. W.: *J. Chemotherapy*, **14**, 1–11, 91–105 (1938).
1982 ——, ——, ——, and ——: *Proc. Soc. Exptl. Biol. Med.*, **40**, 434–5 (1939).
1983 Rajagopalan, S.: *Current Sci.*, **11**, 146, 394–6 (1942); *Brit. Chem. Abst.*, **1942, A2**, 289; *Chem. Abst.*, **36**, 6511; *ibid.*, **37**, 4059.
1984 ——: *Proc. Indian Acad. Sci.*, **18A**, 100–12 (1943); *Brit. Chem. Abst.*, **1944, A2**, 25–6; *Chem. Abst.*, **38**, 729, 1217.
1985 ——, and Ganapathi, K.: *Proc. Indian Acad. Sci.*, **15A**, 432–6 (1942).
1986 Rake, G., and Hamre, D. M.: *Proc. Soc. Exptl. Biol. Med.*, **55**, 90–1 (1944).
1987 ——, Jones, H., and Nigg, C.: *Ibid.*, **49**, 449–52 (1942).
1988 ——, and McKee, C. M.: *Ibid.*, **43**, 561 (1940).
1989 ——, ——, and Shaffer, M. F.: *Arch. Path.*, **29**, 733 (1940).
1990 ——, and Shaffer, M. F.: *J. Immunol.*, **38**, 177–200 (1940).
1991 Rammelkamp, C. H., and Keefer, C. S.: *Ann. Intern. Med.*, **16**, 659–65 (1942).
1992 ——, and Keefer, C. S.: *New Engl. J. Med.*, **223**, 877–85 (1940).
1993 ——, and Keefer, C. S.: *Proc. Soc. Exptl. Biol. Med.*, **43**, 664–8 (1940).
1994 ——, and Jewell, M. L.: *Ibid.*, **45**, 169–74 (1940).
1995 Rankin, L. M., and Eger, S. A.: *Am. J. Surg.*, **59**, 136–7 (1943).
1996 Ransmeier, J. C.: *J. Infectious Diseases*, **72**, 77–82, 83–5 (1943).
1997 ——, and Major, J. W.: *Arch. Intern. Med.*, **72**, 319–28 (1943).
1998 Ransone, B., and Elvehjem, C. A.: *J. Biol. Chem.*, **151**, 109–15 (1943).
1999 Rantz, L. A., and Kirby, W. M. M.: *Arch. Intern. Med.*, **71**, 516–28 (1943).
2000 ——, and ——: *J. Immunol.*, **48**, 29–37 (1944).
2001 Rao, P. L. N.: *J. Indian Chem. Soc.*, **18**, 316–20 (1941); *Chem. Abst.*, **36**, 2910.
2002 Rao, R. S., and Ganapathi, K.: *Indian Med. Gaz.*, **75**, 674 (1940); *ibid.*, **76**, 78–81 (1941).
2003 Ratish, H. D., and Bullowa, J. G. M.: *Proc. Soc. Exptl. Biol. Med.*, **54**, 216–8 (1943).
2004 Raudnitz, H.: *Ber.* **60B**, 743–8 (1927).
2005 Raybin, H. W.: *J. Am. Pharm. Assoc. (Sci. Ed.)*, **33**, 158–9 (1944).
2006 Redlich, O., and Maranville, L. F.: *Northwest Sci.*, **17**, No. 1, 4–5 (1943).
2007 Reed, G. B.: *Trans. Roy. Soc. Can.*, **37**, 1 (1943).
2008 ——, and Orr, J. H.: *War Med.*, **2**, 59–78, 83–6 (1942); *ibid.*, 639–45.
2009 Reed, L. J., and Muench, H.: *Am. J. Hyg.*, **27**, 493–7 (1938).
2010 Reid, R. D.: *J. Bact.*, **38**, 236 (1939).
2011 ——: *Proc. Soc. Exptl. Biol. Med.*, **41**, 437–42 (1939).
2012 Reimann, H. A.: *Arch. Intern. Med.*, **72**, 388–426 (1943).
2013 Reinhart, F. E.: *J. Franklin Inst.*, **236**, 316–20 (1943); *Chem. Abst.*, **37**, 6652.
2014 Reinhold, J. G., Flippin, H. F., and Schwartz, L.: *Am. J. Med. Sci.*, **199**, 393–401 (1940).
2015 ——, ——, ——, and Domm, A. H.: *Ibid.*, **201**, 106–14 (1941).
2016 Remsen, I.: *J. Am. Chem. Soc.*, **18**, 150.
2017 Reque, P. G., and Bergsma, D.: *Bull. U. S. Army Med. Dept.*, **78**, 97–102 (1944).
2018 Research Corporation (Proescher, F., and Sycheff, V. M.): U. S. 2,318,968 (May 11, 1943).
2019 —— (Proescher, F., and Sycheff, V. M.): U. S. 2,348,417 (May 9, 1944).
2020 Rest, A.: *Am. Rev. Tuberc.*, **47**, 406–12 (1943).
2021 Reynolds, F. W., Evans, M. S., and Walsh, F. B.: *Am. J. Syphilis, Gonorrhea and Venereal Diseases*, **27**, 2–14 (1943).
2022 ——, and Shaffer, G. W.: *Ibid.*, **563**–71 (1943).
2023 Riba, L. W., Schmidlapp, C. J., and Bosworth, N. L.: *War Med.*, **6**, 72–9 (1944).
2024 Ribeiro, F.: *J. Biol. Chem.*, **152**, 665–7 (1944).
2025 Rich, A. R., and Follis, R. H., Jr.: *Bull. Johns Hopkins Hosp.*, **62**, 77–84 (1938).
2026 Richards, G. G.: *Ann. Intern. Med.*, **17**, 78–82 (1942).
2027 Richards, P., Forster, W. G., and Thygeson, P.: *Arch. Ophthalmol.*, **21**, 577–9 (1939).
2028 Richards, V.: *Surgery*, **14**, 308–19 (1943).
2029 Riesz, E.: *Monatsh.*, **50**, 263–8 (1928).
2030 Rigdon, R. H., Haines, A., and Lipscomb, A.: *J. Lab. Clin. Med.*, **26**, 1111–5 (1941).
2031 Roasonda, G.: *J. Am. Med. Assoc.*, **116**, 259(1941).
2032 Roberts, T. L., and Daniels, W. B.: *Ibid*, **122**, 651–3 (1943).
2033 Robertson, O. H., and Hamburger, M.: *J. Exptl. Med.*, **72**, 275–88 (1940).
2034 ——, and Coggeshall, L. T.: *Ibid.*, **67**, 597–608 (1938).
2035 ——, and Fox, J. P.: *Ibid.*, **69**, 229–46 (1939).
2036 ——, and Loosli, C. G.: *Ibid.*, **67**, 575–6 (1938).
2037 Robinson, E. J., and Crossley, M. L.: *Arch. Biochem.*, **1**, 415–23 (1943).
2038 Robinson, H. J., Graessle, O. E., and Smith, D. G.: *Science*, **99**, 540–2 (1944).
2039 ——, Siegel, H., and Graessle, O. E.: *J. Pharmacol.*, **79**, 354–63 (1943).

2040 Robinson, H. M., and Robinson, H. M., Jr.: *Southern Med. J.*, **34**, 1093–5 (1941).
2041 Robson, J. M., and Scott, G. I.: *Brit. J. Exptl. Path.*, **24**, 50–6 (1943); *Brit. Med. J.*, **1942, 1**, 5–8; *Lancet*, **1943, 1**, 100–3.
2042 Rodaniche, E. C.: *J. Infectious Diseases*, **70**, 58–61 (1942).
2043 ——: *Ibid.*, **73**, 173–9 (1943).
2044 ——, and Kirsner, J. B.: *J. Parasitol.*, **28**, 441–9 (1942).
2045 ——, Palmer, W. L., and Kirsner, J. B.: *J. Infectious Diseases*, **72**, 222 (1943); *Gastro-enterology*, **1**, 135–9 (1943).
2046 Rohr, J. H., and Christopher, F.: *Surg. Gynecol. Obstet.*, **78**, 515 (1944).
2047 Römcke, O., and Vogt, E.: *Lancet*, **1939, 2**, 779–80.
2048 Romence, H. L., and Harkins, A. N.: *Proc. Soc. Exptl. Biol. Med.*, **54**, 8–10 (1943).
2049 Rose, F. L., and Bevan, H. G. L.: *Biochem. J.*, **38**, 116 (1944).
2050 ——, Martin, A. R., and Bevan, H. G. L.: *J. Pharmacol.*, **77**, 127–42 (1943).
2051 Rosen, N.: *J. Am. Dental Assoc.*, **31**, 622–7 (1944).
2052 Rosenbaum, J. J., and Cass, W. E.: *J. Am. Chem. Soc.*, **64**, 2444–5 (1942).
2053 Rosenthal, L.: *Proc. Soc. Exptl. Biol. Med.*, **43**, 78–80 (1940).
2054 Rosenthal, S. M.: *Med. Ann. Dist. Columbia*, **6**, 337–43 (1937).
2055 ——: *U. S. Pub. Health Repts.*, **58**, 5–9 (1943).
2056 ——, and Bauer, H.: *J. Pharmacol.*, **63**, 32–3 (1938).
2057 Rosicky, J.: Ger. 731,912 (Jan. 21, 1943); *Chem. Abst.*, **38**, 552.
2058 Rothbard, S.: *Proc. Soc. Exptl. Biol. Med.*, **44**, 379–81 (1940).
2059 Rothman, M., Tamerin, J., and Bullowa, J. G. M.: *J. Am. Med. Assoc.*, **120**, 803–5 (1942).
2060 Roughton, F. W. J., *et al.*: *Am. J. Physiol.*, **137**, 593–8 (1942); *Chem. Abst.*, **37**, 183.
2061 Rouslacroix, A., Schafer, E., and Mosser, H.: *Compt. rend. soc. biol.*, **133**, 146–7 (1940).
2062 Roy, A. C.: *Ind. J. Med. Res.*, **28**, 235–40 (1940).
2063 Rubbo, S. D., Maxwell, M., Fairbridge, R. A., and Gillespie, J. M.: *Australian J. Exptl. Biol. Med. Sci.*, **19**, 185–98 (1941).
2064 Ruegsegger, J. M., Brookens, N. L., Hamburger, M., Jr., and Grupen, E. S.: *Am. J. Med. Sci.*, **206**, 323–7 (1943).
2065 ——, and Hamburger, M.: *J. Infectious Diseases*, **64**, 18–21 (1939).
2066 ——, Hamburger, M., Jr., Turk, A. S., Spies, T. D., and Blankenhorn, M. A.: *Am. J. Med. Sci.*, **202**, 432–5 (1941).
2067 Rusk, H. A., and VanRavenswaay, A. C.: *J. Am. Med. Assoc.*, **122**, 495–6 (1943).
2068 Ryan, J. D., Bauman, E., and Mulholland, J. H.: *Ibid.*, **119**, 484–6 (1942).
2069 Sabin, A. B.: *Science*, **89**, 228–9 (1939).
2070 ——, and Warren, J.: *J. Bact.*, **41**, 80 (1941).
2071 ——, and ——: *Proc. Soc. Exptl. Biol. Med.*, **51**, 15–23 (1943).
2072 Sacharow, B.: *Zentr. Bakt. Parasitenk. Orig.*, **142**, 450–72 (1938).
2073 Sadusk, J. F., Jr., Blake, F. G., and Seymour, A.: *Yale J. Biol. Med.*, **12**, 681–96 (1940).
2074 ——, and Hirshfield, J. W.: *J. Clin. Investigation*, **19**, 768 (1940).
2075 ——, ——, and Seymour, A.: *Yale J. Biol. Med.*, **13**, 351–62 (1941).
2076 ——, and Oswald, E.: *Am. J. Trop. Med.*, **23**, 275–9 (1943).
2077 ——, and Tredway, J. B.: *Yale J. Biol. Med.*, **13**, 539–56 (1941).
2078 Sager, W. W., and Pudenz, R. H.: *U. S. Naval Med. Bull.*, **42**, 1275–82 (1944).
2079 Saker, G.: *Z. klin. Med.*, **138**, 317–33 (1940); *Chem. Abst.*, **36**, 7137.
2080 Sako, W., Stewart, C. A., and Fleet, J.: *J. Am. Med. Assoc.*, **119**, 327–31 (1942); *J. Pediat.*, **25**, 114–26 (1944).
2081 Salman, L. D.: *Arch. Otolaryngol.*, **37**, 710–12 (1943).
2082 Sanders, M.: *Arch. Path.*, **28**, 541–86 (1939).
2083 Sandusky, W. R., and Meleney, F. L.: *Arch. Surg.*, **45**, 890–912 (1942).
2084 Sanna, G.: *Rend. Siminar. facoltá. sci. univ. Cagliari*, **10**, 46–9 (1940); *ibid.*, 54–7; *Chem. Abst.*, **37**, 1718; *ibid.*, 2356; *Gazzetta*, **72**, 313–7 (1942); *Brit. Chem. Abst.*, **1943, A2**, 244.
2085 ——, Sollai, V.: *Gazz. chim. ital.*, **72**, 313–7 (1942); *Chem. Abst.*, **38**, 4920.
2086 Saphir, W., Baer, W. H., and Plotke, F.: *J. Am. Med. Assoc.*, **118**, 964–7 (1942).
2087 Sapinsky, H.: *Deut. Arch. f. klin. Med.*, **191**, 70–86 (1943).
2088 Sarvis, E. S.: *Northwest Med.*, **41**, 208–9 (1942).
2089 Satterthwaite, R. W., Hill, J. H., and Huffer, V.: *Venereal Disease Information*, **23**, 249–54 (1942); *Chem. Abst.*, **36**, 6236.
2090 Savino, E.: *Rev. Inst. bacteriol. Buenos Aires*, **9**, 593–607 (1940).
2091 ——, and Morales-Villazon, N.: *Ibid.*, **11**, 70–6 (1942).
2092 ——, and ——: *Semana med. Buenos Aires*, **1942, 2**, 297–300; *Chem. Abst.*, **37**, 686.
2093 Sayliss, H. F., Paine, C. G., and Patrick, L. B.: *Lancet*, **1937, 2**, 792–5.
2094 Saz, A. K., and Bernheim, F.: *J. Bact.*, **43**, 41–2 (1942).

2095 ——, and ——: *Ibid.*, **44,** 385–6 (1942).
2096 ——, and ——: *J. Pharmacol.*, **73,** 78–84 (1941).
2097 ——, Johnston, F. R., Burger, A., and Bernheim, F.: *Am. Rev. Tuberc.*, **48,** 40–50 (1943).
2098 Schenck, L. M., and Henze, H. R.: *J. Am. Chem. Soc.*, **64,** 1499–1501 (1942).
2099 Scherer, H.: *Schweiz. med. Wochschr.*, **71,** 907–8 (1941); *Bull. War Med.*, **3,** 296 (1943).
2100 Schering, A. G.: Brit. 541,958 (Jan. 15, 1942).
2101 Schering Corp. (Dohrn, M., and Diedrich, P.): U. S. 2,340,584 (Feb. 1, 1944).
2102 —— (Dohrn, M., and Diedrich, P.): U. S. 2,341,086 (Feb. 8, 1944).
2103 —— (Dohrn, M., and Diedrich, P.): U. S. 2,345,385 (Mar. 28, 1944).
2104 —— (Dohrn, M., and Laubereau, O. A. A.): U. S. 2,351,936 (June 20, 1944); Ger. 738,565 (July 15, 1943); *Chem. Abst.*, **38,** 4271.
2105 —— (Dohrn, M., Schoeller, W., Laubereau, O. A. A., Fox, H., Leckzyck, E., and Inhoffen, H. H.): U. S. 2,328,548 (Sept. 7, 1943).
2106 —— (Vonkennel, J., and Kimmig, J.): U. S. 2,343,162 (Feb. 29, 1944).
2107 Scherlis, S.: *Ann. Intern. Med.*, **16,** 666–75 (1942).
2108 Schlesinger, B. E., and Martin, N. H.: *Lancet*, **1942, 1,** 527–9.
2109 Schlotthauer, C. F.: *North Amer. Vet.*, **25,** 155–62 (1944).
2110 Schmelkes, F. C.: *J. Bact.*, **45,** 67–8 (1943).
2111 ——: *Surg. Gynecol. Obstet.*, **77,** 69–73 (1943).
2112 ——, and Wyss, O.: *Proc. Soc. Exptl. Biol. Med.*, **49,** 263–7 (1942).
2113 ——, Wyss, O., Marks, H. C., Ludwig, B. J., and Strandskov, F. B.: *Ibid.*, **50,** 145–8 (1942).
2114 Schmidt, E. G.: *J. Biol. Chem.*, **122,** 757–62 (1938).
2115 ——: *J. Lab. Clin. Med.*, **23,** 648–50 (1938).
2116 ——: *Ibid.*, **24,** 795–8, 982–5 (1939).
2117 Schmidt, L. H., Claugus, C. E., and Starkes, E.: *Proc. Soc. Exptl. Biol. Med.*, **45,** 256–9 (1940).
2118 ——: *Ibid.*, **37,** 205–6 (1937).
2119 ——, and Dettwiler, H.: *J. Biol. Chem.*, **133,** 85–6 (1940).
2120 ——, and Hilles, C.: *J. Bact.*, **38,** 236 (1939).
2121 ——, and ——: *J. Infectious Diseases*, **65,** 273–84 (1939).
2122 ——, and ——: *Proc. Soc. Exptl. Biol. Med.*, **40,** 611–14 (1939).
2123 ——, and ——: *Ibid.*, **41,** 111–31 (1939).
2124 ——, and ——: *Ibid.*, **43,** 288–93 (1940).
2125 ——, ——, and Dettwiler, H.: *Div. Med. Chem. Amer. Chem. Soc. Abst. Papers*, p. 8, Cincinnati, Ohio, April 8 to 12, 1942.
2126 ——, ——, ——, and Starks, E.: *J. Infectious Diseases*, **67,** 232–42 (1940).
2127 ——, and Hughes, H. B.: *Proc. Soc. Exptl. Biol. Med.*, **40,** 409–11 (1939).
2128 ——, ——, Badger, E. A., and Schmidt, I. G.: *J. Pharmacol.*, **81,** 17–42 (1944).
2129 ——, and Sesler, C. L.: *Ibid.*, **72,** 311–15 (1941).
2130 ——, and ——: *Ibid.*, **77,** 165–74, 277–89 (1943).
2131 ——, and ——: *Proc. Soc. Exptl. Biol. Med.*, **52,** 353–7 (1943).
2132 ——, ——, and Hamburger, M., Jr.: *J. Bact.*, **45,** 26, 27–8, 28–9 (1943).
2133 ——, ——, and Hughes, H. B.: *J. Pharmacol.*, **81,** 43–57 (1944).
2134 Schmidt, P. W.: *Deut. med. Wochschr.*, **66,** 210–13 (1940); *Chem. Abst.*, **34,** 3817.
2135 Schmith, K.: *Acta. Path. Microbiol. Scand.*, **20,** 563–72 (1943); *Chem. Abst.*, **38,** 2685–6.
2136 ——, and Reymenn, F. E.: *Nord. Med.*, **8,** 2493–2500; 2500–3 (1940); *Chem. Abst.*, **35,** 4055 (1941).
2137 Schmitt, G. F.: *Am. J. Med. Sci.*, **207,** 661–78 (1944).
2138 Schoeffel, E. W.: *J. Am. Med. Assoc.*, **115,** 122–3 (1940).
2139 Schonholzer, G.: *Klin. Wochschr.*, **19,** 790–1 (1940).
2140 Schoop, G., and Stoltz, A.: *Deut. tierärztl. Wochschr.*, **49,** 153–8, 181–3 (1941); *Chem. Abst.*, **37,** 5490.
2141 Schreus, H. T.: *Deut. med. Wochschr.*, **66,** 1121–4 (1940).
2142 ——: *Ibid.*, **69,** 73–6; 101–4 (1943); *Bull. War Med.*, **4,** 6–7.
2143 ——: *Klin. Wochschr.*, **21,** 14–7, 671–2 (1942).
2144 ——, Brauns, A., and Schümmer, H.: *Klin. Wochschr.*, **20,** 1233 (1941).
2145 ——, and Peltzer, E.: *Ibid.*, 504, 529–35 (1941).
2146 Schröer, W.: *Zent. f. Bakt.* **1** Abst. Orig., **149,** 1–14 (1942); *Bull. War Med.*, **3,** 253–4 (1943).
2147 Schultz, E. W., and Robinson, F.: *J. Infectious Diseases*, **70,** 193–200 (1942).
2148 ——, Williams, G., and Hetherington, A.: *Proc. Soc. Exptl. Biol. Med.*, **38,** 799–800 (1938).
2149 Schutt, R., Battelle Memorial Institute: Personal communication (Dec. 1, 1942).
2150 Schutze, H.: *Lancet*, **1939, 1,** 266–8.

2151   Schwartz, L., Flippin, H. F., Reinhold, J. G., and Domm, A. H.: *J. Am. Med. Assoc.*, **117**, 514–5 (1941).
2152   Schweinburg, F. B., and Yetwin, I. J.: *New Engl. J. Med.*, **230**, 510–4 (1944).
2153   Scorgie, N. J.: *J. Path. Bact.*, **46**, 165–6 (1938).
2154   Scott, J. C.: *J. Am. Med. Assoc.*, **122**, 588–91 (1943).
2155   Scudi, J. V.: *J. Biol. Chem.*, **122**, 539–47 (1938).
2156   ——: *Proc. Soc. Exptl. Biol. Med.*, **55**, 197–9 (1944).
2157   ——, and Jelinek, V. C.: *J. Pharmacol.*, **81**, 218–23 (1944).
2158   ——, and Radish, H. D.: *J. Lab. Clin. Med.*, **23**, 615–7 (1938).
2159   ——, and Robinson, H. J.: *Am. J. Med. Sci.*, **201**, 711–7 (1941).
2160   Seastone, C. V.: *J. Immunol.*, **33**, 403–6 (1937).
2161   ——: *J. Exper. Med.*, **70**, 347–59 (1939).
2162   Seelemann: *Deut. tierärztl. Wochschr.*, **51**, 41–5 (1943); *Chem. Abst.*, **38**, 4692.
2163   Seeler, A. O., Graessle, O., and Dusenbery, E. D.: *J. Bact.*, **45**, 205–9 (1943).
2164   Senekji, H. A.: *J. Infectious Diseases*, **66**, 111–2 (1940).
2165   Sesler, C. L., and Schmidt, L. H.: *J. Bact.*, **43**, 73–4 (1942).
2166   ——, and ——: *J. Pharmacol.*, **75**, 356–62 (1942).
2167   ——, and ——: *Ibid.*, **79**, 117–26 (1943).
2168   ——, ——, and Belden, J.: *Proc. Soc. Exptl. Biol. Med.*, **56**, 42–5 (1944).
2169   Sevag, M. G.: *J. Am. Chem. Soc.*, **65**, 110–3 (1943).
2170   ——, and Green, M. N.: *Am. J. Med. Sci.*, **207**, 686–7 (1944).
2171   ——, and ——: *J. Bact.*, **47**, 450–1 (1944).
2172   ——, and Shelburne, M.: *Ibid.*, **43**, 411–20; 421–45; 447–62 (1942).
2173   ——, ——, and Mudd, S.: *J. Gen. Physiol.*, **25**, 805–17 (1942).
2174   Sewell, R. L.: *Texas State J. Med.*, **40**, 12–4 (1944).
2175   ——, Dowdy, A. H., and Vincent, J. G.: *Surg. Gynecol. Obstet.*, **74**, 361–7 (1942).
2176   Shackman, N. H., and Bullowa, J. G. M.: *Arch. Intern. Med.*, **72**, 329–45 (1943).
2177   Shaffer, B., Lentz, J. W., and McGuire, J. A.: *J. Am. Med. Assoc.*, **123**, 17–23 (1943).
2178   Shannon, J. A.: *Ann. N. Y. Acad. Sci.*, **44**, 455–76 (1943).
2179   Sharpe & Dohme Inc.: Personal communication from M. L. Moore (Dec. 28, 1942).
2180   ——: Personal communication from J. M. Sprague (Jan. 25, 1943).
2181   —— (Abbey, A.): Brit. 546,076 (June 26, 1942); *Chem. Abst.*, **37**, 2519.
2182   —— (Moore, M. L.): Brit. 562,763 (Aug. 10, 1944).
2183   —— (Moore, M. L.): U. S. 2,324,013–5 (July 13, 1943).
2184   Shay, H., Komarov, S. A., Siplet, H., and Fels, S. S.: *Gastroenterology*, **2**, 432–6 (1944).
2185   Sheftel, A. G.: U. S. 2,331,573 (Oct. 12, 1943).
2186   Shelton, L., Jr.: *Virginia Med. Monthly*, **70**, 283–9 (1943).
2187   Shemyakin, M. M., and El'kina, E. I.: *J. Gen. Chem.* (*U.S.S.R.*), **11**, 349–52 (1941); *Chem. Abst.*, **35**, 5893.
2188   Shen, Chao-Wen, and Chen, Hung-Nien: *J. Chinese Chem. Soc.*, **8**, 4–6 (1941); *Chem. Abst.*, **37**, 352.
2189   Shepherd, R. C., Bratton, A. C., and Blanchard, K. C.: *J. Am. Chem. Soc.*, **64**, 2532–7 (1942).
2190   Shinn, L. E., Main, E. R., and Mellon, R. R.: *Proc. Soc. Exptl. Biol. Med.*, **39**, 591–4; *ibid.*, **40**, 640–5 (1939).
2191   ——, ——, and ——: *Ibid.*, **44**, 596–600 (1940).
2192   Shonle, H. A., Eli Lilly & Co.: Unpublished work (see Reference 1574).
2193   ——, and Morrison, R. T., Eli Lilly & Co.: Unpublished work (see Reference 1574).
2194   ——, and Rhodehamel, H. W., Jr., Eli Lilly & Co.: Unpublished work (see Reference 1574).
2195   ——, and VanArendonk, A. M.: *J. Am. Chem. Soc.*, **65**, 2375–7 (1943).
2196   Siebenmann, C., and Schnitzer, R. J.: *Ibid.*, 2126–8 (1943).
2197   Siebert, W. J., and Loose, F.: *J. Lab. Clin. Med.*, **26**, 371–81 (1940).
2198   Siegel, L. S., Rosove, L., and Bower, A. G.: *Ann. Intern. Med.*, **16**, 262–8 (1942).
2199   Siegel, M.: *J. Am. Med. Assoc.*, **119**, 783–5 (1942); *Am. J. Diseases Children*, **66**, 114–20 (1943); *ibid.*, **67**, 365–70 (1944); *ibid.*, **68**, 23–7 (1944).
2200   Silcox, L. E., and Schenck, H. P.: *Arch. Otolaryngol.*, **36**, 171–86 (1942).
2201   Silver, B., and Elliott, M.: *J. Am. Med. Assoc.*, **112**, 723–9 (1939).
2202   Simenson, M. H.: *Arch. Internal pharmacodynamie*, **64**, 250 (1940).
2203   Singer, E.: *Med. J. Sidney, Australia*, **2**, 275–300 (1940); *Am. Med. Assoc.*, **115**, 2317 (1940).
2204   Singer, F. W., Smyth, C. J., and Yonkman, F. F.: *Fed. Proc.*, **2**, 92 (1943).
2205   Sise, H. S.: *Proc. Soc. Exptl. Biol. Med.*, **40**, 451–4 (1939).
2206   Sjogren, B.: *Nature*, **150**, 431 (1942).
2207   ——, and Berlin, E.: *Svensk. Kem. Tid.*, **54**, 200–4 (1942).

2208 Skelton, F. M.: *J. Bact.*, **47**, 273–5 (1944).
2209 Slocumb, C. H., and Polley, H. F.: *Med. Clin. North Am.*, **28**, 838–42 (1944).
2210 S. M. A. Corporation (Szabo, L. J.): U. S. 2,321,332 (June 8, 1943).
2211 Smith, C. H.: *Vet. Record*, **54**, 259 (1942).
2212 Smith, C. R.: *Am. Rev. Tuberc.*, **50**, 163–6 (1944).
2213 Smith, F. E., Riley, R., and Jones, O. R.: *Ann. Intern. Med.*, **14**, 1032–41 (1940.)
2214 Smith, G. B. L., Carroll, R., *et al.*: *Div. Med. Chem. of Amer. Chem. Soc.*, meeting Boston, Mass., Sept. 1939, p. 12.
2215 Smith, H. G.: *Brit. Med. J.*, **1944, 1**, 287; *ibid.*, 730.
2216 Smith, M. G.: *Proc. Soc. Exptl. Biol. Med.*, **40**, 191–4 (1939).
2217 Smith, M. I., Emmart, E. W., and Stohlman, E. F.: *Am. Rev. Tuberc.*, **48**, 32–9 (1943).
2218 ——, Lille, R. D., and Stohlman, E. F.: *U. S. Pub. Health Repts.*, **56**, 24–7 (1941).
2219 ——, Rosenthal, S. M., and Jackson, E. L.: *Ibid.*, **57**, 1534–42 (1942).
2220 Smith, P. K.: *Amer. J. Med. Sci.*, **200**, 183–4 (1940).
2221 Smith, W. F., and Rice, J. M.: *N. Y. State J. Med.*, **41**, 686–7 (1941).
2222 Smithburn, K. C.: *Proc. Soc. Exptl. Biol. Med.*, **38**, 574–5 (1938).
2223 Smyth, C. J., Finkelstein, M. B., Gould, S. E., Koppa, T. M., and Leeder, F. S.: *J. Am. Med. Assoc.*, **121**, 1325–30 (1943).
2224 ——, Gould, S. E., and Finkelstein, M. B.: *Ibid.*, 1244–5 (1943).
2225 Snell, E. E., Chan, L., Spiridanoff, S., Way, E. L., and Leake, C. D.: *Science*, **97**, 168 (1943); *Fed. Proc.*, **2**, 92 (1943).
2226 ——, and Mitchell, H. K.: *Arch. Biochem.*, **1**, 93–101 (1942).
2227 Snodgrass, W. R., Anderson, T., and Renne, J. L.: *Brit. Med. J.*, **1938, 2**, 399–43; *ibid.*, **1937, 2**, 1156–9.
2228 Sobin, S. S.: *J. Lab. Clin. Med.*, **27**, 1567–8 (1942).
2229 Society of Chemical Industry in Basle: Brit. 545,419 (May 26, 1942); Ger. 725,072 (July 30, 1942).
2230 ——: Brit. 546,557 (July 20, 1942).
2231 ——: Brit. 560,284 (Apr. 27, 1944).
2232 ——: Brit. 557,037 (Dec. 2, 1943); *Brit. Chem. Abst.*, **1944, B3**, 34.
2233 ——: Brit. 560,345 (Apr. 27, 1944); *Brit. Chem. Abst.*, **1944, B3**, 142.
2234 Soehring, K.: *Biochem. Z.*, **295**, 265–82 (1938).
2235 Sokhey, S. S.: *Indian J. Med. Res.*, **27**, 313–9 (1939).
2236 ——, and Dikshit, B. B.: *Current Sci.*, **9**, 116–7 (1940); *Chem. Abst.*, **34**, 5163 (1940).
2237 Sokolova, V. N., and Mashkovskii, M. D.: *Farmakol. i Toksikol.*, **3**, 87–8 (1940); *Chem. Abst.*, **36**, 3005.
2238 Somaglino, J. C.: *Rev. facultad. cienc. quím.*, **16**, 227–34 (1941); *Chem. Abst.*, **36**, 6148.
2239 Somers, R. B. O.: *Lancet*, **1939, 1**, 921–2.
2240 Speert, H.: *Surg. Gynecol. Obstet.*, **75**, 699–703 (1942).
2241 Sorsby, A., and Hoffa, E. L.: *Brit. Med. J.*, **1944, 1**, 353–4.
2242 Spaulding, E. H., and Bondi, A., Jr.: *Proc. Soc. Exptl. Biol. Med.*, **44**, 321–6 (1940).
2243 Spencer, F. R., Whitehead, R. W., and Duffner, G. J.: *Trans. Am. Acad. Ophthal. Otolaryngol.*, **45**, 43–5 (1941).
2244 Spicer, S. S., Daft, F. S., Sebrell, W., and Ashburn, L. L.: *U. S. Pub. Health Repts.*, **57**, 1559–66 (1942).
2245 Spink, W. W.: *J. Clin. Investigation*, **18**, 471–2 (1939).
2246 ——: *J. Immunol.*, **37**, 345–58 (1939).
2247 ——: *Minnesota Med.*, **25**, 988–90 (1942).
2248 ——: "Sulfanilamide and Related Compounds in General Practice," 2nd ed., The Year Book Publishers, Inc., Chicago, Ill., 1942. (Revised reprint July, 1943.)
2249 ——, Ferris, V., and Vivino, J. J.: *Proc. Soc. Exptl. Biol. Med.*, **55**, 207–10 (1944).
2250 ——, and Hansen, A. E.: *J. Am. Med. Assoc.*, **115**, 840–7 (1940).
2251 ——, ——, and Paine, J. R.: *Arch. Intern. Med.*, **67**, 25–35 (1941).
2252 ——, and Jermsta, J.: *Proc. Soc. Exptl. Biol. Med.*, **47**, 395–7 (1941).
2253 ——, and Vivino, J. J.: *J. Clin. Investigation*, **23**, 267–78 (1944).
2254 ——, and ——: *Proc. Soc. Exptl. Biol. Med.*, **50**, 37–41 (1942).
2255 ——, and ——: *Science*, **98**, 44–5 (1943).
2256 ——, ——, and Mickelson, O.: *Proc. Soc. Exptl. Biol. Med.*, **50**, 31–6 (1942); *J. Clin. Investigation*, **21**, 645–6 (1942).
2257 ——, Wright, L. D., Vivino, J. J., and Skeggs, H. R.: *J. Exptl. Med.*, **79**, 331–9 (1944).
2258 Spitz, S. H., Loughlin, E. H., and Bennett, R. H.: *J. Lab. Clin. Med.*, **26**, 1284–8 (1941).
2259 Spray, R. S.: *Ibid.*, **23**, 609–14 (1938).
2260 Spring, F. S., and Young, E. H. D.: *J. Chem. Soc.*, **1944**, 248–9.
2261 Spring, W. C., Jr., Lowell, F. C., and Finland, M.: *J. Clin. Investigation*, **19**, 163–77 (1940).

2262 Squibb, E. R., and Sons (Braker, W., and Lott, W. A.): U. S. 2,347,242 (Apr. 25, 1944).
2263 —— (Christiansen, W. G.): U. S. 2,184,279 (Dec. 26, 1939).
2264 —— (Christiansen, W. G.): U. S. 2,242,237 (May 20, 1941).
2265 Stableforth, A. W., Hignett, S. L., and Roach, R. W.: *Vet. J.*, **99**, 42–7 (1943).
2266 Stacey, M., and Schlüchterer, E.: *Nature*, **143**, 724 (1939).
2267 Stafford, C. E., Beswick, J., and Deeb, P. H.: *Am. J. Surg.*, **64**, 227–34 (1944).
2268 Stahle, D. C.: *J. Am. Med. Assoc.*, **118**, 440–7 (1942).
2269 Stamp, T. C.: *Lancet*, **1939, 2**, 10–17.
2270 Stanier, M. W., and Stapleton, T.: *Lancet*, **1944, 1**, 366–7.
2271 Steele, C. W., and Gottlieb, J.: *Arch. Intern. Med.*, **68**, 211–31 (1941).
2272 Steenken, W., Jr., and Heise, F. H.: *Proc. Soc. Exptl. Biol. Med.*, **52**, 180–3 (1943).
2273 ——, Heise, F. H., and Wolinsky, E.: *Am. Rev. Tuberc.*, **48**, 453–60 (1943).
2274 Steiger, R. E.: *Bull. soc. chim.*, **53**, 1254–9 (1933).
2275 Steinbach, M. M., and Dillon, B. M.: *Proc. Soc. Exptl. Biol. Med.*, **41**, 613–6 (1939).
2276 Steinfield, E., Byrlawski, M., and Nash, C. B.: *J. Lab. Clin. Med.*, **28**, 1544–7 (1943).
2277 Steinhaus, E. A., and Parker, R. R.: *U. S. Pub. Health Repts.*, **58**, 351–2 (1943).
2278 ——, and McKee, M. T.: *U. S. Pub. Health Repts.*, **59**, 78–9 (1944).
2279 Sterne, M.: *S. African Med. J.*, **16**, 121–4 (1942).
2280 Stevens, J. E., Taliaferro, I., and Haag, H. B.: *Proc. Soc. Exptl. Biol. Med.*, **48**, 223–6 (1941).
2281 Stickl, O., and Gartner, K.: *Z. f. Hyg. u. Infektionskrankh.*, **123**, 591–611 (1942); *Bull. War Med.*, **3**, 345 (1943).
2282 Stillman, E. G., and Schulz, R. Z.: *J. Infectious Diseases*, **65**, 246–51 (1939).
2283 ——, and ——: *J. Infectious Diseases*, **66**, 174–7 (1940).
2284 Stokes, J. L., Gunness, M., and Foster, J. W.: *J. Bact.*, **47**, 293 (1944).
2285 Stokinger, H. E.: *Bull. N. Y. Acad. Med.*, **15**, 252–7 (1939).
2286 ——: *Proc. Soc. Exptl. Biol. Med.*, **40**, 61–5 (1939).
2287 Strakosch, E. A., and Clark, W. G.: *Am. J. Med. Sci.*, **205**, 518–24 (1943); **206**, 610–7 (1943).
2288 Strauss, E., Dingle, J. H., and Finland, M.: *J. Immunol.*, **42**, 313–29; 331–42 (1941).
2289 ——, ——, and ——: *Proc. Soc. Exptl. Biol. Med.*, **46**, 131–3 (1941).
2290 ——, Finland, M.: *Am. J. Med. Sci.*, **201**, 730–4 (1941).
2291 ——, and ——: *Proc. Soc. Exptl. Biol. Med.*, **47**, 432–4 (1941).
2292 ——, Lowell, F. C., and Finland, M.: *J. Clin. Investigation*, **20**, 189–97 (1941).
2293 ——, ——, Taylor, F. H. L., and Finland, M.: *Ann. Intern. Med.*, **14**, 1360–82 (1941).
2294 Strauss, H., and Grunstein, I.: *J. Am. Med. Assoc.*, **121**, 1187–90 (1943).
2295 ——, Goldstein, S., Horowitz, E. A., and Meyer, E.: *Am. J. Obstet. Gynecol.*, **47**, 838–44 (1944).
2296 Strawinski, R. J., Verwey, W. F., and Ciminera, J. L.: *Arch. Biochem.*, **3**, 369–74 (1944).
2297 Strom, G. W., and Thompson, G. J.: *Proc. Staff Mayo Clin.*, **17**, 248–50 (1942).
2298 Stuart, E. H., Eli Lilly & Co.: Unpublished work (see Reference 1574).
2299 Styron, C. W., Bromley, H., and Root, H. F.: *J. Am. Med. Assoc.*, **118**, 1423–7 (1942).
2300 Surrey, A. R., and Lindwall, H. G.: *J. Am. Chem. Soc.*, **62**, 173–4 (1940).
2301 Sutliff, W. D., Helpern, M., Griffin, G., and Brown, H.: *J. Am. Med. Assoc.*, **121**, 307–13 (1943).
2302 Svartz, N.: *Nord. Med.*, **9**, 554 (1941); *ibid.*, **11**, 2261–4 (1941); *Acta Med. Scand.*, **110**, 577 (1942); *Lancet*, **1943, 1**, 181–2.
2303 Swain, R. H. A.: *Brit. Med. J.*, **1940, 1**, 722–5.
2304 Sweet, L. A., Tullar, B. F., and Gruhzit, O. M.: Div. Medicinal Chem. ACS, Dallas, Texas, Apr., 1938).
2305 Swyer, R.: *Brit. Med. J.*, **1943, 1**, 485.
2306 ——: *Lancet*, **1943, 2**, 71–2.
2307 Tager, M.: *Yale J. Biol. Med.*, **13**, 238–52 (1940).
2308 Talbot, T. R., and Adcock, J. D.: *Am. J. Med. Sci.*, **205**, 841–5 (1943).
2309 Tamura, J. T.: *J. Bact.*, **47**, 529–33 (1944).
2310 ——, and Gibby, I. W.: *Ibid.*, **45**, 361–71 (1943).
2311 Taplin, G. V., and Custer, E. A.: *J. Am. Med. Assoc.*, **121**, 313–5 (1943).
2312 Tappi, G.: *Rec. trav. chim.*, **62**, 207–9 (1943); *Chem. Abst.*, **38**, 2325.
2313 ——, and Migliardi, C.: *Arch. sci. biol.* (*Italy*), **27**, 170–5 (1941); *Chem. Abst.*, **38**, 2325.
2314 Taranto, M.: *U. S. Naval Med. Bull.*, **41**, 961–5 (1943).
2315 Tate, B. C., and Klorfajn, I.: *Lancet*, **1944, 1**, 39–44; *ibid.*, **2**, 554–8.
2316 Teply, L. J., Axelrod, A. E., and Elvehjem, C. A.: *J. Pharmacol.*, **77**, 207–14 (1943).
2317 Tenenberg, D. J., Tsuchiya, H. M., Clark, W. G., and Strakosch, E. A.: *Proc. Soc. Exptl. Biol. Med.*, **51**, 247–9 (1942).

2318 Terrell, E. E., Robertson, O. H., and Coggeshall, L. T.: *J. Clin. Investigation*, **12,** 393–432 (1933).
2319 Thelander, H. E.: *J. Pediat.*, **18,** 479–82 (1941).
2320 Thibault, P., and Rist, N.: *Compt. rend. soc. biol.*, **133,** 605–8 (1940).
2321 Thomas, C. B.: *Bull. N. Y. Acad. Med.*, **18,** 508–26 (1942).
2322 Thomas, H. M., Jr.: *J. Am. Med. Assoc.*, **123,** 264–72 (1943).
2323 Thomas, J. C.: Thesis Yale University (1942). Personal communication from Prof. A. J. Hill.
2324 Thomas, L., and Dingle, J. H.: *Proc. Soc. Exptl. Biol. Med.*, **51,** 76–8 (1942).
2325 Thomas, R. B.: *Am. J. Syphilis, Gonorrhea and Venereal Diseases*, **26,** 691–774 (1942).
2326 Thompson, R. C., Isbell, E. R., and Mitchell, H. K.: *J. Biol. Chem.*, **148,** 281–7 (1943).
2327 Thorp, W. T. S.: *Am. J. Vet. Res.*, **4,** 374–81 (1943).
2328 ——, Pisciotta, V. S., and Grundy, C. B.: *J. Am. Vet. Med. Assoc.*, **104,** 274–8 (1944).
2329 Throckmorton, T. D.: *Surgery*, **12,** 906 (1942); *Proc. Staff Mayo Clin.*, **16,** 423–5 (1941).
2330 Thygeson, P., and Stone, W., Jr.: *N. Y. State J. Med.*, **43,** 1409–14 (1943); *J. Am. Med. Assoc.*, **119,** 407–8 (1942).
2331 Todd, C. W., Fletcher, J. H., and Tarbell, D. S.: *J. Am. Chem. Soc.*, **65,** 350–4 (1943).
2332 Todd, W. R.: *Arch. Biochem.*, **4,** 343–6 (1944).
2333 ——, Dodson, M. C., Trainer, J. B., and McKee, J.: *Arch. Biochem.*, **4,** 337–41 (1944).
2334 Tolk, N. R., and Popkin, M. S.: *Conn. State Med. J.*, **7,** 408–10 (1943).
2335 Tonndorf, W.: *Deutsch. med. Wochschr.*, **68** (16), 393–6 (1942); *Biol. Abst.*, **17,** 16511 Sec. C (1943).
2336 Toomey, J. A.: *Arch. Pediat.*, **60,** 22–3 (1943).
2337 ——: *J. Am. Med. Assoc.*, **113,** 250–1 (1939).
2338 ——, Reichle, H. S., and Takacs, W. S.: *J. Bact.*, **38,** 237 (1939); *J. Pediat.*, **16,** 179–90 (1940).
2339 ——, and Roach, F. E.: *J. Pediat.*, **18,** 1–5 (1941); *Chem. Abst.*, **36,** 3256.
2340 ——, and Takacs, W. S.: *Am. J. Diseases Children*, **59,** 94–6 (1940).
2341 ——, and ——: *Arch. Pediat.*, **56,** 384 (1939).
2342 ——, and ——: *J. Immunol.*, **48,** 49–55 (1944).
2343 ——, and ——: *J. Pediat.*, **18,** 10–11 (1941).
2344 Topping, N. H.: *U. S. Pub. Health Repts.*, **54,** 1143–7 (1939).
2345 Torrey, R. G., Julianelle, L. A., and McNamee, H. G.: *Ann. Intern. Med.*, **15,** 431–45 (1941).
2346 Toumey, J. W.: *Surgery*, **14,** 531–40 (1943).
2347 Townsend, S. L.: *J. Roy. Nav. Med. Serv.*, **30,** 25–9 (1944); *Bull. War Med.*, **4,** 597 (1944).
2348 Trautman, J. A., and Emenhiser, D. C.: *Venereal Diseases Information*, **23,** 203–4 (1942).
2349 Travagli, G.: *Ann. chim. farm.*, **1940,** 48–54; *Chem. Abst.*, **37,** 1998.
2350 Travin, A. I., and Mashkovskii, M. D.: *Farmakol. i Toksikol.*, **3,** No. 6, 87 (1940); *Chem. Abst.*, **36,** 3005.
2351 Treadway, J. B., and Sadusk, J. G., Jr.: *Yale J. Biol. Med.*, **14,** 143–53 (1941).
2352 Trefouel, J., Trefouel, Mme. J., Nitti, F., and Bovet, D.: *Presse Med.*, **45,** 839–40 (1937).
2353 Trevett, G. I.: *Bull. Johns Hopkins Hosp.*, **74,** 299–307 (1944).
2354 ——, and Blackman, S. S., Jr.: *Ann. Intern. Med.*, **20,** 971–80 (1944).
2355 ——, Nelson, R. A., and Long, P. H.: *Bull. Johns Hopkins Hosp.*, **69,** 303–13 (1941).
2356 Tschelincev, G. B., and Zakotin, V. N.: *J. Gen. Chem. Russ.*, **11,** 729–30 (1941); *Brit. Chem. Abst.*, **1942, A2,** 330.
2357 Tsuchiya, H. M., Tenenberg, D. J., Clark, W. G., and Strakosch, E. A.: *Proc. Soc. Exptl. Biol. Med.*, **50,** 262–6 (1942); *ibid.*, **51,** 245–7 (1942).
2358 Tudor, R. B.: *J. Pediat.*, **22,** 652–4 (1943).
2359 T'ung, T.: *Proc. Soc. Exptl. Biol. Med.*, **56,** 8–11 (1944).
2360 Tunnicliff, R.: *J. Infectious Diseases*, **64,** 59–65 (1939).
2361 ——: *Ibid.*, **66,** 189–91 (1940).
2362 Turnbull, F. M., Hamilton, W. F., Simon, E., and George, M. F., Jr.: *J. Am. Med. Assoc.*, **123,** 536–7 (1943).
2363 Turnbull, G. C.: *Illinois Med. J.*, **81,** 412–4 (1942).
2364 Tyōbei Takeda Syōten, K. K. (Ida, M.): Japan. 130,481 (June 13, 1939).
2365 Uhley, M. H., and Katz, L. N.: *J. Infectious Diseases*, **68,** 291–300 (1941).
2366 Ungar, J.: *Nature*, **150,** 432 (1942).
2367 Ungerleider, H. E., Steinhaus, H. W., and Gubner, R. S.: *Am. J. Pub. Health*, **33,** 1093–1102 (1943).
2368 United States Government (Rosenthal, S. M., and Bauer, H.): U. S. 2,280,856 (Apr. 28, 1942).
2369 Unna, K.: *Proc. Soc. Exptl. Biol. Med.*, **54,** 55–7 (1943).

2370 Upjohn Company, The Laboratories of the: Personal communication by Alan H. Nathan (Dec. 8, 1942).
2371 Vanags, G., and Veinberg, A.: *Ber.*, **75B**, 1558–69 (1942); *Chem. Abst.*, **38**, 1221.
2372 ——, and ——: *Ber.*, **76B**, 479–83 (1943); *Chem. Abst.*, **37**, 6651.
2373 VanArendonk, A. M., Eli Lilly & Co.: Unpublished work (see Reference 1574).
2374 vanArkel, C. G.: *Chem. Abst.*, **36**, 3321.
2375 VanDyke, H. B.: *Ann. N. Y. Acad. Sci.*, **44**, 477 (1943).
2376 VanOrden, Th.D., and Armentrout, C. H.: *U. S. Naval Bull.*, **41**, 973 (1943).
2377 VanWinkle, W., Jr., and Cutting, W. C.: *J. Pharmacol.*, **69**, 40–4 (1940).
2378 Veldstra, H., and Wiardi, P. W.: *Rec. trav. chim.*, **61**, 627–37 (1942); *Chem. Abst.*, **38**, 3263; *ibid.*, **62**, 661–71 (1943); *Chem. Abst.*, **38**, 4571.
2379 Ventura, J. C.: *J. Am. Pharm. Assoc.*, **31**, 157–8 (1942).
2380 Vera, H. D.: *J. Bact.*, **47**, 59–70 (1944).
2381 Villafane Lastra, T. de, Goober, G. K., Rodeiro, M., and Nidella, L. F.: *Prin. Congr. Nac. Enferm. Endemo-Ebid, Buenos Aires*, **1942**, 586–95.
2382 Vivino, J. J., and Spink, W. W.: *Proc. Soc. Exptl. Biol. Med.*, **50**, 336–8 (1942).
2383 Volini, I. F., Levitt, R. O., and O'Neil, H. B.: *J. Am. Med. Assoc.*, **116**, 938–40 (1941); *Am. J. Med. Sci.*, **200**, 778–84 (1940).
2384 Vonkennel, J., and Kimmig, J.: *Klin. Wochschr.*, **20**, 2–8 (1941).
2385 ——, and Korth, B.: *Munch. Med. Wochschr.*, **85**, 2018–21 (1938).
2386 Wagener, H. P.: *Am. J. Med. Sci.*, **206**, 261–8 (1943).
2387 Wagner-Jauregg, Th.: *Naturwissenschaften*, **31**, 335–44 (1943).
2388 Wagoner, S. C., and Hunting, W. F.: *J. Am. Med. Assoc.*, **116**, 267–70 (1941).
2389 Wallersteiner, W. K. S.: *Nature*, **151**, 586–7 (1943).
2390 Walsh, E. O.: *J. Chem. Soc.*, **1942**, 726.
2391 Walter, L., and Cole, W. H.: *Surg. Gynecol. Obstet.*, **76**, 524–32 (1943).
2392 Walter, L. A.: *J. Am. Chem. Soc.*, **65**, 739 (1943).
2393 Walther, G.: *Munch. med. Wochschr.*, **89**, 299 (1942); *J. Am. Med. Assoc.*, **122**, 1148 (1943).
2394 Wander, A. A. G.: Swiss 214,045 (July 1, 1941); *Chem. Abst.*, **37**, 1228.
2395 Wander, G., and Schenk, J.: *Hundert Jahre Schweiz. Apoth-Ver.*, 1843–1943, 597–603 (1943); *Chem. Abst.*, **38**, 2022.
2396 Ward Blenkinsop & Co., Ltd. (Katscher, E.): Brit. 558,225 (June 22, 1942); *Brit. Chem. Abst.*, **1944, B3**, 73.
2397 —— (Pickholz, S.): Brit. 555,296 (Sept. 9, 1943); *Brit. Chem. Abst.*, **1943, B3**, 279.
2398 —— (Weisner, B. P. H., and Craven, A. B.): Brit. 547,564 (Sept. 2, 1942); *Chem. Abst.*, **37**, 6094.
2399 —— (Weisner, B. P. H., and Katscher, E.): Brit. 546,158 (June 30, 1942).
2400 Warner, Wm. R. & Co. (Martin, G. J., and Thompson, M. R.): U. S. 2,342,879 (Feb. 29, 1944).
2401 Warren, J., Street, J. A., and Stokinger, H. E.: *Proc. Soc. Exptl. Biol. Med.*, **40**, 208–12 (1939).
2402 Watson, R. F., Schwenther, F. F., Fetherston, J. E., and Rothbard, S.: *J. Am. Med. Assoc.*, **122**, 730–3 (1943).
2403 Watt, A. C., and Alexander, G. L.: *Lancet*, **1942, 1**, 483–6.
2404 Watt, J., and Peterson, J. S.: *U. S. Pub. Health Repts.*, **57**, 872–3 (1942).
2405 Wattenberg, C. A., and Heinbecker, P.: *Surgery*, **12**, 576–83 (1942).
2406 Way, E. L., and Oneto, J. F.: *J. Am. Chem. Soc.*, **64**, 1287–8 (1942).
2407 Wayson, N. E., and McMahon, M. C.: *U. S. Pub. Health Repts.*, **59**, 385–401 (1944).
2408 Weil, A. J., and Gall, L. S.: *J. Immunol.*, **41**, 445–52 (1941).
2409 ——, and ——: *J. Infectious Diseases*, **69**, 97–101 (1941).
2410 ——, and McFarlane, J. A.: *J. Immunol.*, **48**, 291–5 (1944).
2411 ——, and Valentine, J. A.: *Proc. Soc. Exptl. Biol. Med.*, **44**, 160–1 (1940).
2412 Weilbaecher, J. O., Jr., and Moss, E. S.: *New Orleans Med. Surg. J.*, **92**, 694–7 (1940).
2413 Weiner, A. L.: *J. Am. Med. Assoc.*, **121**, 411–3 (1943); *ibid.*, **123**, 436 (1943).
2414 Weinman, D., and Berne, R.: *Ibid.*, **124**, 6–8 (1944).
2415 Weiss, O., and Jones, L. R.: *J. Bact.*, **41**, 82 (1941).
2416 Welch, A. D.: *Fed. Proc.*, **1**, 171 (1942).
2417 ——, Mattis, P. A., and Latven, A. R.: *J. Pharmacol.*, **75**, 231–46 (1942).
2418 ——, ——, Koelle, E. S., and Latven, A. R.: *Am. J. Med. Sci.*, **208**, 187–92 (1944).
2419 ——, ——, Latven, A. R., Benson, W. M., and Shiels, E. H.: *J. Pharmacol.*, **77**, 357–91 (1943).
2420 Welch, H.: *J. Bact.*, **37**, 109–10 (1939).
2421 ——, Slocum, G. G., and Herwick, R. P.: *J. Am. Med. Assoc.*, **120**, 361–4 (1942).
2422 Wellcome Foundation Ltd. (Henry, T. A., and Gorvin, J. H.): Brit. 562,349 (June 28, 1944).

2423 —— (Henry, T. A., and Gray, W. H.): Brit. 562,216 (July 20, 1944).
2424 —— (McDougall, A. C., and Shotton, E.): Brit. 562,546 (July 6, 1944).
2425 Weld, J. T., and Mitchell, L. C.: *J. Bact.*, **38**, 335–50 (1939).
2426 Welebir, F., and Barnes, R. W.: *J. Am. Med. Assoc.*, **117**, 2132–5 (1941).
2427 Wells, E. H.: *J. Assoc. Official Agr. Chem.*, **25**, 747–55 (1942).
2428 Wengatz, H. F., Boak, R. A., and Carpenter, C. M.: *J. Bact.*, **35**, 36 (1938).
2429 Werling, E. H.: *J. Oklahoma State Med. Assoc.*, **35**, 103–6 (1942).
2430 Werner, A. E. A.: *Lancet*, **1939, 1**, 18–20.
2431 Wernicoff, N. E., and Goldhaft, T. M.: *Cornell Vet.*, **34**, 199–212 (1944).
2432 West, R., and Coburn, A. F.: *J. Exptl. Med.*, **72**, 91–7 (1940).
2433 Westphal, L., Charles, R. L., and Carpenter, C. M.: *Venereal Disease Information*, **21**, 183–6 (1940).
2434 Weygand, F.: *Ber.*, **73B**, 1259–78 (1940).
2435 Whipple, A. O.: *Ann. Surg.*, **118**, 187–92 (1943).
2436 Whitby, L.: *Lancet*, **1938, 2**, 1095–1102.
2437 White, H. J.: *Bull. Johns Hopkins Hosp.*, **71**, 213–34 (1942).
2438 ——: *J. Bact.*, **38**, 549–62 (1939).
2439 ——: *J. Pharmacol.*, **66**, 39–41 (1939).
2440 ——: *Proc. Soc. Exptl. Biol. Med.*, **43**, 214–6 (1940).
2441 ——, Bratton, A. C., Litchfield, J. R., Jr., and Marshall, E. K., Jr.: *J. Pharmacol.*, **72**, 112–22 (1941).
2442 ——, and Parker, J. M.: *J. Bact.*, **36**, 481–98 (1938).
2443 Wiedling, S.: *Nature*, **150**, 290–1 (1942); *Botan. Notiser (Sweden)*, **1941**, 375–92; *Chem. Abst.*, **36**, 4523.
2444 ——: *Naturwissenschaften*, **31**, 114–5 (1943).
2445 ——: *Science*, **94**, 389 (1941).
2446 Wien, R.: *Quart. J. Pharm. Pharmacol.*, **11**, 217–24 (1938).
2447 Wile, U. J., Johnson, S. A. M., and Arbor, A.: *Am. J. Syphilis, Gonorrhea, Venereal Diseases*, **28**, 187–91 (1944).
2448 Wilkerson, A. S.: *J. Am. Chem. Soc.*, **64**, 2230 (1942).
2449 Wilkinson, P. B.: *Lancet*, **1942, 2**, 67–9.
2450 Williams, A. C., and Guralnick, W. C.: *New Engl. J. Med.*, **228**, 443–50 (1943).
2451 Williams, H.: *Med. J. Australia*, **11**, 535, 557 (1942).
2452 Williams, M. F.: *Lancet*, **1940, 2**, 642–3.
2453 Williams, R. D.: *J. Bact.*, **47**, 452–3 (1944); *J. Biol. Chem.*, **156**, 85–94 (1944).
2454 Williams, R. T.: *Biochem. J.*, **35**, 1169–74 (1941).
2455 ——: *J. Chem. Soc.*, **1942**, 708–9.
2456 Willis, H. B.: *Iowa State Coll. J. Sci.*, **18**, 98–101 (1943); *Brit. Chem. Physiol. Abst.*, **1944, A2**, 55.
2457 Willstaedt, H.: *Svensk. Kem. Tid.*, **54**, 223–35 (1942); *Chem. Abst.*, **38**, 3627.
2458 Wilson, G. S., and Maier, I.:*Brit.Med. J.*, **1940, 1**, 47–50; *ibid.*, **1939, 1**, 8–9.
2459 Winnek, P. S., Anderson, G. W., Marson, H. W., Faith, H. E., and Roblin, R. O., Jr.: *J. Am. Chem. Soc.*, **64**, 1682–5 (1942).
2460 Winthrop Chemical Company (Clingestein, H., and Schrum, H.): U. S. 2,308,675 (Jan. 19, 1943).
2461 —— (Klarer, J.): U. S. 2,288,531 (June 30, 1942); Ger. 726,386 (Sept. 3, 1942) to I. G. Farbenindustrie; Ger. 730,120 (Dec. 3, 1942) to I. G. Farbenindustrie.
2462 —— (Klarer, J., and Mietzsch, F.): U. S. 2,288,530 (June 30, 1942).
2463 —— (Mietzsch, F., and Bauer, K.): U. S. 2,299,555 (Oct. 20, 1942).
2464 —— (Mietzsch, F., Klarer, J., and Behnisch, R.): U. S. 2,289,029 (July 7, 1942); Can. 402,835 (Feb. 10, 1942).
2465 —— (Pöhls, P.): U. S. 2,328,490 (Aug. 31, 1943).
2466 —— (Pöhls, P., and Behnisch, R.): U. S. 2,282,211 (May 5, 1942).
2467 —— (Pöhls, P., and Behnisch, R.): U. S. 2,291,285 (July 28, 1942).
2468 —— (Pöhls, P., and Mietzsch, F.): U. S. 2,297,024 (Sept. 29, 1942).
2469 Wise, B.: *J. Pharmacol.*, **76**, 156–60 (1942); *Arch. Intern. Med.*, **72**, 346–52 (1943).
2470 Wise, G. H., and Anderson, G. W.: *J. Am. Vet. Med. Assoc.*, **100**, 160 (1942); *J. Dairy Sci.*, **27**, 965–7 (1944).
2471 Wohlrab, R.: *Klin. Wochschr.*, **21**, 455 (1942).
2472 Wojahn, H.: *Arch. Pharm.*, **281**, 193–201 (1943); *ibid.*, 124–40; *Chem. Abst.*, **38**, 4919.
2473 Wolff, L. K.: *Acta Brevia Neerland Physiol. Pharmacol. Microbiol.*, **8**, 29–32 (1938).
2474 ——: *Bruxelles Med.*, **18**, 1506–13 (1938).
2475 ——: *Deut. med. Wochschr.*, **67**, 334–6 (1941); *Chem. Abst.*, **38**, 2391.
2476 Wong, R. T.: *Arch. Opthalmol. (Chicago)*, **27**, 670–87 (1942).
2477 Wood, W. B., Jr.: *J. Exptl. Med.*, **75**, 369–81 (1942).
2478 ——, and Austrian, R.: *Ibid.*, 383–94 (1942).

2479   Wooley, D. W.: *J. Biol. Chem.*, **152,** 225–32 (1944).
2480   ——: *Ibid.*, **154,** 31–7 (1944).
2481   Wright, L. D., and Welch, A. D.: *Science*, **97,** 426–7 (1943).
2482   Yonkman, F. F., Lehman, A. J., and Chase, J. F.: *Fed. Proc.*, **1,** 172 (1942).
2483   ——, and Walton, C.: *Ibid.*, 173 (1942).
2484   Zozaya, J.: *Salubridad y Enfem. Trop.* **2** (2), 129–52, 153–60 (1941); *ibid.*, **3** (1), 29–40 (1942); *Biol. Abst.*, Sec. C. **17,** 13986–8 (1943).

Second Supplementary References

2485   Adler, E., Euler, H. von, and Skarzynski, B.: *Arkiv Kemi, Mineral., Geol.*, **16A,** No. 9 (1943).
2486   Aktieb. H. Lundbeck & Co. (Kinberg, T.): Brit. 563,936 (Sept. 6, 1944).
2487   ——: Brit. 564,092 (Sept. 13, 1944).
2488   American Cyanamid Co. (Anderson, G. W.): U. S. 2,359,280 (Oct. 3, 1944).
2489   —— (Crossley, M. L.): Brit. 560,601 (Aug. 3, 1944).
2490   —— (Kaiser, D. W.): U. S. 2,359,363 (Oct. 3, 1944).
2491   —— (Roblin, R. O., Jr., and Winnek, P. S.): U. S. 2,358,031 (Sept. 12, 1944).
2492   —— (Anderson, G. W.): U. S. 2,362,336 (Nov. 7, 1944).
2493   Appelbaum, I. L.: *Diseases of Chest*, **10,** 415–21 (1944); *J. Am. Med. Assoc.*, **126,** 919 (1944).
2494   Ayers, W. W.: *U. S. Naval Med. Bull.*, **41,** 714–6 (1943).
2495   Bambas, L. L.: *Abst. New York Meeting Am. Chem. Soc.*, Sept. 1944, p. 12K; *J. Am. Chem. Soc.*, **67,** 671–3 (1945).
2496   Bang, F. B.: *J. Urol.*, **47,** 299–301 (1942).
2497   Barber, H. J., and Slack, R.: *J. Am. Chem. Soc.*, **66,** 1607 (1944).
2498   Baur, E., and Rüf, H.: *Helv. Chem. Acta*, **25,** 523–7 (1942); *Chem. Abst.*, **36,** 6175–6 (1942).
2499   Bernstein, H. I., and Rothstein, L. R.: *J. Am. Chem. Soc.*, **66,** 1886–8 (1944).
2500   Blanchard, K. C.: *J. Biol. Chem.*, **140,** 919–26 (1941).
2501   Bliss, C. I., and Cattell, M.: *Am. Rev. Physiol.*, **5,** 479–539 (1943).
2502   Bliss, E. A., and Deitz, H. C.: *Bull. Johns Hopkins Hosp.*, **75,** 1–13 (1944).
2503   Borodkina, L. B.: *Problems of Tuberculosis (U.S.S.R.)*, No. **2,** 41–4 (1944).
2504   Boroff, D. A., Cooper, A., and Bullowa, J. G. M.: *J. Immunol.*, **43,** 341–8 (1942).
2505   Brewer, A. E.: *Lancet*, **1944, 2,** 471–2.
2506   Buchman, E. R., Heegaard, E., and Bonner, J.: *Proc. Nat. Acad. Sci.*, **26,** 561–3 (1940); *Chem. Abst.*, **34,** 7943.
2507   Bullowa, J. G. M., and Patish, H. D.: *J. Clin. Investigation*, **23,** 676–81 (1944).
2508   Burnet, Et., Cuénod, E., and Nataf, R.: *Bull. acad. méd.*, **121,** 317–24 (1939); *Chem. Abst.*, **34,** 168.
2509   Butler, T. C., Dickison, H. L., Govier, W. M., Greer, C. M., and Lamson, P. D.: *J. Pharmacol.*, **72,** 298–305 (1941).
2510   Chamelin, I. M., and Funk, C.: *Arch. Biochem.*, **2,** 9–14 (1943).
2511   Chávez, A.: *Farm. pervana*, **2,** No. 5, 15–21 (1944); *Chem. Abst.*, **38,** 5360.
2512   Ciusa, R.: *Gazz. chim. ital.*, **72,** 567–70 (1942); *Chem. Abst.*, **38,** 5505; *Arch. ital. sci. farmacol.*, **12,** 45–9 (1943); *Chem. Abst.*, **38,** 6390.
2513   Coatney, G. R., and Cooper, W. C.: *U. S. Pub. Health Repts.*, **59,** 1455–8 (1944).
2514   Coggeshall, L. T., Porter, R. J., and Laird, R. L.: *Proc. Soc. Exptl. Biol. Med.*, **57,** 286–92 (1944).
2515   Collier, H. B.: *Can. J. Research*, **B18,** 345–50 (1940).
2516   Cook, A. H., Heilbron, I. M., and Reed, K. J.: *J. Chem. Soc.*, **1944,** In Press.
2517   Cooperstock, M.: *Am. J. Diseases Children*, **68,** 269–70 (1944).
2518   Dahlbom, R., and Ekstrand, T.: *Svensk Kem. Tid.*, **55,** 122–7 (1943); *Chem. Abst.*, **38,** 5208.
2519   Denenholz, E. J., and Cheney, G.: *Arch. Intern. Med.*, **74,** 311–30 (1944).
2520   Dittmer, K., and Vigneaud, V. du: *Science*, **100,** 129–31 (1944).
2521   Doerman, A. H.: *Arch. Biochem.*, **5,** 373–84 (1944).
2522   Domagk, G.: *Med. u. Chem.*, **4,** 82–129 (1942); *Chem. Abst.*, **38,** 6377.
2523   ——: *Z. Immunitäts.*, **104,** 298–310 (1943).
2524   Dowdy, A. H., Sewall, R. L., and Vincent, J. G.: *N. Y. State J. Med.*, 1890–1 (1944).
2525   Dyer, H. M.: *J. Biol. Chem.*, **124,** 519–24 (1938).
2526   Eagle, H.: *J. Pharmacol.*, **64,** 164–89 (1938).
2527   Earle, D. P., Jr.: *J. Clin. Investigation*, **23,** 914–20 (1944).

2528 Eckert, H. W.: *J. Biol. Chem.*, **148**, 197–204 (1943).
2529 Edlin, J. S., Bobrowitz, I. D., Safford, F. K., Jr., and Butler, F. S.: *Am. Rev. Tuberc.*, **50**, 543–55 (1944).
2530 English, J. P., Clapp, R. C., Cole, Q. P., Halverstadt, I. F., Lampen, J. O., and Roblin, R. O., Jr.: *J. Am. Chem. Soc.*, **67**, 295–302 (1945).
2531 Euler, H. V.: *Ber.*, **75B**, 1876–85 (1942).
2532 ——, and Ahlstrom, L.: *Z. physiol. Chem.*, **279**, 175–86 (1943).
2533 Evans, D. G., Fuller, A. T., and Walker, J.: *Lancet*, **1944, 2,** 523–7.
2534 Finerman, W. B., and Weiss, J. E.: *Bull. U. S. Army Med. Dept.*, **81**, 71–82 (1944).
2535 Finklestone-Sayliss, H., Paine, C. G., and Patrick, L. B.: *Lancet*, **1937, 2,** 792–5.
2536 Fischer, E., Hoffmann, O., and Prado, E.: *Science*, **100**, 576–7 (1944).
2537 Foley, E. J., Epstein, J. A., and Lee, S. W.: *J. Immunol.*, **49**, 129–38 (1944).
2538 Fox, C. L., Jr.: *J. Bact.*, **43**, 68–9 (1942).
2539 Fox, S. W., Fling, M., and Bollenbeck, G. N.: *J. Biol. Chem.*, **155**, 465–8 (1944).
2540 Geigy, J. R., A. G. (Balaban, I. E., and Levy, M. B.): Brit. 563,621 (Aug. 23, 1944).
2541 Giese, A. C., and Tatum, E. L.: *Collecting Net*, **17**, No. 5 (1942).
2542 Gladstone, G. P.: *Brit. J. Exp. Path.*, **20**, 189–200 (1939).
2543 Greig, M. E., and Hoogerheide, J. C.: *J. Bact.*, **41**, 557–62 (1941).
2544 Grob, D.: *J. Gen. Physiol.*, **26**, 431–42 (1943).
2545 Gross, P., Axelrod, A. E., and Bosse, M. D.: *Am. J. Med. Sci.*, **208**, 642–60 (1944).
2546 Gsell, O.: *Deut. Arch. klin. Med.*, **188**, 582–99 (1942); *Chem. Abst.*, **38**, 5590.
2547 ——: *Schweiz. med. Wochschr.*, **73**, 692–9 (1943); *Chem. Abst.*, **38**, 5597.
2548 Gubner, R.: *J. Clin. Investigation*, **23**, 929 (1944).
2549 Guha, P. C., Rao, P. L. N., and Manadevan, V.: *Current Sci.*, **12**, 325–6 (1943); *Chem. Abst.*, **38**, 5208.
2550 Haldane, J. B. S.: "Enzymes," Longmans, Green and Co., New York (1930).
2551 Harrow, B., Mazur, A., and Sherwin, C. P.: *J. Biol. Chem.*, **102**, 35–8 (1933).
2552 Hartelius, V.: *Naturwissenschaften*, **31**, 440 (1943).
2553 Hartman, M., and Druey, J.: *Schweiz. med. Wochschr.*, **73**, 558–60 (1943).
2554 Henkel, H.: *Z. Immunitäts.*, **104**, 413–21 (1943).
2555 Hinshaw, H. C., and Feldman, W. H.: *Am. Rev. Tuberc.*, **50**, 202–13 (1944).
2556 Holder, E. C., Levine, S., and Bullowa, J. G. M.: *J. Pharmacol.*, **74**, 99–105 (1942).
2557 Hurevitz, H.: *War Med.*, **6**, 247–50 (1944).
2558 Ivánovics, G.: *Naturwissenschaften*, **30**, 104 (1942); *Klin. Wochschr.*, **21**, 343–6 (1942).
2559 ——: *Z. Immunitäts.*, **102**, 238–58 (1942).
2560 ——: *Z. physiol. Chem.*, **276**, 33–5 (1942).
2561 Jackson, A. V.: *Lancet*, **1944, 2, 422.**
2562 Jackson, E. L.: *J. Org. Chem.*, **9**, 457–69 (1944).
2563 Jacoby, F., Medawar, P. B., and Willmer, E. N.: *Brit. Med. J.*, **1941, 2,** 149–53.
2564 Janeway, C. A.: *J. Am. Med. Assoc.*, **116**, 941–2 (1941).
2565 ——: *New Engl. Med. J.*, **227**, 989–95 (1942).
2566 Johnson, F. H., Chase, A. M.: *J. Cellular. Comp. Physiol.*, **19**, 151–62 (1942).
2567 ——, Eyring, H. B., and Williams, R. W.: *J. Cellular Comp. Physiol.*, **20**, 247–68 (1942).
2568 ——, and Moore, K.: *Proc. Soc. Exptl. Biol. Med.*, **48**, 323–5 (1941).
2569 Karel, L., and Chapman, C. W.: *J. Pharmacol.*, **82**, 86–8 (1944).
2570 Keefer, C. S., and Rammelkamp, C. H.: *Trans. Assoc. Am. Physicians*, **56**, 165–72 (1941).
2571 Kenney, W. E.: *Surgery*, **16**, 477–83 (1944).
2572 Kikuth, W.: *Med. Welt.*, **17**, 453–6 (1943); *Chem. Abst.*, **38**, 6382.
2573 Kilham, L., and Steigman, A. J.: *Lancet*, **1942, 2,** 452–4.
2574 King, J. A.: *J. Am. Chem. Soc.*, **66**, 2076–80 (1944).
2575 Kirby, W. M. M.: *Proc. Soc. Exptl. Biol. Med.*, **57**, 149–51 (1944).
2576 Kornberg, A., Daft, F. S., and Sebrell, W. H.: *J. Biol. Chem.*, **155**, 193–200 (1944).
2577 Kuhn, R.: *Die Chemie*, **55**, 1–6 (1942).
2578 ——, and Schwartz, K.: *Ber.*, **74B**, 1617–24 (1941); *Chem. Abst.*, **37**, 357.
2579 Lamanna, C.: *Science*, **95**, 304–5 (1942).
2580 Landy, M., and Dicken, D. M.: *Nature*, **149**, 244 (1942).
2581 ——, and Streightoff, F.: *Proc. Soc. Exptl. Biol. Med.*, **52**, 127–8 (1943).
2582 Larson, W. P., Bieter, R. N., Levine, M., and Hoyt, R. E.: *Ibid.*, **41**, 200–3 (1939).
2583 Laüger, P., Suter, R., and Martin, H.: *Z. Immunitäts.*, **105**, 78–96 (1944).
2584 Lawrence, C. A., and Goetchius, G. R.: *Proc. Soc. Exptl. Biol. Med.*, **57**, 180–3 (1944); *ibid.*, **58**, 356–8 (1945).
2585 Leblond, C. P., and Hoff, H. E.: *Endocrinology*, **35**, 229–33 (1944).
2586 Lee, R. V.: *California Western Med.*, **61**, 133–4 (1944); *J. Am. Med. Assoc.*, **126**, 630–1 (1944).

2587 Lee, S. W., Epstein, J. A., and Foley, E. J.: *Proc. Soc. Exptl. Biol. Med.*, **53,** 245–7 (1943).
2588 ——, and Foley, E. J.: *Ibid.*, 243–5 (1943).
2589 Leishman, A. W., and Kelsall, A. R.: *Lancet*, **1944, 2,** 231–3.
2590 Levaditi, C.: *Compt. rend. soc. biol.*, **135,** 1109–11 (1941); *Chem. Abst.*, **38,** 5961.
2591 Lewis, K. H., and Snyder, J. E.: *J. Bact.*, **39,** 28–9 (1940).
2592 Loomis, T. A., Hubbard, R. S., and Neter, E.: *Proc. Soc. Exptl. Biol. Med.*, **47,** 159–63 (1941).
2593 McCarty, M.: *Ibid.*, **46,** 133–6 (1941).
2594 Macht, D. I., and Kehoe, D. B.: *Fed. Proc.*, **2,** 30 (1943).
2595 McIlwain, H., and Hughes, D. E.: *Biochem. J.*, **38,** 187–95 (1944).
2596 Mackenzie, D. H.: *Brit. Med. J.*, **1944, 2,** 722–3.
2597 MacLeod, C. M., and Mirick, G. S.: *J. Bact.*, **44,** 277–87 (1942).
2598 Manchester Oxide Co. (Wheeler, D. E., Bann, B., Krug, P., and Taylor, W.): Brit. 564,659 (Oct. 6, 1944).
2599 Mann, T., and Keilin, D.: *Nature*, **146,** 164–5 (1940).
2600 Martin, A. R., Rose, F. L., and Swain, G.: *Nature*, **154,** 639 (1944).
2601 Mayer, R. L.: *J. Bact.*, **48,** 93–6 (1944).
2602 ——: *Ibid.*, 337–44 (1944).
2603 Meacham, W. F., Smith, E., and Pilcher, C.: *War Med.*, **6,** 378–81 (1944).
2604 Mellon, R. R.: *Diseases Chest*, **8,** 166–72 (1942).
2605 Miller, J. L.: *J. Pharmacol.*, **72,** 354–62 (1941).
2606 Mirick, G. S.: *J. Bact.*, **45,** 66–7 (1943).
2607 Mitchell, H. K., Isbell, E. R., and Thompson, R. C.: *J. Biol. Chem.*, **147,** 485–6 (1943).
2608 Mutch, N.: *Lancet*, **1944, 2,** 775–80.
2609 Navmed 284, "The Prevention of Respiratory Tract Bacterial Infections by Sulfadiazine Prophylaxis in the United States Navy," Bureau of Medicine and Surgery, Navy Department, Washington, D. C. (1944).
2610 Nielson, N.: *Naturwissenschaften*, **31,** 146 (1943).
2611 ——, and Johansen, G.: *Ibid.*, 235 (1943).
2612 Ohnysty, J., and Wolfson, W. Q.: *New Engl. J. Med.*, **231,** 381–7 (1944).
2613 Oliver, C. S., and Anderson, D. G.: *Am. J. Med. Sci.*, **208,** 597–602 (1944).
2614 Osborn, W. H., and Jones, R. N.: *Lancet*, **1944, 2,** 470–1.
2615 Painton, J. F.: *Military Surgeon*, **95,** 267–9 (1944).
2616 Pinner, M.: *Am. Rev. Tuberc.*, **50,** 257–9 (1944).
2617 Pollack, M. A.: *J. Am. Chem. Soc.*, **65,** 1335–9 (1944).
2618 Praetorius, G.: *Z. Urol.*, **37,** 147–55 (1943); *Chem. Abst.*, **38,** 5962–3.
2619 Ratner, S., Blanchard, M., Coburn, A. E., and Green, D. E.: *J. Biol. Chem.*, **155,** 689–90 (1944).
2620 Reed, G. B., Orr, J. H., and Reed, R. W.: *J. Bact.*, **48,** 233–42 (1944).
2621 Reiman, H. A.: *Arch. Intern. Med.*, **74,** 281–3 (1944).
2622 Rieben, G.: *Schweiz. med. Wochschr.*, **73,** 797–801 (1943); *Chem. Abst.*, **38,** 5304.
2623 Roback, R. A., and Ivy, A. C.: *Surg. Gynecol. Obstet.*, **79,** 469–77 (1944).
2624 Robbins, W. J.: *Proc. Nat. Acad. Sci.*, **27,** 419–22 (1941).
2625 Roblin, R. O., Jr., and Bell, P. H.: *Ann. N. Y. Acad. Sci.*, **44,** 449–54 (1943).
2626 ——, and Bell, P. H.: *Science*, **90,** 327–9 (1939).
2627 ——, Lampen, J. P., English, J. P., Cole, Q. P., and Vaughan, J. R., Jr.: *J. Am. Chem. Soc.*, **67,** 290–4 (1945).
2628 Rosenthal, S. M.: *Sci. Monthly*, **56,** 232–7 (1943).
2629 Ross, A., Kieth, G. S., and Thompson, R. K.: *Canadian Med. Assoc. J.*, **51,** 214–9 (1944).
2630 Roth, J. S., and Degering, E. F.: *J. Am. Chem. Soc.*, **67,** 126–8 (1945).
2631 Sandground, J. H.: *J. Pharmacol.*, **80,** 393–8 (1944).
2632 Schmelkes, F. C., and Rubin, M.: *J. Am. Chem. Soc.*, **66,** 1631–2 (1944).
2633 Schmidt, L. H., Sesler, C. L., and Dettwiler, H. A.: *J. Pharmacol.*, **74,** 175–89 (1944).
2634 Schnitker, M. A., and Lenhoff, C. D.: *J. Lab. Clin. Med.*, **29,** 889–98 (1944).
2635 Scudi, J. V., and Silber, R. H.: *J. Biol. Chem.*, **156,** 343–8 (1944).
2636 Sevag, M. G., Henry, J., and Richardson, R.: *Am. J. Med. Sci.*, **205,** 877–8 (1944).
2637 Shaffer, J. M.: *Fed. Proc.*, **1,** 165 (1942).
2638 Sharp and Dohme, Inc. (Johnson, T. B.): U. S. 2,350,900 (June 6, 1944).
2639 Smith, D. G., and Robinson, H. J.: *Proc. Soc. Exptl. Biol. Med.*, **57,** 292–5 (1944).
2640 Smith, L. B., Cohen, F., and Nichols, R. G.: *J. Am. Med. Assoc.*, **126,** 1027–8 (1944).
2641 Snell, E. E.: *Arch. Biochem.*, **2,** 389–94 (1942).
2642 Soodak, M., and Cerecedo, L. R.: *J. Am. Chem. Soc.*, **66,** 1988–9 (1944).
2643 Strangmann, E.: *Arch. Kinderheilk*, **129,** 124–9 (1943); *Chem. Zentr.*, **1943, 11,** 2175.
2644 Sung, C., and Helmholz, H. F.: *Proc. Staff Mayo Clin.*, **19,** 577–80 (1944).

2645 Surrey, A. R., and Hammer, H. F.: *J. Am. Chem. Soc.*, **66**, 2127–9 (1944).
2646 Tabone, J., Nitti, F., and Moussel, H.: *Ann. Inst. Pasteur*, **68**, 470–97 (1942); *Chem. Abst.*, **38**, 5513–4.
2647 Thomas, C. B.: *J. Am. Med. Assoc.*, **126**, 490–5 (1944).
2648 Ulrich, I.: *Arch. Dermat. Syphilis*, **182**, 452–62 (1941).
2649 Vandegrift, H. N.: *J. Pediatrics*, **25**, 386–93 (1944).
2650 Vandenbelt, J. M., and Doub, L.: *J. Am. Chem. Soc.*, **66**, 1633–6 (1944).
2651 VanWinkle, W., Jr., Herwick, R. P., Calvery, H. O., and Smith, A.: *J. Am. Med. Assoc.*, **126**, 958–61 (1944).
2652 Vilter, C. F., and Blankenhorn, H. A.: *Ibid.*, 691–5 (1944).
2653 Vincent, J. G., and Vincent, H. W.: *Proc. Soc. Exptl. Biol. Med.*, **55**, 162–4 (1944).
2654 Vonkennel, J., and Lenz: *Arch. Dermatol. Syphilis*, **183**, 654–62 (1943); *Chem. Abst.*, **38**, 5594.
2655 Warren, H. A.: *J. Indiana State Med. Assoc.*, **37**, 447–51 (1944).
2656 Weijlard, J., Tishler, M., and Erickson, A. E.: *J. Am. Chem. Soc.*, **66**, 1957–9 (1944).
2657 Weiner, L.: *J. Am. Dental Assoc.*, **31**, 1358 (1944).
2658 Weissberger, A., and Porter, H. D.: *J. Am. Chem. Soc.*, **66**, 1849–51 (1944).
2659 ——, Porter, H. D., and Gregory, W. A.: *Ibid.*, 1851–5 (1944).
2660 Williams, R. D.: *J. Biol. Chem.*, **156**, 85–9 (1944).
2661 Woods, D. D., and Fildes, P.: *Chemistry & Industry*, **59**, 133–4 (1940).
2662 Woolley, D. W.: *Proc. Soc. Exptl. Biol. Med.*, **55**, 179–80 (1944).
2663 ——, Strong, F. M., Elvehjem, C. A., and Madden, R. J.: *J. Biol. Chem.*, **124**, 715–23 (1938).
2664 ——, and White, A. G. C.: *J. Biol. Chem.*, **149**, 285–9 (1943).
2665 ——, and ——: *J. Exptl. Med.*, **78**, 489 (1943).
2666 Wright, H. N.: *J. Am. Pharm. Assoc.*, **30**, 177–80 (1941).
2667 Wurm, K.: *Z. Immunitäts.*, **104**, 263–74 (1943); *Chem. Abst.*, **38**, 6322.
2668 Youmans, G. P.: *Proc. Soc. Exptl. Biol. Med.*, **57**, 119–24 (1944).

APPENDIXES

Appendix A

Key to Activities

+++ More active than reference compound.
++ Approximately equal activity to reference compound.
+ Slight to moderate activity.
± Very slight or uncertain activity.
0 Inactive.
− Toxic, *i.e.* treated animals dead before controls.

Key to Organisms or Diseases

A *Actinomycetes*
Aa *Aerobacter aerogenes*
Ae *Salmonella aertryche* (typhi-murium)
An *Bacillus anthracis*
B *Blastomyces dermatiditis*
Ba *Brucella abortus*
Bd *Borrelia duttoni* (*Spirochaeta, Treponema* or *Trypanosoma duttoni*)
Bm *Brucella melitensis*
Bmu *Bartonella muris*
Br *Borrelia* (*Spirochaeta* or *Treponema*) *recurrentis*
Bs *Brucella suis*
C Coliform bacteria (in dogs or mice): Sulfaguanidine = + +
Ca Cancer, regression of tumor = +
Cd *Corynebacterium diphtheriae*
Ch *Clostridium histolyticum*
Cn *Clostridium novyi* (*Clostridium oedematiens*)
Cs *Clostridium septicum* (*Vibrio septique*)
Cso *Clostridium sordelli* (*Clostridium bifermentans*)
Csp *Clostridium sporogenes*
Ct *Clostridium tetani*
Cv Choriomeningitis virus
Cw *Clostridium welchii* (*Clostridium perfringens*)
D Diphtheria toxin
Dr *Dermacentroxenus rickettsii* (Rocky Mountain spotted fever)
Dy Dysentery bacteria (unspecified)
Ea *Eimeria acervulia* (in chickens)
Eb *Eimeria brunetti* (in chickens)
Ebo *Eimeria bovis* (in calves)
Ec *E. coli, in vitro* tests (in a synthetic medium)*
Eh *Eimeria hagani* (in chickens)
Em *Endamoeba muris*
Ema *Eimeria maxima* (in chickens)
Emi *Eimeria mitis* (in chickens)
En Encephalitis virus, St. Louis strain (in mice)

---

* In terms of minimum molar concentrations necessary to inhibit growth, $C_r \times 10^5$, the approximate values are: $+++ = 0.3$ (sulfathiazole or sulfadiazine = .08); $++ = 0.3$ to 2.0 (sulfapyridine = 0.6); $+ = 2.0$ to 30.0 (sulfanilamide = 20); $± = 30$ to 80; 0 = 80; $−$ = stimulation of growth. See reference[719] for list of values.

Ene   *Eimeria necatrix* (in chickens)
Ep   *Eimeria praecox* (in chickens)
Er   *Erysipelothrix rhusiopathiae*
Et   *Eberthella typhosa* (*B. typhosus*), *in vitro* usually
Ete   *Eimeria tenella*, cecal coccidiosis (in chickens)
F   Friedlander bacillus (*Klebsiélla pneumoniae*): Sulfadiazine = ++
G   Gonococcus (*Neisseria gonorrheae*) clinical: Sulfanilamide = ++
Gm   *Giardia muris*
H   *Hemophilus influenzae* (Pfeiffer's bacillus): Sulfapyridine = ++
Hd   *Hemophilus ducreyi*
Hm   *Hexamita muris*
Hp   *Hemophilus pertussis*
I   Influenza virus, usually PR8 strain (in mice)
Ko   *Klebsiella ozaenae*
Kr   *Klebsiella rhinoscleroma*
L   *Lymphopathia* (*Lymphogranuloma*) *venereum* virus: Sulfanilamide = ++
La   *Lactobacillus arabinosus*, *in vitro*
Lc   Lymphocytic choriomeningitis virus
Le   Leprosy (clinical): Promin = ++
Lm   *Listerella monocytogenes*
Lt   *Leishmania tropica*
M   Meningococcus (*Neisseria intracellularis*): Sulfanilamide = ++
Mp   Meningo-pneumonitis virus (in mice)
Ne   Neurolymphomatosis virus (in chickens): Sulfadiazine = ++
P   Pneumococcus (*Diplococcus pneumoniae*), various types and strains: Sulfapyridine = ++
Pa   *Pseudomonas aeruginosa* (*B. pyocyaneous*)
Pc   *Plasmodium circumflexum* (in canaries)
Pcy   *Plasmodium cynomolgi*
Pf   *Plasmodium falciparum* (in humans)
Pg   *Plasmodium gallinacium* (in chickens)
Pi   *Plasmodium inui* (in monkeys)
Pk   *Plasmodium knowlesi* (in monkeys)
Pl   *Plasmodium lophurae* (in ducks)
Pm   *Plasmodium malariae* (in humans)
Pn   *Plasmodium nucleophilum* (in canaries)
pn   Pneumonitis virus (in mice)
Po   Poliomyelitis virus
Pp   *Pasturella pestis* (Bubonic plague): Sulfathiazole = ++
pr   *Proteus vulgaris*
Pr   *Plasmodium relictum* (in canaries)
Ps   *Pasturella septica*
Pv   *Plasmodium vivax* (in humans)
R   Rabies virus
Rp   *Rickettsia prowazeki* (Typhus fever)
S   β-*Hemolytic streptococci*, various strains Group A: Sulfanilamide = ++
Sa   *Staphylococcus aureus:* Sulfathiazole = ++
Sc   *Salmonella choleraesuis* (suipestifer)
Sd   *Shigella dysenteriae* (Shiga type)
Se   *Salmonella enteritidis*
Sf   *Streptococcus faecalis* (Group D) (enterococci)
Sp   *Salmonella paratyphi* (A)
Spd   *Shigella paradysenteriae* (Flexner)

Spl	*Streptobacterium plantarum, in vitro*
Spy	*Streptococcus pyogenes*
Ss	*Shigella sonnei*
Ssc	*Salmonella schottmülleri* (paratyphi B)
Sv	*Streptococcus viridans* (*S. salivarius*)
T	*Mycobacterium tuberculosis* (in guinea pigs usually): Promin = $++$
Tb	*Trypanosoma brucei*
Tc	*Trypanosoma cruzi*
Te	*Trypanosoma equiperdum*
Tl	*Trypanosoma lewisi*
Tm	*Trichomonas muris*
To	*Toxoplasma*
Tp	*Treponema pallidum* (syphilis)
Tr	*Trachoma* virus (in humans)
Ts	*Trichinella spiralis*
Tt	*Tetanus toxin*
Tu	*Pasteurella tularense, in vitro*
Tv	*Trichomonas vaginalis*
V	*Vaccinia virus*
Vc	*Vibrio cholerae*
Y	Yellow fever virus

Appendix B

Trade Names for Sulfanilamide

Albosal
Ambesid
Antistrept
Astreptine
Astrocid
Bacteramide
Bactesid
Cepticide
Collomide
Colsulanyde
Deseptyl
Ergaseptine
Erysipan
Estreptocida
1162
Gerison
Gombardol
Lusil
Lysococcine
Neococcyl

Orgaseptine
P.A.B.S.
Prontalbin
Prontosil Album
Prontylin
Pronzin Album
Proseptal
Proseptine
Proseptol
Pysococcine
Rubiazol A
Sanamide
Septamide Album
Septanilam
Septinal
Septolix
Septoplex
Septoplix
Stopton Album
Stramid
Strepamide

Strepsan
Streptagol
Streptal
Streptamid
Streptasol
Streptazol
Streptocid Album
Streptocide
Streptoclase
Streptocom
Strepton
Streptosil
Streptozone
Sulfamidyl
Sulfana
Sulfanalone
Sulfanil
Sulfocidine
Sulfonamide P
Therapol

Appendix C

Trade Names for Sulfanilamide Derivatives and Related Compounds

Trade or Medical Name	Chemical Name	Chemical Structure
Acetylpyriamid	2- (N^4- Acetylsulfanilamido) - pyridine	$CH_3CONH\langle\ \rangle SO_2NH\langle N\rangle$
Albasil	see Uleron	
Albasil C	see Disulon	
Albucid	see Sulfacetamide	
Albucid Soluble	see Sulfacetamide Soluble	
Aldanil	Sodium p-Sulfamylanilino-methanesulfinate	$NaOSOCH_2NH\langle\ \rangle SO_2NH_2$
Ambesid Soluble	Sodium N^4-Succinylsulfanil-amide	$NaO_2CCH_2CH_2CONH\langle\ \rangle SO_2NH_2$
Amonal A	n-Hexyl p-Nitrobenzoate	$O_2N\langle\ \rangle COO(CH_2)_5CH_3$
Anabion	see Diseptal B	
Azosulfamide	see Prontosil Soluble	
Badional	see Sulfathiourea	
Bayer 102	see Prontosil Soluble	
B1034	Disodium 2-Acetamido-7-[4'-(2-pyridylsulfamyl)phenyl-azo]- 8- naphthol -3,6- disul-fonate	$\langle N\rangle NHSO_2\langle\ \rangle -N=N-\ \overset{OH}{\underset{NaO_3S\quad SO_3Na}{\langle\ \rangle}} NHCOCH_3$
Bemural	N^1-(3,5- dibromophenyl)sulfa-nilamide	$NH_2\langle\ \rangle SO_2NH\langle\ \rangle\ ^{Br}_{Br}$
Butamide	N^4-Butyrylsulfanilamide	$CH_3(CH_2)_2CONH\langle\ \rangle SO_2NH_2$
Carboxysulfamido-chrysoidine	see Rubiazole	
Chemosept	see Sulfathiazole	
Ciba 3714	Sulfathiazole	
Ciba 3753	see Sulfamethylthiazole	
Cibazol	see Sulfathiazole	
Cibagen 4	Calcium Salt of 2-Sulfanil-amidopyridine	$\left[NH_2\langle\ \rangle SO_2N-\langle N\rangle\right]_2 Ca$
Coccoclase	see Sulfapyridine	
Colistatin	2- (N^4- Succinylsulfanilamido)-thiazole	$HOOCCH_2CH_2CONH\langle\ \rangle SO_2NH\langle^S_N\rangle$

Trade or Medical Name	Chemical Name	Chemical Structure
Dagenan	*see* Sulfapyridine	
Dagenan Sodium	*see* Sulfapyridine Sodium	
Debenal	*see* Sulfadiazine	
Diasone	Disodium [(sulfonyldi-*p*-phenylene)diimino] dimethanesulfinate	$NaO_2SCH_2NH\langle\rangle$ $\quad\quad\quad\quad SO_2\cdot 4H_2O$ $NaO_2SCH_2NH\langle\rangle$
Diazin	*see* Sulfadiazine	
Dimethylgerison	N^1-Dimethylsulfanilamide	$NH_2\langle\rangle SO_2N(CH_3)_2$
Diseptal A (DB90, DB373)	*see* Uleron	
Diseptal B (DB87)	N^1- Methyl- N^4- sulfanilylsulfanilamide	$NH_2\langle\rangle SO_2NH\langle\rangle SO_2NHCH_3$
Diseptal C (DB32)	*see* Disulon	
Disulfane	*see* Disulon	
Disulfanilamide	Disulfanilamide (name is frequently misapplied to N^4-Sulfanilylsulfanilamide)	$NH_2\langle\rangle SO_2NHSO_2\langle\rangle NH_2$
Disulon	N^4-Sulfanilylsulfanilamide	$NH_2\langle\rangle SO_2NH\langle\rangle SO_2NH_2$
Disulon sodium	Sodium N^4-Sulfanilylsulfanilamide	$NH_2\langle\rangle SO_2NH\langle\rangle SO_2NHNa$
DN77	1,5- Naphthalenedisulfonate Salt of 4-Aminomethylbenzenesulfonamide	$\left[\begin{array}{c}SO_3H\\ \\HO_3S\end{array}\right]\cdot\left[NH_2CH_2\langle\rangle SO_2NH_2\right]_2$
Elektyl	N^1-Dimethylsulfanilamide	$NH_2\langle\rangle SO_2N(CH_3)_2$
Eleudron	*see* Sulfathiazole	
Euvernil	Sulfanilylurea	$NH_2\langle\rangle SO_2NHCONH_2$
Eubasin	*see* Sulfapyridine	
Eubasinum	*see* Sulfapyridine	
1399 F	*see* Rodilone	
Geigy 867	*see* Irgafen	
Globucid	*see* Sulfaethylthiadiazole	
Glucostreptocide	Glucoside of Sulfanilamide	
Guamide	*see* Sulfaguanidine	
Haptocil	Calcium Salt of 2-Sulfanilamidopyridine	

Trade or Medical Name	Chemical Name	Chemical Structure
Homosulfanilamide	4-(Aminomethyl)benzenesulfonamide Hydrochloride	$HCl \cdot NH_2CH_2$⟨benzene⟩SO_2NH_2
Homosulfamethazine	2-[4'-(Aminomethyl)phenylsulfonamido]-4,6-dimethylpyrimidine	NH_2CH_2⟨benzene⟩SO_2NH—pyrimidine with CH_3, CH_3
Homosulfathiazole	2-[4'-(Aminomethyl)phenylsulfonamido]thiazole Hydrochloride	$HCl \cdot NH_2CH_2$⟨benzene⟩SO_2NH—thiazole
Ilvin	N^1-(4'-Acetylphenyl)sulfanilamide	NH_2⟨benzene⟩SO_2NH⟨benzene⟩$COCH_3$
Irgafen	N^1-(3,4-Dimethylbenzoyl)sulfanilamide	NH_2⟨benzene⟩SO_2NHCO⟨benzene⟩ with CH_3, CH_3
Irgamid(e)	N^1-Senecioylsulfanilamide or N^1-Dimethylacroylsulfanilamide	NH_2⟨benzene⟩$SO_2NHCOCH{=}C(CH_3)_2$
Lu, tazol	Lithium 4-Sulfamylphenylazosalicylate	NH_2SO_2⟨benzene⟩$N{=}N$⟨benzene⟩ with $COOLi$, OH
Lucosil	2-Sulfanilamido-5-methyl-1,3,4-thiadiazole	NH_2⟨benzene⟩SO_2NH—thiadiazole—CH_3
Lysamide	Aluminum Sulfanilamide	$\left(NH_2\text{⟨benzene⟩}SO_2NH\right)_3 Al \cdot 2.5H_2O$
Lysapyrine	Aluminum 2-Sulfanilamidopyridine	$\left(NH_2\text{⟨benzene⟩}SO_2N{-}\text{pyridine}\right)_3 Al$
M109	Sodium N^4-(Sulfomethyl)sulfanilamide	NaO_3SCH_2NH⟨benzene⟩SO_2NH_2
M541	Sulfanilamide Ethylsulfonate	$C_2H_5OSO_3H \cdot NH_2$⟨benzene⟩SO_2NH_2
Marfanil (Mesudin)	4-(Aminomethyl)benzenesulfonamide Hydrochloride	$HCl \cdot NH_2CH_2$⟨benzene⟩SO_2NH_2
M and B 125	*see* Septazine	
M and B 137	*see* Soluseptazine	
M and B 693	*see* Sulfapyridine	
M and B 693 Soluble	*see* Sulfapyridine Sodium	
M and B 760	*see* Sulfathiazole	
M and B 761 Soluble	*see* Sulfathiazole Sodium	
M and B 838	*see* Sulfamethylthiazole	
Metazin	*see* Sulfamethazine	

APPENDIX C—*Continued*

Trade or Medical Name	Chemical Name	Chemical Structure
Methylsulfidine	2- Sulfanilamido-6-methyl-pyridine	NH_2⟨⟩SO_2NH⟨N⟩CH_3
Neo-Diseptal	*see* Sulfamethylthiazole	
Neoprontosil	*see* Prontosil Soluble	
Neosanamid	N^4-(N^4-Acetylsulfanilyl)-sulfanilamide	CH_3CONH⟨⟩SO_2NH⟨⟩SO_2NH_2
Neostrepsan	*see* Sulfathiazole	
Neostreptosil	*see* Neosanamid	
Neouliron	*see* Diseptal B	
Nisulfadine	2-(*p*-Nitrophenylsulfon-amido)pyridine	NO_2⟨⟩SO_2NH⟨N⟩
Nisulfazole	2-(*p*-Nitrophenylsulfon-amido)thiazole	NO_2⟨⟩SO_2NH⟨S/N⟩
Novamide	Sodium N^4-(Sulfomethyl)sulf-anilamide	NaO_3SCH_2NH⟨⟩SO_2NH_2
Orsulon Calcium	Calcium Salt of 2-Sulfanil-amidopyridine	$Ca\left[NH_2⟨⟩SO_2N⟨N⟩\right]_2$
Percoccide	*see* Sulfamerazine	
Phonocasil	1,3-Bis(N^4-Sulfanilylsulf-anilyl)urea	$\left(NH_2⟨⟩SO_2NH⟨⟩SO_2NH-\right)_2CO$
Phthalylsulfa-thiazole	2-($N^{4'}$-Phthalylsulfanilamido)-thiazole	⟨CONH/COOH⟩⟨⟩SO_2NH⟨S/N⟩
Phthalylsulfadiazine	2- N^4-Phthalylsulfanilamido)-pyrimidine	⟨CONH/COOH⟩⟨⟩SO_2NH⟨N—/N⟩
Phthalylsulfa-merazine	2-(N^4-Phthalylsulfanilamido)-4-methylpyrimidine	⟨CONH/COOH⟩⟨⟩SO_2NH⟨N—/N⟩CH_3
Plurazol	*see* Sulfapyridine	
Promanide	*see* Promin	
Promin	"Sodium Salt of *p,p'*-Diamino-diphenyl sulfone-*N,N'*-di-dextrose sulfonate"	SO_3Na $CHNH$⟨⟩SO_2⟨⟩$NHCHSO_3Na$ $HCOH$　　　　$HCOH$ $HOCH$　　　　$HOCH$ $HCOH$　　　　$HCOH$ $HCOH$　　　　$HCOH$ CH_2OH　　　CH_2OH

APPENDIX C—*Continued*

Trade or Medical Name	Chemical Name	Chemical Structure
Promizole	4-Aminophenyl 2-Amino-5'-thiazyl Sulfone or 2-Amino-5-sulfanilylthiazole	NH_2—⟨⟩—SO_2—[thiazole]—NH_2
Prontosil	4'-Sulfamyl-2,4-diaminoazobenzene Hydrochloride	NH_2SO_2—⟨⟩—$N{=}N$—⟨⟩—$NH_2 \cdot HCl$, NH_2
Prontosil Flavum	*see* Prontosil	
Prontosil Rubrum (red)	*see* Prontosil	
Prontosil (Soluble), (11)	Disodium 2-(4'-Sulfamylphenylazo)- 7- acetamido- 1- hydroxynaphthalene- 3,6- disulfonate	NH_2SO_2—⟨⟩—$N{=}N$—[naphthalene] $NHCOCH_3$, NaO_3S, SO_3Na
Pronzin rubrum	*see* Prontosil	
Pronson rubrum	*see* Prontosil	
Proseptazine(e)	*see* Septazine	
Pyriamid	*see* Sulfapyridine	
Pyridin-derganil	*see* Sulfapyridine	
Pyrimal	*see* Sulfadiazine	
Pyrofanil	5-Phenyl-1-(*p*-sulfamylphenyl)-3-(*p*-sulfamylphenylimino)-2-pyrrolidone	SO_2NH_2 [phenyl], H N ... O, H_2...N—⟨⟩—SO_2NH_2
R-120	*see* Supron	
Roche 4217	*see* Sulfadimethylisoxazole	
R.P. 40	*see* Soluseptazine	
R.P. 46	*see* Septazine	
R.P. 2090	*see* Sulfapyridine	
R.P. 2254	*see* Sulfaisopropylthiadiazole	
Region	*see* Sulfacetamide	
Rodilone	Bis(4-acetylaminophenyl) Sulfone	CH_3CONH—⟨⟩—SO_2—⟨⟩—$NHCOCH_3$
Ronin	*see* Sulfapyridine	
Rubiazol(e) IV	3,5- Diamino- 2-[4'-(sulfamylphenyl)azo]benzoic Acid	NH_2SO_2—⟨⟩—$N{=}N$—⟨⟩ NH_2, NH_2, $COOH$

APPENDIX C—*Continued*

Trade or Medical Name	Chemical Name	Chemical Structure
Rubiazol(e) Injectable	*see* Prontosil S	
Salazopyrin	4-[(2'-Pyridylsulfamyl)-phenyl]azosalicylic acid	
Septazin(e) (Setazine)	N^4-Benzylsulfanilamide	$C_6H_5CH_2NH\langle\rangle SO_2NH_2$
Septinal Soluble	*see* Ambesid Soluble	
Septipulmon	*see* Sulfapyridine	
Septurit	Molecular Compound of Sulfanilamide and Hexamethylenetetramine	
Soludagenan	*see* Sulfapyridine Sodium	
Soluseptazin(e)	N^4-(Disodium-1,3-disulfo-3-phenylpropyl)sulfanilamide	
STAB	2-[N^4-(1-Sodium sulfoethyl)-sulfanilamido]thiazole	
Steramide	*see* Sulfacetamide	
Streptal Soluble	N^4-Quinolinylsulfanilamide	
Streptasol	N-Sulfanilylglycine	$NH_2\langle\rangle SO_2NHCH_2COOH$
Streptocid Rubrum	*see* Prontosil S	
Streptosilpyridine	*see* Sulfapyridine	
Streptosilthiazole	*see* Sulfathiazole	
Streptozon	*see* Prontosil	
Streptozon S	*see* Prontosil S	
Streptozon II	*see* Prontosil S	
Substance 33	Sodium Potassium 4-Sulfamylphenylazosalicylate	
Succinylsulfathiazole	2-(N^4-Succinylsulfanilamido)-thiazole	
Sulamyd	*see* Sulfacetamide	
Sulamyd Soluble	*see* Sulfacetamide Soluble	
Sulfa-allantoin	Loose Addition Product of Sulfanilamide and Allantoin	

Trade or Medical Name	Chemical Name	Chemical Structure
Sulfabenamide	N^1-Hydroxy-N^4-caproylsulf-anilamide	$CH_3(CH_2)_4CONH\langle\ \rangle SO_2NHOH$
Sulfabenzamide	N^1-Benzoylsulfanilamide	$NH_2\langle\ \rangle SO_2NHCO\langle\ \rangle$
Sulfabenzamine	4-(Aminomethyl)benzene-sulfonamide	$NH_2CH_2\langle\ \rangle SO_2NH_2$
Sulfacamphal	$N^4, N^{4'}$-Camphorylidenebis-sulfanilamide	$(C_{11}H_{16}O)CH=\left(NH\langle\ \rangle SO_2NH_2\right)_2$
Sulfacarbamide	Sulfanilylurea	$NH_2\langle\ \rangle SO_2NHCONH_2$
Sulfacet	*see* Sulfacetamide	
Sulfacetamide	N^1-Acetylsulfanilamide	$NH_2\langle\ \rangle SO_2NHCOCH_3$
Sulfacetamide Soluble	Sodium N^1-Acetylsulfanil-amide	$NH_2\langle\ \rangle SO_2N(Na)COCH_3$
Sulfacetimide	*see* Sulfacetamide	
Sulfacholazine	N-Sulfanilylcholhydrazide	$NH_2\langle\ \rangle SO_2NHNHCOCH_2CH_2\cdot CHCH_3$
Sulfac(z)id	4-Aminophenyl 4'-Ureido-phenyl Sulfone or 4-Sulf-anilylphenylurea	$NH_2\langle\ \rangle SO_2\langle\ \rangle NHCONH_2$
Sulfacridine	*see* Sulfazoacridine	
Sulfadiamine	*see* Rodilone	
Sulfadiazine	2-Sulfanilamidopyrimidine	$NH_2\langle\ \rangle SO_2NH\langle\substack{N-\\ \\ N}\rangle$
Sulfadiazine Sodium	Sodium 2-Sulfanilamidopyr-imidine	$NH_2\langle\ \rangle SO_2N\overset{Na}{\langle\substack{N-\\ \\ N}\rangle}$
Sulfadimethyl-diazine	*see* Sulfamethazine	
Sulfadimethyl-isoxazole	3,5-Dimethyl-4-sulfanilamido-isoxazole	$NH_2\langle\ \rangle SO_2NH\overset{CH_3\ \ \overset{O}{\diagdown}}{\underset{CH_3}{\diagup N}}$
Sulfadimethylpy-rimidine	*see* Sulfamethazine	
Sulfadine (Sulfidin(e))	*see* Sulfapyridine	

Trade or Medical Name	Chemical Name	Chemical Structure
Sulfaethylthiadiazole	5-Ethyl-2-sulfanilamido-1,3,4-thiadiazole	NH_2〈〉SO_2NH thiadiazole ring C_2H_5 (N—N, S)
Sulfaethylthiazolone	5-Ethyl-2-sulfanilamido-4-thiazolone	NH_2〈〉SO_2NH thiazolone ring C_2H_5, H, N—O
Sulfaguanidine	Sulfanilylguanidine	NH_2〈〉$SO_2N=C(NH_2)_2$
Sulfahydantoin	5-Sulfanilamidohydantoin	NH_2〈〉SO_2NH hydantoin ring (H, N—H, O, O, NH)
Sulfaisobutylthiadiazole	5-Isobutyl-2-sulfanilamido-1,3,4-thiadiazole	NH_2〈〉SO_2NH ring $CH_2CH(CH_3)_2$ (N—N, S)
Sulfaisopropylthiadiazole	5-Isopropyl-2-sulfanilamido-1,3,4-thiadiazole	NH_2〈〉SO_2NH ring $CH(CH_3)_2$ (N—N, S)
Sulfalaural	$N^4,N^{4'}$-Dodecylidinebissulfanilamide	$CH_3(CH_2)_{10}C$〈NH〈〉SO_2NH_2〉$_2$
Sulfamerazine	4-Methyl-2-sulfanilamido-pyrimidine	H_2N〈〉SO_2NH ring (N—, N, CH_3)
Sulfamerizine (obs.)	*see* Sulfamerazine	
Sulfamethazine	4,6-Dimethyl-2-sulfanilamido-pyrimidine	NH_2〈〉SO_2NH ring (N—CH_3, N—CH_3)
Sulfamethyldiazine	*see* Sulfamerazine	
Sulfamethylpyridine	6-Methyl-2-sulfanilamido-pyridine	NH_2〈〉SO_2NH pyridine ring (N, CH_3)
Sulfamethylpyrimidine	*see* Sulfamerazine	
Sulfamethylselenazole	4-Methyl-2-sulfanilamido-selenazole	NH_2〈〉SO_2NH selenazole ring (Se, N—CH_3)
Sulfamethylthiazole	4-Methyl-2-sulfanilamido-thiazole	NH_2〈〉SO_2NH thiazole ring (S, N—CH_2)
Sulfamethylthiadiazole	5-Methyl-2-sulfanilamido-1,3,4-thiadiazole	NH_2〈〉SO_2NH ring CH_3 (N—N, S)
Sulfamezathine	*see* Sulfamethazine	
Sulfamidochrysoidine	*see* Prontosil	
Sulfamylon	4-(Aminomethyl)benzenesulfonamide	NH_2CH_2〈〉SO_2NH_2

APPENDIX C—*Continued*

Trade or Medical Name	Chemical Name	Chemical Structure
Sulfanaphtho-quinone	2-Sulfanilamido-1,4-naphtho-quinone	NH_2—SO_2NH—structure
Sulfaphenyloxazole	5-Phenyl-2-sulfanilamido-oxazole	NH_2—SO_2NH—C_6H_5 structure
Sulfaphenylthiazole	4-Phenyl-2-sulfanilamido-thiazole	NH_2—SO_2NH—C_6H_5 structure
Sulfapyrazine	2-Sulfanilamidopyrazine	NH_2—SO_2NH—structure
Sulfapyridine	2-Sulfanilamidopyridine	NH_2—SO_2NH—structure
Sulfapyridine Sodium	Sodium 2-Sulfanilamido-pyridine	NH_2—SO_2N—Na structure
Sulfapyrimidine	*see* Sulfadiazine	
Sulfapropylthiadi-azole	5-n-Propyl-2-sulfanilamido-1,3,4-thiadiazole	NH_2—SO_2NH—$(CH_2)_2CH_3$ structure
Sulfapyrrole	2-Sulfanilamidopyrrole	NH_2—SO_2NH—structure
Sulfaquinoxaline	2-Sulfanilamidoquinoxaline	NH_2—SO_2NH—structure
Sulfasuxidine	2-(N^4-Succinylsulfanilamido)-thiazole	$HOOCH_2CH_2CONH$—SO_2NH—structure
Sulfathalidine	2-(N^4-Phthalylsulfanilamido)-thiazole	$COOH$ / $CONH$—SO_2NH—structure
Sulfathiadiazole	2-Sulfanilamido-1,3,4-thiadi-azole	NH_2—SO_2NH—structure
Sulfathiazole Sodium	Sodium 2-Sulfanilamidothia-zole	NH_2—SO_2—N—Na structure

APPENDIX C—*Continued*

Trade or Medical Name	Chemical Name	Chemical Structure
Sulfathiazoline	2-Sulfanilamidothiazoline	NH_2⟨⟩SO_2NH (thiazoline ring)
Sulfathiocarbamide	*see* Sulfathiourea	
Sulfathiophene	2-Sulfanilamidothiophene	NH_2⟨⟩SO_2NH (thiophene ring)
Sulfathiourea	Sulfanilylthiourea	NH_2⟨⟩$SO_2NHCSNH_2$
Sulfazide	Sulfanilylazide; *also see* Neoprontosil	NH_2⟨⟩SO_2N_3
Sulfazoacridine	1-(*p*-Sulfamylphenylazo)-3,9-diamino-8-ethoxyacridine Hydrochloride	C_2H_5O (acridine structure) NH_2 $N=N$⟨⟩SO_2NH_2 ... NH_2 ... H Cl
Sulfazole	*see* Sulfamethylthiazole	
Sulfidine	*see* Sulfapyridine	
Sulfoglycoside	Diglycoside of Bis(4-amino-phenyl) Sulfone	
Sulfonamide E.O.S.	Sodium N^4-(1-Sulfoethyl)sulfanilamide	CH_3CHNH⟨⟩SO_2NH_2 SO_3Na
Sulfonamide L.S.F.	"Sulfanilamide Lactoside Sodium Formaldehydesulf-oxalate"	
Sulfonamide	*see* Prontosil	
Supron	Sodium Quinolinylsulfanilamide	(quinoline)$COONa$ $CONH$⟨⟩SO_2NH
T. 693	*see* Sulfapyridine	
Tetracid	*see* Sulfamethylthiadiazole	
Thiazamide	*see* Sulfathiazole	
Thiazamide Sodium	*see* Sulfathiazole Sodium	
Thiazomide	*see* Sulfathiazole	
Thioseptal	*see* Sulfapyridine	
Tibatin	Digalactoside of Bis(4-amino-phenyl) Sulfone	$[C_6H_{12}O=N$⟨⟩$-]_2 SO_2$
Trianon	*see* Sulfapyridine	

APENDIX C—*Continued*

Trade or Medical Name	Chemical Name	Chemical Structure
Toriseptin M	*see* Sulfamethylthiazole	
TS84	4-Formamidophenyl 4'-Amino-phenyl Sulfone or 4-Sulf-anilylformanilide	$HCONH\langle\ \rangle SO_2\langle\ \rangle NH_2$
Uleron	N^1,N^1-Dimethyl-N^4-sulfanil-ylsulfanilamide	$NH_2\langle\ \rangle SO_2NH\langle\ \rangle SO_2N(CH_3)_2$
Uliron(e)	*see* Uleron	
Ultraseptyl	*see* Sulfamethylthiazole	
Urea Sulfazide	Urea Salt of 2(4'-Sulfamyl-phenylazo)-7-acetamido-1-hydroxynaphthalene-3,6-di-sulfonic Acid	
V.K. 53	*see* Sulfamethylthiadiazole	
V.K. 55	*see* Sulfaethylthiadiazole	
V.K. 57	*see* Sulfaisopropylthiadiazole	
V.K. 57a	5-Diethylmethyl-2-sulfanil-amido-1,3,4-thiadiazole	
V.K. 58	5-Isobutyl-2-sulfanilamido-1,3,4-thiadiazole	
Yuron	*see* Uleron	

Index

A